MW01012229

THE SEA

Ideas and Observations on Progress in the Study of the Seas

Volume 1 PHYSICAL OCEANOGRAPHY

Volume 2 COMPOSITION OF SEA-WATER

COMPARATIVE AND DESCRIPTIVE OCEANOGRAPHY

Volume 3 THE EARTH BENEATH THE SEA

HISTORY

Volume 4 NEW CONCEPTS OF SEA FLOOR EVOLUTION (IN THREE PARTS)

Volume 5 MARINE CHEMISTRY

THE SEA

Ideas and Observations on Progress in the Study of the Seas

Edited by

EDWARD D. GOLDBERG

VOLUME 5

Marine Chemistry

1974

A Wiley-Interscience Publication

JOHN WILEY & SONS · New York · London · Sydney · Toronto

Library of Congress Cataloging in Publication Data:

Main entry under title:

The Sea; ideas and observations on progress in the study of the seas.

Vol. 5: "A Wiley-Interscience publication."
General editor, v. 1–3: M. N. Hill; v. 4, pts 1– A. E. Maxwell; v. 5: E. D. Goldberg.
Vol. 4, pts. 1– have imprint: New York, Wiley-Intersciences; v. 5 has imprint: New York, J. Wiley.
Includes bibliographies.
CONTENTS: v. 1. Physical oceanography.—v. 2. The composition of sea-water. Comparative and descriptive oceanography.—v. 3. The earth beneath the sea. History.—v. 4. New concepts of sea floor evolution. pt. 1. General observations. pt. 2. Regional observations, concepts.—v. 5. Marine chemistry.
1. Oceanography. 2. Submarine geology. I. Hill, Maurice Nevill, 1919– ed. II. Maxwell, Arthur Eugene, 1925– ed. III. Goldberg, Edward D. ed.
GC11.S4 551.4'6 62–18366
ISBN 0–471–31090–5 (v. 5)

Printed in the United States of America

10 9 8 7 6 5 4 3 2 1

CONTRIBUTORS TO VOLUME 5

HANNES ALFVÉN, Royal Institute of Technology, Stockholm, Sweden

RAYMOND J. ANDERSEN, Scripps Institution of Oceanography, La Jolla, California 92037

GUSTAF ARRHENIUS, Scripps Institution of Oceanography, La Jolla, California 92037

ROBERT A. BERNER, Department of Geology and Geophysics, Yale University, New Haven, Connecticut 06520

RUDOLF H. BIERI, Virginia Institute of Marine Science, Gloucester Point, Virginia 23062

W. G. BRECK, Department of Chemistry, Queens University, Kingston, Ontario, Canada

KEN BRULAND, Scripps Institution of Oceanography, La Jolla, California 92037

D. S. CRONAN, Department of Geology, Faculty of Pure and Applied Science, University of Ottawa, Ottawa, Canada

BIBHAS R. DE, Royal Institute of Technology, Stockholm, Sweden

A. DISTECHE, Department of General Biology, 22 quai Van Beneden, University of Liège, Liège, Belgium

JAMES I. DREVER, Department of Geology, University of Wyoming, Laramie, Wyoming 82070

DAVID DYRSSEN, Department of Analytical Chemistry, University of Göteborg, Göteborg 5, Sweden

D. JOHN FAULKNER, Scripps Institution of Oceanography, La Jolla, California 92037

G. DONALD GARLICK, California State University, Humboldt State College, Arcata, California 95521

R. M. GARRELS, Department of Oceanography, University of Hawaii, Honolulu, Hawaii 96822

JORIS M. GIESKES, Scripps Institution of Oceanography, La Jolla, California 92037

EDWARD D. GOLDBERG, Scripps Institution of Oceanography, La Jolla, California 92037

MARTIN GOLDHABER, Department of Geology, University of California at Los Angeles, Los Angeles, California 90024

ARNE JERNELÖV, WHO Regional Office for Europe, Copenhagen, Denmark

IAN KAPLAN, Department of Geology, University of California at Los Angeles, Los Angeles, California 90024

HEINZ LOWENSTAM, Department of Geology, California Institute of Technology, Pasadena, California 91109

FERREN MACINTYRE, 5560 Casitas Pass Road, Carpinteria, California 93013

F. T. MANHEIM, United States Geological Survey, Woods Hole, Massachusetts 02543

DAVID W. MENZEL, Skidaway Institute of Oceanography, Savannah, Georgia 31406

FRANK J. MILLERO, School of Marine Sciences, University of Miami, 10 Rickenbacker Causeway, Miami, Florida 33149

EDWARD A. PERRY, JR., Department of Geology, University of Massachusetts, Amherst, Massachusetts 01002

A. PRESTON, Radioactivity Laboratory, Ministry of Agriculture, Fisheries and Food, Lowestoft, Suffolk, England

F. L. SAYLES, Woods Hole Oceanographic Institution, Woods Hole, Massachusetts 02543

U. SCHMIDT, Max Planck Institute for Chemistry, Saarstrasse 23, Postfach 3060, D 65 Mainz, West Germany

W. SEILER, Max Planck Institute for Chemistry, Saarstrasse 23, Postfach 3060, D 65 Mainz, West Germany

MARGARETA WEDBORG, Department of Analytical Chemistry, University of Göteborg, Göteborg 5, Sweden

R. WOLLAST, Institute of Industrial Chemistry, Free University of Brussels, Brussels, Belgium

Lars Gunnar Sillén, 1916–1970

PREFACE

This volume of *The Sea* is dedicated to Lars Gunnar Sillén (1916–1970) whose quest to understand the chemical reactions determining the composition of seawaters laid a new foundation for investigations in marine chemistry. His venturesome and innovative concepts about the character of ocean waters still provide the bases for many present-day researches. The contributors seek to share with their colleagues both an assessment of knowledge relative to the problems proposed by Sillén and explorations into hitherto unexplored realms of marine chemistry.

Before his association with ocean science, Sillén had established himself as one of the world's foremost inorganic chemists. His early works involved the X-ray analyses of oxides and basic salts. His forte, however, was solution chemistry, especially that involving complex species. His "core plus links" hypothesis is basic to the understanding of polynuclear equilibria. He collated existing data on equilibrium constants in the publication *Stability Constants of Metal-Ion Complexes*, a volume of immeasureable value that went through two editions and occupied a substantial amount of time in preparation. At the time of his death he was working on the third edition, which would have updated and critically evaluated existing data. His prodigious activities resulted in about 500 papers.

His entry to marine science began with a lecture at the International Oceanographic Congress held in New York between August 31 and September 12, 1959. Professor Gustaf Arrhenius and myself invited him to speak with the sense that one of the world's outstanding chemists could provide fresh and vigorous thoughts about the complex and difficult-to-understand medium: seawater. Today we realize how woefully we underestimated the impact of such a presentation. His lecture, "The Physical Chemistry of Sea Water" (Sillén, 1961), was taken from the first of a series of studies concerning the implications of equilibrium calculations to the seawater system. Each of these studies was to challenge existing gospel and to provide new interpretations of natural phenomena consistent with the prevailing concepts of the mother science, chemistry. He assembled these considerations for presentation at the Bat-Sheva Seminar on Marine Chemistry, held in Rehovot, Israel, June 1969, one of his last participations with the marine science community. His mimeographed lecture notes are an invaluable summary of our present knowledge of the nature of seawater.

A recurring theme in the writings of Sillén is the utilization of equilibrium models for seawater. He argued (Sillén, 1961, p. 552) that:

"...it may be worth while to try to find out what the true equilibrium would be like, and that one might learn from a comparison with the real system. We shall often find that sufficient data are lacking to make the discussion very precise. Neither the laboratory data on chemical equilibria (needed for the model), nor the geochemical data (for the real system) are always as accurate as one might wish. Still, it may be worth while to try this approach."

The development of the thermodynamics of the seawater system follows logically from such guidance. Consequently Chapters 1 to 8 are dedicated to such an end. These chapters interpret the composition of seawater, and the reactions occurring in this multicomponent electrolyte solution, on the bases of equilibrium states. There are overlaps and sometimes conflicts in these presentations. This situation could have been minimized, but not eliminated, perhaps by a pruning of the articles. To maintain continuity in the arguments of the contributors, it was thought more reasonable to alter only the writing for a consistent editorial style.

Some of the boundary conditions used by Sillén are critically examined. For redox equilibria he employed a pE of 12.5 $\pm$ 0.2, based on the oxygen-water couple. Chapter 4 suggests that the pE of oxic seawater may be around 8.5 with the redox level governed by the O_2/H_2O_2 couple. Such a change could remove, for example, the dilemma (Sillén, 1964) about the speciation of nitrogen:

> "There is still no good explanation of the fact that nitrogen exists mainly as $N_2(g)$ whereas at equilibrium with H_2O at pE = 12.5 and pH = 8.1, it should have been converted to NO_3^- in the ocean. . .riddle No. 1 in the regulation of the present composition of air and seawater."

With a lower value of the pE, the observed nitrate and nitrogen concentrations in deep seawaters can be reconciled with equilibrium values.

The extension of equilibrium models to the higher hydrostatic pressures and lower temperatures of the deep ocean is a necessary and logical broadening of Sillén's ideas. Chapter 2 is dedicated to such propositions.

Sillén's influence on chemical descriptions of the major sedimentary cycle has been enormous. Garrels notes in Chapter 9 that "because of the article (Sillén, 1961) and that conversation (with Sillén shortly after it was published), the whole direction of my research was changed toward the development and testing of his concepts." The hypothesis that the dissolved species in seawater might be in equilibrium with the solid phases of the sediments stimulated large-scale laboratory and field studies of the relationships between seawaters and sedimentary phases. Such investigations are considered in Chapters 9 to 17.

For those systems in the major sedimentary cycle where equilibrium descriptions appear inadequate, one notes a decided trend to the use of kinetic approaches. The direction to look at nonequilibrium processes was clearly charted by Sillén (1963): "More serious for the equilibrium picture are the non-equilibrium processes: biological processes, photochemical processes, etc." Perhaps a succinct appraisal of present moods is that given in Chapter 13 by Berner: "Equilibrium models predict in what direction reactions are proceeding, but what is needed, in addition, are kinetic models actually describing the reactions."

The remaining chapters, except for the final one, are descriptions of the interactions between seawater and living organisms. Their importance to the equilibrium hypothesis was defined by Sillén (1961, p. 55): "life processes will take the sea water far from the equilibrium composition. This is true especially in the surface layer. . .in the remainder of the ocean, however, it seems that the processes working toward equilibrium will predominate." This idea finds confirmation in the arguments presented in Chapter 18 where Menzel points out that the vertical homogeneity of dissolved and particulate organic carbon below a depth of 300 m is a general characteristic of the oceans. He indicates that "there is no evidence to suggest that the included compounds are decomposed at depth or that they in any way influence the concentration of non-conservative properties."

There is a pragmatic side to the writings of Sillén. Concerned with the future of ocean chemistry, he writes (Sillén, 1963): "We are living in a time of Mamon worship and hence it is proper to end this article with a pious contemplation of the economic profit that mankind can derive in the future from the chemistry of the oceans." He was concerned with the mineral resources of the sea (treated in Chapter 15) and with the factors regulating plant and animal productivity (treated in Volume II of *The Sea*).

In addition he was aware of the problems that plague those involved with the intergovernmental management of marine resources (Sillén, 1963):

"It may prove economical to fertilize a restricted region of the sea, such as the Baltic or some part of it. This, however, raises certain practical questions, the two fundamental of which are: Who is going to pay for the fertilizer and Who is going to eat the fish? By the way, where are the boundaries of individual states in such a pasture sea?"

He recognized the role of the oceans as space for man's wastes and directed his thoughts toward possible changes in climate due to the entry of carbon dioxide from fossil fuel burning. Chapters 21 and 22 further develop our knowledge about man's alterations of the environment.

Chapter 23 deals with the history of the ocean, a problem that attracted Sillén's attention during the latter part of his life. He sought to develop the chemical restraints on the compositions both of the atmosphere and of the oceans for systems with little or no free oxygen at the earth's surface.

Thirty-two scientists have provided this tribute to Lars Gunnar Sillén. Some never met him, yet all clearly have come under his influence in one way or another.

EDWARD D. GOLDBERG

La Jolla, California
March 1973

References

Sillén, L. G., 1961. "The Physical Chemistry of Sea Water." In *Oceanography*, edited by Mar Sears. American Association for the Advancement of Science, Washington, D.C., pp. 549–581.

Sillén, L. G., 1963. "How Has Sea Water Got Its Present Composition." *Svensk Kemisk Tidskrift*, **75**, 161–177.

Sillén, L. G., 1964. "Processes Regulating the Oxidation State of the System (Air + Sea + Sediments) in Past and Present." *Acta Chemica Scandinavica*, **18**, 1016–1018.

CONTENTS

MARINE CHEMISTRY

Marine Chemistry

I. THERMODYNAMICS OF THE SEAWATER SYSTEM

1. SEAWATER AS A MULTICOMPONENT ELECTROLYTE SOLUTION*

Frank J. Millero

1. Introduction

In recent years, there has been a number of major advances made on the interpretation of interactions in multicomponent electrolyte solutions (Friedman, 1962; Harned and Robinson, 1968; Wood and Reilly, 1970; Millero, 1971a). In this chapter we shall review some of these new concepts of multicomponent electrolyte solutions and show how they can be applied to seawater. We hope that the application of these methods to the medium of seawater will provide a new approach to understanding the physical chemistry of seawater.

Classically, the ionic interactions in seawater have been treated by using Bjerrum's (1926) ion pairing model, as exemplified by the work of Garrels and Thompson (1962). Since the ion pairing models for ionic interactions in seawater are discussed in other chapters of this book, we shall not discuss in great detail this method of examining the ionic interactions in seawater. We hope to show that although the ion pairing models have proven to be very useful in discussing the interactions in seawater, it is not necessary to use this model to examine the physical chemistry of seawater. By using some of the new models for multicomponent electrolyte interaction, we shall show that it is possible to estimate and treat the ionic interactions in seawater without invoking the concept of ion-pairing (even though ion pairing may occur). We shall attempt to answer such fundamental questions as: Can the physical chemical properties of seawater be treated as a simple electrolyte (e.g., sea salt)? What are the properties of this sea salt? How do the properties of sea salt depend on the major components of seawater?

Before we review the ionic interactions in multicomponent electrolyte solutions, we shall briefly examine the methods used to study ionic interactions in single (i.e., binary solutions) electrolyte solutions. In the latter sections we shall examine the use of the new methods to predict the properties of seawater and solutes in the medium of seawater.

2. Ion-Ion Interactions in Single Electrolyte Solutions

A. *The Debye-Hückel Theory*

For the last 50 years, most discussions of the physical chemical properties of solutions have been dominated by the use of the Debye-Hückel theory and the resultant

* Contribution Number 1650 From the Rosenstiel School of Marine and Atmospheric Science, University of Miami.

ionic strength principles (Lewis and Randall, 1961; Harned and Owen, 1958; Robinson and Stokes, 1959). The experimental proof of the validity of the theory has been available for some time and the theory can now be accepted as a fundamental law. The problem of treating high ionic strength electrolyte solutions as seawater, however, remains, since the theory is only valid as one approaches infinitely dilute solutions. At finite concentrations, the theory fails because of (1) defects in some of the basic assumptions (e.g., treating ions as point charges or hard charged spheres) and (2) deviations that occur because of noncoulombic effects such as hydration (the Debye–Hückel theory deals only with coulombic forces).

The extended Debye–Hückel theory (i.e., with the inclusion of the ion size parameter) gives for the mean activity coefficient ($f_\pm$) of an electrolyte in water

$$-\ln f_\pm = \frac{S_f I_V^{1/2}}{1 + AaI_V^{1/2}} \tag{1}$$

$$S_f = (1/\gamma) \sum \gamma_i Z_i^2 (DT)^{-3/2} 1.8243 \times 10^6 \tag{2}$$

$$A = \frac{50.29 \times 10^8}{(DT)^{1/2}} \tag{3}$$

where γ is the total number of ions formed when one molecule of electrolyte dissociates into γ_i ions of type i and charge Z_i, I_V is the volume ionic strength ($I_V = \frac{1}{2}\sum C_i Z_i^2$), D is the dielectric constant of pure water, T is the absolute temperature, and a is the ion size parameter. For a 1-1 electrolyte in water at 25°C, $S_f = 0.5091$ mol$^{-1/2}$ liter$^{1/2}$ and $A = 0.3286 \times 10^8$ cm^{-1} mol$^{-1/2}$ liter$^{1/2}$ (Harned and Owen, 1958). Equations for other thermodynamic functions can be derived by appropriate differentiation. Two such equations (Harned and Owen, 1958) representing the relative partial molal volume and the relative partial molal heat content are

$$\bar{V} - \bar{V}^0 = \frac{(3/2)S_V I_V^{1/2}}{1 + AaI_V^{1/2}} + \frac{W_V I_V}{(1 + AaI_V^{1/2})^2} \tag{4}$$

$$\bar{H} - \bar{H}^0 = \frac{(3/2)S_H I_V^{1/2}}{1 + AaI_V^{1/2}} + \frac{W_H I_V}{(1 + AaI_V^{1/2})^2} \tag{5}$$

where the theoretical limiting slopes

$$S_V = 2.303\gamma\, RT\, S_f \left[\frac{\partial \ln D}{\partial P} - \frac{\beta}{3}\right] \tag{6}$$

$$S_H = -2.303\gamma\, RT\, S_f \left[\frac{\partial \ln D}{\partial T} + \frac{1}{T} + \frac{\alpha}{3}\right] \tag{7}$$

are derived by differentiation of $S_f I_V^{1/2}$. The symbols α and β represent, respectively, the expansibility [$\alpha = 1/v(\partial v/\partial T)$, where v is the specific volume] and compressibility [$\beta = -1/v(\partial v/\partial P)$]. At 25°C, $(3/2)S_V = 2.802$ cm^3 liter$^{1/2}$ mol$^{-3/2}$ and $(3/2)S_H = 707.1$ cal liter$^{1/2}$ mol$^{-3/2}$ for a 1-1 electrolyte in water. The terms for the coefficients

$$W_V = -2.303\gamma\, RT\, S_f A(1/2)\left[\frac{\partial \ln D}{\partial P} - \beta - \frac{2\partial \ln a}{\partial P}\right] \tag{8}$$

$$W_H = 2.303\gamma\, RT\, S_f(1/2)\left[\frac{\partial \ln D}{\partial T} + \frac{1}{T} - \partial - \frac{2\partial \ln a}{\partial T}\right] \tag{9}$$

result from the differentiation of the term $(1 + AaI_V^{1/2})$ and cannot normally be evaluated, since the effect of temperature and pressure on the ion size parameter ($\partial \ln a/\partial T$ and $\partial \ln a/\partial P$) is unknown.

In general, equations 1, 4, and 5 give reasonable results up to about $I_V = 0.1$ (Harned and Owen, 1958; Robinson and Stokes, 1959; Lewis and Randall, 1961) and experimentally are approached for all electrolytes as a limiting law. The deviations from the limiting law can be ascribed to (1) defects of the basic assumptions of the theory at higher concentrations or (2) the noncoulombic interactions becoming important. Determining which of these two factors causes the deviations or how much each contributes is a problem that presently has not been solved. The basic assumptions and deficiencies of the Debye-Hückel theory have been adequately discussed elsewhere (Harned and Owen, 1958). The recent theoretical treatments of Friedman and co-workers (1959–1972) based on Mayer's cluster theory (1950) essentially bypasses this problem. In Friedman's statistical mechanical methods, coulombic and noncoulombic effects are treated on an equal level and separation is possible only as one approaches infinite dilution.

The classical method of examining deviations from the limiting law in concentrated solutions is to use various extended forms involving one or more arbitrary constants (such as the ion size parameter). The difference between this form and the experimental data is attributed to noncoulombic effects such as specific interactions (Guggenheim, 1935) or hydration (Stokes and Robinson, 1948). Although these noncoulombic effects are reasonable, they cannot be explicitly determined since the arbitrary constants, such as the ion size parameter, cannot be determined independently.

Since the purely coulombic Debye-Hückel terms are unknown at finite concentrations, the meanings of the new parameters are uncertain and it is difficult to attach to them a definite physical meaning. The addition of more parameters, needed in fitting the experimental data at high concentrations, further complicates the picture.

Although this approach is quite unsatisfactory, until the recent developments of Friedman and co-workers there was no alternative. Since such parameters as the distance of nearest approach or the hydration number appear to be plausible, and the newer methods are complicated mathematically, the older methods will probably continue in use.

Although the distance of closest approach is considered to be part of the basic theory, and is physically necessary, its use deviates from the basic objection of a limiting law—that of requiring only fundamental constants and measurable properties of pure water. The parameter is also vague, unmeasurable, and, when it is needed (i.e., when two ions are close together), other assumptions of the theory (such as a constant dielectric constant) are invalid.

In conclusion, the meaning of the Debye-Hückel theory at high concentrations is uncertain and noncoulombic effects must be considered. For many electrolytes, the Debye-Hückel contribution is almost constant in concentrated solutions and small compared to noncoulombic effects. Even though various empirical approaches are important, many uncertainties cannot be resolved by using these methods. In the next two sections we shall briefly review other coulombic and noncoulombic ionic interactions (Vaslow, 1972).

B. Non-Debye-Hückel Coulombic Treatments

A number of non-Debye-Hückel coulombic or electrical treatments have been developed in attempts to obtain more reasonable theoretical coulombic effects in concentrated solutions. Vaslow (1972) has recently discussed these effects in detail. Some of the methods are briefly discussed below.

Dielectric Constant Variations

Hückel (1925) attempted to modify the Debye-Hückel equation to allow for the changing of the dielectric constant of pure water by the electrolyte. Since little is known about the exact form of ion-water interactions, any corrections involving changes in the dielectric constant are purely empirical. Although most workers (Millero, 1971b) feel that dielectric saturation is important in ion-water interactions, it is difficult to discuss the changes that occur in the dielectric constant when two ions approach each other (Glueckauf, 1964). The dielectric constant is most likely a very complicated function of the distance and the structure of the cospheres (i.e., the ion plus its hydrated waters).

Quasilattice Treatment

Before the Debye-Hückel theory was developed, Bjerrum (1920) represented the concentration dependence of thermodynamic functions by a $c^{1/3}$ relationship (instead of $c^{1/2}$). Since this approach is similar to the energy behavior of a crystal lattice, it is frequently called a quasilattice treatment. Many workers have represented the log $f_{\pm}$ by a $c^{1/3}$ relationship (Bernal and Fowler, 1933; Frank and Thompson, 1959; Desnoyers and Conway, 1964; Bahe, 1972). For example, Bahe (1972) has recently shown that the combination of the repulsive force between ions (due to the gradient of the dielectric constant near the surface) and classical coulombic force leads to a description of 1-1 electrolyte solutions in terms of a "loose" face centered cubic lattice. He has shown that the $\log f_{\pm}$ for many 1-1 electrolytes can be represented by the equation $\log f_{\pm} = -Ac^{1/3} + Bc$. Although the quasilattice theories appear to be reasonable at high concentrations and yield good experimental fits, there is no definite evidence of its validity and the parameters tend to be empirical.

Nonlinearized Poisson Boltzmann Equation

Kirkwood (1934) has shown that by assuming that the fluctuation term of the potential of average force is small and by neglecting the thermodynamic inconsistencies, the nonlinear Poisson-Boltzmann equation can be solved (Fowler and Guggenheim, 1939). As with the linear solution of Debye-Hückel, an arbitrary parameter is necessary. The nonlinear form gives more reasonable and consistent values for the parameter. The nonlinear form can also fit activity coefficient data that fall below the Debye-Hückel limiting law without the use of negative ion size parameters or the arbitrary assumption of ion pairs (Guggenheim, 1960).

Ion Pair Treatments

The most popular method of treating coulombic interactions in high concentrations is the ion-pair treatment. This method was originally developed by Bjerrum (1926). The basic assumption in this approach is that short-range interactions can be represented by the formation of ion pairs.

The ion pair is formed by ions of opposite sign (i.e., cations and anions) and may be separated by one or more solvent molecules. The ion association of an electrolyte (MA) may be represented by

$$M^+ + A^- = MA^0 \tag{10}$$

A characteristic association equilibrium constant is given by

$$K_A = a_{MA^0}/a_{M^+}a_{A^-} \tag{11}$$

where a_i is the activity of species i ($a_i = \gamma_i m_i$, where γ_i is the activity coefficient and m_i the molality). One can generally (Griffiths and Symons, 1960) classify ion pairs into four classes: (1) complexes—when the ions are held in contact by covalent bonds; (2) contact ion pairs—when the ions are in contact (linked electrostatically) and do not have any covalent bonding; (3) solvent shared ion pairs—pairs of ions linked electrostatically separated by a single water molecule; and (4) solvent-separated ion pairs—pairs of ions linked electrostatically but separated by more than one water molecule.

Bjerrum (1926) defined, from electrostatic grounds, the distance between oppositely charged ions that can be classified as being associated. This distance, q, the ionic separation at which the mutual potential energy is equal to $2kT$ (k is Boltzmann constant) represents the position of minimum probability of finding ions of opposite charge within a spherical shell surrounding the central ion. The q is given by

$$q = \frac{(Z_+ Z_-)e^2}{2DkT} \tag{12}$$

where Z_i is the charge on the ion i, e is the electrostatic charge, and the other terms are the same as described earlier. In this treatment, two oppositely charged ions between a (the ion size parameter) and q are considered to form an ion pair. This includes ion pairs of classes 2 and 3. The association constant of the Bjerrum method is given by

$$K_A = \frac{4\pi N}{1000}\left[\frac{e^2}{DkT}\right]^3 Q(b) \tag{13}$$

where N is Avogadro's number and $Q(b)$ is a complicated function computed by Bjerrum for $1 < b < 15$ (Robinson and Stokes, 1959). The theory predicts greater ion-pair formation the higher the valencies and the smaller the dielectric constant, which is in agreement with experimental results (Harned and Owen, 1958).

Bjerrum's theory has been criticized (Swarcz, 1968; Flaherty and Stern, 1958) because of the somewhat arbitrary cutoff distance q, that differs for the same electrolyte in different solvents and its prediction that beyond a given dielectric constant no association occurs. It has now been superseded by the theories of Fuoss (1934), Denison and Ramsey (1955), and Fuoss and Kraus (1957). Fuoss (1934) corrected the Bjerrum model by allowing for the probability of finding one ion pair at a distance r. Poirier and Delap (1961) further improved the model by introducing a factor that allows the q distance to have any desired value. Denison and Ramsey (1955) treated ions as hard spheres (of radii r_1 and r_2) in a continuous dielectric medium. They considered ions to be paired only when they are in contact. They found that K_A is given by

$$\ln K_A = \ln K_A{}^0 + \frac{(Z_+ Z)e^2}{aDkT} \tag{14}$$

where $a = r_1 + r_2$ and $K_A{}^0$ is the association constant of the two uncharged ions. Only when $a = 5.1A^0$ do the Bjerrum and the Denison and Ramsey approaches yield the same value for K_A. For small ions the two theoretical values for K_A deviate widely (Flaherty and Stern, 1958).

The model of Fuoss (1958) consists of cations of radius a in volume $v = 2.52a^3$ and point charge anions, both in a continuous dielectric medium. Only anions on the surface of the cation or within the sphere of volume v of the cation are counted as ion pairs. By using the ion potential of Debye-Hückel and the Boltzmann method, Fuoss obtained

$$K_A = \frac{4\pi Na^3}{3000} \exp [Z_+ Z_- e^2/DakT] \tag{15}$$

which is similar to that obtained by Denison and Ramsey. The vaguely defined $K_A{}^0$ term of the Denison and Ramsey model is now explicitly defined as an excluded volume. Others have made further elaborations on these methods (Popovych and Dill, 1969; Guggenheim, 1960) and discussed the shortcomings of the model. As with the other coulombic treatments, there are arbitrary constants (q or a) that cannot be assigned definite meaning.

C. Noncoulombic Treatments

The electrostatic treatments normally fit the experimental data to only moderate concentrations. It is thus necessary to consider other noncoulombic effects, such as those that occur for nonelectrolytes in water. For nonelectrolyte solutions the noncoulombic effect becomes quite large above $0.1m$. The strong electric field of ions interacting with a highly structured solvent such as water can often accentuate these effects. It is difficult, however, to separate the coulombic and noncoulombic effects except in dilute solutions.

Classically, various attempts to separate the coulombic and noncoulombic effects have been made by selecting one of the electrostatic treatments and considering the difference between this term and the experimental data as caused by noncoulombic effects. Three methods of accounting for noncoulombic effects, namely virial expansions, hydration, and water structure effects, are briefly described below.

Virial Expansions

The virial series expansion for electrolyte solution properties is based on Van't Hoff's expression for the osmotic pressure. Since the osmotic pressure (π) in dilute solutions is analogous to the pressure of an ideal gas, Van't Hoff expanded the osmotic pressure in a manner similar to an imperfect gas:

$$PV/RT = 1 + B_1/V + B_2/V^2 + \cdots \tag{16}$$

where the constants B_i are virial coefficients. For electrolyte solutions, the expansion terms are in addition to the term given by the Debye-Hückel theory. The coefficients contain terms related to each possible combination of ions in solution (Scatchard, 1943). The concentration dependence of the osmotic pressure can be used to obtain the activity (or free energy) of the electrolyte, while the temperature and pressure terms can be differentiated to give the excess enthalpies and volumes. Although the gas phase virial coefficients have a definite meaning, it is difficult to attach more than empirical significance to the osmotic solution values. Another difficulty with interpreting the solution virial coefficients in terms of specific interactions stems from the uncertainty of the assignment of the coulombic term.

Mayer's cluster theory (1950) gives direct meaning to the virial coefficients of the expansion of the excess free energy, provided that the solvent is kept at unit activity. Although the coefficients are complex functions of ionic strength, for mixing processes at constant ionic strength the coefficients are constant and can be related to specific type ion-ion interactions (Friedman, 1960).

Hydration

Since ions interact with water molecules and this interaction will change the excess free energy, one can treat the deviations from the Debye-Hückel theory using the concept of hydration. One type of hydration effect would be to remove water molecules from solution and thus raise the concentration of the solution. Another type of hydration effect is caused by the free energy necessary to separate a pair of ions from their hydrated water molecules. Although these effects are quite valid, the parameters can only be obtained by curve fittings and the hydration numbers are not very meaningful.

Stokes and Robinson (1948) derived the following equation to represent the effect of hydration on the activity coefficient of an electrolyte:

$$\ln \gamma_{\pm} = \ln \gamma_{\pm}\ (\text{elect}) - \frac{h}{\gamma} \ln a_w + \ln \left[\frac{1 - (h - \gamma)m}{55.51}\right] \tag{17}$$

where $\ln \gamma_{\pm}$(elect) is the coulombic Debye-Hückel term, h is the hydration number (average number of water molecules hydrated to the salt), a_w is the activity of water, and γ is the number of moles of ions in 1 mol of salt. Glueckauf (1955) used a model similar to the Stokes and Robinson model to determine the effect of hydration on activity coefficients. He, however, used volume statistics. The "hydration numbers" obtained by Glueckauf for cations and anions are additive and linearly related to ionic radii or hydration entropies. There are two major defects with the hydration treatments: (1) the coulombic contribution is indefinite; and (2) the meaning of the hydration number is vague. For example, the assignment of hydration numbers (representing the average number of water molecules influenced by a given ion) at high concentrations where the hydration cospheres overlap cannot be strictly correct.

Water Structure Effects

Since water is a highly structured solvent, one might expect this structure to influence the interaction of ions with one another. For example, the deviations of the partial molal volumes of electrolytes from the limiting law are much greater at low temperatures where water is more structured than at higher temperatures (Millero, 1970; Millero, 1971b). The large temperature dependence of the deviation of electrolytes from the limiting law can be interpreted as being caused by changes in the structure of bulk water between the interacting ions with temperature. Desnoyers et al. (1969) have recently used a water structural interaction model to examine the deviations of thermodynamic properties (such as volume and enthalpy) from the limiting law. The model is based on Frank and Robinson's suggestion (1940) that ion-ion interactions can be affected by the influence of ions on the structure of water. The model also considers the ideals developed by Gurney (1953) with his cosphere theory and by Frank (1963, 1965) through his concepts of structural salting in and out. The general rule developed by these workers is as follows: "Two solutes will attract each other if their structural influences or their tendencies to orient water molecules, are compatible with each other; conversely, an incompatibility in these structural influences or tendencies will result in repulsive forces". Many other workers (Conway, 1966; Vaslow, 1972) have also discussed water structure effects on ion-ion interactions. For large ions like R_4N^+ (Wen, 1972), the size ratio (ion to water) can also play a factor in ion-ion interactions (Conway and Verrall, 1966).

Since the structure of liquid water is uncertain (for two contrasting views, see Kell, 1972 and Davis and Jarzynski, 1972), it is difficult, at present, to discuss water structure effects in great detail or in other than a qualitative manner.

D. *Statistical Mechanical Treatments*

Although statistical mechanical treatments are normally complicated, in recent years new methods have been developed to treat electrolyte solutions (Vaslow, 1972). Statistical mechanical calculations have been carried out by Friedman et al. (1969–1972) and Rasiah (1968–1970) to concentrations as high as $1m$; these results have provided an insight into the meaning of the ion size parameter and the effect of hydration. Vaslow (1972) has outlined in greater detail the development of statistical mechanical treatments of electrolytes.

The major development was made by Mayer, McMillan, and co-workers (1940, 1945, 1950), who developed simple methods to calculate the virial coefficients in terms of repulsive and attractive forces of clusters of molecules. McMillan and Mayer (1945) showed how the radial distribution function (which gives the probability of finding a molecule of gas or liquid at a specified distance from an arbitrary central molecule) that is valid for imperfect gases or dense fluids could be directly related to the properties of nonionic solutions. The application of these methods to ionic solutions was made by Mayer (1950) when he first applied the virial cluster expansion. More recent developments have been made by Friedman and co-workers (1959–1972), Rasaiah (1968, 1970), and Poirier (1953). These recent developments appear to be the most important theoretical developments since the Debye-Hückel theory.

Two general methods have been used in studying the statistical mechanical treatments of ionic solutions, the cluster expansion theory and the radial distribution theory (Vaslow, 1972). These are briefly described below.

Cluster Expansion Theory

The statistical mechanical methods are based on the equation

$$A = kT \ln Q \tag{18}$$

where A is the Helmholtz free energy per molecule and Q is the partition function. The partition function Q, in principle, can be solved from the geometry, mass, and intra- and intermolecular potential energy curves of the molecules of the system. From the temperature and pressure dependence of Q, any thermodynamic property can be determined. The Q can be factored into three terms:

$$Q = Q_{\mathrm{KE}} Q_{\mathrm{Int}} Q_C \tag{19}$$

where Q_{KE} is the kinetic energy term, Q_{Int} is the internal motions and energy term, and Q_C is the configuration term related to all the molecules of the system. The Q_C term for liquids is the one that is difficult to determine and must normally be solved by approximate methods. Q_C is given by

$$Q_C = \int \exp\left[-U(x, y, z, \ldots)/kT\right] dx \cdots dz \tag{20}$$

where U is the total intermolecular potential energy of the system of molecules at the coordinates x, y, z, etc. The quantity U is given by

$$U = 1/2 \sum_{i}^{n} \sum_{j \neq i}^{n} \mu_{ij} \tag{21}$$

where μ_{ij} is the potential energies of the individual interactions between i and j. The μ_{ij} depends on forces of van der Waals, repulsive, coulombic, etc. The evaluation of U is extremely difficult to solve for a large number of molecules. Mayer (1950) showed how this integral could be broken down into a series of separate terms involving the interaction of clusters of molecules.

Radial Distribution Methods

The radial distribution, $g(r)$, gives the probability of finding a molecule of the gas or solution at a given distance from a central molecule. The average energy $\bar{U}$, the pressure P, and the compressibility β are related to the distribution function by

$$\bar{U} = (\rho/2) \int^{v} g_{12}\mu_{12}\, dr_{12} \tag{22}$$

$$P/\rho kT = 1 - (\rho/6kT) \int g_{12}(\partial\mu_{12}/\partial r_{12}) r_{12}\, dr_{12} \tag{23}$$

$$kT(\beta\rho) = 1 + \rho \int (g_{12} - 1)\, dr_{12} \tag{24}$$

where $\bar{U}$ is the average energy of the molecules of the system, ρ is the density in molecules/cm^3, β is the compressibility $[=1/\rho(\partial\rho/\partial P)]$, g_{12} is the radial distribution function, and μ_{12} is the potential energy corresponding to a distance, r, between molecules 1 and 2. The radial distribution method depends on the properties of pairs of molecules (involving only the pair distribution function), while the virial expansion method depends on the interaction of groups of molecules of all sizes. Most of the methods used to solve g_{12} involve integral equations that are obtained by statistical mechanical methods (Vaslow, 1972).

Friedman's Theory

The ion-ion pair correlation functions of Friedman et al. (1968–1970) are based on an ion-ion pair potential function $\mu_{ij}(r)$ of four terms:

$$\mu_{ij}(r) = \mathrm{COUL}_{ij} + \mathrm{COR}_{ij} + \mathrm{CAV}_{ij} + \mathrm{GUR}_{ij} \tag{25}$$

where the coulombic term $\mathrm{COUL}_{ij} = e_i e_j/Dr$ (e_i is the charge on the ion i, D is the dielectric constant, and r is the crystal radius); the core repulsion term $\mathrm{COR}_{ij} = B_{ij}/r^9$ (B_{ij} is obtained from the electrostatic lattice energy of the salt crystal); the dielectric cavity term $\mathrm{CAV}_i = (1/2Dr^4)(D - D_c)/[2d - D_c]\ [e_i^2 r_j^3 + e_j^2 r_i^3]$, which accounts for the fact that each ion occupies a cavity of dielectric constant $D_c \simeq 2$; and the Gurney term $\mathrm{GUR}_{ij} = A_{ij} V_W^{-1} V_{mu}(r_i + wr_b + wr)$, which represents the effect of the overlap of cospheres around the ions (where V_W is the mean volume of water, V_{mu} is the mutual volume of overlapping of a sphere of the ions when the distance between their centers is r, and w is the cosphere thickness taken to be $2.76A^0$—the diameter of a water molecule). The only adjustable parameter is the Gurney A_{ij} term. In general, the model gives computed properties that agree very well with the experimental properties. The adjustable Gurney term A_{ij} appears to be related to hydration and water structural effects. For a somewhat different approach, see the recent work of Jones and Mohling (1971) and the comments of Friedman (1972).

3. Ion-Ion Interactions in Multicomponent Electrolyte Solutions

As mentioned in the Introduction, in recent years considerable advances have been made on the interpretation of the ionic interactions in multicomponent electrolyte solutions. In this section we shall highlight some of these advances. The reader is referred to a number of these developments for a more detailed description of these advances (Friedman, 1962; Harned and Robinson, 1968; Wood and Reilly, 1970;

Millero, 1971a). The older methods of treating short-range interactions in multicomponent electrolyte solutions exemplified by the equations of Bjerrum, Brønsted, and Guggenheim are reviewed in the classical texts on electrolyte solution chemistry (Harned and Owen, 1958; Robinson and Stokes, 1959; Lewis and Randall, 1961). The use of the ion pairing methods are described in other chapters of this book (also, see Millero, 1971a).

A. Young's Rule

Charge Symmetric Mixtures

During the last 20 years, a number of generalizations concerning the behavior of multicomponent electrolyte solutions have been developed, one of the most important being Young's (1951) rule, given by

$$\Phi = \sum y_i \phi_i \tag{26}$$

where Φ is the apparent molal property of the mixture (such as volume, enthalpy, or heat capacity), ϕ_i is the apparent molal property for the ionic or electrolyte component i at the same ionic strength of the total mixture, and y_i is a molal weighting factor ($y_i = m_i/m_T$), where m_i is the molality of component i and $m_T = \sum m_i$ is the total molality. This equation essentially states that as a first approximation the excess properties (such as heat, volume, and free energy) of mixing two electrolyte solutions at constant ionic strength could be neglected. This relationship is a very useful (Wu, 1970) first approximation and, as will be shown later, can prove very useful in examining the physical chemical properties of seawater.

Young and Smith (1954) showed that equation 26 accurately represented the apparent molal volume data of Wirth and co-workers (1937, 1940, 1950) for KCl-NaCl, KBr-NaCl, and $NaClO_4$-$HClO_4$ mixtures. Further volume studies by Wirth et al. (1963, 1968), Wen et al. (1967, 1968), and others have yielded information on the excess volumes of mixing electrolyte solutions, which are a measure of the deviations from Young's rule. In general, these excess volumes and enthalpies of mixing are small; thus, Young's rule can still be used as a first approximation.

Studies on the excess heat of mixing electrolyte solutions with a common ion (e.g., NaCl-KCl) have been made by Wu, Smith, and Young (1957, 1965); Wood and co-workers (1965, 1966a, b; 1967a, b; 1969a, b; 1970); Stern and co-workers (1963, 1964); Anderson et al. (1970, 1971); and Jolicoeur, Picker, and Desnoyers (1969). For most of the systems studied, the heats of mixing $\Delta_m H$ were parabolic and approximately symmetrical around the solute mole fraction $y = 0.5$. Since many of these heats of mixing of two electrolytes with a common ion (e.g., NaCl-KCl) were quite large, these results can be taken as direct proof that the specific ion interaction theory of Brønsted (1922) and Guggenheim (1935) (which assumes that like-charged ions do not interact) is not valid. It also supports the predictions of Friedman (1960), who showed (using Mayer's ionic solution theory, 1950) that like-charged ions should have specific interactions and that these interactions should be more important than triplet interactions for most systems.

For many of the simple systems the heats of mixing two salts with different cations and a common anion ($MX + NX$) were approximately independent of the common anion and vice versa. For example, at a constant ionic strength the heat of mixing NaCl + KCl is approximately equal to the heat of mixing NaBr + KBr; also, the heat of mixing NaCl + NaBr is approximately equal to the heat of mixing KBr + KCl.

Using a modified form of the nomenclature of Friedman (1962), the excess free energy, heat, and volume of mixing NX with MX is given by (neglecting higher order terms)

$$\Delta_m G = y(1 - y)\, RT\, I^2 g_{N,MX} \tag{27}$$

$$\Delta_m H = y(1 - y)\, RT\, I^2 h_{N,MX} \tag{28}$$

$$\Delta_m V = y(1 - y)\, RT\, I^2 v_{N,MX} \tag{29}$$

where $g_{N,MX}$, $h_{N,MX}$, and $v_{N,MX}$ are the coefficients for the interaction of N and M in the presence of X. The g_i, v_i, and h_i are interrelated by the thermodynamic relationships

$$h_i = -RT^2\left(\frac{\partial g_i}{\partial T}\right) \tag{30}$$

and

$$v_i = (\partial g_i/\partial P) \tag{31}$$

Friedman's (1962) multicomponent electrolyte solution theory shows that in the limit of $I \rightarrow O$ that the interaction terms $g_{N,MX}$, $h_{N,MX}$, and $v_{N,MX}$ are independent of the anion X—in agreement with the heat of mixing results for simple systems.

Several observations of Young and co-workers and Wood and co-workers (on heats of mixing at $y = 0.5$) yield conclusions that are not generally derived from Friedman's theory. They are as follows: (1) In the presence of a common ion, $\Delta_m H$ of cations is much larger than the $\Delta_m H$ of anions; (2) in the $\Delta_m H$ common anion mixtures, the cations can be divided into two groups (structure makers $-H^+$, Li^+, Na^+, Bu_4N^+, etc., and structure breakers $-K^+$, Rb^+, Cs^+). The heats of mixing two ions in the same group gives positive heats, and the mixing of two ions in different groups gives negative heats; (3) for reciprocal salt pairs (NY and MX), the sum of the heats of mixing of common ion mixings equals the sum of the heats of mixing of the uncommon ion mixing (the cross-square rule, $\sum \square = \sum X$). For the mixing of the reciprocal salts NY and MX, the cross-square rule can be illustrated by the figure

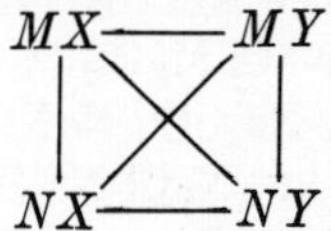

If one goes around the side of the square one obtains the four single electrolyte solutions MX, MY, NX, and NY, whose component ions are limited to two different cations and two anions. There are six possible mixings for this system as represented by the sides and diagonals. The cross-square rule simply states that the heats of mixing represented by the sides ($\sum \square$) equals the heats of mixing the diagonal ($\sum X$). This cross-square relationship has been shown to represent the excess volume, enthalpy, and free energy of mixing reciprocal salt pairs (Wood and Reilly, 1970; Millero, 1971a; Harned and Robinson, 1968).

The first two generalizations are probably related to the effect of the ions on the water molecules (either the water molecules hydrated on the ion or the structured water between the hydrated ions). Desnoyers et al. (1969), for example, have shown that the sign of the excess thermodynamic mixing functions can be predicted using their structural interaction model.

Wood and Anderson (1966) proposed an equation that illustrates the incorporation of the above generalizations to predict the properties of multicomponent electrolyte solutions. The equation for the mean relative apparent molal enthalpy is given by

$$\Phi_L = \sum_{M,X} y_M y_X \phi_L(MX) + (RT\,I^2/m) \sum_{M<N,X} y_M y_N y_X h_{M,NX} + (RT\,I^2/m) \sum_{X<Y,M} y_X y_Y y_M h_{X,YM} \quad (32)$$

where y_M is the molal fraction of M, $\phi_L(MX)$ is the relative apparent molal heat content of the pure electrolyte MX at ionic strength I and h_{MNX} and h_{XYM} are the interaction parameters, respectively, for the mixing of N and M in the presence of X and the mixings of X and Y in the presence of M. (The summation $N < M$ means that each h_{MNX} term is taken only once.)

Young's first approximation consists of assuming that all the h terms in equation 32 are zero. The formulation of Wood and Anderson is equivalent to applying Young's rule to only common ion mixtures. Wood and Anderson's revised rule can be considered to be an embodiment of Brønsted's principle of specific ion interaction. It also essentially eliminates plus-minus interactions that one might classify as ion-pair formation. The last two terms in equation 32 are the result of Young's second approximation where $h_{M,NCl} = h_{M,NX}$, etc., where X is any univalent anion. This approximation consists of neglecting both triplet interactions and the effects of ion atmospheres on the pairs. If g, h or v are strongly dependent on ionic strength, this approximation will no longer hold [since triplet interactions are proportional to I (Wood and Anderson, 1966)].

The above generalizations and equations for predicting the properties of symmetrically charged electrolyte mixtures have been thoroughly tested using experimental heats, volumes, and free energies of mixing (Wood and Reilly, 1970; Millero, 1971a; Harned and Robinson, 1968; Wen et al., 1971; Lilley, 1968; Boyd, Lindenbaum, and Robinson, 1971; Robinson, Wood, and Reilly, 1972).

Charge Asymmetric Mixtures

In recent years the free energy of electrolytes of different charge types have been studied by a number of workers. Studies on sea salt solutions include the work of Robinson and Bower (1965a,b) on the NaCl-KCl-BaCl system; Lanier (1965) on the NaCl-Na_2SO_4, NaCl-$MgSO_4$, and NaCl-$MgCl_2$-$CaCl_2$-Na_2SO_4 systems; Yeatts and Marshall (1967, 1969) on the $CaSO_4$-Na_2SO_4-$NaNO_3$ and $Ca(OH)_3$ systems; Platford and co-workers (1965–1972) on the NaCl-Na_2SO_4, NaCl-$MgCl_2$-$Mg(NO_3)_2$-$CaCl_2$-$Ca(NO_3)_2$, and NaCl-seawater and Na_2SO_4-seawater systems; Butler and co-workers (1967–1970) on the NaCl-$MgSO_4$, NaCl-$MgCl_2$, NaCl-$CaCl_2$-NaCl-Na_2SO_4, and NaCl-Na_2CO_3 systems; Robinson and Covington (1968) on the KCl-$CaCl_2$ system; Lietzke and co-workers (1968–1969) on the HCl-$MgCl_2$, HCl-$SrCl_2$, and HCl-CsCd-$BaCl_2$ systems; Wu, Rush, and Scatchard (1968, 1969) on the NaCl-Na_2SO_4, $MgCl_2$-$MgSO_4$, Na_2SO_4-$MgSO_4$, and $Na_2SO_4MgCl_2$ systems; Pytkowicz and Kester (1969) on the NaCl-Na_2SO_4 system; Reilly and Stokes (1970) on the NaCl-$CdCl_2$ system; Leyendekkers and Whitfield (1971) on the NaCl-$CaCl_2$ system; Christenson and Gieskes (1971) on the KCl-$MgCl_2$, KCl-$CaCl_2$, KCl-$BaCl_2$, KCl-$MgSO_4$, and KCl-K_2SO_4 systems; and Childs and Platford (1971) on the NaCl-Na_2SO_4 and NaCl-$MgCl_2$ systems.

Scatchard (1969) derived an analytical equation describing the excess free energy of solutions that contain any number of electrolytes of different valence types. Although Scatchard's equation is adequate to express the experimental data for various mixtures, it is difficult to use to predict the properties of a multicomponent mixture (since the interaction coefficients are given in sets of ions—Wood and Reilly, 1970). Scatchard, Rush, and Johnson (1970) have recently used Scatchard's equations to examine the system $NaCl$-$MgSO_4$.

Recently, Reilly and Wood (1969) have extended Wood and Anderson's equation to charge asymmetric mixtures. This equation expresses the free energy of a multicomponent charge asymmetric mixture in terms of the properties of pure electrolytes and of two component mixtures of electrolytes with a common ion. The equation is

$$G = \sum_{M,X} E_M E_X (Z_M - Z_X)(G_{MX}{}^0/2EI) + (RT/4E) \sum_{N<M,X} E_M E_N E_X (Z_M - Z_X) \times (Z_N Z_X) g_{M,NX} + (RT/4E) \sum_{X<Y,M} E_M E_X E_Y (Z_M - Z_X)(Z_M - Z_Y) g_{XYM} \quad (33)$$

where the $G_{MX}{}^0$ terms are the excess free energies of the pure electrolytes, the g_{MNX} terms result from measurements on common ion mixtures (MX and NX), E is the total equivalents per kilogram of solvent, E_X is the equivalent fraction of species X, and Z_X is the charge on ion X.

Since Friedman's theory as well as experimental work (Wood, Patton, and Ghamhar, 1969) has shown that for charge asymmetric mixtures g_{MNX} no longer remains finite as $I \to O$, one would expect this equation for asymmetric mixtures to be less reliable than the equation for symmetric mixtures.

Wood, Ghamkhar, and Patton (1969) have used the equation of Reilly and Wood to predict heats of mixing of two alkali chlorides with an alkaline earth chloride with reasonable success. Wu, Rush, and Scatchard's work on $NaCl$-$MgSO_4$ mixtures have been shown to obey the cross-square rule within experimental error. Reilly and Wood (1969) have shown that the cross-square rule for asymmetric mixtures should be weighted by an appropriate valence factor. Their equation for the $MgSO_4$-$NaCl$ system (Wood and Reilly, 1970)

$NaCl$ —— Na_2SO_4

$MgCl_2$ —— $MgSO_4$

is given by

$$6[\Delta_m G(MgSO_4\text{-}NaCl) + \Delta_m G(MgCl_2\text{-}Na_2SO_4)] = 5\Delta_m G(MgCl_2\text{-}NaCl) + 7\Delta_m G(MgSO_4\text{-}Na_2SO_4) + 7\Delta_m G(MgCl_2\text{-}MgSO_4) + 5\Delta_m G(NaCl\text{-}Na_2SO_4) \quad (34)$$

Wood and Reilly found that the weighted cross-square rule is also obeyed within experimental error; thus, it is not possible at present to select whether the weighted or unweighted methods are best.

Wood and Reilly (1970) have shown that the volume of mixing data of Wirth and Mills (1968) and Wirth and LoSurdo (1968) on $LiCl$-Na_2SO_4 mixtures can also be represented by a weighted and unweighted cross-square rule.

Scatchard, Rush, and Johnson (1970) have derived equations for the excess free energy, osmotic coefficient, and activity coefficients for asymmetric mixtures of electrolytes using the ion component treatment of Scatchard (1968). In this method the excess free energy is divided into a Debye-Hückel part, $(G^{ex})^{DH}$ and two non-Debye-Hückel parts, $(G^{ex})^{nI}$ and $(G^{ex})^{nII}$:

$$\frac{G^{ex}}{RTW} = \left(\frac{G^{ex}}{RTW}\right)^{DH} + \left(\frac{G^{ex}}{RTW}\right)^{nI} + \left(\frac{G^{ex}}{RTW}\right)^{nII} \quad (35)$$

where W is the number of kilograms of solvent. The non-Debye-Hückel terms are expressed as a series of interaction terms involving products of the equivalents of each species and are resolved into two components $(G^{ex}/RTW)^{nI}$ and $(G^{ex}/RTW)^{nII}$. These two components can be evaluated from measurements on two ion (single salt) solutions and from three ion (common ion) solutions. By appropriate differentiation, the osmotic coefficient is to be given by

$$\phi - 1 = (\phi - 1)^{DH} + (\phi - 1)^{nI} + (\phi - 1)^{nII} \tag{36}$$

and the activity coefficients by

$$\ln \gamma_{\pm} = (\ln \gamma_{\pm})^{DH} + (\ln \gamma_{\pm})^{nI} + (\ln \gamma_{\pm})^{nII} \tag{37}$$

Scatchard, Rush, and Johnson (1970) have applied these equations to the NaCl-$MgSO_4$ system and synthetic seawater solutions. They compared the results with their earlier calculations using the neutral-electrolyte treatment of Scatchard (1961), in which the components are considered to be neutral salts and water rather than ions.

Gibbard and Scatchard (1972) have recently applied these equations to synthetic seawater solutions from 25 to 100°C. Also, Reilly, Wood, and Robinson (1971) recently used equation 33 of Reilly and Wood (1969) to derive expressions for the osmotic and activity coefficients of multicomponent charge asymmetric mixtures of electrolytes. The osmotic coefficient (ϕ) was obtained from equation 33 by differentiating according to the equation

$$RTm(1 - \phi) = G - m(\partial G/\partial m) = \partial(G/m)/\partial(1/m) \tag{38}$$

and using the relations for the pure electrolyte in water

$$G_{MX}{}^{0} = RTm(1 - \phi_{MX}{}^{0} + \ln \gamma_{MX}{}^{0}) \tag{39}$$

$$\partial G_{MX}{}^{0}/\partial m = RT \ln \gamma_{MX}{}^{0} \tag{40}$$

where the superscript zero refers to the pure electrolyte in water. In a simplified form (i.e., neglecting the limits of summation) the osmotic coefficient of the mixture is given by

$$\begin{aligned} RTm(1 - \phi) = {} & -RT/E\left(\sum E_M E_X/Z_M Z_X\right)(Z_M - Z_X)(1 - \phi_{MX}{}^{0}) - (RT/4E) \\ & \times \sum E_M E_N E_X (Z_M - Z_X)\{g_{MN}X + I(\partial/\partial I)(g_{MN}X)\} - RT/4E \\ & \times \sum E_M E_X E_Y (Z_M - Z_X)(Z_M - Z_Y)\{g_{XY}M + I(\partial/\partial I)(g_{XY}M)\} \end{aligned} \tag{41}$$

From the equations for two salts with a common ion (MX and NX) they obtain values for the trace activity coefficients

$$\ln \gamma_{\pm}(MX) = \ln \gamma_{\pm}{}^{0}(MX) + [1 - \phi_{MX}{}^{0} - (Z^M/Z^N)(1 - \phi_{NX}{}^{0})] - \tfrac{1}{2}Z^M Z^X I g_{MN}X \tag{42}$$

$$\begin{aligned} \ln \gamma_{\pm}(NX) = {} & \ln \gamma_{\pm}{}^{0}(NX) + [-(Z^N/Z^M)(1 - \phi_{MX}{}^{0}) + 1 - \phi_{NX}{}^{0}] \\ & - \tfrac{1}{2}Z^N Z^X I g_{MN}X \end{aligned} \tag{43}$$

These equations are of the same form as Harned's rule (Harned and Owen, 1958):

$$\ln \gamma_{\pm}(MX) = \ln \gamma_{\pm}{}^{0}(MX) + \alpha I_{NX} \tag{44}$$

Reilly, Wood, and Robinson (1971) obtained the activity coefficient of a salt in a multicomponent electrolyte solution from equation 33 by differentiating according to the equation

$$RT \ln \gamma_{\pm}(MX) = \partial G/\partial m \tag{45}$$

The equation is quite lengthy and the reader is referred to the original paper for its exact form. As with the osmotic coefficient equation the activity coefficient equation is given by three terms: (1) a term related to the activity coefficient and osmotic coefficient of the electrolyte in pure water; (2) a term related to the mixing of solutions with a common cation; and (3) a term related to the mixing of solutions with a common anion. There are, thus, two levels of approximation that can be used. The first level of approximation uses only data on single electrolyte solutions. The second level of approximation uses data on common ion mixtures of electrolytes. Reilly, Wood, and Robinson (1971) applied the first level approximation to HCl-$Mg(ClO_4)_2$ (Stokes and Stokes, 1963) and HCl-$Ca(ClO_4)_2$ (Weeks, 1967) and showed that their estimates were superior to the ionic strength principle (which gives the trace activity coefficient the same value as the activity coefficient of the pure electrolyte at the same ionic strength). The full equations were applied to LiCl-NaCl-KCl, LiCl-NaCl-CsCl, LiCl-NaCl-$BaCl_2$, NaCl-KCl-$BaCl_2$ (Robinson and Bower, 1965a, b) and HCl-CsCl-$BaCl_2$ mixtures (Lietzke, Hupf, and Stoughton, 1969). In all cases the predictions agree with the experimental measurements to within the experimental error.

In a recent paper, Robinson and Wood (1972) have applied the equations of Reilly, Wood, and Robinson (1971) to the NaCl-$MgSO_4$ system. As discussed later these estimations are in excellent agreement with the experimental results (Wu, Rush, and Scatchard, 1968, 1969).

The success of the equations of Reilly, Wood, and Robinson (1971) is quite remarkable and they should prove to be very useful in future work. It is difficult at present, however, to make a valid judgment as to which of the methods (Scatchard et al., 1961–1969 or Wood et al., 1969–1971) are more reliable. We prefer the equations of Wood et al., since they are based on Friedman's theory for multicomponent electrolyte solutions.

Other methods of estimating activity coefficients are still being successfully used. For example, Lakshaman and Rangarajan (1970) have successfully used the Guggenheim relation (1935)

$$\ln \gamma_{MX} = -A_\gamma Z_M Z_X[I^2/1 + I^2] + [\gamma_+/\gamma_+ + \gamma_-] \times 2 \sum_X \beta_{MX} m_X + [\gamma_-/\gamma_+ + \gamma_-]2 \sum_{M'} \beta_{M'X} m_{M'} \tag{46}$$

where M and X denote, respectively, a cation and an anion, A_γ is the theoretical Debye-Hückel slope, and β_{MX} are specific interaction coefficients characteristic of the electrolytes MX. They predicted the $\gamma_\pm$(NaCl) in NaCl-$NaNO_3$, NaCl-$NaClO_4$, NaCl-Na_2SO_4, and NaCl-$NaC_2H_3O_2$ solutions to 6 m providing the β term is expressed as a function of ionic strength. As pointed out by Rosseinsky and Hill (1971), part of the concentration dependence of β is due to the particular choice of the Debye-Hückel term (which would cancel for electrolytes of the same charge type).

Since the Guggenheim (1935) equation treats only cation-anion pairs (ignoring cation-cation and anion-anion pairs) and has restrictions imposed on the ion size parameter, it is generally not as reliable as the equation of Reilly, Wood, and Robinson (1971) at high ionic strengths. More recently, Guggenheim (1966) has proposed an equation that includes pairs formed by two ions of the same charge, but this treatment has been applied only to mixtures of univalent electrolytes.

As is apparent from the previous discussion, most of the recent treatments on the ionic interactions in multicomponent electrolyte solutions have been mainly confined to the methods of Friedman (1962) and Scatchard (1968). Little work has been done on hydration effects in multicomponent electrolyte solutions. One such study is the recent work of Leyendekkers (1971). She has illustrated a linear correlation of Harned coefficients, excess free energy, and enthalpy of mixing two electrolytes with a common ion with the ionic entropy (which is related to ion-water interactions). She has also used Glueckauf's volume statistics to predict the activity coefficients of electrolytes in 1:1/1:1 mixtures. Her predictions are reasonable; however, she suggested the need to express hydration numbers as a function of concentration. It is interesting to note that Stokes and Robinson (1972) have recently shown that if hydration numbers are expressed as a function of concentration, their activity equations can fit the experimental data to very high concentrations.

The estimation of the partial molal volume of ions in seawater has been made by Millero (1969) by using a simple model for ion-water interactions in the medium of seawater. He found that the partial molal volume of transfer of ions from pure water to seawater $\Delta\bar{V}(trans)$ could be represented by the semiempirical equation

$$\Delta\bar{V}(trans) = a(Z^2/r) + b \tag{47}$$

where Z is the charge on the ion and r is the crystal radius of the ion (in A^0 units). The constant $a = 0.37_2$ is related to differences in electrostriction between the two media and the constant $b = 0.83_3$ is related to differences in packing effects. Presently, we (Millero and Wood, in preparation) are attempting to use the differentiated (with regard to pressure) equations of Reilly, Wood, and Robinson (1971) to calculate the $\bar{V}$ of salts in the medium of seawater. It will be interesting to compare these estimates with Millero's (1969) semiempirical equation.

In summary, the revised Young's rule of Wood and Anderson (1968) and the extensions made by Reilly and Wood (1969) and Reilly, Wood, and Robinson (1971) based on the ionic solution theories of Friedman (1962) appear to predict the properties of multicomponent electrolyte solutions within experimental error. In the next sections of this chapter we shall examine the use of some of these methods of predicting the properties of seawater as well as solutes in the medium of seawater.

4. The Composition and Stoichiometry of Seawater

Before we can examine the interactions of the major components of seawater, we must characterize the composition of seawater. As has been adequately demonstrated by numerous workers (see Culkin, 1965; Riley and Chester, 1971) the relative composition of the major (greater than 1 ppm by weight) 11 components of seawater is nearly constant. Thus, by measuring one constituent of seawater, the composition of the other components can be characterized. The constituent normally selected to characterize a given seawater sample is the chlorinity, Cl(‰). The chlorinity is determined by the titration of seawater with $AgNO_3$ and is defined as the mass in grams of Ag necessary to precipitate the halogens (Cl and Br) in 328.5233 g of seawater. The ratios of the mass of the major constituents of natural seawater (grams/kilogram of solution) to chlorinity (grams/kilogram of solution) are given in column two of Table I (Lyman and Fleming, 1940; Culkin, 1965; Riley and Chester, 1971). The results given for HCO_3^- are actually values of the carbonate alkalinity expressed as though it were all bicarbonate. At a pH = 8 and 25°C, the carbonate alkalinity is ~91% HCO_3^- and ~9% CO_3^{2-} (Edmond, 1970). Boron in seawater exists primarily as boric acid, which

TABLE I

Composition of One Kilogram of Natural Seawater of Various Chlorinities

Species	$g_i/\mathrm{Cl}(‰)$	$n_i/\mathrm{Cl}(‰)$	$e_i/\mathrm{Cl}(‰)$	$n_iZ_i^2/\mathrm{Cl}(‰)$
Na^+	0.55556	0.0241655	0.0241655	0.0241655
Mg^{2+}	0.06680	0.0027484	0.0054968	0.0109936
Ca^{2+}	0.02125	0.0005302	0.0010604	0.0021208
K^+	0.02060	0.0005268	0.0005268	0.0005268
Sr^{2+}	0.00041	0.0000047	0.0000094	0.0000188
Cl^-	0.99894	0.0281765	0.0281765	0.0281765
SO_4^{2-}	0.14000	0.0014575	0.0029149	0.0058298
HCO_3^-	0.00735	0.0001205	0.0001205	0.0001205
Br^-	0.00348	0.0000436	0.0000436	0.0000436
F^-	0.00006_7	0.0000035	0.0000035	0.0000035
		0.0577772	0.0625179	0.0719994
		$\frac{1}{2}\sum = 0.0288886$	$\frac{1}{2}\sum = 0.0312590$	
$B(OH)_3$	0.00132	0.0000213	0.0000213	$\frac{1}{2}\sum = 0.0359997$
	$\sum = 1.81577_7$	$\sum = 0.0289099$	$\sum = 0.0312803$	

is only slightly hydrolyzed ($\sim$20%) to $B(OH)_4^-$ at the pH of seawater ($\sim$8.2). These assumptions will have only a small effect on the calculations to follow. The value given for Na^+ was determined by difference (i.e., by making the $\sum$ of cation equivalents equal to the $\sum$ of the anion equivalents). Recent measurements of $g_i/\mathrm{Cl}(‰)$ for Na^+ vary from 0.5555 (Culkin and Cox, 1966) to 0.5567 (Riley and Tongudai, 1967). The maximum standard deviation of $g_i/\mathrm{Cl}(‰)$ is $\sim$0.0007 (for Na^+) and most of the values for the other species are good to $\sim$1%.

The total grams of sea salt[1] (g_T) for 1 kg of solution is related to the chlorinity by

$$g_T = 1.81578\ \mathrm{Cl}(‰) \tag{48}$$

Using the definition of salinity (UNESCO, 1966)

$$S(‰) = 1.80655\ \mathrm{Cl}(‰) \tag{49}$$

we have

$$g_T = 1.005109 S(‰) \tag{50}$$

The ratios of the moles of the major constituents of seawater to chlorinity (moles/kilogram of solution) [$n_i = g_i/M_i$, where M_i is the molecular weight of species i (*J. Amer. Chem. Soc.*, **93**, 2579–2580, 1971)] are given in column three of Table I. The total moles of sea salt ($n_T = \frac{1}{2}\sum n_i + n_B$, where n_i is the moles of the ionic components i and n_B is the moles of boric acid) for 1 kg of solution is related to chlorinity by

$$n_T = 0.0289099\ \mathrm{Cl}(‰) \tag{51}$$

and to salinity by

$$n_T = 0.0160028 S(‰) \tag{52}$$

The ratio of the equivalents of the major constituents of seawater to chlorinity

[1] Although seawater contains one nonelectrolyte, $B(OH)_3$, as one of its major constituents, we will use the term "sea salt" to refer to the major solutes of seawater.

(equivalents/kilogram of solution) ($e_i = g_i/M'_i$, where M'_i is the equivalent weight of species i; $M'_i = M_i/Z_i$, where Z_i is the charge on the ion) are given in column four of Table I. The total equivalents of sea salt ($n'_T = \frac{1}{2}\sum e_i + n_B$) for 1 kg of solution is related to chlorinity and salinity by

$$n'_T = 0.0312803\ \mathrm{Cl}(‰) \tag{53}$$

and

$$n'_T = 0.0173149S(‰) \tag{54}$$

The ratio of the ionic strength of the major constituents to chlorinity (moles/kilogram of solution) are given in column five of Table I. The total ionic strength ($I_T = \frac{1}{2}\sum n_i Z_i^2$, where Z_i is the charge of species i) of sea salt/kilogram of solution are related to chlorinity and salinity by

$$I_T = 0.0359997\ \mathrm{Cl}(‰) \tag{55}$$

and

$$I_T = 0.0199273S(‰) \tag{56}$$

The weight fraction, mole fraction, equivalent fraction, and ionic strength fraction of solutes in sea salt calculated from Table I are given in Table II. For most of the discussion and calculations we shall make, the equivalent fractions will be used. The calculation for the mean molecular weight and equivalent weight of sea salt from

$$M_T = \sum N_i M_i \tag{57}$$

and

$$M_T = \sum E_i M'_i \tag{58}$$

are shown in Table III. The M_T and M'_T can be used to convert g_T to n_T and n'_T, respectively.

TABLE II

The Weight Fraction, Mole Fraction, Equivalent Fraction, and Ionic Strength Fraction of Solutes in Sea Salt

Solute	X_i	N_i	E_i	I_i
Na^+	0.305963	0.835890	0.772547	0.671269
Mg^{2+}	0.036789	0.095068	0.175727	0.305380
Ca^{2+}	0.011703	0.018340	0.033900	0.058912
K^+	0.011345	0.018222	0.016841	0.014633
Sr^{2+}	0.000226	0.000163	0.000301	0.000522
Cl^-	0.550145	0.974632	0.900775	0.782687
SO_4^{2-}	0.077102	0.050415	0.093186	0.161940
HCO_3^-	0.004048	0.004168	0.003852	0.003347
Br^-	0.001916	0.001508	0.001394	0.001211
$B(OH)_3$	0.000727	0.000737	0.000681	—
F^-	0.000037	0.000121	0.000112	0.000097

TABLE III

Calculation of the Molecular and Equivalent Weight of Sea Salt

Species	M	M_i'	N_iM_i	E_iM_i'
Na^+	22.9898	22.9898	19.2169	17.7607
Mg^{2+}	24.305	12.1525	2.3106	2.1355
Ca^{2+}	40.08	20.0400	0.7351	0.6794
K^+	39.102	39.1020	0.7125	0.6585
Sr^{2+}	87.62	43.8100	0.0143	0.0132
Cl^-	35.453	35.4530	34.5536	31.9352
SO_4^{2-}	96.0576	48.0288	4.8427	4.4756
HCO_3^-	61.0172	61.0172	0.2543	0.2350
Br^-	79.904	79.9040	0.1205	0.1114
$B(OH)_3$	61.8322	61.8322	0.0456	0.0421
F^-	18.9984	18.9984	0.0023	0.0021
			62.8084	58.0487

The total molarity (c_T), molality (m_T), equivalent molarity and normality (N_T), equivalent molality (e_T), volume ionic strength (I_V), and weight ionic strength (I_m) of seawater solution of various chlorinities and salinities can be calculated from the equations

$$c_T = 0.0289099\,\mathrm{Cl}(‰) \times d \tag{59a}$$

$$c_T = 0.0160028S(‰) \times d \tag{59b}$$

$$m_T = \frac{28.9099\,\mathrm{Cl}(‰)}{1000 - 1.81578\,\mathrm{Cl}(‰)} \tag{60a}$$

$$m_T = \frac{16.0028S(‰)}{1000 - 1.005109S(‰)} \tag{60b}$$

$$N_T = 0.0312803\,\mathrm{Cl}(‰) \times d \tag{61a}$$

$$N_T = 0.0173149S(‰) \times d \tag{61b}$$

$$e_T = \frac{31.2803\,\mathrm{Cl}(‰)}{1000 - 1.81578\,\mathrm{Cl}(‰)} \tag{62a}$$

$$e_T = \frac{17.3149S(‰)}{1000 - 1.005109S(‰)} \tag{62b}$$

$$I_V = 0.0359997\,\mathrm{Cl}(‰) \times d \tag{63a}$$

$$I_V = 0.0199273S(‰) \times d \tag{63b}$$

and

$$I_m = \frac{35.9997\,\mathrm{Cl}(‰)}{1000 - 1.81578\,\mathrm{Cl}(‰)} \tag{64a}$$

$$I_m = \frac{19.9273S(‰)}{1000 - 1.005109S(‰)} \tag{64b}$$

where d is the density of the solution. As will be demonstrated in later calculations, it is frequently convenient to define Cl(‰) × d by Cl_V, which is the volume chlorinity (equal to the chlorosity at 20°C).

The Debye-Hückel limiting law slope for various thermodynamic functions contains a valence factor that must be considered when comparing the properties of sea salt to other electrolytes (e.g., NaCl). The valence factor w is defined as

$$w = \tfrac{1}{2} \sum \gamma_i Z_i^2 \tag{65}$$

where γ_i is the number of ions i of charge Z_i. For a monovalent ion, $w = \frac{1}{2}$ and for a divalent ion, $w = 1$. When the property of interest is expressed in moles, w for sea salt equals $\sum N_i w_i = 1.081$, and when the property of interest is expressed in equivalents, w for sea salt equals $\sum E_i w_i = 1.151$. These results are very important, since they indicate that according to the Debye-Hückel theory, sea salt should behave in dilute solutions as either 1.081 or 1.151 times the behavior of a 1-1 electrolyte (depending on whether the property of interest is expressed in moles or equivalents). This is an important fact, since many workers have incorrectly compared sea salt properties to the 1-1 electrolyte NaCl.

It should be pointed out that all of the concentration equations derived in this section are valid for "average" seawater and dilutions made with pure water. The small changes in pH that occur when seawater is diluted with pure water will not cause large changes in relative concentrations; however, diluting seawater with other than pure water can cause significant effects (Lyman and Fleming, 1940).

5. Prediction of the Properties of Seawater Using Young's Rule

In the following sections we shall examine the use of Young's rule in predicting the apparent equivalent volume, apparent equivalent compressibility, osmotic coefficient, apparent equivalent heat capacity, relative apparent equivalent enthalpy, and viscosity of seawater (Millero, 1971d). These predictions will be made from the properties of pure water and binary solutions of the major component of seawater in pure water. Except in the case of free energies, the excess properties for mixing sea salts with each other are unknown. We are thus forced to use only the first term of Wood and Anderson's (1966) revised form for Young's rule given by

$$\Phi = \sum_{MX} E_M E_X \phi_{MX} + E_B \phi_B \tag{66}$$

where Φ is an apparent molal property (such as volume, expansibility, compressibility, heat capacity, etc); E_M and E_X are, respectively, the equivalent fraction of cation M and anion X; ϕ_{MX} is the apparent equivalent property of MX; E_B is the equivalent fraction of boric acid; and ϕ_B is the apparent equivalent property of boric acid. The extension of Young's rule to electrolyte and nonelectrolyte solutions (i.e., the addition of $E_B\phi_B$ to equation 66) has recently been demonstrated to be reliable for the apparent molal volumes of boric acid–NaCl solutions over a wide concentration range (Ward and Millero, 1972).

By making the summation for each cation over all its possible salts, one obtains the equivalent weighted cation contribution. For example, for the Na^+ anion contribution, we have

$$\phi\left(\text{Na} \sum X_i\right) = E_{\text{Na}} E_{\text{Cl}} \phi(\text{NaCl}) + E_{\text{Na}} E_{\text{SO}_4} \phi(\tfrac{1}{2}\text{Na}_2\text{SO}_4) + E_{\text{Na}} E_{\text{HCO}_3} \phi(\text{NaHCO}_3) + E_{\text{Na}} E_{\text{Br}} \phi(\text{NaBr}) + E_{\text{Na}} E_{\text{F}} \phi(\text{NaF}) \tag{67}$$

The total Φ is given by

$$\Phi = \phi\left(\text{Na} \sum X_i\right) + \phi\left(\text{Mg} \sum X_i\right) + \phi\left(\text{Ca} \sum X_i\right) + \phi\left(K \sum X_i\right) + \phi\left(\text{Sr} \sum X_i\right) + \phi(B) \quad (68)$$

where $\phi(M \sum X_i)$ is the cation contributions and $\phi(B) = E_B\phi_B$ is the boric acid contribution.

The difficulty of using these equations to calculate the apparent properties of seawater rests in the paucity of reliable physical chemical data for all the major sea salts over the concentration (0.1 to 0.8 molal ionic strength) and temperature (0 to 40°C) range of interest. Since salts like $CaSO_4$ are not soluble in pure water at high ionic strengths, one must estimate its properties by some additivity method [e.g., $\phi(Ca_2SO_4) = \phi(CaCl_2) + \phi(Na_2SO_4) - 2\phi(NaCl)$]. Since the two major cations (Na^+ and Mg^{2+}) make up 95% of the total and the two anions (Cl^- and $SO_4{}^{2-}$) make up 99% of the total (on an equivalent basis) of the sea salt ions, it is often possible as a first approximation to make the assumption that $\phi(Na^+) = \phi(K^+)$, $\phi(Mg^{2+}) = \phi(Ca^{2+}) = \phi(Sr^{2+})$ and $\phi(Cl^-) = \phi(Br^-) = \phi(HCO_3{}^-) = \phi(F^-)$.

By dividing the apparent property into an infinite dilution term (Φ^0) and one or more concentration terms (S' or b),

$$\Phi = \Phi^0 + S'I_V^{1/2} \quad (69)$$

$$\Phi = \Phi^0 + SI_V^{1/2} + bI_V \quad (70)$$

it is possible to simplify the use of Young's rule. Since the infinite dilution volume properties are always additive, the ϕ^0's for the major ionic components can be estimated from data on soluble salts. Thus, Wood and Anderson's (1966) revised form of Young's rule need only be applied to the concentration dependent terms (S' and b); S is the theoretical Debye-Hückel term and can be estimated for any system without using Young's rule. Since the concentration dependent terms appear to be additive for the simple alkali halides and alkaline earth halides (Millero, 1972) (which are the major components of seawater), it is also possible as a first approximation to use the "best" additivity ionic concentration terms.

Although the additivity of the concentration terms for the halide salts has been adequately demonstrated for the volume properties, the concentration terms for the sulfate salts are not additive. For example, at 0, 25, and 50°C, we obtain the volume concentration terms for $\frac{1}{2}SO_4{}^{2-}$ ion, $S_V^*(\frac{1}{2}SO_4{}^{2-})$, shown in Table IV (assuming $S_V^*(H^+) = 0$). The values for $S_V^*(\frac{1}{2}SO_4{}^{2-})$ obtained from Na_2SO_4 and K_2SO_4 are quite similar; however, the value obtained from $MgSO_4$ is much larger [presumably because of ion pairing in the $MgSO_4$ system (Millero, 1971c and Millero and Masterson, 1973)]. By weighting the $S_V^*(\frac{1}{2}2SO_4{}^{2-})$ obtained from Na_2SO_4, K_2SO_4, and $MgSO_4$, according to the equivalent concentration of the cations and assuming the $S_V^*(\frac{1}{2}SO_4{}^{2-})$'s for Ca^{2+} and Sr^{2+} are equal to the Mg^{2+} contribution, we have

$$S_V^*(\tfrac{1}{2}SO_4{}^{2-}) = E_{Na} \times S_V^*(\tfrac{1}{2}SO_4{}^{2-})^{Na_2SO_4} + E_K \times S_V^*(\tfrac{1}{2}SO_4{}^{2-})^{K_2SO_4} + (E_{Mg} + E_{Ca} + E_{Sr}) \times S_V^*(\tfrac{1}{2}SO_4{}^{2-})^{MgSO_4} \quad (71)$$

The weighted values obtained in this manner are shown in Table IV.

Table IV

Calculation of the Weighted Masson Volume S_V^* for $\frac{1}{2}SO_4{}^2$ Ion at 0, 25, and 50°C

	0°C	25°C	50°C
		$S_V^*(\frac{1}{2}SO_4{}^{2-})^{M\,a}$	
From Na_2SO_4	2.591	2.293	3.194
From K_2SO_4	2.461	2.118	2.977
From $MgSO_4$	3.563	3.749	4.191
		$E_M S_V^*(\frac{1}{2}SO_2{}^{4-})^M$	
$E_{Na}S_V^*(\frac{1}{2}SO_4{}^{2-})^{Na}$	2.001	1.771	2.467
$E_K S_V^*(\frac{1}{2}SO_4{}^{2-})^K$	0.041	0.035	0.049
$(E_{Mg} + E_{Ca} + E_{Sr})S_V^*(\frac{1}{2}SO_4{}^{2-})^{Mg}$	0.750	0.790	0.883
Weighted $S_V^*(\frac{1}{2}SO_4)$	2.792	2.596	3.399

[a] Calculated from the Masson S_V^*'s, tabulated by Millero (1972a) and the work of Millero and Masterson (1973). The ionic values are based on $S_V^*(H^+) = 0$, where M refers to cation Na^+, K^+, or Mg.

The reliability of this weighted additivity method of obtaining the total concentration terms compared to the use of the full equation

$$S_V' = S_V^*\left(\text{Na}\sum X_i\right) + S_V^*\left(\text{Mg}\sum X_i\right) + S_V^*\left(\text{Ca}\sum X_i\right) + S_V^*\left(\text{K}\sum X_i\right) + S_V^*\left(\text{Sr}\sum X_i\right) \quad (72)$$

where $S_V^*(MX_i) = E_M E_{Cl} S_V^*(\text{MCl}) + E_M E_{SO_4} S_V^*(\frac{1}{2}\text{M}_2\text{SO}_4) + E_M E_{HCO_3} S_V^*(\text{MHCO}_3) + E_M E_{Br} S_V^*(\text{MBr}) + E_M E_F S_V^*(MF)$; M is the cation Na, Mg, Ca, K, or Sr. Table V shows the results of calculating the volume concentration term S_V' for sea salt at 0°C using equation 72 and the S_V^*'s for sea salts taken from Millero's compilation (1972) and some of our recent results (Millero and Knox, 1973). Similar calculations at 25 and 50°C yield, respectively, $S_V' = 2.247$ and 1.952. These values for S_V' agree very well with the values of S_V' calculated by the weighted additivity method 3.285, 2.245, and 1.955, respectively, at 0, 25, and 50°C (see Table XI). Thus, the two methods of calculating the concentration terms S_V' are equivalent (within experimental error). Since reliable physical chemical data are not available for many of the major sea salts, we shall use the additivity method in subsequent calculations.

The apparent molal or equivalent quantities are directly related to measured physical properties by

$$\Phi = (P_{\text{Soln}} - P_{H_2O})/n_T \quad (73)$$

where P_{Soln} and P_{H_2O} are, respectively, the physical property of the seawater solution and pure water, and n_T is the total moles or equivalents. By combining equations 69 and 70 with equation 73 and noting that $n_T \alpha \text{Cl}_V$ and $I_V \alpha \text{Cl}_V$ (where $\text{Cl}_V = \text{Cl}(‰) \times d$ is the volume chlorinity), we have

$$P_{\text{Soln}} = P_{H_2O} + A'\text{Cl}_V + B'\text{Cl}_V{}^{3/2} \quad (74)$$

TABLE V

Calculations of S'_V at 0°C for Sea Salt Using the Equation $S'_V = \sum_{MX} E_M E_X S^*_V(MX)$

Salt	$S^*_V(MX)$	$E_M E_X S^*_V(MX)$	$\sum E_M E_X S^*_V(MX)$
NaCl	3.323	2.311	
$\frac{1}{2}Na_2SO_4$	5.095	0.367	
$NaHCO_3$	9.400	0.028	2.710
NaBr	2.976	0.003	
NaF	8.051	0.001	
$\frac{1}{2}MgCl_2$	2.200	0.351	
$\frac{1}{2}MgSO_4$	4.915	0.081	
$\frac{1}{2}Mg(HCO_3)_2$	8.248	0.005	0.438
$\frac{1}{2}MgBr_2$	1.960	0.001	
$\frac{1}{2}MgF_2$	6.899	0.000	
$\frac{1}{2}CaCl_2$	2.123	0.063	
$\frac{1}{2}CaSO_4$	4.824	0.015	
$\frac{1}{2}Ca(HCO_3)_2$	8.200	0.001	0.079
$\frac{1}{2}CaBr_2$	1.960	0.000	
$\frac{1}{2}CaF_2$	6.851	0.000	
KCl	3.291	0.049	
$\frac{1}{2}K_2SO_4$	4.933	0.003	
$KHCO_3$	9.640	0.001	0.058
KBr	3.219	0.000	
KF	9.041	0.000	
$\frac{1}{2}SrCl_2$	2.409	0.001	
$\frac{1}{2}SrSO_4$	5.110	0.000	
$\frac{1}{2}Sr(HCO_3)_2$	8.486	0.000	0.001
$\frac{1}{2}SrBr_2$	2.286	0.000	
$\frac{1}{2}SrF_2$	7.137	0.000	
			S'_V = 3.286

and

$$P_{\text{Soln}} = P_{H_2O} + A\text{Cl}_V + B\text{Cl}_V{}^{3/2} + C\text{Cl}_V{}^2 \tag{75}$$

where A and A' = const × [Φ^0], B' = const × [S'], B = const × [S], and C = const × [b]. The constants A and A' are related to ion water interactions, and the constants B', B, D, and C are related to ion-ion interaction (B is related to the theoretical Debye-Hückel ion-ion interaction). The physical properties of seawater at a given concentration (Cl_V) can be visualized, thus, as being equal to

$$P_{\text{Soln}} = P_{H_2O} + \sum \text{ion-water interactions} + \sum \text{ion-ion interactions} \tag{76}$$

where P_{H_2O} is the physical property of water (at a given T and P), the second term is a perturbation due to the weighted ion-water interactions of the major sea salts at infinite dilution, and the third term is a perturbation due to the weighted ion-ion interactions of the major sea salts. The ion-ion interaction term (B') can be split up into a theoretical Debye-Hückel limiting law term (B) and a term due to deviations from the limiting law (C).

$$\sum \text{ion-ion interactions} = \text{Debye-Hückel term} + \sum \text{deviations from Debye-Hückel} \tag{77}$$

This general approach of examining the physical chemical properties serves two purposes: (1) it provides the theoretical concentration dependence of the physical chemical properties of seawater, and (2) it emphasizes the importance of ion-water and ion-ion interactions of the major components of seawater. It should be pointed out that in the low concentration region (when $Cl_V \rightarrow 0$), where the composition of natural seawater changes because of changes in the relative composition of the diluting fresh water (Lyman and Fleming, 1940), these equations will not represent the concentration dependence of seawater. We feel that the best way to handle the changes in Cl_V at the low concentrations is to follow the suggestions of Wirth (1940a). He used Lyman and Fleming's (1940) equation for changes in the ratio of major components of diluting waters to Cl(‰). Taking these corrections into consideration gives for Mg^{2+}, Ca^{2+}, HCO_3^-, and SO_4^{2-} (for Baltic waters):

$$n'_{Mg} = 0.000165 + 0.0054968 \, Cl(‰) \tag{78}$$

$$n'_{Ca} = 0.000769 + 0.0010604 \, Cl(‰) \tag{79}$$

$$n'_{HCO_3} = 0.000808 + 0.0001205 \, Cl(‰) \tag{80}$$

$$n'_{SO_4} = 0.000127 + 0.0029149 \, Cl(‰) \tag{81}$$

where n'_i is the number of equivalents of species i/kilogram of solution. When other water of known composition are the dilution waters, the appropriate correction can be made to Cl_V.

Since all of the predictions we plan to examine are for seawater solutions diluted with pure water, we shall not be concerned with the source of the dilution waters and their appropriate corrections to Cl_V.

In the following sections, we shall examine the use of Young's rule in estimating the volume properties, the thermal properties, and the transport properties of seawater.

A. Thermodynamic Properties

Apparent Equivalent Volumes of Sea Salt (at 1 atm)

Experimental results

The volume properties of a multicomponent electrolyte solution such as seawater can be conveniently treated by using the concept of the apparent equivalent volume (Wirth, 1940; Wirth and Mills, 1968; Wirth and LoSurdo, 1968; Millero, 1971a; Lepple and Millero, 1971; Millero and Lepple, 1973; Millero, 1973a) given by

$$\Phi_V = (V_{Soln} - V_{H_2O})/n'_T \tag{82}$$

where V_{Soln} is the volume of the solution, V_{H_2O} is the volume of water in the solution, and n'_T is the total number of equivalents in solution ($n'_T = \frac{1}{2} \sum n'_i + n_B$). Substituting for V_{Soln} and V_{H_2O}, we have (using molar equivalent concentration units)

$$\Phi_V = \frac{1000(d^0 - d)}{d^0 N_T} + \frac{M'_T}{d^0} \tag{83}$$

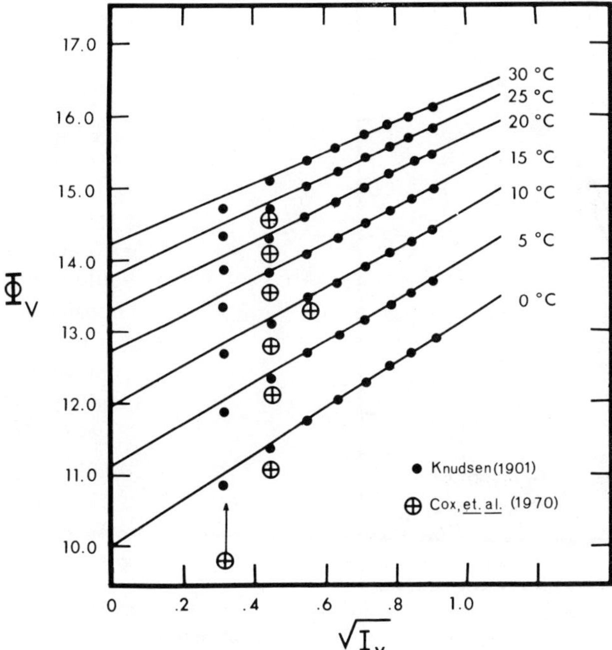

Fig. 1. The apparent equivalent (Φ_V) volume of sea salt plotted versus the square root of the volume ionic strength ($I_V^{1/2}$) at various temperatures.

where d^0 is the density of pure water (Kell, 1967), d is the density of seawater (Knudsen, 1901; Cox, McCartney, and Culkin, 1970), N_T is the total equivalent molarity (or normality) of seawater (equation 61), and M_T' is the mean equivalent weight of sea salt (58.0487). Recently, we (Millero, 1971d, 1973a; Millero and Lepple, 1973) have analyzed the densities of an artificial seawater solution using equation 83. In our present calculations we will be concerned only with natural seawater solutions and the recent calculations made by Schrager and Millero (1972, in preparation). In these calculations we have determined the Φ_V of sea salt from the density data of Knudsen (1901) and Cox, McCartney, and Culkin (1970). The resulting Φ_V's at various temperatures are shown plotted versus the square root of the volume ionic strength (I_V) in Fig. 1. In the high concentration region (20‰ to 40‰ S) the densities of Knudsen (1901) and Cox et al. (1970) give Φ_V's to within ± 0.01 ml/eq. The deviations in the low concentration region (5‰ to 15‰ S) are caused by differences in the diluting waters in the work of Knudsen (1901) and Cox et al. (1970). In the high concentration region, the Φ_V's appear to follow the Masson (1929) equation

$$\Phi_V = \Phi_V{}^0 + S_V' I_V^{1/2} \tag{84}$$

where $\Phi_V{}^0$ is the infinite dilution apparent equivalent volume of sea salt equal to the weighted summation of the apparent equivalent volumes of the major components of seawater [$\Phi_V{}^0 = \sum E_i \phi_V{}^0(i)$] and S_V' is the Masson slope equal to the weighted summation of the Masson slopes of the major components of seawater [$S_V' = \sum E_i S_V^*(i)$]. The nonlinear behavior of the Φ_V''s at concentrations below 20‰ S ($I_V \simeq 0.4$) are due to the fact that diluting waters are not pure water. Since the composition of these diluting waters is unknown (at least for the work of Cox et al.), we will examine only the results above 20‰. The Masson $\Phi_V{}^0$ and S_V' constants for seawater solutions at various

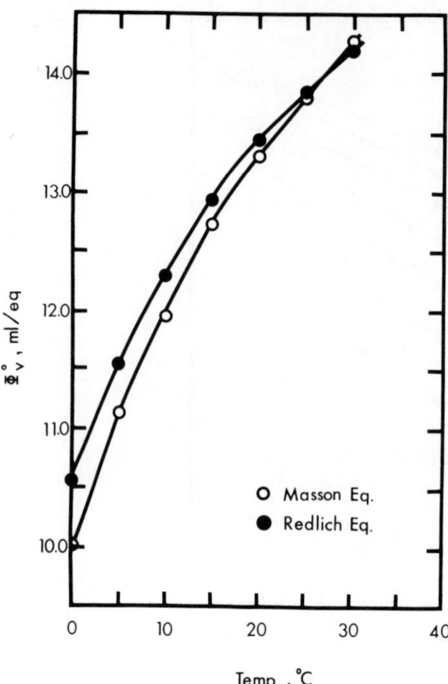

Fig. 2. The apparent equivalent volume of sea salt at infinite dilution ($\Phi_V{}^0$) at various temperatures.

temperatures are given in Table VI along with the average deviations (average ± 0.007 ml/eq over the entire range). Over the concentration range where the Masson equation is valid, the $\Phi_V{}^0$'s and (S_V')'s calculated from the work of Knudsen and Cox et al. are within ± 0.06 ml eq^{-1} liter$^{1/2}$ mol$^{-1/2}$. The Masson Φ_V's for sea salt as a function of temperature are shown in Fig. 2. As with many simple 1-1 electrolytes (Millero, 1971b, 1972) the $\Phi_V{}^0$'s of sea salt appear to go through a maximum near 50°C. As discussed elsewhere (Millero, 1972), this effect is presumably caused by the competition between the electrostriction $\bar{V}^0$ (elect) and void space packing or disordered $\bar{V}^0$ (disord) components of the individual ions of sea salt.

By combining equations 61a, 63a, 83, and 84, we have the Root (1933) density equation for seawater.

$$d = d^0 + A_V' \, \mathrm{Cl}_V + B_V' \, \mathrm{Cl}_V{}^{3/2} \tag{85}$$

where $A_V' = 10^{-3}[M_T' - \Phi_V{}^0 d^0] \times 0.0312803$ and $B_V' = -10^{-3}[S_V' d^0] \times 0.0059350$. As with binary solutions (Millero, 1971a; 1971b; 1972), the A_V' is related to ion water interactions and B_V' is related to ion-ion interactions of the major (weighted) ionic components of seawater. This equation predicts that $(d - d^0)/\mathrm{Cl}_V$ versus $\mathrm{Cl}_V^{1/2}$ should be a straight line for seawater solutions. Although equation 85 was first derived for seawater by Wirth (1940a) 32 years ago, oceanographers still do not fit the densities of seawater to equations of this form (which Wirth showed to be more reliable than other empirical fits). In Fig. 3, a plot of $(d - d^0)/\mathrm{Cl}_V$ versus $\mathrm{Cl}_V^{1/2}$ for seawater solutions is shown. As with the Φ_V's, the $(d - d^0)/\mathrm{Cl}_V$ data at the low concentrations show large deviations from linearity due to the dilution waters not being pure water [and unlike our results for an artificial seawater solution diluted with pure water (Millero and Lepple, 1973)]. The A_V' and B_V' constants calculated for seawater solutions between 20 to 40‰ S are given in Table VII along with the average deviations.

TABLE VI

Constants for the Masson Apparent Equivalent Volume Equation for Seawater at Various Temperatures

Temperature (°C)	Φ_V^0		S_V'		Average Deviation	
	Experimental[a]	Calculated[b]	Experimental	Calculated	Experimental	Calculated
0	10.004 (9.967)	10.012	3.173 (3.207)	3.285	0.006 (0.007)	0.10 (0.11)
5	11.126 (11.073)	10.959	2.874 (2.909)	3.017	0.007 (0.006)	0.05 (0.03)
10	11.969 (11.933)	11.806	2.722 (2.732)	2.780	0.012 (0.006)	0.11 (0.09)
15	12.728 (12.664)	12.554	2.514 (2.571)	2.570	0.007 (0.005)	0.13 (0.11)
20	13.306 (13.286)	13.202	2.386 (2.409)	2.394	0.008 (0.005)	0.10 (0.10)
25	13.793 (13.782)	13.751	2.258 (2.261)	2.246	0.009 (0.005)	0.05 (0.04)
30	14.270	14.200	2.060	2.128	0.009)	0.02

[a] The first values were determined from the densities of Knudsen (1901) while the values in parentheses were determined from the densities of Cox, McCartney, and Culkin (1970).
[b] The calculated values were estimated from the Young's rule values calculated at 0, 25, and 50°C, using equations 89 and 90.

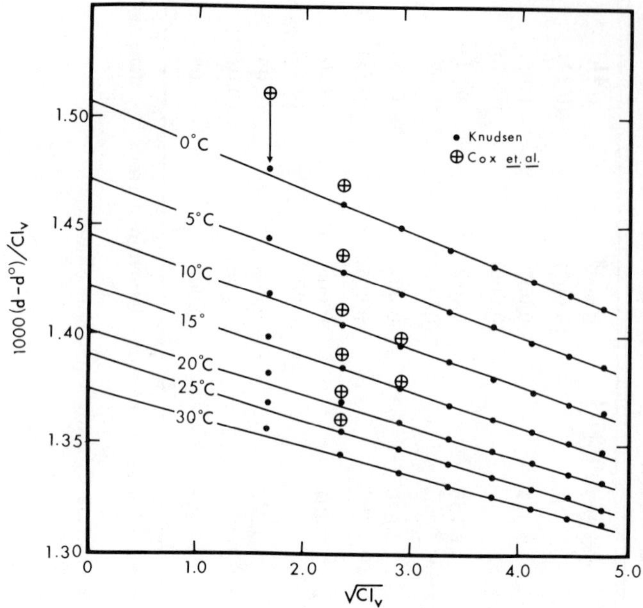

Fig. 3. A plot of $(d - d^0)\ 10^3/\mathrm{Cl}_V$ versus $\mathrm{Cl}_V^{1/2}$ for seawater at various temperatures.

Although the empirical Masson equation has proven useful in representing the concentration dependence of Φ_V at high concentrations, the Redlich equation (Redlich et al., 1931, 1940, 1965) based on the Debye-Hückel limiting law is preferred (Millero, 1971a; 1971b) since it yields more reliable infinite dilution $\Phi_V{}^0$'s. The Redlich equation for sea salt is given by

$$\Phi_V = \Phi_V{}^0 + S_V I_V^{1/2} + b_V I_V \tag{86}$$

where the infinite dilution $\Phi_V{}^0 = \sum E_i \phi_V{}^0(i)$, the theoretical slope $S_V = \sum E_i S_V(i) = k \sum E_i w_i = 1.151k$ [k is the theoretical slope for a 1-1 electrolyte (Millero, 1971b)] and the deviation constant $b_V = \sum E_i b_V(i)$. A plot of $\Phi_V - S_V I_V^{1/2}$ versus I_V for seawater solutions at various temperatures is shown in Fig. 4. The Φ_V's, S_V's, and b_V's for seawater solutions determined by a least squares best fit are given in Table VIII along with the average deviations.

The $\Phi_V{}^0$'s determined from the Redlich equation 86 (also shown in Fig. 2) are more reliable than those determined using the Masson equation 84. The Redlich equation also has an advantage over the Masson equation in that both $\Phi_V{}^0$ and S_V can be estimated from infinite dilution properties and are independent of higher order ion-ion interactions responsible for the deviations from the limiting law. Since the b_V for sea salt [as well as most 1-1 electrolytes (Millero, 1971b; 1972)] is small, errors involved in estimating b_V from ionic $b_V(i)$'s are minimal.

By combining equations 61a, 63a, 83, and 86, we obtain the theoretical Redlich (1940) density equation for seawater:

$$d = d^0 + A_V \mathrm{Cl}_V + B_V \mathrm{Cl}_V^{3/2} + C_V \mathrm{Cl}_V{}^2 \tag{87}$$

where $A_V = 10^{-3}[M'_T - \Phi_V{}^0\, d^0] \times 0.0312803$, $B_V = -10^{-3}(S_V\, d^0) \times 0.0059350$, and $C_V = -10^{-3}(b_V\, d^0) \times 0.0011261$. The constants A_V, B_V, and C_V for seawater determined from the densities of Knudsen (1901) and Cox et al. (1970) are given in Table

TABLE VII

Constants for the Root Density Equation for Seawater at Various Temperatures

Temperature (°C)	d^{0} [a]	$10^3 A'_V$		$-10^3 B'_V$		Average Deviation (ppm)	
		Experimental[b]	Calculated	Experimental	Calculated[c]	Experimental	Calculated[d]
0	0.999868	1.50284 (1.50402)	1.50265	0.018828 (0.019029)	0.019524	3 (4)	41 (55)
5	0.999992	1.46771 (1.46936)	1.47289	0.017058 (0.017267)	0.017924	4 (3)	20 (24)
10	0.999728	1.44142 (1.44255)	1.44640	0.016149 (0.016208)	0.016495	6 (3)	43 (42)
15	0.999129	1.41792 (1.41995)	1.42350	0.014905 (0.015243)	0.015240	4 (3)	50 (52)
20	0.998234	1.40025 (1.40087)	1.40355	0.014133 (0.014272)	0.014160	4 (3)	38 (47)
25	0.997075	1.38554 (1.38583)	1.38688	0.013364 (0.013381)	0.013315	5 (2)	19 (27)
30	0.995678	1.37129	1.37346	0.012174	0.012587	5	9

[a] Taken from Kell (1967). d^0 is in units of grams/milliliter.

[b] The first values were determined from the densities of Knudsen (1901); the values in parentheses were determined from the densities of Cox et al. (1970), both between 20 to 40‰ S.

[c] Calculated from the estimated $\Phi_V{}^0$'s and (S'_V)'s given in Table VI, using the relations $A'_V = 10^{-3}[M'_T - \Phi_V{}^0 d^0] \times 0.0312802$ and $B'_V = -10^{-3}[S'_V d^0] \times 0.0059350$.

[d] Average deviations over the entire concentration range of 5 to 40‰ S.

TABLE VIII

Constants for the Redlich Apparent Equivalent Volume Equation for Seawater at Various Temperatures

Temperature (°C)	Φ_V^0		S_V	B_V		Average Deviation	
	Experimental[a]	Calculated[b]		Experimental	Calculated	Experimental	Calculated
0	10.581 (10.557)	10.466	1.662	0.974 (0.997)	1.237	0.014 (0.028)	0.04 (0.06)
5	11.551 (11.512)	11.521	1.760	0.718 (0.741)	0.829	0.012 (0.011)	0.04 (0.06)
10	12.301 (12.267)	12.312	1.857	0.555 (0.564)	0.574	0.016 (0.010)	0.02 (0.04)
15	12.943 (12.900)	12.946	1.953	0.360 (0.398)	0.281	0.010 (0.008)	0.05 (0.03)
20	13.435 (13.423)	13.487	2.051	0.214 (0.230)	0.065	0.010 (0.007)	0.04 (0.04)
25	13.836 (13.825)	13.914	2.150	0.067 (0.070)	−0.027	0.009 (0.005)	0.02 (0.03)
30	14.200	14.228	2.250	−0.127	−0.062	0.009	0.06

[a] The first values were determined from the densities of Knudsen (1901), while the values in parentheses were determined from the densities of Cox, McCartney, and Culkin (1970).

[b] The calculated values were estimated from Young's rule (Tables XII and XIII).

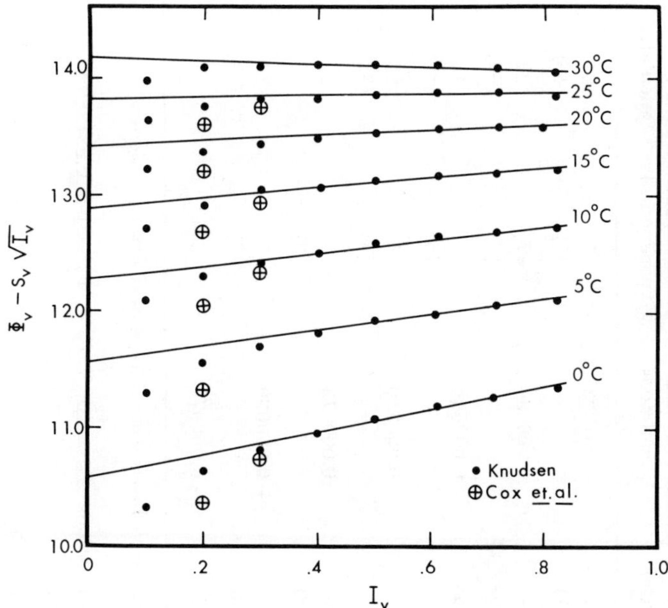

Fig. 4. A plot of $\Phi_V - S_V I_V^{1/2}$ versus I_V for sea salt at various temperatures.

IX along with the average deviations. Since the densities determined by Knudsen (1901) and Cox et al. (1970) were not made in dilute solutions (below $I_V = 0.1$) and the seawater densities in the low concentration range are for a solution of different composition (than 35‰ S seawater), it is not possible to verify the limiting law behavior of sea salt. Since proof of the limiting law has been adequately demonstrated (Millero, 1971b), equation 87 based on the limiting law is the preferred equation for representing the concentration dependence for the density of seawater (even though it does not significantly improve the fit).

Theoretical calculations

Since no data are available for the excess volumes of mixing the major ionic components of seawater, we are forced to use only the first term of the revised form of Young's rule (Wood and Anderson, 1966). Since the volume data for electrolytes have been tabulated by using both the Masson and Redlich equation, we shall use both equations to estimate the apparent volume properties of seawater.

Reliable Masson $\Phi_V{}^0$'s and S_V^*'s for the major ionic components of seawater given by

$$\phi_V(i) = \phi_V{}^0(i) + S_V^*(i)I_V^{1/2} \tag{88}$$

are known only at 0, 25, and 50°C. Using this data, the Masson $\Phi_V{}^0$'s and (S_V')'s for sea salt have been calculated in Tables X and XI. By fitting these Φ_V's and (S_V')'s to the equations

$$\Phi_V{}^0 = 10.012 + 0.19928t - 0.0019888t^2 \tag{89}$$

$$S_V' = 3.285 - 0.05620t + 0.0005984t^2 \tag{90}$$

we have estimated $\Phi_V{}^0$ and S_V' for sea salt from 0 to 30°. The results are given in Table VI along with the average deviations between the calculated and experimental Φ_V's between 20 to 40‰ S. The calculated $\Phi_V{}^0$'s agree with the measured values to

Table IX

Constants for the Redlich Density Equation for Seawater at Various Temperatures

Temperature (°C)	$10^3 A_V$		$-10^3 B_V$	$-10^3 C_V$		Average Deviation (ppm)	
	Experimental[a]	Calculated[b]		Experimental	Calculated	Experimental	Calculated[c]
0	1.48480	1.48839	0.009863	0.001097	0.001393	7	22
	(1.48555)			(0.001121)		(7)	(46)
5	1.45439	1.45534	0.010446	0.000808	0.000934	7	22
	(1.45849)			(0.000985)		(12)	(48)
10	1.43105	1.43070	0.011018	0.000625	0.000646	8	15
	(1.43210)			(0.000635)		(5)	(42)
15	1.41121	1.41112	0.011581	0.000405	0.000316	5	22
	(1.41256)			(0.000447)		(4)	(32)
20	1.39746	1.39459	0.012151	0.000306	0.000073	7	22
	(1.39658)			(0.000258)		(3)	(35)
25	1.38420	1.38176	0.012723	0.000075	−0.000030	5	14
	(1.38453)			(0.000079)		(3)	(29)
30	1.37347	1.37259	0.013296	−0.000142	−0.000070	5	31

[a] The first values were determined from the densities of Knudsen (1901); the values in parentheses were determined from the densities of Cox et al. (1970), both between 20 to 40‰ S.

[b] Calculated from the estimated $\Phi_V{}^0$'s, S_V's, and b_V's given in Table VIII, using the relations $A_V = 10^{-3}[M'_T - \Phi_V{}^0 d^0] \times 0.0312802$, $B_V = -10^{-3}[S_V d^0] \times 0.0059350$, and $C_V = -10^{-3}[b_V d^0] \times 0.0011261$.

[c] Average deviations over the entire concentration range of 5 to 40‰ S.

TABLE X

Calculation of the Masson $\Phi_V{}^0$ for Seawater at 0, 25, and 50°C

	0°C		25°C		50°C	
Solute	$\phi_V{}^a$	$E_i\phi_V{}^0$	$\phi_V{}^0$	$E_i\phi_V{}^0$	$\phi_V{}^0$	$E_i\phi_V{}^0$
Na^+	−4.06	−3.137	−1.67	−1.290	0.05	0.039
$\frac{1}{2}Mg^{2+}$	−11.19	−1.966	−10.97	−1.928	−10.56	−1.856
$\frac{1}{2}Ca^{2+}$	−9.99	−0.339	−8.72	−0.296	−8.36	−0.283
K^+	6.56	0.110	8.54	0.144	9.92	0.167
$\frac{1}{2}Sr^{2+}$	−10.62	−0.003	−9.02	−0.003	−8.01	−0.002
Cl^-	16.42	14.791	18.07	16.277	17.91	16.133
$\frac{1}{2}SO_4{}^{2-}$	4.46	0.416	7.43	0.692	6.99	0.651
$HCO_3{}^-$	21.59	0.083	23.85	0.092	23.96	0.092
Br^-	23.01	0.032	24.95	0.035	25.43	0.035
H_3BO_3	37.0	0.025	40.5	0.028	41.5	0.028
F^-	−1.94	-0.000_2	−0.73	0.000_1	−1.15	-0.000_1
		10.012		13.751		15.004

[a] The ionic $\phi_V{}^0$'s are based on $\phi_V{}^0(H^+) = 0$. The ionic $\phi_V{}^0$'s were taken from Millero's compilation of data (1972a) and the recent works of Millero and Knox (1973). The $\phi_V{}^0$'s for H_3BO_3 were taken from the work of Ward and Millero (1972).

TABLE XI

Calculation of the Masson S'_V for Seawater at 0, 25, and 50°C

	0°C		25°C		50°C	
Solute	S_V^{*a}	$E_iS_V^*$	S_V^*	$E_iS_V^*$	S_V^*	$E_iS_V^*$
Na^+	2.504	1.934	1.217	0.940	0.287	0.222
$\frac{1}{2}Mg^{2+}$	1.352	0.238	0.889	0.156	0.169	0.030
$\frac{1}{2}Ca^{2+}$	1.307	0.044	0.726	0.025	0.107	0.004
K^+	2.472	0.042	1.407	0.024	0.577	0.010
$\frac{1}{2}Sr^{2+}$	1.654	0.000	1.073	0.000	0.393	0.000
Cl^-	0.819	0.738	0.950	0.856	1.517	1.366
$\frac{1}{2}SO_4{}^{2-}$	2.792	0.260	2.596	0.242	3.399	0.317
$HCO_3{}^-$	6.896	0.027	0.543	0.002	1.111	0.004
Br^-	0.569	0.001	0.620	0.001	1.167	0.002
F^-	5.547	0.001	1.143	0.000	1.052	0.000
		3.285		2.246		1.955

[a] The ionic S_V^*'s are based on $S_V^*(H^+) = 0$. The ionic S_V^*'s were taken from Millero's compilation of data (1972a) and the recent work of Millero and Knox (1973).

TABLE

Calculation of the Redlich Infinite Dilution

Solute	0°C		5°C		10°C	
	$\phi_V{}^{0a}$	$E_i\phi_V{}^0$	$\phi_V{}^0$	$E_i\phi_V{}^0$	$\phi_V{}^0$	$E_i\phi_V{}^0$
Na^+	−3.46	−2.673	−2.70	−2.086	−2.21	−1.707
$\frac{1}{2}Mg^{2+}$	−11.16	−1.961	−11.04	−1.940	−10.92	−1.919
$\frac{1}{2}Ca^{2+}$	−9.85	−0.334	−9.55	−0.324	−9.34	−0.317
K^+	7.26	0.122	7.82	0.132	8.22	0.138
$\frac{1}{2}Sr^{2+}$	−10.31	−0.003	−10.01	−0.003	−9.74	−0.003
Cl^-	16.37	14.746	16.79	15.124	17.15	15.448
$\frac{1}{2}SO_4{}^{2-}$	4.63	0.431	5.12	0.477	5.67	0.528
$HCO_3{}^-$	20.99	0.081	21.39	0.082	21.94	0.085
Br^-	22.98	0.032	23.43	0.033	23.94	0.033
H_3BO_3	37.0	0.025	37.9	0.026	38.7	0.026
F^-	−2.54	0.000	−2.34	0.000	−1.98	0.000
		10.466		11.521		12.312

[a] The ionic $\phi_V{}^0$'s are based on $\phi_V{}^0(H^+) = 0$. The ionic $\phi_V{}^0$'s were taken from Millero's compilation of data (1972a) and the recent work of Millero and Knox (1973). The $\phi_V{}^0$'s for H_3BO_3 were taken from the work of Ward and Millero (1972).

within ± 0.17 ml/eq, while the calculated (S'_V)'s agree with the experimental values to within ± 0.14 ml eq^{-1} liter$^{1/2}$ mol$^{-1/2}$. The average deviations between the measured and theoretically calculated Φ_V's from the Masson equation (equation 84) are within ± 0.13 ml/eq over the entire temperature range (average $= \pm 0.08$ ml/eq). The calculated A'_V and B'_V for seawater solutions from 0 to 30°C determined from the Masson $\Phi_V{}^0$'s and (S'_V)'s are given in Table VII along with the average deviations between the calculated and measured densities of seawater. The calculated densities agree with the measured values within an average deviation of ± 60 ppm over the entire temperature and concentration range (average $= \pm 42$ ppm). Since the Masson data is not very reliable, it is not possible at present to state with certainty that deviations are caused by unreliable ϕ_V data or deviations in Young's rule.

Using more reliable ϕ_V data for the major sea salts fitted to the Redlich equation

$$\phi_V = \phi_V{}^0(i) + S_V(i)I_V^{1/2} + b_V(i)I_V \qquad (91)$$

we have determined the Redlich Φ_V and $b_V{}^0$ for sea salt. The calculations of the Redlich $\Phi_V{}^0$ and b_V for sea salt from 0 to 30°C are shown in Tables XII and XIII. The calculated $\Phi_V{}^0$'s (Table VIII) agree with the experimental values to within ± 0.11 ml/eq and calculated by b_V's (Table VIII) with the experimental values to within ± 0.3 ml eq^{-1} liter mol^{-1}. It is interesting to note that even though the experimental seawater Φ_V's were not measured in dilute solutions, the experimental $\Phi_V{}^0$'s are in reasonable agreement with the theoretically calculated values (showing the value of using the Redlich equation). The average deviations between the calculated and measured Φ_V's between 0 to 40‰ are within ± 0.06 ml/eq over the entire temperature range.

The theoretically calculated A_V, B_V, and C_V for seawater solutions for the Redlich density equations are given in Table IX. The average deviations between the measured and calculated densities are within 48 ppm (average ± 21 ppm) for Knudsen's

XII

$\Phi_V{}^0$ for Seawater at Various Temperatures

15°C		20°C		25°C		30°C	
$\phi_V{}^0$	$E_i\phi_V{}^0$	$\phi_V{}^0$	$E_i\phi_V{}^0$	$\phi_V{}^0$	$E_i\phi_V{}^0$	$\phi_V{}^0$	$E_i\phi_V{}^0$
−1.84	−1.421	−1.50	−1.159	−1.21	−0.935	−0.99	−0.765
−10.80	−1.898	−10.70	−1.880	−10.59	−1.861	−10.49	−1.843
−9.19	−0.312	−9.03	−0.306	−8.93	−0.303	−8.86	−0.300
8.54	0.144	8.82	0.149	9.03	0.152	9.19	0.155
−9.49	−0.003	−9.28	−0.003	−9.08	−0.003	−8.92	−0.003
17.44	15.710	17.67	15.917	17.83	16.061	17.93	16.151
6.20	0.578	6.64	0.619	6.99	0.651	7.28	0.678
22.50	0.087	22.98	0.089	23.39	0.090	23.76	0.092
24.39	0.034	24.57	0.034	24.71	0.034	25.01	0.035
39.4	0.027	40.0	0.027	40.5	0.028	40.9	0.028
−1.63	0.000	−1.36	0.000	−1.16	0.000	−1.01	0.000
	12.946		13.487		13.914		14.228

densities and ±39 ppm for the densities of Cox et al., over the entire temperature (0 to 30°C) and concentration (0 to 40‰) range. The improved fit (i.e., compared to the Masson equation) is due to the use of more reliable ϕ_V data in determining the Redlich density constants. The improved fit also supports the earlier contention that the use of the Redlich equation is preferred over the use of the Masson equation.

In Fig. 5, we have plotted the difference between the Redlich Φ_V(meas.) − Φ_V(calc.) versus ionic strength and temperature. This plot indicates that the excess volume of mixing sea salts is negative from 0 to 10°C and positive from 10 to 25°C. Until direct volume of mixing measurements are made on the major sea salts (NaCl, Na_2SO_4, $MgCl_2$, and $MgSO_4$), it will not be possible to state with certainty the magnitude of the excess volume of mixing terms. Since the theoretically calculated Φ_V's and densities are in reasonable agreement with the directly measured values, Young's rule without the excess terms appears to give reliable estimates for the Φ_V that are almost within the experimental error of the single electrolyte sea salt data.

Apparent Equivalent Expansibility of Sea Salt (at 1 atm)

Experimental results

The expansibilities of seawater solutions can be examined in terms of the apparent equivalent expansibility given by

$$\Phi_E = \partial\Phi_V/\partial T \tag{92}$$

By differentiating equation 82 with respect to temperature and setting the same conditions as in the derivation of Φ_V, we obtain the apparent equivalent expansibility of sea salt:

$$\Phi_E = \left[\frac{1000(\alpha - \alpha^0)}{N_T}\right] + \alpha^0\Phi_V \tag{93}$$

TABLE

Calculation of Redlich b_V for

Solute	0°C		5°C		10°C	
	$b_V{}^a$	$E_i b_V$	b_V	$E_i b_V$	b_V	$E_i b_V$
Na^+	2.709	2.093	2.190	1.692	1.802	1.392
$\frac{1}{2}Mg^{2+}$	2.031	0.357	1.334	0.234	1.079	0.190
$\frac{1}{2}Ca^{2+}$	1.626	0.055	1.249	0.042	0.922	0.031
K^+	2.699	0.045	2.286	0.038	1.878	0.032
$\frac{1}{2}Sr^{2+}$	1.722	0.001	1.421	0.000	1.134	0.000
Cl^-	−1.494	−1.346	−1.339	−1.206	−1.215	−1.094
$\frac{1}{2}SO_4{}^{2-}$	0.435	0.041	0.383	0.036	0.327	0.030
$HCO_3{}^-$	−1.806	−0.007	−1.417	−0.005	−1.215	−0.005
Br^-	−1.615	−0.002	−1.552	−0.002	−1.305	−0.002
F^-	1.244	0.000	0.930	0.000	0.570	0.000
		1.237		0.829		0.574

[a] The ionic b_V's are based on $b_V(H^+) = 0$. The ionic b_V's were taken from Millero's compilation of data (1972a) and the recent work of Millero and Knox (1973).

where α and α^0, respectively, are the expansibility of seawater, $\alpha = -1/d\ (\partial d/\partial T)$, and pure water, $\alpha^0 = -1/d^0\ (\partial d^0/\partial T)$ (Kell, 1967). Since there is no direct expansibility data for seawater (at 1 atm), we have determined the Φ_E from equation 92 after fitting the Φ_V's to equations of the form (Millero and Schrager, in preparation):

$$\Phi_V = a + bt + ct^2 + dt^3 + et^4 \tag{94}$$

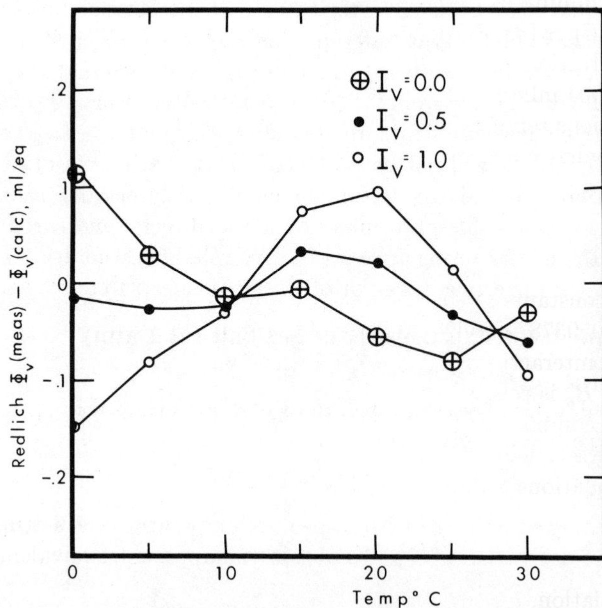

Fig. 5. Comparison of the measured and calculated apparent equivalent volume for sea salt at various temperatures and concentrations.

XIII

Seawater at Various Temperatures

15°C		20°C		25°C		30°C	
b_V	E_ib_V	b_V	E_ib_V	b_V	E_ib_V	b_V	E_ib_V
1.491	1.152	1.239	0.957	1.078	0.833	1.002	0.774
0.401	0.070	0.088	0.015	−0.197	0.035	−0.398	0.070
0.738	0.025	0.419	0.014	0.242	0.008	0.116	0.004
1.538	0.026	1.299	0.022	1.129	0.019	1.072	0.018
0.904	0.000	0.716	0.000	0.569	0.000	0.464	0.000
−1.122	−1.011	−1.061	−0.956	−1.030	−0.928	−1.030	−0.928
0.267	0.025	0.203	0.019	0.134	0.012	0.061	0.006
−1.137	−0.004	−1.055	−0.004	−1.026	−0.004	−1.076	−0.004
−1.122	−0.002	−1.119	−0.002	−1.107	−0.002	−1.201	−0.002
0.168	0.000	−0.201	0.000	−0.538	0.000	−0.851	0.000
	0.281		0.065		−0.027		−0.062

The Φ_E obtained from the differentiation of equation 94 are shown in Fig. 6 plotted versus $I_V^{1/2}$. As with the Φ_V's in the high concentration region, the Masson equation appears to hold:

$$\Phi_E = \Phi_E{}^0 + S'_E I_V^{1/2} \tag{95}$$

where the infinite dilution $\Phi_E{}^0 = \partial\Phi_V{}^0/\partial T = \sum E_i\phi_E{}^0(i)$ and the Masson slope $S'_E = \sum E_i S_E^*(i) \simeq [\partial S'_V/\partial T - (\alpha^0/2)S'_V]$. The Masson $\Phi_E{}^0$'s and (S'_E)'s determined in the high concentration region are given in Table XIV along with the average deviations (within ± 0.004 ml/eq degree over the entire temperature range). The infinite dilution $\Phi_E{}^0$'s at various temperatures are shown in Fig. 7.

By combining equations 61a, 63a, 93, and 95 we obtain the Root expansibility equation

$$\alpha = \alpha^0 + A'_E \mathrm{Cl}_V + B'_E \mathrm{Cl}_V^{3/2} \tag{96}$$

where the constants $A'_E = 10^{-3}[\Phi_E{}^0 - \alpha^0\Phi_V{}^0] \times 0.0312867$ and $B'_E = 10^{-3}\,[S'_E - \alpha^0 S'_V] \times 0.0059378$. As with binary solutions A'_E is related to the effect of temperature on ion water interactions and B'_E is related to the effect of temperature on ion-ion interactions and B'_E is related to the effect of temperature on ion-ion interactions of the major ionic components of seawater. In Fig. 8, the linearity of $(\alpha - \alpha^0)/\mathrm{Cl}_V$ versus $\mathrm{Cl}_V^{1/2}$ for seawater solutions is demonstrated. The α's were determined from the densities fit to equations of the form

$$\mathrm{d} = a + bt + ct^2 + dt^3 + et^4 \tag{97}$$

by differentiation, $\alpha = 1/d(\partial d/\partial t)$. The A'_E and B'_E constants are given in Table XV along with the average deviations.

As with the Φ_V's, a more reliable Φ_E concentration equation based on the limiting

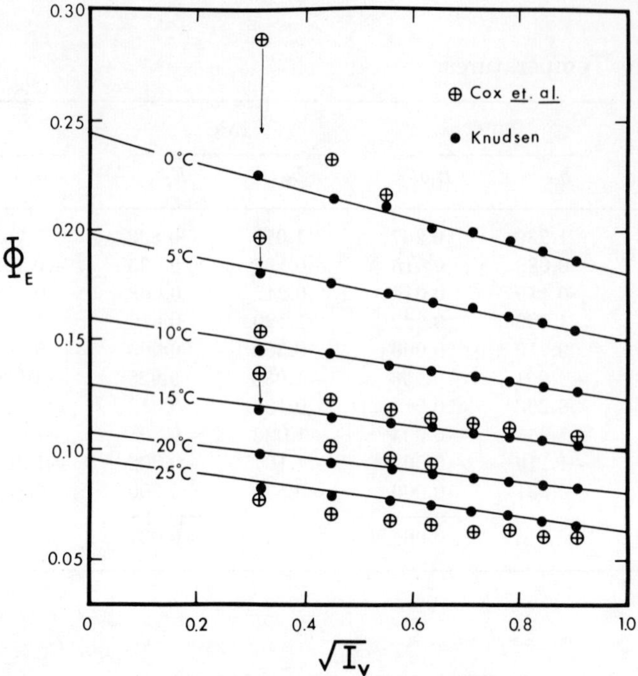

Fig. 6. The apparent equivalent expansibility (Φ_E) of sea salt plotted versus the square root of the volume ionic strength ($I_V^{1/2}$) at various temperatures.

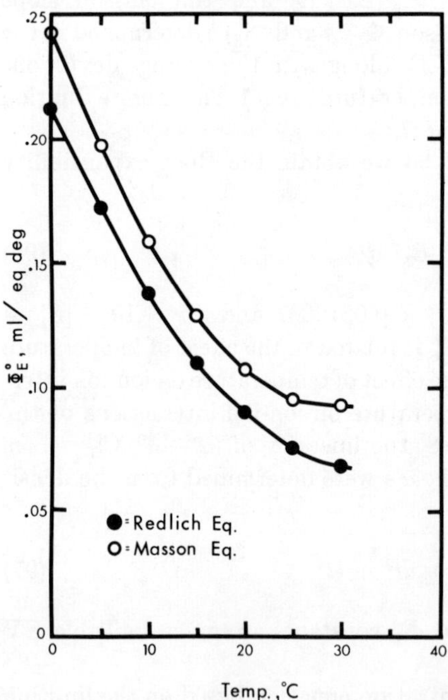

Fig. 7. The apparent equivalent expansibility of sea salt at infinite dilution ($\Phi_E{}^0$) at various temperatures.

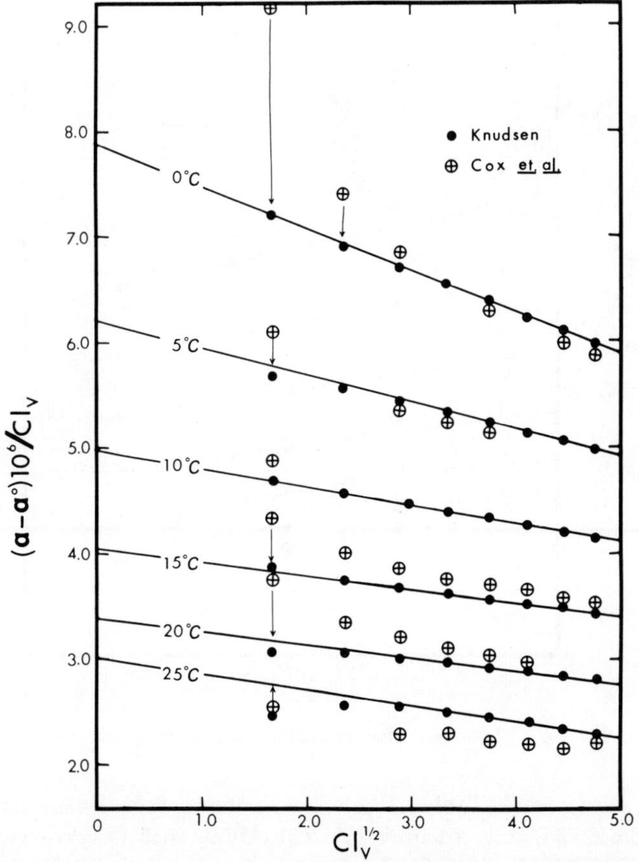

Fig. 8. A plot of $(\alpha - \alpha^0)\ 10^6/Cl_V$ versus $Cl_V^{1/2}$ for seawater at various temperatures.

law can be derived by differentiating the Redlich Φ_V equation with respect to temperature giving

$$\Phi_E = \Phi_E{}^0 + S_E I_V^{1/2} + b_E I_V \tag{98}$$

where $\Phi_E{}^0 = \sum E_i \phi_E{}^0(i) = \partial\Phi_V{}^0/\partial T$, $S_E = \sum E_i S_V(i) \simeq [\partial S_V/\partial T - (\alpha^0/2)S_V]$, and $B_E = \sum E_i b_E(i) \simeq [\partial b_V/\partial T - \alpha^0 b_V]$. A plot of $\Phi_E - S_E I_V^{1/2}$ versus I_V is shown in Fig. 9. The Redlich $\Phi_E{}^0$, S_E, and b_E for sea salts are given in Table XVI along with the average deviations.

Combining equations 61a, 83a, 93, and 98 we have the Redlich expansibility equation

$$\alpha = \alpha^0 + A_E Cl_V + B_E Cl_V^{3/2} + C_E Cl_V{}^2 \tag{99}$$

where $A_E = 10^{-3}[\Phi_E{}^0 - \alpha^0\Phi_V{}^0] \times 0.0312867$, $B_E = 10^{-3}[S_E - \alpha^0 S_V] \times 0.0059378$, and $C_E = 10^{-3}[b_E - \alpha^0 b_V] \times 0.0011269$. The constants A_E, B_E, and C_E are given in Table XVII along with the average deviations.

Theoretical calculations

The temperature dependence of the estimated Masson $\Phi_V{}^0$ and S_V' (equations 89 and 90) can be used to estimate the theoretical Masson $\Phi_E{}^0$ and S_E'. The resulting Masson

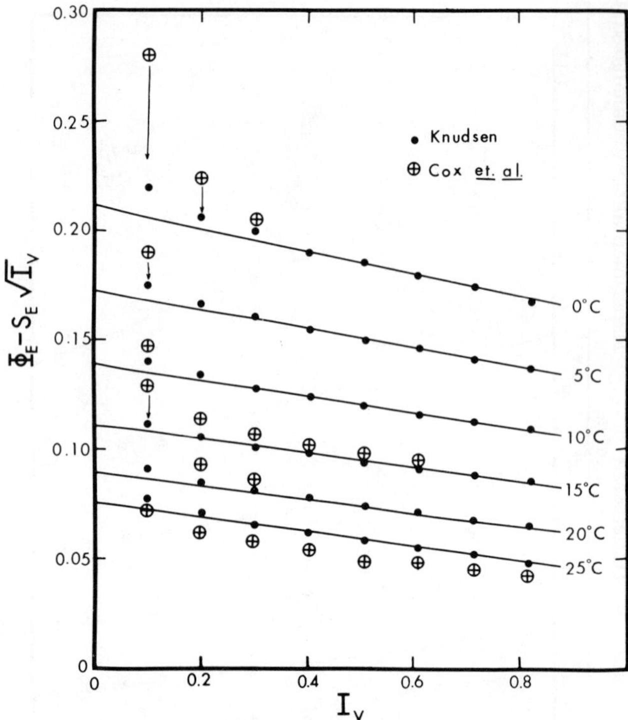

Fig. 9. A plot of $\Phi_E - S_E I_V^{1/2}$ versus I_V for sea salt at various temperatures.

$\Phi_E{}^0$'s and (S'_E)'s are given in Table XVI along with the average deviations between the calculated (equation 95) and measured Φ_E's. The estimated $\Phi_E{}^0$'s agree with the experimental values to ± 0.05 ml/eq degree, while the estimated (S'_E)'s agree with the experimental values to ± 0.01 ml eq^{-1} deg^{-1} liter$^{1/2}$ mol$^{-1/2}$.

The theoretical Masson A'_E and B'_E for seawater calculated from the theoretical Masson $\Phi_E{}^0$ and S'_E are given in Table XV along with the average deviations (average = ± 5 ppm) over the entire temperature range. The larger errors at 0°C are due to the limited Masson ϕ_V single electrolyte temperature data available at low temperatures (i.e., between 0 and 25°C).

The theoretical constants for the Redlich Φ_V's and b_V's have been fit to the equations

$$\Phi_V{}^0 = 10.461 + 0.2485t - 7.84347 \times 10^{-3}t^2 + 1.789687 \times 10^{-4}t^3 - 1.689045 \times 10^{-6}t^4 \quad (100)$$

$$b_V = 1.232 - 0.0800t + 6.765851 \times 10^{-4}t^2 + 4.322766 \times 10^{-5}t^3 - 9.067599 \times 10^{-7}t^4 \quad (101)$$

By appropriate differentiation of equations 100 and 101, $\Phi_E{}^0$ and b_E can be determined: $\Phi_E{}^0 = \partial\Phi_V{}^0/\partial T$ and $b_E = (\partial b_V/\partial T - \alpha^0 b_V)$. The theoretical Redlich $\Phi_E{}^0$'s and b_E's calculated in this manner are given in Table XVI along with the average deviations. The measured and calculated $\Phi_E{}^0$'s agree to within ± 0.021 ml eq^{-1} deg^{-1} and the b_E's agree to within ± 0.02 ml eq^{-1} deg^{-1} liter$^{1/2}$ mol$^{-1/2}$. The theoretically calculated Φ_E's from equation 98 agree with the measured values to within an average deviation ± 0.008 ml/eq deg over the entire temperature and concentration range.

Table XIV

Constants for the Masson Expansibility Equation for Seawater at Various Temperatures

Temperature (°C)	$\Phi_E{}^0$		$-S'_E$		Average Deviation	
	Experimental[a]	Calculated[b]	Experimental	Calculated	Experimental	Calculated
0	0.2433 (0.2555)	0.1992	0.0625 (0.0798)	0.0567	0.009 (0.005)	0.041 (0.051)
5	0.1979 (0.1923)	0.1793	0.0477 (0.0439)	0.0508	0.003 (0.001)	0.026 (0.019)
10	0.1595 (0.1569)	0.1595	0.0362 (0.0323)	0.0449	0.000_4 (0.001)	0.007 (0.005)
15	0.1288 (0.1353)	0.1396	0.0290 (0.0327)	0.0399	0.000_2 (0.000_1)	0.005 (0.002)
20	0.1073 (0.1143)	0.1197	0.0277 (0.0335)	0.0329	0.000_1 (0.000_1)	0.009 (0.006)
25	0.0952 (0.0805)	0.0998	0.0323 (0.0230)	0.0269	0.000_1 (0.008)	0.006 (0.016)
30	0.0930	0.0799	0.0438	0.0209	(0.000_5)	(0.003)

[a] The first values were determined from the densities of Knudsen (1901), while the values in parentheses were determined from the densities of Cox, McCartney, and Culkin (1970).
[b] The calculated values were estimated from the Young's rule values calculated at 0, 25, and 50°C, using equations 89 and 90.

TABLE XV

Constants for the Root Expansibility Equations for Seawater at Various Temperatures

Temperature (°C)	$10^6\ \alpha^0$ [a]	$10^6\ A'_E$		$-10^6\ B'_E$		Average Deviation	
		Experimental[b]	Calculated[c]	Experimental	Calculated	Experimental	Calculated[d]
0	−68.1	7.632	6.252	0.370	0.335	2	18
		(8.013)		(0.472)		(2)	(18)
5	16.0	6.185	5.603	0.283	0.302	2	10
		(6.010)		(0.261)		(2)	(9)
10	87.9	4.956	4.957	0.216	0.268	4	5
		(4.875)		(0.193)		(4)	(5)
15	150.7	3.969	4.308	0.174	0.233	5	2
		(4.173)		(0.196)		(5)	(4)
20	206.6	3.270	3.659	0.167	0.198	5	0.8
		(3.489)		(0.202)		(5)	(2)
25	257.0	2.867	3.011	0.195	0.163	6	0.7
		(2.407)		(0.140)		(7)	(2)
30	303.1	2.774	2.365	0.264	0.128	7	3

[a] Taken from Kell (1967). α^0 is in units of $\deg^{-1}$.
[b] The first values were determined from the densities of Knudsen (1901); the values in parentheses were determined from the densities of Cox et al. (1970), both between 20 to 40‰ S.
[c] Calculated from the estimated $\Phi_V{}^0$'s and (S'_V)'s given in Table XIV.
[d] Average deviations over the entire concentration range of 5 to 40‰ S.

TABLE XVI

Constants for the Redlich Apparent Equivalent Expansibility Equation for Seawater at Various Temperatures

	$\Phi_E{}^0$			$-B_E$		Average Deviation	
Temperature (°C)	Experimental[a]	Calculated[b]	S_E	Experimental	Calculated	Experimental	Calculated
0	0.2122 (0.2175)	0.2845	0.0197	0.0535 (0.0641)	0.0802	0.000_6 (0.001)	0.057 (0.056)
5	0.1724 (0.1682)	0.1838	0.0195	0.0435 (0.0410)	0.0705	0.000_2 (0.000_4)	0.004 (0.005)
10	0.1383 (0.1372)	0.1385	0.0193	0.0359 (0.0334)	0.0571	0.000_3 (0.000_3)	0.011 (0.012)
15	0.1104 (0.1155)	0.1112	0.0194	0.0312 (0.0336)	0.0480	0.000_3 (0.000_3)	0.0005 (0.012)
20	0.0985 (0.0942)	0.0954	0.0194	0.0303 (0.0341)	0.0302	0.000_3 (0.000_1)	0.005 (0.005)
25	0.0756 (0.0744)	0.0863	0.0197	0.0339 (0.0274)	0.0319	0.000_1 (0.000_2)	0.011 (0.026)
30	0.0692	0.0787	0.0201	0.0411	0.0206	0.000_2	0.018

[a] The first values were determined from the densities of Knudsen (1901), while the values in parentheses were determined from the densities of Cox, McCartney, and Culkin (1970).
[b] The calculated values were estimated from Young's rule (Tables XII and XIII).

TABLE XVII

Constants for the Redlich Expansibility Equation for Seawater at Various Temperatures

Temperature (°C)	$10^6 A_E$		$10^6 B_E$	$-10^6 C_E$		Average Deviation (ppm)	
	Experimental[a]	Calculated[b]		Experimental	Calculated	Experimental	Calculated[c]
0	6.660	8.922	0.118	0.059	0.090	2	21
	(6.826)			(0.071)		(1)	(21)
5	5.387	5.744	0.116	0.049	0.080	2	4
	(5.256)			(0.046)		(2)	(3)
10	4.292	4.298	0.114	0.042	0.066	4	8
	(4.258)			(0.039)		(4)	(8)
15	3.392	3.417	0.113	0.037	0.050	5	6
	(3.552)			(0.040)		(5)	(8)
20	2.713	2.897	0.112	0.037	0.037	6	2
	(2.860)			(0.042)		(7)	(4)
25	2.254	2.588	0.111	0.042	0.040	7	0.6
	(1.903)			(0.035)		(8)	(2)
30	2.030	2.327	0.110	0.051	0.028	8	3

[a] The first values were determined from the densities of Knudsen (1901); the values in parentheses were determined from the densities of Cox et al. (1970), both between 20 to 40‰ S.
[b] Calculated from the estimated $\Phi_E{}^0$'s, S_E's, and b_E's given in Table XVI.
[c] Average deviations over the entire concentration range of 5 to 40‰ S.

The theoretically calculated Redlich A_E, B_E, and C_E determined from the theoretical $\Phi_E{}^0$, S_E, and b_E are given in Table XVII along with the average deviations. The theoretically calculated α's agree with the measured values within an average deviation of 3 ppm over the entire temperature and concentration range. These results indicate that the simple Young's rule without the excess term can be used to predict the expansibilities of seawater solutions to within the experimental error of the single electrolyte data.

Apparent Equivalent Compressibilities of Sea Salt (at 1 atm)

Experimental results

The apparent equivalent compressibility of sea salt defined by

$$\Phi_K = -\frac{\partial \Phi_V}{\partial P} \tag{102}$$

can be calculated from the compressibility data of Lepple and Millero (1971). By differentiating equation 82 with respect to pressure (P) and setting the same conditions as in the derivation of Φ_V, we obtain

$$\Phi_K = [1000(\beta - \beta^0)/N_T] + \beta^0\Phi_V \tag{103}$$

where β and β^0 are, respectively, the 1 atm compressibilities of seawater (Lepple and Millero, 1971) and pure water (Kell, 1970). The Φ_K's for seawater calculated from equation 103 are shown in Fig. 10, plotted versus $I_V^{1/2}$. In the high concentration region, the Φ_K's follow the Masson compressibility equation

$$\Phi_K = \Phi_K{}^0 + S_K' I_V^{1/2} \tag{104}$$

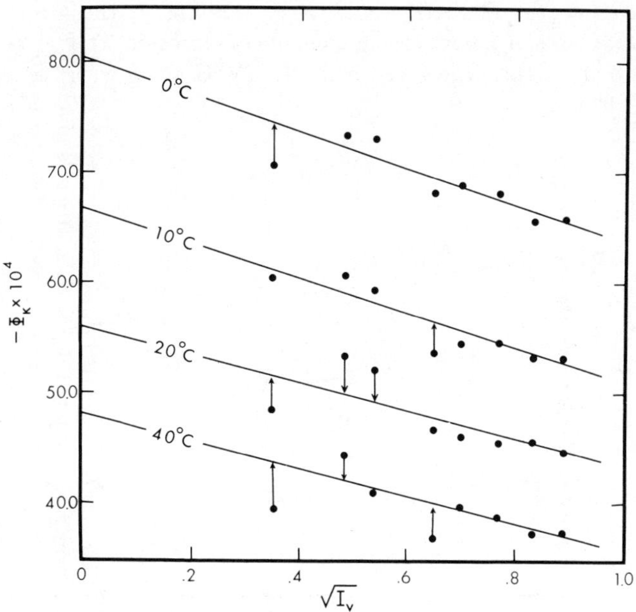

Fig. 10. The apparent equivalent compressibility (Φ_K) of sea salt plotted versus the square root of the volume ionic strength ($I_V^{1/2}$) at various temperatures. From Millero (1973a) with permission of Plenum Publishing Corporation.

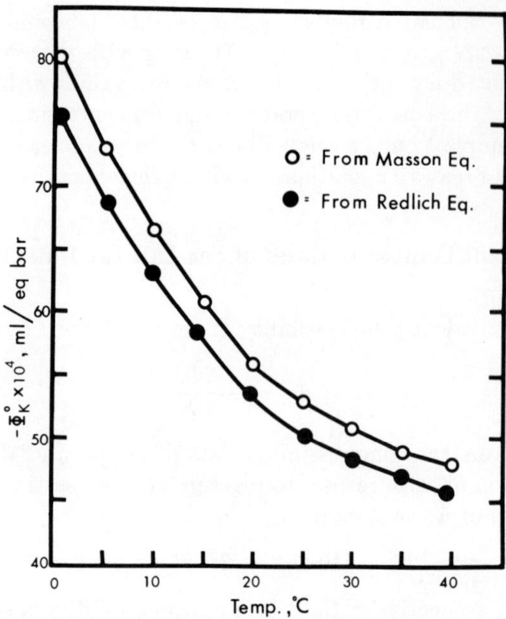

Fig. 11. The apparent equivalent compressibility of sea salt at infinite dilution ($\Phi_K{}^0$) at various temperatures.

where the infinite dilution apparent equivalent expansibility $\Phi_K{}^0 = \sum E_i \Phi_K(i) = -\partial\Phi_V{}^0/\partial P$ and the Masson compressibility slope $S_K = \sum E_i S_K^*(i) \simeq [\partial S_V'/\partial P - (S_V/2)\beta^0]$. As with the single electrolyte solutions, the $\Phi_K{}^0$ is related to the effect of pressure on the ion-water interactions and the S_K' is related to the effect of pressure on the ion-ion interactions of the major components of seawater. The $\Phi_K{}^0$ and S_K' for sea salt at various temperatures are given in Table XVIII along with the average deviations (Millero, 1973a).

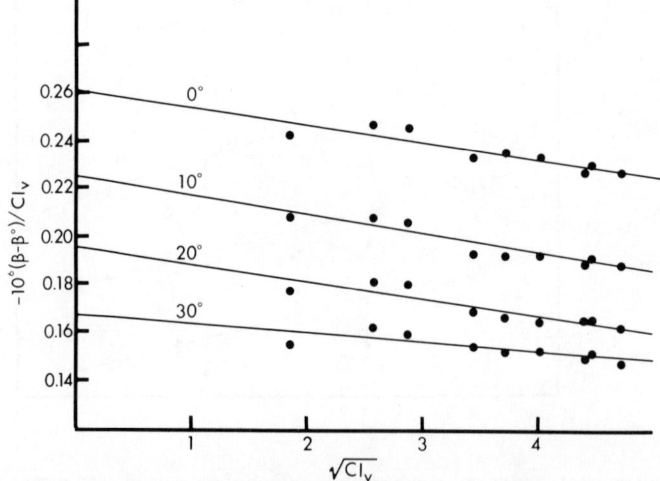

Fig. 12. A plot of $(\beta - \beta^0)\ 10^6/Cl_V$ versus $Cl_V^{1/2}$ for seawater at various temperatures. From Lepple and Millero (1971) with permission of Pergamon Press.

Table XVIII

Constants for the Masson Apparent Equivalent Compressibility Equation for Seawater at Various Temperatures[a]

Temperature (°C)	$-10^4\ \Phi_K{}^0$ Experimental	$-10^4\ \Phi_K{}^0$ Calculated	$10^4\ S'_K$ Experimental	$10^4\ S'_K$ Calculated	10^4 Average Deviation Experimental	10^4 Average Deviation Calculated
0	80.4	80.3	16.4	17.3	1.4	1.4
5	73.0	73.3	16.3	15.8	1.2	1.5
10	66.6	67.1	15.9	14.5	1.0	1.6
15	60.9	61.7	13.4	13.2	1.4	1.7
20	55.9	57.1	12.3	12.3	1.6	2.2
25	53.0	53.3	10.0	11.4	1.7	1.5
30	50.9	50.4	12.0	10.8	1.2	1.4
35	49.0	48.2	10.8	10.3	1.4	1.5
40	48.0	46.9	12.4	10.0	1.4	1.5

[a] Taken from the work of Millero (1973a).

A plot of $\Phi_K{}^0$ versus temperature is given in Fig. 11. By combining equations 61a, 63a, 103, and 104, we have the Root compressibility equation for seawater:

$$\beta = \beta^0 + A'_K \mathrm{Cl}_V + B'_K \mathrm{Cl}_V^{3/2} \tag{105}$$

where $A'_K = 10^{-3}(\Phi_K{}^0 - \beta^0\Phi_V{}^0) \times 0.0312803$ and $B'_K = 10^{-3}(S'_K - \beta^0 S'_V) \times 0.0059350$. In Fig. 12 a plot of $(\beta - \beta^0)/\mathrm{Cl}_V$ versus $\mathrm{Cl}_V^{1/2}$ is given. The constants A'_K and B'_K determined from these plots are given in Table XIX along with the average deviations.

Table XIX

Constants for the Root Compressibility Equation for Seawater at Various Temperatures[a]

Temperature (°C)	$10^6\ \beta^{0\,b}$	$-10^7\ A'_K$ Experimental	$-10^7\ A'_K$ Calculated	$10^9\ B'_K$ Experimental	$10^9\ B'_K$ Calculated	10^6 Average Deviation Experimental	10^6 Average Deviation Calculated
0	50.886	2.62	2.67	7.4	9.3	0.03	0.06
5	49.171	2.40	2.46	7.4	8.4	0.04	0.05
10	47.811	2.22	2.27	7.3	7.8	0.04	0.07
15	46.736	2.05	2.11	6.1	7.1	0.04	0.06
20	45.895	1.91	1.97	5.9	6.6	0.05	0.07
25	45.250	1.80	1.86	4.8	6.1	0.04	0.04
30	44.774	1.71	1.77	4.9	5.8	0.03	0.04
35	44.444	1.65	1.71	3.9	5.5	0.05	0.05
40	44.243	1.61	1.67	4.4	5.4	0.04	0.05

[a] Taken from the work of Lepple and Millero (1971a) and Millero (1937b).
[b] Kell (1970); units of bar^{-1}.

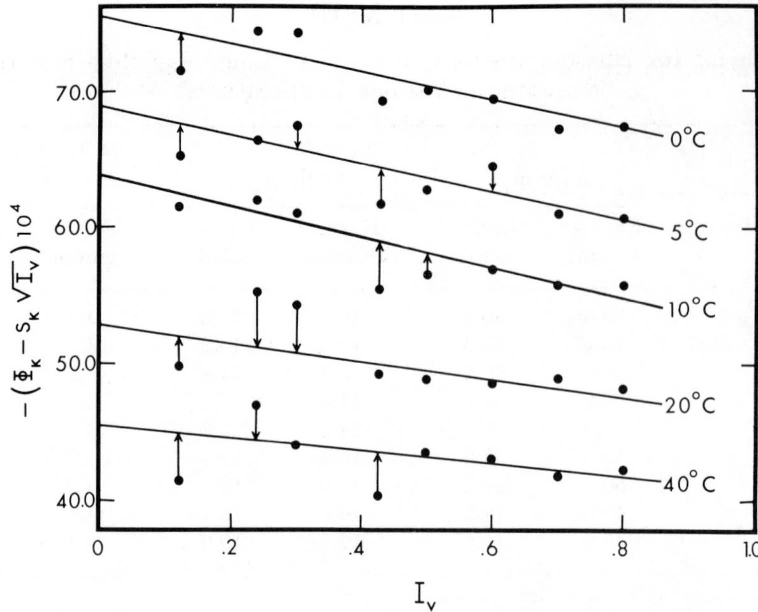

Fig. 13. A plot of $-(\Phi_K - S_K I_V^{1/2})\ 10^4$ versus I_V for sea salt at various temperatures.

A more reliable equation to represent the concentration dependence of the Φ_K can be obtained by differentiating the Redlich Φ_V equation with respect to pressure, which gives

$$\Phi_K = \Phi_K{}^0 + S_K I_V^{1/2} + b_K I_V \tag{106}$$

where the infinite dilution apparent equivalent compressibility $\Phi_K{}^0 = -\partial\Phi_V{}^0/\partial P$, the limiting law slope $S_K = \sum E_i S_K(i) = [(\partial S_V/\partial P) - (\beta^0/2)S_V]$, and the deviation constant $b_K = \sum E_i b_V(i) \simeq [\partial b_V/\partial P - \beta^0 b_V]$. A plot of $\Phi_K - S_K I_V^{1/2}$ versus I_V is shown in Fig. 13. The Redlich constants Φ_K', S_K, and b_K for sea salt at various temperatures are given in Table XX along with the average deviations of the fit. Although the fit using equation 106 is not improved over equation 104, the $\Phi_K{}^0$'s are more reliable. As shown in Fig. 11, the Redlich $\Phi_K{}^0$'s are higher by approximately 2×10^{-4} ml/eq bar over the entire temperature range.

Theoretical calculations

In a recent paper, we estimated the $\Phi_K{}^0$ and S_K' for seawater from 0 to 40° using the $\phi_K{}^0(i)$ and $S_K^*(i)$ for the major components of seawater (Lepple and Millero, 1971; Millero, 1972, 1973b; Millero, Ward, Hoff, and Lepple, 1973). Calculations of the Masson $\Phi_K{}^0$ and S_K' for sea salt are given in Tables XXI and XXII. The theoretically calculated $\Phi_K{}^0$ and S_K' agree very well with the experimental values (see Table XVIII). The theoretically calculated Φ_K's from equation 104 agree with the measured values to $\pm 2.2 \times 10^{-4}$ ml eq^{-1} bar^{-1} over the entire temperature range (average $\pm 1.6 \times 10^{-4}$ ml eq^{-1} bar^{-1}), which is within the experimental error of the $\phi_K(i)$'s.

The theoretically calculated Masson compressibility constants A_K' and B_K' are given in Table XIX along with the experimental error of the back calculated β's. The average deviations of $\pm 0.06 \times 10^{-6}$ bar^{-1} in the β's are almost within the precision of the original measurements [$\pm 0.05 \times 10^{-6}$ bar^{-1} (Lepple and Millero, 1971)]. Thus, the

TABLE XX

Constants for the Redlich Apparent Equivalent Compressibility Equation for Seawater at Various Temperatures

Temperature (°C)	$-10^4\ \Phi_K{}^0$	$10^4\ S_K{}^a$	$10^4\ b_K$	10^4 Average Deviation
0	75.8	1.61	11.4	1.2
5	68.6	2.21	10.4	1.2
10	63.3	2.81	10.6	1.1
15	59.0	3.34	10.0	1.5
20	53.8	3.87	7.5	1.5
25	50.3	4.34	4.3	1.5
30	48.4	4.82	5.5	1.1
35	47.2	5.26	4.5	1.4
40	45.7	5.67	4.9	1.0

[a] Calculated from $S_K \simeq -[\partial S_V/\partial P - (\beta^0/2)S_V]$ at 1 atm derived from the dielectric constant data of Owen et al. (1961) and the compressibility data of Kell and Whalley (1965).

simple Young's rule predicts compressibility properties of seawater that are nearly within the experimental error of the direct measurements.

At present, there are no reliable $\phi_K(i)$ data for all the sea salts in dilute solutions from which reliable Redlich constants can be estimated. Our experimental $\Phi_K{}^0$ results for sea salt given in Table XX indicate that the true infinite dilution values are probably higher by as much as 4.6×10^{-4} (average 2.8×10^{-4}). The limited amount of data available for $\phi_K{}^0$'s, obtained from dilute solution data, supports this general trend. For example, the $\phi_K{}^0$ of NaCl at 25° determined from sound velocity data (Owen and Kronick, 1961) is -46.2×10^{-4} ml/mol bar compared to the Masson value of -51.6×10^{-4} ml/mol bar. Until reliable dilute solution compressibility data (from sound velocity measurements) become available for seawater and sea salts, it will not be possible to state with certainty how reliable our infinite dilution $\phi_K{}^0$'s are for sea salt.

In future work it will be interesting to treat (theoretically and experimentally) the volume properties of seawater to high pressures in the methods used in this chapter at 1 atm.

In summary, it appears from these calculations that the simple Young's rule (without the excess terms) yields estimates for the apparent equivalent volume, expansibility, and compressibility that are nearly within the experimental error of the measured values.

Osmotic and Activity Coefficients of Seawater Solutions

The osmotic coefficient of seawater

The free energy (relative to the standard state G^0) of a solution containing (55.51 mol) of water is given by

$$G - G^0 = 55.51\ RT \ln a_W + 2m_T\ RT \ln a_S \tag{107}$$

where a_W is the activity of water in the solution, a_S is the activity of sea salt, and m_T is the molality of the solution. The activity of water in seawater is related to the ratio

TABLE

Calculation of the Masson Φ_K^{0a} ($\times 10^{-4}$)

Solute	0°C		5°C		10°C		15°C	
	$-\phi_K^0$	$-E_i\phi_K^0$	$-\phi_K^0$	$-E_i\phi_K^0$	$-\phi_K^0$	$-E_i\phi_K^0$	$-\phi_K^0$	$-E_i\phi_K^0$
Na^+	53.0	40.945	51.2	39.554	49.3	38.087	47.3	36.541
$\frac{1}{2}Mg^{2+}$	45.3	7.960	45.1	7.925	44.7	7.855	44.1	7.750
$\frac{1}{2}Ca^{2+}$	37.5	1.271	37.3	1.264	36.9	1.251	36.3	1.231
K^+	46.8	0.788	44.9	0.756	43.0	0.724	41.0	0.690
$\frac{1}{2}Sr^{2+}$	37.8	0.011	37.6	0.011	37.2	0.011	36.6	0.011
Cl^-	26.0	23.420	20.8	18.736	16.4	14.773	12.9	11.620
$\frac{1}{2}SO_4^{2-}$	61.1	5.694	52.7	4.911	45.7	4.259	40.2	3.746
HCO_3^-	17.4	0.067	12.1	0.047	7.2	0.028	3.4	0.013
Br^-	17.7	0.025	12.1	0.017	7.5	0.010	3.7	0.005
F^-	58.8	0.003	51.7	0.006	45.5	0.005	40.0	0.004
		80.188		73.227		67.003		61.611

[a] The ionic ϕ_K^0's are based on $\phi_K^0(H^+) = 0$.

of the vapor pressure (P) of seawater (corrected for nonideal behavior) and the vapor pressure of pure water (P^0):

$$a_W = \frac{P}{P^0} \tag{108}$$

It is frequently more convenient to express the deviation from ideal behavior of a solution in terms of the practical osmotic coefficient that can be defined for seawater by (Robinson and Stokes, 1959):

$$\phi_S = -\left(\frac{55.51}{2m_T}\right) \ln a_W \tag{109}$$

where $2m_T = \sum m_i$, the sum of the molality of the ionic components. From Robinson's (1954) isopiestic measurements on seawater using NaCl solutions as a standard, the ϕ_S is given by

$$\phi_S = R\phi_{NaCl} \tag{110}$$

where R is the osmotic ratio ($R = m_{NaCl}/m_T$ at isopiestic equilibrium). Robinson (1954) found that over the range of 9 to 22‰ chlorinity the osmotic ratio was given by

$$R' = 0.02782 + 0.000079\ Cl(‰) \tag{111}$$

where $R' = m_{NaCl}/Cl(‰)$. By examining his experimental results in terms of m_T for seawater, we obtain (Millero and Leung, in preparation)

$$R = 0.96385 + 0.02685m_T \tag{112}$$

with an average deviation of $\pm 0.001_7$. The osmotic coefficient can be calculated from equations 110 and 112 using known osmotic coefficient data for NaCl solutions (Robinson and Stokes, 1959). Between 0.1 to 1.0m the ϕ_{NaCl} can be represented by the equation

$$\phi_{NaCl} = 0.9420_4 - 0.1195_3 m + 0.1948_3 m^2 - 0.0821_5 m^3 \tag{113}$$

XXI

for Seawater at Various Temperatures

20°C		25°C		30°C		35°C		40°C	
$-\phi_K{}^0$	$-E_i\phi_K{}^0$	$-\phi_K{}^0$	$-E_i\phi_K{}^0$	$-\phi_K{}^0$	$-E_i\phi_K{}^0$	$-\phi_K{}^0$	$-E_i\phi_K{}^0$	$-\phi_K{}^0$	$-E_i\phi_K{}^0$
45.3	34.996	43.3	33.451	41.2	31.829	39.1	30.207	36.9	28.507
43.4	7.627	42.5	7.468	41.6	7.310	40.5	7.117	39.2	6.888
35.6	1.207	34.7	1.176	33.8	1.146	32.7	1.109	31.4	1.064
39.0	0.657	36.9	0.621	34.9	0.588	32.8	0.552	30.7	0.517
35.9	0.011	35.0	0.011	34.1	0.010	33.0	0.010	31.7	0.010
10.2	9.188	8.3	7.476	7.2	6.486	6.9	6.215	7.5	6.756
36.0	3.355	33.1	3.084	31.7	2.954	31.6	2.945	33.0	3.075
0.4	0.002	−1.9	−0.007	−3.3	−0.013	−3.9	−0.015	−3.7	−0.014
0.7	0.001	−1.6	−0.002	−3.0	−0.004	−3.6	−0.005	−3.4	−0.005
35.1	0.004	31.0	0.002	27.5	0.003	24.8	0.003	22.8	0.003
	57.048		53.281		50.309		48.138		46.801

with an average deviation of ± 0.0003. Combining equations 110, 112, and 113, we obtain for seawater

$$\phi_S = 0.9079_9 - 0.0899_2 m_T + 0.1845_8 m_T{}^2 - 0.0739_5 m_T{}^3 - 0.00221 m_T{}^4 \quad (114)$$

This equation can be converted to a function of molal ionic strength (I_m) using the relation $m_T = 0.80306 \times I_m$, which gives

$$\phi_S = 0.9079_9 - 0.0722_1 I_m + 0.1190_4 I_m{}^2 - 0.0383_0 I_m{}^3 - 0.0009_2 I_m{}^4 \quad (115)$$

valid only between $I_m = 0.3$ to 0.8. The osmotic coefficients of seawater calculated from equation 115 are given in Table XXIII, also, given for comparison are the osmotic coefficients of NaCl solutions. As is quite apparent from Table XXIII, the ϕ_S and ϕ_{NaCl} are quite different, indicating that assuming the $\phi_{NaCl} = \phi_S$ is not a good approximation.

Robinson and Wood (1973) have recently used the equations of Robinson, Wood, and Reilly (1971) to predict the osmotic coefficient of a synthetic seawater (NaCl + $MgCl_2$ + Na_2SO_4 + $MgSO_4$) and its concentrates at 25°C. Their calculation is based on the use of equation 41 and requires a knowledge of the osmotic coefficients of NaCl, $MgCl_2$, Na_2SO_4, and $MgSO_4$ in their own solutions (Robinson and Stokes, 1959) and of the common ion interaction parameters of Na–Mg–Cl, Na–Mg–SO_4, Na–Cl–SO_4, and Mg–Cl–SO_4 (Platford, 1968; Wu, Rush, and Scatchard, 1968). Their calculated osmotic coefficients for the NaCl–$MgSO_4$ and Na_2SO_4–$MgCl_2$ system below $I_m = 5.0$ agree with the work of Wu, Rush, and Scatchard (1969) with an average deviation of $\pm 0.001_4$. These predictions appear to be as good as the experimental measurements.

Robinson and Wood (1973) also calculated the osmotic coefficient for a solution equivalent to seawater of 0.4958m NaCl + 0.0367m $MgCl_2$ + 0.0293m $MgSO_4$ (where the Ca and Sr content is counted in with Mg, the K in with the Na, and the HCO_3, Br, and F in with Cl) and for a solution equivalent to seawater of 0.4852m NaCl + 0.0106m KCl + 0.0367m $MgCl_2$ + 0.0293m $MgSO_4$. The observed values for this

TABLE

Calculation of S'_K ($\times 10^4$) for

Solute	0°C		5°C		10°C		15°C	
	S^{*a}_K	$E_i S^*_K$	S^*_K	$E_i S^*_K$	S^*_K	$E_i S^*_K$	S^*_K	$E_i S^*_K$
Na^+	15.0	11.588	13.3	10.275	11.9	9.193	10.6	8.189
$\frac{1}{2}Mg^{2+}$	8.4	1.476	7.7	1.353	7.1	1.248	6.5	1.142
$\frac{1}{2}Ca^{2+}$	8.4	0.285	7.7	0.261	7.1	0.241	6.5	0.220
K^+	16.2	0.273	14.6	0.246	13.1	0.221	11.8	0.199
$\frac{1}{2}Sr^{2+}$	8.4	0.003	7.7	0.002	7.1	0.002	6.5	0.002
Cl^-	3.0	2.702	3.0	2.702	3.0	2.702	3.0	2.702
$\frac{1}{2}SO_4{}^{2-}$	10.4	0.969	9.6	0.895	9.0	0.839	8.4	0.783
$HCO_3{}^-$	2.0	0.008	2.0	0.008	2.0	0.008	2.0	0.008
Br^-	2.0	0.003	2.0	0.003	2.0	0.003	2.0	0.003
F^-	5.2	0.001	5.2	0.001	5.2	0.001	5.2	0.001
		17.308		15.746		14.458		13.249

[a] The ionic values are based on $S^*_K(H^+) = 0$.

artificial mixture given in the fourth column of Table XXIII were interpolated from the results of Rush and Johnson (1966). The artificial mixture has osmotic coefficients that are on the average 0.004 units higher than the values obtained for seawater from Robinson's measurements (1954). Since the measurements of Robinson (1954) made on both natural seawaters and an artificial mixture containing $NaCl + KCl + MgCl_2 + CaCl_2 + MgSO_4$ were in agreement to within ± 0.002 in ϕ_S, the difference between the artificial seawater of Robinson and Wood (1973) and natural seawater is probably due to the Ca ion contribution (not included in the artificial mixture of Robinson and Wood).

The theoretical predictions made by Robinson and Wood (1973) are given in Table XXIII in various levels of sophistication. The first estimate (column five) was made using only the single salt solution for a mixture of $Na_2SO_4 + NaCl + MgCl + MgSO_4$. The second estimate (column six) was made on the same mixture using all the interaction parameters. The third estimate (column seven) was made for a mixture of $NaCl + KCl + Na_2SO_4 + K_2SO_4 + MgCl_2 + MgSO_4$ using all the interaction parameters.

The first calculation gave an average difference between the observed and calculated value of ϕ_S for the artificial mixture of 0.002 over the range $I = 0.5$ to 2.0 (0.003 over the entire range). The second calculation, which includes the interaction parameters, gave an average difference of 0.0006 in the low range and 0.002 over the entire range. The third calculation gives almost perfect agreement between 0.5 to 4.0 (average deviation 0.001_4 over the entire range). In the ionic strength of artificial seawater 0.5 to 0.8, all of the calculated values are in excellent agreement with the artificial seawater mixture and in good agreement with the natural seawater mixture. As more free energy data becomes available for sea salts and their mixtures, these calculations can be improved.

XXII

Seawater at Various Temperatures

20°C		25°C		30°C		35°C		40°C	
S^*_K	$E_iS^*_K$	S^*_K	$E_iS^*_K$	S^*_K	$E_iS^*_K$	S^*_K	$E_iS^*_K$	S^*_K	$E_iS^*_K$
9.5	7.339	8.5	6.567	7.8	6.026	7.2	5.562	6.8	5.253
6.0	1.054	5.5	0.966	5.2	0.914	4.8	0.843	4.6	0.808
6.0	0.203	5.5	0.186	5.2	0.176	4.8	0.163	4.6	0.156
10.6	0.179	9.4	0.158	8.3	0.140	7.3	0.123	6.1	0.103
6.0	0.002	5.5	0.002	5.2	0.002	4.8	0.001	4.6	0.001
3.0	2.702	3.0	2.702	3.0	2.702	3.0	2.702	3.0	2.702
8.2	0.764	8.4	0.783	8.7	0.811	9.3	0.867	10.4	0.969
2.0	0.008	2.0	0.008	2.0	0.008	2.0	0.008	2.0	0.008
2.0	0.003	2.0	0.003	2.0	0.003	2.0	0.003	2.0	0.003
5.2	0.001	5.2	0.001	5.2	0.001	5.2	0.001	5.2	0.001
	12.255		11.376		10.783		10.273		10.004

TABLE XXIII

The Osmotic Coefficient of Seawater at 25°C

	ϕ			Calculated		
I_m	NaCl[a]	Seawater[b]	Artificial Seawater[c]	d	e	f
0.5	0.9209	0.897	0.9018	0.9004	0.9020	0.9014
0.6	0.9230	0.899	0.9037	0.9021	0.9038	0.9032
0.7	0.9257	0.902	0.9062	0.9043	0.9062	0.9055
0.8	0.9288	0.906	0.9091	0.9070	0.9090	0.9082
0.9	0.9320	—	0.9121	0.9099	0.9121	0.9112
1.0	0.9355	—	0.9155	0.9131	0.9154	0.9144
2.0	0.9833	—	0.9619	0.9615	0.9635	0.9618
3.0	1.0453	—	1.0232	1.0253	1.0258	1.0233
4.0	1.1158	—	1.0938	1.0990	1.0982	1.0948
5.0	1.1916	—	1.1716	1.1791	1.1785	1.1740
6.0	1.2706	—	1.2536	1.2635	1.2659	1.2604

[a] From Robinson and Stokes (1959).
[b] Calculated from equation 115.
[c] Interpolated by Robinson and Wood (1973) from the results of Rush and Johnson (1966).
[d] Calculated by Robinson and Wood (1973) for the mixture NaCl + $MgCl_2$ + Na_2SO_4 + $MgSO_4$, using only single solution data.
[e] Calculated by Robinson and Wood (1973) for the mixture NaCl + $MgCl_2$ + Na_2SO_4 + $MgSO_4$, using all the interaction parameters.
[f] Calculated by Robinson and Wood (1973) for the mixture NaCl + KCl + Na_2SO_4 + $MgCl_2$ + K_2SO_4 + $MgSO_4$, using all the interaction parameters.

Activity of sea salt

The activity of sea salt a_S or the mean activity coefficient of sea salt $\gamma_\pm{}^S$ can be calculated from the osmotic coefficient by using the Gibbs-Duheim equation:

$$-55.51\, d \ln a_W = 2\, d(m_T\phi_S) = 2m_T\, d \ln a_S = 2m_T\, d \ln (\gamma_\pm{}^S m_T) \quad (116)$$

By integrating this equation it is possible to determine $\gamma_\pm{}^S$:

$$\ln \gamma_\pm{}^S = \phi_S - 1 + \int_0^m (\phi_S - 1)\, d \ln m \quad (117)$$

and $a_S = m_T\gamma_\pm{}^S$. Because of problems in evaluating $\phi_S - 1$ in dilute solutions, $\gamma_\pm$'s estimated from equation 117 are not very reliable (Robinson and Stokes, 1959).

Since ϕ, $\gamma_\pm$, and a are known for the reference solution NaCl used by Robinson (1954), it is more useful (and reliable) to relate a_S to a_{NaCl} and $\gamma_\pm{}^S$ to $\gamma_\pm$(NaCl). Since both solutions have equal water activities at isopiestic equilibrium, we have

$$m_T\, d \ln a_S = m_{NaCl}\, d \ln a_{NaCl} \quad (118)$$

or

$$d \ln a_S = R\, d \ln a_{NaCl} \quad (119)$$

By integrating equation (119), the a_S or $\gamma_\pm{}^S$ of sea salt can be determined from

$$\ln \gamma_\pm{}^S = \ln \gamma_\pm(\mathrm{NaCl}) + \ln R + \int_0^m (R - 1)\, d \ln \gamma_\pm(\mathrm{NaCl}) m_{NaCl} \quad (120)$$

Recently, we (Millero and Leung, in preparation) calculated the $\gamma_\pm$ of sea salt by integrating equations 117 and 119 using Robinson's (1954) results for seawater and Robinson and Stokes' (1959) results for NaCl solutions. The results are given in Table XXIV.

Leyendekkers (1973) has integrated equation 118 between 18 to 40‰ S and obtained

$$p \log a_S = -0.0131 \log c + 670.37c - 11480c^2 + 86420c^3 + 49270c^4 - 86820c^5 + \text{const.} \quad (121)$$

where $p = (m_S/2)[10^3/S(‰) - 1]$, $c = [10^{-3}S(‰)]$, and $m_S = m_T/1.089$. Leyen-

TABLE XXIV

The Mean Activity Coefficient of Sea Salt at 25°C

S(‰)	m_T	$\gamma_\pm$(NaCl)[a]	$\gamma_\pm{}^S$	
20	0.3266	0.705	0.690[b]	(0.628)[c]
25	0.4104	0.692	0.675	(0.614)
30	0.4950	0.682	0.664	(0.604)
35	0.5805	0.675	0.656	(0.598)
40	0.6669	0.670	0.651	(0.593)

[a] From Robinson and Stokes (1959).
[b] From the integration of equation 117 (Millero and Leung, in preparation).
[c] From the integration of equation 120 (Millero and Leung, in preparation).

dekkers (1973) evaluated the integration constant from data on single and two electrolyte solutions using the equations of Guggenheim (Leyendekkers, 1971a, b). Using the Lyman and Fleming (1940) recipe for seawater, she obtained -23.048 for the constant, while the recipe of Kester et al. (1967) gives -23.042 for the constant.

It should be pointed out that the a_S defined by Leyendekkers (1973) is different from our definition ($a_S = m_T\gamma_\pm{}^S$). Thus, the values of a_S calculated from equation 121 do not agree with the values calculated from $a_S = m_T\gamma_\pm{}^S$ (using the values of $\gamma_\pm$ given in Table XXIV); they differ by a constant of integration. Leyendekkers (1973) treats sea salt as a mixture of salts, while we treat sea salt as a mixture of ions.

The Relative Apparent Equivalent Enthalpy of Sea Salt

The enthalpies of seawater have been determined at 25°C by Bromley et al. (1968, 1973) and calculated from 0 to 25°C by Connors (1970). Recently, we measured the relative apparent enthalpy of seawater solutions from 0 to 40‰ S and 0 to 40°C (Millero, Hansen, and Hoff, 1972, 1973). In this paper we showed that the enthalpy of seawater can be treated in a manner similar to single electrolyte solutions (Harned and Owen, 1958).

The apparent equivalent enthalpy of sea salt is defined:

$$\Phi_H = \left(\frac{H - n_1\bar{H}_1{}^0}{n_2}\right) \tag{122}$$

where H is the enthalpy of the solution and $\bar{H}_1{}^0$ is the enthalpy of pure water, and n_1 and n_2 are, respectively, the number of moles of water and equivalents of sea salt. Since absolute values of enthalpies cannot be measured experimentally, it is necessary to use the corresponding relative enthalpies (relative to infinite dilution) given by

$$L = n_1\bar{L}_1 + n_2\bar{L}_2 = n_2\Phi_L \tag{123}$$

where the relative enthalpy of the solution $L = H - H^0$, the relative partial equivalent enthalpy of water $\bar{L}_1 = \bar{H}_1 - \bar{H}_1{}^0$, the relative partial equivalent enthalpy of sea salt $\bar{L}_2 = \bar{H}_2 - \bar{H}_2{}^0$, and the relative apparent enthalpy of sea salt $\Phi_L = \Phi_H - \Phi_H{}^0$ (equal to and opposite in sign to the heat of dilution). The relative partial equivalent enthalpy of sea salt, $\bar{L}_2$, is related to the effect of temperature on the activity of sea salt (a_S):

$$\left(\frac{\partial \ln a_S}{\partial T}\right) = \left(\frac{-\bar{L}_2}{RT^2}\right) \tag{124}$$

while the relative partial equivalent enthalpy of water in seawater, $\bar{L}_1$, is related to the effect of temperature on the activity of water (a_W)

$$(\partial \ln a_W/\partial T) = (-\bar{L}_1/RT^2) \tag{125}$$

The partial equivalent quantities [like other partial thermodynamic functions (Millero, 1972)] can be determined from the concentration dependence of the relative apparent enthalpy:

$$\bar{L}_2 = \Phi_L + n_2(\partial\Phi_L/\partial n_2)_{T,P,n_1} \tag{126}$$

and by combining equations 123 and 126:

$$\bar{L}_1 = (-n_2/n_1)^2[\partial\Phi_L/\partial n_2]_{T,P,n_1} \tag{127}$$

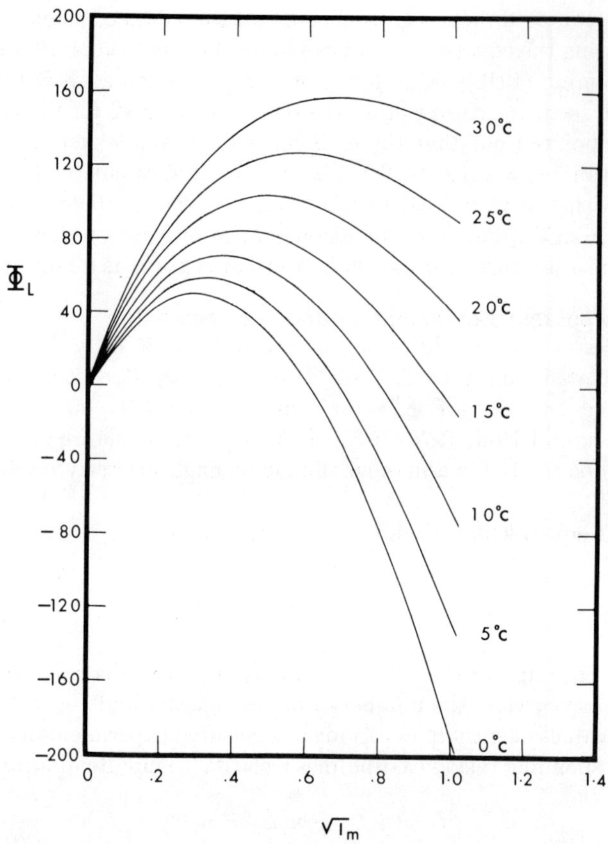

Fig. 14. The relative apparent equivalent enthalpy (Φ_L) of sea salt plotted versus the square root of the weight ionic strength (I_m) at various temperatures.

Since Φ_L data does not readily approach the limiting law at moderate concentrations, it is necessary to use some form of an extended Debye-Hückel equation. The extrapolation equation used for sea salt (Millero, Hansen, and Hoff, 1973) is given by

$$\Phi_L = S_H I_m^{1/2}\left[\frac{1}{(1 + I_m^{1/2})} - \frac{\sigma}{3}\right] + B_L I_m + C_L I_m^{3/2} \tag{128}$$

where S_H is the Debye-Hückel limiting law slope for sea salt (Lewis and Randall, 1961), $\sigma = (3/I_m^{3/2})[(1 + I_m^{1/2}) - 1/(1 + I_m^{1/2}) - 2\ln(1 + I_m^{1/2})]$ and B_L and C_L are temperature dependent adjustable parameters. The Φ_L's for sea salt at various I_m's are shown in Fig. 14.

The S_H's for sea salt have been fit to the equation

$$S_H = 534 + 8.51t + 0.073t^2 \tag{129}$$

while the constants B_L and C_L were fit to the equations (Millero, Hansen, and Hoff, 1973)

$$B_L = -418 - 0.40t + 0.166t^2 \tag{130}$$

and

$$C_L = 22 + 9.96t - 0.257t^2 \tag{131}$$

from 0 to 30°C (when Φ_L is expressed in units of cal/eq).

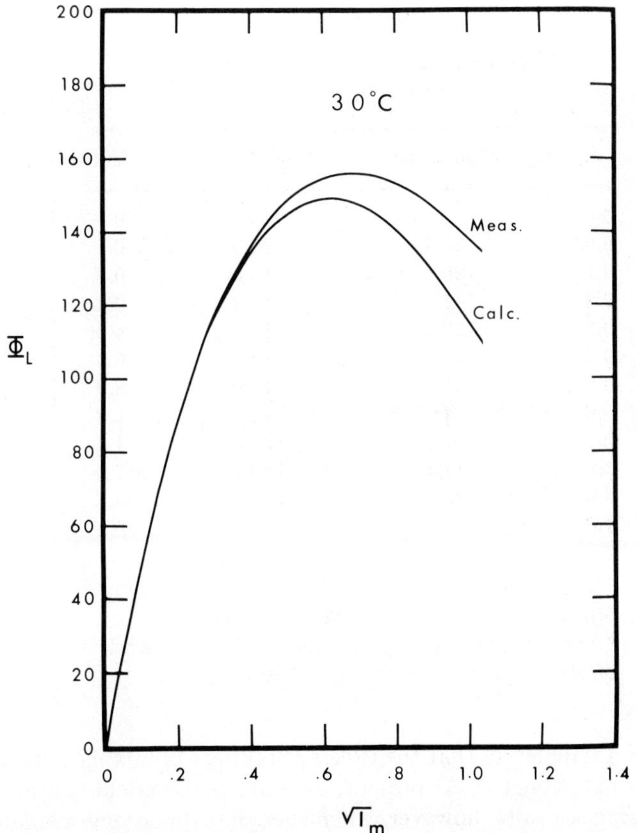

Fig. 15. Comparison of the measured and calculated relative equivalent enthalpy of sea salt at various concentrations and at 25°C.

The simple Young's rule (neglecting the excess enthalpy terms) for the relative apparent enthalpy of sea salt is given by

$$\Phi_L = \sum E_M E_X \Phi_L(MX) \tag{132}$$

Recently, we (Millero and Leung, in preparation) have estimated the Φ_L of sea salt from equation 132 at 25 and 30°C. If the Φ_L's of major sea salts (Parker, 1965; Lewis and Randall, 1961; Harned and Owen, 1958; Millero, Leung, and Hoff, in preparation) are fit to equation 128, it is necessary to use Young's rule only to estimate the B_L and C_L terms:

$$B_L = \sum E_M E_X B_L(MX) \tag{133}$$

$$C_L = \sum E_M E_X C_L(MX) \tag{134}$$

The B_L and C_L calculated from equations 133 and 134 at 30°C are, respectively, $B_L = -280$ and $C_L = 60$ (Millero and Leung, in preparation). The calculated Φ_L's for sea salt at 30°C are given in Table XXV and shown in Fig. 15, along with the measured values. In the low concentration region (below 20‰), the calculated values are in excellent agreement with the measured values. The maximum deviation of

TABLE XXV

The Measured and Calculated Φ_L's of Sea Salt at 30°C

I_m	Measured[a]	Calculated[b]	Δ
0	0	0	0
0.05	95.7	95.6	0.1
0.1	120.1	119.3	0.8
0.2	142.7	140.3	2.4
0.3	152.1	147.8	4.3
0.4	155.7	149.1	6.6
0.5	155.9	147.0	8.9
0.6	154.3	142.7	11.6
0.7	151.3	136.9	14.4
0.8	147.4	130.2	17.2
0.9	143.1	123.0	20.1
1.0	138.4	115.4	23.0

[a] The measured values are taken from the work of Millero, Hansen, and Hoff (1972, 1973).
[b] The calculated values are taken from the work of Millero and Leung (in preparation).

23 cal/eq at $I_m = 1.0$ indicates that the excess enthalpies of mixing salts become important at high ionic strengths. At present, data are not available for all the excess enthalpies of mixing sea salts; however, when such data do become available (Millero and Leung, in preparation) the revised form (Wood and Anderson, 1966) of Young's rule can be used to estimate the enthalpy of seawater.

The Apparent Equivalent Heat Capacity of Sea Salt

The heat capacity of seawater solutions (Millero, 1971d; Millero and Leung, in preparation) can be examined by the same general methods that have been applied earlier to the volume and enthalpy properties. The apparent equivalent heat capacity (Φ_{Cp}) of sea salt is given by

$$\Phi_{Cp} = \frac{[Cp(\text{soln}) - Cp(\text{H}_2\text{O})]}{e_T} \tag{135}$$

where Cp(soln) is the heat capacity of the seawater solution and $Cp(H_2O)$ is the heat capacity of pure water. The apparent equivalent heat capacity can be related to the measured specific heats (cp) by the equation

$$\Phi_{Cp} = \left[\frac{1000(cp - cp^0)}{e_T}\right] + M'_T cp \tag{136}$$

where cp and cp^0 are, respectively, equal to the specific heat of seawater and pure water.

The Φ_{Cp} calculated from the specific heat measurements of Cox and Smith (1959) and Bromley et al. (1967–1970) using equation 136 are shown plotted versus $I_m^{1/2}$ in Fig. 16. In the high concentration, the Φ_{Cp}'s appear to follow a Masson-type equation

$$\Phi_{Cp} = \Phi_{Cp}{}^0 + S'_{Cp} I_m^{1/2} \tag{137}$$

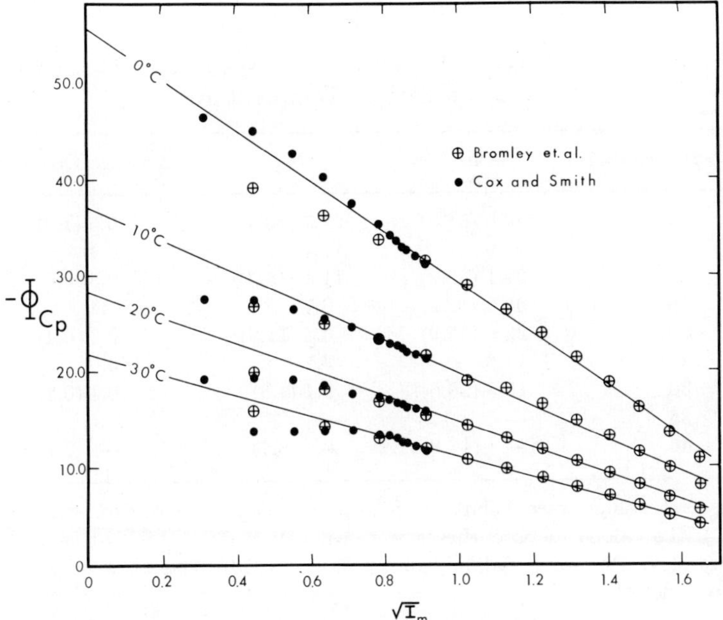

Fig. 16. The apparent equivalent heat capacity (Φ_{Cp}) of sea salt plotted versus the square root of the weight ionic strength ($I_m^{1/2}$) at various temperatures.

where the infinite dilution apparent equivalent heat capacity $\Phi_{Cp}{}^0 = \sum E_i \phi_{Cp}{}^0(i)$ and the Masson apparent heat capacity slope $S'_{Cp} = \sum E_i S^*_{Cp}(i)$ [$\phi_{Cp}{}^0(i)$ and $S^*_{Cp}(i)$ are, respectively, the ionic infinite dilution apparent equivalent heat capacity and the Masson slope]. It should be pointed out that classically (Lewis and Randall, 1961; Harned and Owen, 1958) the ϕ_{Cp}'s of electrolytes have been plotted versus the square root of the molal concentration, not the molar concentration; the difference in the (S^*_{Cp})'s obtained using the two different units are normally very small. The Masson $\Phi_{Cp}{}^0$ and S'_{Cp} for sea salt from 0 to 40°C determined from the high concentration data are given in Table XXVI along with the average deviations.

A plot of $\Phi_{Cp}{}^0$ versus temperature (Bromley et al., 1970) is shown in Fig. 17. Like the $\Phi_{Cp}{}^0$ for most electrolytes (Criss and Cobble, 1964), the $\Phi_{Cp}{}^0$ for sea salt goes through a maximum near 50°C.

The combination of equations 136 and 137 do not yield equations for the specific heat of seawater similar to the Root density equation. If we define the heat capacity of seawater in volume units, $\sigma = cp \times d$, and use volume concentration units to represent the Masson Φ_{Cp} equation, we have

$$\Phi_{Cp} = \left[\frac{1000(\sigma - \sigma^0)}{N_T}\right] + \sigma^0 \Phi_V \tag{138}$$

$$\Phi_{Cp} = \Phi_{Cp}{}^0 + S'_{Cp} I_V^{1/2} \tag{139}$$

where $\sigma^0 = cp^0 \times d^0$ (the volume specific heat for pure water in cal cm^{-3} deg^{-1}). The combination of these equations with equations 61a, 63a, and 84 gives

$$\sigma = \sigma^0 + A'_{Cp}\mathrm{Cl}_V + B'_{Cp}\mathrm{Cl}_V^{3/2} \tag{140}$$

TABLE XXVI

Constants for the Masson Apparent Equivalent Heat Capacity of Sea Salt at Various Temperatures

Temperature (°C)	$-\Phi_{Cp}{}^{0}$ [a]	S'_{Cp}	Average Deviation
0	56.8 (51.8)	27.7 (23.7)	0.5 (1.0)
5	41.9	17.7	0.4
10	32.1 (35.2)	11.4 (15.7)	0.3 (0.6)
15	25.0	6.7	0.4
20	22.0 (25.9)	6.4 (11.9)	0.3 (0.4)
25	17.6	3.7	0.6
30	15.3 (20.6)	3.1 (9.8)	0.4 (0.2)
35	—	—	—
40	— (17.8)	— (8.7)	— (0.1)

[a] The first values were calculated for the heat capacities of Cox and Smith (1965); the values in parentheses were calculated from the heat capacities of Bromley, Diamond, Salami, and Wilkins (1970). The units of Φ_{Cp} are cal eq^{-1} deg^{-1}.

where $A'_{Cp} = 10^{-3}[\Phi_{Cp}{}^{0} - \sigma^{0}\Phi_{V}{}^{0}] \times 0.0312803$ and $B_{Cp} = 10^{-3}[S'_{Cp} - \sigma^{0}S'_{V}] \times 0.0059350$. This equation predicts that $(\sigma - \sigma^{0})/\text{Cl}_V$ should be a linear function of $\text{Cl}_V^{1/2}$. Since d and d^0 are near 1 and $\text{Cl}_V \simeq \text{Cl}(‰)$, one might expect that $(cp - cp^0)/\text{Cl}(‰)$ should also be a linear plot of $\text{Cl}(‰)^{1/2}$. In Table XXVII we give the constants A_{Cp} and B_{Cp} for the equation

$$cp = cp^0 + A_{Cp}\text{Cl}(‰) + B_{Cp}\text{Cl}(‰)^{3/2} \tag{141}$$

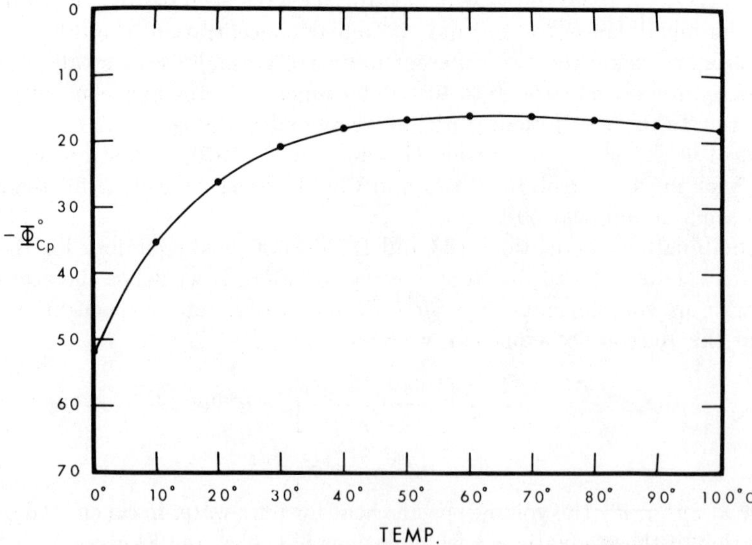

Fig. 17. The apparent equivalent heat capacity of sea salt at infinite dilution ($\Phi_{Cp}{}^{0}$) at various temperatures.

TABLE XXVII

Constants for a Root-Type Equation for the Specific Heat of Seawater[a]

Temperature (°C)	cp^0 (cal/g)	$-10^3 A_{Cp}$	$-10^3 B_{Cp}$	Average Deviation ($\pm$)
0	1.0080	3.7045	0.1899	0.00011
5	1.0044	3.1954	0.1200	0.00010
10	1.0019	2.8870	0.0839	0.00009
15	1.0004	2.6993	0.0644	0.00013
20	0.9995	2.5873	0.0580	0.00008
25	0.9990	2.4260	0.0386	0.00030
30	0.9987	2.3580	0.0338	0.00015

[a] Calculated from the specific heat data (cal g^{-1}) of Cox and Smith (1959).

determined from Cox and Smith's *cp* data along with the average deviations. As is quite apparent from the deviations given in Table XXVII, equation 141 fits the data to within the experimental error of the measurements (± 0.0005 cal g^{-1} deg^{-1}).

The prediction of the $\Phi_{Cp}{}^0$ and S'_{Cp} for sea salt using Young's rule (in its simple form) can be calculated from the major components of seawater in a manner similar to the volume calculations described earlier. The calculation of $\Phi_{Cp}{}^0$ and S'_{Cp} at 25°C are shown in Table XXVIII. The estimated $\Phi_{Cp}{}^0$ and S'_{Cp} are in reasonable agreement with the measured values. The average deviation of the back calculated Φ_{Cp}'s are ± 0.6 cal. eq^{-1} deg^{-1}. The specific heats calculated from (Young's rule) the estimated

TABLE XXVIII

Calculation of the Masson Φ_{Cp} and S'_{Cp} for Sea Salt at 25°C

Solute	$-\phi^*_{Cp}{}^{0a}$	$-E_i\phi_{Cp}{}^0(i)$	S^*_{Cp}	$E_i S^*_{Cp}(i)$
Na^+	8.55	6.617	8.65	6.694
$\frac{1}{2}Mg^{2+}$	16.05	2.814	0.05	0.009
$\frac{1}{2}Ca^{2+}$	18.90	0.641	2.22	0.075
K^+	13.75	0.231	5.45	0.092
$\frac{1}{2}Sr^{2+}$	19.95	0.006	3.11	0.001
Cl^-	15.25	13.732	5.75	5.178
$\frac{1}{2}SO_4{}^{2-}$	17.20	1.602	8.12	0.756
$HCO_3{}^-$	15.75	0.061	5.15	0.020
Br^-	15.75	0.022	5.15	0.007
H_3BO_3	—	—	0.00	0.000
F^-	13.75	0.002	5.45	0.001
		25.728		12.833

[a] Based on $\phi_{Cp}(H^+) = 0$. Data taken from the tabulations of Harned and Owen (1958) and Lewis and Randall (1961). The values for F^-, $HCO_3{}^-$, and Sr^{2-} have been estimated.

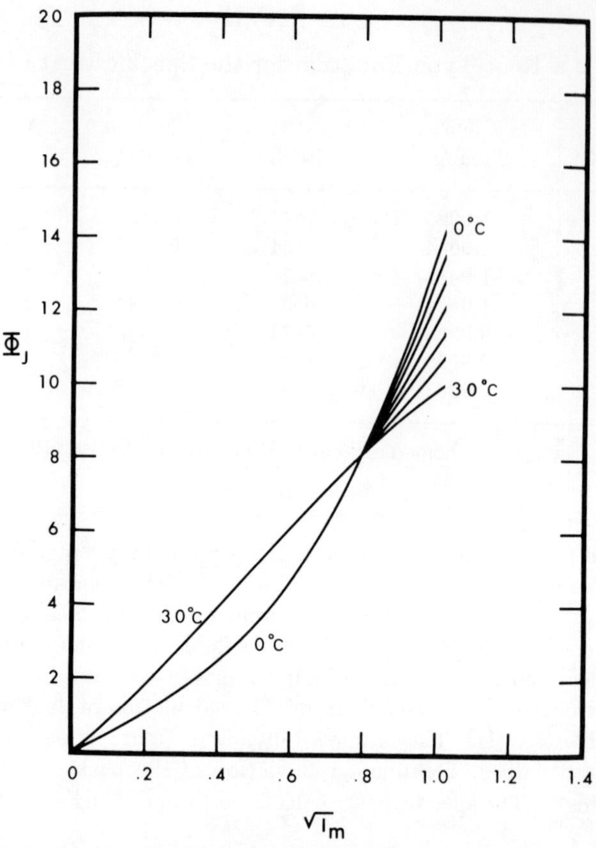

Fig. 18. The relative apparent heat capacity (Φ_J) of sea salt plotted versus the square root of the weight ionic strength (I_m) at various temperatures.

$\phi_{Cp}{}^0$ and S'_{Cp} (using equation 136) agree with the measured value to within an average deviation of ± 0.001 cal g^{-1} deg^{-1}.

Since the relative apparent equivalent heat capacity (Φ_J) is related to Φ_L by

$$\Phi_J = \Phi_{Cp} - \Phi_{Cp}{}^0 = (\partial \Phi_L / \partial T) \tag{142}$$

it is possible to use an extended Debye-Hückel equation similar to equation 128 to fit the Φ_{Cp} of seawater (Bromley, 1968). Differentiating equation 128 with respect to temperature, we obtain

$$\Phi_J = \Phi_{Cp} - \Phi_{Cp}{}^0 = S_{Cp} I_m^{1/2} \left[\frac{1}{(1 + I_m^{1/2}) - \sigma/3} \right] + B_J I_m + C_J I_m^{3/2} \tag{143}$$

where the theoretical Debye-Hückel slope is given by

$$S_{Cp} = 8.51 + 0.146t \tag{144}$$

and the constants are given by

$$B_J = 0.40 + 0.332t \tag{145}$$

and

$$C_J = 9.96 - 0.514t \tag{146}$$

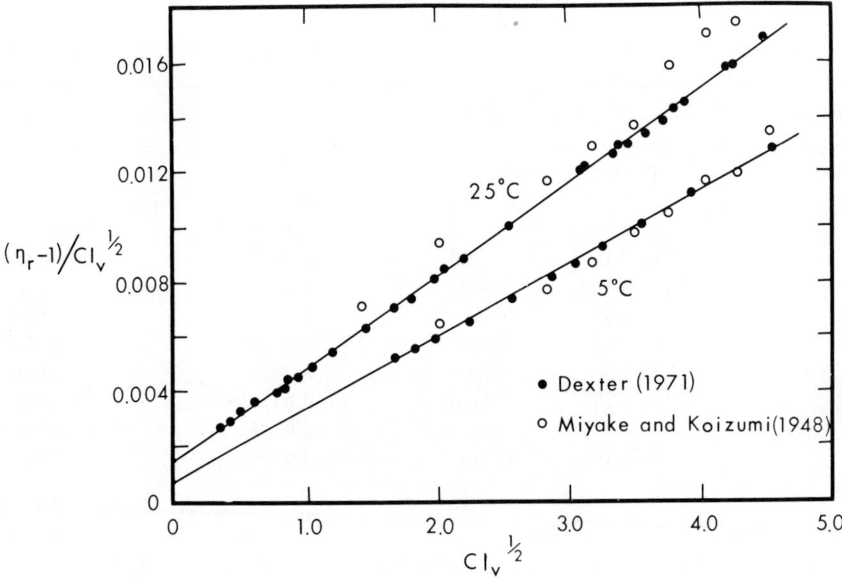

Fig. 19. A plot of $(\eta_r - 1)/Cl_V^{1/2}$ versus $Cl_V^{1/2}$ for seawater at 5°C and 25°C.

A plot of the Φ_J for sea salt at 0 and 30°C (calculated from equation 143) is shown in Fig. 18. As demonstrated elsewhere (Millero, Hansen, and Hoff, 1973), equation 143 yields Φ_J data that are in good agreement with the results of Bromley et al. (1968–1970). Since this equation has not been applied to single electrolyte data, it is not possible at present to use Young's rule to estimate B_J and C_J.

B. Transport Properties

Viscosity of Seawater

The viscosity of electrolyte solutions as a function of concentration is normally examined by using the Jones-Dole equation (1929). The Jones-Dole (1929) equation for seawater expressed in concentration units of normality (N_T) is given by Millero (1971d):

$$\eta_r = \frac{\eta}{\eta^0} = 1 + A_S N_T^{1/2} + B_S N_T \qquad (147)$$

where η_r the relative viscosity equals the viscosity of seawater η divided by the viscosity of pure water (Korson, Drost-Hansen, and Millero, 1969). The constant $A_S = \sum E_i A_i$ is related to the weighted sum of the ion-ion interactions of the major components and the constant $B_S = \sum E_i B_i$ is related to the weighted sum of the ion-water interactions of the major components (Gurney, 1953).

Since the volume chlorinity of seawater (Cl_V) is proportional to the normality (N_T) (see equation 61a), one would expect the relative viscosity of seawater to be given by

$$\eta_r = 1 + A_\eta Cl_V^{1/2} + B_\eta Cl_V \qquad (148)$$

where $A_\eta = A_S \times 0.001274 = \sum E_i A_i \times 0.001274$ and $B_\eta = B_S \times 0.00312803 \times \sum B_i A_i \times 0.00312803$. In Fig. 19, we have plotted $(\eta_r - 1)/Cl_v$ versus $Cl_V^{1/2}$ for seawater solutions using the viscosity data of Miyake and Koizumi (1948) and Dexter

TABLE XXIX

Calculation of the Jones-Dole Coefficients for Seawater Solutions at 25°C

Solute	A_i[a]	E_iA_i	B_i[b]	E_iB_i
Na^+	0.0024	0.0019	0.0863	0.0667
$\frac{1}{2}Mg^{2+}$	0.0071	0.0013	0.1926	0.0342
$\frac{1}{2}Ca^{2+}$	0.0050	0.0002	0.1425	0.0047
K^+	0.0016	0.0000	−0.0070	−0.0001
$\frac{1}{2}Sr^{2+}$	0.0042	0.0000	0.1325	0.0000
Cl^-	0.0032	0.0029	−0.0070	−0.0063
$\frac{1}{2}SO_4^{2-}$	0.0092	0.0009	0.1043	0.0097
HCO_3^-	0.0020	0.0000	0.0460	0.0002
Br^-	0.0023	0.0000	−0.0420	−0.0001
H_3BO_3	—	—	0.0380	0.0000
F^-	0.0036	0.0000	0.0960	0.0000
		A_S = 0.0072		B_S = 0.1090

[a] The A_i's have been divided into ionic components using the relation $A^+/A^- = \lambda_+^0 Z^+/\lambda_-^0 Z^-$ where λ^0 is the mobility and Z is the charge on the ion (Harned and Owen, 1958).
[b] The B_i's have been divided into ionic components by assuming $B(K^+) = B(\mathrm{Cl})$ (Gurney, 1953).

(1971). As is quite apparent from Fig. 16, the Jones-Dole (1929) equation (equation 148) represents the viscosity of seawater over the entire concentration range. The recent work of Dexter (1971) represents the most precise viscosity measurements made on seawater. His results at 5 and 25°C have been fit, respectively, to the equations (Millero, 1971d; Millero and Emmet, in preparation)

$$\eta_r = 1 + 0.000366\ \mathrm{Cl}_V^{1/2} + 0.002756\ \mathrm{Cl}_V \tag{149}$$

$$\eta_r = 1 + 0.001403\ \mathrm{Cl}_V^{1/2} + 0.003416\ \mathrm{Cl}_V \tag{150}$$

If we convert A_η and B_η at 5 and 25°C to units of normality, we obtain at 5°C, $A_S = 0.0021$ and $B_S = 0.0891$ and at 25°C, $A_S = 0.0079$ and $B_S = 0.1092$.

Recently, Millero and Emmet (Millero, 1971d; Millero and Emmet, in preparation) have calculated the $A_S = \sum E_iA_i$ and $B_S = \sum E_iB_i$ for seawater solutions at 25°C using A_i and B_i for the major components of seawater (Gurney, 1953; Harned and Owen, 1958; Robinson and Stokes, 1959; Kaminsky, 1957). Calculation of A_S and B_S for seawater at 25°C are shown in Table XXIX. The calculated $A_S = 0.0072$ and $B_S = 0.1090$ for seawater solutions at 25°C are in excellent agreement with measured values ($A_S = 0.0079$ and $B_S = 0.1092$). The calculated viscosities obtained using the A_S and B_S given in Table XXIX are within the experimental error of the measured values. Unfortunately, at present there is little or no reliable viscosity for electrolyte solutions below 25°C, thus, we cannot make similar calculations at low temperatures.

Conductivity of Seawater

Although few attempts (Harned and Owen, 1958) have been made to predict the conductance of mixed electrolyte solutions by adding the conductances of the components, because of the success of Park (1964), Connors and Park (1967), and Connors and Weyl (1968) in using partial equivalent conductances to estimate the specific conductance of seawater, one might expect a Young's rule approach to work on the conductance of seawater.

The partial equivalent conductances ($\overline{\Lambda}_i$) of the major sea salts in seawater, defined by (Connors and Weyl, 1968)

$$\overline{\Lambda}_i = \left(\frac{\partial L}{\partial n_i}\right)_{T,P,n_j \neq i} \tag{151}$$

where $\overline{\Lambda}_i$ is the increase in the total conductance L of an infinitely large volume of seawater contained between two parallel plates 1 cm apart. Connors and Weyl (1968) found that the partial equivalent conductances of sea salt, $\overline{\Lambda}_S$, calculated from the relation

$$\overline{\Lambda}_S = \sum E_i \overline{\Lambda}_i \tag{152}$$

are in good agreement with values calculated from the electrical conductance of seawater.

Recently, we (Hatcher and Millero, unpublished results) have found that over the salinity range of 30 to 35‰ the ionic partial equivalent conductances could be fit to a Masson-type equation (originally developed by Kohlrausch, 1916):

$$\overline{\Lambda}_i = \overline{\Lambda}_i{}^0 + S_i^* I_V^{1/2} \tag{153}$$

The ionic partial equivalent conductances fit to the Masson-type equation also gives good estimates for the $\overline{\Lambda}_S$ (i.e., by using equation 152).

It will be interesting in future work to see if ionic conductance data in single electrolyte solutions can be used to predict the conductance of sea salt.

6. Prediction of the Properties of Solutes in Seawater

The estimation of the thermodynamic properties such as activity coefficients for solutes in seawater are of great importance since the data are very useful in interpreting various geochemical (e.g., solubilities) and biochemical (e.g., ion transport) processes. The thermodynamic equilibrium of a chemical process

$$A + B = C + D \tag{154}$$

can be characterized by an equilibrium constant

$$K = \left(\frac{a_C a_D}{a_A a_B}\right) = \left(\frac{[C][D]}{[A][B]}\right) \times \left(\frac{\gamma_C \gamma_D}{\gamma_A \gamma_B}\right) \tag{155}$$

where a_i, $[i]$, and γ_i are, respectively, the activity, concentration, and activity coefficient for species i. The effect of pressure on the chemical process (equation 154) can be determined from

$$(\partial \ln K/\partial P) = (-\Delta \overline{V}/RT) \tag{156}$$

where

$$\Delta \overline{V} = \overline{V}(C) + \overline{V}(D) - \overline{V}(A) - \overline{V}(B) \tag{157}$$

[$\overline{V}(i)$ is the partial molal volume of species i.] While the effect of temperature on the chemical process (equation 154)

$$(\partial \ln K/\partial T) = (\Delta \overline{H}/RT^2) \tag{158}$$

where

$$\Delta\bar{H} = \bar{H}(C) + \bar{H}(D) - \bar{H}(A) - \bar{H}(B) \tag{159}$$

[$\bar{H}(i)$ is the partial molal enthalpy of species (i).] The determination of the equilibrium constant, its pressure dependence, and its temperature dependence can be made by two general methods: (1) direct measurements in the medium of seawater, and (2) estimation from known properties in pure water. Needless to say, the first method will require years of work and may be impossible for some processes because of the chemical nature of seawater. In this section we will briefly examine some of the methods that can be used to estimate activity coefficients, partial molal volumes, and partial molal enthalpies in the medium of seawater.

A. *Activity Coefficients*

A number of methods are available for the estimation of the activity coefficients in mixed electrolyte solutions (some of them described earlier). The simplest method is the ionic strength principle (Lewis and Randall, 1961), which gives the trace activity coefficient the same value as the activity coefficient of the pure electrolyte at the same ionic strength. As demonstrated by Reilly, Wood, and Robinson (1971) and others, the ionic strength principle gives reasonable values for some electrolytes at low ionic strength; however, at high concentrations the equations of Reilly, Wood, and Robinson (1971) are consistently better. The activity coefficients of some of the major ionic components in seawater are given in Table XXX. The calculated activity coefficients of some of the major ions (HCO_3^-, CO_3^{2-}, SO_4^{2-}, Mg^{2+}, and Ca^{2+}) obtained by using the ionic strength principle are higher than the experimentally measured values. As discussed elsewhere (Millero, 1971a), many workers have interpreted these differences in terms of ion pair formation.

Another method that can be used to estimate the activity coefficients of ionic

Table XXX

The Activity Coefficients of the Major Ions in Seawater (at $I_m = 0.7$)

Ion	Measured[a]	Calculated: Ionic Strength Principle[a]	Calculated: Guggenheim[b]
Na^+	0.68	0.71	0.68
Mg^{2+}	0.23	0.36	0.23
Ca^{2+}	0.21	0.28	0.21
K^+	0.64	0.64	0.63
Cl^-	0.68	0.64	0.66
SO_4^{2-}	0.11	0.17	0.11
HCO_3^-	0.55	0.68	0.59
CO_3^{2-}	0.02	0.20	0.03

[a] Taken from the tabulation of Millero (1971a).

[b] Taken from the tabulation of Leyendekkers (1973). The values for HCO_3^- and CO_3^{2-} are for an ionic strength of 0.51.

TABLE XXXI

The Activity Coefficients of Salts in Seawater at I = 0.5 and 0.7

	Measured[a]		Calculated			
			Leyendekkers[b]		Robinson and Wood[c]	
Salt	$I = 0.52$	$I = 0.72$	$I = 0.51$	$I = 0.74$	$I = 0.5$	$I = 0.7$
NaCl	0.69	0.67	0.681	0.669	0.684	0.669
$MgCl_2$	—	—	0.486	0.466	0.483	0.467
$CaCl_2$	—	—	0.475	0.453	—	—
KCl	—	—	0.663	0.644	0.661	0.639
Na_2SO_4	0.41	0.38	0.406	0.368	0.398	0.366
$MgSO_4$	—	—	0.189	0.158	0.181	0.158
$CaSO_4$	—	—	0.183	0.152	—	—
K_2SO_4	—	—	0.392	0.350	0.381	0.345
$CaCO_3$	—	—	—	0.069	—	—
$NaHCO_3$	—	—	0.640	0.612	—	—

[a] The results for NaCl are taken from Gieskes (1966) and Platford (1965); the results for Na_2SO_4 were taken from Platford and Dafoe (1965).
[b] Taken from Leyendekkers (1973).
[c] Taken from Robinson and Wood (1973).

solutes in seawater is to use an equation based on Guggenheim's (1966) treatment that inclues all the pairwise interactions (+ +, + −, and − −) (Leyendekkers, 1971a, b). Recently, Leyendekkers (1973) has used a modified Guggenheim equation to estimate the activity coefficient of the major ionic components of seawater. The results of her estimations are given in Table XXX. As is quite apparent, her estimates are in excellent agreement with the directly measured values and showing that it is not necessary to invoke the concept of ion pairing to estimate activity coefficients in seawater (and vice versa, one cannot prove ion pairing is important in seawater by examining measured and calculated activity coefficients).

Recently, Robinson and Wood (1973) have estimated the activity coefficients of salts in seawater by using the equations of Reilly, Wood, and Robinson (1971).

Their calculated values for the $\gamma_{\pm}$ of NaCl, Na_2SO_4, $MgCl_2$, $MgSO_4$, KCl, and K_2SO_4 in seawater at I = 0.5 and 0.7 are given in Table XXXI, along with some directly measured values. Also included in this table are the estimates made by Leyendekkers (1973) for some salts using the modified Guggenheim equation. Both the estimates of Leyendekkers (1973) and Robinson and Wood (1973) are in excellent agreement with each other as well as with the directly measured values of Gieskes (1966), Platford (1965), and Platford and Dafoe (1965).

In future work, both methods of Guggenheim (1966) as used by Leyendekkers (1973) and the methods of Reilly, Wood, and Robinson (1971) as used by Robinson and Wood (1973) should prove very useful in estimating the activity coefficients of electrolytes and ions in the medium of seawater.

B. Partial Molal Volumes

Owen and Brinkley (1941) were the first to estimate the partial molal volume of salts in seawater. They used the ionic strength principle and the Masson equation to estimate the partial molal volumes of ions in seawater:

$$\bar{V}^* = \bar{V}^0 + \tfrac{3}{2} S_V I_V^{1/2} \tag{160}$$

where $\bar{V}^*$ is the partial molal volume of the salt in seawater, $\bar{V}^0$ is the partial molal volume of the salt in pure water (equal to $\phi_V{}^0$), and I_V is the volume ionic strength of seawater ($I_V = 0.712$ for 35‰ S seawater). Owen and Brinkley (1941) also estimated the $\bar{V}^*$ for salts in seawater by assuming that $0.725m$ NaCl was equivalent to seawater of 35‰ S.

In Table XXXII the $\bar{V}^*$ for various salts in seawater estimated by the methods of Owen and Brinkley (1941) are given along with the directly measured values of Duedall and Weyl (1967) and Duedall (1968, 1972). For most of the simple electrolytes the measured results in seawater and $0.725m$ NaCl are in reasonable agreement (note that the exceptions are $MgSO_4$ and $CaCl_2$). The estimates made by Owen and Brinkley (1941) are also in reasonable agreement with the measured values (with the exception of $KHCO_3$, $MgCl_2$, and $NaCO_3$).

Millero (1969) has taken another approach to the estimation of ions in the medium of seawater. He noted that the volume change for transferring ions from pure water to $0.725m$ NaCl or seawater (35‰) followed an empirical equation (equation 47) shown in Fig. 20. This semiempirical equation is based on the fact that the partial molal volumes of simple ions can be broken down into two major components:

$$\bar{V}^0(\text{ion}) = \bar{V}^0(\text{elect}) + \bar{V}^0(\text{int}) \tag{161}$$

where the electrostriction partial molal volume $\bar{V}^0(\text{elect}) = AZ^2/r$ and the intrinsic

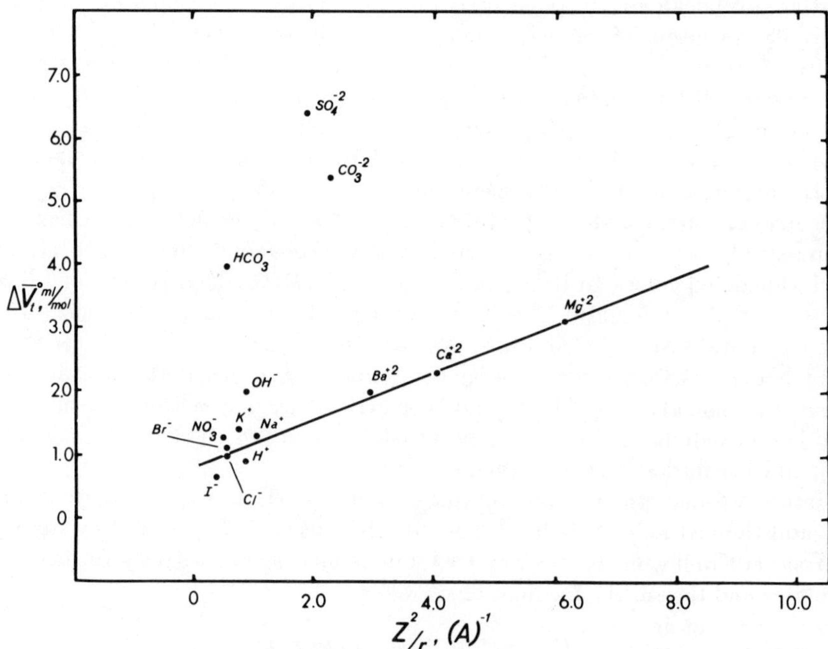

Fig. 20. The change in the partial molal volumes of ions transferred from water to seawater plotted versus Z^2/r. From Millero (1969) with permission of *Limnology and Oceanography*.

TABLE XXXII

The Partial Molal Volumes of Salts in Seawater at 25°C

Salt	Measured		Calculated	
	Seawater[a]	0.725*m* NaCl[b]	Owen and Brinkley[c]	Millero[d]
HCl	—	19.6	—	20.1
NaCl	18.9	19.0	—	18.8
KCl	29.2	29.3	—	28.9
NaBr	—	25.8	—	25.7
KBr	—	36.2	—	35.8
KI	—	—	47.3	47.4
KOH	—	—	8.4	7.2
$NaNO_3$	30.5	—	—	30.0
KNO_3	40.7	—	41.1	40.1
$KHCO_3$	37.4	—	36.0	34.0
Na_2SO_4	21.0	20.6	21.0	15.4
K_2SO_4	41.6	41.4	—	35.6
$MgCl_2$	19.6	19.3	18.4	19.6
$CaCl_2$	22.0	23.0	22.6	22.0
$BaCl_2$	—	—	27.1	27.0
$MgSO_4$	2.9	1.9	—	−2.6
$Ca(NO_3)_2$	45.1	—	—	44.4
Na_2CO_3	11.0	—	1.5	−2.4
K_2CO_3	30.3	—	—	—

[a] Taken from Duedall and Weyl (1967) and Duedall (1972). The 25° values for Na_2CO_3 and K_2CO_3 were estimated from 20°C data (Millero and Berner, 1972).
[b] Taken from the work of Wirth (1939) and Lee (1966).
[c] Taken from Owen and Brinkley (1941).
[d] Taken from Millero (1969) for free ions only.

partial molal volume (equal to the crystal partial molal volume plus a void space effect) $\bar{V}(\text{int}) = Br^3$. From the transfer equation the $\bar{V}$ for ions in seawater can be estimated by

$$\bar{V}^*(\text{ion}) = \bar{V}^0(\text{ion}) + aZ^2/r + b \tag{162}$$

where $a = 0.01585\ S(‰)$ and $b = 0.02373\ S(‰)$ at 25°C. As is apparent from Fig. 20, the ions HCO_3^-, CO_3^{2-}, and SO_4^{2-} show large deviations from the straight line. These deviations have been interpreted (Millero, 1969, 1971c) in terms of ion pairing (when an ion pair is formed, electrostricted water molecules are released and the volume of the solution increases). In recent papers these methods have been used to correct the free ion values given by equation 162. For example, the $\bar{V}^*$ of CO_3^{2-} has been estimated to be 22.1 ml/mol in seawater (Millero and Berner, 1972), which compares very well with the measured value of 19.2 ml/mol by Duedall (1972).

In summary, the semiempirical equations corrected for ion pairing effects yields results for $\bar{V}^*$ that are in excellent agreement with the measured values.

Whether the semiempirical equation is better than the differentiated equations of Reilly, Wood, and Robinson (1971) remains to be seen (Millero and Wood, in preparation). Judging by the success in estimating the Φ_V for seawater, one would expect the method of Reilly, Wood, and Robinson (1971) to give reliable estimates for the $\bar{V}^*$'s of salts in seawater without the necessity of involving the concept of ion pairing.

C. *Partial Molal Enthalpies*

No direct experimental measurements have been made on the partial molal enthalpy of salts in seawater ($\bar{H}^*$) or the relative partial molal enthalpy ($\bar{L}^*$). We presently are making such measurements (Millero and Schrager, in progress); thus, in the near future we can expect some experimental results. At present, the best way to estimate the $\bar{L}^*$ or $\bar{H}^*$ of salts in seawater is to use the ionic strength principle

$$\bar{H}^* - \bar{H}^0 = \bar{L}^* = \bar{L}_2 \qquad (163)$$

where $\bar{L}_2$ is the relative partial molal enthalpy of the salt in pure water (equation 127) at the ionic strength of seawater and the $\bar{L}^*$ is relative to infinite dilution. $\bar{L}_2$ values for salts at the ionic strength of seawater can be obtained from the tabulations of Parker (1965).

Again, one might expect the methods of Reilly, Wood, and Robinson (1971) to yield the best estimates for the $\bar{L}^*$ of salts in the medium of seawater.

7. Summary

To summarize briefly, the recent developments in the physical chemistry of multicomponent electrolyte solutions have been very useful in obtaining a better understanding of the physical chemistry of seawater, both as the pseudoelectrolyte-sea salt and as an ionic medium. We hope that the reader has obtained an overall view of these developments and will follow future work in this field closely. The understanding of seawater as an electrolyte solution and as an ionic medium should prove to be very useful to other fields, such as geochemistry and biochemistry (both of marine and nonmarine systems). Although seawater is a complex mixture of many components, it is still possible to handle its properties by using classical thermodynamics.

Acknowledgments

I would like to first acknowledge the Office of Naval Research (Contract NONR-4008-02) and the Oceanographic Branch of the National Science Foundation (GA-17386) for their support of this study. I wish to thank my graduate students, Robert Emmet, Rana Fine, Wing Leung, Sheldon Schrager, and Gary Ward, who aided in the literature research; Col. Jon Knox for the drawings; Augustin Gonzalez for checking the references; and my secretary, Carolyn Beaty, for her patience in typing this manuscript. I also thank Dr. Robert Wood, Dr. Jacques Desnoyers, and Dr. Robert Robinson for reading the manuscript and offering many helpful comments.

Last, but not least, I wish to dedicate this chapter to my good friend, Dr. Henry Anderson, who recently passed away. His classical work under the direction of Dr. Robert Wood, and later with his own graduate students, has been very important to the advancement of the understanding of multicomponent electrolyte solutions such as seawater.

References

Anderson, H. L. and L. A. Petree, 1970. Heats of mixing. I. Temperature dependence of aqueous electrolytes with a common anion. *J. Phys. Chem.*, **74**, 1455–1459.

Anderson, H. L., R. D. Wilson, and D. E. Smith, 1971. Heats of Mixing. II. Temperature dependence of aqueous electrolytes with a common ion. *J. Phys. Chem.*, **75**, 1125–1128.

Bahe, L. W., 1972. Structure in concentrated solutions of electrolytes. Field dielectric gradient forces and energies. *J. Phys. Chem.*, **76**, 1062–1071.

Bernal, J. D. and R. H. Fowler, 1933. A theory of water and ionic solution, with particular reference to hydrogen and hydroxyl ions. *J. Chem. Phys.*, **1**, 515–548.

Bjerrum, N., 1920. Der Aktivitätskoeffizient der Ionen. *Z. Anorg. Chem.*, **109**, 275–292.

Bjerrum, N., 1926. Ionic association. I. Influence of ionic association on the activity of ion at moderate degree of association. *Kgl. Danske Videnskab Selskab. Mat-Fys. Medd.*, **7** (9), 1–48.

Boyd, G. E., S. Lindenbaum, and R. A. Robinson, 1971. Estimation of solute activity coefficients in dilute aqueous mixtures of sodium and zinc bromides at 25°—Comparisons with predictions from the Guggenheim theory of solutions. *J. Phys. Chem.*, **75**, 3153–3159.

Bromley, L. A., 1968a. Heat capacity of seawater solutions partial and apparent values for salts and water. *J. Chem. Eng. Data*, **13**, 60–62.

Bromley, L. A., 1968b. Relative enthalpies of sea salt solutions at 25°C. *J. Chem. Eng. Data*, **13**, 399–402.

Bromley, L. A., V. A. DeSaussure, J. C. Clipp, and J. A. Wright, 1967. Heat capacities of seawater at salinities of 1 to 12% and temperatures of 2° to 80°C. *J. Chem. Eng. Data*, **12**, 202–206.

Bromley, L. A., A. E. Diamond, E. Salami, and D. G. Wilkins, 1970. Heat capacities and enthalpies of sea salt solutions to 200°C. *J. Chem. Eng. Data*, **15**, 246–253.

Brønsted, J. N., 1922. Studies on solubility. IV. Principles of the specific interaction of ions. *J. Amer. Chem. Soc.*, **44**, 877–898.

Butler, J. N., 1968. The thermodynamic activity of calcium ion in sodium chloride-calcium chloride electrolytes. *Biophys. J.*, **8**, 1426–1433.

Butler, J. N., P. T. Hsu, and J. C. Synnot, 1967. Activity coefficient measurements in aqueous sodium chloride-sodium sulfate electrolytes using sodium amalgam electrodes. *J. Phys. Chem.*, **71**, 910–914.

Butler, J. N. and R. Huston, 1967. Activity coefficient measurements in aqueous $NaCl \cdot CaCl_2$ and $NaCl \cdot MgCl_2$ electrolytes using sodium amalgam electrodes. *J. Phys. Chem.*, **71**, 4479–4485.

Butler, J. N. and R. Huston, 1970. Activity coefficients and ion pairs in the systems sodium chloride-sodium bicarbonate water and sodium chloride-sodium carbonate-water. *J. Phys. Chem.*, **74**, 2976–2983.

Childs, C. W. and R. F. Platford, 1971. Excess free energies of mixing at temperatures below 25°. Isopiestic measurements on the systems $H_2O–NaCl–Na_2SO_4$ and $H_2O–NaCl–MgSO_4$. *Aust. J. Chem.*, **24**, 2487–2491.

Christenson, P. G. and J. M. Gieskes, 1971. Activity coefficients of KCl in several mixed electrolytes solutions at 25°C. *J. Chem. Eng. Data*, **16**, 398–400.

Connors, D. N., 1970. On the enthalpy of seawater. *Limnol. Oceanog.*, **15**, 587–594.

Connors, D. N. and K. Park, 1967. The partial equivalent conductances of electrolytes in seawater: a revision. *Deep-Sea Res.*, **14**, 481–484.

Connors, D. N. and P. K. Weyl, 1968. The partial equivalent conductances of salts in seawater and the density/conductance relationship. *Limnol. Oceanog.*, **13**, 39–50.

Conway, B. E., 1966. Electrolyte solutions: solvation and structural aspects. *Annual Rev. of Phys. Chem.*, **17**, 481–528.

Conway, B. E. and R. E. Verrall, 1966. Ion-solvent size ratio as a factor in the thermodynamics of electrolytes. *J. Phys. Chem.*, **70**, 1473–1477.

Cox, R. A., M. J. McCartney, and F. Culkin, 1970. The specific gravity/salinity/temperature relationship in natural seawater. *Deep-Sea Res.*, **17**, 679–689.

Cox, R. A. and N. D. Smith, 1959. The specific heat of seawater. *Proc. Roy. Soc.*, (A) **252**, 51–62.

Criss, C. M. and J. W. Cobble, 1964. The thermodynamic properties of high temperature aqueous solution. IV. Entropies of the ions up to 200° and the correspondence principle. *J. Amer. Chem. Soc.*, **86**, 5385–5390.

Culkin, F., 1965. The major constituents of seawater. In *Chemical Oceanography* Vol. 1. J. P. Riley and G. Skirrow, eds. Academic Press, New York, pp. 121–161.

Culkin, F. and R. A. Cox, 1966. Sodium, potassium, magnesium, calcium and strontium in seawater. *Deep-Sea Res.*, **13**, 789–804.

Davis, C. M. and J. Jarzynski, 1972. Mixture models of water. In *Water and Aqueous Solutions*. R. A. Horne, ed. Wiley, New York, pp. 377–424 (Chapter 10).

Denison, J. T. and J. B. Ramsey, 1955. Free energy, enthalpy and entropy of dissociation of some perchlorates in ethylene chloride and ethylidene chloride. *J. Amer. Chem. Soc.*, **77**, 2615–2621.

Desnoyers, J. E., M. Arel, G. Perron, and C. Jolicoeur, 1969. Apparent molal volumes of alkali halides in water at 25°C. *J. Phys. Chem.*, **73**, 3346–3351.

Desnoyers, J. E. and B. E. Conway, 1964. Activity coefficients of electrolytes and intermediate concentrations and the "cube-root" law. *J. Phys. Chem.*, **68**, 2305–2311.

Desnoyers, J. E. and C. Jolicoeur, 1969. Hydration effects and thermodynamics properties of ions. In *Modern Aspects of Electrochemistry*. Vol. 5. J. O. M. Bockris and B. E. Conway, eds. Plenum Press, New York.

Dexter, R., 1971. I. Viscosity of heavy water and artificial seawater. II. *In situ* measurements of some oceanography important chemical parameters. M.S. thesis, School of Marine and Atmospheric Science, University of Miami, Miami, Florida.

Duedall, I. W., 1968. Partial molal volumes of 16 salts in seawater. *Environ. Sci. Tech.*, **2**, 706–707.

Duedall, I. W., 1972. The partial molal volume of calcium carbonate in seawater. *Geochim. Cosmochim. Acta*, **36**, 729–734.

Duedall, I. W. and P. K. Weyl, 1967. The partial equivalent volumes of salts in seawater. *Limnol. Oceanog.*, **12**, 52–59.

Edmond, J. M., 1970. High precision determination of titration alkalinity and total carbon dioxide content of seawater by potentiometric titration. *Deep-Sea Res.*, **17**, 737–750.

Flaherty, P. H. and R. H. Stern, 1958. Thermodynamics of ion pair dissociation—tetrabutylammonium picrate in chlorobenzene, *o*- and *m*-dichlorobenzene. *J. Amer. Chem. Soc.*, **80**, 1034–1038.

Fowler, R. H. and E. A. Guggenheim, 1939. *Statistical Thermodynamics*. Cambridge University Press, London.

Frank, H. S., 1963. Single-ion activities and ion-solvent interactions in dilute aqueous solutions. *J. Phys. Chem.*, **67**, 1554–1558.

Frank, H. S., 1965. Structural influences on activity coefficients (γ) in aqueous electrolytes. *Z. Physik. Chem.* (*Leipzig*), **228** (5/6), 364–372.

Frank, H. S. and A. L. Robinson, 1940. The entropy of dilution of strong electrolytes in aqueous solutions. *J. Chem. Phys.*, **8**, 933–938.

Frank, H. S. and P. T. Thompson, 1959a. Single-ion activities and ion-solvent interactions in dilute aqueous solutions. *J. Chem. Phys.*, **31**, 1086–1095.

Frank, H. S. and P. T. Thompson, 1959b. A point of view on ion clouds. In *The Structure of Electrolyte Solutions*. W. J. Hamer, ed., New York, (Chapter 8).

Friedman, H. L., 1959. Singularities of the integrals in Mayer's ionic solution theory. *Mol. Phys.*, **2**, 190–205.

Friedman, H. L., 1960a. Thermodynamic excess functions for electrolyte solutions. *J. Chem. Phys.*, **32**, 1351–1362.

Friedman, H. L., 1960b. Mayer's ionic solution theory applied to electrolyte mixtures. *J. Chem. Phys.*, **32**, 1134–1144.

Friedman, H. L., 1962. Computed thermodynamic property and distribution functions for simple models of ionic solutions. In *Modern Aspects of Electrochemistry*. Vol. 6. J. O. M. Bockris and B. E. Conway, eds. Plenum Press, New York, pp. 1–86 (Chapter 1).

Friedman, H. L., 1972. Comment on Theories of the primitive model of ionic solutions. *J. Phys. Chem.*, **76**, 1229–1230.

Friedman, H. L. and P. S. Ramanathan, 1970. Theory of mixed electrolyte solutions and application to a model for aqueous lithium chloride-cesium chloride. *J. Phys. Chem.*, **74**, 3756–3765.

Fuoss, R. M., 1934. Distribution of ions in electrolyte solution. *Trans. Faraday Soc.*, **30**, 967–980.

Fuoss, R. M., 1958. Ionic association. III. The equilibrium between ion pairs and free ions. *J. Amer. Chem. Soc.*, **80**, 5059–5061.

Fuoss, R. M. and C. A. Kraus, 1957. Ionic association. I. Deviation of constants from conductance data. *J. Amer. Chem. Soc.*, **79**, 3301–3313.

Garrels, R. M. and M. E. Thompson, 1962. A chemical model for seawater at 25°C and one atmosphere total pressure. *Amer. J. Sci.*, **260**, 57–66.

Gibbard, Jr., H. F. and G. Scatchard, 1972. Vapor-liquid equilibria of synthetic seawater solutions from 25° to 100°C. *J. Chem. Eng. Data*. In press.

Gieskes, J. M. T., 1966. The activity coefficients of sodium chloride in mixed electrolyte solutions at 25°C. *Physik. Chemie. Neue Folge*, **50**, 78–90.

Glueckauf, E., 1955. The influence of ionic hydration on activity coefficients in concentrated electrolyte solutions. *Trans. Faraday Soc.*, **51**, 1235–1244.

Glueckauf, E., 1964. Effect of the dielectric constant on activity coefficients of electrolytes in aqueous solutions. *Trans. Faraday Soc.*, **60**, 776–782.

Griffiths, T. R. and M. C. R. Symons, 1960. Ionic interactions in solutions of electrolytes as studied by ultraviolet spectroscopy. *Mod. Phys.*, **3**, 90–102.

Guggenheim, E. A., 1935. Thermodynamic properties of aqueous solutions of strong electrolytes. *Phil. Mag.*, **19**, 588–643.

Guggenheim, E. A., 1960. Definition of entropy in classical thermodynamics. *Trans. Faraday Soc.*, **56**, 1152–1159.

Guggenheim, E. A., 1966. Mixture of 1 : 1 electrolytes. *Trans. Faraday Soc.*, **62**, 3446–3450.

Gurney, R. W., 1953. *Ionic Processes in Solution.* Dover Publications, New York.

Harned, H. S. and B. B. Owen, 1958. *The Physical Chemistry of Electrolytes Solutions.* A.C.S. Monograph Series, No. 137, 803 pp. Reinhold, New York.

Harned, H. S. and R. A. Robinson, 1968. *Multicomponent Electrolyte Solutions.* Pergamon Press, Oxford, England.

Hückel, E., 1925. The theory of concentrated aqueous solutions of strong electrolytes. *Physik. Z.*, **26**, 93–147.

Jolicoeur, R., P. Picker, and J. E. Desnoyers, 1969. The concentration dependence of the enthalpies of mixing of some aqueous electrolytes at 25°C; a test of Young's Rule. *J. Chem. Thermodynamics*, **1**, 485–493.

Jones, G. and M. Dole, 1929. Viscosity of aqueous solutions of strong electrolytes with special reference to barium chloride. *J. Amer. Chem. Soc.*, **51**, 2950–2964.

Jones, R. W. and F. Mohling, 1971. On the accuracy of theories of the primitive model of ionic solutions. *J. Phys. Chem.*, **75**, 3790–3796.

Kaminsky, M., 1957. Interaction in ionic solutions. *Disc. Faraday. Soc.*, **24**, 171–179.

Kell, G. S., 1967. Precise representation of volume properties of water at one atmosphere. *J. Chem. Eng. Data*, **12**, 66–69.

Kell, G. S., 1970. Isothermal compressibility of liquid water at one atmosphere. *J. Chem. Eng. Data*, **15**, 119–122.

Kell, G. S., 1972. Continuum theories of liquid water In *Water and Aqueous Solutions.* R. A. Horne, ed. Wiley, New York, pp. 331–376 (Chapter 9).

Kell, G. S. and E. Whalley, 1965. The P-V-T properties of water. I. Liquid water in the temperature range 0 to 150°C and at pressures up to 1 kb. *Phil. Trans. Roy. Soc.* (*London*), (A) **258**, 565–617.

Kester, D. R., I. W. Duedall, D. N. Connors, and R. M. Pytkowicz, 1967. Preparation of artificial seawater. *Limnol. Oceanog.*, **12**, 176–179.

Kirkwood, J. G., 1934. Theory of solutions of molecules containing widely separated charges with special application to amphoteric ions. *J. Chem. Phys.*, **2**, 351–361.

Knudsen, M. (ed.), 1901. *Hydrographical Tables According to the Measurings of Carl Forch, P. Jacobsen, Martin Knudsen and S. P. L. Sorensen.* G. E. C. Gad, Copenhagen, Williams Norgate, 63 pp.

Korson, L., W. Drost-Hansen, and F. J. Millero, 1969. Viscosity of water at various temperatures. *J. Phys. Chem.*, **73**, 34–39.

Kohlraush, F. and L. Hoborn, 1916. *Das Leitvermögen der Elekrolyte Teubuer*, Leipzig.

Lakshmanam, S. and S. K. Rangarajan, 1970. Activities coefficients in mixed electrolytes: A note on Guggenheim's relations. *N. Electranal. Chem.*, **29**, 170–174.

Lanier, R. D., 1965. Activity coefficient of sodium chloride in aqueous three-components solutions by cation-sensitive glass electrodes. *J. Phys. Chem.*, **69**, 3992–3998.

Lee, J., 1966. The apparent and partial molal volumes of electrolytes in water and in aqueous sodium-chloride solution. Ph.D. dissertation, Yale University. University Microfilms, Ann Arbor, Michigan. *#66-4906*, *Abst. B*27, 131 (1966).

Lepple, F. K. and F. J. Millero, 1971. The isothermal compressibility of seawater near one atmosphere. *Deep-Sea Res.*, **18**, 1233–1254.

Levine, A. S., N. Bhatt, M. Ghamkhar, and R. H. Wood, 1970. Heats of mixing of some aqueous alkali metal chloride solutions. *J. Chem. Eng. Data*, **15**, 34–37.

Lewis, G. N. and M. Randall, 1961. *Thermodynamics*, 2d ed. Revised by K. S. Pitzer and F. Brewer. McGraw-Hill, New York, 723 pp.

Leyendekkers, J. V., 1971a. Single ion activities in multicomponent systems. *Anal. Chem.*, **43** 1835–1843.

Leyendekkers, J. V., 1971b. Thermodynamics of mixed electrolyte solutions. Ionic entropy correlations and volume fraction statistics. *J. Phys. Chem.*, **75**, 946–956.

Leyendekkers J. V., 1973. The chemical potentials of seawater components. *Mar. Chem.* In press.

Leyendekkers, J. V. and M. Whitfield, 1971. Measurement of activity coefficients with liquid ion-exchange electrodes for the system calcium (II)-sodium(I)-chloride(I)-water. *J. Phys. Chem.*, **75**, 957–963.

Lietzke, M. H., H. B. Hupf, and R. W. Stoughton, 1969. Electromotive force studies in aqueous solutions at elevated temperatures. XII. Thermodynamic properties of hydrochloric acid-cesium chloride-barium chloride mixtures. *J. Inorg. Nucl. Chem.*, **31**, 2481–3489.

Lietzke, M. H. and H. A. O'Brien, Jr., 1968. Electromotive force studies in aqueous solutions at elevated temperatures. X. The thermodynamic properties of HCl–KCl, HCl–RbCl, HCl–CsCl, HCl–$MgCl_2$, HCl–$CaCl_2$, HCl–$SrCl_2$, and HCl–$AlCl_3$ mixtures. *J. Phys. Chem.*, **72**, 4408–4414.

Lilley, T. H., 1968. Thermodynamic relationships of 1:1 electrolytes. *Trans. Faraday Soc.*, **64** 2947–2950.

Lyman, J. and R. H. Fleming, 1940. Composition of seawater. *J. Mar. Res.*, **3**, 134–146.

Masson, D. O., 1929. Solute molecular volumes in relation to solvation and ionization. *Phil. Mag.*, **8**, 218–235.

Mayer, J. E., 1950. The theory of ionic solutions. *J. Chem. Phys.*, **18**, 1426–1436.

Mayer, J. E. and M. G. Mayer, 1940. *Statistical Mechanics*. Wiley, New York.

McMillan, Jr., W. G. and J. E. Mayer, 1945. Thermodynamics of multicomponent systems. *J. Chem. Phys.*, **13**, 276–305.

Millero, F. J., 1969. The partial molal volumes of ions in seawater. *Limnol. Oceanog.*, **14**, 376–385.

Millero, F. J., 1970. The apparent and partial molal volume of aqueous sodium chloride solutions at various temperatures. *J. Phys. Chem.*, **74**, 356–362.

Millero, F. J., 1971a. The physical chemistry of multi-component salt solutions. In *Biophysical Properties of Skin*. H. R. Elden, ed. Wiley, New York, pp. 329–337 (Chapter 9).

Millero, F. J., 1971b. The molal volume of electrolytes. *Chem. Rev.*, **71**, 147–176.

Millero, F. J., 1971c. Effect of pressure on sulfate ion association in seawater. *Geochim. Cosmochim. Acta*, **35**, 1089–1098.

Millero, F. J., 1971d. Seawater—a test for multicomponent salt solution theories. Abstract, Paper #235, 162 National A.C.S. Meeting, September, Washington, D.C.

Millero, F. J., 1972. The partial molal volumes of electrolytes in aqueous solutions. In *Water and Aqueous Solutions*. R. A. Horne, ed. Wiley, New York, pp. 519–595 (Chapter 13).

Millero, F. J., 1973a. Seawater—a test for multicomponent electrolyte solutions theories I. The apparent equivalent volume expansibility and compressibility of artificial seawater. *J. Soln. Chem. 2*, 1–22.

Millero, F. J., 1973b. Theoretical estimates of the isothermal compressibility of seawater. *Deep-Sea Res. 20*, 101–105.

Millero, F. J. and R. A. Berner, 1972. Effect of pressure on carbonate equilibria in seawater. *Geochim. Cosmochim. Acta*, **36**, 92–98.

Millero, F. J., L. D. Hansen, and E. V. Hoff, 1972. The enthalpy of seawater from 0 to 30°C and 0 to 40‰ salinity. Abstract, 26 Annual Calorimetry Conf., N.B.S., Brigham Young University, Provo, Utah.

Millero, F. J., L. D. Hansen, and E. V. Hoff, 1973. The enthalpy of seawater from 0 to 30°C and 0 to 40‰ salinity. *J. Mar. Res. 31*, 21–39.

Millero, F. J. and F. K. Lepple, 1973. The density and expansibility of artificial seawater solutions from 0 to 40°C and 0 to 21‰ chlorinity. *Mar. Chem. 1*, 89–104.

Millero, F. J., G. Ward, F. K. Lepple, and E. V. Hoff, 1973. The isothermal compressibility of aqueous NaCl, $MgCl_2$, Na_2SO_4 and $MgSO_4$ solutions from 0 to 40°C at one atmosphere. *J. Soln. Chem.* To be submitted.

Millero, F. J. and J. H. Knox, 1973. Apparent molal volumes of aqueous NaF, Na_2SO_4, KCl, K_2SO_4, $MgCl_2$ and $MgSO_4$ solutions at 0 to 50°C. *J. Chem. Eng. Data.* In press.

Miyake, Y. and M. Koizumi, 1948. The measurement of the viscosity coefficient of seawater. *J. Mar. Res.*, **7**, 63–66.

Owen, B. B. and S. R. Brinkley, Jr., 1941. Calculation of the effect of pressure upon ionic equilibrium in pure water and in salt solutions. *Chem. Rev.*, **29**, 461–472.

Owen, B. B. and P. L. Kronick, 1961. Standard partial molal compressibilities by ultrasonics. II. Sodium and potassium chlorides and bromides from 0 to 30°C. *J. Phys. Chem.*, **65**, 84–87.

Owen, B. B., R. C. Miller, C. E. Milner, and H. L. Cogan, 1961. The dielectric constant of water as a function of temperature and pressure. *J. Phys. Chem.*, **65**, 2065–2070.

Park, K., 1964. Partial equivalent conductances of electrolytes in seawater. *Deep Sea Res.*, **11**, 729–736.

Parker, V. B., 1965. Thermal properties of aqueous uni-univalent electrolytes. NSRDS-NBS2, Superintendent of Documents, U.S. Government Printing Office, Washington, D.C., April. 66 pp.

Platford, R. F., 1965a. The activity coefficient of sodium chloride in seawater. *J. Mar. Res.*, **23**, 55–62.

Platford, R. F., 1965b. Activity coefficient of the magnesium ion in seawater. *J. Fish Res. Bd.* (Canada), **22**, 113–116.

Platford, R. F., 1967. Activity coefficients in the system H_2O–NaCl–$MgSO_4$ at 25°C. *Can. J. Chem.*, **45**, 821–825.

Platford, R. F., 1968a. Isopiestic measurements on the system water-sodium chloride-magnesium chloride at 25°C. *J. Phys. Chem.*, **72**, 4053–4057.

Platford, R. F., 1968b. Isopiestic measurements on the system H_2O–NaCl–Na_2SO_4 at 25°C. *J. Chem. Eng. Data*, **13**, 46–48.

Platford, R. F., 1971. Thermodynamics of mixed salt solutions excess Gibbs energies of mixing for the six ternary systems from aqueous $MgCl_2$, $Mg(NO_3)_2$, $CaCl_2$ and $Ca(NO_3)_2$ at 25°C. *J. Chem. Thermodynamics*, **3**, 319–324.

Platford, R. F. and T. Dafoe, 1965. The activity coefficient of sodium sulfate in seawater. *J. Mar. Res.*, **23**, 63–68.

Poirier, J. C., 1953. Thermodynamic functions from Mayer's theory of ionic solutions, I. Equations for thermodynamic functions. *J. Chem. Phys.*, **21**, 965–972.

Poirier, J. C. and J. H. DeLap, 1961. On the theory of ion pairs in solution. *J. Chem. Phys.*, **35**, 213–227.

Popovych, O. and A. J. Dill, 1969. Single scale for ion activities and electrode potentials in ethanol-water solvents based on the trisoamylbutylammonium. *Anal. Chem.*, **41**, 456–462.

Pytkowicz, R. M. and D. R. Kester, 1969. Harned's Rule behavior of NaCl–Na_2SO_4 solutions explained by an ion association model. *Amer. J. Sci.*, 217–229.

Ramanathan, P. S. and H. L. Friedman, 1971. Study of a refined model for aqueous 1-1 electrolytes. *J. Chem. Phys.*, **54**, 1086–1099.

Rasaiah, J. C., 1970. Equilibrium properties of ionic solutions; the primitive model and its modification for aqueous solutions of the alkali halides at 25°C. *J. Chem. Phys.*, **52**, 704–715.

Rasaiah, J. C., 1972. Computations for higher valence electrolytes in the restricted primitive model. *J. Chem. Phys.*, **56**, 3071–3085.

Rasaiah, J. C. and H. L. Friedman, 1968a. Integral equation methods in the computation of equilibrium properties of ionic solutions. *J. Chem. Phys.*, **48**, 2742–2752.

Rasaiah, J. C. and H. L. Friedman, 1968b. Charged square-well model for ionic solutions. *J. Phys. Chem.*, **72**, 3352–3353.

Rasaiah, J. C. and H. L. Friedman, 1969. Integral equation computations for aqueous 1-1 electrolytes; accuracy of the method. *J. Chem. Phys.*, **50**, 3965–3976.

Redlich, O., 1940. Molal volumes of solutes IV. *J. Phys. Chem.*, **44**, 619–629.

Redlich, O. and D. M. Meyer, 1964. The molal volume of electrolytes. *Chem. Rev.*, **64**, 221–227.

Redlich, O. and P. Rosenfeld, 1931. Theory of the molal volumes of a dissolved electrolyte. *Z. Electrochem.*, **37**, 705–711.

Reilly, P. J. and R. H. Stokes, 1970. The activity coefficient of cadmium chloride in water and sodium chloride solution at 25°C. *Aust. J. of Chem.*, **23**, 1397–1405.

Reilly, P. J. and R. H. Wood, 1969. The prediction of the properties of mixed electrolytes from measurements on common ion mixtures. *J. Phys. Chem.*, **73**, 4292–4297.

Reilly, P. J., R. H. Wood, and R. A. Robinson, 1971. The predictions of osmotic and activity coefficients in mixed electrolyte solutions. *J. Phys. Chem.*, **75**, 1305–1315.

Riley, J. P. and R. Chester, 1971. *Introduction to Marine Chemistry*. Academic Press, London and New York.

Riley, J. P. and M. Tongudai, 1967. The major cation chlorinity ratios in seawater. *Chem. Geol.*, **2**, 263–269.

Robinson, R. A., 1954. The vapor pressure and osmotic equivalence of seawater. *J. Mar. Biol. Assoc. U.K.*, **33**, 449–455.

Robinson, R. A., 1972. Excess Gibbs energy of mixing of the systems H_2O–CsCl–Na_2SO_4 and H_2O–CsCl–Na_2SO_4 at 25°C. *J. Soln. Chem.*, **1**, 71–75.

Robinson, R. A. and V. E. Bower, 1965a. An additive rule for the vapor pressure lowering of aqueous solutions. *J. Res. Nat. Bur. Stand.*, **69A**, 365–367.

Robinson, R. A. and V. E. Bower, 1965b. Properties of aqueous mixtures of pure salts; thermodynamics of the system, water-potassium chloride-barium chloride at 25°C. *J. Res. Nat. Bur. Stand.*, **69A**, 439–448.

Robinson, R. A. and A. K. Covington, 1968. The thermodynamics of the ternary system: water-potassium chloride-calcium chloride at 25°C. *J. Res. Natl. Bur. Std.*, **72A**, 239–245.

Robinson, R. A. and R. H. Stokes, 1959. *Electrolyte Solutions*. Butterworths, London.

Robinson, R. A. and R. H. Woods, 1972. Calculations of the osmotic and activity coefficients of seawater at 25°C. *J. Soln. Chem. 1*, 481–488.

Robinson, R. A., R. H. Wood and P. J. Reilly, 1971. Calculation of excess Gibbs energies and activity coefficients from isopiestic measurements on mixtures of lithium and sodium salts. *J. Chem. Thermodynamics*, **3**, 461–471.

Robinson, R. A., R. F. Platford and C. W. Childs, 1972. Thermodynamics of aqueous mixtures of sodium chloride, sodium sulfate and potassium sulfate at 25°C. *J. Soln. Chem.*, **1**, 167–172.

Root, W. C., 1933. An equation relating density and concentration. *J. Amer. Chem. Soc.*, **55**, 850.

Rosseinsky, D. R. and R. J. Hill, 1971. Approximate prediction of mixed electrolyte activity coefficients. *J. Electroanal. Chem.*, **30**, 7–10.

Rush, R. M. and J. S. Johnson, 1966. Osmotic coefficients of synthetic seawater solutions at 25°C. *J. Chem. Eng. Data*, **11**, 590–592.

Scatchard, G., 1943. Thermodynamics and simple electrostatic theory. In *Proteins, Amino Acids and Peptides*. E. J. Cohn and J. T. Edsall, eds. Reinhold, New York, pp. 20–74 (Chapter 3).

Scatchard, G., 1961. Effect of dielectric constant difference on hyperfiltration of salt solutions. *J. Amer. Chem. Soc.*, **83**, 2636–2642.

Scatchard, G., 1968. The excess free energy and related properties of solutions containing electrolytes. *J. Amer. Chem. Soc.*, **90**, 3124–3127.

Scatchard, G., 1969. The excess free energy and related properties of solutions containing electrolytes. *J. Amer. Chem. Soc.*, **91**, 2410–2411.

Scatchard, G., R. M. Rush, and J. S. Johnson, 1970. Osmotic and activity coefficients for binary mixtures of sodium chloride, sodium sulfate, magnesium sulfate and magnesium chloride in water at 25°C. III. Treatment with the ions as components. *J. Phys. Chem.*, **74**, 3786–3796.

Schrager, S. R. and F. J. Millero, 1972. The apparent equivalent volume and expansibility of seawater. Abstract Paper #6, F.L.A.C.S. Vol. XXV, A.C.S. Meeting-in-Miniature, May, Key Biscayne, Florida.

Stern, J. H. and C. W. Anderson, 1964. Thermodynamic properties of aqueous solutions of mixed electrolytes, KCl–NaCl and LiCl–NaCl systems. *J. Phys. Chem.*, **68**, 2528–2533.

Stern, J. H. and A. A. Passchier, 1963. Thermodynamic properties of aqueous solution of mixed electrolytes, HCl–NaCl systems. *J. Phys. Chem.*, **67**, 2420–2424.

Stokes, R. H., 1972. Debye model and the primitive model for electrolyte solutions. *J. Chem. Phys.*, **56** (7), 3382–3383.

Stokes, R. H. and R. A. Robinson, 1948. Ionic hydration and activity in electrolyte solutions. *J. Am. Chem. Soc.*, **70**, 1870–1878.

Stokes, R. H. and R. A. Robinson, 1972. Ion solvent interactions in very concentrated electrolytes. *J. Soln. Chem.* In press.

Stokes, J. M. and R. H. Stokes, 1963. Activity coefficients in $Ca(ClO_4)_2$–HCl mixtures in water. *J. Phys. Chem.*, **67**, 2442–2446.

Swarcz, M., 1968. *Cabanions, Living Polymers and Electron Transfer Processes*. Wiley-Interscience, New York.

Synnot, J. C. and J. N. Butler, 1968. Mean activity coefficients of sodium sulfate in aqueous Na_2SO_4–NaCl electrolytes. *J. Phys. Chem.*, **72**, 2474–2477.

UNESCO, 1966. Second report of the Joint Panel on Oceanographic Tables and Standards. *UNESCO Techn. Pap. Mar. Sci.*, **4**, 9 pp. (mimeographed).

Vaslow, F., 1972. Thermodynamics of solutions of electrolytes. In *Water and aqueous solutions*. R. A. Horne, ed. John, New York, pp. 465–518 (Chapter 12).

Ward, G. K. and F. J. Millero, 1972. The apparent molal volume of boric acid and sodium borate in pure water and sodium chloride solutions. Abstract Paper #9, F.L.A.C.S. Vol. XXV, A.C.S. Meeting-in-Miniature, May, Key Biscayne, Florida.

Weeks, J. A., 1967. Activity coefficients in some alkaline earth metal perchlorates-hydrochloric acid mixtures at 25°C. *Aust. J. Chem.*, **20** 2367–2374.

Wen, W. Y., 1972. Aqueous solutions of symmetrical tetraalkylammonium salts. In *Water and Aqueous Solutions*. R. A. Horne, ed. Wiley, New York, (Chapter 15).

Wen, W. Y., K. Miyajima, and A. Otsuka, 1971. Free energy changes on mixing solutions of alkali halides and symmetrical tetraalkylammonium halides. *J. Phys. Chem.*, **75**, 2148–2157.

Wen, W. Y. and K. Nara, 1967. Volume changes on mixing solutions of potassium halides and symmetrical tetraalkylammonium halides: an evidence for cation-cation interaction. *J. Phys. Chem.*, **71**, 3907–3927.

Wen, W. Y. and K. Nara, 1968. Volume changes on mixing solutions of alkali halides and symmetrical tetraalkylammonium halides. II. Effects of deuterium oxide and temperature. *J. Phys. Chem.*, **72**, 1137–1139.

Wen, W. Y., K. Nara, and R. H. Wood, 1968. Volume changes on mixing solutions of potassium halides and symmetrical tetraalkylammonium halides: evidence for cation-cation interactions. A correction and further comment. *J. Phys. Chem.*, **72**, 3048–3049.

Wirth, H. E., 1937. The partial molal volumes of potassium chloride, potassium bromide and potassium sulfate in sodium chloride solutions. *J. Amer. Chem. Soc.*, **59**, 2549–2554.

Wirth, H. E., 1940a. The problem of the density of seawater. *J. Mar. Res.*, **3**, 230–247.

Wirth, H. E., 1940b. Apparent and partial molal volumes of sodium chloride and hydrochloric acid in mixed solutions. *J. Amer. Chem. Soc.*, **62**, 1128–1134.

Wirth, H. E. and F. N. Collier, 1950. Apparent and partial molal volumes of $NaClO_4$ and $HClO_4$ in mixed solutions. *J. Amer. Chem. Soc.*, **72**, 5292–5296.

Wirth, H. E., R. E. Lindstrom, and J. N. Johnson, 1963. Volume changes on mixing solutions of sodium chloride, hydrochloric acid, sodium perchlorate and perchloric acid at constant ionic strength. A test of Young's rule. *J. Phys. Chem.*, **67**, 2339–2344.

Wirth, H. E. and A. LoSurdo, 1968. Temperature dependence of volume changes on mixing electrolyte solutions. *J. Chem. Eng. Data*, **13**, 226–231.

Wirth, H. E. and W. L. Mills, 1968. Volume changes on mixing solutions of lithium chloride, sodium chloride, lithium sulfate, and sodium sulfate at constant ionic strength. *J. Chem. Eng. Data*, **13**, 102–107.

Wood, R. H. and H. L. Anderson, 1966a. Heats of mixing of aqueous electrolytes. II. Alkaline earth halides. *J. Phys. Chem.*, **70**, 992–996.

Wood, R. H. and H. L. Anderson, 1966b. Heats of mixing of aqueous electrolytes. III. A test of the general equations with quarternary mixtures. *J. Phys. Chem.*, **70**, 1877–1879.

Wood, R. H. and H. L. Anderson, 1967a. Heats of mixing of aqueous electrolytes. IV. Potassium salts of the fluoride, chloride, bromide and acetate ions. *J. Phys. Chem.*, **71**, 1869–1871.

Wood, R. H. and H. L. Anderson, 1967b. Heats of mixing of aqueous electrolytes. V. Tetraalkylammonium chlorides. *J. Phys. Chem.*, **71**, 1871–1874.

Wood, R. H., M. Ghamkhar, and J. D. Patton, 1969. Heats of mixing aqueous electrolytes. VIII. Prediction and measurement of charge-asymmetric mixtures of three salts. *J. Phys. Chem.*, **73**, 4298–4302.

Wood, R. H., J. D. Patton, and M. Ghamkhar, 1969. Heats of mixing aqueous electrolytes. VI. Magnesium chloride with some alkali metal chlorides. *J. Phys. Chem.*, **73**, 346–349.

Wood, R. H. and P. J. Reilly, 1970. Electrolytes. *Annual Rev. Phys. Chem.*, **21**, 287–406.

Wood, R. H. and R. W. Smith, 1965. Heats of mixing aqueous electrolytes. I. Concentration dependence of 1:1 electrolytes. *J. Phys. Chem.*, **69**, 2974–2979.

Wu, Y. C., 1970. Young's mixture rule and its significance. *J. Phys. Chem.*, **74**, 3781–3786.

Wu, Y. C., R. M. Rush, and G. Scatchard, 1968. Osmotic and activity coefficients for binary mixtures of sodium chloride, sodium sulfate, magnesium sulfate and magnesium chloride in water at 25°C. I. Isopiestic measurements on the four systems with common ions. *J. Phys. Chem.*, **72**, 4048–4053.

Wu, Y. C., R. M. Rush, and G. Scatchard, 1969. Osmotic and activity coefficients for binary mixtures of sodium chloride, sodium sulfate, magnesium chloride in water at 25°C. II. Isopiestic and electromotive force measurements on the two systems without common ions. *J. Phys. Chem.*, **73**, 2047–2053.

Wu, Y. C., M. B. Smith, and T. F. Youngs, 1965. Heats of mixing of electrolytes of the 1:1 charge type. *J. Phys. Chem.*, **69**, 1873–1876.

Yeatts, L. B. and W. L. Marshall, 1967. Aqueous system at high temperatures XVIII. Activity coefficient behavior of calcium hydroxide in aqueous sodium nitrate to the critical temperatures of water. *J. Phys. Chem.*, **71**, 2641–2650.

Yeatts, L. B. and W. L. Marshall, 1969. Apparent invariance of activity coefficients of calcium sulfate at constant ionic strength and temperature in the system, $CaSO_4$–$NaNO_3$–H_2O to the critical temperatures of water association equilibria. *J. Phys. Chem.*, **73**, 81–90.

Young, T. F., 1951. Recent developments in the study of interactions between molecules and ions, and of equilibrium in solutions. *Rec. Chem. Progr.*, **12**, 81–95.

Young, T. F. and M. B. Smith, 1954. Thermodynamic properties of mixtures of electrolytes in aqueous solution. *J. Phys. Chem.*, **58**, 716–724.

Young, T. F., Y. C. Wu, and A. A. Krawetz, 1957. Thermal effects of interaction between ions of like charge. *Disc. Faraday Soc.*, **24**, 37–42, 77–80.

2. THE EFFECT OF PRESSURE ON DISSOCIATION CONSTANTS AND ITS TEMPERATURE DEPENDENCY

A. Disteche

1. Methods and Theory

In solutions, the effect of pressure on the thermodynamic dissociation constant K^0 ($-\log K^0 = pK^0$) is given by the classical equation

$$2.303\,RT\left(\frac{\partial \log K^0}{\partial p}\right)_{T,m} = -\Delta\bar{V}^0 = -\left[\sum^{p}\bar{V}_2{}^0 - \sum^{r}\bar{V}_2{}^0\right] \tag{1}$$

where m refers to molal concentrations, the subscript 2 to a solute, R is the gas constant, T the absolute temperature, and $\Delta\bar{V}^0$ is the algebraic difference between the partial molal volumes of the products (p) and reactants (r) in their standard states, where the activity coefficients (γ) are unity ($\bar{V}_2{}^0 = (\partial V/\partial m_2)_{m_1 \neq m_9}$; V = total volume of the system). If $\gamma^{\nu}{}_{\pm} = \gamma_{+}^{\nu+}\,\gamma_{-}^{\nu-}$ ($\nu = \nu_+ + \nu_-$) defines the mean activity coefficient of an electrolyte, it can be shown that

$$\nu 2.303\,RT\left(\frac{\partial \log \gamma_{\pm}}{\partial p}\right)_{T,m} = \bar{V}_2 - \bar{V}_2{}^0 \tag{2}$$

where $\bar{V}_2$ is the apparent partial molal volume of the solute at any concentration m. $\bar{V}_2$ tends to $\bar{V}_2{}^0$ at infinite dilution of all solute species in the pure solvent (m_1). A component that takes part in the reaction as a "pure phase" is in its standard state by convention.

The standard state can be shifted, for instance, from pure water to water containing a given amount of salt. In this case one will assume that the activity coefficients of all subsequently added solutes will become unity at infinite dilution in the new medium where the activity of water and that of the salt are then unity by definition. The thermodynamic constant K^{*0} for a reaction in the salt solution is equal to the mass action constant at infinite dilution in the new medium, and equation 1 can be rewritten

$$2.303\,RT\left(\frac{\partial \log K^{*0}}{\partial p}\right)_{m,T} = -\Delta\bar{V}_2^{*0} = \left[\sum^{p}\bar{V}_2^{*0} - \sum^{r}\bar{V}_2^{*0}\right] \tag{3}$$

where $\bar{V}^{*0}$ refers to partial molal volumes extrapolated to infinite dilution in the chosen ionic medium.

This standard-state shift is of particular interest to study equilibria in seawater (see Owen and Brinkley, 1941) because activity coefficients vary only slightly at ionic strengths of the order of 0.725 ($I = 0.5 \sum_2^i Z_i^2\, m_i$, where Z is the charge of ion i) and need not be considered in many cases ($\Delta\bar{V}^{*0} \simeq \Delta\bar{V}^{*}$). A $0.725m$ NaCl solution is often used to simulate the ionic environment in seawater. In such a solution the solubility products, the stoichiometric dissociation constants, are nearly equivalent to the corresponding thermodynamic constants K^* if only long-range ionic interactions are considered (ionic strength effect).

In seawater chemistry, equilibria studies intended to be useful in field work are necessarily restricted to reactions between the major ionic species, which are fast relative to water transport and to biological and geological processes that may alter the water composition. The effect of pressure and temperature on the dissociation of weak acids and of ion pairs and on the solubility of various salts are of prime importance to determine the deep ocean concentrations of ionic and molecular species, which cannot be found by direct analytical methods. The compositions of the interstitial water of sediments, particulate matter, and body fluids of deep-sea animals may be understood if the effects of pressure and temperature on both equilibrium and rate constants of chemical reaction involving them are known.

Most of the work done so far deals with the effects of pressure on ionic equilibria. Equation 3 shows that there are only two ways to approach the problem: either one measures $2.303\ RT\ (\partial \log K^{*0}/\partial \mathrm{p})_{m,T}$, or calculates $-\Delta \bar{V}^{*0}$ from the partial molal volumes $\bar{V}^{*0}$ of products and reactants.

A. The Partial Molal Volume Approach

Partial molal volumes are pressure dependent and the partial molal compressibility $\bar{K}_2{}^0$ is equal to $-(\partial \bar{V}_2{}^0/\partial \mathrm{p})_{T,m}$. Over the moderate pressure ranges encountered in the ocean, $\bar{K}_2{}^0$ is constant and one can write

$$(\bar{V}_2{}^0)_p = (\bar{V}_2{}^0)_1 - \bar{K}_2{}^0(\mathrm{p} - 1) \tag{4}$$

Integration of equation 1 or 3 then yields

$$2.303\ RT \log \bar{K}_p{}^0/\bar{K}_1{}^0 = -\Delta\bar{V}^0(\mathrm{p} - 1) + 0.5\ \Delta\bar{K}^0(\mathrm{p} - 1)^2 \tag{5}$$

Partial volumes are obtained from density and dilatometry experiments; $\bar{K}_2{}^0$ can be calculated from high pressure and sound velocity measurements. In many instances, $\bar{V}_2{}^0$ is independent of pressure, an observation that simplifies the problem. Partial molal volumes are known for most electrolytes in pure water. Additivity rules allow the calculation of $\bar{V}^0_{(\mathrm{ion})}$. In earlier work (see Owen and Brinkley, 1941), $\bar{V}^0_{H^+}$ was taken to zero by convention. It is now generally admitted that $\bar{V}^0_{H^+} = -4.5$ ml/mol at 25°C; the recent data has been compiled by Millero (1971).

A few experimental values have been obtained by direct density measurements in seawater using the magnetic float method (Duedall and Weyl, 1967; Duedall, 1968). A great deal of effort and thought, however, has been spent to calculate $\bar{V}_2^{*0}$ in seawater, for example, in $0.725m$ NaCl, from $\bar{V}_2{}^0$ values found in pure water.

Owen and Brinkley (1941) calculated $\bar{V}_2^{*0}$ by the following equation:

$$\bar{V}_2^{*0} = \bar{V}_2{}^0 + A_v\sqrt{\Gamma} \tag{6}$$

where for a given ion, A_v is a constant derived from the Debye-Hückel limiting law, $\Gamma = \sum_2^i Z_i^2 C_i$, where C is the concentration on the molar scale and Z is the charge of ion species i. ($\Gamma = 2 \times 0.723$ in $0.725m$ NaCl).

In a recent review of all available data, Millero (1969) suggests the following semi-empirical formula:

$$\bar{V}^{*0} = \bar{V}^0 + a\left(\frac{Z^2}{r}\right) + b \tag{7}$$

with

$$\bar{V}^0 = Ar^3 - \left(\frac{BZ^2}{r}\right) \tag{8}$$

where Z is again the charge of the ion, r is the crystal radius, a and b are constants equal to 0.37 Å/mol, and 0.83 ml/mol for 35.1% salinity water; A and B are constants equal to 4.48 (Å)$^{-3}$ ml/mol and 8.0 Å ml/mol in pure water. Ar^3 corresponds to the intrinsic partial molal volume ($\bar{V}^0_{(\mathrm{int})}$) plus void space effects and $-BZ^2/r$ is the electrostriction partial molal volume ($\bar{V}_{(\mathrm{elect})}$) due to the ion-water reaction.

Equations 7 and 8 can be rearranged to give

$$\bar{V}_2^{*0} = \left(A + \frac{b}{r^3}\right)r^3 - (B - a)\frac{Z^2}{r} \tag{9}$$

and new values A^* and B^* can be calculated for A and B in seawater (4.58 and 7.5, respectively). The difference $\bar{V}^{*0} - \bar{V}^0$ is called $\Delta\bar{V}^*_{(\text{trans})}$ to refer to the volume change related to the process of transferring a given ion from pure water to seawater. $\Delta\bar{V}^*_{(\text{trans})}$ is of the order of 1 to 6 ml/mol, depending on the ionic charge and the crystal radius.

$\bar{V}^{*0}$ values are additive and any deviation from equation 7 or 9 is thought to arise from the formation of ion pairs. It is assumed that when an ion pair is formed, the electrostricted water of the individual ions is diminished and the volume of the system therefore is increased. The difference between $\bar{V}^{*0}$ observed and $\bar{V}^{*0}$ calculated from equation 9 can in the first approximation be equated to $\bar{V}^{*0}_{(\text{elect})}$ times the percent of contact ion-pair formation. $\bar{V}^{*0}_{(\text{elect})}$ can be estimated from $-B^*Z^2/r$ or by using equations derived from the Debye-Hückel limiting law. For contact, ion pairs reequal the ionic radius. When the components of complex ions are separated by one water molecule, $r = r_{(\text{ion})} + r_{(H_2O)}$ and the percentage of complexed ions can be evaluated (Millero, 1969).

To determine $\Delta\bar{V}^*$ at $m_2 \neq 0$, for ion-pair dissociation and $\bar{V}^*_{(\text{ion-pair})}$, the value of the dissociation or association constant at 1 atm, K^*, or $1/K^* = K_A^*$ is used to evaluate the amount α of free ions present:

$$K_A^* = \frac{1 - \alpha}{\alpha^2\gamma^2 m_T} \tag{10}$$

where m_T refers to the total solute concentration. We can then write (see equation 1)

$$\Delta\bar{V}^*_{(\text{ion pair})} = \bar{V}^*_{(\text{ion pair})} - \bar{V}^*_{(\text{ions})} = \frac{[\bar{V}^*_{(\text{obs})} - \bar{V}^*_{(\text{ions})}]}{(1 - \alpha)} \tag{11}$$

in which $\bar{V}_{(\text{ions})}$ values, calculated as above and using the additivity rules can be introduced; $\bar{V}^*_{(\text{obs})} = (1 - \alpha)\bar{V}^*_{(\text{ion pair})} + \alpha\bar{V}^*_{(\text{ions})}$ is the observed partial molal volume at total molality m_T. If K_A^0 or $1/K^0$ is only known from low ionic strength determinations, assumptions must be made to evaluate the activity coefficients in order to derive K_A^*.

The effect of temperature on $\Delta\bar{V}^*_{(\text{ion pair})}$ can be estimated from the partial molal expansibility determinations or from the equation

$$\Delta\bar{V}^*_{(\text{ion pair})} = \text{k}\beta \tag{12}$$

where β is the compressibility of the solvent and k is a constant related to the number of water molecules attached to the ions and the ion pairs. If K^* or K_A^* is known at different temperatures, the change of enthalpy $\Delta\bar{H}^*$ which occurs upon the formation of ion pairs, is given by the relation

$$\Delta\bar{H}^*_{(\text{ion pair})} = \frac{2.303\ R(\log K^*_{A,T_2}/K^*_{A,T_1})}{(1/T_1 - 1/T_2)} \tag{13}$$

from which, if one assumes $\Delta\bar{H}^*$ constant within a given absolute temperature T range, K^* or K_A^* can be calculated at any temperature within that temperature interval.

It is obvious that a rather large number of assumptions must be made to carry out the type of calculations listed above to evaluate, from partial molal volume data and from dissociation constants at 1 atm, the effect of pressure on the equilibrium constants of weak acids and ion pairs in seawater. Even the assumption that seawater is equivalent to 0.725m NaCl is questionable. The choice of the method to compute $\bar{V}_{(\text{ions})}$ in the case of $MgSO_4$, for example, leads to values of $\Delta\bar{V}^*$ ($MgSO_4{}^0$) ranging from 6.6 to 11.4 ml/mol (Millero, 1971).

The only way to test the validity of the assumptions is an experimental evaluation of the right-hand side of equation 5, that is, 2.303 $RT \log K_p^{*0}/K_1^{*0}$.

B. The Dissociation and Association Constant Approach

Conductivity measurements allow the determination of K at 1 atm or at high pressure only in dilute solutions that contain only a few ionic species. The values of K_p^{*0}/K_1^{*0} in seawater can be calculated from the corresponding $-\Delta\bar{V}^0$, using the transfer rules as discussed above or by estimating the effect of pressure on the activity coefficients, which are essentially equivalent (see equation 2). Fisher (1962) has calculated $\Delta\bar{V}^0$ for $MgSO_4{}^0$ from conductivity data and ultrasonic measurements under high pressure. Data for many other electrolytes from conductance measurements can be found in reviews by Hamann (1963) and Hills and Ovenden (1966).

Electromotive force measurement using concentration cells is a classical tool to evaluate dissociation constants of electrolytes, in particular of weak acids. A large variety of ion-selective electrodes are now available (Durst, 1969, 1971) for work at 1 atm. Some of these electrodes, glass electrodes sensitive to H^+ and Na^+ have been tried successfully at high pressure (1000 to 2000 atm) (Disteche, 1959, 1962, 1972; Disteche and Disteche, 1965, 1967; Hamann, 1963; Culberson and Pytkowicz, 1968; Whitfield, 1969, 1970, 1972; Kester and Pytkowicz, 1970). The effect of pressure on the dissociation of many weak acids of interest in oceanographic work and in biology has been determined (see Disteche, 1972). Sea-going pressure compensated pH electrodes have been made (Disteche and Dubuisson, 1960; Disteche, 1964; Ben-Yaakov and Kaplan, 1968). A fluoride electrode for *in situ* measurements, using LaF_3 crystals is described by Brewer and Spencer (see Durst, 1971). Unfortunately, Mg- and Ca-sensitive electrodes of the liquid ion exchange or heterogenous membrane type have been shown to be unreliable under high pressure (Whitfield, 1969; Kester and Pytkowicz, 1970).

The concentration cells used for the direct determinations of 2.303 $RT \log K_p^0/K_1^0$ at high pressure are junctionless (Disteche, 1959; Disteche and Disteche, 1965, 1967):

$$\text{Ag–AgCl}\left|\begin{array}{l}\text{Ref}\\ \text{HCl } 0.01\\ \text{MCl } (m_3-0.01)\end{array}\right|\text{glass}\left|\begin{array}{l}\text{X}\\ \text{HA } (m_1)+\text{MA } (m_2)\\ \text{MCl } m_3\end{array}\right|\text{AgCl–Ag}$$

for $[H^+]$ measurements in solutions containing the weak acid HA and its salt MA,

$$\text{Ag–AgCl}\left|\begin{array}{l}\text{Ref}\\ \text{NaCl}(m_1)\end{array}\right|\text{glass}\left|\begin{array}{l}\text{X}\\ \text{NaCl}(m_1)\\ \text{NaA}(m_2)\end{array}\right|\text{AgCl–Ag}$$

for $[Na^+]$ determinations (Whitfield, 1969; Kester and Pytkowicz, 1970) in mixtures of NaCl and a weak acid salt NaA.

The electromotive force E (emf) of such cells is given at pressure 1 or p atm by:

$$\frac{E_{1,p}F}{2.303\ RT} = \log\,(m_{H^+})^{\text{Ref}}_{1,p} - \log\,(m_{H^+})^{X}_{1,p} + 2\log\frac{(\gamma_{\text{HCl}})^{\text{Ref}}_{1,p}}{(\gamma_{\text{HCl}})^{X}_{1,p}} \tag{14}$$

$$\frac{E_{1,p}F}{2.303\ RT} = \log\,(m_{\text{Na}^+})^{\text{Ref}}_{1,p} - \log\,(m_{\text{Na}^+})^{X}_{1,p} + 2\log\frac{(\gamma_{\text{NaCl}})^{\text{Ref}}_{1,p}}{(\gamma_{\text{NaCl}})^{X}_{1,p}} \tag{15}$$

In these expressions $\gamma^2_{\text{HCl}} = \gamma_{\text{H}^+}\gamma_{\text{Cl}^-}$ and $\gamma^2_{\text{NaCl}} = \gamma_{\text{Na}^+}\gamma_{\text{Cl}^-}$. It is further assumed that the chloride concentrations are equal in both the Ref (reference solution) and X (test solution) compartments. Were this not the case, a term $\log\,(m_{\text{Cl}^-})^{\text{Ref}}_{1,p}/(m_{\text{Cl}^-})^{X}_{1,p}$ would have to be added to the right-hand side of equations 14 and 15.

For an acid of the strength of carbonic acid, for instance, m_{H^+} is negligible compared to the acid or the corresponding salt concentration. The dissociation constant K^0 is given by $\log K^0 = (m_{\text{H}^+} m_1)/m_2 + 2\log\gamma_{\text{A}}$ where $2\log\gamma_{\text{A}} = \log\,(\gamma_{\text{H}^+}\gamma_{\text{A}^-})/\gamma_{\text{HA}}$ and $(m_{\text{H}^+} m_1)/m_2 = k$ the ionization function, equivalent to the stoichiometric dissociation constant at a given ionic strength.

Equation 14 leads then to the following expression, valid if m_1 and m_2 are independent of pressure p:

$$(E_1 - E_p)F\ 2.303\ RT = \log\frac{K^0_{\text{p}}}{K^0_1} + 2\log\frac{\gamma_{A1}}{\gamma_{Ap}} + 2\log\frac{(\gamma_{\text{HCl}})^{\text{Ref}}_1}{(\gamma_{\text{HCl}})^{\text{Ref}}_p} - 2\log\frac{(\gamma_{\text{HCl}})^{X}_1}{(\gamma_{\text{HCl}})^{X}_p} \tag{16}$$

The terms in γ_{HCl} cancel each other at infinite dilution of the weak electrolyte and, if its salt effect is small, cancellation practically occurs for finite values of m_1 and m_2. Equation 16 then simplifies to:

$$\frac{(E_1 - E_p)F}{2.303\ RT} = \log K^0_{\text{p}}/K^0_1 + 2\log\gamma_{A1}/\gamma_{Ap} = \log k'_p/k'_1 \tag{17}$$

the primes indicating that k' is only known approximately because of the assumptions regarding γ_{HCl}.

At infinite dilution of the weak acid components in pure water or in a given MCl solution used to define a new standard state (0.725m NaCl, for instance), $2\log\gamma_{A1}/\gamma_{Ap}$ becomes zero by definition and values of $\log K^{*0}_1/K^{*0}_p = \log k^{*0}_1/k^{*0}_p$ can be obtained by extrapolation of $(E_1 - E_p)F/2.303\ RT$, care being taken to maintain the ionic strength and the Cl^- concentration equal in both electrode compartments at each selected ionic strength value. The extrapolation methods are discussed in Disteche and Disteche (1965) and Disteche (1972). In the case of carbonic acid and corresponding salts, the extrapolation can be carried out on the $\sqrt{I}$ scale, in the case of phosphoric acid, double extrapolation is required, first to zero weak acid component concentrations at a given I, then to zero NaCl or KCl concentrations.

The symbols m_1 and m_2 in the definition of K^0 refer to free ions or concentrations of molecules. When ion pairs are formed, the total concentrations m_T can be used to define apparent dissociation constants or ionization functions. It is obvious that the ratio m_1/m_2 of the free ions or molecules will not be independent of pressure, since the amount of ion pairs formed will change with pressure.

In the case of a reaction of the type $\text{HA}^- \leftrightarrows \text{A}^{2-} + \text{H}^+$, the expression for the apparent ionization function is a given salt solution, $k^{*\prime\prime}_2 = m_{\text{H}^+} m_{1T}/m_{2T}$, can be written $k''_2 = [\text{H}^+][\text{A}^{2-}](1 + [\text{Ma}^-]/[\text{A}^{2-}])/[\text{HA}^-](1 + [\text{MHA}^0]/[\text{HA}^-])$, where MA^-

and MHA^0 represent ion pairs. The respective association constants of these ion pairs are $K^*_{A2} = [MA^-][M^+]/[A^{2-}]$ and $K^*_{A1} = [MHA^0]/[M^+][HA^-]$ at a given ionic strength. If $k^{*\prime}_2 = [H^+][A_2^-]/[HA^-]$ were known in a medium where, at equal ionic strength and hydrogen ion concentration, ion-pair formation is negligible, one can write

$$1 + K^*_{A2}[M^+] = \frac{k^{*\prime\prime}_2}{k^{*\prime}_2}(1 + K^*_{A1}[M^+]) \tag{18}$$

For reaction $H_2A \leftrightharpoons HA^- + H^+$, (k_1), since the undissociated acid is uncharged, ion pairing is expected only for HA^-, and it is easy to show that

$$\frac{k^{*\prime\prime}_1}{k^{*\prime}_1} = 1 + K^*_{A1}[M^+] \tag{19}$$

and

$$1 + K^*_{A2}[M^+] = k^{*\prime\prime}_1 k^{*\prime\prime}_2 / k^{*\prime}_1 k^{*\prime}_2 \tag{20}$$

Equations 19 and 20 should in principle allow the calculation of K^*_{A1} and K^*_{A2} at 1 atm and at pressure p from the ratios of the true and apparent ionization functions of a diacid.

The problem is to find a medium where ion pairing is small. Perhaps this occurs for the case of certain potassium salts, because the single-ion form of the Debye-Hückel limiting law is obeyed. This is, however, a matter of controversy (see Butler and Huston, 1970, and p. 71 in this chapter).

If one assumes that it is possible to calculate k^{*0} from K^0/γ_A^2 where γ_A is the mean activity of the weak acid in the absence of ion pairing, evaluated from hypothetical single-ion values, equation 19a can be derived from equation 19:

$$k^{*\prime\prime}_2 = \frac{K^0}{\gamma_A^2}\frac{(1 + K^*_{A2}[M^+])}{(1 + K^*_{A1}[M^+])} \tag{19a}$$

this expression shows how $k^{*\prime\prime}_2$ is affected by ionic strength and the corresponding long-range ionic interaction effects and by a short-range interaction term depending on the association constants. This equation and the similar expression for $k^{*\prime\prime}_1$ might prove useful in high-pressure work. Ionization constants and function ratios can then be determined experimentally (see equation 17), but not the absolute values, and log γ_{Ap}/γ_{A1} can be evaluated with more confidence than γ_{Ap} or γ_{A1} separately. Equation 2 shows that log γ_{Ap}/γ_{A1} can be computed from $\bar{V}^*_{(\text{trans})}$ values for free ions, which do seem to obey a well-defined law (equations 7 and 9) in the absence of ion pairing (Millero, 1969). The evaluation of the ratios

$$\frac{(1 + K^*_{A2}[M^+])_p}{(1 + K^*_{A2}[M^+])_1}$$

and

$$\frac{(1 + K^*_{A1}[M^+])_p}{(1 + K^*_{A1}[M^+])_1}$$

with reasonable accuracy seems therefore possible and if K^*_{A1} and K^*_{A2} can be determined by other methods at 1 atm, it would then be easy to calculate their value at pressure p from the $k^{*\prime\prime}_p/k^{*\prime\prime}_1$ values from electromotive force measurements.

Nakayama (1970) has derived a mathematical treatment applicable to this type of measurement to separate the ionic strength effect (γ_{A2}) and the ion associations term in equation 19a. The method uses single-ion values for the individual activity coefficients and selects K^0_{A1} and K^0_{A2} values that fit equation 19a to obtain consistent values of K^0 at any ionic strength and concentrations of the components. Here, mass and charge balance relations must further be obeyed taking into account the formation of ion pairs. This treatment aims to show how to split the global activity coefficient estimate used to extrapolate electromotive force data to obtain K^0 into a factor, depending only on the long-range ionic interaction and another that depends on ion pairing, both tending to zero at infinite dilution.

Experimental values of k^{*0} at 1 or p atm or of the ratio k_p^{*0}/k_p^{*0} could in principle be obtained by extrapolation of the electromotive force data to zero weak electrolyte concentration at a given ionic strength. Examples of such treatment can be found in Disteche and Disteche (1965) at low ionic strengths for a series of weak acids, as previously mentioned. Harned and Bonner (1945) have shown how to determine k^{*0} for carbonic acid (first step) over a wide ionic strength range at 1 atm. The results obtained by Disteche (1962) and Disteche and Disteche (1965), indicate, however, that even at very high dilutions log k_p^0/k_1^0, obtained by extrapolation at zero NaCl or KCl and zero weak acid and salt concentrations, is always smaller in buffered solutions than in the corresponding pure acid solutions, which might indicate that ion pairing exists at concentrations where activity coefficients are very close to unity.

Another approach to the ion-pairing problem tries to measure their formation constants in a more direct way. Kester and Pytkowicz (1968, 1969, 1970) have used an elegant method based on electromotive force measurements to determine K_{2A}^* in solutions containing MCl and M_2A for instance, at hydrogen ion concentrations where the ionic species HA^- is negligible. At 1 atm, a cation-sensitive calomel electrode pair is used. The activity of the free cation (M^+, for example) is measured in a standard MCl solution and in a test solution containing MCl + M_2A. The concentration of the test solution is adjusted to fulfill the condition

$$([M^+]\gamma_{M^+})_{test} = ([M^+]\gamma_{M^+})_{Std} \tag{21}$$

at which the electromotive force of the electrode pair is equal in both test and standard solution. γ_{M^+} is calculated in an iterative way from the mean salt method $\gamma_{M^+} = (\gamma_{MCl})^2/\gamma_{KCl}$ at the respective ionic strengths of the test and standard solutions.

$K_{A2}^* = [MA^-]/[M^+][A^{2-}]$ can be calculated from the relations

$$[MA^-] = T(M) - [M^+] \tag{22}$$

$$[A^{2-}] = T(A) - [MA^-] \tag{23}$$

where $T(M)$ and $T(A)$ refer to total concentrations.

If $T(M)$, $T(A)$, and K_{A2}^* are known, it is in turn possible for a given solution to calculate $[A^{2-}]$ and $[M^+]$ from the following expressions:

$$[A^{2-}]^2K_{A2}^* + [A^{2-}](1 + K_{A2}^*[T(M) - T(A)]) - T(A) = 0 \tag{24}$$

$$[M^+] = T(M) - (T(A) - [A^{2-}]) \tag{25}$$

K_{A2}^* at pressure p can be estimated experimentally for sodium salts, using a junctionless pressure compensated cell for which equation 15 applies. The ratio $[M^+]_p/[M^+]_1$ is measured and allows the calculation of $(K_{A2}^*)_p$, using equations 22 and 23. For other cations such as Ca^{2+} and Mg^{2+}, direct measurements at high pressure cannot be made because of the unreliability of the corresponding ion sensitive electrodes. The association constant can easily be measured at 1 atm, but its value at pressure p has to be computed from partial molal volume data, as shown earlier.

Instead of trying to measure the free cation concentration, the method used by

Garrels, Thompson, and Siever (1961) was designed to measure the free anion concentrations. Starting from the relation

$$[A_2^-]\gamma_{A^{2-}} = T(A^{2-})\gamma_T = a_{A^{2-}} \tag{26}$$

and a similar expression for HA^- (where "a" corresponds to the activity of a given anion), γ_T is evaluated from conventional paH measurements (glass-calomel electrode pair) at different ionic strengths and component concentrations, using the equilibrium relations

$$\frac{a_{H^+}a_{A^{2-}}}{a_{HA^-}} = K_2{}^0 = \frac{a_{H^+}T(A^{2-})(\gamma_{A^{2-}})_T}{T(HA^-)(\gamma_{HA^-})_T} \tag{27}$$

$$\frac{a_{H^+}a_{HA^-}}{a_{H_2A}} = K_1{}^0 = \frac{a_{H^+}T(HA^-)(\gamma_{HA^-})_T}{a_{H_2A}} \tag{28}$$

To calculate $[A^{2-}]$ and $[HA^-]$, Garrels et al., make the simple assumption that potassium salts are totally dissociated. They use the single-ion activity coefficients obtained for potassium salts, at a given ionic strength, to calculate the free anion concentration, using equation 26 and the $T(A^{2-})$ and $T(HA^-)$ values evaluated from a_{H^+}, $K_1{}^0$, $K_2{}^0$, and γ_T for different ratios and concentration of MCl, MHA, and M_2A. The concentrations of the ion pairs are then equated to $T(A^{2-}) - [A^{2-}]$ and $T(HA^-) - [HA^-]$. To evaluate K^0_{A1} and K^0_{A2} is then in principle possible if further assumptions are made to calculate the activity coefficients of the ion pairs and of the free cations. Uncharged ion pairs are estimated to behave like uncharged molecules of the type H_2A, while charged ion pairs interact as free HA^- ions. The activity coefficients of the free cations are calculated from $\gamma_{M^+} = (\gamma_{MCl})^2/\gamma_{KCl}$.

This type of approach is open to criticism essentially because of the assumption that the potassium salts are totally dissociated, and because it is almost entirely based on the validity of single-ion activity values estimations for which only electrically neutral combinations (e.g., $\gamma_{Na^+}\gamma_{Cl^-}$ or $\gamma_{Na^+}\gamma_{HA^-}$) can be empirically determined.

Butler and Huston (1970) have used the cells

$$\text{M(Hg)}\left|\ \text{MCl}(m_1)\ \begin{matrix}\text{M}_2\text{A}(m_2)\\ \text{or}\\ \text{MHA}(m_3)\end{matrix}\right|\ \text{AgCl–Ag}$$

$$\text{M–glass}\left|\ \text{MCl}(m_1)\ \begin{matrix}\text{M}_2\text{A}(m_2)\\ \text{or}\\ \text{MHA}(m_3)\end{matrix}\right|\ \text{AgCl–Ag}$$

at 1 atm to measure $2 \log \gamma_{MCl}$, the mean activity coefficient of MCl, in mixtures MCl + MHA or MCl + M_2A where the total formal ionic strength $(m_1 + m_3)$ or $(m_1 + 3m_2)$ is kept constant. They observed that Harned's rule (see Harned and Owen, 1958, p. 600) holds in the case of NaCl–$NaHCO_3$, NaCl–Na_2CO_3 solutions, and that the expression

$$[\log \gamma_{12} = \log \gamma_{10} - \alpha_{12}I(1 - X_1)] \tag{29}$$

is verified ($\log \gamma_{12}$) is the mean total activity coefficient of NaCl in the presence of the added salts and $\log \gamma_{10}$ is the same in pure NaCl at the given ionic strength I ($X = m_1/I$).

Pytkowicz and Kester (1969) have shown that for weak ion associations, a relationship approximating Harned's rule can be obtained from an ion-pairing model. Butler and Huston (1970) arrive at the same conclusion: a linear expression between log γ_{12} (experimental) and $X' = m_1/I_E$ can be found if the effective ionic strength I_E (corresponding to the concentration of the free ions) is substituted for the formal value I_T Since

$$I_E = \tfrac{1}{2}([M^+] + [Cl^-] + [HA^-] + 4[A^{2-}] + [MA^-]) \tag{30}$$

it follows that log γ_{12} can be expressed as a function of the equilibrium concentrations calculated by the following set of equations:

$$\begin{aligned} [HA^-] &= 1/k_2^{*0}[H^+][A^{2-}] \\ [MA^-] &= K_{A2}^*[M^+][A^{2-}] \\ [MHA] &= k_{A1}^*[M^+][HA^-] \\ [Cl^-] &= m_1 \\ T(M) &= m_1 + 2m_2 + m_3 \\ T(A) &= m_2 + m_3 \end{aligned} \tag{31}$$

Butler and Huston assume that the mean activity of MCl only changes as a result of ion-pair formation if the total formal ionic strength is held constant, which they express in the following equation:

$$[M^+][Cl^-]\gamma_{M^+}\gamma_{Cl^-} = T(M)[Cl^-]\gamma_{12}{}^2 \tag{32}$$

This is the equivalent of equation 26 for mean activity coefficients. Since $[Cl^-] = m_1$, equation 32 becomes

$$[M^+]\gamma_{10}'^2 = T(M)\gamma_{12}{}^2 \tag{33}$$

where γ_{10}' is the mean activity of MCl in pure MCl solutions at the effective ionic strength I_E.

These equations can be used to calculate, with an iterative procedure, the concentions of the free ions and I_E. Values of K_{A2}^* and K_{A1}^* resulting from a less rigorous treatment and I_T are used to start the calculations, $[M^+]$ being evaluated from the experimental γ_{12} values and equation 33. The values of k_2^{*0} can be derived from $k_2^{*0}\gamma_A{}^2 = K_2{}^0$, with estimates of γ_A based on single-ion values. Butler and Huston derive k_2^{*0} from experimental data based on a titration method using a junctionless glass electrode cell as indicator. It is not clear in their paper how they derive k_2^{*0} from what is obviously an apparent constant $k_2^{*''}$ related to k^{*0} by equation 19.

It would be of great interest to evaluate log γ_{NaCl} in the presence of MHA and M_2A at high pressure using a junctionless glass electrode.

The conclusion from this review of the methods and theories for directly measuring and for interpreting the effect of pressure on the dissociation constants of weak electrolytes at the ionic strength of seawater, is that they involve practically as many assumptions as the calculations based on partial molal volume determinations. The two methods are complementary and often need to be used simultaneously. The advantage of the electromotive force measurements is their specificity, which rests on the use of ion-sensitive electrodes, some of which can be used for direct high-pressure work.

The greatest theoretical difficulty is the separation of the pure ionic strength effects from those related to the formation of ion pairs. This is best resolved by the direct determination of ion-pairing constants whenever possible.

We shall now describe the experimental results which have been obtained, either from partial molal volume determinations or from dissociation constants measurements using electromotive force methods, on the effect of pressure and temperature on the sulfate and carbonate systems in seawater, the only ones that have been studied in detail.

2. Results

A. The Sulfate System

The sulfate system in seawater is less complicated than the carbonate–carbon dioxide system because the protonation of SO_4 can be neglected. SO_4 ions are either free or combined with Na, Mg, and Ca to form $NaSO_4^-$, $MgSO_4^0$, and $CaSO_4^0$, respectively. The problem of the sulfate speciation has been well studied, since $MgSO_4^0$ plays an important role in sound-wave transmission in seawater.

Fisher (1962, 1965, 1967) has shown, using conductivity and an ultrasonic technique on aqueous solution of $MgSO_4$, that only 90% of the Mg is present as free ions in seawater at 1 atm. His results show that a pressure increase of 1000 atm produces a 60% decrease in ultrasonic absorption and only a 10% decrease in the number of $MgSO_4^0$ ion pairs.

This effect is explained by the Eigen and Tamm (1962) theory, which postulates the existence of the following reactions:

$$\begin{array}{cccc} Mg^{2+} + SO_4^{2-} \leftrightharpoons & Mg\overset{H}{\underset{H}{O}}\overset{H}{\underset{H}{O}}SO_4 \leftrightharpoons & Mg\overset{H}{\underset{H}{O}}SO_4 \leftrightharpoons & MgSO_4^0 \\ \bar{V}_1(m_1 + m_1) & \bar{V}_2(m_2) & \bar{V}_3(m_3) & \bar{V}_4(m_4) \end{array}$$

Eigen and Tamm calculated $\bar{V}_1 \leqslant \bar{V}_2 < \bar{V}_3 < \bar{V}_4$. The transition from state 4 to state 3 controls the relaxation frequency observed in aqueous solutions.

According to Fisher (1972), m_4 decreases when pressure is applied, and the ultrasonic absorption should decrease with depth in the ocean. This prediction is based on the calculated values of $\Delta\bar{V}_{23} = -18$ ml/mol, $\Delta\bar{V}_{34} = -3$ ml/mol, with $K_{23} = m_2/m_3 = 1$ and $K_{34} = m_3/m_4 = 9$ at 1 atm, from Fisher's data in diluted aqueous solutions and

$$K^*_{A(MgSO_4)} = \frac{[MgSO_4^0]_T}{[Mg^{2+}][SO_4^{2-}]} = 10.2 \text{ at } 25°C$$

determined experimentally by Kester and Pytkowicz (1970) and the corresponding $\Delta\bar{V}^* = 3.7$ ml/mol calculated by the same authors on the basis of theoretical considerations and molal volume data.

Kester and Pytkowicz (1968, 1969, 1970) have made an extensive use of the potentiometric method described on p. 64, using ion-selective electrodes to determine K^*_A for $NaSO_4^-$, $MgSO_4^0$, and $CaCO_3^0$, at 25 and 2°C. They have measured $K^*_{A(NaSO_4^-)}$ directly at 1000 atm with a sodium-sensitive electrode, but the Ca and Mg electrodes proved, as pointed out previously, to be erratic at high pressure. Figure 1 shows that $2.303 \log K^*_{A(NaSO_4^-)}$ varies linearly with pressure. Their calculation of the activity coefficients takes into account the difference between I_T and I_E, the total and effective ionic strength, respectively. Their results are represented in Table I. The distribution of sulfate species according to Kester and Pytkowicz (1970) is given in Table II, where we have also included the results of Garrels and Thompson (1962).

The major difference between the model of Garrels and Thompson and that of Kester and Pytkowicz lies essentially in the difference in the $NaSO_4^-$ and free SO_4^{2-} concentrations caused by the use by the latter of the experimental value of $K^*_{A(NaSO_4^-)}$.

From their results, Kester and Pytkowicz conclude that the effect of pressure on $NaSO_4^-$ liberates SO_4^{2-} ions that partly combine with Mg and Ca so that there is a

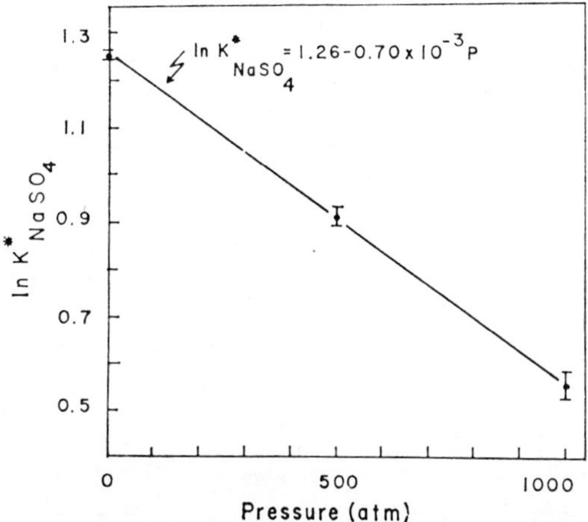

Fig. 1. Variations of ln K_{NaSO_4} with pressure at 1.5°C and I_E^m = 0.61; the vertical bars represent the average deviation of the mean of three measurements. From Kester and Pytkowicz (1970).

slight net increase in the amounts of Mg and Ca sulfate ion pairs. This would indicate an increase of ultrasonic absorption with depth. Fisher (1971) comes, as we have seen, to the opposite conclusion, arguing that Kester and Pytkowicz measure an increase in the sum total of the three possible $MgSO_4$ ion pairs. Fisher shows that this might be compatible with a decrease of the form $MgSO_4$. His arguments are, however, based on results obtained in a dilute aqueous solution for the intermediate equilibria between the three types of $MgSO_4$ ion pairs.

Millero (1971) has examined the problem of sulfate ion association in seawater on the basis of partial molal volume determinations. He uses the method outlined on p. 61, taking values for the dissociation constant $K_A^* = (1 - \alpha)/\alpha^2\gamma_\pm{}^2 m_T$ from Kester and Pytkowicz (1968) with α = 0.52, and

$$\bar{V}_{(obs)} = (1 - \alpha)\bar{V}_{(MgSO_4{}^0)} + \alpha\bar{V}_{(Mg^{2+},SO_4{}^{2-})} = 2.9 \text{ ml/mol}$$

from Lee (1966) in pure $MgSO_4$ solutions and in 0.725*m* NaCl solutions, and

$$\bar{V}^0_{(Mg^{2+},SO_4{}^{2-})} = -7.2 \text{ ml/mol}$$

from Lee, also. Millero uses three different methods to evaluate the $\bar{V}$ of the free ions: additivity rules in pure water and in 0.725*m* NaCl; the Debye-Hückel limiting law in pure water; and the transfer equation (see p. 60).

The values for $\Delta\bar{V}^*_{(MgSO_4{}^0)}$ are 10.2, 8.6, 6.6, and 11.4 ml/mol, depending on the method used. The difference with the estimate of Kester and Pytkowicz lies essentially in the fact that they used the transfer equation valid for free ions (equation 7) which, according to Millero, is not applicable to $MgSO_4{}^0$. $\Delta\bar{V}^*_{(trans)}$ = 1.2 ml/mol when one uses the transfer equation, and Millero expects it to be 5.0 ml/mol, making use of the value $\bar{V}^0_{(Mg^{2+},SO_4{}^{2-})} = -7.2$ ml/mol, of which Kester and Pytkowicz were unaware. The theoretical approach of Millero (1971) has been extended to the formation of $NaSO_4{}^-$, $CaSO_4{}^0$ using partial volume data and the experimental values of Kester and Pytkowicz (Table III).

The effect of temperature on $\Delta\bar{V}^*$ is estimated by Millero (1971) to be of the order of 1 to 2 ml/mol from 25 to 0°C, with an average value of 1.2 ml/mol, which he suggests can be neglected, until reliable experimental data can be obtained at 0°C.

TABLE I

The Association Constants of Sulfate Ion Pairs in Seawater (34.8‰ Salinity)

$I_E = 0.67$	$t = 25°C$	1 atm
$K^*_{A(NaSO_4^-)}$	2.02[a]	0.69[d]
$K^*_{A(MgSO_4^0)}$	10.2[b]	8.75[d]
$K^*_{A(CaSO_4^0)}$	10.8[a]	6.07[d]
$K^*_{A(KSO_4^-)}$[e]	1.03[a]	1.03[d]

$I_E = 0.67$	$t \simeq 2°C$; 1 atm;	1000 atm	$\Delta\bar{V}^*$ ml/mol	$\Delta\bar{V}^0$ ml/mol
$K^*_{A(NaSO_4^-)}$[g]	3.52 (1°.5)	1.75	15.8	—
$K^*_{A(MgSO_4^0)}$[h]	15.0 (1°.7)[c]	13.0	3.7	7.3[i]
$K^*_{A(CaSO_4^0)}$[h]	15.9[c, f]	13.0	3.7	—

[a] Kester and Pytkowicz (1969).
[b] Kester and Pytkowicz (1968).
[c] Kester and Pytkowicz (1970).
[d] Garrels and Thompson (1962).
[e] Calculated from Garrels and Thompson (1962) (see *a*).
[f] Calculated assuming the same temperature dependency as found experimentally for $MgSO_4^0$.
[g] Determined experimentally (*c*).
[h] Calculated from partial molal volume data.
[i] Fisher (1962).

The distribution of the sulfate species calculated by Millero (1971) is, of course, different from that of Kester and Pytkowicz (Table IV).

Since the pressure effect calculated by Millero for $MgSO_4^0$ and $CaSO_4^0$ is much larger than the theoretical estimate of Kester and Pytkowicz, and is of the order of magnitude of the experimental observed effect on $NaSO_4^-$, this model shows a decrease in the $MgSO_4^0$ concentration. Until further experimentation is made possible at low temperature and high pressure, it will probably be impossible to decide on theoretical basis alone which, if either, of the two models is valid. It should be pointed out that the differences are, in fact, small (Pytkowicz, 1972). Errors on the estimate of K_A^* for $MgSO_4^0$ and $CaSO_4^0$ at high pressure affect the distribution of sulfate species much less than does the value of $NaSO_4^-$, which is known experimentally, because of the relatively low concentration of the Mg and Ca salts compared to NaCl.

B. The Carbon Dioxide-Carbonate System

The chemistry of carbon dioxide in seawater can schematically be represented by the following reaction series:

$$CO_2(\text{gas}) \overset{\alpha}{\rightleftharpoons} CO_2(\text{aq}) + H_2O \overset{K_0}{\rightleftharpoons} H_2CO_3 \overset{K_1}{\rightleftharpoons} H^+ + HCO_3^-$$
$$\overset{K_2}{\rightleftharpoons} CO_3^{2-} + H^+ + Ca^{2+} \overset{K_{sp}}{\rightleftharpoons} CaCO_3(s)$$

TABLE II

Effect of Temperature and Pressure on the Distribution of Sulfate Species in Seawater

		Percent of total sulfate in each species			
T(°C)	P atm	SO_4^{2-}	$NaSO_4^-$	$MgSO_4^0$	$CaSO_4^0$
25[a]	1	39	38	19	4
2	1	28	47	21	4
2	1000	39	32	24	5
25[b]	1	54	21	21.5	3

[a] Kester and Pytkowicz (1960, 1969, 1970).
[b] Taken from the general model of Garrels and Thompson (1962), which includes the carbonate–bicarbonate ion-pair distribution.

TABLE III

$V^*_{(\text{ion pair})}$ and K^*_A for Sulfate Species in Seawater (Millero, 1971)

	$\Delta\bar{V}^*$ (25°C)	K^*_A (2°C, 1000 atm)
$NaSO_4^-$ (at 25°C)	12.8 ml mol	1.7
$MgSO_4^0$ (at 25°C)	11.4 ml mol	9.0
$CaSO_4^0$ (at 25°C)	11.2 ml mol	9.6

TABLE IV

Comparison Between the Data of Kester and Pytkowicz (*a*) (1970) and of Millero (*b*) (1971) on the Distribution of SO_4 Species in Seawater at 1 and 1000 atm and 2°C

	Percent free SO_4^{2-}	Percent $NaSO_4^-$	Percent $MgSO_4^0$	Percent $CaSO_4^0$
(*a*) 1 atm	28.0	47.0	21.0	4.0
(*a*) 1000 atm	39.0	32.0	24.0	5.0
(*b*) 1000 atm	42.0	35.0	19.0	4.0

where α is the solubility of CO_2 in water, K_0, K_1, and K_2 are equilibrium constants, and K_{sp} is the solubility product of $CaCO_3$; the ion-pairing equilibria are omitted. All of the data for this series of reactions have been very carefully and critically reviewed by Edmund and Gieskes (1970). Empirical expressions to calculate the constants as functions of temperature, pressure, salinity, or chlorinity are given in order to compute the *in situ* degree of saturation of seawater with respect to $CaCO_3$.

We will deal here only with the effects of pressure and their temperature dependency.

Effect of Pressure on the Ionization of Carbonic Acid and the Related Ion Pairs

It is useful in describing the effect of pressure on carbonic acid equilibria in seawater to define the following ionization functions (equivalent to the stoichiometric dissociation constants at a given ionic strength):

$$k^{*\prime}_{(1)} = \frac{[H^+][HCO_3^-]}{[CO_2]_T} \quad \text{with} \quad [CO_2]_T = [H_2CO_3] + [CO_2] \tag{34}$$

$$k^{*\prime}_{(2)} = \frac{[H^+][CO_3^{2-}]}{[HCO_3^-]} \tag{35}$$

$$k^{*\prime\prime}_{(1)} = \frac{[H^+][HCO_3^-]_T}{[CO_2]_T} = k^{*\prime}_{(1)}(1 + \sum K^*_{A1}[M^+]) \tag{36}$$

$$k^{*\prime\prime}_{(2)} = \frac{[H^+][CO_3^{2-}]_T}{[HCO_3^-]_T} = k^{*\prime}_{(2)} \frac{(1 + \sum K^*_{A2}[M^+])}{(1 + \sum K^*_{A1}[M^+])} \tag{37}$$

The dots ($\prime$ or $\prime\prime$) indicate that the absolute values of the ionization functions are usually not known with a high precision since only $k_p^{*\prime}/k_1^{*\prime}$ can be directly measured from pressure-compensated junctionless concentration cells (equation 17). The $k^{*\prime}$'s define what might be called the true ionization constants and the $k^{*\prime\prime}$'s are apparent constants where the terms $1 + \sum K^*_{A1}[M^+]$ and $1 + \sum K^*_{A2}[M^+]$ represent the global ion-pairing effect for Ca, Mg, Na, and K.

In oceanographic work apparent mixed constants $K_1^{*\prime} = k_1^{*\prime\prime}\gamma_{H^+}$ and $K_2^{*\prime} = k_2^{*\prime\prime}\gamma_{H^+}$ are used, where γ_{H^+} represents the activity coefficient of the hydrogen ion. These constants relate *pa*H measurements, usually made with a calomel-glass electrode pair and the total ionic concentrations. Junctionless cells measure $m_{H^+}\, m_{Cl^-}\, \gamma^2_{HCl}$ and the hydrogen ion activity has to be calculated from γ_{H^+} computations. It is often assumed that the effect of pressure is small on γ_{H^+} because it is small on γ_{HCl} and $K_p^{*\prime}/K_1^{*\prime}$ is taken equal to $k_p^{*\prime\prime}/k_1^{*\prime\prime}$. In fact, $\Delta\bar{V}^{*0}_{(trans)}$ for H^+ is 0.8 − 1.0 ml/mol according to Millero (1969), which means that $\log K_p^{*\prime}/K_1^{*\prime} = \log k_p^{*\prime\prime}/k_1^{*\prime\prime} + 0.01$.

The effect of pressure on the ionization of carbonic acid in seawater was first estimated by Buch and Gripenberg (1932) on the basis of $\Delta\bar{V}_1{}^0 = -28$ ml/mol for the first step and $\Delta\bar{V}_1{}^0 = -10.5$ ml/mol for the second step, assuming that HCO_3^- would behave as acetic acid.

The first direct experimental determinations have been made at 22°C by Disteche and Disteche (1967) and Culberson and Pytkowicz (1968) at 2, 11.6, and 22°C. The two sets of results at 22°C were difficult to compare because Disteche and Disteche (1967) used reference solutions containing $0.01M$ HCl + $0.49M$ NaCl + $0.026M$ $MgCl_2$ + $0.010\ M$ $CaCl_2$ + $0.030M$ MgSO . They overlooked the fact that HSO_4^- ions were formed and had to apply corrections to their data both at 1 atm and high pressure. The experiments have since been repeated in my laboratory (Disteche, 1972) using either $0.01M$ HCl + $0.49M$ NaCl + $0.056M$ $MgCl_2$ + $0.010M$ $CaCl_2$ or Tris-buffer-seawater as reference solutions. These results will be discussed with some of the earlier data.

As an introduction, we shall examine the effect of pressure on the carbonic acid–carbonate system in NaCl and KCl. Figures 2 and 3 give $(E_1 - E_p)$ from equation 17 as a function of $\sqrt{I_T{}^c}$* in bicarbonate and carbonate buffers at different buffer ratios in presence of KCl or NaCl. For a given buffer ratio $(E_1 - E_p)$ extrapolates linearly and

* Total or formal ionic strength on the molar scale.

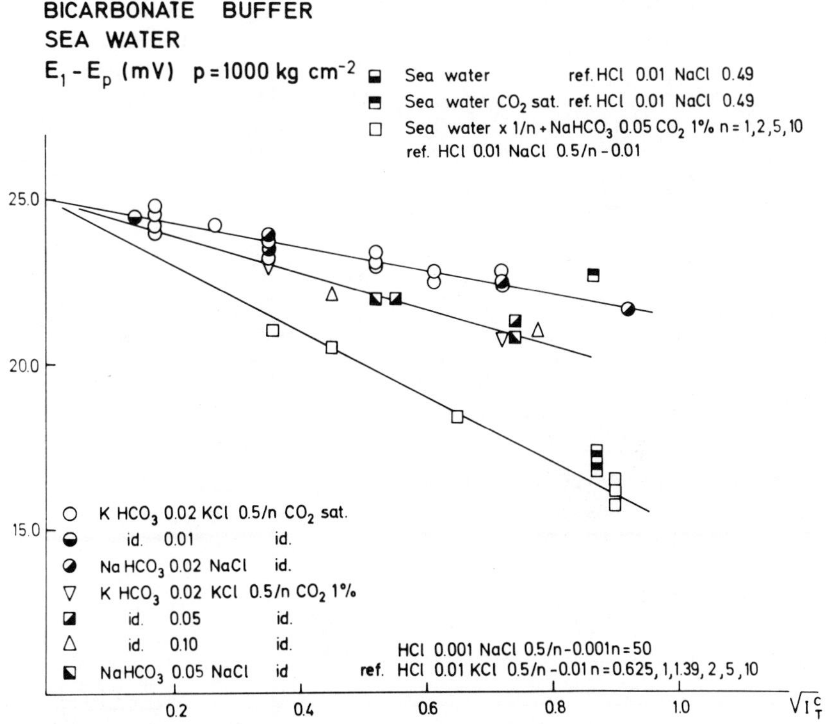

Fig. 2. Effect of pressure (1000 kg/cm^2) on the glass electrode electromotive force in bicarbonate buffer at different buffer ratios and at different ionic strengths in solutions of NaCl and KCl and in seawater at 22°C. Redrawn from Disteche and Disteche (1967).

a change in the buffer concentration has the same effect as the corresponding ionic strength change produced by an increase of the NaCl or KCl concentration.

It is therefore possible, knowing $(E_1 - E_p)$ at zero I, to obtain a graphical estimate of $(E_1 - E_p)$ at a chosen ionic strength. One might think, from these remarks, that $\log k_p^{*0}/k_1^{*0}$ can easily be obtained from the linear plots in Figures 2 and 3. One must, however, bear in mind that very dilute solutions of the buffering species, in NaCl or KCl solutions, have not been studied and their behavior at high pressure might well be very different from what is expected.

Because of its importance in chemical speciation studies in seawater we will discuss first the problem of ion-pair formation and suggest a method to calculate $\Delta\bar{V}^*_{(\text{ion pair})}$ from the high-pressure data on the ionization of carbonic acid in presence of various salts (NaCl; KCl, $MgCl_2$, $CaCl_2$, and SO_4 ions). We will then consider the effect of the initial pH on the pH shifts induced by pressure in seawater and show how it affects the evaluation of the ionization functions of carbonic acid in seawater. The last paragraph will be devoted to the effect of SO_4 ions and boric acid.

Figures 4 and 5 give the first and the second ionization functions of carbonic acid at 1 atm and 1000 kg/cm^2 in KCl or NaCl, over a wide formal ionic strength range. The results are given for both molar (c) and molal (m) scales ($K^m = K^c/d_o$ where d_o is the density of pure water and $\log d_{0,p}/d_0$ is 0.017 at 1000 kg/cm$^2 d_{0,1}$. The function $pK'_{(1)1} = pk'_{(1)1} + 1.01\sqrt{I_T{}^c}/(1 + \sqrt{I_T{}^c})$ is extrapolated to zero ionic strength on the $I_T{}^c$ scale; $pk'_{(2)}$ can be extrapolated on the $\sqrt{I_T{}^c}$ scale directly.

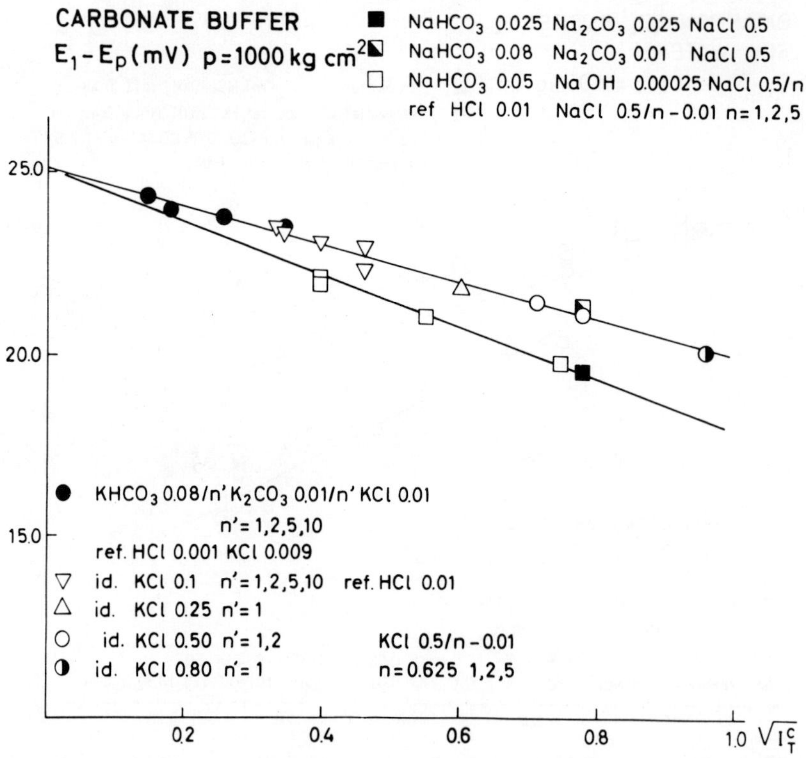

Fig. 3. The effect of pressure (1000 kg/cm²) on the glass electrode electromotive force in carbonate buffer at two buffer ratios in NaCl and KCl solutions of different ionic strengths at 22°C. Redrawn from Disteche and Disteche (1967).

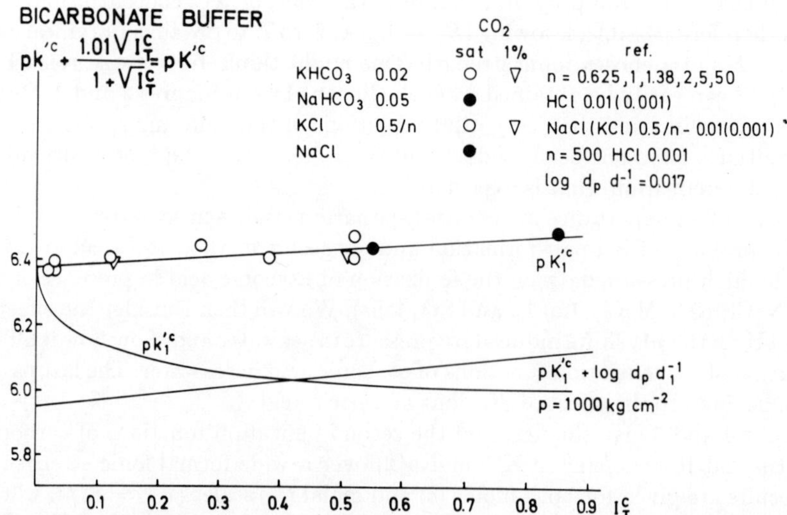

Fig. 4. The first ionization function ($pk'_{(1)}$) and dissociation constant ($K^0_{(1)}$) of carbonic acid in NaCl and KCl solutions at different ionic strengths at 1 atm and 1000 kg/cm². Redrawn from Disteche and Disteche (1967).

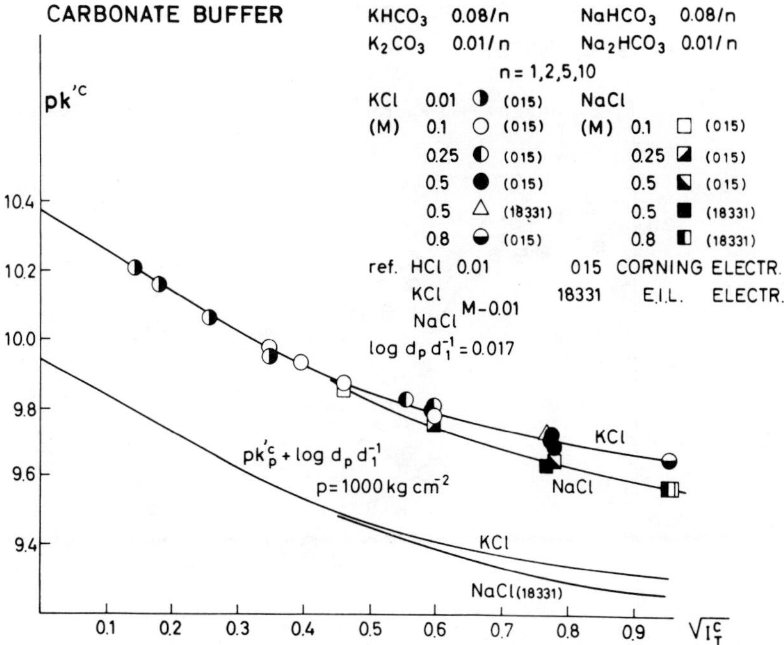

Fig. 5. The second ionization function ($pk'_{(2)}$) and dissociation constant ($K^0_{(2)}$) of carbonic acid in NaCl and KCl solutions at different ionic strengths at 1 atm and 1000 kg/cm². Redrawn from Disteche and Disteche (1967).

No difference is found when NaCl is substituted to KCl in bicarbonate buffer but NaCl lowers $pk'_{(2)}$ at high ionic strength and the effect is pressure dependent. The $pk'_{(1)}$ values in bicarbonate buffer fit very well with the data of Harned and Bonner (1945), who extrapolate $pk'_{(1)}$ at infinite dilution of the buffering species in NaCl solution and came to the conclusion that adding $NaHCO_3$ had the same effect as adding the corresponding amount of NaCl.

Ion pairing must indeed be very small in bicarbonate buffers either in NaCl or KCl, but it is an important factor in carbonate buffers.

$NaCO_3^-$, $NaHCO_3^0$, KCO_3^-, $KHCO_3^0$ *ion-pair formation*

Considering our results for $pk'_{(2)}$ in NaCl and KCl, one might as a first approximation follow Garrels, Thompson, and Siever (1961) and estimate that ion pairing is negligible in potassium salts. One can then use equation 20 and, since $k^{*''}_{(1)} = k^{*'}_{(1)}$, write:

$$\log(1 + {}^{\mathrm{Na}}K^{*'}_{A2}[\mathrm{Na}^+]_T) = {}^{K}pk^{*'}_{(2)} - {}^{\mathrm{Na}}pk^{*''}_{(2)} = 9.675 - 9.60 = 0.075$$

and

$${}^{\mathrm{Na}}K^{*'}_{A2}[\mathrm{Na}^+]_T = [\mathrm{NaCO_3}^-]/[\mathrm{CO_3}^{2-}] = 0.19$$

(The dot on ${}^{\mathrm{Na}}K^{*'}_{A2}$ indicates the approximation that $[\mathrm{Na}^+]_T$ is used instead of $[\mathrm{Na}^+]$.)

At $I_T{}^c = 0.75$, $\log K^{*'}_{A2} = -0.60$ and does not agree with the estimates of Garrels et al. (1961), Butler and Huston (1970), and Nakayama (1970) (see Table V, where $I_T{}^m$ is calculated on the molal scale).

The conclusion is that either our results are at fault or that ion pairing does exist in KCl–$KHCO_3$–K_2CO_3 solutions, but to a lesser extent than in the $NaCl$–$NaHCO_3$–Na_2CO_3–H_2O system.

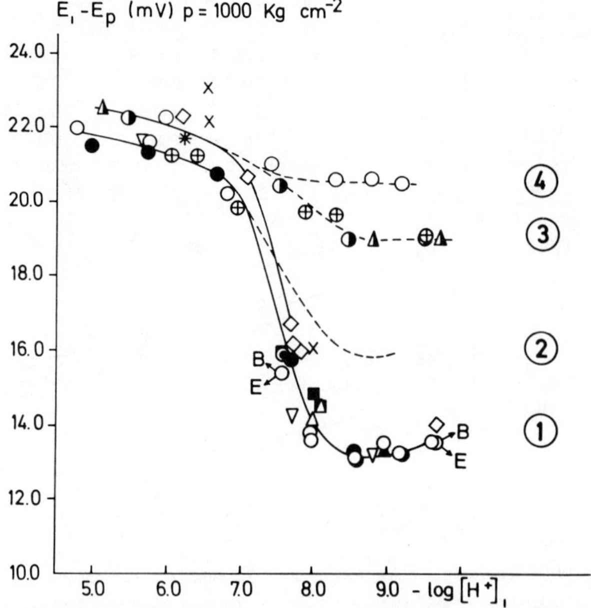

Fig. 6. The effect of pressure (1000 kg/cm²) on the glass electrode electromotive force in carbonate and bicarbonate buffers at $I_T^c = 0.75$ in NaCl or KCl solutions and in solutions resembling sea-water, as a function of $-\log[H^+]$, at 22°C.

Curve 1: effect of Ca^{2+}, Mg^{2+}, and SO_4^{2-}. Curve 2: effect of Ca^{2+}, Mg^{2+}, SO_4^{2-}, and boric acid. Curve 3: buffer in NaCl solutions (⊕ effect of SO_4^{2-}, ◇ effect of Mg^+). Curve 4: buffer in KCl solutions (B. Beckman 14185 electrode; E. E.I.L 18331 electrode). Molar concentration in the two half-cells:

Curve	HCl	NaCl	$MgSO_4$	$MgCl_2$	$CaCl_2$	KCl	Na_2CO_3	Na_2SO_4	Tris
○ Ref.	0.01	0.49	—	0.056	0.010	—	—	—	—
×	—	0.50	0.030	0.026	0.010	—	0.0025	—	—
● Ref.	0.02	0.48	0.030	0.026	0.010	—	—	—	0.05
×	—	0.50	0.030	0.026	0.010	—	0.0025	—	—
△ Ref.	0.01	0.49	—	0.056	0.010	—	—	—	—
×	—	0.50	0.030	0.026	0.010	—	0.0025	—	—
▲ Ref.	0.01	0.71	—	—	—	—	—	—	—
×	—	0.50	0.030	0.026	0.010	—	0.0025	—	—
● Ref.	0.01	0.40	—	0.053	0.010	0.009	—	—	—
×	—	0.46	0.028	0.025	0.010	0.009	0.0023	—	—
■ Ref.	—	0.40	—	0.053	0.010	0.009	—	—	—
×	—	0.41	—	0.053	0.010	0.009	0.0023	0.028	—
* Ref.	0.01	0.71	—	—	—	—	—	—	—
×	—	0.41	—	0.053	0.010	0.009	0.0023	0.028	—
(Prolonged equilibration)									
× Ref.	0.01	0.71	—	—	—	—	—	—	—
×	—	0.41	—	0.053	0.010	0.009	0.0023	0.028	—
(Prolonged equilibration, Culberson and Pytkowicz, 1968)									
▽ Ref.	0.01	0.49	—	0.056	0.010	—	—	—	—
×	—	0.50	—	0.056	0.010	—	0.0025	—	—

TABLE V

$I_T{}^m$	$\log K^*_{A2}$	$\log k^*_{A2}$ at $I = 0$	$\log K^*_{A1}$	$\log K^*_{A1}$ at $I = 0$
3.0[a]	0.37	0.97	—	—
1.0	0.27	0.96	−0.67	−0.30
0.5	0.14	0.77	−0.41	−0.08
0.75[b]	0.61[d]	1.27	−0.58[d]	−0.26
0.75[c]	−0.11[d]	0.55	−0.19[d]	+0.16

[a] Butler and Huston (1970).
[b] Garrels et al. (1961).
[c] Nakayama (1970).
[d] Calculated using the same activity coefficient value as Butler and Huston (1970).

Taking, as a starting point, that the latter hypothesis is correct, we shall use the data of Butler and Huston (1970) to evaluate the effect of pressure on ${}^{\mathrm{Na}}K^*_{A2}$ and other association constants, from our pk determinations.

Equation 19 can be rewritten as

$$\log \frac{{}^{\mathrm{Na}}k^{*\prime\prime}_{(2)p}}{{}^{\mathrm{Na}}k^{*\prime\prime}_{(2)1}} = \log \frac{K^0_{(2)p}}{K^0_{(2)1}} - 2\log \frac{\gamma_{(2)p}}{\gamma_{(2)1}} + \log \frac{(1 + {}^{\mathrm{Na}}K^*_{A2}[\mathrm{Na}^+])_p}{(1 + {}^{\mathrm{Na}}K^*_{A2}[\mathrm{Na}^+])_1} - \log \frac{(1 + {}^{\mathrm{Na}}K^*_{A1}[\mathrm{Na}^+]_p)}{(1 + {}^{\mathrm{Na}}K^*_{A1}[\mathrm{Na}^+]_1)} \tag{38}$$

We will first neglect the $NaHCO_3{}^0$ formation, so that the last term of equation 38 vanishes; $2 \log \gamma_{(2)p}/\gamma_{(2)1}$ is estimated from $\Delta\bar{V}^*_{(\mathrm{trans})}(\mathrm{H}^+, \mathrm{CO_3}^{2-}) - \Delta\bar{V}^*_{(\mathrm{trans})}(\mathrm{HCO_3}^-) = (1.1 + 1.7) - 1.0 = 1.8$ ml/mol, at 1000 kg/cm^2, using equation 7 and assuming that only ionic strength effects contribute to the change of the activity coefficients. One then finds (see Fig. 6: $p\mathrm{H} = -\log[\mathrm{H}^+] = 8.5$, curve 3, and Table VII):

$$0.325 = 0.429 - 0.031 - 0.073$$

Introducing ${}^{\mathrm{Na}}K^*_{A2} = 1.64$ at 1 atm (Ref. *a*, Table V), one obtains at $I_T{}^c = 0.75$ (NaCl 0.75M or 0.763m):

$$\frac{1 + {}^{\mathrm{Na}}K^*_{A2}[\mathrm{Na}^+]_p}{1 + {}^{\mathrm{Na}}K_{A2}[\mathrm{Na}^+]_1} = \frac{1.902}{2.251} = 0.845 \quad \text{and} \quad \Delta\bar{V}^*_{(\mathrm{NaCO_3}^-)} = 7.9 \text{ ml/mol}$$

If one assumes that bicarbonate ion pairing does exist:

$$\log \frac{{}^{\mathrm{Na}}k^{*\prime\prime}_{(1)p}}{{}^{\mathrm{Na}}k^{*\prime\prime}_{(1)1}} = \log \frac{K^0_{(1)p}}{K^0_{(1)1}} - 2\log \frac{\gamma_{(1)p}}{\gamma_{(1)1}} + \log \frac{(1 + {}^{\mathrm{Na}}K^*_{A1}[\mathrm{Na}^+])_p}{(1 + {}^{\mathrm{Na}}K^*_{A1}[\mathrm{Na}^+])_1} \tag{39}$$

Curve 2. Boric acid effect (4.3 × 10^{-4}M) on curve 1 (Disteche and Disteche, 1967)
Curve 3. NaCl and buffer only ◑ ▲

⊕ Ref. 0.01	0.65	—	—	—	—	—	—	—
—	0.66	—	—	—	—	0.0025	0.030	—
◇ Ref. 0.01	0.65	—	—	—	—	—	—	—
—	0.66	—	0.056	—	—	0.0025	—	—

Curve 4. KCl and buffer only ○. Redrawn from Disteche and Disteche (1967) and Disteche (1972).

The values for $\log k_{(1)p}/k_{(1)1}$ have to be read from the acid range of Fig. 6 (curve 3). It is however obvious that, in contrast to $\log k_{(2)p}/k_{(2)1}$, which remains constant from 8.5 to 9.5, $\log k_{(1)p}/k_{(1)1}$ varies in the interval 7.0 to 5.0. If one arbitrarily, takes $\log k_{(1)p}/k_{(1)1}$ at pH 5.0 and calculates $2 \log \gamma_{(1)p}/\gamma_{(1)1}$ from $\Delta \overline{V}^*_{(\text{trans})}$ $(H^+, HCO_3^-) = (1.0 + 1.1) = 2.10$ ml/mol, since $\Delta \overline{V}^*_{(\text{trans})}$ (CO_2) is usually assumed to be zero (Millero, 1972) one finds:

$$0.384 = 0.427 - 0.036 - 0.007$$

With ${}^{\text{Na}}(K^*_{A1})_1 = 0.30$ (Table V, Ref. *a*):

$$\frac{(1 + {}^{\text{Na}}K^*_{A1}[\text{Na}^+])_p}{(1 + {}^{\text{Na}}K^*_{A1}[\text{Na}^+])_p} = \frac{1.210}{1.221} = 0.984 \qquad \text{and} \qquad \Delta \overline{V}^*_{(\text{NaHCO}_3{}^0)} = 2.1 \text{ ml/mol}$$

which is very small indeed. If we now take $\log k_{(1)p}/k_{(1)1} = 0.362$ at pH 7.0 (Fig. 6):

$$0.362 = 0.427 - 0.036 - 0.029$$

$$\frac{(1 + {}^{\text{Na}}\text{Na}_{K^*_{A1}}[\text{Na}^+])_p}{(1 + {}^{\text{Na}}\text{Na}_{K^*_{A1}}[\text{Na}^+])_p} = \frac{1.149}{1.229} = 0.935 \qquad \text{and} \qquad \Delta \overline{V}^*_{(\text{NaHCO}_3{}^0)} = 10.8 \text{ ml/mol}$$

Assuming that the value calculated at pH 7.0 in solutions where CO_2 is practically at infinite dilution is correct and that the observed difference between pH 5.0 and 7.0 is due to the effect of the CO_2 concentration on $2 \log \gamma_{(1)p}/\gamma_{(1)1}$, one can then write at pH 5.0:

$$0.384 = 0.427 - 0.014 - 0.029$$

which tends to show that $\Delta \overline{V}^*_{(\text{trans})}$ for CO_2 would be of the order of 1.3 ml/mol at saturation. Whatever the reason is for this effect, which might reflect an important change in the structure of water due to the presence of CO_2 (aq) we believe it the only possible explanation of the change of $\log k_{(1)p}/k_{(1)1}$ with pH, since obviously, at a given ionic strength $(K^*_{A1})_{1,\,p}$ should be independent of pH.

We can now, taking into account the bicarbonate ion pairing (equation 38), recalculate $\Delta \overline{V}^*_{(\text{NaCO}_3{}^-)} = 11.9$ ml/mol. Taking the data of Garrels et al. (1961) (Table V, Ref. *b*) yields $\Delta \overline{V}^*_{(\text{NaCO}_3{}^-)} = 5.8$ ml/mol if $NaHCO_3{}^0$ is ignored and 8.1 ml/mol when it is taken into account; $\Delta \overline{V}^*_{(\text{NaCHO}_3{}^0)}$ is 12.5 ml/mol. The values obtained with the data of Nakayama (1970 (Table V, Ref. *c*) are apparently quite out of the range of expected $\Delta \overline{V}^*$ (ion pair) values in seawater (see p. 76) ($\Delta \overline{V}^*_{((\text{NaCO}_3{}^-)} = 20.6$ ml/mol when corrected for bicarbonate ion pairing (13.2 ml/mol uncorrected), $\Delta \overline{V}^*_{(\text{NaHCO}_3{}^0)} = 5.4$ ml/mol). The results of Nakayama were, however, obtained at low ionic strength ($I <$ 0.01). The calculations based on Garrels' et al. data (1961) are of restricted value in this analysis, since the hypothesis of totally dissociated potassium salts applied to our electromotive force determinations in NaCl and KCl leads to a value of ${}^{\text{Na}}K^*_{A2}$ which does not fit with theirs, essentially based on that very same hypothesis.

The analysis based on Butler and Huston's work (1970) gives more promising values, although the results depend on the choice of $\log \gamma_1/\gamma_p$. It will be treated again in the next section, where the effect of pressure on $MgCO_3{}^0$ and $CaCO_3{}^0$ will be considered.

Finally, from equations 38 and 39 it is possible to evaluate the absolute value of $-\log (K_{(2)}/\gamma_{(2)}{}^2)_{1,\,p}$ and $-\log (K_{(1)}/\gamma_{(1)}{}^2)_{1,\,p}$, which could be used, being the nearest approach we have to the true $k'_{(2)}$ and $k'_{(1)}$ (equations 34 and 35), to calculate the free $[HCO_3^-]$ and $[CO_3^{2-}]$ concentrations in pure NaCl solutions. We find at $I_T{}^c$ 0.75

$$9.60 + \log \frac{(1 + K_{A2}^*[Na^+])}{(1 + K_{A1}^*[Na^+])} = 9.86 \ (10.37 \text{ at } I = 0)$$

$$6.00 + \log (1 + K_{A1}^*[Na^+]) = 6.09 \ (6.38 \text{ at } I = 0$$

$$\Delta pk'_{(2)} \text{ at } 1000 \text{ kg/cm}^2 = 0.398$$

$$\Delta pk'_{(1)} \text{ at } 1000 \text{ kg/cm}^2 = 0.391 \text{ at pH} \geqslant 7.0$$

At $I_T{}^c$ 0.50 one finds $9.675 + 0.199 = 9.87$ (see Fig. 5).

If we admit as a crude estimate that $pk'_{(2)} = 9.86$ is valid for potassium salts, it is possible to evaluate ${}^{K}K_{A2}^* = 1.16$ and $\Delta\bar{V}^*_{(KCO_3^-)} = 10.7$ ml/mol, taking ${}^{K}pk^{*\prime\prime}_{(2)} = 9.675$, ${}^{K}\Delta pk^{*\prime\prime}_{(2)} = 0.350$, ${}^{Na}K_{A1}^* = {}^{K}K_{A1}^*$.

$MgCO_3{}^0$, $CaCO_3{}^0$, $MgHCO_3{}^+$, $CaHCO_3{}^+$, *ion-pair formation*

Let us now consider the effect of Mg and Ca ions, in the presence or absence of SO_4 ions, on the carbonic acid equilibria in NaCl solutions at the ionic strength of seawater. Figure 7 taken from earlier work by Disteche and Disteche (1967), shows that the addition of Mg, Ca, and SO_4 ions to carbonate and bicarbonate buffers in $0.5M$ NaCl at 1 atm produces a shift of the hydrogen ion concentration obviously due to the formation of ion pairs. The insert scales indicate how to correct for the effect of adding SO_4 ions to the reference solution of the junctionless glass-electrode cell, which contains $0.01M$ HCl plus the same salts (except the buffering species) as the buffered solutions.

The SO_4^{2-} effect, at 1 atm, is for the greatest part one of ionic strength. The fact that no significant pH change is observed at pH 5.0 can be interpreted to mean that Mg and Ca ions bind to HCO_3^- practically to the same extent as Na, although some difference might exist for Ca. The pH shift depends on the total buffer concentration. In concentrated buffers ($T(CO_3) = 0.09M$) a precipitate is formed when $CaCl_2$ ($0.01M$) is added with Mg salts ($0.030M$ $MgSO_4$ and 0.026 $MgCl_2$). This does not happen in a diluted buffer solution ($T(CO_3) = 0.0025M$) but there the shape of the curves in the alkaline range is modified.

This is explained by the hydrolysis of the carbonate species:

$$CO_3^{2-} + H_2O \leftrightharpoons HCO_3^- + OH^-$$

The equilibrium constant of this reaction is $K_w/K_{(2)}$ where K_w is the ion product of water. When CO_3^{2-} is trapped by ion pairing, some of the HCO_3^- reacts with OH^- ions at alkaline pH and the pH shift, observed when $MgCl_2$ is added, is therefore somewhat reduced. The equation

$$\frac{([HCO_3^-] - x)x}{[T(CO_3) + x]/2.53} = \frac{K_w^*}{K_{(2)}^*} \tag{40}$$

can be used to roughly calculate the hydrolysis effect. As shown later in the case of $MgCl_2$ $2.53 = T(CO_3)/[CO_3^{-2}]$, x is the amount HCO_3^- reacting with OH^-. At pH 9.2, the correction amounts to 3.6 mV. It is 1.3 mV at 8.6 and 1.2 mV at 8.1, and it falls within the limits of the experimental errors. When $T(CO_3)$ is $0.09M$, the correction is negligible, since in this case x is of the order of $10^{-4}M$.

If we now look at Fig. 6 where all the data are corrected at $I_T{}^c = 0.75$ and where we see how $(E_1 - E_p)$ varies as a function of the initial pH ($= -\log [H^+]_1$), it is obvious that at pH < 7.0 no distinction can be made between Na- and K-salts, and no effect can be seen when Mg and Ca salts are added. Sulfate has a small unexplained effect

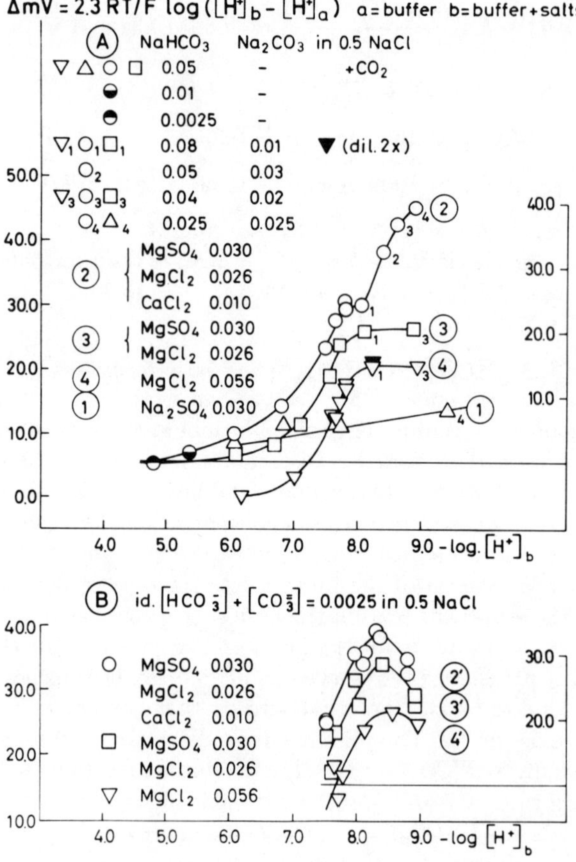

Fig. 7. Glass electrode electromotive force shifts produced by the addition of $MgSO_4$, $MgCl_2$, $CaCl_2$, and Na_2SO_4 to bicarbonate and carbonate buffers at atmospheric pressure. (A) $[HCO_3^-]_T + [CO_3^{2-}]_T$ 0.05 − 0.09 in 0.05 NaCl: Curve 1, effect of Na_2SO_4 (0.030); Curve 2, effect of $MgSO_4$ (0.030), $MgCl_2$ (0.026), and $CaCl_2$ (0.010). Precipitates are obtained at points 2, 3, and 4; result at pH 4.8 corresponds to $[HCO_3^-]_T + [CO_3^{2-}]_T$ 0.0025; Curve 3, effect of $MgSO_4$ (0.030) and $MgCl_2$ (0.026); Curve 4, effect of $MgCl_2$ (0.056). (B) $[HCO_3^-]_T + [CO_3^{2-}]_T = 0.0025$ (2′), (3′), (4′) same as (2), (3), (4). Concentrations on molar scale. Right insert scales correspond to the correction for the dissociation of HSO_4^- in the reference compartment of the glass electrode (see text). Redrawn from Disteche and Disteche (1967).

(see pp. 74 and 79). It is therefore reasonable to admit that pressure affects bicarbonate ion pairing of all cations present in the same way, so that we must consider the expression:

$$[HCO_3^-][1 + K_{A1}^*([Na^+] + [Mg^{2+}] + [Ca^{2+}])] = T(HCO_3^-)$$

to represent the total concentration of bicarbonate species.

In the alkaline range it is clear that Mg and Ca salts have a large effect on $(E_1 - E_p)$. This is obviously because of the dissociation of $MgCO_3^0$ and $CaCO_3^0$, which counteracts the effect of pressure on the dissociation of HCO_3^-.

If one considers the effect of Mg salts alone in NaCl-buffer, then

$$\frac{[CO_3^{2-}] + [NaCO_3^-] + [MgCO_3^0]}{[HCO_3^-] + [NaHCO_3^0] + [MgHCO_3^-]} = \frac{^{Mg}k^{*''}_{(2)}}{[H^+]} \tag{41}$$

and

$$\frac{[CO_2^{2-}] + [NaCO_3^-]}{[HCO_3^-] + [NaHCO_3^0]} = \frac{^{Na}k^{*}_{(2)}}{[H^+]} \tag{42}$$

If one admits that $^{Na}k^{*''}_{(2)}$ can be used to measure the ratio

$$\frac{[CO_3^{2-}] + [NaCO_3^-]}{[HCO_3^-] + [NaHCO_3^0]}$$

in the presence of Mg salts, one obtains at equal $[H^+]$ and I:

$$\frac{[MgCO_3^0]}{[CO_3^{2-}]} = {}^{Mg}K^*_{A2}[Mg^{2+}] = \left[\frac{^{Mg}k^{*''}_{(2)}}{^{Na}k^{*''}_{(2)}}\alpha - 1\right](1 + {}^{Na}K^*_{A2}[Na^+]) \tag{43}$$

with

$$\alpha = \frac{1 + ([Na^+] + [Mg^{2+}])K^*_{A1}}{1 + [Na^+]K^*_{A1}}$$

At 1 atm $^{Mg}pk^{*''}_{(2)} = {}^{Na}pk^{*''}_{(2)} - 0.403 = 9.60 - 0.403 = 9.197$ (curve 4′, Fig. 7, read at pH 8.5, corrected for the I shift, using Fig. 5).

At 1000 kg/cm^2:

$$^{Na}pk^{*''}_{(2)p} = 9.60 - 0.325 = 9.275 \text{ (Fig. 6, curve 3)}$$
$$^{Mg}pk^{*''}_{(2)p} = 9.197 - 0.234 = 8.963 \text{ (Fig. 6, } \diamondsuit)$$

one then finds, after neglecting the bicarbonate ion pairs, and after adjusting $(1 + {}^{Na}K^*_{A2}[Na^+])$ to the concentration of $0.582M$ ($0.592m$) NaCl ($I_{T^c} = 0.75$; $0.056M$ $MgCl_2$ or $0.05695m$)

$$\frac{[Mg^+]_T({}^{Mg}K^{*\prime}_{A2})_p}{[Mg^+]_T({}^{Mg}K^{*\prime}_{A2})_1} = \frac{(2.052 - 1)_p}{(2.53 - 1)_1} \times \frac{1.709}{1.971} = 0.596$$

which corresponds to $\Delta\bar{V}^*_{(MgCO_3^0)} = 13.0$ ml/mol and $({}^{Mg}K^{*\prime}_{A2}) = 52.9$.

If the formation of $NaHCO_3^0$ and $MgHCO_3^-$ is considered $\Delta\bar{V}_{(MgCO_3^0)} = 14.6$ ml/mol, $^{Mg}K^{*\prime}_{A2} = 54.2$. It can be checked, using equation 38 arranged to include Mg species with the above values for $^{Mg}K^{*\prime}_{A2}$, $^{Na}K^*_{A2}$, $^{Na}K^*_{A1} = {}^{Mg}K^{*\prime}_{A1}$ that $\Delta\bar{V}^*_{(trans)}$ has increased from 1.8 to 2.2 ml/mol. If one takes into account that 50% of the $T(CO_3)$ is bound to Mg, one can correct $^{Mg}K^{*\prime}_{A2}$ at pH 8.2 and obtain $^{Mg}K^*_{A2} = 54.5$.

If one now wants to apply the same treatment to the evaluation of $\Delta\bar{V}^*$ ion pair and K^*_{A2} for $CaCO_3^0$, using again the results of Figs. 6 and 7 in the presence of SO_4 ions $[{}^{SW}pk^{*''}_{(2)1} - {}^{SW}pk^{*''}_{(2)p} = 9.09 - 8.862 = 0.228$ (SW stands for NaCl $0.50M$, $CaCl_2$ $0.010M$, $MgCl_2$ $0.026M$, $MgSO_4$ $0.030M$, $T(CO_3) = 0.0025M$), we must take into consideration that I effective (I_E) is now largely different from I total, because of the relatively important concentration of sulphate ion pairs. From Table IV, and taking into account our estimates for the carbonate ion pairs, one finds $I_E{}^c = 0.70$ for the artificial seawater used in our experiments ($I_E{}^m = 0.712$ on the molal scale).

With $^{Na}K^*_{A2} = 1.59$ and $^{Na}K^*_{A1} = 0.31$ (Butler and Huston (1970), Table V), and first neglecting the effect of SO_4 in the acid range (Fig. 6), we recalculate $\Delta\bar{V}^*$ for the different ion pairs and ${}^{Mg}K^*_{A2}$ at $I_E{}^c = 0.70$. The values of $(E_1 - E_p)$ are corrected for the ionic strength change (Figs 2, 3, and 6). We obtain:

$$\begin{aligned} \Delta\bar{V}^*_{(NaCO_3{}^-)} &= 12.0 \text{ ml/mol} \\ \Delta\bar{V}^*_{(NaHCO_3{}^0)} &= 10.5 \text{ ml/mol} \\ \Delta\bar{V}^*_{(MgCO_3{}^0)} &= 13.9 \text{ ml/mol} \\ {}^{Mg}K^*_{A2} &= 51.4 \end{aligned}$$

Equation 43 becomes:

$$\begin{aligned} ([Mg^{2+}]^{Mg}K^*_{A2} + [Ca^{2+}]^{Ca}K^{*\prime}_{A2})_p &= [(2.432 \times \alpha_p) - 1]\,1.500 = 2.185 \\ ([Mg^{2+}]^{Mg}K^{*\prime}_{A2} + 2[Ca^{2+}]^{Ca}K^{*\prime}_{A2})_1 &= [(3.02 \times \alpha_1) - 1]\,1.809 = 3.738 \end{aligned}$$

where $\alpha_1 = 1.0156$ and $\alpha_p = 1.010$. After successive approximations to calculate the free ion concentration, taking the sulfate ion pairs into account, $[Mg^{2+}] = 0.505m$, $[Ca^{2+}] = 0.092m$, and $[Na^+] = 0.509m$, which leads to ${}^{Ca}K^*_{A2} = 124$ at 1 atm and $\Delta\bar{V}^*_{(CaCO_3{}^0)} = 12.5$ ml/mol for the formation of the $CaCO_3{}^0$ ion pair.

Using equation 38 for ${}^{SW}pk^{*\prime\prime}_{(2)}$ and introducing the ratios $[MCO_3]/[CO_3{}^{2-}] = [M]_T K^{*\prime}_{A2} = [M]K^*_{A2}$, one obtains:

$$0.228 = 0.429 - 0.046 - 0.178 + 0.023$$

where 0.023 represents the contribution of the bicarbonate ion pairs, for which ${}^{Na}K^*_{(NaHCO_3{}^0)}$ and $\Delta\bar{V}^*_{(NaHCO_3{}^0)}$ are assumed to be valid for all the ions present.

The activity coefficient term corresponds to $\Delta\bar{V}^*_{(trans)} = 2.6$ ml/mol, which is quite reasonable. One also finds in seawater:

$$pK_{(2)_1}/\gamma^2_{(2)_1} = 9.774 \text{ and } pK_{(2)p}/\gamma^2_{(2)p} = 9.774 - 0.383$$

If we now rewrite equation 38 for $pk_{(1)}$ (Fig. 6) and consider the small effect of SO_4 ions in the acid range, we obtain for pure NaCl solutions at $I_T{}^c = 0.70$, in the presence or absence of SO_4 ions, respectively:

$$\begin{aligned} 0.347 &= 0.427 - 0.036 - 0.028 - \theta(\theta = 0.016) \\ 0.363 &= 0.427 - 0.036 - 0.038 \end{aligned}$$

where θ represents the sulphate effect. If -0.016 is added to the log $\gamma_p/\gamma_\cdot$ term $(-0.036 - 0.016 = -0.052)$, one has to admit that SO_4 ions and associated ion pairs have a large effect on the mean activity coefficient related to the first dissociation step of carbonic acid.

If one adds -0.016 to the log term

$$\frac{(1 + {}^{Na}K^*_{A1}[Na^+])_p}{(1 + {}^{Na}K^*_{A1}[Na^+])_1}$$

then either $[Na^+]$ or ${}^{Na}K^*_{A1}$ has changed. The first alternative would mean that about $0.2m[Na^+]$ should have disappeared, which is obviously impossible; the second would lead to the acceptance of the pressure-induced dissociation of $NaHCO_3{}^0$ and of other bicarbonate ion pairs being enhanced by the presence of SO_4 ions. Although there is no explanation available for such a change of $\Delta\bar{V}^*$ for the bicarbonate species, we have recalculated the $\Delta\bar{V}^*$'s for all the ions in seawater, taking it into consideration and obtaining the following results:

$$\begin{aligned} \Delta\bar{V}^*_{(NaHCO_3{}^0)} &= 19.1 \text{ ml/mol}, \ \Delta\bar{V}^*_{(NaCO_3{}^-)} = 14.3 \text{ ml/mol} \\ \Delta\bar{V}^*_{(MgCO_3{}^0)} &= 14.7 \text{ ml/mol}, \ \Delta\bar{V}^*_{(CaCO_3{}^0)} = 13.0 \text{ ml/mol} \end{aligned}$$

Compared with the results where the SO_4 effect was neglected, the change is important for $\Delta\bar{V}^*_{(NaHCO_3{}^0)}$ and $\Delta\bar{V}^*_{(NaCO_3{}^-)}$ only.

If equation 38 is solved for ${}^{SW}pk^{*''}_{(1)}$, one finds:

$$0.346 = 0.427 - 0.058 - 0.023$$

and $\Delta\bar{V}^*_{(trans)}$ has increased to 3.3 ml/mol, or one writes:

$$0.346 = 0.427 - 0.045 - 0.036$$

admitting that $\Delta\bar{V}^*$ has changed for $NaHCO_3{}^0$ and $NaCO_3{}^-$, which corresponds for ${}^{SW}pk^{*''}_{(2)}$ to the following solution of equation 38:

$$0.228 = 0.429 - 0.046 - 0.191 - 0.036$$

We believe that it is more reasonable to accept a medium effect of SO_4 ions and related species on the activity coefficient term than to imagine a change in $\Delta\bar{V}^*$ for $NaCO_3{}^-$ and $NaHCO_3{}^0$.

Our results further show that in seawater $pK_{(1)}/\gamma_{(1)} = 5.97 + 0.07 = 6.04$ at 1 atm and $6.04 - 0.369$ at 1000 kg/cm^2.

The above analysis leads to a partition model of the bicarbonate and carbonate species in seawater, which takes into account the formation of sulfate ion pairs as described p. 68. The model could be refined to become a general model by solving the four equations $[M] = T(M)/(1 + \sum K^*_A[A])$ with M for Mg^{2+}, Ca^{2+}, Na^+, and K^+ and A for the $SO_4{}^{2-}$, $CO_3{}^{2-}$, and $HCO_3{}^-$ anions and the three equations $[A] = T(A)/(1 + \sum K^*_A[M])$ (see Kester and Pytkowicz, 1969), but this iterative procedure would only introduce very slight changes to the data presented in Table VI, smaller than the errors involved in the analysis of our electromotive force data.

TABLE VIa

Distribution of Bicarbonate and Carbonate Species in Seawater

T(°C)	P atm	Percent of total CO_3 as each species				
		$CO_3{}^{2-}$	$NaCO_3{}^-$	$MgCO_3{}^0$	$CaCO_3{}^0$	$KCO_3{}^-$
22[a]	1	18	14.5	46.8	20.5	0.2
	1000	27.4	13.5	40.1	19.5	0.2
		$HCO_3{}^-$	$NaHCO_3{}^0$	$MgHCO_3{}^+$	$CaHCO_3{}^+$	$KHCO_3{}^0$
	1	84.75	13.4	1.35	0.25	0.25
	1000	89.5	9.1	0.9	0.2	0.2
25	1	CO^{2-}	$NaCO_3{}^-$	$MgCO_3{}^0$	$CaCO_3{}^0$	$KCO_3{}^-$
[a]		9.1	17.3	67.3	6.4	—
[c]		8.0	16.0	43.9	21.0	—
				$Mg_2CO_3{}^{2+}$	$CaMgCO_3{}^{2+}$	
				7.4	3.8	
		$HCO_3{}^-$	$NaHCO_3{}^0$	$MgHCO_3{}^+$	$CaHCO_3{}^-$	$KCO_3{}^0$
[a]		70.0	8.6	17.8	3.3	—
[c]		81.3	10.7	6.5	1.5	—

[a] This work, $I_E{}^m = 0.712$ ($I_E{}^c = 0.70$).

[b] From Garrels and Thompson (1961), revised by Kester and Pytkowicz (1969) ($I_E{}^m = 0.67$).

[c] Hawley (1973).

The comparison of the K_A^*'s calculated by Garrels and Thompson (1961) with our values based essentially on the data of Butler and Huston (1970) for Na and our electromotive force determinations shows no agreement whatsoever. There is a large increase in free CO_3^{2-} and HCO_3^- in our model due to the value of the constants of Butler and Huston. There is also an important change in the partition of CO_3^{2-} between Mg and Ca. The present analysis further shows that the constants taken from Garrels and Thompson for the Mg and Ca ion pairs are incompatible with our electromotive force measurements. Starting with their values for ${}^{Na}K_{A1}^*$ and ${}^{Na}K_{A2}^*$, and taking our electromotive force results there evolves a ratio 2:1 for ${}^{Ca}K_{A2}^*/{}^{Mg}K_{A2}^* \simeq 92.5$ (neglecting the α correction in equation 43 and the ionic strength corrections, which, in fact, are not very important).

In a recent thesis Hawley (1973, personal communication) shows that K_{A1}^* values can be computed at 1 atm from paH measurements in seawaterlike solutions of different compositions, at constant I_E, by solving a set of equations similar to 36. Activity coefficients assumptions are made to evaluate $k_{(1)}^{*1}$. Similarily, at the experimentally determined hydrogen ion concentration $[H^+] = \sqrt{k_{(1)}^{*\prime\prime}k_{(2)}^{*\prime\prime}}$ (where the addition of HCO_3^- produces no paH shift), a set of equations equivalent to 20 (or 36 and 37), written for different $[M^+]$'s, can be used to calculate K_{A2}^* values; $k_{(1)}^{*\prime}k_{(2)}^{*\prime}$ is estimated from activity coefficients assumptions and the thermodynamic constants. The results are listed in Table VIb; triple ion formation is also considered.

If one takes Hawley's values for K_{A1}^* to estimate α in equation 43 and starts with his result for ${}^{Ng}K_{A2}^*$ (4.25) that agrees with Garrels and Thompson's, one obtains with our method and using our electromotive force data ${}^{Mg}K_{A2}^* = 100.4$ and ${}^{Ca}K_{A2}^* = 238.4$. The agreement with Hawley's results is reasonable, and the ratio of the two association constants is of the same order.

Hawley has no explanation for the difference between his result for ${}^{Na}K_{A2}^*$ and that of Butler and Huston. It might rest on the different assumptions made to evaluate the activities. Probably only direct determinations of K_{A2}^* with ion selective electrodes will make it possible to ascertain the value of K_{A2}^* not only for $NaCO_3^-$ but also for $MgCO_3^0$ and $CaCO_3^0$.

The speciation model computed by Hawley is of course intermediate between ours and that of Garrels and Thompson. It fits with our estimate of the amounts of $MgCO_3^0$ on $CaCO_3^0$, the major difference being in the free CO_3^{2-} (see Table VIa). We feel that at this stage there is no need to go further into a detailed comparison of the various models, nor will we discuss the model of Lafon (1969) based essentially on the data of Garrels and Thompson.

It seems obvious that a final model is within reach, and that it will be achieved by proper evaluations and intercalibration of the various methods.

Since the effect of temperature on the association constant at 1 atm is unknown and since no detailed high-pressure electromotive force determinations over a wide pH scale have so far been made at low temperature, we cannot calculate the partition of the ionic species at 1000 atm and 2°C. The values in Table VI given at 22°C and 1000 atm are only of academic interest in oceanography but indicate at least the qualitative shifts to be expected. For instance, it shows that the concentration of $CaCO_3^0$ changes very little with pressure. The increase in free CO_3^{2-} results from the dissociation of $NaCo_3^-$ and $MgCO_3^0$.

If one compares this with the sulphate distribution, one should bear in mind that sulphate ion pairing is much more important since $T(SO_4) = 0.030M$ and that $T(CO_3) \simeq 0.5\ 10^{-3}M$ at pH 8.2.

Table VIb shows that the values found for $\Delta\bar{V}^*$ for carbonate and bicarbonate except for $NaCO_3{}^0$ are relatively independent of the absolute values of the K_A^*'s, because only the ratio's $(1 + K_A^*[M]_p)/(1 + K_A^*[M]_1)$ come into the formulas. If one compares the data for the sulfate species calculated by Millero (1970) (Table III) with the experimental value of Kester and Pytlowicz (1970) (Table I) for $NaSO_4{}^-$, one comes to the conclusion that $\Delta \bar{V}^*$ is very similar for all ion pairs considered, with an average value $\simeq 12.5$ ml/mol. The agreement might be fortuitous and only of practical interest, but it might also be related to some similarity in the organization of the water molecules that hydrate the ion pairs.

The pH dependency of the ionization of carbonic acid and related species in seawater at high pressure and the calculation of the apparent ionization function; the effect of SO_4 *ions and boric acid on the pH of seawater at high pressure*

The ionization of carbonic acid at high pressure at different initial pH values; the effect of temperature. We shall consider here in more detail the shift of the apparent ionization functions of carbonic acid in artificial seawater when pressure is applied. At $p\mathrm{H} \geqslant 8.5$ $\log k_{(2)1}^{*\prime\prime}/k_{(2)p}^{*\prime\prime}$ can be read directly, as we have done in the preceding paragraphs, from the $(E_1 - E_p)$ values. At lower pH, $pk_{(2)p}^{*\prime\prime}$ has to be calculated, assuming that $pk_{(1)p}^{*\prime\prime}$ is known. These calculations have to be done to ascertain that $pk_{(2)p}^{*\prime\prime}$ remains constant whatever the value of $p\mathrm{H}_1$. They are made as follows, without making any initial assumption regarding the Na ion pairing:

1. The initial equilibrium concentration of the carbonate species are computed from $p\mathrm{H}_1$, and the value of $\sum CO_2$ using equations 44–48.

$$[CO_2]_1 = \sum CO_2/(A_1 + B_1 + 1) \tag{44}$$

$$A_1 = [CO_3{}^{2-}]_1/[CO_2]_1 \tag{45}$$

$$\log A_1 = -2 \log [H^+]_1 - (pk_{(1)1} - k_{(2)1}) \tag{46}$$

$$B_1 = [HCO_3{}^-]_1/[CO_2]_1 \tag{47}$$

$$\log B_1 = -\log [H^+]_1 - pk_{(1)1} \tag{48}$$

When ${}^{Na-SO_4}pk_{(1)}^{*\prime\prime}$ and ${}^{Na-SO_4}pk_{(2)}^{*\prime\prime}$ are used, one obtains $[CO_3{}^{2-}]'$ and $[HCO_3{}^-]_1'$, which correspond respectively to $[CO_3{}^{2-}] + [NaCO_3{}^-]$ and $[HCO_3{}^-] + [NaHCO_3{}^0]$. Knowing ${}^{SW}pk_{(1)1}''$ $(= {}^{Na-SO_4}pk_{(1)1}'')$ and ${}^{SW}pk_{(2)1}''$ one can evaluate $[CO_3{}^{2-}]_1' + [CO_3{}^{2-}]_1^B = [CO_3^{2-}]_1^T$ where B refer to the bound CO_3, $[CaCO_3{}^0] + [MgCO_3{}^0]$, and T to total.

2. The effect due to the release, at pressure p, of an amount of free $CO_3{}^{2-}$ (some of which binds to Na^+) resulting from the dissociation of $MgCO_3{}^0 + CaCO_3{}^0$ is estimated by solving the simultaneous equations 49 and 50:

$${}^{Na-SO_4}pk_{(1)p}^{*\prime\prime} + \log [H^+]_p + \log([HCO_3{}^-]_1' + 2x)_p = \log([CO_2]_1 - x)_p \tag{49}$$

$${}^{Na-SO_4}pk_{(2)p}^{*\prime\prime} + \log [H^+]_p - \log([HCO_3{}^-]_1' + 2x)_p = \log([CO_3{}^{2-}]_1' - x + \Delta)_p \tag{50}$$

where x represents the amount of CO_2 and free $CO_3{}^{2-}$ that combine because of the displacement of the equilibrium $2HCO_3{}^- \leftrightharpoons CO_3{}^{2-} + CO_2 + H_2O$ when an amount Δ of $MgCO_3{}^0$ and $CaCO_3{}^0$ ion pairs is dissociated by pressure. Since x is small compared to $[HCO_3{}^-]_1'$, a first estimate, x' can be obtained from equation 49 by using the initial $[HCO_3]_1'$ concentration and $\log [H^+]_p$; $2x'$ is then added to $[HCO_3]_1'$ and a better value for x is found. Two successive approximations are usually sufficient to determine x and $([HCO_3]_1' + 2x)_p$. It is then easy, using equation 50, to calculate $([CO_3{}^{2-}]_1' - x + \Delta)_p$, and, since $[CO_3{}^{2-}]_1'$ is known, Δ can be computed.

Table VIb

Ion-Pair Association Constants at 1 atm and $\Delta\bar{V}^*$ for Ion-Pair Formation (ml/mol) in Seawater

(T°C)		HCO_3^-				CO_3^{2-}			
		K_A^*	$\Delta\bar{V}^*$	K_A^*	$\Delta\bar{V}^*$	K_A^*	$\Delta\bar{V}^*$	K_A^*	$\Delta\bar{V}^*$
22[a]	Na^+	0.31[c]	10.5	0.28[e]	11.8	1.59[c]	12.0	4.25[e]	7.8
	Mg^{2+}	(0.31)[d]	10.5			51.4	13.9	100.4	14.8
	Ca^{2+}	(0.31)	10.5			124.0	12.5	238.4	13.7
	K^+	(0.31)	10.5			1.16	10.7		
25[b]	Na^+	0.26[b]		0.28[e]		4.16[b]		4.25[e]	
	Mg^{2+}	5.22[b]		1.62[e]		160.0[b]		112.5[e] ($MgCO_3^0$)	
								386.6[e] (Mg_2CO^{2+})	
	Ca^{2+}	5.10[b]		1.96[e]		78.0[b]		279.6[e] ($CaCO_3^0$)	
								1042.0[e] ($MgCaCO_3^{2+}$)	

[a] This work, $I_E{}^m = 0.712$ ($I_E{}^c = 0.70$, $I_T{}^c = 0.75$).
[b] From Garrels and Thompson (1961) and Kester and Pytkowicz (1969) ($I_E = 0.67$).
[c] Butler and Huston (1970).
[d] Numbers in parentheses are assumed to be equal to ${}^{Na}K_A^*$ (see text).
[e] Hawley (1973).

One then finds:

$$[CO_3{}^{2-}]_1^B - \Delta = [CO_3{}^{2-}]_p^B \text{ and } [CO_3{}^{2-}]_1^T - x = [CO_3{}^{2-}]_p^T$$

$[CO_3{}^{2-}]_p^T$, $\log [H^+]_p$,$([HCO_3{}^-]_1' + 2x)_p$ can then be used to evaluate ${}^{SW}pk_{(2)p}^{*''}$.

Table VII summarizes the results calculated from the experimental data of Fig. 6, assuming that $\log k_{(1)p}''/k_{(1)1}^{*''}$ is chosen at pH 7.0.

The fact that ${}^{SW}\Delta pk_{(2)}^{*''}$ is reasonably independent of $p\mathrm{H}_1$ tends to validate the choice of $\log {}^{Na-SO_4}k_{(1)p}^{*''}/{}^{Na-SO_4}pk_{(1)1}^{*''}$ at pH 7.0. If $pk_{(1)p}^{*''}$ is taken at $p\mathrm{H}_1 = 6.5$, for instance, ${}^{SW}\Delta pk_{(2)}^{*''}$ can be shown to vary with decreasing pH. It drops to 0.217 at pH 7.53. This finally means that curve 1 and also curves 3 and 4 in Fig. 6 have to be symmetric with respect to $p\mathrm{H}_1 = \frac{1}{2}(pk_{(1)1}^{*''} + pk_{(2)1}^{*''})$ for the formulas representing the dissociation of a diacid to be valid for the apparent ionization functions at high pressure. It can also be checked that $\frac{1}{2}({}^{SW}\Delta pk_{(1)}^{*''} - {}^{SW}\Delta pk_{(2)}^{*''}) = 0.287$. The experimental value read on Fig. 6 is 0.288 or 16.8 mV at $p\mathrm{H}_1 = 7.53 = \frac{1}{2}(5.97 + 9.09)$. The results show also that the ratio $[CO_3{}^{2-}]^B/[CO_3{}^2]'$ remains constant in the whole pH range, which is consistent with the assumption that association constants for ion pairs should not depend on pH.

The fact that one has to take $\log {}^{SW}k_{(1)p}^{*''}/{}^{SW}k_{(1)1}^{*''}$ at pH 7.0 to obtain constant values for $\log {}^{SW}k_{(2)p}^{*''}/{}^{SW}k_{(2)1}^{*''}$ at $p\mathrm{H} \geqslant 7.0$ fits well with the remark (p. 72) that a change in $\log \gamma_{(1)p}/\gamma_{(1)1}$ had to be postulated to obtain constant values for the formation constant of $NaHCO_3{}^0$ in the range pH 5.0 to 7.0. It finally comes to an acceptance that $\log \gamma_{(1)p}/\gamma_{(1)1}$ stays constant from pH 7.0 to 9.0, that is, at practically infinite dilution of CO_2, and that it increases to reach a minimum value when the solution is saturated with CO_2.

The data indicated by X in Fig. 6 refer to the results obtained by Culberson and Pytkowicz (1968) corrected at $I_T{}^c = 0.75$. These data have been obtained with $0.01M$ HCl + $0.71M$ NaCl as reference solution and are about 2 mV higher than our

TABLE VII

The Effect of Pressure (1000 kg/cm²) on the Apparent Ionization Constants of Carbonic Acid in Seawater at 22°C, $I_T{}^m = 0.712$

${}^{\text{Na-SO}_4}\Delta pk^{*''}_{(1)} = {}^{\text{SW}}\Delta pk^{*''}_{(1)}$	${}^{\text{Na-SO}_4}\Delta pk^{*''}_{(2)}$	${}^{\text{SW}}\Delta pk^{*''}_{(2)}$
0.346 (pH 7.0)	0.325	0.228
	${}^{\text{SW}}\Delta pk^{*''}_{(2)}$ at different $p\text{H}_1$ values	
$p\text{H}_1$	${}^{\text{SW}}\Delta pk^{*''}_{(2)}$	$(E_1 - E_p)$ (p = 1000 kg/cm²)
9.0	0.228	13.3 mV
8.5	0.226	13.3 mV
8.0	0.219	14.1 mV
7.8	0.228	15.0 mV
7.56	0.230	16.8 mV
7.30	0.225	18.6 mV

results. Half of the difference, can be explained by the choice of the reference solution, in our case 0.01M HCl + 0.49M NaCl + 0.056M $MgCl_2$, or Tris-seawater with an ionic composition identical to that of the artificial seawater except for the buffering species. When the two 0.01M HCl salt solutions are compared with the same glass-electrode, a shift of 1 mV is observed at 1000 kg/cm², which could perhaps be an indication of ion pairing between Mg^{2+} and Cl^-. The remaining 1 mV difference between Culberson and Pytkowicz's data and ours is not explained. It might rest in the fact that they use prolonged equilibration times and that we operate by pressure steps of 250 kg/cm² lasting 30 min each. In the case of prolonged equilibration, we often observe aging effects, depending on the electrode type. Such effects were apparently not observed by Culberson and Pytkowicz (Pytkowicz, private communication).

Taking ${}^{\text{SW}}\Delta pk^{*''}_{(1)} = 0.359$ at pH 7.0 from Culberson and Pytkowicz's measurements, and their observed pH shift at pH 8.0, one finds, using the method described above, ${}^{\text{SW}}\Delta pk^{*''}_{(2)} = 0.243$, at 1000 kg/cm², with our data for ${}^{\text{Na-SO}_4}pk^{*''}_{(2)}$ at 1000 kg/cm². If one takes ${}^{\text{SW}}\Delta pk^{*''}_{(1)} = 0.370$ at pH 6.5, as Culberson and Pytkowicz do, ${}^{\text{SW}}\Delta pk^{*''}_{(2)}$ is 0.242 in the alkaline range, but drops to 0.227 at pH 7.53. Culberson and Pytkowicz solve the following equation at two different pH values in their calculations:

$$\sum CO_2/\text{CA} = (1 + k^{*''}_{(2)}/[\text{H}^+] + [\text{H}^+]/k^{*''}_{(1)})/(1 + 2k^{*''}_{(2)}/[\text{H}^+]) \tag{51}$$

with

$$\text{CA} = [\text{HCO}_3{}^-]^T + 2[\text{CO}_3{}^{2-}]^T$$

This equation can be derived from equations 44 to 48, and it also implies that the ΔpH or $(E_1 - E_p)$ values data should lie symmetric with respect to $p\text{H}_1 = \frac{1}{2}(pk_{(1)} + pk_{(2)})$. In the present case this is only so between pH 7.0 and 8.5–9.0, where one then can assume that $pk_{(1)}$ and $pk_{(2)}$ are constants, with $\Delta pk_{(2)}$ well defined in the alkaline range. Between pH 6.5 and 7.0 $pk_{(1)p}$ is not a constant in our opinion, because of the effect of CO_2 on the activity coefficient term log $\gamma_{(1)p}/\gamma_{(1)1}$. It would indeed be interesting to verify at 1 atm whether in the pH region, where the two equilibria overlap, $pk_{(1)1}$ does behave like a constant, since the $pk_{(1)1}$ determinations have all been done at high CO_2 concentration.

In the above calculations, at alkaline $p\text{H} \simeq 9.00$, the hydrolysis of the CO_3 species has not been taken into account. Pressure should have a very small effect on $K^*_w/K^*_{(2)}$

(equation 40), since the pressure effect on K^*_w practically cancels the effect on $K^*_{(2)}$ [extensive data on the effect of pressure on K^*_w at low ionic strength over a large range of temperatures has been recently published by Whitfield (1972), using glass electrode cells].

Culberson and Pytkowicz (1968) have measured the linear effect of temperature on $\Delta pk_{(1)}$ and $\Delta pk_{(2)}$:

$$^{\mathrm{SW}}\Delta pk^{*\prime\prime}_{(1)2^\circ} - {}^{\mathrm{SW}}\Delta pk^{*\prime\prime}_{(1)22^\circ} = 0.061$$
$$^{\mathrm{SW}}\Delta pk^{*\prime\prime}_{(2)2^\circ} - {}^{\mathrm{SW}}\Delta pk^{*\prime\prime}_{(1)22^\circ} = 0.039$$

Applying the same coefficients to our results and taking the corrected Culberson and Pytkowicz data (for the difference in reference solution, the choice of $^{\mathrm{SW}}\Delta pk^{*\prime\prime}_{(1)}$ at pH $= 7.0$ instead of 6.5), one arrives at the Table VIII, valid at 1000 atm.

Millero and Berner (1972) discuss the available data for $-\Delta\bar{V}$ in carbonic acid equilibria, both from electromotive force, conductivity measurements, and partial molal volume data. One should notice, however, that they did not correct our data for the dissociation of HSO_4^- in the electrode reference solution, although a correction is proposed in our 1967 paper They come to the conclusion that:

$$-\Delta\bar{V}^0(\Delta pK^0_{(1)}) = 26.5 \text{ ml/mol (Ellis, 1959)}$$
$$-\Delta\bar{V}^0(\Delta pK^0_{(2)}) = 27.2 \text{ ml/mol}$$
$$-\Delta\bar{V}^*(^{\mathrm{SW}}\Delta pK^{*\prime}_{(1)}) = 22.4 \text{ ml/mol}$$
$$-\Delta\bar{V}^*(^{\mathrm{SW}}\Delta pK^{*\prime}_{(2)}) = 24.8 \text{ (using } \bar{V}^*_{(CO_3{}^{2-})} = 10.3 \text{ ml/mol)}$$
$$= 15.9 \text{ (using } \bar{V}^*_{(CO_3{}^{2-})} = 19.2 \text{ ml/mol)}$$

(The value $\bar{V}^*_{(CO_3{}^{2-})} = 19.2$ ml/mol was taken from Duedall (see Millero and Berner, 1972).

The agreement with the data of Table VIII is reasonable, but it is obvious that the partial molal volume data are always higher than the results from direct electromotive force measurements (except for $-\Delta\bar{V}^0$ $(\Delta pK^0_{(1)})$ where the value of Ellis (1959) (conductivity) was found by Millero to agree with other partial molal volume data). His first value for $\Delta\bar{V}^*(^{\mathrm{SW}}\Delta pK^*_{(2)}) = -24.8$ ml/mol might well correspond to $\Delta pK_{(2)}/\gamma^2_{(2)}$, since $\Delta\bar{V}^*_{(CO_3{}^{2-})} = 10.3$ ml/mol was calculated using the ionic strength principle (see p. 60).

The absolute value of the ionization functions and the dissociation constants are at 22°C and 1 atm at $I_E{}^m = 0.712$, given in Table IX. The status of our knowledge about the oceanographic mixed constants can be found in the review by Edmond and Gieskes (1970), Conflicting values for $pK^{*\prime}_{(2)}$ have been reported from field experiments by Takahashi et al. (1970): the value of Lyman (see Riley and Skirrow, 1965) for $K^{*\prime}_{(2)}$ should be 30% greater to fit with their experimental data (pH, $\sum CO_2$, alkalinity, CO_2 partial pressure).

The determination of the sulfate effect. The effect of sulfate on the ionization of carbonic acid was obscured in the earlier work of Disteche and Disteche (1967) because of the addition of $0.030M$ $MgSO_4$ to the reference cell, which then contained $0.01M$ HCl $+$ $0.49M$ NaCl $+$ $0.010M$ $CaCl_2$ $+$ $0.026M$ $MgCl_2$ $+$ $0.030M$ $MgSO_4$. The $-\log\,[H^+]$ of this cell is 2.085 (Disteche and Disteche, 1967) and the values of $pk_{(1)}$ and $pk_{(2)}$ in the presence of SO_4 published in 1967 have been corrected accordingly.

The correction to take into account the dissociation of HSO_4^- at 1000 kg/cm² and the eventual effect of SO_4 on the activity coefficients is however not as simple as proposed in 1967. It has now been shown (see Fig. 6) that the effect of SO_4 on $(E_1 - E_p)$ in pure NaCl solutions is negligible in the alkaline range. Furthermore, a small effect can still be detected in the acid range and the possible significance of this has been

Table VIII

$\Delta pk_{(1)}$, $\Delta pk_{(2)}$, $\Delta pK_{(1)}$, $\Delta pK_{(2)}$, $\Delta pK_{(1)}/\gamma^2_{(1)}$, $\Delta pK_{(2)}/\gamma^2_{(2)}$, $-\Delta \bar{V}^*$ (ml/mol), and for Carbonic Acid in Seawater ($I_T{}^c = 0.75$, $I_E = 0.70$, $I_E{}^m = 0.712$), and NaCl at 1000 atm, 22 and 2°C

	D and D[a]				C and P[c]			
	22°C	$-\Delta \bar{V}^*$	2°C	$-\Delta \bar{V}^*$	22°C	$-\Delta \bar{V}^*$	2°C	$-\Delta \bar{V}^*$
$^{SW}\Delta pk^{*''}_{(1)}$	0.357	19.9	0.418	21.7	0.370	20.6	0.431	22.4
					[d] (0.396)	(22.1)	(0.457)	(23.8)
					[e] (0.395)	(22.0)	(0.456)	(23.7)
$^{SW}\Delta pk^{*}_{(2)}$	0.235	13.1	0.274	14.2	0.251	14.0	0.290	15.1
					[d] (0.275)	(15.3)	(0.314)	(16.3)
					[e] (0.269)	(15.0)	(0.308)	(16.0)
$^{Na-SO_4}\ \Delta pk^{*''}_{(1)}$	0.358	20.0						
$^{Na}\Delta pk^{*''}_{(2)}$	0.338	18.9						
$^{Na-SO_4}\ \Delta pk^{*''}_{(2)}$	0.338	18.9						
$\Delta pK^0_{(1)}/\gamma^2_{(1)}$	0.381	21.3		In seawater				
$\Delta pK^0_{(2)}/\gamma^2_{(2)}$	0.395	22.1		In seawater				
		$-\Delta \bar{V}^0$						
$\Delta pK^0_{(1)}$	0.441[a]	24.6		In bicarbonate buffer				
$\Delta pK^0_{(1)}$	0.462[a]	25.8		In NaCl + CO_2				
	0.475[b]	26.5		In NaCl + CO_2				
$\Delta pK^0_{(2)}$	0.443[a]	24.7						

2.303 RT = 55.785 at 22°C and 52.006 at 2°C

[a] Disteche and Disteche (1965, 1967, corrected and this work, see text). The values for $-\Delta \bar{V}$ given in Table III differ from our earlier published data by 3% due to an unfortunate error in the direct conversion of $(E_1 - E_p)$, at 1000 kg cm^2 in millivolts to $-\Delta \bar{V}$ in ml/mol; $E_1 - E_p = 1.016\,\Delta \bar{V}$ (see Disteche, 1962) and not $\Delta \bar{V}/1.016$ as erroneously indicated in later papers.

[b] Ellis (1959).

[c] Culberson and Pytkowicz (1968) corrected, see text.

[d] Parentheses indicate original data of Culberson and Pytkowicz (1968) at $I_E{}^m = 0.67$.

[e] Parentheses indicate original data of Culberson and Pytkowicz (1968) at $I^E{}_m = 0.712$.

TABLE IX

Ionization Functions and Dissociation Constants of Carbonic Acid Valid in Seawater and Other Aqueous Solutions at 1 atm and 22°C ($I_E{}^m = 0.712$)

${}^{SW}pk^{*\prime\prime}_{(1)}$	5.97
${}^{Na}pk^{*\prime\prime}_{(1)}$	6.00
${}^{SW}pk^{*\prime\prime}_{(2)}$	9.09
${}^{Na}pk^{*\prime\prime}_{(2)}$	9.61 (-0.03 in presence of $T(SO_4)0.03M$) (-0.01 at $I_E{}^m = 0.763$)
${}^{Na-Mg}pk^{*\prime\prime}_{(2)}$	9.20 (-0.03 in presence of $SO_4(0.03M)$ (-0.01 at $I_E{}^m = 0.763$)
$pK^{*\prime\prime}_{(1)}$	6.00 (oceanographic mixed constant)
$pK^{*\prime\prime}_{(2)}$	9.12 (oceanographic mixed constant)
${}^{Na}pK_{(1)}/\gamma^2_{(1)}$	6.09 (-0.03 in presence of $T(SO_4)0.03M$) (-0.01 at $I_E{}^m = 0.763$)
${}^{Na}pK_{(2)}/\gamma^2_{(2)}$	9.87 (-0.03 in presence of $T(SO_4)0.03M$) (-0.01 at $I_E{}^m = 0.763$)
${}^{SW}pK_{(1)}/\gamma^2_{(1)}$	6.04
${}^{SW}pK_{(2)}/\gamma^2_{(2)}$	9.77

discussed in the section dealing with ion pairing. The new $(E_1 - E_p)$ values measured with different types of electrodes for artificial seawater solutions of slightly different composition are in accord whether established with $0.01M$ HCl + $0.49M$ NaCl + $0.010M$ $CaCl_2$ + $0.056M$ $MgCl_2$ or with Tris-seawater-buffer as reference, the latter having exactly the same composition as the artificial seawater under test except for the buffering species. The effect of pressure on the pH of Tris-buffer is quite small, as can be seen from Fig. 8. This is because the dissociation constant is of the type K_w/K_b (Disteche, 1972) and the effect of pressure on K_w cancels the one on K_b, the basic dissociation constant of the amine group of Tris (hydroxymethyl) aminomethane (reaction $BH^+ + H_2O \leftrightharpoons B + H_3O^+$). It is also well known that no Ca or Mg complexes are formed in Tris-buffer (Bates, 1961). We can see from Fig. 8 that indeed Mg or Ca salts (and also SO_4) have only a very small effect on $(E_1 - E_p)$.

The scatter of the results in Fig. 6 is rather high where the curve slopes, probably because very slight changes in the CO_2 concentrations are important. Some of the results are in the range of the observations of Culberson and Pytkowicz (1968) when one takes into account the reference solution difference. The scatter is much less in the acid and alkaline range where the buffering is higher. One successfully prolonged equilibration experiment in acid pH is also in the range of Culberson and Pytkowicz's data. Only systematic intercalibration will probably resolve the discrepancies between Culberson and Pytkowicz's results and ours. However, we believe it essential to be in possession of the whole curve, giving $E_1 - E_p$ as a function of pH, at different temperatures, to come to a full understanding of the effect of pressure on the carbon dioxide-bicarbonate-carbonate system.

The values we proposed in 1967 for $K^{*\prime}_{(2)}$ and $K^{*\prime}_{(1)}$ (the mixed oceanographic constants) are unaffected by the corrections and agree with the data of Lyman (see Riley and Skirrow, 1965). This suggests that $\log\gamma_{H^+} = 0.03$, a small value, but in reasonable agreement with the data obtained in pure NaCl (Disteche and Disteche, 1967).

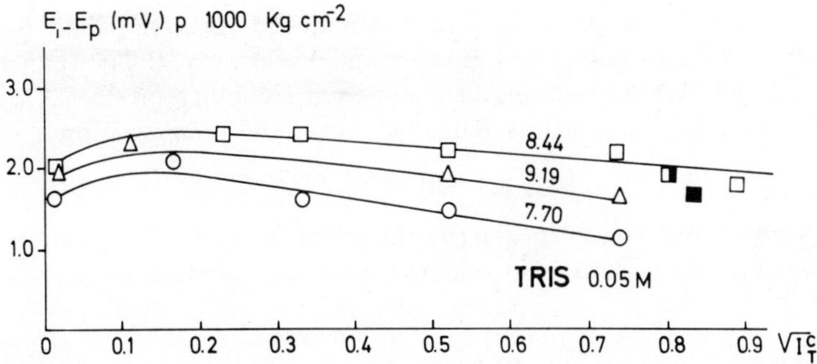

Fig. 8. The effect of pressure (1000 kg cm^{-2}) on the glass electrode e.m.f. for Tris-buffer (0.05*M*) in NaCl solution of different ionic strengths at three values of pH, at 22°C. The effect of addition of 0.030*M* Na_2SO_4(◨) and of 0.026*M* $MgCl_2$, 0.030*M* $MgSO_4$ and 0.010*M* $CaCl_2$ (■) are also shown. The reference solution contains 0.01*M* HCl and an appropriate concentration of NaCl; 0.010*M* $CaCl_2$ and 0.056*M* $MgCl_2$ are added for the (■) measurement.

The effect of boric acid on the pH of seawater at high pressure. When boric acid ($4.310^{-4}M$) is added to artificial seawater the ($E_1 - E_p$) data are altered in the alkaline range (Disteche and Disteche, 1967), as indicated by dotted line 2 in Fig. 6. $\Delta pK_B{}^0 = 0.531$ at 1000 kg/cm² and 22°C, ΔpK_B^{*0} drops to 0.433 in artificial seawater at zero borate concentration. Culberson and Pytkowicz (1968) calculated from their high-pressure data on artificial seawater, taking their values for $\Delta pK_{(1)}^{*\prime}$ and $\Delta pK_{(2)}^{*\prime}$, that $\Delta pK_B^{*\prime}$ was equal to 0.462 at 1000 atm or 0.447 at 1000 kg/cm². Their value for the linear temperature dependency of $\Delta pK_B^{*\prime}$ is:

$$\Delta pK_{B2^\circ}^{*\prime} = \Delta pK_{B22^\circ}^{*\prime} - 0.071$$

The high value of $\Delta pK_B^{*\prime}$ corresponds to $-\Delta\bar{V}^0 = 30.6$ ml/mol. This is because of the small diameter of the boron atom and also because hydration probably plays an important role in the reaction:

$$B(OH)_3 + H_2O \leftrightharpoons H^+ + B(OH)_4{}^-$$

which should be substituted for:

$$B(OH)_3H^+ + H_2BO_3{}^-$$

according to Edwards et al. (1955), Ingri et al. (1957) (see Culberson's thesis, 1968). Nothing seems to be known about possible borate ion association and polyanions in seawater.

The Effect of Pressure on the Solubility of $CaCO_3$ (Aragonite, Calcite)

Edmond and Gieskes (1970) have made an exhaustive compilation of the available data on the solubility of different forms of calcium carbonate in seawater at 1 atm and have reviewed the available data at high pressure and low temperature.

The first direct determination of the solubility of $CaCO_3$ at high pressure was made by Pytkowicz, Disteche, and Disteche (1967), using a glass-electrode as saturometer. The electrode is filled with seawater in equilibrium with a solid phase made up of the carbonate material to be investigated. The change of the solubility at high pressure increases $T(CO_3)$. A *p*H shift is observed from which the amount of released CO_3 can be calculated, provided the effect of pressure on the ionization of carbonic acid is known.

Pytkowicz and Fowler (1967) used this technique at 22°C for calcitic foraminifera, while Pytkowicz et al. (1967) and Hawley and Pytkowicz (1969) studied aragonite oolites at 22 and 2°C, respectively. The apparent solubility product K'_{sp} at a given temperature and ionic strength is defined at 1 atm and pressure p by

$$(K^{*\prime}_{sp})_{1,p} = [Ca^{2+}]^T_{1,p}[CO^{2-}]^T_{1,p} \tag{52}$$

where T refers to total concentration (free ions plus ion pairs) at saturation. The apparent solubility product is related to the true solubility product K_{sp} by:

$$K^{*\prime}_{(sp)} = K_{sp}/\gamma_{Ca_T}\gamma_{CO_{3T}}$$

Since total CO_3 and Ca concentrations are used, γ_{Ca_T} and $\gamma_{CO_{3T}}$ refer to total activity coefficient, which include both ionic strength and ion-pairing effects. Both of these effects on γ_{Ca_T} and $\gamma_{CO_{3T}}$ explain why the solubility of calcite in seawater is about 200 times as large as in distilled water. This illustrates the importance of the ion-pairing problem (Pytkowicz, 1969).

If CA is the carbonate alkalinity ($[HCO_3{}^-]^T + 2[CO_3{}^{2-}]^T$), the ratio $(K^{*\prime}_{sp})_p(K^{*\prime}_{sp})_1$ can be computed from

$$\frac{(K^{*\prime}_{sp})_p}{(K^{*\prime}_{sp})_1} = \frac{(\text{CA } K^{*\prime}_{(2)})_p\,(a_H + 2K^{*\prime}_{(2)})_1}{(\text{CA } K^{*\prime}_{(2)})_1\,(a_{H^+} + 2K^{*\prime}_{(2)})_p} \tag{53}$$

where $K^{*\prime}_{(2)}$ is the mixed oceanographic apparent dissociation constant for the second ionization step of carbonic acid and a_{H^+} is the hydrogen ion activity. This equation, if the ratio $[HCO_3{}^-]_p{}^T/[HCO_3{}^-]_1{}^T$ is unity, reduces to

$$\frac{(K^{*\prime}_{sp})_p}{(K^{*\prime}_{sp})_1} = K^{*\prime}_{(2)p} \cdot (a_{H^+})_1/K^{*\prime}_{(2)1} \cdot a_{(H^+)p} \tag{54}$$

The error made by this assumption is only about 2% and falls within the experimental errors.

If boric acid is present, Hawley and Pytkowicz (1969) use equation 55 to calculate $(CA)_s$ at saturations with $CaCO_3$:

$$\frac{\sum CO_2}{(CA)_s} = \frac{T(CO_2)_o + \Delta}{(TA)_o - (BA)_s + 2\Delta} = \frac{(1 + K^{*\prime}_{(2)}/a_{H^+} + a_{H^+}/K^{*\prime}_{(1)})_s}{(1 + 2K^{*\prime}_{(2)}/a_{H^+})_s} \tag{55}$$

where $T(CO_2)_o$ and $(TA)_o$ are the values of total CO_2 and alkalinity before the introduction of $CaCO_3$ in the seawater sample, Δ is the number of moles of $CaCO_3$ that dissolve or precipitate upon addition of $CaCO_3$, $(BA)_s = \sum B(1 + a_{H^+}/K^{*\prime}_B)_s$ ($\sum B$ = total boron concentration and $K^{*\prime}_B$ is the apparent mixed dissociation content of boric acid). $(BA)_s$ is calculated from $K^{*\prime}_B$ and $(a_{H^+})_s$ at 1 atm and pressure p, $T(CO_2)_o$ and (TA) are known, hence Δ can be estimated and also $(CA)_s$ at 1 and p atm, using suitable values for log $K^{*\prime}_p/K^{*\prime}_1$ for boric acid and carbonic acid.

The results depend directly on the value of $K^{*\prime}_{(2)p}/K^{*\prime}_{(2)1}$. They are represented in Table X calculated on the basis of (*a*) the original data of Culberson and Pytkowicz's (1967), (*b*) the corrected values for $K^{*\prime}_{(2)p}/K^{*\prime}_{(1)1}$ resulting from the analysis of the data of Culberson and Pytkowicz (1967) presented earlier in this chapter, and (*c*) the author's estimates for $K^{*\prime}_{(2)p}/K^{*\prime}_{(2)1}$ (see Table VIII).

Since the change of log $K^{*\prime}_{(sp)})_p/K^{*\prime}_{(sp)1}$ is practically a linear function of pressure (see

Table X

Effect of Pressure (p = 1000 atm) on the Apparent Stoichiometric Solubility Product of $CaCO_3$ in Seawater at 22° and 2°C ($I_E = 0.67$) (see text for explanations of *a*, *b*, and *c*)

	$\log (K^{*\prime}_{sp})_p/(K^{*\prime}_{sp})_1$	$\log (K^{*\prime}_{sp})_p/(K^{*\prime}_{sp})_1$ corr.	
At 22°C[1]	*a*	*b*	*c*
Calcite	0.5514	0.5334	0.5174
Aragonite	0.4969	0.4789	0.4629
	$(K^{*\prime}_{sp})_p/(K^{*\prime}_{sp})_1$	$(K^{*\prime}_{sp})_p/(K^{*\prime}_{sp})_1$ corr.	
Calcite	$3.56(\Delta\bar{V}^* = -30.8)$	$3.42(\Delta\bar{V}^* = -29.7)$	$3.29(\Delta\bar{V}^* = -28.9)$
Aragonite	$3.16(\Delta\bar{V}^* = -27.7)$	$3.01(\Delta\bar{V}^* = -26.7)$	$2.90(\Delta\bar{V}^* = -25.9)$
	$\log (K^{*\prime}_{sp})_p/K^{*\prime}_{(sp)1}$	$\log (K^{*\prime}_{sp})_p/(K^{*\prime}_{sp})_1$ corr.	
At 2°C[2]	*a*	*b*	*c*
Aragonite	0.6263	0.6083	0.5923
	$(K^{*\prime}_{sp})_p(K^{*\prime}_{sp})_1$	$(K^{*\prime}_{sp})_p/(K^{*\prime}_{sp})_1$ corr.	
	$4.23(\Delta\bar{V}^* = -32.6)$	$4.06(\Delta\bar{V}^* = -31.6)$	$3.91(\Delta\bar{V}^* = -30.8)$

$(K^{*\prime}_{sp})_1$ calcite $= (0.1614 + 0.02892.\ \text{Cl} - 0.0063\,t)10^{-6}$
$(K^{*\prime}_{sp})_1$ aragonite $= (0.5115 + 0.2892\ \text{Cl} - 0.0063\,t)10^{-6}$
From Edmond and Gieskes, 1970.

[1] 22°C, 19.16‰ Cl (Pytkowicz and Fowler, 1967).
[2] 2°C, 19.16‰ Cl (Hawley and Pytkowicz, 1969).
Cl = chlorinity.
t = temperature (°C).

Fig. 9), only the value at 1000 atm is given; the values for $\Delta\bar{V}^*_{(CaCO_3)sp}$ are also given in ml/mol.

The corrections are of the order of 4 and 7.5% and in final analysis depend partially on the value taken for $\log K^{*\prime}_{(1)p}/K^{*\prime}_{(1)1}$, for the first dissociation step of carbonic acid as well as on experimental discrepancies (see p. 78). The difficulty could certainly be solved by making more measurements at alkaline pH between 8.5 and 9.0, where $\Delta pk^{*\prime\prime}_{(2)}$ can be estimated directly and is practically independent of $\Delta pk^{*\prime\prime}_{(1)}$.

The degree of saturation of seawater *in situ* is usually expressed by $\Omega = (IP/K^{*\prime}_{(sp)}) \times 100\%$ where IP is the observed ion product $[Ca^{2+}]^T[CO_3]^T_{obs}$. Since the calculation of $[CO_3]^T_{obs}$ is made starting from total alkalinity or $\sum CO_2$ and paH measurements, the results depend on the value of the mixed dissociation constant of carbonic acid approximately in the same way as $K^{*\prime}_{(sp)}$. The slight difference is due to the borate alkalinity correction and the initial paH (at lower paH values $K^{*\prime}_{(1)}$ plays a more and more important role in the evaluation of $[CO_3]^T_{obs}$). Edmond and Gieskes (1970) have calculated that a change of 10% in the pressure term in the evaluation of the constants would cause a change less than 1% in Ω, but, of course, the total amount of soluble $CaCO_3$ in the ocean is affected by the value of $(K^{*\prime}_{sp})_p$.

The problem of the chemical solution of calcium carbonate in seawater is not simple and the process depends on many factors, some of which are rate dependent, while

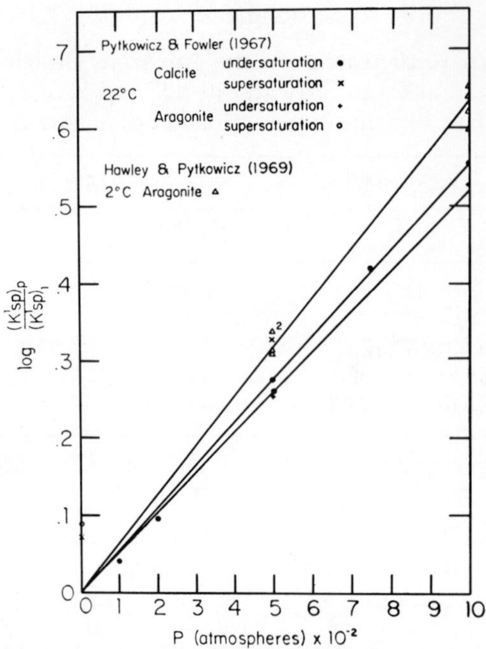

Fig. 9. The effect of pressure on the apparent solubility of calcium carbonate. Edmond and Gieskes (1970), based on data from Pytkowicz and Fowler, Hawley, and Pytkowicz.

others are related to particle size, structure, and organic matrix. Many papers deal with these aspects and have been reviewed by Pytkowicz (1965, 1968, 1969, 1971). A recent study of the kinetics of carbonate seawater interactions has been made by Pespret (1972).

The pattern of distribution of $CaCO_3$ with depth is well known. There is surface supersaturation, followed by a minimum, then a maximum, and lastly a monotonic decrease with depth. This pattern was first explained by Pytkowicz and Fowler (1967) and Hawley and Pytkowicz (1969) as the result of oxidation at the oxygen minimum, which depresses the *p*H and causes the saturation minimum, followed by an increase and then a deeper decrease resulting from the effect of pressure (Pytkowicz, 1972). The determination of these patterns from water samples depends largely on the reliability on the values for the dissociation constants of carbonic and related ion pairs, and the solubility product of calcite and aragonite, and it is unfortunate that so much uncertainty still reigns in this field, even for the values at 1 atm. Ben-Yaakov and Kaplan (1971) have devised a deep ocean *in situ* saturometer using a glass-electrode imbedded in calcite grains. Seawater is pumped through the probe and is allowed to react with the calcite; the recorded *p*H shifts indicate the initial degree of saturation. The profiles obtained agree at least qualitatively with the pattern described above, but one might wonder whether equilibration is really attained and how adsorption of clay minerals or organic material might interfere. Another semidirect approach is to rely on *in situ* *p*H measurements and surface measurements of $\sum CO_2$. Deep-sea probes have been successfully tested (see p. 61) but have not systematically been used to investigate the carbonate distribution in the ocean, principally because of the lack of data at low temperature on the ion pairs association constants and related apparent and true ionization functions for carbonic acid.

3. Conclusions and Summary

The oceans have an average depth of 4000 m, and below 1000 m, the temperature is $\leqslant 4°C$. We still know very little about the simultaneous effects of low temperature and high pressure on the chemistry of seawater.

We know the apparent ionization functions and the mixed oceanographic dissociation constants of carbonic acid and boric acid from direct electromotive force measurements using concentration cells over a wide temperature acid pressure scale, but more precision is still required (Disteche and Disteche, 1967, and this chapter; Culberson and Pytkowicz, 1968). The interpretation of these data rests entirely on our knowledge of the stoichiometric association constants of the major ion pairs existing in seawater: those belonging to the bicarbonate and carbonate species, which determine the amount of free HCO_3^- and CO_3^{2-}, those belonging to the sulphate species, which essentially determine the concentration of the free cations Na^+, Mg^{2+}, and K^+, which in turn are in equilibrium with the carbon dioxide-bicarbonate-carbonate system.

From all these association constants, only that of $NaSO_4^-$ (Kester and Pytkowicz, 1970) is known with precision in the required temperature and pressure range. The other constants for the sulphate system are known only at 25°C in seawater (Kester and Pytkowicz, 1968, 1969, 1970). These determinations have been carried out with ion-selective electrodes. We have attempted to show how to calculate the value and the pressure dependency of the association constants of the carbonate and bicarbonate ion pairs from high-pressure *p*H measurements, but low-temperature data are lacking. Our estimates are based on the experimental values determined by Butler and Huston (1970) for the formation constants of $NaCO_3^-$ and $NaHCO_3^0$ from mean activity coefficients determinations from electrochemical techniques. The data of Garrels and Thompson (1961) and Hawley (1973) for these constants have also been used for comparison. This has shown that the calculated pressure dependency of the association constants is very little affected by relatively large changes of the absolute values of the measured constants.

It is impossible to calculate the effect of temperature on the constants known only at 25°C, but the effect of pressure and its temperature coefficient can be, in principle, estimated from partial molal volume data. This has been done by Millero and Berner (1972) for the effect of pressure on the apparent dissociation constants of carbonic acid, the results being of the order of magnitude of the directly measured effect. Millero (1971) has also used partial molal volume data to predict the effect of pressure on $MgCO_4^0$ and $CaSO_4^0$. His estimates do not agree with those of Kester and Pytkowicz (1970), based also on partial molal volume determinations. Most of these are unfortunately only known in dilute solutions, and the data from direct measurements in seawater are still scarce (Duedall, 1968; Duedall and Weyl, 1967; Duedall in Millero et al., 1972.)

Despite all these shortcomings, one slowly arrives at models for the speciation of the major ionic constituents of seawater that rest on firmer experimental bases than the earlier models based for a great deal on single ion activity coefficients computations (Garrels and Thompson, 1961). It is clear, however, that more experimental work is required, combining wherever possible the partial molal volume approach and the direct determination of the ionization and association constants with electromotive force techniques.

Since the apparent ionization constants of carbonic acid are relatively well known at high pressure, it has been possible to measure directly the solubility of $CaCO_3$

(aragonite and calcite) using a glass-electrode as saturometer (Pytkowicz et al., 1967; Pytkowicz and Fowler, 1967; Hawley and Pytkowicz, 1969).

The solubility of $CaCO_3^0$ in seawater depends largely on the existence of $CaCO_3^0$, $MgCO_3^0$, and $NaCO_3^-$, which reduces the amount of free CO_3^{-2} to about 18% of the total carbonate concentration. It is obvious that ion pairing has the same effect on the solubility of many other minerals and that electrical conductance, viscosity, water structure, sound absorption, and the colligative properties in general, in some way or another depend on the extent of ion association as well as on the effects of the ionic environment, that is, the ionic strength.

The importance of chemical speciation has long been recognized (Sillen, 1961, 1964; Garrels and Thompson, 1962). Its role has been emphasized by Goldberg (1965). Ion pairs and complex ions exist in multitude in seawater; hundreds of them are possible, as shown by a recent theoretical analysis of Mangel (1971). Kester and Pytkowicz (1967) have shown that Mg^{2+} and Ca^{2+} form complexes with phosphates from determination of the apparent dissociation constants of phosphoric acid in seawater. Warner (1969a, 1969b), using CaF_3 fluoride sensitive electrodes, has shown the existence of MgF^- and CaF^-. The effect of pressure and temperature on none of these complex ions are known. Most of them are minor constituents but some occupy a significant position in seawater chemistry. It is unfortunate that so little is known about the effect of pressure on silicic acid and related compounds. Only recently (Jones and Pytkowicz, 1973) has the solubility of amorphous silica been measured in seawater at 1000 atm and 2°C ($\Delta V^* = -5.3$ ml/mol).

Pressure in the ocean affects not only water [the self ionization of which at high pressure is only known at low ionic strength (Whitfield, 1972), but over a wide temperature scale], the solute species, the inanimate matter, but also the life processes. The effect of pressure on but a few buffers of importance in body fluids are known (Disteche, 1972). Not much is understood about how animals living at great depth are "bio-engineered" to compensate or adapt to the ionization shifts induced by pressure (see Sleigh, 1972).

The effect of pressure on rate processes is another unknown in seawater chemistry and biochemistry. This might be the greatest shortcoming of all, because finally equilibrium states, except perhaps for some very fast ionic reactions between major species, must be confined to very local conditions in the ocean.

From the viewpoint of the physical chemistry of electrolyte solutions, the results from high-pressure work on seawater allow a distinction to be made between the non-specific ionic strength effects and the specific interaction, which involve ion pairing. Pressure has a small effect on the former and in many instances a much larger effect on the latter. Total activity coefficients can thus be split and the effect of ionic association can be shown even to very high dilution (Disteche and Disteche, 1967). In seawater chemistry one often takes 0.725*m* NaCl as a new reference for the standard state, and one often assumes that the activity coefficients of added solutes at low concentration are then close to unity. This is true for that part of the total activity coefficients that represents the long-range interaction.

It is also true for the "ionic strength" activity coefficient of the charged ion pairs, but one wonders how far one would have to go in dilution to reach a state where ion pairs disappear and whether such expressions as $\Delta \bar{V}^{*0}$, that is, the volume change due to ionic association, at infinite dilution in 0.725*m* NaCl has a meaning. One might also wonder whether 0.725*m* NaCl is really an ionic medium worth to be taken as reference, since obviously the addition of $MgCl_2$, for instance, affects the mean activity of HCl in NaCl solutions and thus also the activity of other ions so that deviations from the new reference standard have to be considered. Besides, the existence of ion pairs implies a distinction between effective and total formal ionic strength. It seems also from our results that for noncharged species, like CO_2, relatively large effects of pressure can be detected that depend on the CO_2 concentration and that lead to the concept that for such species the activity does vary, although it is generally accepted for ions that at the ionic strengths of sea water, activities vary only slightly with concentration or ionic strength. The case of CO_2 is probably an extreme case that reveals strong interactions with water molecules. It draws attention to the need for a general theory, taking into consideration the interactions of water-uncharged molecules, water-ion pairs, water-ions, and water-water clusters, besides the ion-ion, and so on, interactions. It is well known (see Horne, 1969) that at very high pressure, water clusters due to hydrogen bonding tend to disappear and that ions are stripped of their water sheath. This situation might well represent the ideal case of pure coulomb force interactions, even at large ionic concentrations. Pressure studies might throw needed light on the fundamental problems of electrolytic solutions, since it has a large effect on hydration and on water structure. These changes in water structure must be of great importance at interfaces where water is organized differently than in the bulk of the solutions. What happens at interfaces is another problem that should be studied in detail.

References

Bates, R. G., 1961. Amine buffers for pH control. *Ann. N.Y. Acad. Sci.*, **92**, 341–356.

Ben-Yaakov, S. and I. R. Kaplan, 1968. High pressure pH sensor for oceanographic applications. *Rev. Scient. Instrum.*, **39**, 1113–1138.

Ben-Yaakov, S. and I. R. Kaplan, 1971. Deep sea calcium carbonate saturometry. *J. Geophys. Res.*, **76**, 722–731.

Buch, K. and S. Gripenberg, 1932. Ueber den Einfluss des Wasserdruckes auf pH und das Kohlensauren gleichgewicht in grosseren Meerstiefen. *J. Conseil Perm. Intern Exploration Mer*, **7**, 233–245.

Butler, J. K. and R. Huston, 1972. Activity coefficients and ion pairs in the systems sodium chloride–sodium bicarbonate–water and sodium chloride–sodium carbonate–water. *J. Phys. Chem.*, **74**, 2976–2983.

Culberson, C. H., 1968. Pressure dependence of the apparent dissociation constants of carbonic and boric acids in sea water. Thesis, Oregon State University.

Culberson, C. H. and R. M. Pytkowicz, 1968. Effects of pressure on carbonic acid, boric acid and the pH of sea water. *Limnol. Oceanog.*, **13**, 403–417.

Disteche, A., 1959. pH measurements with a glass electrode withstanding 1500 kg cm^{-2} hydrostatic pressure. *Rev. Scient. Instrum.*, **30**, 474–478.

Disteche, A., 1962. Electrochemical measurements at high pressures. *J. Electrochem. Soc.*, **109**, 1084–1092.

Disteche, A., 1964. Nouvelle cellue à électrode de verre pour la mesure directe de pH aux grandes profondeurs sous-marines. *Bull. Inst. Oceanogr. Monaco*, **64**, No. 1320, 10 pp.

Disteche, A., 1972. Effect of pressure on the dissociation of weak acids. *Symp. Soc. Exp. Biol.*, **XXVI**, 27–60. Cambridge University Press.

Disteche, A. and S. Disteche, 1965. The effect of pressure on pH and dissociation constants from measurements with buffered and unbuffered glass electrode cells. *J. Electrochem. Soc.*, **112**, 350–354.

Disteche, A. and S. Disteche, 1967. The effect of pressure on the dissociation of carbonic acid from measurements with buffered glass electrode cells. The effect of NaCl, KCl, Mg^{2+}, Ca^{2+}, SO_4^{2-}, and boric acid with special reference to sea water. *J. Electrochem. Soc.*, **114**, 330–340.

Disteche, A. and M. Dubuisson, 1960. Mesures directes de pH aux grandes profondeurs sous-marines. *Bull Inst. Océanog. Monaco*, **57**, No. 1174, 8 pp.

Duedall, I. W. and P. K. Weyl, 1967. The partial equivalent volumes of salts in seawater. *Limnol. Oceanog.*, **12**, 52–59.

Duedall, I. W., 1968. Partial molal volumes of 16 salts in seawater. *Environ. Sci. Technol.*, **2**, 706–707.

Durst, R. A., (ed.), 1969. Ion-selective electrodes. *NBS Spec. Publ. 134*, U.S. Government Printing Office, Washington, D.C.

Durst, R. A., 1971. Ion selective electrodes in science, medicine and technology. *Ann. Scientist.*, **59**, 353–361.

Edmond, J. M. and J. M. T. M. Gieskes, 1970. On the calculation of the degree of saturation of seawater with respect to calcium carbonate under *in situ* conditions. *Geochim. Cosmochim. Acta*, **34**, 1261–1291.

Edwards, J. O. et al., 1955. The structure of the aqueous borate ion. *J. Amer. Chem. Soc.*, **77**, 266–268.

Eigen, M. and K. Tamm, 1962. Schallabsorption in Elektrolytlösungen als folge chemischer relaxation. *Z. Elektrochem.*, **66**, 93–121.

Ellis, A. J., 1959. The effect of pressure on the first dissociation constant of carbonic acid. *J. Chem. Soc.*, 750, 3689–3699.

Fisher, F. H., 1962. The effect of pressure on the equilibrium of magnesium sulfate. *J. Phys. Chem.*, **66**, 1607–1611.

Fisher, F. H., 1965. Ultrasonic absorption in $MgSO_4$ solution as a function of pressure and dielectric constant. *J. Acoust. Soc. Amer.*, **38**, 805–815.

Fisher, F. H., 1967. Ion pairing of magnesium sulphate in seawater: determined by ultrasonic absorption. *Science*, **157**, 823.

Fisher, F. H., 1972. Effect of pressure on sulfate ion association and ultrasonic absorption in seawater. *Geochim. Cosmochim. Acta*, **36**, 99–101.

Garrels, R. M., M. E. Thompson, and R. Siever, 1961. Control of carbonate solubility by carbonate complexes. *Amer. J. Sci.*, **259**, 24–25.

Garrels, R. M. and M. E. Thompson, 1962. A chemical model for seawater at 25°C and one atmosphere total pressure. *Amer. J. Sci.*, **260**, 57–66.

Goldberg, E. D., 1965. Minor elements in seawater. *Chemical Oceanography*. Vol. I. J. P. Riley and G. Skirrow, eds. Academic Press, New York, pp. 163–196.

Hamann, S. D., 1963. Chemical equilibria in condensed systems. In *High Pressure Physics and Chemistry*. R. S. Bradley, ed. Academic Press, New York and London, pp. 130–162.

Hamann, S. D., 1963. The ionization of water at high pressure. *J. Phys. Chem.*, Ithaca, **67**, 2233–2235.

Harned, H. S. and F. T. Bonner, 1945. The first ionization of carbonic acid in aqueous solutions of sodium chloride. *J. Am. Chem. Soc.*, **67**, 1026–1031.

Harned, M. S. and B. B. Owen, 1958. *The Physical Chemistry of Electrolytic Solutions*, 3rd ed. Reinhold, New York.

Hawley, J. E. 1973. Bicarbonate and carbonate ion association with sodium, magnesium and calcium at 25°C and 0.72 ionic strength. Thesis, Oregon State University.

Hawley, J. and R. M. Pytkowicz, 1969. Solubility of calcium carbonate in seawater at high pressure and 2°C. *Geochim. Cosmochim. Acta*, **33**, 1557–1561.

Hills, G. J. and P. J. Ovenden, 1966. Electrochemistry at high pressures. *Adv. Electrochem. Electrochem. Eng.*, **4**, 1845–1847.

Horne, R. A., 1969. Marine Chemistry. Wiley, New York.

Ingri, N. et al., 1957. Equilibrium studies of polyanions. II. Polyborates in $NaClO_4$ medium. *Acta Chem. Scand.*, **11**, 1034–1058.

Jones, M. M. and Pytkowicz, R. M. 1973. Solubility of silica in sea water at high pressures (in press *Bull. Soc. Roy. Sc. Liege*).

Kester, D. and R. M. Pytkowicz, 1967. Determination of the apparent dissociation constants of phosphoric acid in seawater. *Limnol. Oceanog.*, **12**, 243–252.

Kester, D. R. and R. M. Pytkowicz, 1968. Magnesium sulfate association at 25°C in synthetic seawater. *Limnol. Oceanog.*, **13**, 670–674.

Kester, D. R. and R. M. Pytkowicz, 1969. Sodium, magnesium and calcium sulfate ion pairs in seawater at 25°C. *Limnol. Oceanog.*, 14, 686–692.

Kester, D. and R. M. Pytkowicz,, 1970. Effect of temperature and pressure on sulfate ion association in seawater. *Geochim. Cosmochim. Acta*, **34**, 1039–1051.

Lafon, G. M., 1969. Some quantitative aspects of the chemical evolution of the oceans. Ph.D. thesis, Northwestern University, Evanston, Illinois.

Lee, S., 1966. The apparent and partial molal volumes of electrolytes in water and in aqueous sodium chloride solutions. Ph.D. thesis, Yale University, New Haven, Conn. University Microfilm, Ann Arbor, Michigan. *Ord. no. 66–4906. Diss. Abstr. B. 27.131.*

Mangel, M. S., 1971. A treatment of complex ions in seawater. *Marine Geol.*, **11**, M24–M26.

Millero, F. J., 1969. The partial molal volume of ions in seawater. *Limnol. Oceanog.*, **14**, 376–385.

Millero, F. J., 1971. The molal volumes of electrolytes. *Chemical Reviews*, **71**, 147–176.

Millero, F. J., 1971. Effect of pressure on sulfate ion association in seawater. *Geochim. Cosmochim. Acta*, **35**, 1089–1098.

Millero, F. J. and R. A. Berner, 1972. Effect of pressure on carbonate equilibria in seawater. *Geochim. Cosmochim. Acta*, **36**, 92–98.

Nakayama, F. S., 1970. Sodium bicarbonate and carbonate ion pairs and their relation to the estimation of the first and second dissociation constants of carbonic acid. *J. Phys. Chem.*, Ithaca, **74**, 2726–2728.

Owen, B. and S. Brinkley, 1941. Calculation of the effect of pressure upon ionic equilibria in pure water and in salt solutions. *Chemical Reviews*, **29**, 461–474.

Pespret, F., 1972. Kinetics of carbonate seawater interactions. Thesis, Hawaii Institute of Geophysics, University of Hawaii.

Pytkowicz, R. M., 1965. Carbonate cycle and the buffer mechanism of recent oceans. *Geochim. Cosmochim. Acta*, **31**, 63–73.

Pytkowicz, R. M., 1968. The carbon dioxide-carbonate system at high pressure in the oceans. *Oceanogr. Mar. Biol. Ann. Rev.*, **6**, 83–135.

Pytkowicz, R. M., 1969. Chemical solution of calcium carbonate in seawater. *Am. Zoologist.*, **9**, 673–679.

Pytkowicz, R. M., 1971. The physical chemistry of seawater. *Oceanogr. Mar. Biol. Ann. Rev.*, **9**, 11–60.

Pytkowicz, R. M., 1972. The status of our knowledge on sulfate association in seawater. *Geochim. Cosmochim. Acta*, **36**, 631–633.

Pytkowicz, R. M., 1972. Comments on a paper by S. Ben Yaakov and I. R. Kaplan, Deep sea *in situ* carbonate saturometry. *J. Geophys. Res.*, **77**, Letters 2733–2734.

Pytkowicz, R. M., A. Disteche, and S. Disteche, 1967. Calcium carbonate solubility in seawater at *in situ* pressures. *Earth and Planet. Sci. Letters*, **2**, 430–432.

Pytkowicz, R. M. and G. A. Fowler, 1967. Solubility of foraminifera in seawater at high pressures. *Geochem. J.*, **1**, 169–182.

Pytkowicz, R. M. and D. R. Kester, 1969. Harned's rule behavior of NaCl–Na_2SO_4 solutions explained by an ion association model. *Am. J. of Sci.*, **267**, 217–229

Riley, J. P. and G. Skirrow, 1965. *Chemical Oceanography*, Vol. I. Academic Press, London and New York.

Sillen, L. G., 1961. The physical chemistry of seawater. In *Oceanography*, M. Sears, ed. AAAS Publ. no. 67, Washington, D.C., pp. 549–581.

Sleigh, M. A., ed. 1972. The effects of pressure on organisms. *Symposia Soc. Exp. Biol.*, no. XXVI. Cambridge University Press.

Takahashi, T., R. F. Weiss, C. H. Culberson, J. M. Edmond, D. E. Hammond, C. S. Wong, Li Yvan-Hui, and A. E. Bainbridge, 1970. A carbonate chemistry profile at the 1969 Geosecs intercalibration station in the Eastern Pacific Ocean. *J. Geophys. Res.*, **75**, 7648–7666.

Warner, T. B., 1969. Fluoride in seawater; measurements with lauthanum fluoride electrode. *Science*, **165**, 172–180.

Warner, T. B., 1969. Lauthanum fluoride electrode response in water and sodium chloride. *Anal. Chem.*, **41**, 527–529.

Whitfield, M., 1969. Multicell assemblies for studying ion-selective electrodes at high pressures. *J. Electrochem. Soc.*, **116**, 1042–1046.

Whitfield, M., 1970. Effect of membrane geometry on the performance of glass electrode cells. *Electrochim. Acta*, **15** (1) 83–96.

Whitfield, M., 1972. Self-ionization of water in dilute sodium chloride solutions from 5–35°C and 1–2000 bars *J. of Chem. and Eng. Data*, **17**(2), 124–128.

3. THE ALKALINITY—TOTAL CARBON DIOXIDE SYSTEM IN SEAWATER

JORIS M. GIESKES

1. Introduction

The chemistry of carbon dioxide in natural waters has long interested a wide spectrum of investigators. Whereas biologists have focussed their attention on the role of carbon dioxide in photosynthetic processes, geochemists and chemical oceanographers were interested in the participation of carbon dioxide in the major geochemical cycles and also in the processes that led to the distribution of carbon dioxide in the oceans.

Much attention has been given to the solution chemistry of carbon dioxide in natural waters, especially with regard to thermodynamic relationships. Among the first to present a quantitative characterization of the carbon dioxide system were Johnston (1916) and Buch (1917). Johnston found that the alkalinity and total carbon dioxide content of natural waters could best be used for these purposes. With the development of modern electrolyte theories, particularly the Debye-Hückel (1923) theory, a powerful tool became available that allowed a thermodynamic basis for the description of the carbon dioxide equilibria in natural waters. Hastings and Sendroy (1925) and Hastings, Murray, and Sendroy (1928) were among the first to use this approach in the carbon dioxide system in sodium chloride solutions. With regard to seawater, this work was taken up by two groups of workers; one group was in Europe, under the auspices of the International Council for the Exploration of the Sea led by Buch (Buch et al., 1932), and the other was at the Scripps Institution of Oceanography under the direction of Moberg (Moberg et al., 1934; Lyman, 1957). Subsequent work on the solution equilibria of the carbon dioxide system in seawater has introduced essentially no new concepts, but has greatly improved the data.

The distribution of carbon dioxide in the atmosphere, the surface waters of the ocean, and the deep sea has been studied during various major expeditions, particularly the "Meteor" expedition in the South Atlantic (Wattenberg, 1933), the "Snellius" expedition in the Indonesian Archipellago (Postma, 1957, 1958), and the Swedish deep sea expedition on the "Albatross" (Bruneau et al., 1953). The data collected during these expeditions did establish some general trends in the distribution of alkalinity and CO_2 in the oceans, although the accuracy of some of the data has been questioned. For instance, Keeling (1968) was able to show that the values of the partial pressure of CO_2 in surface waters as calculated from the pH and alkalinity data of Bruneau et al. (1953) disagreed with the direct measurements of this property. Accurate data are necessary to obtain reliable partial pressure data so that areas can be identified in the ocean where surface waters act as sources or sinks for atmospheric CO_2. Refinements in analytical techniques now make it possible to make a quantitative study of the distribution of alkalinity and CO_2 in the ocean, so that many geochemical questions can be answered with more confidence than before.

This chapter aims at a survey of the various problems currently under investigation by workers in this field. A discussion will be presented of the thermodynamic information presently available, followed by a discussion of the general distribution of alkalinity and CO_2 in the ocean. Finally, some specific geochemical problems will be considered in more detail.

2. Carbon Dioxide Equilibria in Seawater—Thermodynamic Relations

Carbon dioxide, unlike most other dissolved gases in seawater, reacts with water to form a weak acid, carbonic acid. This, in turn, dissociates into bicarbonate and carbonate ions. The latter react with the alkaline earth ions, particularly calcium, to form solid carbonates. The various equilibria involved are represented in the following reaction scheme:

$$CO_2(gas) \overset{K_0}{\rightleftharpoons} CO_2(aq) \tag{1}$$

$$CO_2(aq) + H_2O \overset{K_H}{\rightleftharpoons} H_2CO_3 \tag{2}$$

$$H_2CO_3 \overset{K_1}{\rightleftharpoons} H^+ + HCO_3^- \tag{3}$$

$$HCO_3^- \overset{K_2}{\rightleftharpoons} H^+ + CO_3^{2-} \tag{4}$$

$$Ca^{2+} + CO_3^{2-} \overset{K_{sp}}{\rightleftharpoons} CaCO_3(s) \tag{5}$$

Here K_0 is the solubility of CO_2 in seawater and the other constants are the equilibrium constants governing these reactions.

Data on the solubility of CO_2 in seawater have until recently been very scarce, and usually the data of Bohr (1899) for the solubility of CO_2 in sodium chloride solutions have been applied to seawater of the same salinity (Buch et al., 1932). Li and Tsui (1971) concluded that the above procedure was correct. However, based on a more extensive set of measurements Murray and Riley (1973) found that at temperatures above 15°C, solubilities in seawater were higher by as much as 2.7%. The latter data have been selected (Table I), even though more work seems necessary to settle the disagreement between the two sets of measurements.

In principle, a dissociation reaction can be described by a thermodynamic equilibrium constant, which is a function of temperature and pressure, in conjunction with the "effective" concentrations of the various species involved in the reaction expressed in terms of activities (Lewis and Randall, 1961). The activity of an ion or a neutral dissolved species can be calculated from the actual concentration through multiplication with an appropriate activity coefficient. The values of the dissociation constants as well as those of the activity coefficients depend on the choice of the standard or reference state (Lewis and Randall, 1961). A rigorous description of the equilibria described above in terms of thermodynamic constants and species activities is an enormous task for which we are not yet adequately equipped (c.f. Edmond, 1972). Buch et al. (1932) and Moberg et al. (1934) understood this problem, and, using the concept of acidity constants introduced by Brönsted (1928), they defined "apparent dissociation constants," which describe the above equilibria in terms of the activity of the hydrogen ion and the stoichiometric concentrations of the other ions involved in these equilibria. The hydrogen ion activity is determined on the basis of a conventional pH scale, for instance that of the National Bureau of Standards (Bates, 1964). The stoichiometric concentrations represent the actual free ionic concentration of a species plus the concentrations of the various complexes with other ionic species present in the solution. Greenberg and Moberg (1932) suggested that calcium and magnesium could form complexes with carbonate ions, thus leading to the low value of about 0.02 of the apparent activity coefficient of the CO_3^{2-} ion. Buch et al. (1932) argued that this low value could be explained on the basis of the interionic interaction theory alone. Very little reliable information is available on the stability constants

TABLE I

Thermodynamic Data on CO_2 System in Seawater

	Estimated Error
$-{}^{10}\log K_1{}^1 = 3404.71/T + 0.032786T - 14.712 - 0.19178\ \mathrm{Cl}^{1/3}$	$\pm 0.01(\log K)$
$-{}^{10}\log K_2{}^1 = 2902.39/T + 0.02379T - 6.471 - 0.4693\ \mathrm{Cl}^{1/3}$	$\pm 0.03(\log K)$
$-{}^{10}\log K_B{}^1 = 2291.9/T + 0.01756T - 3.385 - 0.32051\ \mathrm{Cl}^{1/3}$	$\pm 0.02(\log K)$
$K_{sp}^{1\mathrm{Ca}} = (0.1614 + 0.02892\ \mathrm{Cl} - 0.0063t) \times 10^{-6}$	$\pm 5\%$
$K_{sp}{}^{1a} = (0.5115 + 0.02892\ \mathrm{Cl} - 0.0063t) \times 10^{-6}$	$\pm 5\%$
${}^{10}\log (K_i{}^1)_p/(K_i{}^1)_1 = -\Delta V^1(P - 1)/2.303\ RT$	
$\Delta V_1{}^1 = -(24.2 - 0.085t)\ \mathrm{cm^3/mol}$	$\pm 0.5\ \mathrm{cm^3/mol}$
$\Delta V_1{}^2 = -(16.4 - 0.040t)\ \mathrm{cm^3/mol}$	$\pm 0.5\ \mathrm{cm^3/mol}$
$\Delta V_B{}^1 = -(27.5 - 0.095t)\ \mathrm{cm^3/mol}$	$\pm 1\ \mathrm{cm^3/mol}$
$\Delta V_{Ca}{}^1 = -(47.5 - 0.23t)\ \mathrm{cm^3/mol}$	$\pm 1\ \mathrm{cm^3/mol}$
$\Delta V_a{}^1 = -(45.0 - 0.23t)\ \mathrm{cm^3/mol}$	$\pm 1\ \mathrm{cm^3/mol}$
$-{}^{10}\log (K_0) = -2622.38/T + 15.5873 - 0.0178471T + \mathrm{Cl}\,(0.0117950 + 2.77676 \times 10^{-5}T)$	

where $2.303\ RT = 5.636 \times 10^4\ \mathrm{cm^3\ atm/mol}$
P = pressure in atmospheres
T = °K
t = °C
Ca = calcite
a = aragonite
Cl = chlorinity
K_0 = solubility of CO_2 in moles/l at 1 atm partial pressure of CO_2 (data of Murray and Riley, 1971).

governing these possible complex-forming reactions, and modern interionic interaction theories can explain the results equally well without specifically invoking the concept of ion association (Millero, this volume).

For the weak acids carbonic acid and boric acid, the definitions of the apparent constants by Lyman (1957) are generally accepted

$$K_1{}^1 = \frac{a_H[HCO_3{}^-]}{\{[CO_2] + [H_2CO_3]\}} \tag{6}$$

$$K_2{}^1 = \frac{a_H[CO_3{}^{2-}]}{[HCO_3{}^-]} \tag{7}$$

$$K_B{}^1 = \frac{a_H[H_2BO_3{}^-]}{[B(OH)_3]} \tag{8}$$

where a_H is the hydrogen ion activity and the quantities in brackets represent the stoichiometric concentrations of the various species. In the definition of $K_1{}^1$, the hydrate convention (Lewis and Randall, 1961) has been invoked in which the constant K_H for the hydration reaction of CO_2 is set equal to unity. In fact, K_H is about equal to 1000 in seawater (Lyman, 1957), so that most of the undisssociated CO_2 in seawater is present as the dissolved CO_2(aq) species and not as H_2CO_3. Edmond and Gieskes (1970) pointed out that in the case of boric acid, the $H_2BO_3{}^-$ species does not really exist, but that the dissociation of boric acid occurs according to the reaction (Edwards et al., 1955; Ingri, 1963).

$$B(OH)_3 + H_2O = B(OH)_4^- + H^+ \tag{9}$$

As stoichiometric concentrations are used here, it makes no difference in what form the actual ionic species occur. One important point is that the apparent dissociation constants as defined above are not only functions of temperature and pressure, but also of the salinity of the seawater solution. This is because of ionic medium effects, that is, effects of differences in ionic strength as well as of specific ionic interactions. In fact, Disteche and Disteche (1967) found that the value of K_2^1 at a fixed salinity was also a function of the pH, showing a variation of 0.015 pK_2^1 units from pH = 7.5 to 8.5, with a minimum at pH = 8.3. Because of the constancy in composition of sea salt with respect to its major constituents (Culkin, 1965), the salinity dependence of the apparent dissociation constants can be expressed as a function of the chlorinity.

Edmond and Gieskes (1970) critically reviewed the various sets of apparent dissociation constants of carbonic acid and boric acid in seawater. Few data were available, especially as far as temperature dependence was concerned. Therefore, comparisons with infinite dilution data were made and interpolation formulas were developed that gave the most appropriate representation of the available data (Table I). Recently Hansson (1972) measured K_1^1, K_2^1, and K_B^1 for a series of salinities (20 to 40‰) and temperatures (5 to 30°C) using a slightly different pH reference scale, in which the activity coefficient of the hydrogen ion approaches unity when the concentration of H^+ approaches zero in pure synthetic seawater. A comparison of this new set of constants with the formulas presented in Table I will be given in a subsequent section.

The solubility product of calcium carbonate in seawater for the same reasons as stated for the apparent dissociation constants is expressed in terms of an apparent solubility product

$$K_{sp}^1 = [Ca^{2+}] \cdot [CO_3^{2-}] \tag{10}$$

where the terms in brackets represent the stoichiometric concentrations of calcium and carbonate ions. The values for K_{sp}^1 for both calcite and aragonite are given in Table I as functions of temperature and chlorinity (cf. Edmond and Gieskes, 1970). The useful range of these formulas is from 15 to 25‰ Cl and from 0 to 40°C. It should be emphasized that the scatter in the calcium carbonate solubility data indicates the need for additional work.

Buch and coworkers realized that pressure effects on the dissociation equilibria of carbonic acid in seawater could be appreciable. Due to lack of data, an analogy was made using acetic acid, since some pressure data were available for pure acetic acid solutions. Similarly, the effect of pressure on the solubility of calcium carbonate was ignored in earlier work. Owen and Brinkley (1941) attempted to remedy this situation, but they were not completely successful in their effort because their model pertained to calcium carbonate in sodium chloride, without the complicating effects of interionic interactions with other anions and cations in the solution. The task of the experimental determination of the pressure effects on the dissociation and solubility equilibria of carbonic acid, boric acid, and calcium carbonate was taken up by Disteche and Disteche (1967), Culberson and Pytkowicz (1968), and Hawley and Pytkowicz (1969). The pressure dependence of an apparent dissociation constant or solubility product can be represented by

$$\frac{RT\, d \ln K_i^1}{dP} = -\Delta V_i' \tag{11}$$

in analogy to the usual expression for thermodynamic constants. In this expression, $\Delta V_i'$ is an apparent partial molal volume change, which is subject to the same restrictions in its thermodynamic significance as the apparent dissociation constant. Edmond and Gieskes (1970) proposed that $\Delta V_i'$ could best be considered as a pressure coefficient, because this parameter is not rigorously defined in terms of specific chemical interactions. Millero and Berner (1972) and Duedall (1972) misinterpreted this statement by assuming that Edmond and Gieskes (1970) implied that $\Delta V_i'$ cannot be considered in terms of specific chemical interactions. In principle, this apparent partial molal volume change can be seen as the sum total of all volume changes involving all the ionic species of importance in the reaction under consideration. At present, however, we are not able to calculate $\Delta V_i'$ from first principles.

The values of the apparent partial molal volume changes of Culberson and Pytkowicz (1968) and Hawley and Pytkowicz (1969) were selected by Edmond and Gieskes (1970) despite their disagreement with the values reported by Disteche and Disteche (1967). Duedall (1972) measured the apparent partial molal volumes of K_2CO_3 and Na_2CO_3 in seawater and from these data computed the $\Delta V_i'$ for calcite in seawater at 20°C. In addition, Millero and Berner (1972) showed that the apparent partial molal volumes of the various carbonic acid species are additive and that the experimental value of calcite as determined by Hawley and Pytkowicz (1969) is in error. They also showed that Duedall's (1972) experimental work agrees well with the value of $\Delta V_2{}^1$ from Culberson and Pytkowicz (1968). At 25°C and a salinity of 35‰, the following apparent partial molal volume changes are estimated from Duedall's measurements:

$$\Delta V^1 \text{ calcite} = -41.8 \text{ cm}^3/\text{mol (25°C)}$$
$$\Delta V^1 \text{ aragonite} = -39.1 \text{ cm}^3/\text{mol (25°C)}$$

These data are distinctly different from those selected by Edmond and Gieskes (1970), and the work of Duedall (1972) suggests that more experimental evidence is necessary over a wider range of temperature and salinity on the pressure dependence of the solubility of calcium carbonate in seawater. The formulas in Table I are adjusted to the above values, assuming the temperature dependence of the $K_{sp}{}^1$ to be the same as found by Hawley and Pytkowicz (1969).

$$\Delta V^1 \text{ calcite} = -(47.5 - 0.23t) \text{ cm}^3/\text{mol} \tag{12}$$

$$\Delta V^1 \text{ aragonite} = -(45.0 - 0.23t) \text{ cm}^3/\text{mol} \tag{13}$$

From the above studies it follows that in seawater the solubility of calcium carbonate increases with a decrease in temperature and an increase in pressure. This is also true in solutions of calcium carbonate in pure water. This is of great importance with regard to the distribution of calcium carbonate in the sediments of the oceans, as will be discussed in a further section.

It should be emphasized that the apparent dissociation constants were mainly developed as a set of suitable parameters by means of which measured values of the alkalinity of seawater and its total CO_2 content can be used in the estimation of geochemically important quantities, such as the partial pressure of CO_2 or the state of saturation with respect to calcium carbonate. In order to investigate the state of saturation of interstitial waters of marine sediments, which sometimes show large deviations from the major ion composition of seawater, we need to know the apparent constants in this medium. For this, the chemical model of Garrels and Thompson (1962) is useful. In this model the speciation of all the major ionic constituents is calculated from a knowledge of the total ion concentrations and the stability constants

TABLE II

Changes in Apparent Constants as Functions of Composition at Cl = 19‰ and 25°C[a]

	Ratio of K_i^1/K_i^1 (Seawater)			
	K_1^1	K_2^1	K_B^1	$K_{sp}^{1\,Ca}$
Seawater	1.00	1.00	1.00	1.00
Seawater; no $[SO_4^{2-}]$[b]	1.03	1.07	1.03	1.01
Seawater; 0.5 × $[Mg^{2+}]$	0.91	0.72	0.91	0.67
Seawater; 0.5 × $[Ca^{2+}]$	0.98	0.98	0.98	0.97
Seawater; 2 × $[Ca^{2+}]$	1.03	1.03	1.03	1.07
Seawater; 10 × $[HCO_3^-]$	0.99	0.97	0.99	1.02

[a] After Hammond, 1973.
[b] Concentrations in brackets are "normal" seawater concentrations.

governing the ion association reactions. This model yields apparent dissociation constants for carbonic acid in seawater, the values of which depend on the choice of the stability constants (cf. Gieskes and Edmond, 1972). There is considerable disagreement about the values of these constants, particularly those governing association reactions of HCO_3^- and CO_3^{2-} ions (Nakayama, 1968, 1970; Butler and Huston, 1969) and apparent dissociation constants predicted from this model do not necessarily agree with the measured values. However, from a knowledge of the latter one can manipulate the stability constants in the model until good agreement is reached. Then the model can be used to calculate variations in the apparent constants due to changes in the composition. Hammond (1973) used a similar approach and investigated the state of saturation in the interstitial waters of Caribbean sediments. The variations in the constants (Table 2) are relatively small except in the case of magnesium depletion. Changes in K_2^1 and K_{sp}^1, however, are almost equal in sign and magnitude, so that the ratio K_2^1/K_{sp}^1 does not change by more than 10%. This ratio is of importance in the calculation of the degree of saturation of a water sample with respect to calcium carbonate. An analysis similar to that of Hammond (1973) was made by Ben-Yaakov and Goldhaber (1973).

3. Titration Alkalinity and Total CO_2 in Seawater

In the study of geochemistry of carbon dioxide in seawater, two quantities play an important role: the titration alkalinity and the total CO_2 content. In seawater there are anions of various weak acids, particularly carbonic acid, boric acid, phosphoric acid, and silicic acid that are not necessarily charge balanced by hydrogen ions, but rather by some of the major cations present in seawater, that is, sodium, magnesium, calcium, and potassium ions. This means that seawater is a base and that upon titration with a strong acid, the added hydrogen ions will balance this original "excess" of weak acid anions until the equivalence points of these acids are reached. Carbonic acid is the most prevalent weak acid in seawater and, therefore, the titration alkalinity is generally defined as the amount of strong acid, in equivalents, required to titrate 1 kg of seawater to the bicarbonate end point. Only the weak acids with dissociation constants smaller than the first dissociation constant of carbonic acid are

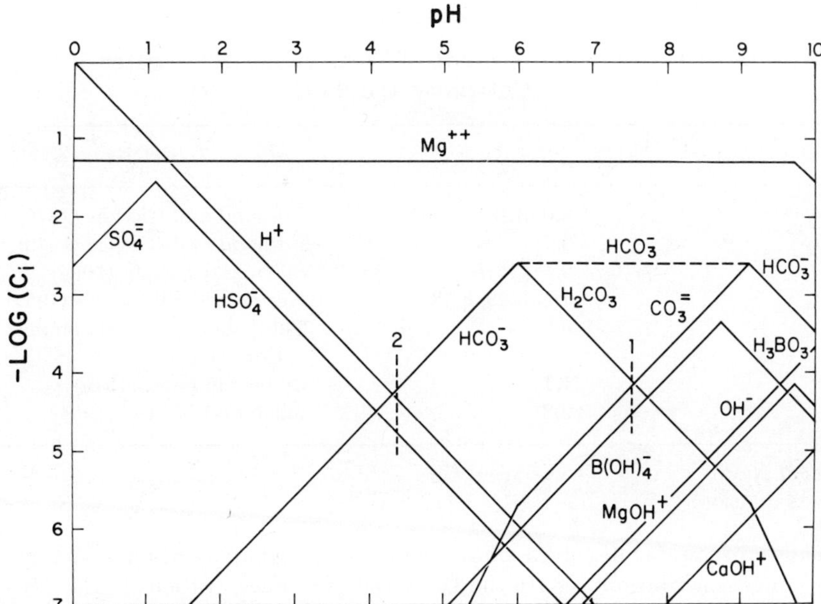

Fig. 1. Logarithmic diagram of some important species in seawater; for more detail, see Edmond (1970a); c_i = species concentration (mol/kg). (1) First equivalence point carbonic acid-proton condition (Sillén, 1959): $[CO_3{}^{2-}] + [B(OH)_4^-] = [H_2CO_3]$. (2) Second equivalence point carbonic acid-proton condition: $[HCO_3^-] = [H^+] + [HSO_4^-]$.

included (Edmond, 1970a). Rakestraw (1949) suggested the use of the Lowry-Brönsted acid base convention, and that the alkalinity be defined as the balance between the hydrated cations that act as acids (proton donors) and the anions that act as bases (proton acceptors). It is important to note that the definition of the alkalinity is empirical, that is, the second end point of the carbonic acid titration is chosen because it can be detected. Appropriate corrections must be made for the contributions of proton acceptors other than $HCO_3{}^-$ and $CO_3{}^{2-}$ in order to evaluate the contribution of the CO_2 system to the alkalinity.

The use of logarithmic equilibrium diagrams was propagated by Sillén in 1959. In complex systems such diagrams are particularly useful because at any given pH an immediate estimate can be obtained on the relative amounts of the various species present. Edmond (1970a) provided such a diagram for seawater (see Fig. 1). Seawater normally has a pH range of 7.4 to 8.3, and we can use

$$\begin{aligned} TA = {} & [HCO_3{}^-] + 2[CO_3{}^{2-}] + [B(OH)_4{}^-] \\ & + [Si(OH)_3O^-] + 2[HPO_4{}^{2-}] + 3[PO_4{}^{3-}] + [NH_3] + [OH^-] - [H^+] \end{aligned} \tag{14}$$

for the titration alkalinity. In this the contribution of ammonia is included because in anoxic waters and in interstitial waters this constituent shows appreciable concentrations. The concentrations are expressed in terms of millimoles per kilogram of seawater.

The contributions of the various species in the above equation can be evaluated from a knowledge of the total concentration of the weak acid under consideration and the apparent dissociation constants, as reported in Table III.

TABLE III

Apparent Dissociation Constants of Weak Acids in Seawater of 19‰ Chlorinity and 25°C

Acid or Base	$-\log K$	Reference
H_2CO_3	6.0, 9.1	Edmond and Gieskes (1970)
H_3BO_3	8.7	Edmond and Gieskes (1970)
H_4SiO_4	9.4[a], 12.7[a]	Sillén and Martell (1964)
H_3PO_4	1.6, 6.08, 8.58	Kester and Pytkowicz (1967)
H_2S	6.7	Goldhaber (personal communication)
H_2SO_4	1.1	Culberson et al. (1970)
NH_3	9.2[b]	Sillen and Martell (1964)

[a] In 0.5*M* NaCl.
[b] Infinite dilution.

Usually in seawater dissolved silica, inorganic phosphate, and ammonia are relatively minor contributors, as are the OH^- and H^+ concentrations in the pH range 7.4 to 8.3. The CO_2 component of the alkalinity, the carbonate alkalinity is

$$CA = [HCO_3^-] + 2[CO_3^{2-}] \tag{15}$$

and is equal to the titration alkalinity corrected for the borate contribution.

If one considers a seawater sample of a given titration alkalinity in equilibrium with the atmosphere, and the partial pressure in either phase is changed while maintaining equilibrium in the system, the seawater will gain or lose some CO_2. This will result in a change in pH because of a shift in the weak acid equilibria. The titration alkalinity, however, will not be affected, as follows from the reactions

$$\begin{aligned} CO_2 + H_2O + CO_3^{2-} &= 2HCO_3^- \\ CO_2 + B(OH)_4^- &= H_3BO_3 + HCO_3^- \end{aligned} \tag{16}$$

Only upon addition of acids stronger than carbonic acid will the titration alkalinity as defined in this section be affected. Addition of salts of acids weaker than carbonic acid will change the alkalinity. Similarly, if free ammonia (NH_3) is added, the titration alkalinity will change, addition of an ammonium salt of a strong acid will have no influence.

The carbonate alkalinity, even in cases where the titration alkalinity is constant, is a function of the state of the system. For instance, if a seawater sample is brought up from great depth and no CO_2 exchange occurs with the surroundings, the titration alkalinity and total CO_2 content are constant, whereas the carbonate alkalinity changes because of changes in pressure and temperature, and subsequently, in the weak acid anion distribution. This led Dyrssen and Sillen (1967) to advocate the use of titration alkalinity and total CO_2 as the important parameters to characterize the CO_2 system in seawater, because these parameters are chemically speaking independent variables. These variables make it possible to calculate the pH under *in situ* conditions of temperature and pressure, as will be demonstrated in the next section.

The total CO_2 content includes the carbonate, bicarbonate, and undissociated dissolved CO_2 species. In the following section, it will be shown how the titration alkalinity and the total CO_2 content can be used to calculate some important parameters in the CO_2 system. In addition, a brief discussion of methods for the determination of these quantities will be presented.

4. Computations in the Alkalinity—Total CO_2 System in Seawater

With a knowledge of the titration alkalinity and the total CO_2 content ($\sum CO_2$) we are able to evaluate the species distribution of CO_2 in seawater. This information is necessary as an intermediate step for the computation of (1) the partial pressure of $CO_2(pCO_2)$ in surface seawater, and (2) the *in situ* degree of calcium carbonate saturation (Ω) in seawater.

For this it is useful to evaluate the hydrogen ion activity for the *in situ* conditions of temperature, pressure, and salinity from

$$TA = \frac{(a_H K_1{}^1 + 2K_1{}^1 K_2{}^1)}{(a_H{}^2 + a_H K_1{}^1 + K_1{}^1 K_2{}^1)} \cdot \sum CO_2 + \frac{K_B{}^1 \sum B}{(a_H + K_B{}^1)} \tag{17}$$

where the first term on the right-hand side is equal to the carbonate alkalinity and where the bicarbonate and carbonate concentrations are expressed in terms of the total CO_2 content using equations 6, 7, and 15. The second term is the borate alkalinity, calculated from equation 8 and the total boron content ($\sum B$), which follows from the boron/chlorinity ratio of 0.23 mg/kg/Cl‰ (Culkin, 1965). Edmond and Gieskes (1970) rewrote this equation as

$$\begin{aligned} a_H{}^3 A + a_H{}^2(K_1{}^1(A-1) + K_B{}^1(A-B)) \\ + a_H(K_1{}^1 K_B{}^1(A-B-1) + K_1{}^1 K_2{}^1(A-2)) \\ + K_1{}^1 K_2{}^1 K_B{}^1(A-B-2) = 0 \end{aligned} \tag{18}$$

where $A = TA/\sum CO_2$ and $B = \sum B/\sum CO_2$.

The partial pressure of CO_2, in atmospheres, can be computed from

$$pCO_2 = \frac{\{[CO_2] + [H_2CO_3]\}}{Ko} = \frac{\sum CO_2}{Ko} \cdot \frac{a_H{}^2}{a_H{}^2 + a_H K_1{}^1 + K_1{}^1 K_2{}^1} \tag{19}$$

See equations 1, 6, and 7. Similarly, the degree of saturation with respect to calcium carbonate is

$$\Omega = \frac{[Ca^{2+}] \cdot [CO_3{}^{2-}]}{K_{sp}{}^1} = \frac{[Ca^{2+}]}{K_{sp}{}^1} \cdot \frac{K_1{}^1 K_2{}^1}{(a_H{}^2 + a_H K_1{}^1 + K_1{}^1 K_2{}^1)} \cdot \sum CO_2 \tag{20}$$

See equations 6, 7, and 10. The concentration of the calcium ions is obtained from the mean ocean calcium per chlorinity ratio of 0.0213 g/kg/Cl‰ (Culkin, 1965). This ratio varies by about 1.5% in the world ocean, a variation negligibly small compared to the errors involved in estimating the total carbonate ion concentration (see below).

The *in situ* value of a_H is of no great importance and is subject to the errors in the apparent constants, the TA, and the $\sum CO_2$. The calculation of a_H serves mainly as an intermediate step toward the computation of pCO_2 or Ω, in which the same values of the apparent dissociation constants are used. Thus use of the apparent dissociation constants from Table I or of those of Hansson (1972), although they differ in magnitude because of differences in the pH reference scales, should yield similar values for pCO_2 and Ω if the two sets of apparent constants are compatible.

To investigate this, the two sets of data have been used at 35‰ salinity and at 5, 15, and 25°C to calculate the CO_2 speciation for two typical sets of TA and $\sum CO_2$ values representative of North Atlantic surface water and North Pacific deep water, respectively (Table IV). The results show that at high pH's and low temperatures there is

TABLE IV

Comparison of Undissociated CO_2 and Total Carbonate Species Concentrations Calculated from Different Sets of Dissociation Constants at 35‰ Salinity and 5, 15, and 25°C

	mmol/kg 5°C		mmol/kg 15°C		mmol/kg 25°C	
	$[CO_2]$	$[CO_3^{2-}]$	$[CO_2]$	$[CO_3^{2-}]$	$[CO_2]$	$[CO_3^{2-}]$
TA = 2.35 meq/kg; $\sum CO_2$ = 2.00 mmol/kg						
H[a]	0.0076	0.244	0.0085	0.250	0.0095	0.256
EG[b]	0.0083	0.240	0.0087	0.243	0.0092	0.245
δ%	+9	−1.7	+2.5	−3	−3	−4.5
TA = 2.40 meq/kg; $\sum$ 2.35 mmol/kg						
H[a]	0.0460	0.0656	0.0499	0.0702	0.0536	0.0747
Eg[b]	0.0490	0.0661	0.0504	0.0682	0.0525	0.0701
δ%	+6	+0.7	+1	−3	−2	−6

[a] Hansson (1972)
[b] Edmond and Gieskes (1970).

bad agreement for pCO_2 with a possible error as large as 10% at 5°C and probably larger at lower temperatures, Hansson's data yielding lower values. At temperatures higher than 15°C the differences become small, but here the value for the solubility of CO_2 in seawater (K_0) is uncertain, since there occur systematic differences in the measured values as has been discussed previously. It follows, therefore, that the absolute accuracy in the estimation of pCO_2 from TA and $\sum CO_2$ is not better than 5% in waters with $t > 15$°C, and about 10% in waters with colder surface temperatures. In view of the importance of the partial pressure of CO_2 in air-sea interchange studies, direct measurement of pCO_2 (Keeling, 1968; Li et al., 1969) seems preferable to the estimation of this quantity from TA and $\sum CO_2$ measurements. Although Hansson's (1972) data are based on measurements over an extensive range of temperatures and salinities, some confirmation of the low-temperature work still seems warranted. This preferably should be combined with direct measurements of pCO_2.

For the computation of Ω, we are generally interested in the lower temperature range ($t < 15$°C). Agreement between calculated CO_3^{2-} concentrations is good (Table IV), and even at higher temperatures the agreement is satisfactory. In addition, any systematic change in CO_3^{2-} due to a change in K_2^1 will be reflected in the recalculated value of K_{sp}^1 in such a way that the ratio of K_2^1/K_{sp}^1 and hence Ω is affected to less than 1%. Edmond and Gieskes (1970), considering all possible errors, estimated the uncertainty in Ω to be 10%.

5. Methods

As has been discussed in the previous sections, the measurement of the titration alkalinity and the total CO_2 content provide a set of independent variables by means of which the CO_2 system in seawater can be characterized. The determination of the alkalinity can be made with good precision by means of electrometric pH measurements. The original electrometric method proposed by Anderson and Robinson (1946) has been modified by Culberson et al. (1970) to yield accurate values of the titration alkalinity (standard error about $\pm 0.3\%$), and when combined with precise pH measurements, can also yield the total CO_2 content. The latter value depends on the values chosen for K_1^1, K_2^1, and K_B^1. At a pH value of 8.2, a change in K_2^1 of 8% (equal to the uncertainty of 0.03 pK_2^1 units) causes a change in the computed $\sum CO_2$ of about 0.5% in normal seawater. Dyrssen (1965) and Edmond (1970a) described a potentiometric titration for the determination of the alkalinity and total CO_2 that yields data with an accuracy of 0.17% for the titration alkalinity and 0.65% for the total CO_2 content at the 95% confidence level. Hansson and Jagner (1973) discussed in detail the mathematical techniques used to evaluate these quantities from this titration technique. The advantage of this method is that it lends itself to complete automation.

Several excellent independent methods for the total CO_2 content are available in addition to the one described above, such as the gas chromatographic technique of Weiss and Craig (1973) and the infrared absorption technique of Broecker and Takahashi (1966). The most accurate method is the extraction method of Wong (1970), which yields accuracies of better than 0.2% (at the 95% confidence level).

The advancement of the methodologies for obtaining titration alkalinities and total CO_2 contents has yielded methods with standard deviations of 0.3% or better. Systematic errors in sampling, storage, and standardization can lead to differences as large as 5% in the various data reported (Takahashi et al., 1970). There seems, therefore, to be a good case for overdetermining the parameters in the system so that the various values for alkalinity and total CO_2 can be checked for consistency. For example, the total CO_2 content can be estimated both from a potentiometric titration and from gas chromatographic measurements.

In the following section the distribution of TA and $\sum CO_2$ will be discussed in more detail, but as the change in the deep water titration alkalinity from the North Atlantic to the North Pacific is only about 7% (about 0.15 meq/kg), an error of 1% in the estimation of the titration alkalinity can vastly affect any mass balance calculations. Thus, all efforts should be geared to obtaining data with absolute accuracies of 0.5% or better.

6. The Distribution of Alkalinity and Total CO_2 in the Oceans

In consideration of the geochemical cycles that lead to the distribution of titration alkalinity and total CO_2 in the oceans, it is appropriate to start with the input of CO_2 into the ocean via the rivers. The CO_2 dissolved in rainwater and also the CO_2 produced by soil bacteria serve as agents in the weathering reactions of carbonates, silicates, and aluminosilicates, thus causing the relatively high content of bicarbonate in river water. About 85% of this bicarbonate is derived from the weathering of carbonate rocks, the remainder from that of silicates. Garrels and Perry (this volume) provide a detailed discussion on the geochemical cycles that involve carbon dioxide. They give a total flux of dissolved and suspended inorganic carbon of 39×10^{12} mol/yr from the rivers into the ocean. The oceanic reservoir of inorganic carbon is 33×10^{17} mol, so that for a steady-state ocean the residence time of inorganic carbon is 9×10^4 yr. The removal mechanism of inorganic carbon is complex and is treated in detail by Garrels and Perry, who estimate that about 30% is deposited in the form of calcium carbonate and the remainder is returned to the atmosphere as CO_2 by "reverse weathering" reactions (Siever, 1968; Garrels and MacKenzie, 1971), such as the formation of authigenic silicates in continental shelf and deep sea sediments. The mechanism of this process is not clear (c.f. Garrels and Perry, this volume). The amount of calcium carbonate that is permanently deposited on the ocean floor is determined by the flux of calcium from the rivers, about 12×10^{12} mol/yr. The residence time of inorganic carbon (total CO_2) in the ocean is relatively short because of its activity in both inorganic and biological cycles, and a nonuniform distribution is expected. Even in the case of calcium, which has an oceanic residence time of about 12×10^5 yr (Garrels and Perry, this volume), small variations of up to 1.5% in the calcium/chlorinity ratio are found in the ocean (Tsunogai et al., 1968).

Some typical vertical distributions of temperature, salinity, titration alkalinity, and total CO_2 are presented in Fig. 2. From this it is apparent that the distribution pattern is complex. In the following paragraphs the processes that lead to these observations, that is, calcium carbonate formation and dissolution, photosynthesis, respiration, air-sea exchange, and oceanic circulation, will be discussed in some greater detail.

The main mechanism by which calcium carbonate is removed from seawater is by the formation of calcium carbonate tests of marine organisms, particularly planktonic foraminifera and calcareous nannoplankton (Berger, 1971). Other less important amounts are formed as coral reefs, or even as inorganic precipitates (Cloud, 1965; Broecker and Takahashi, 1966). The formation of calcium carbonate skeletal material and its subsequent removal by sedimentation results in a decrease in the alkalinity and total CO_2 in surface waters (Fig. 2), whereas dissolution at depth leads to increases in the quantities in the deep water. This is not immediately clear from the profiles in the North Atlantic Ocean and the Brazil Basin (Fig. 2), but this is caused by the complications introduced by oceanic circulation processes, as will be discussed presently. That dissolution of calcium carbonate at greater depths occurs in the oceans is indicated by the occurrence of a "snowline" of calcium carbonate in the sediments, that is, a depth horizon below which there occurs a sudden drop in the calcium carbonate content in recent sediments. This phenomenon was first observed during the "Challenger" expedition by Murray and Renard (1891). The depth of this snowline, the calcium carbonate compensation depth, and the processes that affect this depth will be treated in more detail in a subsequent section. Li, Takahashi, and Broecker (1969) and Berger (1970, 1971) considered the supply of calcium carbonate to the ocean floor and estimated that about 80% must redissolve at depth in order to maintain the steady state, that is, about 48×10^{12} mol/yr.

The distribution of total CO_2 is also profoundly influenced by photosynthesis and respiration. Photosynthesis is a complex biochemical process in which carbon dioxide is converted into living organic matter. For this process, nutrients are also necessary, especially nitrate (for the formation of organic nitrogen compounds) and inorganic phosphates (among others for the formation of high energy phosphates). The main "product" of photosynthesis is marine plankton, which has a fairly constant composition with respect to carbon, nitrogen, and phosphorous. The average ratio of these three elements was determined to be C:N:P = 106:16:1 (Fleming, 1940). The work of Redfield et al. (1963) and of Richards (1965) led to a stoichiometric relationship describing the photosynthetic production of average marine plankton:

$$106\,CO_2 + 122\,H_2O + 16\,HNO_3 + H_3PO_4 = (CH_2O)_{106}(NH_3)_{16}H_3PO_4 + 138\,O_2 \quad (21)$$

Respiration and decomposition by microbiological agents reverse the above process. In near-surface waters photosynthesis exceeds respiration and decomposition; the depth zone over which this is the case is often called the euphotic zone. In this zone there occurs a net depletion in CO_2, whereas deeper down in the water column

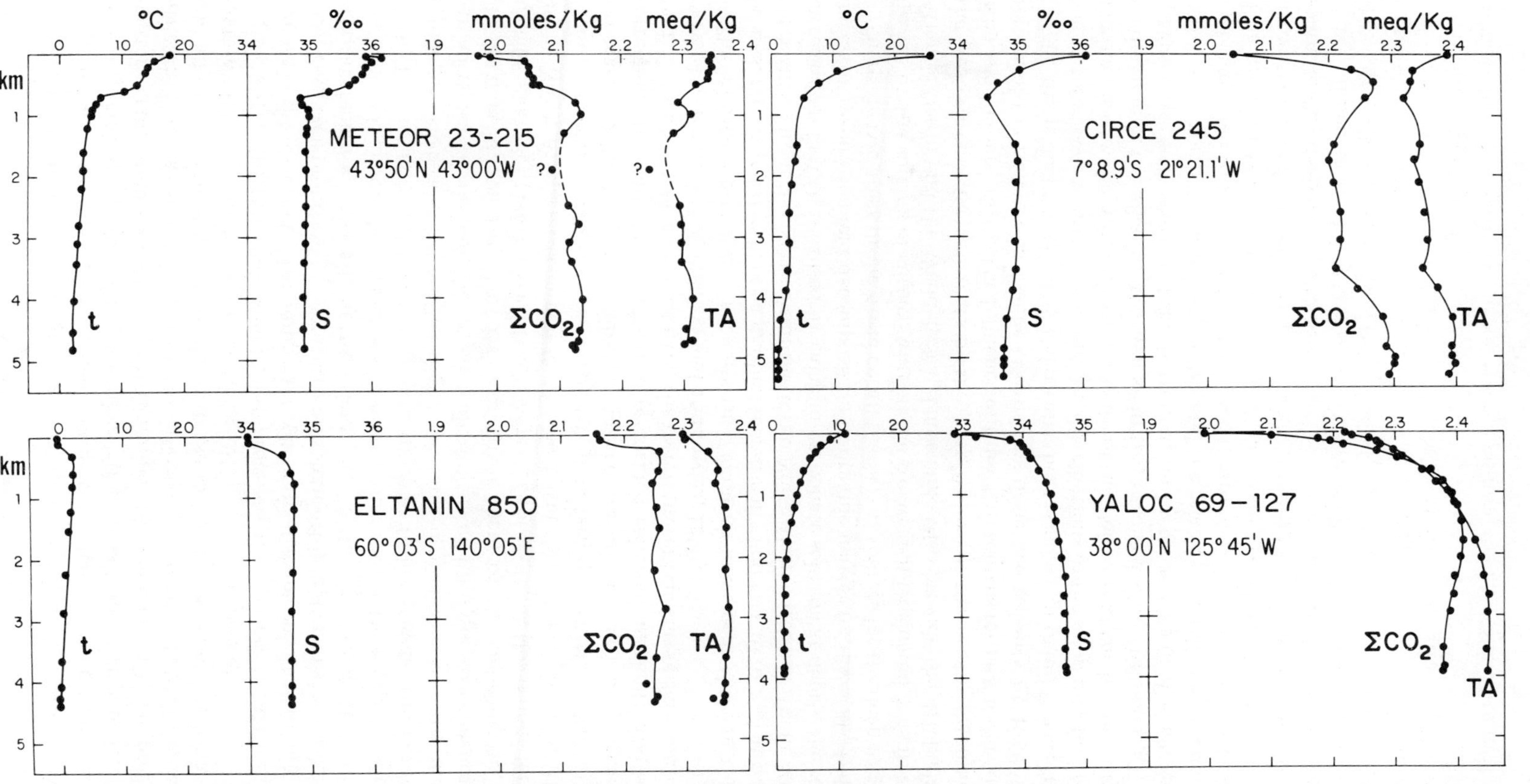

Fig. 2. Temperature, salinity, total CO_2, and titration alkalinity at representative locations in world ocean. Sources: Meteor (Gieskes, unpublished data) North Atlantic; Circe (Edmond and Gieskes, 1970) South Atlantic; Eltanin (Edmond, 1970b) Antarctic; Yaloc 69 (Culberson and Pytkowicz, 1970) North Pacific.

respiration and decomposition become more important, leading to the production of CO_2 and the consumption of oxygen. Respiration and decomposition are complex processes and of the manifold of material that constitutes living or dead organic matter, compounds containing nitrogen and phosphorous will be preferentially utilized. This was substantiated by the laboratory experiments of Kamatani (1969) and also by the observations of the increase in the C/N ratio of particulate organic matter with depth in the ocean (Gordon, 1971).

In addition to the above-mentioned processes the general circulation of water masses in the oceans plays an important role in the distribution of alkalinity and total CO_2. The given profiles of temperature and salinity (Fig. 2) demonstrate a complicated vertical structure, especially in the Atlantic and Antarctic Oceans. Much of the classical information on the various water masses that lead to these profiles is contained in the treatise of Sverdrup et al. (1942). In order to investigate whether in a given profile any variations occur other than those caused by mixing of water masses, one can normalize the data on the titration alkalinity and total CO_2 to a constant salinity (Li, Takahashi, and Broecker, 1969) or divide them by the chlorinity to yield the specific alkalinity (Wattenberg, 1933) or specific total CO_2. If this is done for the data in the North Atlantic Ocean and the Brazil Basin (Fig. 2), it is apparent that in all oceans a decrease occurs in the alkalinity of surface waters (cf. Li, Takahashi, and Broecker, 1969). These normalization procedures are not entirely justified, unless corrections are made for the so-called preformed values of alkalinity and total CO_2, that is the alkalinity and total CO_2, that were present at the surface sources of the various water masses (Culberson and Pytkowicz, 1970).

The information in Fig. 2 suggests that upon its movement through the various oceans, the deep water shows a gradual increase in alkalinity (6 to 7%) and total CO_2 (11 to 12%) from the North Atlantic to the North Pacific Oceans. About 30% of the increase in total CO_2 is caused by calcium carbonate solution at depth; the rest is produced by respiration and decomposition of organic matter (cf. Li et al., 1969).

There are two areas in the world ocean that act as sources for the deep waters of the oceans by the sinking of surface waters: the Norwegian-Greenland Seas in the North Atlantic Ocean and the Weddell Sea. These sinks also provide the driving forces for the western boundary currents in the deep waters of the oceans (Stommel, 1958; Kuo and Veronis, 1970). The influence of these two sources for new water to the deep waters of the Indian and Pacific Oceans was described recently by Reid and Lynn (1971). In the deep waters of all the oceans there is sufficient detail in the structure of the water masses to lead to nonuniform distributions of the alkalinity and total CO_2. For instance, in the Antarctic Ocean south of the Polar Front the bottom water shows a minimum in the alkalinity as well as in the dissolved silica (Edmond, 1970b). This is caused by the formation of this bottom water by the mixing of Weddell Sea surface water with North Atlantic Deep water and the relatively small deposition of calcium carbonate due to lack of calcium carbonate productivity south of the Polar Front. This Antarctic Ocean bottom water flows north into the Atlantic, where it shows the highest values of alkalinity and total CO_2 (Fig. 2) because of the low values in the south-flowing deep water. The Antarctic Ocean bottom water in the Southern Pacific shows minima in alkalinity and total CO_2 because here the south-flowing deep water shows high alkalinity and total CO_2 (Bacon and Edmond, 1972). Thus it is necessary to possess detailed information on the oceanography in a certain area of the ocean before geochemical considerations on the basis of alkalinity and total CO_2 distributions can be attempted.

There has been disagreement on where and how changes take place in the concentrations of nutrients, dissolved oxygen, alkalinity, and total CO_2. Much of the respiration and microbiological oxidation of organic matter occur in the upper layers of the ocean, causing an often sharply defined oxygen minimum, especially in areas of high productivity. This respiration and decomposition depends on the availability of organisms and of reactive organic matter. From a study of the distribution of particulate and dissolved organic carbon in the ocean, Menzel and Ryther (Menzel and Ryther, 1968, 1971; Menzel, 1970) showed a remarkable constancy of these properties below depths of a few hundred meters. This observation led them to conclude that below a depth of about 400 m no measurable amount of organic matter was consumed. As a consequence also no oxygen consumption or CO_2 production by biological degradation of organic matter would take place below this depth, thus making dissolved oxygen a conservative component in the deep ocean. The observed distribution of dissolved oxygen would then be due to advection and mixing (often called diffusion) in the deeper water layers, depending on the circulation patterns in the oceans. Williams and Gordon (1970) supported this conclusion from their studies of the carbon-13 : carbon-12 ratios in dissolved and particulate organic matter in the ocean. Riley (1970) and Gordon (1971) disputed the contention that the distribution of particulate organic carbon is constant with depth, time, and space in the deep ocean. Gordon (1971) found a significant variability in time and depth in his particulate organic carbon and nitrogen data, and in addition showed a gradual change in the C/N ratio of particulate organic matter with depth at Station Gollum off Hawaii in the North Pacific Ocean. This observation suggests that biological fractionation does occur in the deep ocean. The problem is that the various workers involved in these disputes chose different areas of the ocean and different treatments of their data, so that no unique answers can be given to the question of whether, in fact, consumption of organic matter takes place in the deep ocean. The possibility of this actually occurring in the deep ocean cannot be dismissed. Perhaps the *in situ* consumption rates are very slow and because of the existence of an almost steady state these rates cannot be measured directly. Thus the increase in CO_2 in the deep ocean is not necessarily caused only by the dissolution of calcium carbonate from the sea floor and the advection of CO_2 from the oxygen minimum layers, but some CO_2 may be produced *in situ* by the combustion of organic matter.

Another way to establish whether an input of CO_2 caused by *in situ* dissolution of calcium carbonate or combustion of organic matter takes place in deep waters is by means of mass balance calculations. In the Atlantic Ocean such calculations are difficult, but in the deep waters of the Pacific Ocean this is possible. In the South Pacific Ocean a salinity maximum occurs in the deep water, the origins of which can be traced to the high salinity water that sinks down in the Norwegian-Greenland Seas (Reid and Lynn, 1971). This maximum gradually dissipates due to mixing with bottom waters and overlying intermediate waters, and disappears at about 9°S in the Pacific Ocean. The bottom water retains different characteristics with respect to temperature, silicate, and alkalinity, as described by Edmond et al. (1971), Craig et al. (1972), and Bacon and Edmond (1972). A discontinuity layer ("benthic front") has been demonstrated to exist over a large area in the southern Pacific Ocean. This front separates the deep water from the bottom water, and along it strong horizontal mixing takes place. Above this benthic front the deep water was demonstrated to be essentially a linear mixture of water advected along this front and overlying intermediate water (Craig et al., 1972). Any vertical profile through this deep water is characterized by a linear potential temperature (Θ)-salinity (S) relationship, the boundary values of which are determined by the characteristics of waters in the benthic front and the intermediate water at that point. If linear mixing of two or more water masses has led to such a relationship, then all other properties must also show a linear relationship with either potential temperature or salinity. Deviations from linearity must be attributed to production or consumption within the water column for which the linear potential temperature-salinity relationship is valid. On this basis, Bacon and Edmond (1972) showed that alkalinity is conservative within the deep water of the South Pacific and that dissolution of calcium carbonate within the column of deep water is negligible. On the other hand, Craig (1971) and Craig et al. (1972) showed that oxygen and total CO_2 were nonconservative in this region.

In a water column, characterized by a linear Θ-S relationship, the vertical distribution of various conservative and nonconservative properties can formally be described by simple vertical advection and mixing models (Wyrtki, 1962; Munk, 1966; Craig, 1969). As pointed out by Craig et al. (1972), these models assume that horizontal advection in the interior of the mixing interval is negligible, and that their validity can be questioned until more is known about the actual physical processes that lead to the mixing in the deep water under consideration. Mass balance considerations are not dependent on such models, but only on the condition that the linear Θ-S relation is caused by the mixing of well-defined water types (cf. Sverdrup et al., 1942).

As an illustration, stations off the coasts of California and Peru have been chosen (Culberson and Pytkowicz, 1970). Below a certain depth the deep water is characterized by a linear Θ-S diagram (Fig. 3). The potential temperature-alkalinity relations are essentially linear, that is, within the precision of the data, whereas this is not true for total CO_2. Thus, if the deep water is affected by mixing processes only, production of CO_2 must take place in the water column. Simultaneous consumption of oxygen (which was measured but is not shown here) suggests that this CO_2 input is from metabolic processes. For both stations, the Θ-S diagram is linear to the bottom, which precludes a meaningful use of vertical advection-mixing models that require negligible horizontal advection. Horizontal advection of water mass characterized by potential temperatures and salinities such that they would give perfect linearity on a Θ-S diagram, but not on a Θ-total CO_2 diagram is possible although highly unlikely. The conclusion is, therefore, that metabolism does indeed affect the distribution of oxygen and total CO_2 in deep waters. The diagrams in Fig. 3 show that off the coast of South America the production of CO_2 from biological degradation of organic matter within the water column is very small, tentatively supporting the conclusions of Menzel and Ryther (1971) for the region to the south of this station. Off the coast of California, however, *in situ* deep metabolism is quite important, but no data are available on the vertical distribution of particulate and dissolved organic carbon in the region of the station under consideration.

The above considerations indicate that in some areas of the ocean CO_2 production due to deep metabolism can be significant, whereas in other areas this is not the case. Until now no method has been able to show, without making certain assumptions, that biological decomposition has a significant effect. Also, the number of stations with detailed and accurate data are still too small to make any estimates as to the regional aspects of this problem. Whereas carbon dioxide can be produced *in-situ* in deep waters by metabolic processes, the evidence is strong that alkalinity is "conservative" in deep water and only is affected significantly by dissolution of calcium carbonate at the sediment water interface.

Aspects of the distribution of CO_2 in surface waters and the distribution of alkalinity and total CO_2 in anoxic waters and sediments will be treated in subsequent sections.

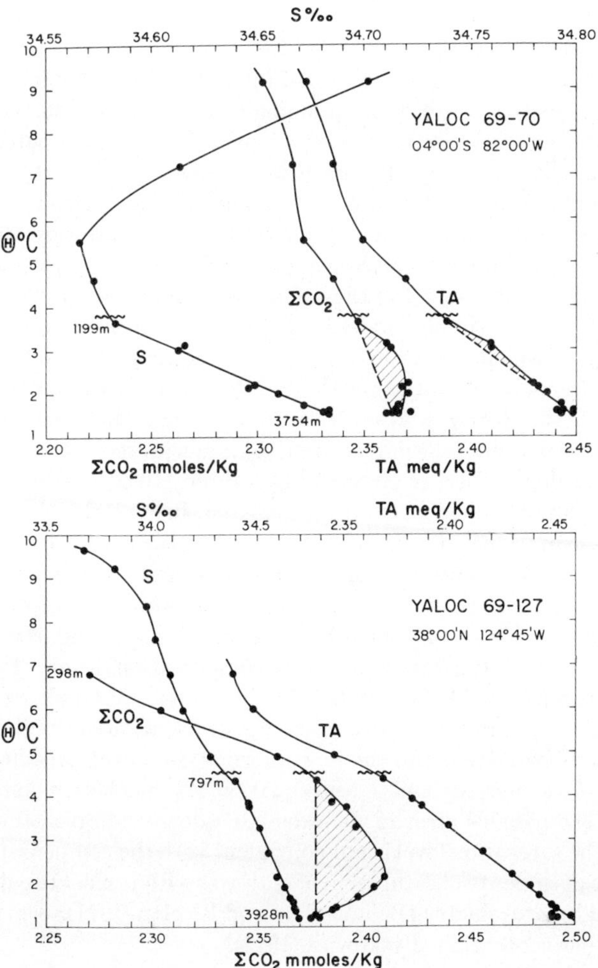

Fig. 3. Potential temperature versus salinity, total CO_2, and titration alkalinity for two Yaloc stations. Culberson and Pytkowicz (1970).

7. Sedimentation and Dissolution of Calcium Carbonate—The Calcium Carbonate Compensation Depth

Section 6 showed that the formation and sedimentation of calcium carbonate skeletons of marine organisms profoundly affect the distribution of the titration alkalinity in the ocean. As much as 80% of the calcium carbonate sedimented must redissolve in the deep ocean. From mass balance considerations it appears that little or no dissolution occurs within the deep water column, but that alkalinity is "conservative" in the deep water and only increases because of dissolution of calcium carbonate at the sediment-water interface. More observations, particularly in areas of high calcium carbonate productivity, may modify these views, but most information available supports this. In the oceans this is reflected by the existence of a depth horizon below which a drastic decrease occurs in the calcium carbonate content of deep sea sediments. Below this horizon the sedimentation of calcium carbonate may be said to be compensated by its removal. In this section the origin and nature of the "compensation depth" will be considered in more detail.

In the section on the thermodynamics of the CO_2 system it was observed that calcium carbonate has the property of becoming increasingly soluble with a decrease in temperature and an increase in pressure (depth). Sillén (1967) noted that if, in an isothermal stagnant ocean, equilibrium between seawater and calcium carbonate on the bottom would exist, that then only the bottom water would be saturated with respect to calcium carbonate because of gravitational and pressure effects. If such an ocean would be stirred up, thus advecting waters from lesser depths, the lower layers would become undersaturated and the upper layers supersaturated. This observation immediately suggests a simple model in which the compensation depth is identified with the depth at which the water becomes undersaturated with respect to calcium carbonate. It is postulated that below this depth removal of calcium carbonate by dissolution exceeds the incrementation by sedimentation. This model can be critically tested by the calculation of the degree of saturation with respect to calcium carbonate as a function of depth. Berner (1965) and Lyakhin (1968) observed that these two depth horizons did not coincide. On the other hand, Li et al. (1969) concluded that the marked decrease in the calcium carbonate content in the sediments reflects the transition of the overlying seawater from saturation to undersaturation with respect to calcite. More accurate data on the distribution of alkalinity and total CO_2, as well as on the pressure dependence of the solubility of calcite, have reinforced the conclusions of the nonidentity of the saturation and compensation levels (Pytkowicz, 1970; Edmond and Gieskes, 1970; Edmond, 1972). Edmond and Gieskes (1970) computed the degree of saturation with respect to calcite for a station in the Brazil Basin in the South Atlantic Ocean. Here also the new information on the pressure dependence of the solubility of calcium carbonate (see equation 12), has been taken into consideration (Fig. 4). The possible error in the calculated degree of saturation is about 10%. The depth of the saturation level is not coincident with the compensation level. Direct measurements of the state of saturation of seawater with respect to calcite by means of *in situ* carbonate saturometry (Ben-Yaakov and Kaplan, 1971) seem too inconclusive to support either contention (Pytkowicz, 1972).

The depth control on the calcium carbonate compensation level may be due to kinetic factors, which, among others, can involve difference in rates of supply, in bottom currents, and in sedimentation conditions. Peterson (1966) and Berger (1967) carried out *in situ* experiments in which calcite spheres and also foraminifera were suspended at various depths in a water column in the Pacific Ocean (18°49′N 168°31′ W). It was found that at a depth of about 3700 m a sudden increase occurred in the rate of dissolution of the calcite spheres. Peterson concluded that the position of the compensation depth may be due to such a sharply increased rate of dissolution. Edmond et al. (1971) showed that in this region a "benthic thermocline" occurs at about the same depth. This thermocline also defines the location of the "benthic front" described by Craig et al. (1972). Thus, a straightforward explanation of the sharp increase in the rate of solution of the calcite spheres is a change in the current regime associated with the above hydrographic features. Much research, however, is still required to investigate the various phenomena that affect the rate of dissolution of calcium carbonate, especially under oceanic conditions (c.f. Suess, 1970; Morse and Berner, 1972).

Usually the calcium carbonate compensation is determined from the percentage of calcium carbonate in the surface sediments (Bramlette, 1961). Heath and Culberson (1970) pointed out that a more appropriate measure would be a comparison of the

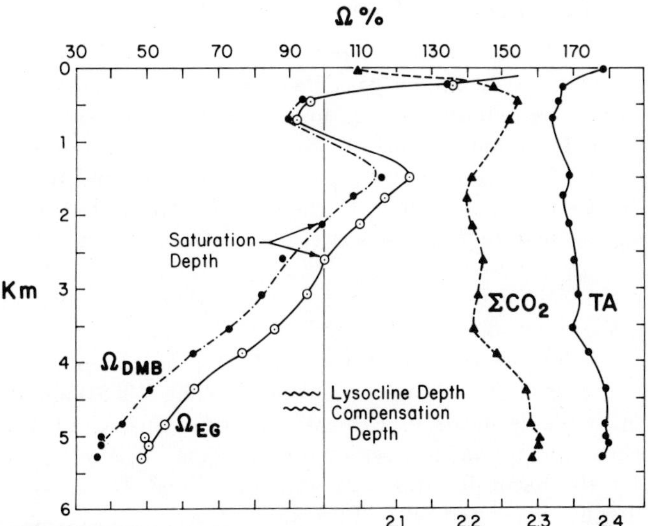

Fig. 4. Total CO_2, titration alkalinity, and degree of saturation with respect to calcite—Circe 245, 7°9′S 21°21′W. Ω EG = Edmond and Gieskes (1970); Ω DMB = Ω EG recalculated using data of Table I.

rate of dissolution with the rate of supply of calcium carbonate. Berger (1971) calculated the amount of calcium carbonate lost by dissolution in terms of the percentage of insoluble residue in the sediment. He showed that whether one assumes a linear increase in the rate of dissolution with depth or an increase in these rates similar to that reported by Peterson (1966), a depth distribution of calcium carbonate in sediments would be obtained similar to the one actually observed (Turekian, 1965).

Another method of looking at the dissolution of calcium carbonate skeletons is the study of the differential solution of planktonic foraminifera (Ruddiman and Heezen, 1967). In these studies comparative studies are made of the solution effects on the various species in an assemblage of sedimented foraminifera. Berger (1970, 1971) made similar extensive studies and observed that there occurs a depth range, the lysocline, over which a rapid change occurs in the so-called solution index of foraminifera. This index gives a relative measure of the abundance of the easier dissolvable species versus the more resistant ones. Studies on the foraminiferal assemblages in the core tops can yield far more information on solution processes than a simple study of the calcium carbonate content. In fact, Berger (1971) was able to show that in some areas, especially the fertile, tropical Pacific Ocean, a pronounced divergence in the depth ranges of the lysocline and the compensation depth does occur. Under fertile regions, relatively more organic matter is deposited, so microbiological degradation can supply additional CO_2. The addition of CO_2 can again cause greater dissolution of the more readily dissolvable foraminiferal tests (Gieskes, 1970; Berger, 1971). Consequently, one observes an increase in the compensation depth due to increased supply and a decrease in the lysocline depth due to increased dissolution. In other areas of the ocean, differences between the position of the calcite compensation depth and the lysocline are less marked (Parker and Berger, 1971). The positions of both lysocline and compensation depth are by no means static, but can vary considerably through time (Berger, 1972) in response to as yet unexplained variations in ocean chemistry, current regimes, and rates of supply.

8. CO_2 in Surface Waters—Air-Sea Interchange

The distribution of CO_2 in surface waters is governed by six principal processes: photosynthesis, calcium carbonate formation as tests of marine organisms, and such advective processes as upwelling, temperature changes, evaporation, and precipitation. Much work has been done recently to study the distribution of CO_2 in surface waters using the partial pressure of CO_2 as a measure (Keeling and Waterman, 1968; Keeling, 1968; Kelley and Hood, 1971; Büchen, 1971). These studies have demonstrated that equilibrium rarely exists between the CO_2 in the atmosphere and in surface waters.

Postma (1964) made an extensive analysis of the exchange of oxygen and carbon dioxide between the ocean and atmosphere based on data obtained in the Pacific Ocean along two north-south sections. He was able to provide tentative patterns of areas that act as sources of CO_2 to the atmosphere. Keeling (1968) summarized much of the information available on the direct measurements of the partial pressure of CO_2 by previous workers and by his own research group (Fig. 5). More recent data will refine this map, but the essential features are well represented. The areas designated as "highs" are generally associated with divergence or coastal upwelling zones. The "lows" occur in regions where cooling and sinking are of importance, for instance, the Norwegian-Greenland Seas, the Weddell Sea, and the region east of Japan, where significant cooling occurs of warm waters transported in the Kuroshio Current (Keeling and Waterman, 1968). All of the above six processes affect the measured pCO_2 distributions, and from Fig. 5 it is clear that air-sea exchange of CO_2 is sufficiently slow to maintain a disequilibrium over much of the ocean's surface. To estimate the magnitude of the effects of the various processes listed above, a detailed knowledge is necessary on the thermodynamics of the CO_2 system in seawater. As was shown in Section 4, the uncertainties in the apparent dissociation constants are too large for this purpose. More work is necessary emphasizing direct relationships between titration alkalinity, total CO_2 and pCO_2 as functions of temperature and salinity.

One of the principal problems in the study of the CO_2 system is to identify areas where the ocean can serve as a possible sink for atmospheric CO_2. This is of particular interest because of the need to find the nature and location of the sink for the excess CO_2 injected into the atmosphere by the combustion of fossil fuel (Broecker et al., 1971; Machta, 1972). Somewhat less than half of the CO_2 produced by fossil fuel remains in the atmosphere. Hence, there must exist an efficient sink for CO_2 in the ocean or elsewhere.

The surface mixed layer of the ocean contains about the same amount of total CO_2 as the atmosphere, 5×10^{16} mol. Intermediate waters contain roughly 18×10^{16} mol, and the deep ocean contains 300×10^{16} mol (c.f. Machta, 1972). Communication between these reservoirs is slow, particularly between the mixed layer and the deep ocean. In addition, the fractional change in the pCO_2 is about 10 times greater than the fractional change in the total CO_2 in the mixed layer (Bolin and Eriksson, 1959; Machta, 1972).

$$\frac{\delta pCO_2}{pCO_2} = \frac{10\,\delta \sum CO_2}{\sum CO_2} \tag{22}$$

Thus the surface waters of the oceans show a strong buffering effect against uptake of CO_2; an 11% increase in CO_2 in the atmosphere will cause a loss of only 1% to the ocean, the remainder will stay in the atmosphere. The observed removal of more than

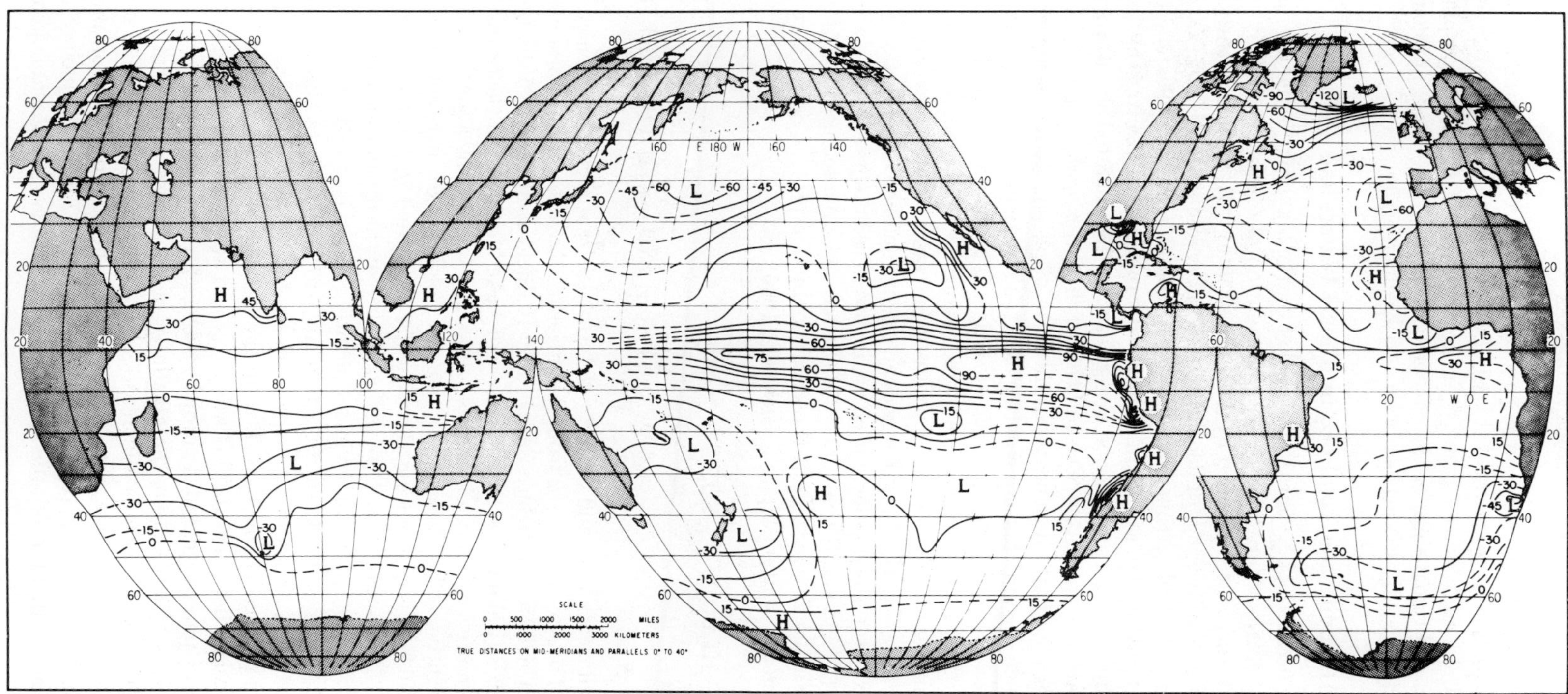

Fig. 5. The distribution of pCO_2 of the world's oceans expressed as departures in parts per million from equilibrium with atmospheric CO_2. H indicates high, L indicates low. After Keeling (1968), with the permission of the American Geographical Union.

50% of the excess fossil fuel CO_2 can in part be explained by the participation of the intermediate layers in the removal of this CO_2, which increases the exchange reservoir about fivefold. In addition, an increase in productivity of the land biosphere can account for an additional sink for the excess atmospheric CO_2. These problems have been discussed in detail by Machta (1972) and Keeling (1973).

9. Alkalinity and Total CO_2 in Anoxic Waters and Sediments

In the open ocean the only measurable effect on the alkalinity is the precipitation or dissolution of calcium carbonate. The degradation of organic matter by oxygen-requiring organisms is accompanied by a change in total CO_2, but not in the titration alkalinity. If the final product of decomposition of organic matter is not CO_2 but CO or some other gas (Seiler, this volume) this becomes more complicated, but the amounts of CO produced in the ocean are generally rather small. During the decomposition of organic matter, nutrients are released ("regenerated"), in particular, inorganic nitrate and phosphate. The addition of the latter could, in principle, lead to a change in the alkalinity, depending on the form of phosphate released. Concentrations in the open ocean (less than 3 μM/kg) are too low to have a significant effect.

In anoxic waters and sediments the situation is rather different. Here further oxidation of organic matter takes place by means of sulfate-reducing microorganisms. This organic matter usually does not have the same composition as "average" marine plankton (see equation 21). Very few measurements on the C:N:P ratio of organic matter in anoxic water bodies have been made, but in sediments this ratio was shown to be variable (Emery and Rittenberg, 1952; Bader, 1955; Arrhenius, 1963; Hartmann et al., 1973). Similar to equation 21 the sulfate reduction process can be summarized by a stoichiometric relationship (c.f. Richards, 1965):

$$(CH_2O)_x(NH_3)_y(H_3PO_4)_z + \frac{x}{2}SO_4{}^{2-} =$$
$$xCO_2 + \frac{x}{2}S^{2-} + yNH_3 + zH_3PO_4 + xH_2O \quad (23)$$

where the coefficients x, y, and z can be determined by direct measurements of the composition of organic matter, or from the ratios in which the various products occur in the water. The latter procedure was used by Redfield at al. (1963) in the Black Sea and by Richards (1965) in the anoxic waters of Lake Nittinat and the Saanich Inlet. This method, however, is not reliable, as several products of the above reactions will not be conservative in an anoxic environment. For instance, particularly in anoxic sediments, sulfides disappear from the aqueous phase due to the formation of iron sulfides and of elemental sulfur. Also, the possibility of the dissolution or precipitation of calcium carbonate, particularly in sediments, cannot be ruled out (Presley and Kaplan, 1968; Gieskes, 1973; Hartmann et al., 1973, Sholkovitz, 1973). Inorganic phosphate has been observed to increase in anoxic basins in "excess" of values expected from any reasonable C:N:P ratio (Fonselius, 1969; Gieskes and Grasshoff, 1969; Gaines and Pilson, 1972). This was suggested to be caused by the dissolution of some form of phosphate, but no direct evidence for this was found.

In general it is observed that the alkalinity of anoxic waters and of interstitial waters of anoxic recent sediments increases above that normally found in seawater. This is mainly because of the proteolytic effect of the sulfate reduction process in which an anion of a weak acid (hydrogen sulfide) is formed from an anion of a strong acid (sulfuric acid). In addition, the formation of ammonia and inorganic phosphate, as well as the dissolution or precipitation or carbonates and phosphates, affect these observed alkalinity changes.

Several models have been proposed to explain variations in the alkalinity on the basis of observed changes in dissolved sulfide, ammonia, and alkaline earth elements (Knull and Richards, 1969; Gaines and Pilson, 1972). Such models are moderately successful in anoxic basins and fjords, where no significant removal of dissolved sulfides has taken place. In anoxic sediments, however, they do not give correct predictions, particularly because of the extensive formation of iron sulfides. Berner, Scott, and Thomlinson (1970) proposed to use the change in dissolved sulfate instead of in dissolved sulfide. They argued that the formation of iron monosulfide and pyrite woud not lead to a change in alkalinity, a contention that it is not necessarily true. For instance, Drever (1971) explained the formation of pyrite in sediments in a different manner than Berner et al. (1970) and predicted a change in alkalinity.

If, in anoxic sediments, the products of diagenetic changes, for instance, iron sulfides, authigenic silicates, and carbonate, have been identified, a model can be developed that explains observed changes in alkalinity, total CO_2, calcium, sulfate, and other reactive components. In general, such information is lacking. This makes the above models only tentative (c.f. Gieskes, 1973; Hartmann et al., 1973, Sholkovitz, 1973).

Also, serious complications arise in studies of the alkalinity and total CO_2 of interstitial waters because of pressure and temperature changes in the core during and after retrieval. Temperature effects, although small, were shown to be of importance (Gieskes, 1973). Pressure effects have not been studied but are probably important. Data obtained on deep sea cores suggest that equilibrium exists between interstitial water and calcite in sediments (Gieskes, 1973; Hammond, 1973; Hartmann et al., 1973). Thus, if estimates can be made of the *in situ* values of dissolved calcium and alkalinity, the pH of interstitial water can be calculated at the *in situ* temperature and pressure. This information is necessary in equilibrium calculations in sediment-interstitial water systems.

10. Summary and Conclusions

Because of its geochemical importance in the major sedimentary cycle, the study of the distribution of carbon dioxide in the ocean is of great interest. Even more important is a better understanding of the processes that lead to this distribution. The most useful parameters for such a study are the total CO_2 content and the titration alkalinity. Not only can changes in these be interpreted in terms of major chemical processes occurring in the oceans, but they also characterize the CO_2 system in seawater.

From our present knowledge of the distribution of the total CO_2 and the titration alkalinity of the ocean, it appears that variations of these quantities are relatively small, that is, 11 to 12% and 6 to 7%, respectively (Fig. 2). Therefore a study of the global distribution of these parameters, particularly in deep waters, requires accurate measurements. Precise methods are presently available, but great care is needed in sampling, sample preservation, and standardization. Accuracies are not yet well specified, and until now there has been little agreement between methods. It is, therefore, good policy to overdetermine the system so that titration alkalinity and/or total CO_2 can be obtained in several ways.

Many processes influence the total CO_2, the alkalinity, and the oxygen distributions in the ocean. Concentrations of CO_2 are affected by photosynthesis, respiration and decomposition of organic matter, air-sea interchange, and precipitation and dissolution of calcium carbonate. The last two processes also influence the alkalinity. In addition, cooling and warming, precipitation and evaporation, and oceanic circulation are of great importance.

Considerable debate exists about where production of CO_2 by biological decomposition of organic matter takes place. Data on the distribution of particulate and dissolved organic carbon in some areas of the ocean suggest that all or most of the decomposition takes place in the first few hundred meters below the surface, but that below these depths oxygen is essentially conservative. On the other hand, mass balance considerations in other areas of the oceans suggest that significant amounts of CO_2 are produced by deep metabolism, that is, biological decomposition at greater depths. There appear to be geographical aspects to this problem, and, in addition, all methods that are used to establish the existence or nonexistence of deep metabolic CO_2 input are necessarily subject to assumptions. It is very important to decide how much, if any, oxygen is consumed in the deep waters by these processes.

Observations on the distribution of the titration alkalinity suggest that this parameter is essentially "conservative" in deep water, that is, no significant dissolution of calcium carbonate occurs in the deep water column. Most of the increase in alkalinity of deep waters is caused by the dissolution of calcium carbonate skeletons of planktonic foraminifera and calcareous nannoplankton after they have reached the bottom by sedimentation. Geochemical considerations based on the accumulation of alkalinity and total CO_2 in the deep Pacific lead to the conclusion that about 80% of the calcium carbonate formed in the surface waters dissolves in the deep ocean after sedimentation. The remainder, which is equivalent to the flux of calcium in the rivers, is permanently deposited in the sediments.

Studies of the depths at which the ocean becomes undersaturated with respect to calcite indicate that this "saturation depth" horizon is usually above the calcite "compensation depth" horizon. The latter is determined by the depths below which calcium carbonate rapidly vanishes as a sediment component. The origin of the compensation depth is kinetic and the depth is determined by the equality of the rates of sedimentation and of dissolution. Among the kinetic factors influencing the position of the compensation depth, deep currents are of great importance. The observation of the existence of a lysocline, that is, a depth horizon below which easier dissolvable species vanish from a sedimented foraminiferal assemblage, indicates the complicated nature of the kinetic processes involved. Studies of the reasons why some species dissolve easier than others, chemical, biological, or physical, will enable a better understanding of the origins of the compensation depth. Very few studies of this type have hitherto been made.

The investigation of the distribution of the partial pressure of CO_2 in surface waters can identify sources or sinks of atmospheric CO_2. This is of particular importance in the search for the sinks for the excess input of CO_2 into the atmosphere due to fossil fuel combustion. Data presently available suggest areas around the equator and in the high latitudes as potential sources of atmospheric CO_2, whereas particularly the subtropical gyres in the oceans constitute sinks. More accurate data are necessary on the thermodynamics of the CO_2 system in seawater in order to unravel the various factors that influence the distribution of pCO_2 in surface waters.

Studies of the thermodynamics of the CO_2 system in seawater have relied mainly on the description of the equilibria in terms of stoichiometric concentrations and apparent dissociation constants. This approach is necessarily empirical in nature and is not founded on a rigorous thermodynamic basis. It leads to a set of parameters that are useful in the estimation of equilibrium values of pCO_2 in seawater of a given temperature, salinity, titration alkalinity, and total CO_2. In addition, the stoichiometric carbonate ion concentration can be estimated, which is useful in studies of the state of saturation of seawater with respect to calcium carbonate. Data available are of sufficient accuracy to calculate the degree of saturation with respect to calcite to within 10%, but for accurate estimates of pCO_2 from titration alkalinity and total CO_2 the apparent constants are not reliable.

More work seems necessary on the thermodynamics of the CO_2 system with a particular emphasis on a more rigorous thermodynamic description of these equilibria. This will be of special importance in detailed studies of the solution kinetics of calcium carbonate in seawater. Such studies must be carried out with emphasis on oceanic conditions of temperature and pressure in order to understand better the kinetic processes that lead to the lysocline and the compensation depth of calcium carbonate in the ocean.

Acknowledgments

I am indebted to Drs. John Edmond, Wolfgang Berger, and David Keeling for many suggestions and improvements of the manuscript, to Dr. Ted Warner for his continuous interest during the drafting of this chapter, and to Dr. A. B. Hastings for reading the manuscript and to making some useful suggestions.

References

Anderson, D. H. and R. J. Robinson, 1946. Rapid electrometric determination of the alkalinity of seawater. *Ind. Eng. Chem.*; *Anal. Ed.*, **18**, 767–769.

Arrhenius, G., 1963. Pelagic Sediments. In The Sea. Vol. 1, M. N. Hill, ed. Wiley-Interscience, New York, pp. 655–727.

Bacon, M. P. and J. M. Edmond, 1972. Barium at Geosecs III in the Southwest Pacific. *Earth and Planet Sci. Letters,* **16**, 66–74.

Bader, R. G., 1955. Carbon and nitrogen relations in surface and subsurface marine sediments. *Geochim. Cosmochim. Acta,* **7**, 205–211.

Bates, R. G., 1946. *Determination of pH, Theory and Practice.* Wiley, New York, 435 pp.

Ben-Yaakov, S. and I. R. Kaplan, 1971. Deep sea calcium carbonate saturometry. *J. Geophys. Res.,* **76**, 722–731.

Ben-Yaakov, S. and M. B. Goldhaber, 1973. The influence of sea water composition on the apparent constants of the carbonate system. *Deep Sea Res.,* **20**, 87–99.

Berger, W. H., 1967. Foraminiferal ooze: solution at depths. *Science,* **156**, 383–385.

Berger, W. H., 1970. Biogenous deep-sea sediments: fractionation by deep-sea circulation. *Geol. Soc. Am. Bull.,* **81**, 1385–1402.

Berger, W. H., 1971. Sedimentation of planktonic foraminifera. *Marine Geol.,* **11**, 325–328.

Berger, W. H., 1972. Deep-sea carbonates: dissolution facies and age-depth constancy. *Nature,* **236**, 392–395.

Berner, R. A., 1965. Activity coefficients of bicarbonate, carbonate, and calcium ions in seawater. *Geochim. Cosmochim. Acta,* **29**, 947–965.

Berner, R. A., M. R. Scott, and C. Thomlinson, 1970. Carbonate alkalinity in the pore waters of anoxic marine sediments. *Limnol. Oceanog.,* **15**, 544–549.

Bohr, C., 1899. Definition and Methode zur Bestimmung der Invasions-und Evasions Koeffizienten bei der Auflösung von Gasen in Flüssigkeiten. *Ann. Phys. Chem.,* **68**, 500–525.

Bolin, B. and E. Eriksson, 1959. Changes in the carbon dioxide content of the atmosphere and the sea due to fossil fuel combustion. Rossby Memorial Volume, B. Bolin, ed., Rockefeller Institute Press, New York, pp. 130–142.

Bramelette, M. N., 1961. Pelagic sediments. In *Oceanography.* M. Sears, ed., AAAS, Washington, D.C., pp. 345–366.

Broecker, W. S. and T. Takahashi, 1966. Calcium carbonate precipitation on the Bahama Banks. *J. Geophys. Res.,* **71**, 1575–1602.

Broecker, W. S., Y. H. Li, and T. H. Peng, 1971. Carbon dioxide—Man's unseen artifact. In *Impingement of Man on the Oceans*, D. W. Hood, ed. Wiley-Interscience, New York, pp. 287–324.

Brönsted, J. N., 1928. Acid and base catalysis. *Chem. Rev.*, **5**, 231–338.

Bruneau, L., N. G. Jerlov, and F. F. Koczy, 1953. Physical and chemical methods. In *Reports of the Swedish Deep Sea Expedition*. Elanders, Göteborg, Vol. 3, pp. 99–112.

Buch, K., 1917. Über die Alkalinität, Wasserstoffionenkonzentration, Kohlensäure, und Kohlensäure-tension in Wasser der Finnland umgebenden Meere. *Finnl. hydrogr.-biolog. Untersuchungen*, No. 14, Helsingfors.

Buch, K., H. W. Harvey, H. Wattenberg, and S. Gripenberg, 1932. Über dem Kohlensäuresystem im Meerwasser. *Rapp. Proc. Verb. C.P.I.E.M.*, **79**, 1–70.

Büchen, M., 1971. Ergebnisse der CO_2-Konzentrationsmessung in der ozeannahen Luftschicht und im Oberflachenwasser während der Atlantischen Expedition 1969. "*Meteor*" *Forsch. Ergeb.*, **B7**, 55–70.

Butler, J. N. and R. Huston, 1969. Activity coefficients and ion pairs in the system sodium chloride-sodium bicarbonate-water and sodium chloride-sodium carbonate-water. *J. Phys. Chem.*, **74**, 2976–2983.

Cloud, P. E., 1965. Carbonate precipitation and dissolution in the marine environment. In *Chemical Oceanography*. Vol. 2. J. P. Riley and G. Skirrow, eds. Academic Press, New York, pp. 127–156.

Craig, H., 1969. Abyssal Carbon and radiocarbon in the Pacific. *J. Geophys. Res.*, **74**, 5491–5506.

Craig, H., 1970. Abyssal carbon-13 in the South Pacific. *J. Geophys. Res.*, **75**, 691–695.

Craig, H., 1971. The deep metabolism: oxygen consumption in abyssal ocean water. *J. Geophys. Res.*, **76**, 5078–5086.

Craig, H., Y. Chung, and M. Fiadeiro, 1972. A benthic front in the South Pacific. *Earth and Planet Sci. Letters*, **16**, 50–65.

Culberson, C. and R. M. Pytkowicz, 1968. Effect of pressure on carbonic acid, boric acid, and the pH in seawater. *Limnol. Oceanog.*, **13**, 403–417.

Culberson, C. and R. M. Pytkowicz, 1970. Oxygen-total carbon dioxide correlation in the eastern Pacific Ocean. *J. Oceanogr. Soc. Japan*, **26**, 95–100.

Culberson, C., R. M. Pytkowicz, and J. E. Hawley, 1970. Seawater alkalinity determination by the pH method. *J. Mar. Res.*, **28**, 15–21.

Culkin, F., 1965. The major constituents of seawater. In *Chemical Oceanography*. Vol. 1. J. P. Riley and G. Skirrow, eds., Academic Press, New York, pp. 121–162.

Debye, P. and E. Hückel, 1923. Zur Theorie der Elektrolyte. I. Gefrierpunktserniedrigung und verwandte Erscheinungen. *Phys. Z.*, **24**, 185.

Disteche, A. and S. Disteche, 1967. The effect of pressure on the dissociation of carbonic acid from measurements with buffered glass electrode cells; the effects of NaCl, KCl, Mg^{2+}, Ca^{2+}, SO_4^{2-} and of boric acid with special reference to seawater. *J. Electrochem. Soc.*, **114**, 330–340.

Drever, J. L., 1971. Magnesium-iron replacement in clay minerals in anoxic marine sediments. *Science*, **172**, 1334–1336.

Duedall, I. W., 1972. The partial molal volume of calcium carbonate in seawater. *Geochim. Cosmochim. Acta*, **36**, 729–734.

Dyrssen, D., 1965. A Gran titration of seawater on board "Sagitta." *Acta Chem. Scand.*, **19**, 1265.

Dyrssen, D. and L. G. Sillen, 1967. Alkalinity and total carbonate in seawater: a plea for t-p independent data. *Tellus*, **19**, 113–121.

Edmond, J. M., 1970a. High precision determination of titration alkalinity and total carbon dioxide content of seawater by potentiometric titration. *Deep-Sea Res.*, **17**, 737–750.

Edmond, J. M., 1970b. Comments on the paper by T. L. Ku, Y. H. Li, G. G. Mathieu, and H. K. Wong, Radium in the Indian-Antarctic Ocean South of Australia. *J. Geophys. Res.*, **75**, 6878–6883.

Edmond, J. M., 1972. The thermodynamic description of the CO_2 system in seawater: development and current status. *Proc. Roy. Soc. Edinburgh*, (**B**)**72**, 371–387.

Edmond, J. M. and J. M. T. M. Gieskes, 1970. On the calculation of the degree of saturation of seawater with respect to calcium carbonate under *in situ* conditions. *Geochim. Cosmochim. Acta*, **34**, 1261–1291.

Edmond, J. M., Y. Chung, and J. G. Sclater, 1971. Pacific bottom water: Penetration east around Hawaii. *J. Geophys. Res.*, **76**, 8089–8097.

Emery, K. O. and S. C. Rittenberg, 1952. Early diagenesis of California basin sediments in relation to origin of oil. *Am. Assoc. Petrol. Geol. Bull.*, **36**, 735–806.

Edwards, J. O., G. C. Morrison, V. F. Ross, and J. W. Schultz, 1955. The structure of the aqueous borate ion. *J. Am. Chem. Soc.*, **77**, 266–268.

Fleming, R. H., 1940. The composition of plankton and units for reporting population and production. *Proc. Sixth Pacific Sci. Conf.*, Calif., 1939, **3**, 535–540.

Fonselius, S. H., 1969. Hydrography of the Baltic Deep Basins III. Fisheries Board of Sweden, Series Hydrography, Report No. 23, Lund, 97 pp.

Gaines, A. G. and M. E. Q. Pilson, 1972. Anoxic water in the Pettaquamscutt River. *Limnol. Oceanog.*, **17, 42–49.**

Garrels, R. M. and M. E. Thompson, 1962. A chemical model for seawater at 25°C and one atmosphere total pressure. *Am. J. Sci.*, **260**, 57–66.

Garrels, R. M. and F. T. Mackenzie, 1971. *Evolution of Sedimentary Rocks.* Norton, New York, 397 pp.

Gieskes, J. M., 1970. Einige Beobachtungen über Lösungsvorgange am Boden dez Ozeans. "*Meteor*" *Forsch. Ergebn.*, **A8**, 12–17.

Gieskes, J. M., 1973. Interstitial water studies, Leg 15. In: Edgar, N. T., Saunders, J. B. et al, *Initial Reports of the Deep Sea Drilling Project.* Vol. 15. In press, U.S. Government Printing Office, Washington.

Gieskes, J. M. and K. Grasshoff, 1969. A study of the variability in the hydrochemical factors in the Baltic Sea on the basis of two anchors stations, September 1967 and May 1968. *Kieler Meeresf.*, **25**, 105–132.

Gieskes, J. M. and J. M. Edmond, 1972. Thermodynamical approaches to geochemical problems in seawater. *J. Geological Ed.* 20, 246–257.

Gordon, D. C., 1971. Distribution of particulate organic carbon and nitrogen at an oceanic station in the central Pacific. *Deep-Sea Res.*, **18**, 1127–1134.

Greenberg, D. M. and E. G. Moberg, 1932. The relation of the buffer mechanism of seawater to the solubility of calcium carbonate. Bull. Nat. Research Council, No. 89, Rep. Comm. on Sedimentation, 73 pp.

Hammond, D. E., 1973. Interstitial water studies, Leg 15. A comparison of the major element and carbonate chemistry data from sites 147, 148, and 149. In: Edgar, N. T., Saunders J. B. et al, *Initial Reports of the Deep Sea Drilling Project.* Vol. 15, in press, U.S. Government Printing Office, Washington.

Hansson, I., 1972. An analytical approach to the carbonate system in seawater. Unpublished Ph.D. thesis, Göteborg University.

Hansson, I. and D. Jagner, 1973. Evaluation of the accuracy of Gran plots by means of computer calculation. Application to the potentiometric titration of the total alkalinity and carbonate content of seawater. *Anal. Chim. Acta.* in press.

Hartmann, M., P. Müller, E. Suess, and C. H. van der Weijden, 1973. Diagenesis of organic matter in recent marine sediments. "Meteor" Forsch. Ergebn., C12, 74–86.

Hastings, A. B. and J. Sendroy, Jr., 1925. The effect of variation in ionic strength on the apparent first and second dissociation constants of carbonic acid. *J. Biol. Chem.*, **65**, 445–455.

Hastings, A. B., C. D. Murray, and J. Sendroy, Jr., 1927. The solubility of calcium carbonate in salt solutions and biological fluids. *J. Biol. Chem.*, **71**, 723–781.

Hawley, J. and R. M. Pytkowicz, 1969. Solubility of calcium carbonate in seawater at high pressures and 2°C. *Geochim. Cosmochim. Acta*, **33**, 1557–1561.

Heath, G. R. and C. Culberson, 1970. Calcite: degree of saturation, rate of dissolution, and the compensation depth in the deep oceans. *Geol. Soc. Am. Bull.*, **81**, 3157–3160.

Ingri, N., 1963. Equilibrium studies of polyanions XI, Polyborates in 3M NaBr, 3M LiBr and 3M KBr; a comparison with data obtained in 3M $NaClO_4$. *Acta. Chem. Scand.*, **17**, 581–589.

Johnston, J., 1916. The determination of carbonic acid, combined and free, in solution, particularly in natural waters. *J. Am. Chem. Soc.*, **38**, 947–975.

Kamatani, A., 1969. Regeneration of inorganic nutrients from diatom decomposition. *J. Oceanogr. Soc. Japan*, **25**, 63–74.

Keeling, C. D., 1968. Carbon dioxide in surface ocean waters, 4. Global distribution. *J. Geophys. Res.*, **73**, 4543–4553.

Keeling, C. D., 1973. The carbon dioxide cycle: Reservoir models to depict the exchange of atmospheric carbon dioxide with the oceans and land plants. In: Chemistry of the lower Atmosphere. Plenum, in press.

Keeling, C. D. and L. S. Waterman, 1968. Carbon dioxide in surface ocean waters, 3. Measurements on Lusiad expedition 1962–1963. *J. Geophys. Res.*, **73**, 4529–4541.

Kelley, J. J. and D. W. Hood, 1971. Carbon dioxide in the Pacific Ocean and Bering Sea: Upwelling and Mixing. *J. Geophys. Res.*, **76**, 745–752.

Kester, D. R. and R. M. Pytkowicz, 1967. Determination of the apparent dissociation constants of phosphoric acid in seawater. *Limnol. Oceanog.*, **12**, 243–252.

Knull, J. R. and F. A. Richards, 1969. A note on the sources of excess alkalinity in anoxic waters. *Deep-Sea Res.*, **16**, 205–212.

Kuo, H. H. and G. Veronis, 1970. Distribution of tracers in the deep oceans of the world. *Deep-Sea Res.*, **17**, 29–46.

Lewis, G. N. and M. Randall, 1961. *Thermodynamics*, 2nd ed. revised by K. S. Pitzer and L. Brewer, McGraw-Hill, New York, p. 723.

Li, Y. H., T. Takahashi, and W. S. Broecker, 1969. Degree of saturation of calcium carbonate in the oceans, *J. Geophys. Res.*, **74**, 5507–5525.

Li, Y. H. and T. F. Tsui, 1971. Solubility of CO_2 in water and in seawater. *J. Geophys. Res.*, **76**, 4203–4207.

Lyakhin, Y. U., 1968. Calcium carbonate saturation of Pacific water. *Oceanology*, **8**, 44–53.

Lyman, J., 1957. Buffer mechanism of seawater. Unpublished Ph.D. thesis, University of California, Los Angeles, 196 pp.

Machta, L., 1972. The role of the oceans and biosphere in the carbon dioxide cycle. In *Changing Chemistry of the Oceans*. Nobel Symposium 20, Almquist and Wiksell, Uppsala, pp. 121–145.

Menzel, D. W., 1970. The role of *in situ* decomposition of organic matter on the concentration of non-conservative properties in the sea. *Deep-Sea Res.*, **17**, 751–764.

Menzel, D. W. and J. H. Ryther, 1968. Organic carbon and the oxygen minimum in the South Atlantic Ocean. *Deep-Sea Res.*, **15**, 327–337.

Menzel, D. W. and J. H. Ryther, 1971. Distribution and cycling of organic matter in the oceans. In *Symposium on Organic Matter in Natural Waters.*, 1968. D. Hood, Institute of Marine Science, Alaska, Occasional Publication No. 1, pp. 31–54.

Millero, F. J. and R. A. Berner, 1972. Effect of pressure on carbonate equilibria in seawater. *Geochim. Cosmochim Acta*, **36**, 92–98.

Moberg, E. G., D. M. Greenberg, R. Revelle, and E. C. Allen, 1934. The buffer mechanism of seawater. Bull. SIO, Techn. Ser. 3, 231–278.

Morse, J. W. and R. A. Berner, 1972. Dissociation kinetics of calcium carbonate in seawater: II. A kinetic origin of the Lysocline. *Am. J. Sci.*, **272**, 840–851.

Munk, W. H., 1966. Abyssal Recipes. *Deep-Sea Res.*, **13**, 707–730.

Murray, C. N. and J. P. Riley, 1971. The solubility of gases in distilled water and seawater-IV. Carbon dioxide. *Deep-Sea Res.*, **18**, 533–541.

Murray, J. and A. F. Renard, 1891. Deep sea deposits based on the specimens collected during the voyage of H.M.S. Challenger in the years 1872–1876. Rep. Voy. Challenger, Longmans, London, 525 pp. (Johnson Reprint, London 1965).

Nakayama, F. S., 1968. Calcium activity, complex and ion-pair in saturated $CaCO_3$ solutions. *Soil Science*, **106**, 429–434.

Nakayama, F. S., 1970. Sodium bicarbonate and carbonate ion pairs and their relation to the estimation of the first and second dissociation constants of carbonic acid. *J. Phys. Chem.*, **74**, 2726–2728.

Owen, B. B. and S. R. Brinkley, 1941. Calculation of the effect of pressure upon ionic equilibria in pure water and in salt solutions. *Chem. Revs.*, **29**, pp. 461–474.

Parker, F. L. and W. H. Berger, 1971. Faunal and solution patterns of planktonic foraminifera in surface sediments of the South Pacific. *Deep-Sea Res.*, **18**, 73–107.

Peterson, M. N. A., 1966. Calcite: rates of dissolution in a vertical profile in the central Pacific. *Science*, **154**, 1542–1544.

Postma, H., 1958. Chemical results and a survey of water masses and currents. "Snellius" expedition 1929–1930. Vol. 2. Oceanographic Results, Part 8. E. J. Brill, Leiden, 116 pp.

Postma, H., 1959. Tables: oxygen, hydrogen ion, alkalinity and phosphate. "Snellius" expedition 1929–1930. Vol. 4, Chemical Results. E. J. Brill, Leiden, 35 pp.

Postma, H., 1964. The exchange of oxygen and carbon dioxide between the ocean and the atmosphere. *Netherlands J. of Sea Res.*, **2**, 258–283.

Presley, B. J. and I. R. Kaplan, 1968. Changes in dissolved sulfate, calcium, and carbonate from interstitial water of near shore sediments. *Geochim. Cosmochim. Acta*, **32**, 1037–1048.

Pytkowicz, R. M., 1970. On the carbonate compensation depth in the Pacific Ocean. *Geochim. Cosmochim. Acta*, **34**, 836–839.

Pytkowicz, R. M., 1972. Comments on a paper by S. Ben-Yaakov and I. R. Kaplan, "Deep Sea in situ Carbonate Saturometry". *J. Geophys. Res.*, **77**, 2733–2734.

Rakestraw, N. W., 1949. The conception of alkalinity or excess base in seawater. *J. Mar. Res.*, **8**, 14–20.

Redfield, A. C., B. H. Ketchum, and F. A. Richards, 1963. The influence of organisms on the composition of seawater. In *The Sea*, Vol. 2. M. N. Hill, ed. Wiley-Interscience, New York, pp. 26–77.

Reid, J. L. and R. J. Lynn, 1971. On the influence of the Norwegian-Greenland and Weddell Seas upon the bottom waters of the Indian and Pacific Oceans. *Deep-Sea Res.*, **18**, 1063–1088.

Richards, F. A., 1965. Anoxic basins and Fjords. In *Chemical Oceanography* Vol. 1. J. P. Riley and G. Shirrow, eds. Academic Press, New York, pp. 611–645.

Riley, G. A., 1970. Particulate matter in seawater. *Adv. Mar. Biol.* **8**, 1–118.

Ruddiman, W. F. and B. C. Heezen, 1967. Differential solution of planktonic Foraminifera. *Deep-Sea Res.*, **14**, 801–808.

Sholkovitz, E. R., 1973. Interstitial water chemistry of the Santa Barbara Basin sediments. *Geochim. et Cosmochim. Acta*, in press.

Siever, R., 1968. Sedimentological consequences of a steady state ocean-atmosphere. *Sedimentology*, **11**, 5–29.

Sillén, L. G., 1959. Graphic representation of equilibrium data. In *Treatise on Analytical Chemistry*. Part 1, Sec. B, Chap. 8. I. M. Kolthoff and P. J. Elving, eds. Wiley-Interscience, New York, pp. 277–317.

Sillén, L. G. 1967. The ocean as a chemical system. *Science*, **156**, 1189–1197.

Sillén, L. G. and A. E. Martell, 1964. Stability constants of metal-ion complexes. The Chemical Society (London), Special Publication No. 17.

Stommel, H., 1958. The abyssal circulation. *Deep-Sea Res.*, **5**, 80–82.

Suess, E., 1970. Interaction of organic compounds with calcium carbonate. I. Association phenomena and geochemical implications. *Geochim. Cosmochim. Acta*, **34**, 157–168.

Sverdrup, H. U., M. W. Johnson, and R. H. Fleming, 1942. *The Oceans*. Prentice Hall, Englewood Cliffs, N.J., 1087 pp.

Takahashi, T., R. F. Weiss, C. H. Culberson, J. M. Edmond, D. E. Hammond, C. S. Wong, Y. H. Li, and A. E. Bainbridge, 1970. A carbonate chemistry profile at the 1969 Geosecs intercalibration station in the Eastern Pacific Ocean. *J. Geophys. Res.*, **75**, 7648–7666.

Turekian, K. K., 1965. Some aspects of the geochemistry of marine sediments. In *Chemical Oceanography* Vol. 2, J. P. Riley and G. Skirrow, eds. Academic Press, London, pp. 81–126.

Tsunogai, S., M. Nishimura, and S. Nakaya, 1968. Calcium and magnesium in seawater and the ratio of calcium to chlorinity as a tracer for water masses. *J. Oceanogr. Soc. Japan*, **24**, 153–159.

Wattenberg, H., 1933. Über die titrationsalkalinität und der Kalziumkarbonatgehalt des Meerwassers. Deutsche Atlantische Expedition, "Meteor", 1925–1927. Wiss. Ergebn. Bd. 8, Teil, 122–231.

Weiss, R. F. and H. Craig, 1973. Precise shipboard determination of dissolved nitrogen, oxygen, argon, and total inorganic carbon by gas chromatography. *Deep-Sea Res.*, **20**, 291–303.

Williams, P. M. and L. I. Gordon, 1970. Carbon-13: Carbon-12 ratios in dissolved and particulate organic matter in the sea. *Deep-Sea Res.*, **17**, 19–27.

Wong, C. S., 1970. Quantitative analysis of total carbon dioxide in seawater: a new extraction method. *Deep-Sea Res.*, **17**; 9–17.

Wyrtki, K., 1962. The oxygen minima in relation to oceanic circulation. *Deep-Sea Res.*, **9**, 11–23.

4. REDOX LEVELS IN THE SEA

W. G. Breck

We shall start with our model system, corresponding to one liter of seawater + solids and gases, and reduce it gradually. We may imagine that H_2 is added to the system in portions and that the system is equilibrated after each addition. Comparing with the real system, we might say that we are carrying back the H_2 that has escaped from outer space; adding the buried C is equivalent to adding $CO_2 + H_2$.

As a convenient measure of the oxidizing power of the system we will use the quantity pE. In the course of this imaginary process our model passes through equilibrium states that might correspond to earlier, less oxidizing states of our planet's ocean and atmosphere.

Lars Gunnar Sillén (1965)

The conceptual liter of seawater shown in Fig. 1 can function not only as a tribute to Sillén's contributions in this area of marine science but also as an index of the history of redox conditions on our planet and more immediately as a chart of the sense of this chapter. Sillén's liter of seawater is for the world ocean somewhat analogous to what the human embryo is to man: a record of present development as well as of past evolution.

Based on the planetary mass balances of Goldschmidt (1933) and Horn (1964), Sillén has shown the basic origin of a liter of seawater by the relation (which can also function in the reverse sense),

$$\underset{0.6\text{ kg}}{\text{igneous rock}} + \underset{1.0\text{ kg}}{\text{volatiles}} = \underset{1.0\text{ liter}}{\text{seawater}} + \underset{0.6\text{ kg}}{\text{sediments}} + \underset{3\text{ liter}}{\text{air}} \tag{1}$$

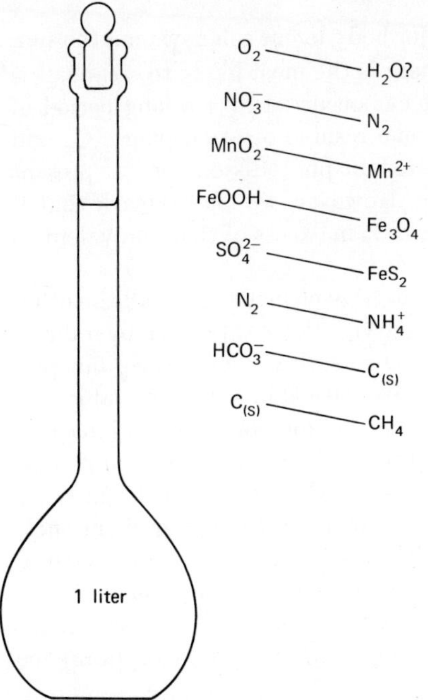

Fig. 1. Sillén's model liter of seawater.

In addition to the above, the following should be considered:

1. The existence of interstitial water in contact with various sorts of sediments.

2. The photochemical dissociation of water, according to

$$2\,H_2O \underset{}{\overset{h\nu}{\rightleftharpoons}} 2\,H_2 + O_2 \tag{2}$$

3. The loss of H_2 to outer space and its unequal replacement from the interior by volcanic action.

4. The photosynthetic reduction of CO_2 and production of O_2, approximated in an overall way by

$$CO_2 + H_2O \overset{h\nu}{\rightleftharpoons} \frac{1}{n}\,(CH_2O)_n + O_2 \tag{3}$$

5. The decay of organic material with consumption of O_2 and release of CO_2, approximated by the reverse of equation 3.

6. The introduction of material from the mantle and the reverse.

Considering O_2 alone in a balance, it is produced chiefly by the reactions of photosynthesis (3) and photodissociation (2), and is consumed by the reverse of (3) in decay and by oxidizing such elements as Fe, Mn, S, and H from the interior. Any exchange with the mantle is likely to consume more oxygen than furnished. Detailed balances have been attempted with uncertain reliability. It is generally accepted that, beginning from a more reduced state, our planet has lost H_2 and steadily built up a stock of O_2. According to Cloud and Gibor (1970), this present stock of oxygen is stoichiometrically roughly equivalent to the inventory of fossil C, implying that the oxygen is mainly of photosynthetic origin. If this is so, the price to be paid for having O_2 in the atmosphere is to leave the fossil C buried; dire consequences would result from the sudden combustion of all the fossil fuel.

On the other hand, by comparison with the major body in our solar system, the sun, our planet is deficient in H_2. Since this light element is the most likely to escape, it is reasonable that some loss of H_2 from the planet has occurred over a long period of time as a consequence of reaction (2), leaving some residue of atmospheric O_2 and perhaps priming the photosynthesis (3). To what extent photodissociation at present competes with photosynthesis is difficult to gage. However, we may remark that if significant this process should produce atmospheric O_2 in excess of that equivalent to the fossil C.

It is only logical to consider the relation of the reactive element, O, to all the other elements in the earth's crust and also that exchanged with the mantle even by indirect redox relations. Most important is the amount of O so stably bound to Si, but presumably this amount does not change much. Reactive with O in a more variable way would be Fe, Mn, S, Ti, V, and other transition elements and complex combinations of elements all of whose reactivities with O and the stabilities of whose compounds would range widely. It is not reasonable to suppose that the O content of such a mélange has not changed over the ages, especially when it is evident that redox gradients now exist with depth in the crust for the elements Fe, Mn, and S. In the course of geological time any increase in the amount of O stored in combination with such elements would constitute a deficit in the amount of O equivalent to the fossil C. This deficit might roughly counteract the excess from the H_2 loss, leaving the C to O ratio to appear even more significant than it really is.

1. The Sillén Model Liter of Seawater

Two classic papers by Sillén (1965) organize the available thermodynamic knowledge relevant to the redox roles of the oceans and atmosphere and whereas most of his development need not be reproduced here, his main findings are too valuable not to be put to more use than they have been, and extended. In considering the evolution of a liter of contemporary seawater, Sillén takes the frame of reference qualified by the points in the following section.

A. Basic Assumptions and Definitions

1. The temperature is taken as 25°C, as thermodynamic data are usually considered at this temperature. The real sea, of course, has considerable variation.

2. The pH is taken as 8.1 and is ultimately determined by equilibria involving clay minerals. It is not significantly changed by the usual redox reactions.

3. The redox potential of the system at equilibrium is expressed by the dimensionless quantity pE, where at 25°C

$$pE = -\log\{e\} = \frac{FEh}{2.3\,RT} = \frac{Eh}{0.059} \tag{4}$$

and $\{e\}$ represents activity of electrons; Eh is the redox potential measured on the conventional hydrogen scale; and F is the faraday. The use of pE is regarded as a property of the system rather than of particular chemicals.

4. The activity of seawater is nearly unity, so its logarithm is nearly zero (-0.008) and the amount of water on the planet is assumed not to change.

5. Activity coefficients for singly charged ions are often taken as ~ 0.7, and for doubly charged ions, ~ 0.1. Sillén uses the respective logarithmic values -0.17 and -0.08.

6. The main elements on the planet that have changes in oxidation states are H, O, C, N, Fe, S, Mn, and I; these are termed the redox elements.

7. The oxidation states are normally fixed for such common crustal species as Al^{3+}, Cl^-, Na^+, K^+, Ca^{2+}, and Mg^{2+}; the concentrations of these are largely determined by sedimentation processes and are presumed, like pH, to be quite uniform. Up-to-date values have been given by Goldberg et al. (1971).

8. Atmospheric partial pressures of the gases N_2, O_2, and CO_2 are known (0.758, 0.203, and 0.000291, respectively); the logarithmic partial pressures are, respectively, -0.120, -0.692, and -3.536.

B. The Method for H, O, *and Atmospheric Gases*

As well as the information contained in the assumptions above, use was made of other thermodynamic data, particularly that of Sillén and Martell (1964), in a convenient logarithmic (to base 10) form by reducing ΔG^0 and E^0 data to log K_f values, and using these to calculate equilibrium constants required for particular reactions. A few examples of important reactions involving the common gases are given below:

$$2H^+ + 2e = H_2 \qquad \begin{aligned} &\log K = \log P_{H_2} + 2pE + 2\text{pH} = 0 \\ &\log P_{H_2} = -2\text{pH} - 2pE = -16.2 - 2pE \end{aligned} \tag{5}$$

$$H_2 + \tfrac{1}{2} O_2 = H_2O \qquad \log K = \log K_f = \log \{H_2O\} - \log P_{H_2} - \tfrac{1}{2} \log P_{O_2} = 41.6 \quad (6)$$

$$C + O_2 = CO_2 \qquad \log K = \log K_f = \log P_{CO_2} - \log \{C\} - \log P_{O_2} = 69.1 \quad (7)$$

$$C + 2\,H_2 = CH_4 \qquad \log K = \log K_f = \log P_{CH_4} - \log \{C\} - 2 \log P_{H_2} = 8.9 \quad (8)$$

Activities of elements in their standard states are taken as unity:

$$\{C\} = 1 \qquad \log \{C\} = 0$$

For the atmospheric gases, the logarithmic partial pressures as calculated at three different levels of pE, namely $+12.5$, -5.5, and -6.1, are given in Table I. Log values lower than -6 are assumed negligible and shown in the table by a slash (/). The value of $pE = +12.5$ corresponds to the redox level that would theoretically be attained if O_2 at a logarithmic partial pressure of -0.69 were equilibrated with water according to the relation at 25°C and pH 8.1,

$$\tfrac{1}{2} O_2 + 2\,H^+ + 2e = H_2O \qquad \log K = 41.6 = -0.008 - \tfrac{1}{2} \log P_{O_2} + 2(8.1) + 2pE \quad (9)$$

where $\log P_{O_2} = -50.7 + 4pE$ and $pE = 12.5$.

TABLE I

Logarithmic Partial Pressures of Atmospheric Gases at Various pE

pE	$\log P_{O_2}$	$\log P_{H_2}$	$\log P_{CO_2}$	$\log P_{CH_4}$	$\log P_{N_2}$	$\log P_{NH_3}$
+12.5	−0.69	/	−3.5	/	−0.12	/
−5.5	/	−5.3	−3.5	−1.6	−0.12	−5.0
−6.1	/	−3.9	/	1.03	−4.1	−5.0

In the real world a value as high as the above is rarely achieved even in the laboratory, but this is to anticipate a later discussion. For the present we can regard the value of $pE = +12.5$ as an upper theoretical limit. The other two levels of pE, at -5.5 and -6.1, will be explained under the following section on carbon.

C. Carbon Species at Three Levels of pE

At higher levels of pE, C exists as CO_2 in equilibrium with the whole carbonate system, the most abundant form in the sea at pH 8.1 being HCO_3^-. It is more difficult to characterize the more reduced forms simply since oxidation states from +4 through zero to −4 are possible; Sillén has simplified the situation for carbon whether as humus, peat, the biomass, or graphite as $C_{(s)}$ with an oxidation state of zero. Further reduction can produce hydrocarbons such as CH_4. Thus there are three pE ranges considered: I, II, III with boundaries as shown in the scheme below:

I		II		III
Carbonaceous		Carboniferous		Hydrocarboniferous
HCO_3^-, CO_2, $CaCO_3$	$pE = -5.5$	$(CH_2O)_n$, $C_{(s)}$	pE −6.1	CH_4, C_2H_6
max. $pE = +12.5$				

From equations 7, 9, 8, and 5, respectively, and values from Table I for $\log P_{CO_2}$, $\log P_{CH_4}$, and with $\log \{C\} = 0$,

$$\log P_{CO_2} = 69.1 + \log P_{O_2} = 69.1 - 50.7 + 4pE = 18.4 + 4pE = -3.5 \qquad pE = -5.5 \quad (10)$$

$$\log P_{CH_4} = 2 \log P_{H_2} + 8.9 = -4(8.1) - 4pE + 8.9 = -23.5 - 4pE = 1.03 \qquad pE = -6.1 \quad (11)$$

Setting pE in turn equal to $+12.5$, -5.5, and -6.1, it is possible to estimate the abundances of the various carbon species as in Table II where dominant species are marked by an asterisk and negligible quantities with a slash. At pE $+12.5$ and somewhat below -5.5, CO_2, and HCO_3^- are the abundant forms. The significance of choosing $pE = -5.5$ as a boundary is that it is where $C_{(s)}$ enters in quantity; the significance of -6.1 is that below this pE $C_{(s)}$ disappears in favor of CH_4 and other hydrocarbons. Thus Range I can be termed "carbonaceous," Range II "carboniferous," and Range III "hydrocarboniferous."

TABLE II

Logarithmic Partial Pressures and Activities of Various C Species in Three pE Ranges

pE	$\log P_{CO_2}$	$\log \{H_2CO_3\}$	$\log \{HCO_3^-\}$	$\log \{CO_3^{2-}\}$	$\log \{C\}$	$\log P_{CH_4}$
+12.5	−3.5	−5.0	−3.2*	−5.5	/	/
−5.5	−3.5	−5.0	−3.2	−5.5	0*	−1.6
−6.1	/	/	−5.9	/	0	−1.03*

Sillén has also estimated abundances of a number of organic species such as acetate, formate, ethanol, but few of these reach activities higher than 10^{-10} which, as he has pointed out, is dilute soup in any man's cuisine, and other sources must be sought for organic solutions concentrated enough to have cradled the sparks of life.

D. Nitrogen Species

Without reproducing Sillén's equilibrium calculations, which are again based on formation reactions, the dominant forms of N for the pE ranges are entered in Table III and plotted in Fig. 2.

TABLE III

Logarithmic Partial Pressures and Activities of Various N Species in Three pE Ranges

pE	$\log P_{N_2}$	$\log \{NO_3^-\}$	$\log P_{NH_3}$	$\log \{NH_3\}$	$\log \{NH_4^+\}$
+12.5	−0.12	+5.8*	/	/	/
−5.5	−0.12	/	−5.0	−3.3	−2.1*
−6.1	−4.1	/	−5.0	−3.3	−2.1*

Species calculated as most abundant are indicated by an asterisk, negligible quantities by a slash. The high value for NO_3^- of $+5.8$ at pE $+12.5$ is incredible. Sillén (1965) has claimed that this value cannot be reached for kinetic reasons. A more basic reason, discussed more fully later, is that such a high pE as $+12.5$ is not

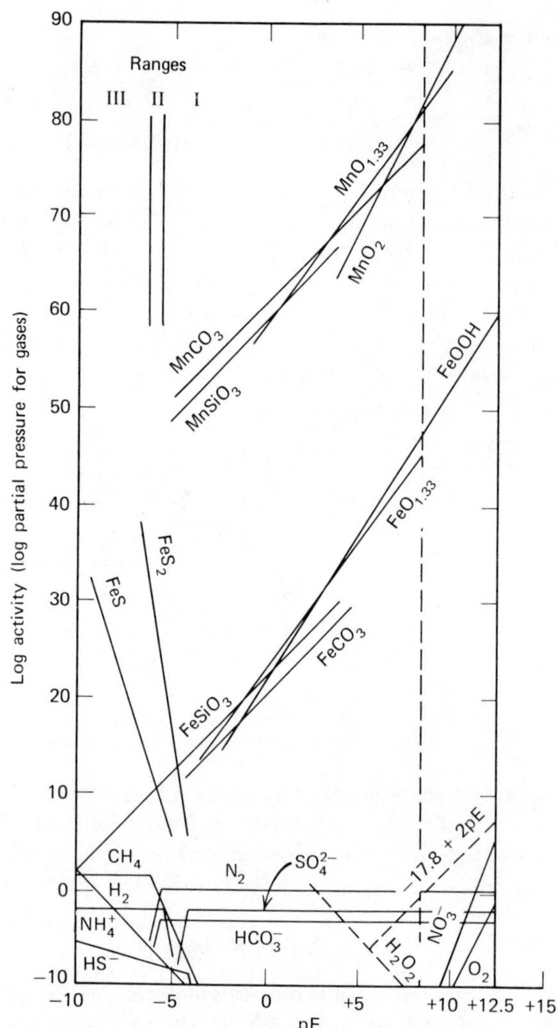

Fig. 2. Log activities of redox species in three ranges of *pE*.

attained in the real sea. At lower *pE* values, $NH_4{}^+$ is dominant and NH_3 considerable. Simply put, in the positive *pE* range the N system is nitrogenous, and at *pE* more negative than −5.5, mainly ammoniacal.

E. Iron Species

Of all the elements the relations for iron developed by Sillén (1965) are the most exciting in their potential for monitoring redox levels. In his paper (1965b) he has given logarithmic activity ratios for the various iron species against Fe^{2+} as datum, being a definite, reliable species. Here it is preferred to use Fe^0 as the datum for the following reasons. First, the Fe^0 can be roughly regarded as referring to the earth's core, so all redox levels are graded outward from the center as datum; and, being a pure solid, the $\{Fe^0\}$ can be taken as unity, so other activities based on it become absolute, allowing data for iron to be plotted on the same diagram with absolute data for other elements. Also, at a *pE* in the sea of about 8.1 it is questionable how much ferrous iron exists as Fe^{2+}_{aq} and how much as particulate oxides and hydroxides and related complex ions. The equilibrium data used to calculate the redox relations for iron are given below in Table IV and plotted in Fig. 2.

TABLE IV

Equilibrium Data and Redox Equations for Fe Species

Half-Cell Reaction	Equation for Plot
$FeOOH_{(s)} + 3H^+ + 3e = Fe^0_{(s)} + 2H_2O$	$\log\{FeOOH\} = 3pE + 21.5$
$FeO_{1.33,(s)} + 2.66H^+ + 2.66e = F^0_{(s)} + 1\ 33H_2O$	$\log\{FeO_{1.33}\} = 2\ 66pE + 22.7$
$FeSiO_{3,(s)} + 2H^+ + 2e = Fe^0_{(s)} + SiO_{2\ (s)} + H_2O$	$\log\{FeSiO_3\} = 2pE + 22.0$
$FeCO_{3,(s)} + 2e = Fe^0_{(s)} + CO_3{}^{2-}$	$\log\{FeCO_3\} = 2pE + 20.1$ (Range I only)
$FeS_{2,(s)} + 8H_2O - 12e = Fe^0_{(s)} + 2SO_4{}^{2-} + 16H^+$	$\log\{FeS_2\} = -12pE - 32.3$
$FeS_{(s)} + 4H_2O - 6e = Fe^0_{(s)} + SO_4{}^{2-} + 8H^+$	$\log\{FeS\} = -6pE - 13\ 7$

F. Sulfur Species With and Without Iron

The last two half-cell reactions in Table IV indicate that the elements Fe and S interact. It should be understood that the amount of S is limited; that is, there is more than enough Fe to react with all the S (except locally), which becomes critical, the quantity being that available from reduction of $SO_4{}^{2-}$ in the sea for which $\log\{SO_4{}^{2-}\} = -2.22$ before any appreciable reduction. Pyrrhotite ($FeS_{1.14}$) has not been included because Sillén has designated it unstable with respect to transformation to FeS_2 and FeS. The first of these to precipitate should be FeS_2 at a *pE* of -3.9.

The abundance of S species in the absence of Fe has also been treated by Sillén, but in too complicated a fashion to reproduce here, or even to outline. It is preferred to emphasize that the main reduction reactions are of $SO_4{}^{2-}$ to HS^- (along with H_2S and S^{2-}) and to $S^0_{(s)}$. The equilibrium data for these are given in Table V as calculated from thermodynamic data of Garrels and Christ (1965) and the plots included in Fig. 2. At $pE < -5.5$, the maximum logarithmic values of activities or partial pressures, as appropriate for the major S species are: $\log\{SO_4{}^{2-}\}$, -2.2; $\log\{S^0\}$, -1.5; $\log\{HS^-\}$, -1.8; $\log\{H_2S\}_{aq}$, -2.9; $\log P_{H_2S}$, -1.9.

TABLE V

Equilibrium Data and Redox Equations for S Species

Half-Cell Reaction		Equation for Plot
$SO_4{}^{2-} + 9H^+ + 8e = HS^- + 4\ H_2O$	$\log K = 34.0$	$\log\{HS^-\} = -8pE - 41.1$
$SO_4{}^{2-} + 8H^+ + 6e = S^0_{(s)} + 4\ H_2O$	$\log K = 36.6$	$\log\{S\} = -6pE - 30.4$

G. Manganese Species

Certain Mn species such as $Mn(OH)_3$, MnOOH, $MnO_4{}^-$, and MnS are quite plausible but have been omitted in view of their predictably low activities. Only data for the

TABLE VI

Equilibrium Data and Redox Equations for Mn Species

Half-Cell Reaction	Equation for Plot
$MnO_{2,(s)} + 4H^+ + 4e = Mn^0_{(s)} + 2H_2O$	$\log\{MnO_2\} = 4pE + 48.0$
$MnO_{1.33,(s)} + 2.66H^+ + 2.66e = Mn^0_{(s)} + 1.33H_2O$	$\log\{MnO_{1.33}\} = 2.66pE + 58.8$
$MnSiO_{3,(s)} + 2H^+ + 2e = Mn^0_{(s)} + SiO_{2,(s)} + H_2O$	$\log\{MnSiO_3\} = 2pE + 59.1$
$MnCO_{3,(s)} + 2H^+ + 2e = Mn^0_{(s)} + CO_3^{2-}$	$\log\{MnCO_3\} = 2pE + 60.8$ (Range I only)

more common species such as MnO_2, $MnO_{1.33}$, $MnCO_3$, and $MnSiO_3$ have been included in Table VI, on the basis that $\log\{Mn^0\} = 0$. The plots for these equations are in Fig. 2.

H. Redox Titration of the Model Liter of Seawater

The logarithmic plots in Fig. 2 indicate the likelihood, at any pE, of the occurrence of dominant species for the redox elements. It is possible from this information to consider taking a liter of primeval seawater (low pE) and by a progressive oxidation process to create, step by step, a liter of modern seawater (high pE). Sillén (1965b) further suggested that the reverse process be considered wherein the appropriate number of equivalents of escaped H_2 is brought back, theoretically speaking, to reduce the liter of modern seawater, by stages and element by element, back in time to a primeval condition when our planet was more reduced; or down in depth in a stratified basin or fiord where the lower layers are present in a much reduced condition; or in oxygenated waters, down into the sediments. Sillén's redox model is thus representative of present depth profiles as well as past time profiles.

The amounts of the various dominant redox elements corresponding to 1 liter of seawater Sillén has calculated from the geochemical balance of Horn (1964) and converted to the number of faradays, or equivalents, per liter of seawater consumed in oxidation; here we consider in reverse the number of faradays, or equivalents of H_2, required to reduce the dominant redox elements in turn in the order displayed in Fig. 2, starting from pE +12.5 and moving to the left, giving the values in Table VII.

TABLE VII

Equivalents of Reductant to Titrate Model Liter of Sea Water

Reduction	pE Range (Fig. 2)	Equivalents of H_2	Totals
$O_2 \rightarrow H_2O$	12.1 to 12.5	0.09	0.09
$MnO_2 \rightarrow Mn^{2+}$	8.0	0.10	0.19
$FeOOH \rightarrow Fe_3O_4$	3.7	0.21	0.40
$SO_4^{2-} \rightarrow FeS_2$	−3.9 to −4.1	0.21	0.61
$N_2 \rightarrow NH_4^+$	−5.5	0.49	1.10
$HCO_3^- \rightarrow C_{(s)}$	−5.5	4.32	5.42
$C_{(s)} \rightarrow CH_4$	−6.1	8.36	13.78
$FeS_2 \rightarrow FeS$	−7.7	0.42	14.20

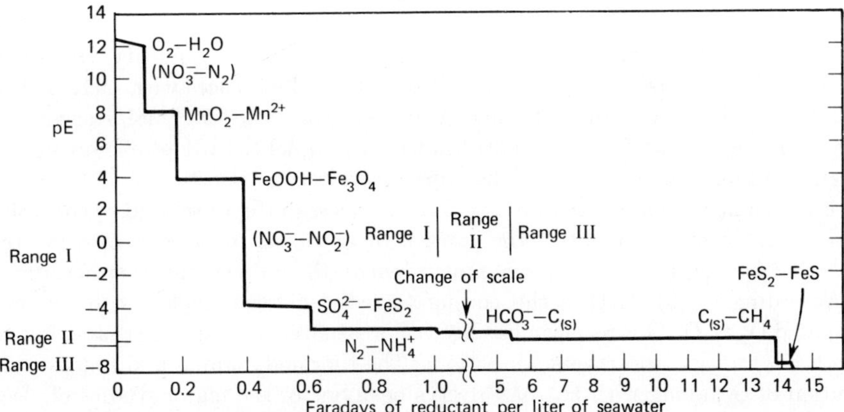

Fig. 3. Reduction titration of model liter of seawater.

The data of Table VII are plotted in Fig. 3, which differs from Sillén's in that *pE* has been put on the ordinate and number of equivalents on the abscissa to make the plot more like the usual reduction titration with multiple steps. Note how well poised the *pE* is in the reduced Ranges II and III, around −5.5 and −6.1, as judged by the long horizontal portions, and how precarious the poise is in Range I, at the top relying ultimately on the continuing success of the photosynthetic process. To be stressed again is that a *pE* of +12.5 is to be viewed as an upper limited and not a usual value.

2. Redox Conditions in the Real Sea

The foregoing must be clearly recognized as an equilibrium model and is strictly applicable as such. Some natural systems are readily equilibrated and others have become so over geologic time; on the other hand, some chemicals that thermodynamically have strong tendencies to interact (e.g., H_2, O_2) under ordinary conditions do not. Other systems are in such a state of stress or rapid change that what is needed is a kinetic or mechanistic model. Here I have in mind biological processes involving constant stresses on the activities of such species as NO_3^- and NH_4^+ and other compounds of N (e.g., NO_2^-), which are probably rarely in equilibrium. Much of the redox chemistry in natural waters turns out to be remarkably well represented by Sillén's model when certain limitations are imposed.

The vast bulk of the world ocean is well enough mixed to contain some dissolved oxygen and can be designated conveniently as "oxic." On the other hand, if oxygen is absent or consumed, the *pE* drops drastically, as in the titration curve of Fig. 3, and control by the sulfur system comes into effect, usually in the presence of iron; this condition is termed "anoxic." Occasionally the water may be found in the sensitive region of drastic *pE* change in between oxic and anoxic, when it may be termed "suboxic."

The steep *pE* gradient between the oxic and anoxic regions will often be found at an interface between layers in the same way that a temperature gradient exists at a thermocline, mainly for the reason that within the separate regions the gradient is confined by mixing. In the case of oxic waters this tender redox gradient may be found just below the surface of the sediment. In a thoroughly anoxic body of water the most marked gradient could be at the water–air interface or between well-stratified layers.

A. The Oxic Regime

In oxic waters the concentration of dissolved O_2 is a variable quantity. Its solubility decreases with increased temperature and salinity and increases with increased pressure. It generally has a range of values between 0 and 5×10^{-3} mol/liter and often has a characteristic profile with depth that may parallel the pH profile owing to the influence of biological processes on both parameters.

It is not sufficient merely to say that O_2 is in excess in the water and so controls the redox level. To clearly identify the control (if any) one must recognize the redox *couple* that is operative; that is, one must identify the reduced member conjugate to O_2. According to (9), H_2O is the conjugate reduced form, so this control can be designated O_2/H_2O. This reaction has been of great interest to scientists and engineers in both the forward and reverse directions. The thermodynamics and kinetics of the evolution of O_2, along with H_2, has always been one of the major studies of electrochemistry. However, the overall way in which equation 9 has been written disguises how complicated this process is in detail. The individual mechanistic acts can be formulated as follows:

$$O_2 \xrightarrow{e} O_2^- \xrightarrow{H^+} HO_2 \xrightarrow{e} HO_2^- \xrightarrow{H^+} H_2O_2 \xrightarrow{e} OH + OH^- \xrightarrow{e} 2\,OH^- \xrightarrow{2H^+} 2\,H_2O \qquad (12)$$

The overall effect of (12) might be described as the net result of four protonations and four electronations, but the crux of the whole matter may well be the breaking of the strong O—O bond, which may require effective catalysis as for the same process in fuel cells. It is not surprising that the set of reactions represented by (12) has rarely been found to be reversible or to follow the Nernst equation.

The reduction of aqueous O_2 is important in polarography. Solutions for analysis of other species must first have the dissolved O_2 removed; otherwise a compound wave is obtained for the reduction of O_2 at the cathode, which usually precedes and may create confusion by adding to the desired waves for the ions being measured. The compound O_2 wave consists of two reduction waves: the first corresponds to the $O_2 \rightarrow H_2O_2$ part; the second and more demanding in terms of applied negative voltage to activate it is the $H_2O_2 \rightarrow 2\,H_2O$ reduction. This polarographic technique has been found reliable enough to be used to measure dissolved O_2 in natural waters. Finally, measurements of redox potentials in the environment have not given values nearly high enough ($Eh = 0.75$ V or $pE = 12.5$) to correspond to control by equilibration of reaction (9).

It is also possible that there is no very strong thermodynamic control of the redox potential at all, and that only a kinetic approach, however difficult, will ultimately suffice. Without denying the usefulness of equilibrium arguments, Morris and Stumm (1967) and Stumm and Morgan (1970) emphasize the *dynamic* nature of oxic aquatic systems, especially those mediated by biochemical activity such as photosynthesis. It is their view that most measurements of *Eh* in natural waters represent *mixed* potentials not amenable to quantitative interpretation. A mixed potential is a complex condition wherein the anodic and cathodic processes involved are not directly related in a reverse sense.

Between a completely dynamic state and one in thermodynamic equilibrium there is hope of making sense by a steady-state approach. Let us return to a closer study of some details known about (12). First, it should be understood that O_2 is the most abundant highly oxidizing species in the environment and, although regenerated by photosynthesis, it is also subject to reduction by many substances with which it comes into contact. The detailed mechanics are given by (12) but all the individual steps will not occur at the same rate.

In a polarographic kinetic study of the reduction of O_2 in aqueous solution Kastening and Kazemifard (1970) found that the reaction

$$O_2 + H_2O + 2e = HO_2^- + OH^- \quad E^0 \text{ reported variously as } -0.05 \text{ to } -0.08 \text{ V} \quad (13)$$

carried out on a dropping mercury cathode was reversible in quite alkaline solution (0.1*M* NaOH). This supported the earlier findings of Berl (1943) who originally operated such a reversible electrode reaction on activated carbon in the absence of peroxide-decomposing catalysts. Berl's results were also corroborated by Weisz and Jaffe (1948). Furthermore, isotopic studies have shown that in the above reaction the O—O is not broken and that both O's in HO_2^- are derived from the same O_2 molecule. The work of Kastening and Kazemifard offers some other pertinent facts. Whereas the reduction of O_2 to HO_2^- was found to occur at about +0.1 V, the more difficult reduction of HO_2^- to H_2O (or OH^-) occurred in the range −0.6 to −1.2 V, according to

$$HO_2^- + H_2O + 2e = 3\,OH^- \quad (14)$$

These waves have been redrawn schematically in Fig. 4. In aprotic solvents the first step found was the reduction of O_2 to O_2^-, involving only a single electronation, and, of course, no protonations. These workers were able to approach the same result by the addition of various amounts of surfactant to inhibit the protonation in aqueous solution. It appears that in aqueous solution, with no inhibitor present, protonation occurs readily (to HO_2) and the reduction proceeds further with another electron to HO_2^-, and then with the easy addition of another proton to H_2O_2 if the pH is not too high. In the pH range near 8 the species H_2O_2 should be vastly more abundant than HO_2^-,

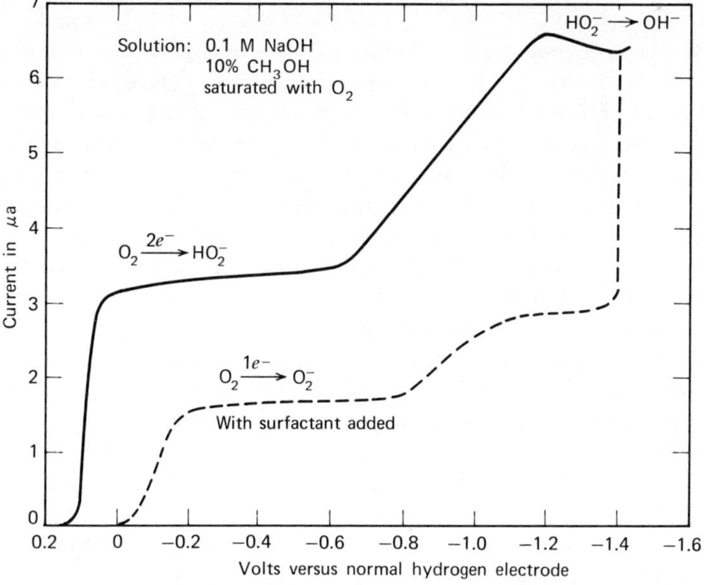

Fig. 4. Polarographic reduction of O_2, data of Kastening and Kazemifard.

so although (13) has been written to represent the mechanism, for most purposes it is more useful to write the analogous protonated form of the reaction:

$$O_2 + 2\,H^+ + 2e = H_2O_2 \qquad E^0 = 0.68\text{ V} \qquad pE^0 = 11.5 \tag{15}$$

The relative ease with which reactions (15) or (13) occur as opposed to (14), corroborates the work of Yeager, Krouse, and Rao (1964), who found that by polarographic reduction on carbon the current density associated with (14) was very small relative to that for (13) or (15). On the other hand, in certain acid solutions with metals present that are known to catalyze (14) it is possible to have O_2 reduced directly to H_2O in quantity, but these conditions are not normally found in the sea.

In the oxic sea, then, with O_2 the dominant oxidizing species that comes into contact with many reduced substances, the selection of the likely form conjugate to O_2 now becomes more clear. On the reduction of O_2 in the absence of specific catalysts, the fact that H_2O_2 (or HO_2^-) is formed by (15) faster than it is used up by (14) demands that $\{H_2O_2\}$ must build up to a steady-state value. In this case its increased activity as a product enables it to slow down (15) and as a reactant to speed up (14) until it is formed as fast as it is consumed. The important reduced form, which, along with O_2, appears to form a labile couple is thus H_2O_2 (or HO_2^-) and the delicate controlling reaction is (15), designated as O_2/H_2O_2 control. But the actual mechanics of the process may follow (13), or in more detail, the sequence in (12).

It has been stated above that the steady-state activity of H_2O_2 is dependent on the existence of a limiting rate in the reduction of H_2O_2 to H_2O according to (14) or alternatively,

$$H_2O_2 + 2\,H^+ + 2e = 2\,H_2O \qquad \text{or} \qquad H_2O_2 + 2e = 2\,OH^- \tag{16}$$

Yet another possibility is that H_2O_2 is capable of acting as both its own oxidant and reductant in the disproportionation

$$2\,H_2O_2 = 2\,H_2O + O_2 \qquad \text{or simply} \qquad H_2O_2 = H_2O + \tfrac{1}{2}\,O_2 \tag{17}$$

A cycle can be considered in which 1 mol of O_2 is reduced by (15) to produce 1 mol of H_2O_2, which can then in turn decompose to give back 0.5 mol of O_2 and 1 mol of H_2O according to (17). However, such a cycle is incomplete and runs down the O_2 supply by 0.5 mol unless regenerated by some other process such as photosynthesis.

Allowing that a strong influence on the control of redox level is by O_2/H_2O_2 instead of $O_2/2\,H_2O$, and for the moment neglecting all the other diverse systems in our complicated real sea, it is now appropriate to calculate what pE or Eh would result from such control. For this purpose $\{H_2O_2\}$ must be known, or, conversely, $\{H_2O_2\}$ might be computed from reliable measurements of Eh or pE. For the moment, an assessment of the upper and lower limits of $\{H_2O_2\}$ may be tried.

The reaction (17) allows a lower limit to be set. This reaction is known to proceed at a slow rate even in the absence of suitable catalysts. If it is assumed that such catalysts are present in the sea (perhaps as compounds of Fe or Mn) in an amount sufficient to allow equilibrium to be attained, the $\{H_2O_2\}$ would then be at a minimum that can be calculated from the known ΔG^0 data at 25°C: $\Delta G^0 = -25.2$ kcal; $\log K = 18.3$ for (17). Taking P_{O_2} at 0.2 atm and $\{H_2O\} = 1$, $\{H_2O_2\} \sim 10^{-19}$. As an approach to an upper limit, it is doubtful if $\{H_2O_2\}$ could have reached levels in the sea as high as for H^+ or OH^-, say 10^{-7}, without being detected. For a precise value, the Eh of oxic water must be reliably determined. This has recently been attempted (Breck,

1970) by an equilibrium method (to be discussed later), yielding an *Eh* value of 0.50 V at pH 8.0, or $pE = 8.5$. Using these values, calculation according to (15) gives a value for $\{H_2O_2\}$ of 10^{-11}.

H_2O_2 can be produced from large reserves of O_2 and H_2O. These abundant chemicals constitute such a reliable supply that the dominant system in setting the poise could ultimately be credited to $O_2/(O_2 + H_2O)$. The stability is thus afforded on the lower side by a plentiful supply of related species in a dynamic cycling process that maintains a relatively steady but small $\{H_2O_2\}$ as a key agent, but by no means the only one, in the mediation of natural waters. But since most reagents act as reductants with O_2, it is the oxidizing member of the O_2/H_2O_2 couple whose poise is under the most stress in the environment, so that the most important *single* agent in maintaining redox poise is the hopefully reliable excess of O_2.

The idea that the O_2/H_2O_2 couple plays an important role in the redox chemistry of waters is not new. Electrochemists have long regarded H_2O_2 as a dynamic intermediate in the electrolysis of H_2O to produce O_2 as well as in the cathodic reduction of O_2. It is difficult, in fact, to see how O_2 can be produced from H_2O or vice versa without going through such a stage. In an experimental study of certain mine waters, Sato (1960) concluded that the redox poise of water was set by the O_2/H_2O_2 couple. His estimate of $\{H_2O_2\}$ is 10^{-6}, which seems too high not to have been observed. Sato also commented on the E^0 values for couples of which H_2O_2 is one member, claiming that such couples were thermodynamically unstable in the presence of a host of non-metals and metals, including especially the transition metals. Many species in the sea may be capable of catalyzing the decomposition of H_2O_2 to form H_2O and O_2. The important roles of Fe and Mn compounds in redox control and indication have been clearly recognized and treated in detail by Sato. In particular he has shown that the oxidation states found for these elements under natural conditions are more in accord with a potential set by the O_2/H_2O_2 couple than one set by the $O_2/2\ H_2O$ couple.

In summary, in the oxic part of the real sea, the redox level is assumed to be poised, somewhat precariously, by the O_2/H_2O_2 couple, the oxidized member, O_2, being present in molarity about 10^{-4} and subject to reduction by many species, especially those of C; the reduced member, H_2O_2, being at a low but steady-state activity of the order of 10^{-11}. For this important couple,

$$O_2 + 2\,H^+ + 2e = H_2O_2 \qquad E^0 = 0.68\text{ V} \qquad \log K = 23.0 \qquad (15)$$
$$pE^0 = 11.5 \qquad \{H_2O_2\} \sim 10^{-11}$$

and

$$pE = pE^0 - \frac{1}{n}\log\{H_2O_2\} + \frac{1}{n}\log P_{O_2} - \text{pH} \qquad (15a)$$

Calculation from (15a) gives $pE = +8.5$ at a pH value chosen as 8.1.

It is now appropriate to see what significance the pE value of $+8.5$ has for some of the key redox elements already dealt with in Sillén's model, by referring to Fig. 2 where a dashed line has been drawn at pE 8.5 to indicate what oxidation states would be expected for these elements in the real oxic sea.

Oxygen. This should be the first element to be reduced. The O_2 line in Fig. 2 was drawn assuming $O_2/2\ H_2O$ equilibration, which is apparently not the case. In conformity with (15a) the equation for the O_2 in the real sea would be given by

$$\log P_{O_2} = -17.8 + 2\,pE \qquad (15b)$$

This line is shown in Fig. 2, marked $-17.8 + 2\,pE$.

Nitrogen. Next to be reduced should be NO_3^- to N_2. In Sillén's model with pE at $+12.5$ this presented a dilemma, for most of the N should be found as NO_3^- instead of N_2. This anomaly was rationalized by assuming that the formation of NO_3^- from N_2 was blocked kinetically by the high energy requirement to break the N≡N bond. However, at pE $+8.5$ the dominant form should be N_2, with NO_3^- permitted at a low level of about $10^{-6}M$, in fact very much as actually found in the real sea.

Manganese. For the dominant form of Mn at pE 8.5 on the diagram of Fig. 2 it is difficult to distinguish between MnO_2 and $MnO_{1.33}$ (or Mn_3O_4), since their lines cross near this value, indicating that the activities of these solid species should be roughly equal. The presence of MnO_2 has been amply verified but the identity of Mn_3O_4 is uncertain; here Mn may exist in both the II and IV states. It is highly significant that manganese nodules have been found to contain the minerals birnessite (MnO_2) and todorokite (containing Mn II and Mn IV). The latter mineral would be an unlikely occurrence at pE $+12.5$, but very likely at pE $+8.5$. A calculation done elsewhere (Breck, 1970) showed that MnO_4^- should be at a negligibly low value.

Iron. The dominant species at pE 8.5 (and at 12.5) is probably FeOOH, although other choices of data are possible with large uncertainties. Where the supply of O_2 is not restricted, FeOOH or at least some form of Fe III is dominant. Rusted iron objects found in the oxic aqueous environment have a reddish-brown coat of FeOOH on the outside, with a black, magnetic layer of Fe_3O_4 underneath, and then perhaps hydrous FeO or $FeCO_3$, and FeS_2 or FeS if S is present, and pure Fe^0 on the inside, all of which parallel the earth's states of Fe.

Sulfur. The dominant form is clearly the soluble anion, SO_4^{2-}, over a wide range of pE.

Carbon. Dominant is HCO_3^-, with lesser amounts of $CO_{2,aq}$, H_2CO_3, and CO_3^{2-}.

Hydrogen. Dominant over a wide range will be H^+ in H_2O down to large negative values of pE.

According to all the redox elements above, their states of oxidation as found in oxygenated waters are in excellent accord with the Sillén model (in fact, much better than he himself claims), providing the pE is taken as 8.5 and not 12.5. Especially significant are the states for Mn and N compounds.

B. The Anoxic Regime

For this section I shall be concerned only with the redox chemistry of such waters. By respiration and microbial decomposition, organic matter consumes O_2 in water, but in the major part of the world ocean the O_2 is replaced by a sufficient circulation. Were it not for physical restrictions on the mixing of O_2 in seawaters it is probable that the whole ocean would be oxic (excluding the sediments). In landlocked bays, submerged craters, deep fiords, trenches, and some basins circulation of enough dissolved O_2 to create an excess is prevented by the presence of a lip, or sill, or equivalent confining feature. The anoxic regions must therefore be regarded as somewhat exceptional from a chemical point of view.

The separation between oxic and anoxic is sudden for at least two reasons. A look at the reduction titration (Fig. 3) confirms that when seawater is subjected to reduction the O_2 is consumed first, followed by NO_3^- in small amount, then MnO_2, FeOOH, before SO_4^{2-} is reduced to HS^-. The O_2 step is well separated vertically from the SO_4^{2-} step by a few poorly poised steps with low reductive capacity. Or, on the composite plot of Fig. 2, it is plain that reduction of O_2 is well separated from reduction of SO_4^{2-}. Also, thermodynamically HS^- (or H_2S, S^{2-}) is unstable in the presence of O_2

and, depending on the ratio of O_2/HS^-, may be oxidized to certain stages in the series represented below:

$$HS^- \xrightarrow{O_2} S^0_{(s)} \xrightarrow{O_2} \tfrac{1}{2}\, S_2O_3^{2-} \xrightarrow{O_2} SO_3^{2-} \xrightarrow{O_2} SO_4^{2-} \tag{18}$$

The presence of free, elemental $S^0_{(s)}$ in the environment is not extensive but Sillén (1965), and Garrels and Christ (1965) show that it is to be expected over a narrow range of pH. One reason that it might escape detection in the free state is that it complexes with S^{2-}:

$$S^0_{(s)} + S^{2-} = S_2^{2-} \qquad \Delta G^0 = -2.2 \text{ kcal} \tag{19}$$

The above are mostly theoretical considerations. A convincing example for the world's major anoxic body, the Black Sea, is presented as a plot in Fig. 5 of the data of Skopintsev, as reported by Richards (1965). The oxic and anoxic regions are clearly seen as two distinct strata. On going from oxic to anoxic, O_2 is consumed and NO_3^- is denitrified to N_2; then SO_4^{2-} is reduced mainly to HS^-, with lesser amounts of H_2S and S^{2-}, the latter of which can precipitate metal ions if the activity product is exceeded. Undecayed organic material and nutrients accumulate in the depths where O_2 is scarce. Throughout these processes in the Black Sea, the pE changes accordingly, being poised in the oxic part at a high value, and poised at a low value in the anoxic part, but in a delicate condition in between, where the curve displays an inflection.

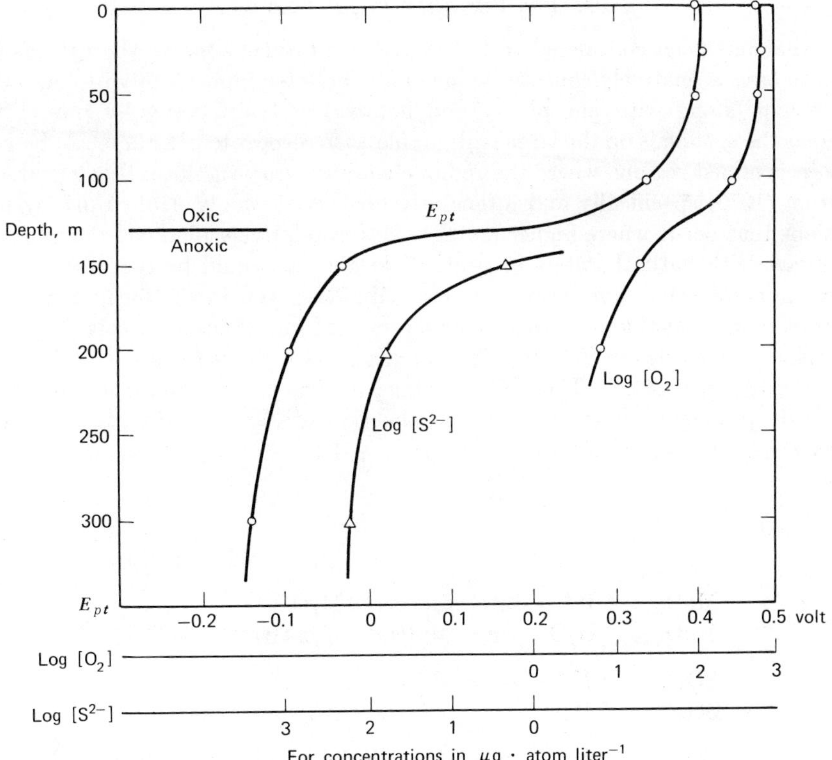

Fig. 5. Plot of data of Skopintsev for Black Sea.

C. Suboxic Conditions

Some basins are permanently anoxic while others are intermittently so, depending on the particular geometry of the basin, height of sill, and how the basin is flushed. According to Richards (1965) stabilization of the water column is sometimes by a halocline (in fiords) and sometimes by thermocline (in tropical basins). Such intermediate conditions are frequently accompanied by the occurrence of NO_2^-, usually regarded as an unstable stage between NO_3^- and N_2. Besides regions that are intermittently anoxic, there are others that can be described as habitually oxygen deficient or suboxic, and these, too, are characterized by the appearance of NO_2^- just below the mixed layer. The partial denitrification process, $NO_3^- \rightarrow NO_2^-$, would be expected to follow closely the O_2 reduction.

Richards and Broenkow (1969) report on a good example of a suboxic regime in Darwin Bay in the Galapagos Islands. Here the basin is a flooded caldera, of maximum depth 240 m, with a sill at 15 m. The bottom salinity was 34.9/mille and the temperature 18°C. Between two sets of observations it was found that NO_3^- had been converted to NO_2^- on a one-to-one basis.

The flushing of Lake Nitinat, periodically anoxic, in 1972 rewarded its fishermen with a bumper crop of salmon.

In summary, anoxic regions are characterized chemically by the reduction of NO_3^- to N_2, of SO_4^{2-} to HS^-, and ultimately of CO_2 and HCO_3^- to hydrocarbons; suboxic regions are characterized by the appearance of NO_2^-, at least intermittently.

D. The Variation of *pE* with pH

In what has been considered so far by following Sillén's model the pH has been taken to have a relatively constant value of 8.1, buffered immediately by the carbonate system (along with phosphates and borates) and ultimately by the silicates. Whereas the system is on the large scale stable with respect to pH, there can be variations in confined regions where the redox chemistry may significantly alter the pH. Boström (1970) specifically and intensively deals with the control of pH by redox reactions that occur where higher metal oxides in relatively high concentrations are in contact with natural waters in confined locales, as would be the case in anoxic basins, mineral veins, hot springs, within sediments, and in the formation of sedimentary rocks. Capable of acting as oxidants that on reduction involve significant pH change are oxides of Fe, Mn, Pb, and As, as well as some anions of nonmetals such as SO_4^{2-} and CO_3^{2-}. The pH-controlling tendency of a redox reaction is shown to depend primarily on the ratio in the reaction of (OH^- produced)/(e's used) or alternatively (H^+ used)/(e's used), or, simply, pH/pE, as may be seen for the reductions below:

	pH/pE	
$MnO_2 + 4\,H^+ + 2e = Mn^{2+} + 2\,H_2O$ $MnO_2 + 2\,H_2O + 2e = Mn(OH)_2 + 2\,OH^-$	2	(20)
$SO_4^{2-} + 8\,H^+ + 8e = S^{2-} + 4\,H_2O$ $SO_4^{2-} + 4\,H_2O + 8e = S^{2-} + 8\,OH^-$	1	(21)
$CO_3^{2-} + 6\,H^+ + 4e = C + 3\,H_2O$ $CO_3^{2-} + 3\,H_2O + 4e = C + 6\,OH^-$	1.5	(22)

Boström's study is concerned with the effect of *pE* on pH as indicated by his values of (OH^- produced)/(*e*'s used); for our purpose in assessing the effect of pH on *pE* the index is simply the reciprocal, or *pE*/pH, for similar relations. But in the main ocean the changes in pH are slight and so one must again look to the unusually restricted regions where water is confined by the sediments, fiords, basins, veins, or craters for any significant effect of pH on *pE*.

The *pE*/pH diagram for the iron system is given in Fig. 6. The plot also bears the stability region for water between the upper O_2/H_2O and lower H_2O/H_2 lines, both at unit slope. These lines represent outer limits whose attainment is not to be expected in natural waters except in unusual circumstances. Also on the diagram at pH 8.1 are entered portions of lines at the proper slopes for the various redox systems considered in the Sillén model, as well as a few others to show where their fields of stability lie with respect to one another and to iron species. Near the top right at *pE* 8.5, pH 8.1 is a circled point that approximates the position of the oxic sea at 25°C and 1 atm. It is significantly close to the MnO_2/Mn_2O_3 boundary; these oxidation states are found together in natural occurrence, for example, in the ferromanganese minerals. The

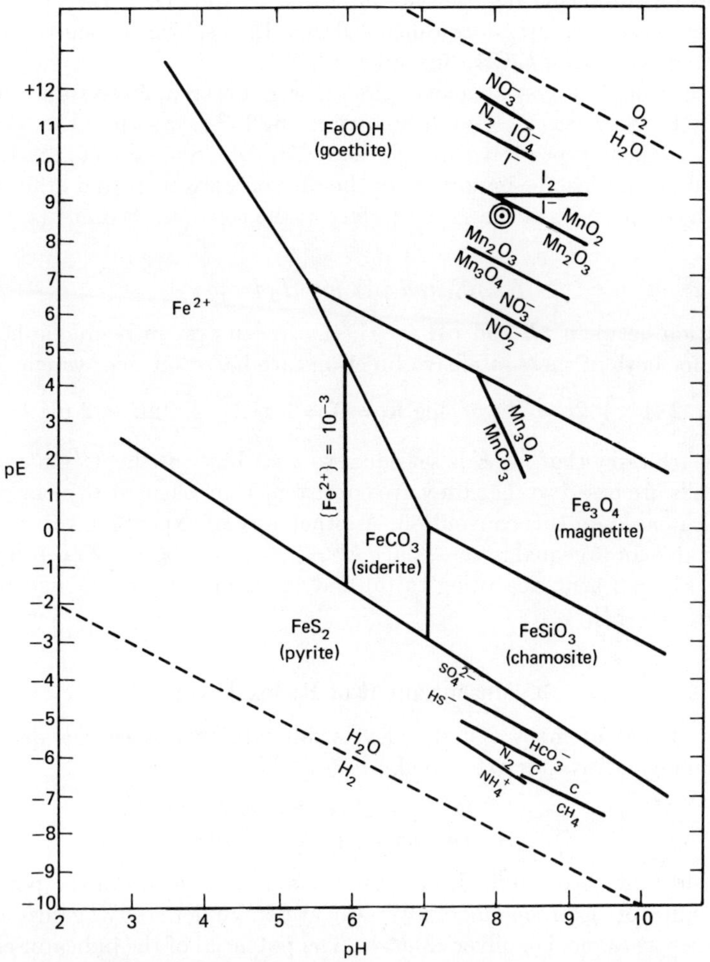

Fig. 6. *pE*/pH diagram for iron and other elements.

position of the circled point relative to the NO_3^-/N_2 line indicates the redox condition for nitrogen, where N_2 is dominant and NO_3^- found at very low concentrations. The suboxic condition where NO_2^- appears is shown by the NO_3^-/NO_2^- line. Another puzzling element has been iodine. If natural waters were at pE 12.5, then the iodine should be mainly found as IO_3^-, but substantial amounts are found as I^-; whereas at the circled point at pE 8.5, I^- should predominate as expected.

In the oxic sea iron exists as FeOOH; this and the more reduced fields of iron species are indicated with the most appropriate formula and a geochemical name to show the actual mineral occurrence of such species. The fields represent the areas of dominance of particular species while the lines represent a boundary condition of equal activities between two species. The construction of such a diagram is in some respects quite an arbitrary matter. Choice is required in the use of such thermodynamic data as activity coefficients of key chemicals and equilibrium constants.

The change over to anoxic conditions can be visualized by dropping vertically down the diagram, thus, for iron going progressively through the FeOOH, Fe_3O_4, $FeSiO_3$, or $FeCO_3$, and FeS fields; for manganese through the MnO_2, Mn_2O_3, Mn_3O_4, and $MnCO_3$ fields, but MnS is considered unlikely. On changing to anoxic conditions the redox states for sulfur and nitrogen are indicated by the SO_4^{2-}/HS^- and N_2/NH_4^+ lines, respectively. The entry into Sillén's Range II is shown by the HCO_3^-/C line, and into Range III by the C/CH_4 line, all at pH 8.1.

On the other hand, if by some means the pH were lowered, for example in the sediments, FeOOH could become solubilized by forming Fe^{2+}, as seen in Fig. 6 by moving horizontally to the left, possibly through the Fe_3O_4 field. Similar solubilization within the sediments might also be important in the case of manganese and other transition metals, with redeposition at the oxic interface at the top of the sediments.

E. pE and pH *for Hydrogen*

The relation between pE and pH for the hydrogen system is unique because the definitions for both of these intensive functions are based on this system. That is,

$$2\,H^+ + 2e = H_2 \qquad \log K = 0 = \log P_{H_2} + 2pE + 2\,\text{pH} \tag{5}$$

It is purely arbitrary that log K is set equal to zero, but it is the datum on which all such half-cells are based so that they are consistent from element to element. Sillén's model is also based on this convention. Another way of expressing this would be to set the E^0 value for (5) equal to zero, since $E^0 = 2.303\,RT \log K/nF$. It is noteworthy that when $P_{H_2} = 1$ atm, according to (5) and the definitions of pE and pH, pH + $pE = 0$; $pE = -\text{pH}$.

3. Measurement of Redox Levels

Methods of measurement of redox levels fall into two categories designated as intensive and capacitive (or extensive).

A. Intensive Measurements

The classical intensive method most used has been to measure the potential of a platinum indicator electrode immersed in the system under study against a reference electrode such as calomel or silver chloride. The potential of the indicator electrode is then calculated relative to the standard hydrogen electrode ($E^0 = 0$ for $P_{H_2} =$

1 atm; $\{H^+\} = 1$). This electromotive force is termed the *Eh* and pertains to the cell designated below:

$$-\mathrm{Pt},\ \underset{1\ \mathrm{atm}}{H_2}\ \Big|\ \underset{a\,=\,1}{H^+}\ \Big|\Big|\ O/R,\ \mathrm{Pt}+$$

where O/R represents the ratio of activities of oxidized and reduced forms of the redox system under study. If this system is one involving natural waters such as the sea, there will be more than one redox system involved. Ideally these would all be reversible and mediated one with another so that in this ideal case the *Eh* applies to all systems present; this feature is one advantage of an intensive type of measurement.

In contrast to the above formally defined situation, the measurement of *Eh* in real waters is complicated. It is a problem to decide which redox couples are active, which of these are dominant, and whether they all have the same potential value. In the oxic sea the dominant oxidized form is likely to be O_2, existing as it does in excess at a molar concentration of about 10^{-4}, but the identity of the reduced partner conjugate to O_2 has not been definitely established. The following approaches do not exhaust possibilities but they are the main ones:

1. The *Eh* value measured may be considered to represent the potential reached by the equilibration of all the reversible redox couples (other than that of O_2) present in the medium. These couples should contribute to the poise of the same potential value for all, registered on a platinum electrode whose behavior is inert with respect to the coupled species, serving only to transfer electrons. The oxic environment is dominated by O_2, which has established the appropriate O/R ratio for each of these reversible systems by slow reaction over a long period of time, or catalyzed microbiologically. In this model the O_2 itself is considered to be inert so far as the electrode is concerned (in the same sense that strongly bonded N_2 is electroinert). The difficulty with this model is that whereas in certain lakes and sediments the water may have sufficient content of dissolved or suspended compounds of redox elements (such as iron), it is doubtful whether this is possible in the sea.

2. Alternatively, the relative abundance of O_2 in the water may be considered to set the poise and to dominate the redox states of other systems (with the required mediation), and the corresponding potential becomes registered on the platinum electrode in accordance with the following half-cell, which has H_2O as its reduced form:

$$O_2 + 4\,H^+\ 4e = 2\,H_2O \qquad E^0 = 1.23\ \mathrm{V} \tag{9}$$

This system has already been discussed and it has been noted that reversible behavior has not been observed in seawater, and not normally in the laboratory, either.

3. There is evidence that platinum is not, in fact, inert to O_2 and a strong possibility is the adsorption of oxygen in some form on the surface of the platinum (Hoare, 1968). The oxygen is not considered to form a definite oxide of platinum; in fact, agreement on the stoichiometric ratio of O to Pt atoms is lacking. Only one of a number of possible formulations is,

$$\mathrm{Pt} - \mathrm{O} + 2\,H^+ + 2e = \mathrm{Pt} + H_2O \qquad E^0 = 0.88\ \mathrm{V} \tag{23}$$

but values for others are made available by Hoare (1968).

4. It is considered by Hoare that the platinum electrode functions rather with a mixed potential regulated by both a cathode mechanism that follows (9) and an anode

mechanism that is the reverse of (23), along with side effects from peroxides and impurities. It is not possible to represent this complex case by a suitable equation.

5. Stumm and Morgan (1970) emphasize that natural waters are in a highly dynamic state rather than in or near equilibrium, and consequently no single potential representing any one of the possible systems present can be expected to be reliably established on the platinum. They also note that redox reactions in general are slower than acid-base reactions. Accordingly, the only accurate descriptions of natural redox conditions are bound to be kinetic, involving different rates of approach to equilibrium rather than the state of poise at equilibrium.

6. Consideration of the mechanism of the reduction of O_2 has earlier been shown to lead logically to the concept of a steady-state activity of HO_2^- (or H_2O_2), which serves as the reduced form of the couple, and O_2 as the oxidized form in the half-cell reaction:

$$O_2 + 2\,H^+ + 2e = H_2O_2 \qquad E^0 = 0.68\ V \tag{15}$$

The oxidative side of the poise is maintained in natural oxic water by the supply of O_2, whereas the poise on the reductive side is more precarious, depending on the steady-state $\{H_2O_2\}$, which is in turn fed dynamically by a supply of O_2 and H_2O. It is not to be expected that a reversible and reliable potential corresponding to the above half-cell will be registered on platinum as an electrode for the reason that this is interfered with by the adsorption of O atoms on the platinum surface to an extent that governs the potential in an uncertain manner as described in 3 above.

All the above might be considered to render redox measurements with a platinum electrode useless. Such is the case only when for theoretical purposes the absolute potential for a half-cell is required and O_2 is dominant. Otherwise, in a relative sense, the measurements with the platinum electrode may show useful and quite reliable trends even if all the values are somewhat low, as is the case when O_2 is present in any quantity. However in a suboxic or anoxic regime where sulfides are present, the platinum may excel, and, according to Berner (1963), give reversible absolute measurements based on sulfide half-cell reactions studied in both natural and artificial sediments:

$$S^0_{(s)} + 2e = S^{2-} \qquad E^0 = -0.48\ V \tag{24}$$

$$S_2^{2-} + 2e = 2S^{2-} \qquad E^0 = -0.48\ V \tag{25}$$

$$S_3^{2-} + 2e = S_2^{2-} + S^{2-} \qquad E^0 = -0.49\ V \tag{26}$$

$$S_4^{2-} + 2e = S_3^{2-} + S^{2-} \qquad E^0 = -0.52\ V \tag{27}$$

The series of polysulfides above are formed in decreasing abundance by complexation of sulfides with sulfur, all with E^0 values close to -0.50 V. Realistically one might prefer HS^- to S^{2-} and write:

$$HS_2^- + 2e = HS^- + S^{2-} \tag{28}$$

and so on for the other polysulfides, but thermodynamic values are uncertain for the ionization data required. Berner states that $S^0_{(s)}$ occurs commonly in recent marine sediments. Stumm and Morgan (1970) have shown that it should be expected within the range of pE, -0.6 to $+0.4$, and pH 7.

A new approach to the measurement of Eh that has the advantage of not being based on the behavior of any particular group of chemicals at an electrode has been described by Breck (1972): the equilibrated redox potential, *Eh*, of a natural system is defined as the potential (on the usual hydrogen scale) of a small amount of a reversible redox indicator couple that has been equilibrated with an infinite amount of the natural system under study. One way to carry out the reaction required by the above definition was in an electric cell that was electrically short-circuited so that it ran itself down rapidly. The compartment for the indicator couple was kept small in volume (0.1 ml) but not too dilute, whereas the natural system was present in large amount, well stirred or circulated. Inert graphite electrodes were used so that bias due to catalysis was not introduced, as might be the case with most metallic elements (e.g., Pt). For the same reason, the use of activated carbon was avoided. The two electrodes were made of one piece of graphite so that the cell was shorted externally to allow a leak of electrons to equilibrate the indicator system (O^*/R^*) with the natural system (O/R) according to the complete cell reaction:

$$O + R^* = O^* + R \tag{29}$$

$$E_{\text{cell}} = -\left(E^{O}_{O^*/R^*} - \frac{RT}{nF}\ln\frac{\{R^*\}}{\{O^*\}}\right) + E_{O/R} - \frac{RT}{nF}\ln\frac{\{R\}}{\{O\}} = 0 \qquad \text{at equilibrium}$$

The graphite had been impregnated with paraffin to prevent it from soaking up any solution and thereby forming a series of indefinite liquid junctions. The electrolytic connection between the two solutions was conveniently effected by a plug of unfired Vycor glass that had been previously soaked in a saturated solution of KCl. The Vycor plug was seated in a rubber sleeve, as shown in Fig. 7*a*. The potential of the indicator couple was taken by means of a commercial combination redox cell fitted into the graphite cell by an O-ring. The combination measuring cell consisted of an external electrode in the form of a button of platinum, connected internally through a saturated KCl solution to an internal silver chloride reference electrode.

Several indicator redox couples were used to test this apparatus: Fe^{3+}/Fe^{2+}, I_3^-/I^-, and $Fe(CN)_6^{3-}/Fe(CN)_6^{4-}$. The last of these was preferred for a variety of reasons. It equilibrates quickly; the anionic species are soluble in slightly alkaline solution as well as in acidic solution; and this couple has a potential slightly below that of the oxic water so that it becomes oxidized up to the potential of the water, thus drawing

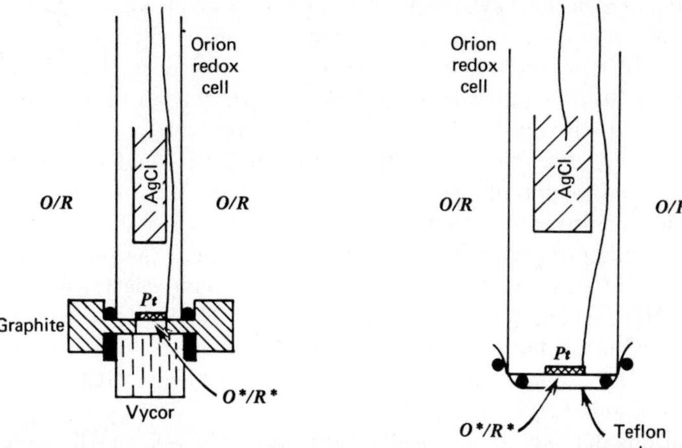

Fig. 7*a*. The graphite equilibration cell.

Fig. 7*b*. The Teflon membrane equilibration cell.

on the poise afforded by excess O_2 instead of being being reduced by the water with poorer poise on the reduced side. A sensible choice of indicator couple is also one whose E^0 value is such that it has reasonable poise at the redox level of the natural system being measured, making for a stable potential by avoiding polarization owing to very low concentrations of O^* or R^*.

The purpose of the above design was not to advance another device for monitoring water for *Eh* so much as to establish a reliable value of the *Eh* of natural oxic water. The method is independent of the reliability of any particular electrode system and of an understanding of its mechanism. Nor is the method limited to indicator couples that are amenable to potentiometric measurement. If, for an indicator couple (O^*/R^*) the different forms O^* and R^* have distinctive radiation, absorption peaks, or difference in another suitable property, then the logarithmic ratio of O^*/R^*, and hence *Eh* and *pE* can be found, although translation through activity coefficients may be required in cases where concentrations are measured. Even redox indicator paper, or colored redox indicator in any suitable physical arrangement to equilibrate small amounts of the O^*/R^* coupled with infinite amounts of the natural system, O/R, should give reliability if not the precision of electrical measurements.

Another means by which a small amount of redox indicator can be equilibrated with a large natural system uses dissolved O_2 as the short-circuiting agent (instead of electrons) by leakage through a semipermeable membrane. A small amount (two drops) of O^*/R^* was enclosed by a Teflon membrane that served as the analog of the liquid junction, but allowed the passage of O_2 gas and not of dissolved electrolyte species within the time of the experiment. To arrange this, two drops of the O^*/R^* solution were placed on the platinum end of the combination redox cell and covered by a small piece of either Saran or Teflon sheet, sealed with a small O-ring, as in Fig. 7*b*. This whole assembly was immersed in the natural water and allowed to equilibrate. *Eh* values obtained using different O^*/R^* couples were in good agreement with one another and with *Eh* values of about 0.50 V from the graphite cell. Potential values measured on a bare platinum electrode in the same media ranged from 0.04 to 0.27 V lower, and averaged about 0.1 V lower.

B. Capacitive Measurements

The oxidative capacity of a natural system with respect to a given *pE* is equal to the sum of all the oxidants in equivalents on the positive side of the given *pE* minus the sum of all the reductants in equivalents on the negative side of it. The above paraphrases a definition by Stumm and Morgan (1970). At a *pE* of 8.5 a natural oxic water would usually have the dissolved oxidants O_2, NO_3^-, and traces of other oxidants such as IO_3^-, and $Cr_2O_7^{2-}$. Particulate MnO_2 and FeOOH could constitute trace oxidants. Any unreacted reductants below *pE* 8.5 would constitute a debt to be charged against this oxidative inventory to get the net oxidative capacity. The traditional method of determining oxidative capacity due to dissolved, gaseous O_2 has been by Winkler titration, the overall effects of which are to have the O_2 oxidize fresh $Mn(OH)_2$ to $MnO(OH)_2$, which in turn releases I_2 from I^- solution for quantitative titration with standard thiosulfate. The oxidative capacity due to O_2 is smaller than that of FeOOH and SO_4^{2-}, but the really large capacities belong to HCO_3^- and $C_{(s)}$, as already noted in the long ranges in Fig. 3.

Under reducing conditions the reductive capacity with respect to a given *pE* can be defined as the equivalent sum of all the reductants on the negative side of this *pE* minus the equivalent sum of all the oxidants on the positive side. ZoBell (1946) estimated reductive capacity in the sediments by titration with an oxidizing solution of Fe^{3+} in Cl^- solution, keeping the iron soluble by complexing.

Just as the alkalinity of seawater is for many purposes more informative than pH, so the redox capacity can be more useful than *Eh* or *pE*. A determination of redox capacity is consumptive of reductant or oxidant, as the case may be, and so is, in general, a type of titration; but also possible is the provision of electrons as the reductant in electrometric titrations. Reduction by electrons is also the basis of the polarographic techniques for measuring dissolved O_2, for example, at a gold cathode inside a Teflon membrane. Such a cell is calibrated with O_2 in air or in aqueous solutions of known O_2 content at known temperatures, or temperature compensation can be built in by inserting a temperature probe in the cell. Suitable probes, stirrers, and leads are designed for *in situ* operation. In the oxic sea it appears that more sensitive and reliable monitoring is possible by measurement of dissolved O_2 or by redox titration than by *Eh* measurement.

C. *Temperature Dependence of Eh*

It is of scientific interest to ascertain how *Eh* depends on temperature; however, the experimental data for such a study are not readily available. It is possible to attempt a thermodynamic thrust by use of a relation that identifies the temperature coefficient of electromotive force of an electric cell reaction or half-cell reaction with the associated change in entropy. Thus, for a reaction at constant pressure:

$$\frac{dEh}{dT} = \frac{\Delta S}{nF} \tag{30}$$

Before ΔS can be evaluated, and hence dEh/dT, a decision is required as to the identity of the reaction controlling the *Eh*. Here let us consider both (9) and (15) as possibilities, and use the appropriate standard values of the entropies as given by Garrels and Christ (1965). This yields, in kilojoule K^{-1}/mol, for: $O_2(g)$, 205.0; $H_2(g)$, 130.6; $H_2O(1)$, 70.0; H^+_{aq}, 0.0 by definition. For $H_2O_2(aq)$ no entropy value is given; but the formation energies, $\Delta G_f{}^0$ and $\Delta H_f{}^0$, are. Accordingly, calculation of $\Delta S_f{}^0 = \Delta H_f{}^0/T - \Delta G_f{}^0/T$ for $H_2O_2(aq)$ in kilojoule K^{-1}/mol gives the value -199.6. From (31) below S^0 for $H_2O_2(aq)$ works out to be 136.0.

$$H_2(g) + O_2(g) = H_2O_2(aq); \qquad \Delta S_f{}^0 = S^0_{H_2O_2(aq)} - S^0_{H_2}(g) - S^0_{O_2}(g) \tag{31}$$

Considering the reactions in Table VIII, each against a standard hydrogen electrode ($E^0 = 0$), we calculate for the two reactions (9) and (15) the values in the table of ΔS^0 and dEh/dT. It must be noted that the above calculations are for standard conditions

TABLE VIII

Calculated Temperature Coefficients of *Eh*

Half-Cell Reaction	E^0 (volt)	$\Delta S^0 \left(\frac{\text{kilojoule}}{\text{K} \times \text{mole}}\right)$	$dEh/dT(10^4$ volt/K)
$\frac{1}{2}O_2 + 2H^+ + 2e = H_2O$	1.23	-32.6	-1.7
$O_2 + 2H^+ + 2e = H_2O_2$	0.68	-69.0	-3.6

and not for the activities operating in the environment, but they suffice to show that the difference in temperature behavior for the two reactions is significant, with both negative but one about twice the other. These estimations are not important in a practical sense simply because the temperature range encountered in the sea is not usually more than about 30°C, making the effect small even at a maximum. Instead, a theoretical use would be to determine the temperature coefficient of *Eh* experimentally as a means of helping to decide whether redox control by (9) or (15) is indicated by the result.

D. Pressure Dependence of Eh

Here again, few reliably known values of *Eh* exist, let alone the set of experimental data to assess the pressure dependence. Classically, the thermodynamic relation for change of *Eh* with pressure would be, at constant temperature

$$dEh/dP = \Delta\overline{V}/nF \tag{32}$$

The change in partial molar volume of the reaction, $\Delta\overline{V}$, could be calculated if all the partial molar volumes of products and reactants were known for the particular reaction; however, it is usually necessary (MacInnes, 1961) to treat only the values for the gaseous substances, and even for these MacInnes shows the ideal gas law usually to be adequate. This means that in treating the pressure dependence of the *Eh* of either (9) or (15), one needs to be concerned in the electrode expression for *Eh* only with the effect of the log P_{O_2} term. On this basis:
(a) for $O_2/2\ H_2O$ control,

$$E = E^0 - \frac{RT}{4F} \ln \frac{\{H_2O\}^2}{\{H^+\}^4 \cdot P_{O_2}} \tag{33}$$

and taking $\{H_2O\} = 1$, pH $= 8.1$,

$$E = 1.23 - 0.06(8.1) - 0.015 \log P_{O_2} = 0.74 - 0.015 \log P_{O_2} \tag{34}$$

(b) for O_2/H_2O_2 control,

$$E = E^0 - \frac{RT}{2F} \ln \frac{\{H_2O_2\}}{\{H^+\}^2 \cdot P_{O_2}} \tag{35}$$

and taking $\{H_2O_2\} = 10^{-11}$, pH $= 8.1$,

$$E = 0.68 - 0.06(8.1) + 0.33 + 0.03 \log P_{O_2} = 0.52 - 0.03 \log P_{O_2} \tag{36}$$

To test the above relations, an as yet unreported experiment was done by Pascoe (1971) in our laboratory in which water thermostatted at 25°C in a round-bottom flask was saturated with pure O_2 at 1 atm. A slow leak allowed the O_2 to escape until eventually the solution became saturated with air ($P_{O_2} = 0.2$ atm), all the while three measurements were made concurrently:

1. The potential on a bare platinum (E_{Pt}) was measured against a calomel electrode as reference and reduced to the potential against the standard hydrogen datum.

2. The equilibrated potential (*Eh*) of an O^*/R^* solution of $Fe(CN)_6{}^{3-}/Fe(CN)_6{}^{4-}$ with added KCl and contained by a Teflon membrane was measured against a reference electrode and referred to the hydrogen datum.

3. The log P_{O_2} was determined with a dissolved O_2 probe and meter, with agitation to avoid local depletion of O_2.

Such an experiment had some serious faults, the worst of which were that this water lacked any natural poise and depended only on the O_2 content, and there was no assurance that equilibration of each of the conditions for the three measured properties had time to be established as the experiment proceeded or that the various properties reported were synchronous at any point. Nevertheless, the plots of Figs. 8 and 9 show valuable features. *Eh*, P_{Pt}, and $-\log P_{O_2}$ all vary similarly with time in Fig. 8, with the *Eh* value coming out at values close to 0.50 V in good agreement with previously determined equilibrated values from graphite and Saran membrane cells. The values for E_{Pt} were found to be about 0.1 V lower than the corresponding *Eh* values.

A plot of (34) in the form of E against $-\log P_{O_2}$ should give a straight line of intercept 0.74 and slope 0.015, whereas the analogous plot of (36) should give a straight line of intercept 0.52 and slope 0.03. The plots of Fig. 9, particularly with respect to the intercept, are compatible with O_2/H_2O_2 control but not with $O_2/2\ H_2O$ control.

A more diagnostic calculation of the slope can be obtained from Fig. 8, where,

$$\frac{\Delta(Eh)}{\Delta(\log P_{O_2})} = \frac{0.504 - 0.494}{0.380 - 0.080} = \frac{0.01}{0.3} \sim 0.03$$

showing that the experimental slope also supports O_2/H_2O_2 control.

If it is accepted that *Eh* depends on $\log P_{O_2}$, according to (36), the next logical question is how P_{O_2} varies in the water column in a typical sea. O_2 profiles (often given in mole per liter, which should parallel P_{O_2}), differ characteristically for the different oceans and appear to be governed more by biological processes than by pressure per se. Usually there is a high concentration of O_2 in the upper layer with good mixing of a plentiful supply from the atmosphere, along with O_2 produced by photosynthesis. Below the euphotic zone, however, decay processes consume O_2, and

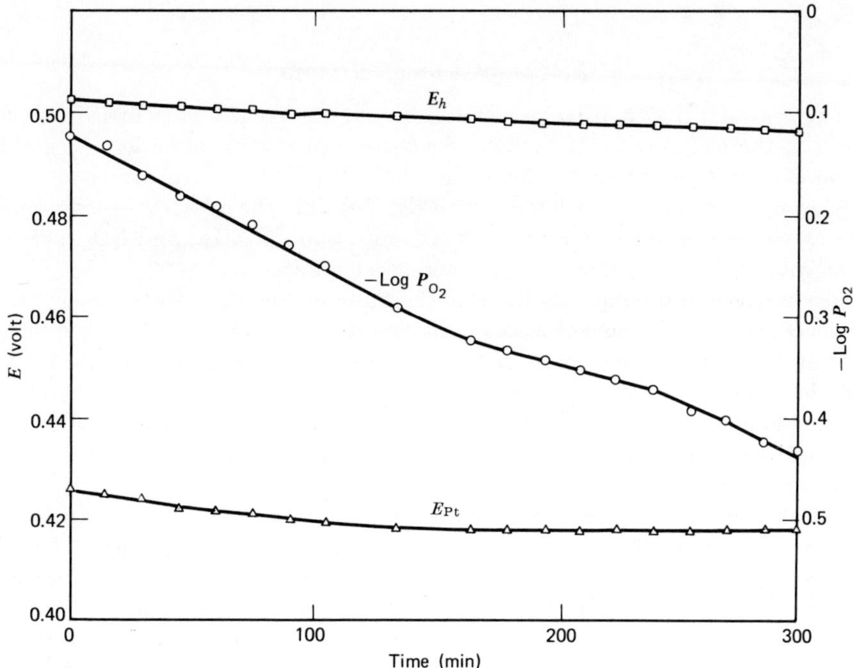

Fig. 8. Variation of *Eh*, E_{Pt}, and $-\log P_{O_2}$ with time.

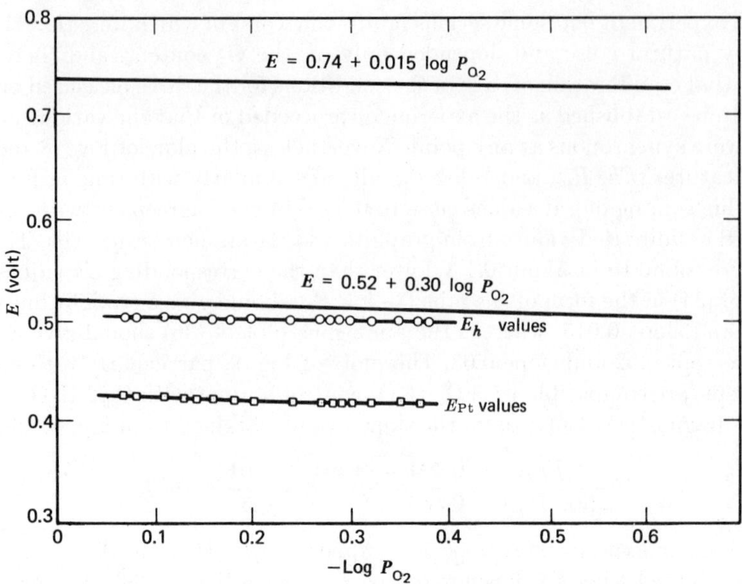

Fig. 9. Plot of Eh, E_{Pt}, and equations 42 and 43 against $-\log P_{O_2}$.

with no reliable supply an O_2 minimum occurs at depths somewhat less than 1000 m. From here down the O_2 concentration gradually increases with depth. The logarithmic O_2 profile should exhibit a much damped version with the same qualitative features. Within the reliability of relation (36), *Eh* and *pH* can be calculated from known P_{O_2} values.

E. Comparison of Methods

In oxic seawater the intensive properties, *Eh* and *pE*, like pH, vary little from place to place in the main ocean. Both *Eh* and *pE* are seen to depend on log P_{O_2} and are relatively insensitive criteria for describing the redox condition; as can be seen from Fig. 8, even log P_{O_2} varies much more than *Eh*. Certainly the capacitive measurement of the O_2 content or, in certain cases, of concentrations of NO_3^- and NO_2^-, give an assessment of redox in a more sensitive and specific way.

Under anoxic and suboxic conditions in the water and beneath the sediments there is evidence that the platinum electrode behaves reversibly; even so, there is difficulty operating the reference electrode in the presence of sulfides, and more sensitivity should be available by capacitive measurement of sulfide concentration. Finally, the value should not be overlooked of the redox analogue of alkalinity, that is, of titrating the sample electrometrically, or using a convenient quantitative reductant such as borohydride ion.

In conclusion, Sillén's equilibrium model for the redox condition of the seas, past and present, is in excellent agreement with experimental measurements of *Eh*, P_{O_2}, corrected E_{Pt}, colored redox indicators, or with the natural indication afforded by chemical speciation of Mn, Fe, N, and I, providing agreement prevails that the *pE* of oxic seawater is taken to be around 8.5, as the equilibration and log P_{O_2} experiments tend to confirm. However, a qualifying clause should also be added to the effect that pockets of irregularity are always to be expected in space and time or, as Sillén said:

At most we may hope that the model may have some resemblance to the average state of the bulk of the ocean at various times in the past; there have certainly always been regions that deviate because of photochemical or (in later stages) biological activity.

References

Berl, W. G., 1943. A reversible oxygen electrode. *Trans. Electrochem. Soc.*, **83**, 253–271.

Berner, R. A., 1963. Electrode studies of hydrogen sulfide in marine sediments. *Geochim. Cosmochim. Acta*, **27**, 563–575.

Boström, K., 1967. Some pH-controlling redox reactions in natural waters. In *Equilibrium Concepts in Natural Water Systems*. R. F. Gould ed. Advan. Chem. Ser. No. 67 (Chapter 14)

Breck, W. G. 1972. Redox potentials by equilibration. *J. Marine Res.* **30** 121–139.

Cloud P. and A. Gibor, 1970. The oxygen cycle. *Scient. American*, **223** (3), 115.

Garrels, R. M. and C. L. Christ, 1965. *Solutions, Minerals, and Equilibria*. Harper and Row, New York, 400 pp.

Goldberg, E. D., W. S. Broecker, M. G. Gross, and K. K. Turekian, 1971. Marine chemistry. In *Radioactivity in the Marine Environment*. National Academy of Sciences (Chapter 5).

Goldschmidt, V. M., 1933. *Fortschr. Mineral Krist. Petr.*, **17**, 112.

Hoare, J. P., 1968. *The Electrochemistry of Oxygen*. Wiley-Interscience, New York, 423 pp.

Horn, M. K., 1964. A computer system for the geochemical balance of the elements. Ph.D. thesis, Geology Department, Rice University, Houston, Texas.

Kastening, B., and G. Kazemifard, 1970. Elektrochemische Reduktion von Sauerstoff. *Berichte der Bunsen-Gesellschaft*, **74**, 551–556.

MacInnes, D. A., 1961. *The Principles of Electrochemistry*. Dover, New York, 465 pp.

Morris, J. C. and W. Stumm, 1967. Redox equilibria and measurement of potentials in the aquatic environment. In *Equilibrium Concepts in Natural Water Systems*. R. F. Gould, ed. Advan. Chem. Ser. No. 67, Chapter 13.

Pascoe, D., 1971. Unpublished work, Queen's University, Kingston, Canada.

Richards, F. A. 1965. Anoxic basins and fiords. In *Chemical Oceanography*. Vol. 1. J. P. Riley and G. Skirrow, eds. Academic Press, London, 613–645 (Chapter 13).

Richards, F. A. and W. W. Broenkow, 1971. Chemical changes, including nitrate reduction, in Darwin Bay, Galapagos Archipelago, over a 2-month period, 1969. *Limnol. Oceanog.*, **16** (5), 758–765.

Sato, M., 1960. Oxidation of sufide ore bodies, 1. Geochemical environments in terms of *Eh* and pH. *Econ. Geol.*, **55**, 928–961.

Sillén, L. G., 1965. "Oxidation States of Earth's Ocean and Atmosphere."

(a) A model calculation on earlier states. The myth of the probiotic soup. *Arkiv. Kemi*, **24**, 431–456.

(b) The behavior of Fe, S, and Mn in earlier states. Regulating mechanisms for O_2 and N_2. *Arkiv. Kemi*, **25**, 159–176.

Sillén, L. G. and A. E. Martell, 1964. *Stability Constants of Metal–Ion Complexes*. Special Publ. No. 17, The Chemical Society, London, 745 pp.

Stumm, W. and J. J. Morgan, 1970. *Aquatic Chemistry*. Wiley-Interscience, New York, 583 pp.

Weisz, R. S. and S. S. Jaffe, 1948. The mechanism of the reduction of oxygen at the air electrode. *Trans. Electrochem. Soc.*, **93**, 128–141.

Yeager, E., P. Krouse, and K. V. Rao, 1964. The kinetics of the oxygen–peroxide couple on carbon. *Electrochemica Acta*, **9**, 1057–1070.

ZoBell, C. E., 1946. Studies on redox potential of marine sediments. *Bull. Amer. Ass. Pet. Geol.*, **30** (4), 477–513.

5. EQUILIBRIUM CALCULATIONS OF THE SPECIATION OF ELEMENTS IN SEAWATER

DAVID DYRSSEN AND MARGARETTA WEDBORG

1. Introduction

Lars Gunnar Sillén was invited in 1959 to present a lecture on the physical chemistry of seawater at the International Oceanographic Congress in New York. For this lecture (Sillén, 1961) he calculated the main dissolved species of major, minor, and microelements in seawater using the pH value of 8.1, the *pE* value of 12.5 and the chloride concentration of 0.5483 mole/liter (*M*). His calculations were based on the second edition of "Stability Constants" (Bjerrum et al., 1958). These principal species were listed by Goldberg (1963), who also commented that ion-pair formation took place between the sulfate and divalent metal ions.

In order to gain an understanding of processes in seawater, one can neither neglect the equilibrium state nor reaction kinetics regardless of whether the rate depends on a pure inorganic reaction or a reaction involving biological or geological matter. The fact that Swedish coastal waters (Lindahl, 1972) can be stimulated by adding chelated trace metals or even by adding chelating substances only shows that the chemical state of biogenic metal ions is very important for primary production. The fact that particulate iron(III) is set free as soluble iron(II) in reducing (anoxic) conditions is understandable with the knowledge of their coordination chemistry. In order to understand different separation procedures such as solvent extraction, ion exchange, adsorption, electrolysis, coprecipitation, and evaporation, it is important to know the chemical state. In fact, such procedures are often used for the determination of different species of trace elements in solution (e.g., Matthews and Riley, 1970).

The aim of the present article is the determination of the speciation of elements in seawater by complex formation equilibrium measurements and computer calculations of the equilibrium state in standard 35‰ seawater.

2. Sodium Chloride. Concentration Units. Activity Scales.

For studies of ionic interactions in seawater 0.7*M* (or *m*) sodium chloride is used as a reference medium. However, the suitable concentration unit for the analysis of the major ions in seawater is moles per kilogram of seawater, M_w (Dyrssen and Sillén, 1967). The difference between these concentration units is demonstrated in Table I.

The ionic strength of 0.7*M* NaCl is 0.7102*m* in the molal unit used by physical chemists dealing with activity coefficients. The mean activity coefficient at 25°C is 0.667 (Robinson and Stokes, 1959). This mean coefficient can be split into f_{Na^+} =

TABLE I

Concentrative Properties of 0.7*M* NaCl

M				*m*	M_w
mol/l	g H_2O/l	g NaCl/l	kg soln/l	mol/kg H_2O	mol/kg soln
0.7000	985.6	40.91	1.0265	0.7102	0.6819

0.700 and $f_{Cl^-} = 0.636$ according to a procedure given by Bates, Staples, and Robinson (1970). These activity coefficients are defined in the usual way, that is, f_{Na^+} or $f_{Cl^-} \rightarrow 1$ when $[Na^+]$ or $[Cl^-] \rightarrow 0$ in pure water. Sillén (1967) pointed out, however, that for minor species X in a salt medium there is a certain advantage to use another activity scale by defining $f_x \rightarrow 1$ when $[X] \rightarrow 0$ in $0.7M$ NaCl or 35‰ seawater. This scale has been extensively used in complex formation studies.

The concentrations of major and minor ionic constituents in standard seawater are given in Table II. (The micro constituents will be discussed in a later section. The formal ionic strength is $0.714M$, but sulfate ion-pairing may lower the real ionic strength to $0.666M$.

Table II

Concentrations of the Main Ionic Constituents of Standard Seawater. S = 35‰, Cl = 19.374‰, and d = 1.02336 g/cm³ at 25°C

	mol/kg (M_w)	mol/l (M)	mg/kg
Na^+	0.468(38) [a]	0.479(32) [a]	107(68)
K^+	0.01021	0.01045	399.1
Mg^{2+}	0.05315	0.05439	1291.8
Ca^{2+}	0.01029	0.01053	412.3
Sr^{2+}	0.000093	0.000095	8.14
Cl^-	0.54587	0.55862	19353
Br^-	0.00084	0.00086	67.3
F^-	0.0000734	0.0000751	1.39
SO_4^{2-}	0.02823	0.02889	2712
Alkalinity	0.00238	0.00244	—
Total carbonate	0.00230	0.00235	27.6 (as C)
HCO_3^-	0.00188	0.00192	—
CO_3^{2-}	0.00023	0.00024	—
Total boron	0.000412	0.000421	4.45 (as B)
$B(OH)_4^-$	0.000081	0.000083	—
$\sum n[X^{n\pm}]$ (equivalent)	0.60566 [a]	0.61981 [a]	
$\frac{1}{2}\sum n^2[X^{n\pm}]$ (formal ionic strength)	0.69765	0.71395	

[a] The sodium concentration has been calculated from the ionic balance: $\sum n[X^{n+}] = \sum n[X^{n-}]$.

3. Interactions Among the Main Constituents

Figure 1 shows the approximate strength of ionic interactions among the main constituents of seawater. This diagram shows that CO_2 (H_2CO_3), HCO_3^-, $B(OH)_3$, and H_2O are strong proton complexes (weak acids, $K > 10^6$), while HSO_4^- and HF are rather weak complexes of intermediate strength ($10 < K < 1000$). The carbonate complexes with Mg^{2+} and Ca^{2+} (and Sr^{2+}) lie in the same intermediate range, as do MgF^+ and $MgOH^+$, also. The divalent metal complexes with sulfate, hydrogen carbonate, and borate are weak ($1 < K < 10$) as are CaF^+ and $CaOH^+$. Complexing with sodium and potassium may in general be neglected except in the case of sulfate. Thus a determination of the protonization constant of SO_4^{2-} in $0.4M$ NaCl + $0.1M$ Na_2SO_4 will be $17M^{-1}$ at 25°C (Elgquist and Wedborg, 1972) using the definition $f_{H^+} \rightarrow 1$ for $[H^+] \rightarrow 0$ in the salt medium. If the reaction $H^+ + SO_4^{2-} \rightleftharpoons HSO_4^-$ is

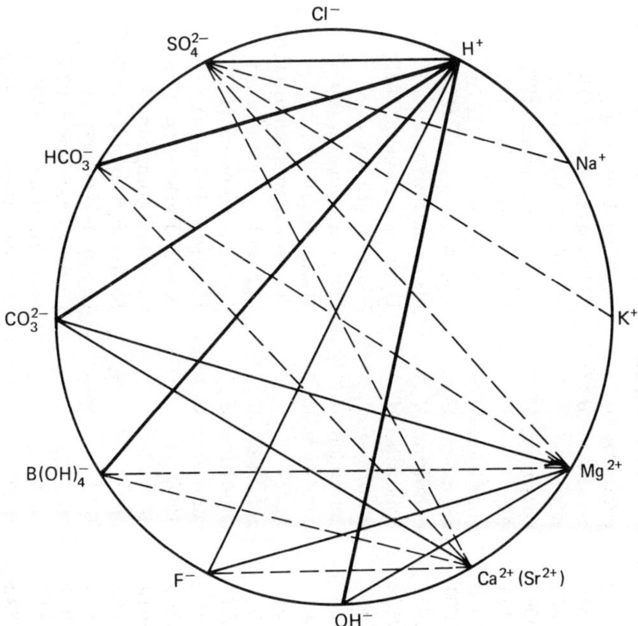

Fig. 1. Ion-pairing diagram for seawater. ▬▬ strong complexes ($K > 10^6$); —— intermediate complexes ($10 < K < 1000$); - - - - weak complexes ($1 < K < 10$).

corrected for the formation of $NaSO_4^-$ using an ion-pairing constant of 2, then $K_{HSO_4^-}$ will be 36 instead of 17, which is a conditional constant. In pure water at 25°C $K_{HSO_4^-}$ is 95 ± 5 according to a compilation of stability constants by Sillén and Martell (1964, supplement 1971). For seawater, Dyrssen and Hansson (1973) obtained a conditional constant of $11.6M^{-1}$ while Culberson, Pytkowicz, and Hawley (1970) obtained $12.3M^{-1}$. It is advisable to use the conditional constants for corrections in the precise determination of the alkalinity of seawater (cf. Hanson and Jagner, 1973). Calculations of the speciation of elements, on the other hand, requires that ion interactions between sulfate and Na^+, K^+, Mg^{2+}, and Ca^{2+} are taken into account.

Table III summarizes constants for the main constituents of standard seawater. Except in the case of sulfate the constants for sodium chloride media may be regarded as working constants for the calculation of the concentration of different species in seawater. For chloride we shall use the concentration $0.54587M_w$ or 0.55862M, ($p\text{Cl} \approx 0.26$), i.e., we regard chloride as not being complexed by the main constituents of seawater.

4. Carbonate Speciation—pH and pOH of Seawater

Seawater is not very well buffered in the absence of minerals with ion-exchange properties (cf. Sillén, 1961). In fact, seawater is close to one of the buffer minima of the carbonate system (cf. Dyrssen and Sillén, 1967). Thus photosynthesis will have a more marked effect on pH than on total inorganic carbonate. For our calculations of metal and carbonate speciation we may then choose 8.00 as a working value of pH (conditional value of $-\log[H^+]_{tot}$). Using a total carbonate concentration of

TABLE III

Complex Formation Constants for the Main Constituents of Seawater at 25°C

Equilibrium	Medium	log K	Remark	Reference
$H^+ + SO_4^{2-} \rightleftharpoons HSO_4^-$	0.4 NaCl + 0.1 $NaSO_4$	1.230	condition M^{-1}	Elgquist-Wedborg (1972)
$H^+ + SO_4^{2-} \rightleftharpoons HSO_4^-$	0.1 NaCl + 0.1 Na_2SO_4 + 0.1 $MgCl_2$	1.230	condition M^{-1}	Elgquist-Wedborg (1972)
$H^+ + SO_4^{2-} \rightleftharpoons HSO_4^-$	0.4 NaCl + 0.1 Na_2SO_4	1.552	M^{-1}	Calculated by authors
$H^+ + SO_4^{2-} \rightleftharpoons HSO_4^-$	SW	1.064	condition M^{-1}	Dyrssen-Hansson (1973)
$H^+ + SO_4^{2-} \rightleftharpoons HSO_4^-$	SW	1.511	M_w^{-1}	Dyrssen-Hansson (1973)
$H^+ + SO_4^{2-} \rightleftharpoons HSO_4^-$	SW	1.090	condition M^{-1}	Culberson et al. (1970)
$H^+ + HCO_3^- \rightleftharpoons H_2CO_3$	0.7 NaCl	6.001	condition M_w^{-1}	Dyrssen-Hansson (1973)
$H^+ + HCO_3^- \rightleftharpoons H_2CO_3$	SW	5.857	condition M_w^{-1}	Hansson (1973a, c)
$H^+ + CO_3^{2} \rightleftharpoons HCO_3^-$	0.7 NaCl	9.538	condition M_w^{-1}	Dyrssen-Hansson (1973)
$H^+ + CO_3^{2-} \rightleftharpoons HCO_3^-$	SW	8.947	condition M_w^{-1}	Hansson (1973a, c)
$H^+ + B(OH)_4^- \rightleftharpoons B(OH)_3$	0.7 NaCl	8.85	condition M_w^{-1}	Dyrssen-Hansson (1973)
$H^+ + B(OH)_4^- \rightleftharpoons B(OH)_3$	SW	8.61	condition M_w^{-1}	Hansson (1973b, c)
$H^+ + F^- \rightleftharpoons HF$	0.5 $NaClO_4$	2.91	M^{-1}	56C in Sillén-Martell (1964)
$H^+ + F^- \rightleftharpoons HF$	SW	2.6	condition M_w^{-1}	Calculated by authors
$H^+ + OH^- \rightleftharpoons H_2O$	0.7 NaCl	13.77	condition M_w^{-1}	Dyrssen-Hansson (1973)
$H^+ + OH^- \rightleftharpoons H_2O$	SW	13.19	condition M_w^{-1}	Hansson (1973a, c)
$Na^+ + SO_4^{2-} \rightleftharpoons NaSO_4^-$	SW	0.305	M^{-1}	Kester-Pytkowicz (1969)
$K^+ + SO_4^{2-} \rightleftharpoons KSO_4^-$	SW	0.013	M^{-1}	Garrels-Thompson (1962)
$Mg^{2+} + SO_4^{2-} \rightleftharpoons MgSO_4$	SW	1.009	M^{-1}	Kester-Pytkowicz (1969)
$Mg^{2+} + SO_4^{2-} \rightleftharpoons MgSO_4$	SW	0.845	M^{-1}	Elgquist-Wedborg (1972)
$Mg^{2+} + HCO_3^- \rightleftharpoons MgHCO_3^+$	SW	0.017	M_w^{-1}	Dyrssen-Hansson (1973)
$Mg^{2+} + CO_3^{2-} \rightleftharpoons MgCO_3$	SW	1.512	M_w^{-1}	Dyrssen-Hansson (1973)
$Mg^{2+} + B(OH)_4^- \rightleftharpoons MgB(OH)_4^+$	SW	0.732	M_w^{-1}	Dyrssen-Hansson (1973)
$Mg^{2+} + F^- \rightleftharpoons MgF^+$	0.7 NaCl	1.274	condition M^{-1}	Elgquist (1970)
$Mg^{2+} + OH^- \rightleftharpoons MgOH^+$	SW	1.58	M_w^{-1}	Dyrssen-Hansson (1973)
$Ca^{2+} + SO_4^{2-} \rightleftharpoons CaSO_4$	SW	1.033	M^{-1}	Kester-Pytkowicz (1969)
$Ca^{2+} + F^- \rightleftharpoons CaF^+$	0.7 NaCl	0.625	condition M^{-1}	Elgquist (1970)
$Ca^{2+} + OH^- \rightleftharpoons CaOH^+$	SW	$\sim$0.25	M^{-1}	Estimated by authors

$0.00230M_w$, we may then calculate the total concentrations of $CO_2 + H_2CO_3$, HCO_3^-, and CO_3^{2-} with the conditional constants in Table III. The result is:

$$\text{Total } [CO_2] + (H_2CO_3] = 0.000015M_w \ (0.64\%)$$
$$\text{Total } (HCO_3^-] = 0.00205M_w \ (89.29\%)$$
$$\text{Total } [CO_3^{2-}] = 0.00023M_w \ (10.07\%)$$

The ratio of $[CO_2]/[H_2CO_3]$ is in the order of 400 to 1000 (Sillén and Martell, 1964). The total concentrations of HCO_3^- and CO_3^{2-} may be split in one part complexed with Mg^{2+} and Ca^{2+} and one "free" part. Thus,

$$0.00205M_w = [HCO_3^-] + [MHCO_3^+]$$

and

$$0.00023M_w = [CO_3^{2-}] + [MCO_3]$$

where

$$[M^{2+}] = [Mg^{2+}] + [Ca^{2+}] \approx 0.0579M_w$$

Using $K = 1.04$ for $MHCO_3^+$ and $K = 32.5$ for MCO_3 we obtain

$$[HCO_3^-] = \frac{0.00205}{(1 + 1.04 \cdot 0.0579)}$$

and

$$[CO_3^{2-}] = 0.00023/(1 + 32.5 \cdot 0.0579)$$

The percentage of the different carbonate species is then

$$CO_2:0.64\%$$
$$HCO_3^-:84.30\%$$
$$MHCO_3^+:4.99\%$$
$$CO_3^{2-}:3.53\%$$
$$MCO_3:6.54\%$$

Likewise, part of the protons are complexed with sulfate:

$$[H^+]_{tot} = [H^+] + [HSO_4^-] = [H^+](1 + 11.5 \cdot 0.02823)$$

and

$$p[H^+] = p[H^+]_{tot} + 0.12 = 8.12$$

The activity scale for pH is so chosen that $f_{H^+} \to 1$ when $[H^+] \to 0$ (M_w scale) in 35‰ seawater (cf., Hansson, 1973d).

In the same way part of the OH^- is in the form of $MgOH^+$:

$$[OH^-]_{tot} = [OH^-] + (MgOH^+] = [OH^-](1 + 38.0 \cdot 0.048)$$

and

$$p[OH^-]_{tot} = p[OH^-] - 0.45$$

Thus the formation of HSO_4^- and $MgOH^+$ will explain the difference in pK_w for $0.7M_w$ NaCl and standard seawater:

$$p[H^+] + p[OH^-] = 13.77$$
$$p[H^+]_{tot} + p[OH^-]_{tot} = 13.19$$

For the calculation of hydroxide complexing (metal ion hydrolysis), we shall use pH = 8.12 or pOH = 5.65, and for the calculation of metal complexes with carbonate or hydrogen carbonate we shall use

$$p\mathrm{HCO_3} = 2.71$$

and

$$p\mathrm{CO_3} = 4.09$$

5. Sulfate Species in Seawater

One way to study sulfate or magnesium complexing is to work at constant formal ionic strength using mixtures of 0.7*M* NaCl, 0.7/3*M* Na_2SO_4, or $MgCl_2$ and 0.7/4*M* $MgSO_4$. However, single ion activity coefficients calculated by Elgquist and Wedborg (1972) show that (see Figs. 2 and 3) although the activity coefficients of the sodium and magnesium ions are much lower in sulfate media than in chloride media, the activity coefficient of sulfate remains practically unaltered by replacing 1 Mg^{2+} with $2\frac{2}{3}$ Na^+ in a sulfate medium of ionic strength 0.7*M* (or *m*). Elgquist and Wedborg (1972) concluded from their measurements that if $K_{NaSO_4^-} = 2$ then $K_{MgSO_4} = 7$

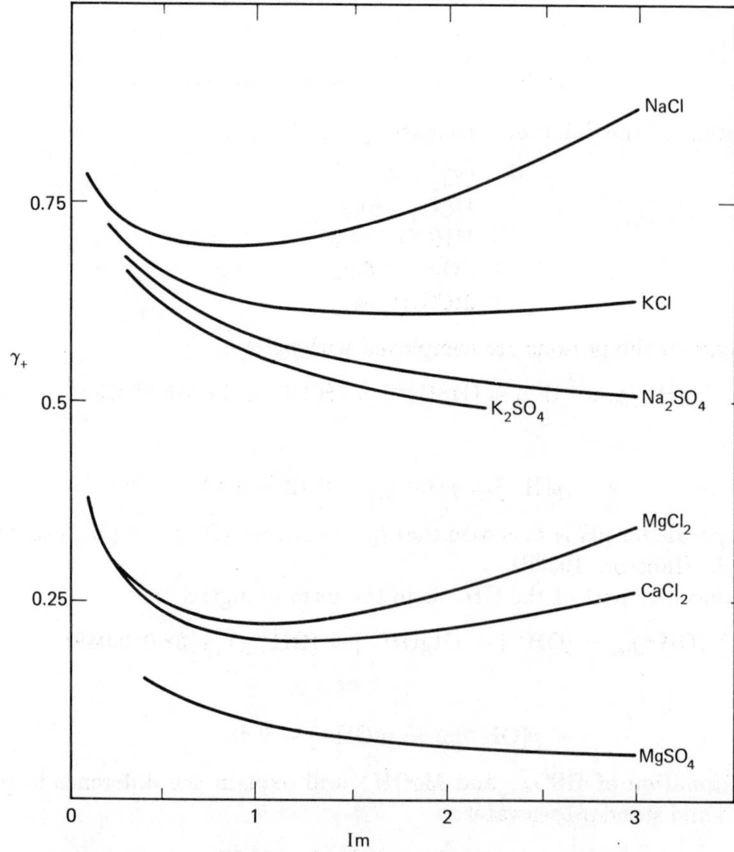

Fig. 2. Total single ion activity coefficients for some cations versus ionic strength (molal scale), according to Elgquist and Wedborg (1972). See also Bates et al. (1970).

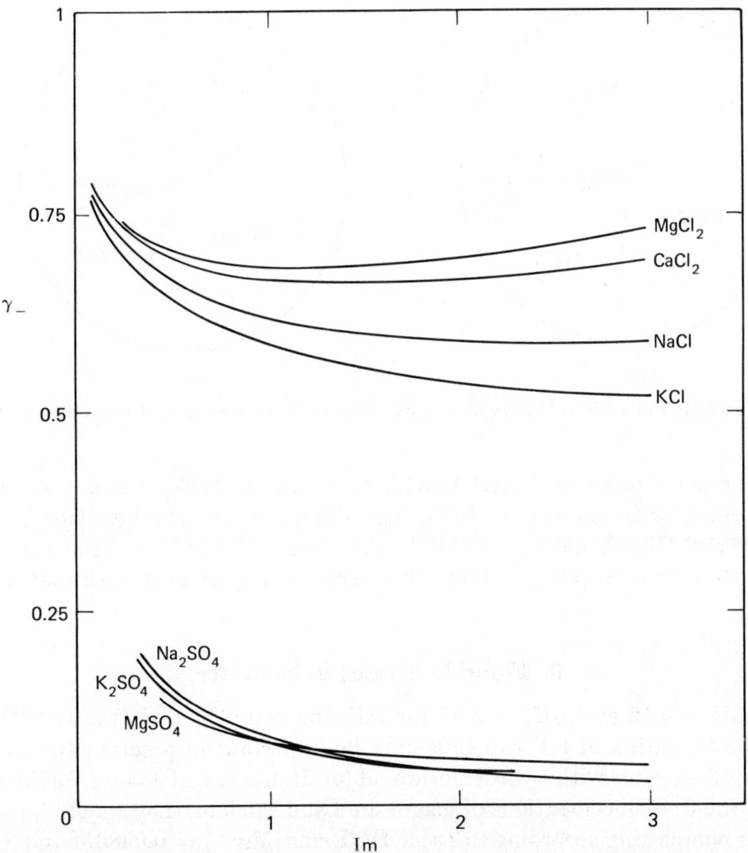

Fig. 3. Total single ion activity coefficients for chloride and sulfate versus ionic strength (molal scale), according to Elgquist and Wedborg (1972). See also Bates et al. (1970).

rather than 10, as determined by Kester and Pytkowicz (1969). We shall therefore calculate the different sulfate species with the two sets of constants in Table IV.

Figure 4 and Table IV show how the sulfate "cake" representing $0.02823M_w$ is divided for these two sets of constants. This calculation is easily performed with

TABLE IV

The Influence of Ion Pairing on the Speciation of Sulfate

	Case 1		Case 2	
Ion Pair	K	Percent	K	Percent
$NaSO_4^-$	2.02	37.0	2	39.6
KSO_4^-	1.03	0.416	1	0.436
$MgSO_4$	10.2	19.4	7	14.8
$CaSO_4$	10.8	3.99	7	2.88
(SO_4^{2-})	—	39.1	—	42.3

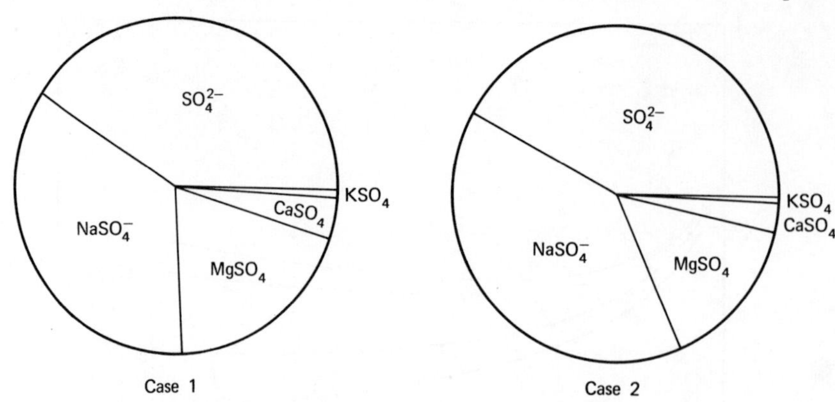

Fig. 4. Speciation of sulfate in seawater calculated with the two sets of constants in Table IV.

Sillén's computer program HALTAFALL (Ingri et al., 1967), the use of which has been described by Dyrssen et al. (1968). The difference between these two cakes is not very large and for calculations of sulfate complexing it will be sufficient to use 42% "free" sulfate, that is, $p\mathrm{SO}_4 = 1.93$. This value is in agreement with that of Millero (1971).

6. Fluoride Species in Seawater

Using pH = 8.12 and pK_a = 2.91 for HF, the ratio $[\mathrm{F}^-]/[\mathrm{HF}]$ is $10^{-2.91+8.12} = 10^{5.21}$. The formation of HF will thus only be important in precise titrations of the alkalinity of seawater with hydrochloric acid (cf. Hansson and Jagner, 1973). In order to obtain the free concentrations of magnesium and calcium, they should be corrected for sulfate complexing according to Table IV. Using $[\mathrm{Mg}^{2+}] = 0.0486M$ and $[\mathrm{Ca}^{2+}] = 0.00945M$ together with the stability constants in Table III for MgF^+ ($K = 18.8$) and CaF^+ ($K = 4.22$), the following percentage of different fluoride species are obtained:

F^-: 51.1% or $0.0000375M_w$
MgF^+: 46.9% or $0.0000344M_w$
CaF^+: 2.0% or $0000015M_w$

The value of $p\mathrm{F}$ is thus 4.43.

7. Borate and Phosphate Species in Seawater

At $p[\mathrm{H}^+]_{\mathrm{tot}} = 8.00$, the ratio $[\mathrm{B(OH)_3}]/[\mathrm{B(OH)_4}^-]_{\mathrm{tot}}$ will be $10^{8.61-8.00} = 4.07$. From the difference between the conditional constants in sodium chloride and seawater, according to Table III it is possible to calculate the amount of borate bound as $\mathrm{MgB(OH)_4}^+$ and $\mathrm{CaB(OH)_4}^+$.

$$[\mathrm{B(OH)_4}^-]_{\mathrm{tot}} = [\mathrm{B(OH)_4}^-] + [\mathrm{MB(OH)_4}^+] = [\mathrm{B(OH)_4}^-](1 + K(\mathrm{M}^{2+}])$$

where $(\mathrm{M}^{2+}] = [\mathrm{Mg}^{2+}] + [\mathrm{Ca}^{2+}] = 0.0579M_w$, Dyrssen and Hansson (1973) calculated K to be 5.4.

Thus, boron has the following speciation at pH 8:

$\mathrm{B(OH)_3}$: 80.2%
$\mathrm{B(OH)_4}^-$: 15.1%
$\mathrm{MB(OH)_4}^+$: 4.7%

Similarly, we may treat determinations of phosphoric acid in 0.7M sodium chloride and standard seawater. At 20°C, Kester and Pytkowicz (1967) obtained the acidity constants in Table V. For comparison the values for pure water and $I = 0.7M$ are included in Table V (cf. Sillén and Martell, 1964). The constants in Table V are defined

TABLE V

Stability Constants for Phosphoric Acid at 20°C

	$\log K_{13}$	$\log K_{12}$	$\log K_1$
0.68M NaCl	1.55	6.39	11.00
35‰ SW	1.64	6.01	8.89
Pure water	2.127	7.123	12.0
$I = 0.7M$	1.90	6.70	11.1

with the usual pH scale, that is, $f_{H^+} \rightarrow 1$ when $(H^+] \rightarrow 0$ in pure water and not 0.7M NaCl or standard seawater, as used previously in this work and by Hansson (1973 a–d). The difference is approximately 0.12 log units, that is, pH 8.00 will be 8.12 using pure water as reference. Thus the following ratios and percentages may be calculated for $p(H^+]_{tot} = 8.00$:

$$\log \frac{[H_3PO_4]_{tot}}{[PO_4^{3-}]_{tot}} = 1.64 + 6.01 + 8.89 - 3 \times 8.12 = -7.82$$

$$\log \frac{[H_2PO_4^-]_{tot}}{[PO_4^{3-}]_{tot}} = 6.01 + 8.89 - 2 \times 8.12 = -1.34$$

$$\log \frac{[HPO_4^{2-}]_{tot}}{[PO_4^{3-}]_{tot}} = 8.89 - 8.12 = 0.77$$

$$[H_2PO_4^-]_{tot} = 0.66\%$$

$$[HPO_4^{2-}]_{tot} = 84.9\%$$

$$[PO_4^{3-}]_{tot} = 14.4\%$$

If we assume that complexing occurs between H^+ and SO_4^{2-} and between Mg^{2+} and Ca^{2+} and $H_2PO_4^-$, HPO_4^{2-}, and PO_4^{3-}, then the following relations are valid (cf. Dyrssen and Hansson, 1973):

$$K_{13}^{NaCl} = K_{13}{}^{SW}(1 + \beta_{HSO_4^-}[SO_4^{2-}])(1 + \beta_{MH_2PO_4^+}[M^{2+}])$$

$$K_{12}^{NaCl} = \frac{K_{13}{}^{SW}(1 + \beta_{HSO_4^-}[SO_4^{2-}])(1 + \beta_{MHPO_4}[M^{2+}])}{(1 + \beta_{MH_2PO_4^+}[M^{2+}])}$$

$$K_{1}^{NaCl} = \frac{K_{1}{}^{SW}(1 + \beta_{HSO_4^-}[SO_4^{2-}])(1 + \beta_{MPO_4^-}[M^{2+}])}{(1 + \beta_{MHPO_4}[M^{2+}])}$$

According to measurements for the carbonate and borate system,

$$1 + \beta_{HSO_4^+}[SO_4^{2-}] = 1.324 = 10^{0.12}$$

(Dyrssen and Hansson, 1973). Since the values of Kester and Pytkowicz (1967) for K_{13} and K_{12} on 0.68M NaCl seem to be too small, we use the values for $I = 0.7M$

estimated from "Stability Constants" (Sillén and Martell, 1964) for the following calculations:

$$1 + \beta_{MH_2PO_4^+}[M^{2+}] = 10^{1.90-1.64-0.12} = 10^{0.14} = 1.38$$
$$1 + \beta_{MHPO_4}[M^{2+}] = 10^{6.70+0.14-6.01-0.12} = 10^{0.71} = 5.13$$
$$1 + \beta_{MPO_4^-}[M^{2+}] = 10^{11.1+0.71-8.89-0.12} = 10^{2.80} = 631$$

Using $[M^{2+}] = [Mg^{2+}] + (Ca^{2+}] = 0.0581M$, constants for the following equilibria may be calculated:

$$M^{2+} + H_2PO_4^- \rightleftharpoons MH_2PO_4^+ \qquad \log \beta_{MH_2PO_4^+} = 0.81$$
$$M^{2+} + HPO_4^{2-} \rightleftharpoons MHPO_4 \qquad \log \beta_{MHPO_4} = 1.85$$
$$M^{2+} + PO_4^{3-} = MPO_4^- \qquad \log \beta_{MPO_4^-} = 4.03$$

These stability constants are not unreasonable, and a redetermination of the phosphoric acid dissociation in $0.7M_w$ NaCl and 35‰ seawater with the techniques introduced by Sillén and used by Hansson (1973a–d) should give reliable values (cf. Dyrssen and Hansson, 1973). Using the constants above the following inorganic species of phosphate can be calculated:

$H_2PO_4^-$: 0.48%
$MH_2PO_4^+$: 0.18%
HPO_4^{2-}: 16.5%
$MHPO_4$: 68.4%
PO_4^{3-}: 0.023%
MPO_4^-: 14.4%

This calculation shows that most of the inorganic phosphate in seawater will be in the uncharged form of $MgHPO_4$ and $CaHPO_4$. This may be of importance for its adsorption properties and ability to penetrate membranes.

8. Complexation of Organic Acids in Seawater

Most complexation of heavy metal ions with organic ligands probably occurs within particulate matter of biological origin even if the amount of dissolved organic matter may be considerably larger (cf. Horne, 1969, p. 229). For this discussion it may be sufficient to use $10^{-6}M$ acetic acid as a model substance for carboxylic acids (≈ 100 μg/l) and $10^{-7}M$ glycine as a model for amino acids (≈ 10 μg/l). The equilibrium state of these dissolved organic substances will mainly depend on the free concentrations of Mg^{2+} ($\approx 0.0486M$), Ca^{2+} ($\approx 0.0095M$), Cu^{2+} ($\approx 5 \cdot 10^{-9}M$), Zn^{2+} ($\approx 2 \cdot 10^{-8}M$), and pH (8.12). The acid dissociation constants (pK_a) of the model substances are in our activity scale approximately:

CH_3COOH: 4.64
$NH_3^+CH_2COOH$: 2.22
$NH_3^+CH_2COO^-$: 9.66

Approximate values of the stability constants ($K_1 = [ML^+]/[M^{2+}][L]$) in seawater ($0.7M_w$ NaCl) may be estimated from values given in the compilation of Sillén and Martell (1969, supplement, 1971) as follows:

	$\log K_1(CH_3COO^-)$	$\log K_1(NH_2CH_2COO^-)$
Mg^{2+}	0.6	3.0
Ca^{2+}	0.5	1.0
Cu^{2+}	1.6	8.1
Zn^{2+}	1.0	4.9

Since $L_{tot} = [L] + [HL] + \sum[ML] = [L](1 + [H^+]/K_a + \sum[M^{2+}]K_1)$, the percentage speciation will be:

	CH_3COO^-	$NH_2CH_2COO^-$
HL	0.027	40.7
L^-	81.6	1.17
MgL^+	15.9	57.3
CaL^+	2.5	0.11
CuL^+	< 0.001	0.74
ZnL^+	< 0.001	< 0.01

This means that dissolved carboxylic acids will be mainly in the form of $RCOO^-$ and $MgRCOO^+$ with some $CaRCOO^+$. Amino acids, on the other hand, will exist mainly in the forms $R(NH_3^+)COO^-$ and $Mg(NH_2)COO^+$, with some $R(NH_2)COO^-$ and $CuR(NH_2)COO^+$.

9. Sodium, Potassium, Magnesium, and Calcium Species in Seawater

Since the total concentrations of most complexing ligands in seawater are considerably lower than the total concentrations of the main metal ions, only a small part of these will be in the form of metal complexes. Table VI shows that besides sulfate complexes most other forms are negligible. Strontium should not be very different from calcium.

The combined concentration of sulfate ion pairs are $0.0116M$ in the form of $NaSO_4^- + KSO_4^-$ and $0.0051M$ in the form of $MgSO_4$ and $CaSO_4$. This will lower the effective ionic strength of seawater with $2 \times 0.0116 + 4 \times 0.0051 = 0.0436M$ from $0.714M$ to $0.670M$.

TABLE VI

The Percentage Speciation of the Main Metal Ions in Seawater

Element	$[M^{n+}]$	$[MSO_4]$	$[MHCO_3]$	$[MCO_3]$	$[MB(OH)_4]$	[MF]
Sodium	97.6	2.4	< 0.1	< 0.1	< 0.1	< 0.1
Potassium	98.8	1.2	< 0.1	< 0.1	< 0.1	< 0.1
Magnesium	89.0 to 92.0 [a]	7.8 to 10.8 [a]	0.1	0.1	< 0.03	0.063
Calcium	89.0 to 92.0 [a]	7.8 to 10.8 [a]	0.1	0.1	< 0.03	0.014

[a] Depending on the value of K (see Table IV).

10. Speciation of Some Heavy Metals

In the tables given by Sillén (1961) and Goldberg (1963) (see also Horne, 1969, pp. 153–155), the principal species in solution were given. In this section we shall consider a few divalent heavy metals with somewhat different complexing abilities than the alkaline earth metals in order to demonstrate the rather large variations in speciation. Table VII summarizes total concentrations and the log β_n values chosen for these calculations together with the free ligand concentrations calculated in earlier sections. Many of the constants given in Table VII must be regarded as educated guesses, and, of course, pOH, pHCO, and $p\mathrm{CO_3}$ vary with pH and the total carbonate. However, with the following expression for the total metal concentration

$$\mathrm{M_{tot}} = [\mathrm{M}^{2+}] + \sum [\mathrm{ML}] = [\mathrm{M}^{2+}](1 + \sum \beta_n[\mathrm{L}]^n)$$

it is possible to calculate the percentage speciation by the following equations:

$$\%[\mathrm{M}^{2+}] = 100[M^{2+}]/\mathrm{M_{tot}} = 100/(1 + \sum \beta_n[\mathrm{L}]^n)$$

$$\%[\mathrm{ML}] = 100[\mathrm{ML}]/\mathrm{M_{tot}} = 100\beta_1[\mathrm{L}]/(1 + \sum \beta_n[\mathrm{L}]^n)$$

At the low concentrations of the microelements in seawater, polynuclear complexes (including metal hydrolysis) may be neglected. Nor will the intrinsic solubility of uncharged complexes be reached (for $\mathrm{PbSO_4}$, HgOHCl, etc.; cf. Dirssen et al., 1969). The results of these calculations are given in Table VIII. This table shows that these metal ions may form a large variety of complexes in standard seawater. Except in the case of zinc the free metal ion is only a minor species. Furthermore, sulfate and fluoride complexing is not important.

TABLE VII

Total Concentrations and Stability Constants for Copper, Zinc, Cadmium, Mercury, and Lead in Seawater. The Stabilities are Estimated from Values given by Sillén and Martell (1964, Supplement, 1971)

	Cu	Zn	Cd	Hg	Pb
Total concentration M	10^{-7}	10^{-7}	$2\cdot10^{-10}$	$5\cdot10^{-10}$	10^{-10}
Total concentration μg/l	6.4	6.5	0.02	0.1	0.02
log $\beta_1(\mathrm{OH^-})$	6.4	4.8	4.3	10.1	6.0
log $\beta^1(\mathrm{HCO_3^-})$	1.5	1.0	1.2	5.6	2.2
log $\beta_1(\mathrm{CO_3^{2-}})$	5.6	3.4	3.2	(10)	3
log $\beta_1(\mathrm{SO_4^{2-}})$	1	1	1	1	1
log $\beta_1(\mathrm{F^-})$	0.7	0.7	0.5	1.0	1.5
log $\beta_1(\mathrm{Cl^-})$	1.2	0.7	1.46	6.74	0.88
log $\beta_1(\mathrm{Cl^-})$	0.9	0.5	1.83	13.22	1.49
log $\beta_3(\mathrm{Cl^-})$	0.8	−0.2	1.96	14.07	1.09
log $\beta_4(\mathrm{Cl^-})$	0.9	0.2		15.07	0.94
log $\beta_{11}(\mathrm{OH^-, Cl^-})$	7.9	5.8	6.1	17.43	6.2
log $\beta_1(\mathrm{Br^-})$	0.7	0.2	2.0	9.05	1.6
log $\beta_1(\mathrm{L^-})$	8.1	5.2	3.9	10.3	5.5

Note. pOH = 5.65, $p\mathrm{HCO_3}$ = 2.71, $p\mathrm{CO_3}$ = 4.09, $p\mathrm{SO_4}$ = 1.93, pF = 4.43, pCl = 0.26, pBr = 3.07, and pL = 9 (HL = glycine).

TABLE VIII

Percentage Speciation of Some Important Heavy Divalent Metals in Seawater. For Mercury (II) see Table II

Complex	Cu	Zn	Cd	Pb
M^{2+}	0.7	*16.1*	1.8	4.5
MOH^+	3.7	2.3	—	*10.2*
$MHCO_3^+$	—	0.3	—	1.4
MCO_3	*21.6*	3.3	0.2	0.4
MSO_4	—	1.9	0.2	0.5
MF^+	—	—	—	—
MCl^+	5.8	*44.3*	*29.2*	*18.9*
MCl_2	1.6	*15.4*	*37.5*	*42.3*
MCl_3^-	0.7	1.7	*27.9*	9.2
MCl_4^{2-}	0.5	2.3	—	3.6
MOHCl	*65.2*	*12.5*	2.9	8.8
MBr^+	—	—	0.2	0.15
ML^+	0.08	—	—	—

Bromide forms very strong complexes with mercury, and $\log \beta_1$ (for $HgCl^+$) $-$ pCl $= 6.48$ is only slightly larger than $\log \beta_1$ (for $HgBr^+$) $- p$Br $= 5.98$. Since mixed complexes are statistically favored, the $HgCl_nBr$ and $HgCl_nBr_2$ complexes must be taken into account. Complexes with three or four Br^- can be neglected since for $HgBr_3^-$

$$\log \beta_3 - 3p\text{Br} = 10.53 \qquad \text{and for } HgBr_4^{2-} \qquad \log \beta_4 - 4p\text{Br} = 8.72$$

Using the formula

$$\beta_{m,n} = \frac{N!}{m!n!} N\sqrt{\text{Cl}\beta_N{}^m \times \text{Br}\beta_N{}^n} \qquad N = m + n$$

given by Dryssen et al. (1968), the stability for the mixed $HgCl_mBr_n$ complexes may be calculated from the stability constants of $HgCl_N$ and $HgBr_N$. The results are given in Table IX.

To summarize Tables VIII and IX we may list those species that are present in the order of 10% or more:

Copper(II): $CuCO_3$, $CuOHCl(CuCl^+)$
Zinc(II): Zn^{2+}, $ZnCl^+$, $ZnCl_2$, ZnOHCl
Cadmium(II): $CdCl^+$, $CdCl_2$, $CdCl_3^-$
Mercury(II): $HgCl_3^-$, $HgCl_4^{2-}$, $HgCl_3Br^{2-}$ ($HgCl_2Br^-$)
Lead(II): $PbOH^+$, $PbCl^+$, $PbCl_2$($PbCl_3^-$, PbOHCl)

Our conclusion is that this complicated speciation cannot be determined by experiments with seawater containing such a mixture of ligands, and that one has to rely on measurements with one or two ligands, such as 0.7*M* NaCl at different pH, 0.7*M* NaCl(Br), 0.7*M* NaCl(HCO_3), etc.

These measurements may be carried out by techniques such as potentiometry, polarography, spectrophotometry, solubility, and solvent extraction determinations.

TABLE IX

Stability Constants for $HgCl_mBr_n$. Percentage of Different Species

Complex	$\log \beta_{mn}$	$\log \beta_{mn} - mp\text{Cl} - np\text{Br}$	Percentage
$HgCl^+$	6.74	6.48	—
$HgCl_2$	13.22	12.70	3.0
$HgCl_3^-$	14.07	13.29	*12.0*
$HgCl_4^{2-}$	15.07	14.03	*65.8*
$HgBr^+$	9.05	5.98	—
$HgBr_2$	17.33	11.19	0.1
$HgBr_3^-$	19.74	10.53	—
$HgBr_4^{2-}$	21.00	8.72	—
HgClBr	15.58 (15.88)[a]	12.25 (12.55)	1.1
$HgCl_2Br^-$	16.44	12.85	4.3
$HgCl_3Br^{2-}$	17.15	13.30	*12.3*
$HgClBr_2^-$	18.33	11.93	0.5
$HgCl_2Br_2^{2-}$	18.64	11.98	0.6
$HgClBr_3^{2-}$	20.12	10.65	—
HgOHCl	17.43	11.52	0.2

[a] Experimental determination.

By studies of this kind Biedermann and Chow (1966) determined the principal solubility product for iron(III) in 0.5*M* (Na)Cl medium:

$$Fe^{3+} + 2.7\ H_2O + 0.3\ Cl^- \rightleftharpoons Fe(OH)_{2.7}Cl_{0.3}(s) + 2.7\ H^+$$

with the equilibrium constant $\log K_s = -3.04$. Since the concentration of iron(III) in seawater is 10–100 μg/l (approximately $10^{-6}M$) and the intrinsic solubility is less than $10^{-7}M$, most iron(III) should be in the particulate form (adsorbed or as the hydroxo chloride complex). This solubility equilibrium must be taken into account when, for example, the influence of reducing conditions or the complexing with NTA on iron(III) is to be calculated. Different studies of this kind are being carried out at our laboratory.

References

Bates, R. G., B. R. Staples, and R. A. Robinson, 1970. Ionic hydration and single ion activities in unassociated chlorides at high ionic strengths. *Anal. Chem.*, **42**, 867–871.

Bjerrum, J., G. Schwarzenbach, and L. G. Sillén, 1958. Stability Constants. *Chem. Soc. Spec. Publ.*, 7.

Chen, K. Y. and J. C. Morris, 1972. Oxidation of sulfide by O_2: Catalysis and inhibition. *J. Sanit. Eng. Div. Amer. Soc. Civil Eng.*, **98** (SA 1), 215–227.

Corner, E. D. and A. G. Davis, 1971. Plankton as a factor in the nitrogen and phosphorus cycles in the sea. *Adv. Mar. Biol.*, **9**, 101–204.

Culberson, C., R. N. Pytkowicz, and J. E. Hawley, 1970. Seawater alkalinity determination by the pH method. *Mar. Res.*, **28**, 15–21.

Dirssen, D., E. Ivonova, and K. Oren, 1969. Krioye rastvorimosti sul'fatov kal'tsiya, strontsiya i svintsa. *Vestnik Moskovskogo Universiteta*, **1**, 41–45.

Dyrssen, D. and I. Hansson, 1973. Ionic medium effects in sea water—A comparison of acidity constants of carbonic acid and boric acid in sodium chloride and synthetic seawater. *Mar. Chem.*, *8*, 137–149.

Dyrssen, D., D. Jagner, and F. Wengelin, 1968. *Computer Calculations of Ionic Equilibria and Titration Procedures*. Almqvist & Wiksell, Stockholm.

Dyrssen, D. and L. G. Sillén, 1967. Alkalinity and total carbonate in seawater. A plea for p-T-independent data. *Tellus*, **XIX**, 113–121.

Elgquist, B., 1970. Determination of the stability constants of MgF^+ and CaF^+ using a fluoride ion selective electrode. *J. Inorg. Nucl. Chem.*, **32**, 937–944.

Elgquist, B. and M. Wedborg, 1972. A relation between the stability constants of sodium sulfate and magnesium sulfate in seawater from a determination of the stability constant of hydrogen sulfate and a calculation of the single ion activity coefficient of sulfate. Manuscript submitted to *Mar. Chem.* for publication.

Garrels, R. M. and M. E. Thompson, 1962. A chemical model for seawater at 25°C and one atmosphere total pressure. *Am. J. Sci.*, **260**, 57–66.

Goldberg, E. D., 1963. The oceans as a chemical system. In *The Sea*. Vol. 2. Wiley-Interscience, New York, pp. 3–25.

Hansson, I., 1973a. The determination of the dissociation constants of carbonic acid in seawater media in the salinity range of 20–40‰ and the temperature range of 5–30°C. *Acta Chem. Scand.*, in print.

Hansson, I., 1973b. Determination of the acidity constants of boric acid in synthetic seawater media. *Acta Chem. Scand.*, in print.

Hansson, I., 1973c. A new set of acidity constants of carbonic acid and boric acid in seawater. *Deep-Sea Res.*, in print.

Hansson, I., 1973d. A new set of pH-scales and standard buffers for seawater. *Deep-Sea Res.*, in print.

Hansson, I. and D. Jagner, 1973. Evaluation of the accuracy in Gran plots by means of computer calculations. Application to the potentiometric titration of the total alkalinity and carbonate content in seawater. *Anal. Chim. Acta*, in print.

Horne, R. A., 1969. *Marine Chemistry*. Wiley-Interscience, New York.

Ingri, N., W. Kakolowicz, L. G. Sillén, and B. Warnqvist, 1967. HALTAFALL, a general program for calculating the composition of equilibrium mixtures. *Talanta*, **14**, 1261–1286. Errata *ibid.*, **15** (xi) (1968).

Kester, D. R. and R. M. Pytkowicz, 1967. Determination of the apparent dissociation constants of phosphoric acid in seawater. *Limnol. Oceanog.*, **12**, 243–252.

Kester, D. and R. M. Pytkowicz, 1969. Sodium, magnesium, and calcium sulphate ion pairs in seawater at 25°C. *Limnol. Oceanog.*, **14**, 686–692.

Lindahl, B., 1972. Dept. of Plant Physiology, University of Uppsala, Sweden. Personal Communication.

Matthews, A. D. and J. P. Riley, 1970. A study of Sugawara's method for the determination of iodine in seawater. *Anal. Chim. Acta*, **51**, 295–301.

Millero, F. J., 1971. The physical chemistry of multi-component salt solutions. In *A Treatise on Skin. I*. Wiley-Interscience, New York, pp. 329–371.

Robinson, R. A. and R. H. Stokes, 1959. *Electrolyte Solutions*. Butterworths, London.

Sillén, L. G., 1961. The physical chemistry of seawater. In *Oceanography*. Amer. Assoc. Adv. Sci., Washington, D.C. pp. 549–582.

Sillén, L. G., 1967. Master variables and activity scales. In *Equilibrium Concepts in Natural Water Systems*, Adv. in Chem. Ser. 67, Amer. Chem. Soc., Washington, D.C.

Sillén, L. G. and A. E. Martell, 1964, 1971. Stability Constants of Metal–Ion Complexes. Chem. Soc., London, Spec. publ. 17 and 25 (supplement).

II. AIR-SEA INTERACTIONS

6. DISSOLVED CONSERVATIVE GASES IN SEAWATER

RUDOLF H. BIERI

Among the conservative parameters available to the oceanographer, dissolved conservative gases—particularly the noble gases on which emphasis will be placed in this presentation—fulfill a special function in a number of applications. By virtue of their chemical inertness, they can be assumed to be truly conservative properties of seawater. As such, the noble gases may serve as standards against which chemical or biochemical alterations of nonconservative gases can be measured; they thus have a supporting function and provide a baseline for investigations of nonconservative parameters.

In other applications, one or more of the noble gases are the object of investigation. The detection of a radiogenic helium component in the abyssal Southeast Pacific (Bieri et al., 1966; Craig et al., 1967) and the subsequent confirmation of this component (Bieri and Koide, 1972) belong in this category. Other examples relate to air-sea interaction mechanisms (Bieri, 1971; Craig and Weiss, 1971; Bieri and Koide, 1972; Bieri et al., 1968). These are problems that may or may not have any relation to other conservative parameters such as temperature, salinity, or density, and therefore are available exclusively through the analysis of these gases.

In investigations of mixing and advection (Bieri et al., 1966; Craig and Weiss, 1968; Bieri and Koide, 1972a; Bieri and Barnes, 1972) the noble gases finally take an equivalent position with other conservative parameters. They are then of advantage only in special situations.

The use of noble gases in oceanography has been limited by analytical problems. Precise and accurate analyses are difficult and time consuming. As a consequence, the detail of concentration profiles is always less than what is desirable. Continuous records, such as those available for other parameters (temperature, salinity, and O_2) are not yet possible. In addition, interpretation of the data in some cases is in question, as published noble gas solubilities could not be confirmed by the mass spectrometric technique employed for the seawater analyses (Bieri and Barnes, 1972). Most of the factors involved in the determination of the *in situ* concentrations are complex and poorly understood, and for that reason require further investigation. Finally, many of the oceanic mechanisms acting on the gases lead to only small concentration changes that are barely detectable by the present methods.

Much work, therefore, remains to be done to detail the different mechanisms that influence the dissolved gas concentrations. The following presentation is a status report emphasizing potential uses of noble gases to air-sea interactions and oceanic mixing processes.

1. Some Factors Determining the Dissolved Gas Content of Ocean Water

A. Solubility

If the oceans and the atmosphere were in thermodynamic equilibrium, the concentration C_ν of a gas ν in seawater would be determined by the partial pressure p_ν of the pure gas ν above the liquid, the temperature T, and the salinity S of the water:

$$C_\nu = C_\nu(p_\nu, T, S) \tag{1}$$

Since the amount of dissolved gas according to Henry's Law is proportional to p_ν, this equation may be written

$$C_\nu = p_\nu f_\nu(T, S) \tag{2}$$

where f_ν is an empirically determined quantity that must be measured separately for each gas. $f_\nu(T, S)$ is intimately related to the structure of the liquid.

It is customary to specify $f_\nu(T, S)$ at a partial pressure $p_\nu = 1$ atm. The resulting concentration C_ν can then be expressed:

1. As the volume of gas, reduced to 0°C and 1 atm of pressure (standard temperature and pressure, abbreviated as STP), contained in a unit volume of water at the temperature T of the measurement (Bunsen coefficient)

$$\beta_\nu = \frac{\text{ml of gas } \nu \text{ (STP)}}{\text{ml of water at } T} \tag{3}$$

2. As the volume of gas (STP) contained in 1 g of water (Kuenen coefficient)

$$s_\nu = \frac{\text{ml of gas } \nu \text{ (STP)}}{\text{g of water}} \tag{4}$$

3. As the volume of gas at temperature T contained in a unit volume of water at T (Ostwald coefficient)

$$1_\nu = \frac{\text{ml of gas } \nu \text{ at } T}{\text{ml of water at } T} \tag{5}$$

β_ν, s_ν, and 1_ν all are solubility coefficients. Here, the Bunsen coefficient will be used exclusively.

For seawater in contact with air of 1 atm total pressure and under conditions of thermodynamic equilibrium, the concentrations of the different atmospheric gases are given by:

$$C_\nu^* = p_\nu \beta_\nu(T, S) = P\left(\frac{1 - p_e(T, S)}{P}\right)\beta_\nu(T, S)x_\nu \tag{6}$$

where P is the total atmospheric pressure, $p_e(T, S)$ is the vapor pressure of seawater of salinity S and at temperature T, and x_ν is the mole fraction of gas ν in the (dry) atmosphere. Note that $P_{\text{dry}} + p_e = 1$ atm. C_ν^*, normally called "solubility" in the literature, will be referred to here as "normal atmospheric equilibrium concentration" or NAEC. Since, as has been pointed out by Benson (1965), the solubility of xenon is from ~30 to 70 times lower than the solubility of helium, while the solubility *coefficient* of xenon at the same time is from ~2 to 22 times higher (Wood and Caputti, 1966; Weiss, 1971), the similarity of these terms can easily lead to confusion. In addition, "solubility" is a much used general term for an effect or mechanism and should, for this reason, not be assigned a *specific* meaning.

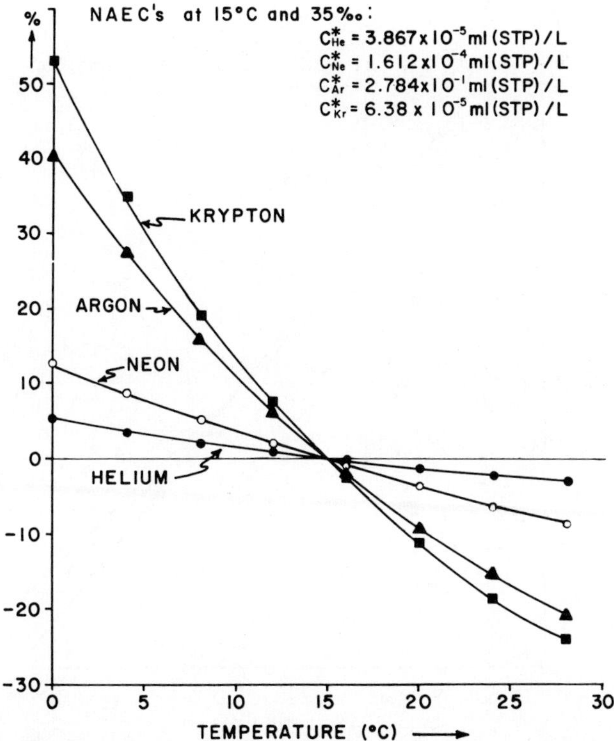

Fig. 1. Normal atmospheric equilibrium concentrations as a function of temperature for He, Ne, Ar, and Kr, plotted relative to the respective values at 15°C and a salinity of 35‰. NAEC's for He, Ne, Ar from Weiss (1970, 1971), Kr from preliminary results of Bieri (unpublished).

An extensive literature is available on the solubility of inert gases in pure and seawater. While earlier research in this field was mainly concerned with theoretical aspects of solubility (for references see Morrison and Johnstone, 1954), some of the recent work has more been oriented toward interpretation of *in situ* concentrations (Klots and Benson, 1963; Koenig, 1963; Douglas, 1964, 1965; Murray et al., 1969; Murray and Riley, 1970; Weiss, 1970) of conservative gases in the oceans. Normal atmospheric concentration curves are plotted in Figs. 1 and 2.

In spite of the progress that has been made in the execution of gas solubility measurements, there are still some unsettled questions. For instance, there is no agreement as to how discrete experimental data points should be fitted to a solubility curve. While computer technology is replacing graphical interpolation, the mathematical form of the equations for the solubility coefficients is not known, and different approaches are used by different investigators (Murray and Riley, 1970; Murray, Riley, and Wilson, 1969; Himmelblau, 1960; Weiss, 1970, 1971).

Perhaps more serious is the fact that all high-precision solubility measurements have been carried out at partial pressures of the order of 1 atm, using a volumetric method to measure the gas content (Klots and Benson, 1963; Koenig, 1963; Douglas, 1964, 1965; Murray, Riley, and Wilson, 1969; Murray and Riley, 1970; Weiss, 1971). Under such experimental conditions, agreement between different workers is generally excellent. A few preliminary mass spectrometric normal atmospheric equilibrium

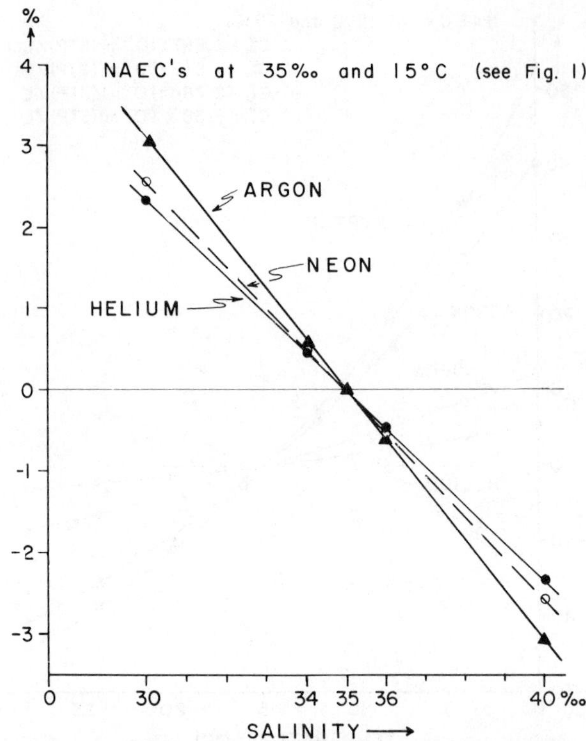

Fig. 2. Normal atmospheric equilibrium concentrations as a function of salinity for He, Ne, and Ar, plotted relative to the respective values at 15°C and a salinity of 35‰. Notice that the ordinate is expanded 10 times. Data from Weiss (1970, 1971).

concentrations, determined by equilibrating air with both distilled water and seawater, however, give values that are on the average high by 6% for He, 4% for Ne, 1.5% for Ar, and 1% for Kr (Bieri and Barnes, 1972). While the preliminary nature of these mass spectrometric NAECs makes a cautious approach for the interpretation of these discrepancies necessary, it also suggests that future solubilities must be evaluated at partial pressures close to what they are in the atmosphere. The validity of extrapolations covering five orders of magnitude (He, Kr) can only be decided by carefully designed and executed experiments.

B. *In situ Concentrations*

As conservative properties of seawater, concentrations of inert gases *per se* can be used as chemical tracers without the need of NAECs; they may contain the same information as salinity and temperature. Thus, if solubility were the only factor determining the *in situ* concentration, and thermodynamic equilibrium were established at all times, little additional information could be derived from such analyses.

Fortunately, the actual situation is somewhat more complex. While analyses of N_2 (Rakestraw and Emmel, 1938; Hamm and Thompson, 1941; Swinnerton and Sullivan, 1962) long ago have suggested that solubility is one of the main factors in determining the *in situ* concentration of this gas, deviations of the order of $\pm 10\%$ have also been suspected to exist (Benson, 1965).

Two closely related parameters are useful in such evaluations—σ_ν, the saturation in percent:

$$\sigma_\nu = 10^2 \frac{C_\nu}{C_\nu^*} \text{ percent} \tag{7}$$

and Δ_ν, the percentage of super- or undersaturation:

$$\Delta_\nu = 10^2 \left(\frac{C_\nu}{C_\nu^*} - 1 \right) \text{ percent} \tag{8}$$

where C_ν is the *in situ* concentration of gas ν and C_ν^* is the NAEC of gas ν, specified for the potential temperature, the potential volume, and the measured salinity of the sample (and, according to the definition of the NAEC, for a total atmospheric pressure, including the saturated water vapor, of 1 atm). σ and Δ both contain C^*, which for volumetric solubility determinations is calculated from the solubility coefficient by equation 6). Since this equation is based on Henry's Law and is valid for solubility effects only, either equations 7 or 8 for any single gas solely allows a quantitative assessment of deviations from the normal atmospheric equilibrium concentration.

Recent analyses of dissolved noble gases in the oceans (Koenig et al., 1964; Hintenberger et al., 1964; Bieri et al., 1964, 1966, 1968; Mazor et al., 1964; Craig et al., 1967; Bieri and Koide, 1972, 1972a; Bieri and Barnes, 1972) have confirmed the existence of deviations from solubility (determined first in analyses of N_2). Supersaturation has been found to be more pronounced and more prevalent than undersaturation. Of a total of 525 samples analyzed, only 87 samples from the North Pacific are slightly undersaturated in Ar and Kr relative to volumetric NAECs (Weiss, 1970; Bieri, preliminary results), and there, this undersaturation is due to diffusive losses (Craig and Weiss, 1968; Bieri and Koide, 1972). Relative to mass spectrometric solubilities, undersaturation is observed more often, but rarely exceeds 5%. Supersaturations of the order of 10%, on the other hand, have been observed in some intermediate waters (Bieri et al., 1968; Bieri and Koide, 1972; Bieri and Barnes, 1972) and in near-surface waters in the North Pacific (Bieri and Koide, 1972).

The extension of analyses from N_2 to the noble gases is important in two respects; first, it allows a systematic inquiry into the cause of deviations, and second, since such deviations are conserved within the water masses, they may serve as distinct tracers over large distances and may be of value for the investigation of advective and diffusive mechanisms within the oceans, especially in situations where gradients in temperature and salinity are very small.

The systematic analysis of mechanisms that affect the *in situ* concentrations are of special interest. As a consequence of the conservative character of the gases under discussion, such mechanisms must act at the boundaries.

C. *Boundary Effects*

Near the air-water interface, the exchange of heat can influence T and S. Changes may be so rapid that large deviations from thermodynamic equilibrium for the dissolved gases result and reasoning based on solubility considerations does not apply. Further complications can be introduced by the presence of submerged gas bubbles near the interface. The dissolved gas concentrations under these circumstances no longer fit simple equations based on their solubilities alone. In the following section, a few of the boundary effects that do play an important role will be considered. Criteria for the special effects such mechanisms may introduce will be derived from approximations.

The Boundary Between the Ocean and the Atmosphere

Effect of submerged bubbles

If bubbles of air are present within the water, a (static) thermodynamic equilibrium cannot exist. Gas bubbles, due to their buoyancy, have limited lifetimes in the water (Liebermann, 1957) and are dynamic variables. The gas pressure in the submerged bubbles is not constant, but depends on the sum of atmospheric and hydrostatic pressure and on the pressure forces due to the surface tension of the water. In collapsing bubbles, adiabatic heating may occur. Temperatures up to 11,000°C have been derived from observations on the spectrum of luminescence (Guenther et al., 1957). There is a critical radius below which bubbles will collapse and above which they will expand (see, for instance, Flynn, 1964).

Collapsing bubbles inject atmospheric gases into the water in amounts that may cause significant deviations from the NAECs. The gas exchange will be dependent on the size distribution of the bubble population, their distance from the sea surface, and the concentration gradients across the bubble interface. To treat such a system in an exact way would be a formidable task and is at this time not possible.

For the purpose of this discussion, the effect of bubbles is approximated by two extreme cases. It is assumed that the bubbles either collapse and inject all their gas into the water, or lose only a small amount of gas before they reach the surface and burst (Bieri, 1971; Craig and Weiss, 1971).

In the first case, if v is the total volume of air (in milliliters (STP) per milliliter of water and at 1 atm pressure) injected into water already saturated with the different gases and $(P_{\text{dry}} + p_e) = 1$ atm, the concentration of gas ν is now

$$C_\nu = p_\nu(\beta_\nu + v) = P\left(1 - \frac{p_e}{P}\right)(\beta_\nu + v)x_\nu \tag{9}$$

With C^*, defined by equation 6, one finds for the percent saturation or the supersaturation (equations 7 and 8):

$$\sigma_\nu = 10^2 \frac{C_\nu}{C^*} = 10^2\left(1 + \frac{v}{\beta_\nu}\right) \text{ percent} \tag{10}$$

$$\Delta_\nu = 10^2 \frac{v}{\beta_\nu} \text{ percent} \tag{11}$$

These two equations, especially equation 11, immediately suggest how air injection can be recognized if more than one gas is analyzed. By choosing a gas with a low solubility coefficient (He or Ne) and another with a high solubility coefficient (Ar, Kr), Δ_ν can be seen to reveal very pronounced and characteristic trends. For He and Kr, these trends are plotted in Fig. 3. An injected air volume of 0.001 ml/ml causes He to be supersaturated by 12.8%, while Kr at the same time is supersaturated by only 1.2%. The same is true for the pair Ne and Ar, except that the difference in the Δ's is not as pronounced. As shown in Fig. 3, the slope of an injection line is a function of temperature (because the solubility coefficients are functions of temperature). This slope is defined by

$$\frac{\Delta_\nu}{\Delta_\mu} = \frac{\beta_\mu}{\beta_\nu} \tag{12}$$

The consequences of air injection have been observed in some surface waters (Bieri et al., 1968; Bieri and Koide, 1972). In deep and bottom waters, except for those of the

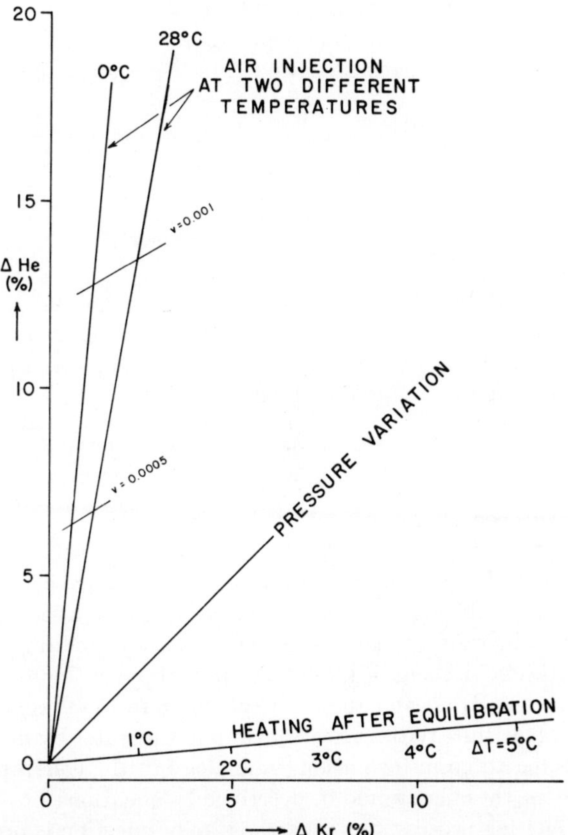

Fig. 3. Δ–Δ correlation for He and Kr and different effects capable of causing deviations from saturation. One air injection line each is drawn for 0°C and 28°C water and two lines of constant injection volume are indicated. It is seen that this mechanism generates large effects on He, but only small effects on Kr. Pressure variation, whether due to deviations of the atmospheric pressure or partial dissolution of submerged air bubbles, affects both gases the same way. Heating after gas equilibration at 15°C by an amount indicated on the heating curve has large effect on Kr, but causes only small apparent supersaturation of He.

Southeast Pacific, the supersaturation patterns of He, Ne, Ar, and Kr as calculated from the solubility coefficients of Weiss (1970, 1971) and preliminary NAECs of Kr by Bieri have indicated that air injection is not a rare phenomenon (Bieri, 1971; Craig and Weiss, 1971). If the Δ's, on the other hand, are calculated by using mass spectrometric NAECs (Bieri and Barnes, 1972), these waters seem close to saturation. Until the accuracy of solubility measurements at low partial pressures has been improved, no further interpretation of such data is possible.

We now turn to the second case. If it is assumed that the gas composition within the bubble is not changed, $(P_{\text{dry}} + p_e) = 1$ atm, the exchange from the gas phase to the liquid phase reaches a quasi equilibrium, is molecular, and the bubble radius is large enough so that surface tension can be neglected, the concentration is determined by:

$$C_\nu = P\left(1 - \frac{p_e}{P} + \frac{\int_0^h \rho_{sw}\, dh}{P}\right)\beta_\nu x_\nu \tag{13}$$

ρ_{sw} is the density of seawater in grams per cubic centimeter and h is an average height for the water column above the bubble population (the integral yields a mean hydrostatic pressure). The percent saturation and Δ in this case are given by:

$$\sigma_\nu = 10^2\left(1 + \frac{1}{P - p_e}\int_0^h \rho_{sw}\, dh\right) \text{ percent} \tag{14}$$

and

$$\Delta_\nu = \frac{10^2}{P - p_e}\int_0^h \rho_{sw}\, dh \text{ percent} \tag{15}$$

respectively. The solubility coefficient cancels and the magnitude of σ and Δ is determined only by the hydrostatic pressure term, which is the same for all gases. The effect of pressure variations, hydrostatic or atmospheric, in a Δ–Δ plot (Fig. 3) for any pair of gases is depicted by a line for which

$$\frac{\Delta_\nu}{\Delta_\mu} = 1 \tag{16}$$

So far, we have been concerned with submerged bubbles having relatively short lifetimes (of the order of minutes) in the liquid phase and a submergence depth of the order of 10 m. In icebergs, different conditions may be expected. While the bulk volume of icebergs is solid ice and the solubilities of gases in ice are negligibly small compared to those in water, it is also known that they contain gaseous occlusions. Analyses of Antarctic iceberg ice (Matsuo and Miyake, 1966) indicate that the occluded gases are mostly air and amount to about 25 to 75 ml/kg. For the submerged part of the iceberg, as the cavities are opened up to the water by melting, most of this gas can be expected to go into solution, in analogy to the collapsing bubbles. Thus, for air filled cavities, the effect would be described by equations 9 to 11. Because of the slowness of the melting process, however, the rate of injection is probably small, and exchange with the atmosphere, where such exchange is possible, for example, where the submerged part of the ice is within the surface layer, will tend to diminish this effect. In addition, the meltwater from the solid ice has a negligible gas content and thus will have a diluting effect on the dissolved concentrations, which again may approach equilibrium values by exchange with the atmosphere. It is difficult to make sound predictions on what the balance of all these effects will be.

Finally, there is the interesting case of the reverse of bubble collapse: bubble cavitation. Although it seems improbable to get cavitation from a solution of conservative gases at or near saturation without excessive negative pressure excursions, it may in principle be possible if this process is assisted by a nonconservative gas in a supersaturated state. In waters where productivity is high, photosynthesis could lead to oxygen supersaturation sufficiently high, especially if assisted by radiative heating, to form gas bubbles into which other gases from the surrounding water would diffuse. Equilibrium might then be established if the bubbles persist for long enough times. If such bubbles rise to the surface and burst, dissolved gases are "stripped" from the solution. Such a procedure is commonly used for gas extraction from liquids. In this process, the loss of gases with low solubility is more pronounced than loss of gases with high solubility, as can be seen from equations 9 to 11 by replacing ν with $-\nu$, or extending the injection lines in Fig. 3 toward negative Δ's. In the open ocean, however, it is very doubtful that such a mechanism can be of importance. Most probable productivity figures appear to be in the range from 40 to 200 g C/m^{2}yr (Strickland, 1965), and with the conversion factors of Westlake (1963), one arrives at a total oxygen production far too small to have any effect. Surface waters at and near the Pacific Equator (Bieri and Barnes, 1972) show a trend that qualitatively would fit this mechanism, but obviously the answer must be sought somewhere else.

Temperature and salinity effects near the interface

Radiation, conduction, and evaporation can create conditions that leave the interface colder than the water below. They may act independently or in combination. Rapid loss of heat from the interface not only increases the gas-absorbing capacity of the water which is in contact with the atmosphere, but also has an influence on density if evaporation is involved. Salinity gradients must be introduced by evaporation. Whether such conditions can have noticeable effects on the dissolved gases at deeper levels or not depends on the stability of the interface layer. While the concentrations with progressive cooling must increase, the layer nearest the interface may not remain stable and sink. It is not clear if turbulent motion breaks down near a gas-liquid boundary, as it does near a liquid-solid boundary. Higbie (1935) and Dankwerts (1951) favor abandonment of the stable laminar layer concept, while the existence of such films is supported by observations of Davis and Crandall (1930), Bolin (1960), Kanwisher (1963), Ewing and McAlister (1960), and McAlister et al., (1969).

Whatever the exact details are, it is clear that one is again looking at a dynamic system and thermodynamic equilibrium for the gas exchange, while it may be approximated at the interface, does not hold for the water below.

If the existence of a stable laminar layer is postulated, the gas exchange across the layer with $T_i < T_m$ (Fig. 4) is given by Kanwisher (1963):

$$F_{im}{}^{v} = -D_v \frac{dC_v}{dz} = -D_v \frac{C_v{}^i - C_v{}^m}{\delta} \tag{17}$$

with $C_v{}^i = C_v^* = p_v\beta_v(T_i, S_i)$ and $C_v{}^m = p_v\beta_v(T, S)$. This assumes that turbulent motion above and below the laminar layer maintains isothermal conditions. Equation 17 states that cooling of the interface must lead to an influx of gas into the water. At the same time, however, there is also an efflux of heat:

$$H_{im} = -k \frac{dT}{dz} = -k \frac{T_i - T_m}{\delta} \tag{18}$$

where k is the thermal conductivity and H the heat flux. If T_i were to remain fixed,

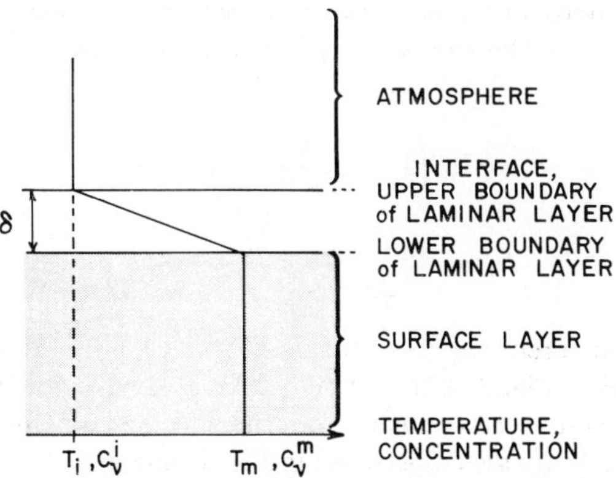

Fig. 4. Simple model used for stable laminar layer.

the system would eventually return toward equilibrium and large deviations from saturation should not be observed.

If rapid evaporation occurs, equations 17 and 18 and the assumptions made for their derivation almost certainly do not apply. There are indications from noble gas measurements that such conditions can create large Δ's (Bieri and Koide, 1972), and it is suspected that instabilities in the laminar layer are responsible. But this interpretation of the results would also require that the sinking layer fragments can penetrate the warmer surface layer without substantial exchange of gas. This may have an analogy in the filament hypothesis proposed by Munk (1966) in his discussion of bottom water formation. In addition, heat by some nonturbulent mechanism must at the same time be exchanged to produce the apparent supersaturation.

A clearer situation exists in areas where meteorological conditions between summer and winter are extreme. Where the density stratification of near-surface water is such that high-density water formed during winter by cold and dry winds can remain at the surface, but an influx of warmer and less saline water in spring or early summer can displace this cold water to a deeper level without causing excessive mixing, radiative heating of the displaced body of cold water is possible. Conditions similar to this have been described by Reid (1972) for the North Pacific. Although they probably are not often encountered, they do exist.

Wherever equilibration of gas at a temperature different from the *in situ* temperature of the water is involved, it leads to characteristic effects that are easily recognized if present in pure form. As with air injection, their recognition requires that more than one gas is analyzed, and again pairs of gases with extreme solubility coefficients are the most suitable.

The concentration of a gas in a water sample of temperature T and salinity S, but equilibrated at temperature $T + \Delta T$ and salinity $S + \Delta S$ is found from

$$C_\nu = p_\nu\left(\beta_\nu \mp \int_{T_0}^{T} \left(\frac{\partial \beta_\nu}{\partial T}\right)_S dT \mp \int_{S_0}^{S} \left(\frac{\partial \beta_\nu}{\partial S}\right)_T\right) dS \tag{19}$$

Since $(\partial\beta_\nu/\partial S)_T\, dS$ is usually negligibly small compared to the temperature term, and the slope of the NAEC curve for T's of a few degrees centigrade can be assumed to be constant, equation 19 simplifies to

$$C_\nu = p_\nu\left(\beta_\nu \mp \frac{d\beta_\nu}{dT}\,\Delta T\right) \tag{20}$$

$d\beta_\nu/dT$ is a linear approximation of the temperature coefficient of the solubility coefficient, determined at the center of ΔT, if necessary by iteration. σ and Δ are given by:

$$\sigma_\nu = 10^2\left(1 \mp \frac{1}{\beta_\nu}\frac{d\beta_\nu}{dT}\,\Delta T\right) \text{ percent} \tag{21}$$

$$\Delta_\nu = 10^2\left(\frac{1}{\beta_\nu}\frac{d\beta_\nu}{dT}\,\Delta T\right) \text{ percent} \tag{22}$$

For He and Kr, the apparent supersaturation of water equilibrated at 15°C and then heated may be found in Fig. 3. For any ΔT, ΔKr is always much more pronounced than ΔHe; the effect is just the opposite from the effects of air injection.

The systematic trends are also illustrated in Fig. 1, but since these curves have been plotted relative to the NAEC at 15°C, the percent deviations are only approximate.

Note that the supersaturation of an *in situ* sample is always compared to the NAEC of the potential temperature of the water.

An example of such heating after equilibration has been found in the extreme North Pacific (Bieri and Koide, 1972). In a near-surface (5 m) sample from ~50°N, 177°W, Kr was found to be supersaturated by 16%, Ar by 12%, Ne by 7%, and He by 5%. At 20 m depth, Δ_{Kr} was +12%, Δ_{Ar} +9%, Δ_{Ne} +6%, and Δ_{He} +4% [He, Ne, Ar, relative to volumetric NAECs of Weiss (1970, 1971), Kr relative to preliminary volumetric NAECs of Bieri]. Concentration ratios C_{Ne}/C_{Kr} and C_{Ar}/C_{Kr} for both samples indicate that the equilibration temperature was about 4.5°C, while the *in situ* temperature was 7.98°C in the 5 m sample and 7.76°C at 20 m depth.

Effects involving interface cooling by evaporation, while the interpretation of observed distributions for noble gases in some high-salinity waters near the equator (Bieri and Koide, 1972) suggest their reality, are definitively not understood. Since nonturbulent heating in the presence of a stable laminar layer is about two orders of magnitude faster than molecular gas exchange ($\tau_{gas}/\tau_H \sim 10^2$),[1] the temperature of the relatively well-mixed regime below the laminar layer should change more rapidly than the gas concentrations, and such conditions should thus lead to undersaturation. Only gravitational instability of the laminar layer could generate the observed effects.

Effect of excessive rain

Rain may also influence the dissolved gas concentrations of surface water. Because of its low salt content and consequently lower density, it may form a low salinity layer floating at the top of more saline water (Newman and Pierson, 1966). Also, depending on the height in the atmosphere at which precipitation of raindrops occurs, dissolved gas concentrations may be low because of lower pressure at the level where condensation before precipitation has taken place. Unfortunately, the concentrations of noble gases in rain have never been measured, but unless the surface layer is very shallow, the gas concentrations low, and $(E - P) \ll 0$, such effects would barely be perceptible.

Interpretation of in situ *concentrations in complex cases*

So far, the effects of a few specific mechanisms have been described, and each generates a characteristic distribution pattern of Δ by which it can be recognized. In principle, the contribution of each mechanism can be found by writing down the complete equations for as many gases as there are unknowns by using matrix algebra. For instance, if the deviations are caused by pressure effects—both atmospheric and

[1] The fluxes given by equations 17 and 18, in addition to the total contents of gas and heat, $Q_{gas} = V \times C$ (Q_{gas} = total gas content of reservoir, V = volume, and C = concentration) and $Q_H = V \times \rho_{sw} \times c_p \times T$ (Q_H = total heat content of reservoir, V = volume, ρ_{sw} = density of seawater, c_p = specific heat of seawater at constant pressure, and T = temperature) allow a calculation of the characteristic times for exchange:

$$\tau_{gas} = \frac{Q_{gas}}{F} = \frac{VC\delta}{\Delta CD} \quad \text{and} \quad \tau_H = \frac{Q_H}{H} = \frac{V\rho_{sw}c_pT\delta}{\Delta Tk}$$

(In both equations, the gradient across the interface has been replaced by the concentration, or temperature difference, respectively, at the upper and lower boundaries of the laminar layer of thickness δ.) Thus, the ratio

$$\frac{\tau_{gas}}{\tau_H} = \frac{1}{\rho_{sw}c_p}\frac{C}{T}\frac{k}{D}\frac{\Delta T}{\Delta C}$$

For argon and water of 20°C, one finds ($C_{Ar} = 0.2531\ 10^{-3}$ ml (STP)/ml, $\rho_{sw}c_p \sim 1$, $k \sim 0.00134$ cal/cm sec °K, $D \sim 2\ 10^{-5}$ cm²/sec) $\tau_{gas}/\tau_H \sim 10^2$. For other gases, the order of magnitude remains unchanged.

hydrostatic—air injection and temperature variations after gas equilibration, ϵ, ΔT, and v can be sought from the equations:

$$\Delta_{He} = \epsilon - \frac{1}{\beta_{He}} \frac{d\beta_{He}}{dT} \Delta T + \frac{v}{\beta_{He}} \tag{23}$$

$$\left.\begin{aligned} \Delta_{Ne} &= \epsilon - \frac{1}{\beta_{Ne}} \frac{d\beta_{Ne}}{dT} \Delta T + \frac{v}{\beta_{Ne}} \\ \Delta_{Ar} &= \epsilon - \frac{1}{\beta_{Ar}} \frac{d\beta_{Ar}}{dT} \Delta T + \frac{v}{\beta_{Ar}} \end{aligned}\right\} \tag{24}$$

$$\Delta_{Kr} = \epsilon - \frac{1}{\beta_{Kr}} \frac{d\beta_{Kr}}{dT} \Delta T + \frac{v}{\beta_{Kr}} \tag{25}$$

This approach, however, because of small difference terms, does require that the solubilities and the *in situ* concentrations are known accurately, to at least 1 per mill (1/10 of 1 percent). Since the *in situ* analyses have accuracies of the order of 1% and in view of what has been said about the solubilities, this method cannot be applied at the present time.

The Boundary Between the Ocean and the Solid Earth

Influx of helium

Radioactive α-decay in the lithosphere supplies the atmosphere with a steady source of helium of atomic mass 4. This isotope constitutes the bulk of all helium present in the atmosphere. A lighter isotope of mass 3 is present with an abundance of 1.2 ppm by volume (Aldrich and Nier, 1948) and results primarily from high-energy interactions between cosmic rays and atmospheric gases. Were it not for this steady production of both isotopes, our atmosphere would long ago have lost all its helium to outer space.

The first suggestion that an influx of He^4 through the sediment-ocean boundary may be possible to detect is due to (or credited to) Revelle and Suess (1962). From a simple box model, it was estimated that 5% of the dissolved helium in the bottom 1000 m may be caused by such an influx.

Today, 10 yr later, our knowledge about the helium fluxes entering the abyssal ocean is not much better. There are several reasons for this state of affairs. First, maintaining the integrity of a sample from the collection at sea to its introduction into analytical instruments in the laboratory, the identification of the excess[2] component of helium in the measured helium concentration and finally the translation of this excess into a flux poses formidable problems. The small concentration of helium, about 4×10^{-8} ml (STP)/ml of seawater in near-bottom samples, are subject to air contamination (discussed in the paragraph on air injection) and require a sampling device that maintains the integrity of the collected samples. I have used a very simple sample container (Bieri, 1965) allowing *in situ* collection and reliable storage over months (although the operational attachment is somewhat difficult to handle).

Gas extraction on shipboard and storage of samples in the gaseous phase has had its pitfalls. Suess and Wänke (1965) find a 6% difference between deep samples from the North Pacific (stored in Pyrex containers) and the Indian Ocean (stored in stainless steel containers) and concluded that helium diffusion through the Pyrex may be the

[2] The term "excess" has been coined to identify the part of the supersaturation that is due to the influx of He through the lower boundary.

reason for this difference. Craig et al. (1967), analyzing a large number of samples from the Southeast Pacific that were extracted aboard ship and stored in valved stainless steel flasks, find variations in Δ_{He} from 8.7 to 50% and had to discard all but the 8.7% value. Because of the simultaneous presence of liquid and gas during gas transfer, "simple" expansions can prove to be very unpredictable. Such complications may have been the reason for the large variations and the fractionation observed in analyses of samples from a profile in the North Pacific (Bieri et al., 1964).

The evaluation of the excess He component has also proved to be more difficult than originally expected, for reasons that have been explained in the preceding paragraphs. In the absence of any detailed knowledge that is needed to find any supersaturation of helium due to mechanisms at the upper boundary, Bieri et al. (1964, 1966, 1967) evaluated the radiogenic component from He/Ne ratios (Benson, 1965):

$$\Delta_{He^4} \sim \left(\frac{C_{He}}{C_{Ne}} - \frac{C^*_{He}}{C^*_{Ne}}\right)\frac{C_{Ne}}{C^*_{He}} \tag{26}$$

or by subtracting the supersaturation of Ne from that of He:

$$\Delta_{He^4} \sim \Delta_{He} - \Delta_{Ne} \tag{27}$$

Bieri et al. (op. cit) find evidence that the deep and bottom waters of the Southeast Pacific contain excess helium in amounts estimated to be between 4 and 7%. With the exception of one sample taken above an area of high heat flow, the radiogenic He appeared to be evenly distributed from the bottom to about the 1000 m level. The single value of Craig et al. (1967) also agrees with these estimates (their 8.7% Δ_{He} is a supersaturation, not an excess; if the Δ_{Ne} of 3.7% found in the same sample is taken into account, the excess helium is 5%).

In contrast to the abyssal waters of the Southeast Pacific, deep samples from the North Atlantic and cold near-surface waters from the Drake Passage reveal supersaturations of He that are 5% lower (Bieri et al., 1968). There is no evidence for excess He in these samples. Lower concentrations of He are also encountered in the North Pacific (Bieri et al., 1968), but these results in addition show a general tendency toward undersaturation, which Craig and Weiss (1968) interpret as diffusional losses. Further profiles (Bieri and Koide, 1972) confirm that Δ_{He} in the North Pacific is also 5% lower than in the Southeast Pacific.

The higher concentrations and the excess of helium in the Southeast Pacific has been confirmed by analysis from three detailed profiles, one of them taken at the equator (Bieri and Koide, 1972). In these three profiles, additional support for the presence of excess He comes from indications of vertical concentration gradients of helium near the bottom (Fig. 5). That such gradients under certain conditions may be expected can again be derived from an idealized model. In formal analogy to linear molecular diffusion, the flux of helium across the lower boundary under steady-state conditions, in the absence of horizontal concentration gradients, vertical advection, and with a removal mechanism present at some higher level, is given by

$$F_{He^4} = -\kappa_z \frac{dC_{He}}{dz} \tag{28}$$

Since the resolution of the sampling is low, dC_{He}/dz is replaced by differences:

$$F_{He^4} = \kappa_z \frac{C_{He}{}^{Z_1} - C_{He}{}^{Z_2}}{Z_1 - Z_2} \tag{29}$$

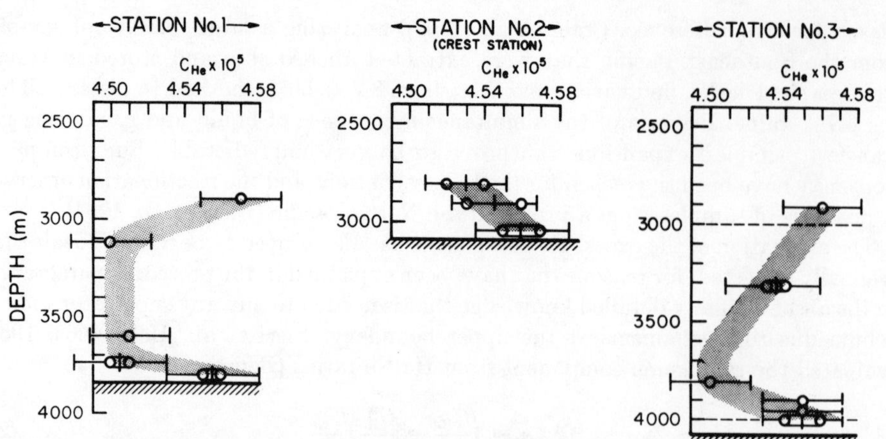

Fig. 5. Helium concentration in near-bottom samples in the Equatorial and Southeast Pacific. Connected points indicate results from double samples. Horizontal bars are 1-sigma limits. The location of the bottom is given by the hatched line. In all three stations, the concentration of He^4 appears to decrease with increasing distance from the bottom. The observed reversal of this trend and the second maximum at the 3000-m level in stations 1 and 3 may be due to leakage of He^4 from the crest of the East Pacific Rise.

where Z_1 is the ordinate nearest the bottom and Z_2 that at a higher level. Note that ${C_{He}}^{Z_1} - {C_{He}}^{Z_2}$ is *not* necessarily ΔHe^4, but if ${C_{Ne}}^{Z_1} = {C_{Ne}}^{Z_1}$, ${C_{Ar}}^{Z_1} = {C_{Ar}}^{Z_2}$ in the same samples, ${C_{He}}^{Z_1} - {C_{He}}^{Z_2}$ can only derive from an influx of helium. It is clear that the conditions specified for this model cannot exist in a natural system such as the ocean and that fluxes calculated from equation 29 have a qualitative meaning only. To obtain quantitative information, the physical parameters of the area would have to be studied in detail and the flux equation solved for the more general three-dimensional case, also taking into account advection components. Any correlation between the excess helium and the flux is by necessity intimately connected with the detailed physical oceanography of the area, and attempts to solve this problem are found in Bieri et al. (1966) and Craig and Clarke (1972).

Recently determined helium and neon solubilities (Weiss, 1971) suggest that both gases in all abyssal waters are supersaturated to a considerable degree—helium by 8 to 12% and neon by about 6.5%. For such waters, the Δ distribution almost exactly fits the distributions predicted by air injection, with the exception of helium in the Southeast Pacific, which was about 4% higher (Bieri, 1971; Craig and Weiss, 1971). Positive identification of an air-sea boundary effect allows a more correct assessment of the excess helium than equations 26 or 27. For air injection in particular:

$$\Delta_{He^4} = \Delta_{He} - \frac{v}{\beta_{He}} \tag{30}$$

The preliminary mass spectrometric solubilities (Bieri and Barnes, 1972), however, lead to an entirely different interpretation of the gas concentrations in deep waters. With the exception of He in the Southeast Pacific, all the gases appear to be essentially at saturation within analytical error. In this case, Δ_{He^4} evaluated from equation 30 is incorrect and would properly have to be derived from equation 27.

A new approach toward the determination of excess helium involving the isotope He^3 is due to Clarke et al. (1969, 1970). Instead of trying to evaluate Δ_{He^4} relative to the Δ's of other dissolved gases, this component theoretically can be directly calculated if He^3 is also measured. Assuming that the atmosphere is the only source of He^3:

$$\frac{C_{He^3}}{C^*_{He^3}} - 1 = \Delta_{He^3} \tag{31}$$

where C_{He^3} is the measured concentration of He^3 in the water, $C^*_{He^3}$ is the NAEC of He^3, and Δ_{He^3} is the supersaturation of He^3. For $\Delta_{He^3} \neq 0$, the supersaturation of He^4 should be the same as that of He^3, except for small deviations due to the slightly lower solubility coefficient of He^3 (Weiss, 1970a) in cases where the supersaturation depends on β. The excess is then given by

$$\Delta_{He^4} = \Delta_{He} - \Delta_{He^3} \tag{32}$$

where Δ_{He} and Δ_{He^3} are the supersaturation components derived from equations 8 and 31, respectively.

The results of Clarke et al., however, suggest that there are additional sources of He^3. A pronounced maximum in the supersaturation of He^3 appears to exist near 2000-m depth in both profiles. In the Southwest Pacific station (Clarke et al., 1969), this maximum was interpreted to derive from an influx of primordial He^3 escaping from the crest of the East Pacific Rise. Since the excess He^4 in a station nearby was also found by Bieri et al. (1968) to have a maximum at a similar level, the assumption of a common source for both helium isotopes is reasonable.

In the Northeast Pacific, however, such a common origin is not evident. Clarke et al. (1970) find Δ_{He} and Δ_{He^3} to be uncorrelated, and earlier results on He^4 from the same area of the Pacific (Bieri et al., 1964) are not accurate enough for a comparison. All other samples collected in the North Pacific give little support for the presence of excess He^4 (Bieri et al., 1968; Bieri and Koide, 1972a) and it is therefore unlikely that the large Δ_{He^3} could derive from the interior of the earth in this case, but it also cannot be a supersaturation.

Thus, instead of getting an accurate hold on the excess of radiogenic helium, one is faced with a problem of even higher complexity, as the source of the excess He^3 is more difficult to identify and evaluate than that of Δ_{He^4}. Also, the question again is whether the NAEC for He^3 can be calculated from the solubility coefficient, as the extrapolation of this isotope is over ~11 orders of magnitude. However, no indication of any deviations can be found in the He^3/He^4 from two surface water samples (Clarke et al., 1969, 1970).

Excess helium is present in the abyssal waters of the Southeast and East Equatorial Pacific. Where samples were collected in the deep North Atlantic, the deep North Pacific, and close to an area where bottom waters are formed (Drake Passage), the supersaturation of helium was found to be about 5% lower than in the Southeast Pacific and is probably zero. In the Southeast Pacific, small He concentration gradients are indicated near the bottom and large gradients are encountered below the intermediate water. In between, the distribution of excess helium is very uniform. With the exception of one sample collected above an area of high heat flow (but the heat flow was not measured), there is no evidence for large helium leaks (hot spots) and it is therefore still unclear where all the excess helium in this area comes from. The average helium flux in the Southeast Pacific is still uncertain. Values between 2–4 × 10^6 helium atoms/cm^2 sec have been derived.

Influx of Heat

The present oceanic heat flow is about 1.5 μcal/sec (Lee and McDonald, 1963). Without any other means of heating (no mixing), one estimates that the temperature difference between the abyssal waters from the North and South Pacific, assuming a general northward flow of such water with removal by vertical advection w, should be (H, ρ and c as defined in footnote on p. 207)

$$T_n - T_s = 2H/\rho_{sw}\, C_p\, W \tag{33}$$

or about 0.2°C (Munk, 1966). This would cause an apparent Δ_{Kr} of 0.6% and a Δ_{Ar} of 0.5%. The influence of the heat flow on the apparent supersaturation is therefore only small and with presently available instrumentation cannot be detected. In addition, eddy diffusion and advection have an effect that works in the opposite direction, for example, causing undersaturation (Bieri and Koide, 1972a).

2. Noble Gas Concentrations Within the Oceans

A. Mixing

As has briefly been mentioned in Section 1, any change in the concentration of conservative gases within the oceans may be reflected in an analogue change of other

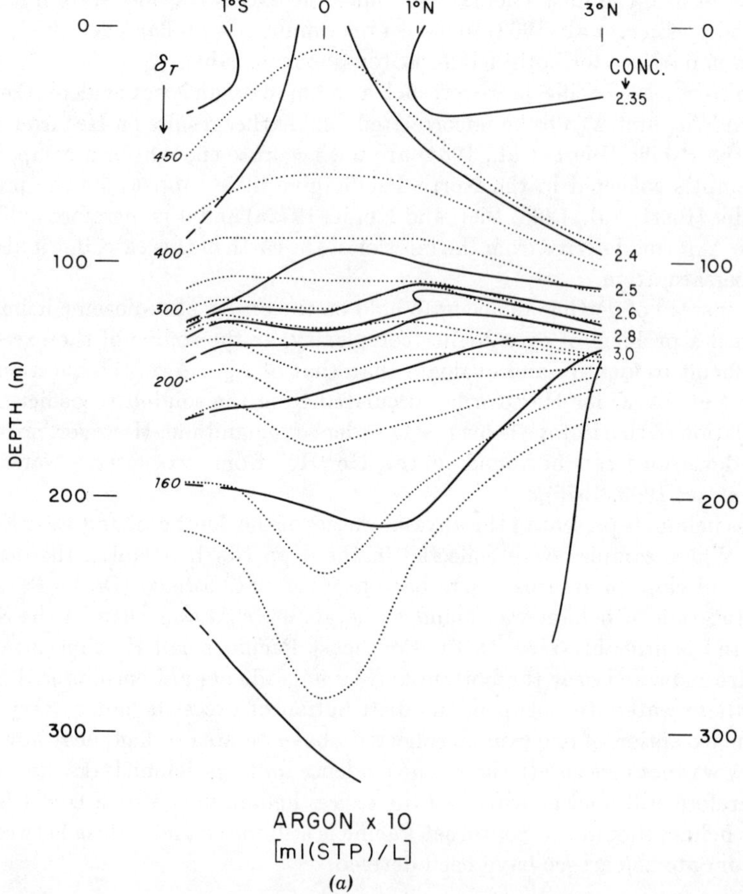

(a)

Fig. 6. Meridional profiles of Ar (Fig. 6a) and Kr (Fig. 6b) at 150°W, displaying ridging and troughing. The velocity core of the undercurrent is at 100-m depth where a lens of water with homogeneous concentrations is seen. Dotted lines are isopleths of thermosteric anomaly.

conservative properties. Since mixing is the only mechanism capable of changing a conservative variable, an exception to this would only be possible for the (highly hypothetical) case that boundary values were identical for one property, but not for the gases. Where mixing of two masses at different temperatures occurs in a steady, linear situation and in the presence of diffusion and advection, the concentration of dissolved gas, the temperature, and the salinity are described by the equation:

$$\left[\kappa \frac{\partial^2}{\partial z^2} - w \frac{\partial}{\partial z}\right] C, S, T = 0 \tag{34}$$

Since the coefficients κ and w must be the same for all conservative variables, the concentration is a linear function of T or S. The normal atmospheric equilibrium concentrations, on the other hand, are curves of increasing convexity (toward coordinates) from He to Kr (Fig. 1). Thus, mixing will lead to a Δ which depends on the separation of the NAEC curve and the mixing line. If the concentrations at the boundaries are close to saturation, mixing effects will lead to a similar distribution of Δ's as heating. Such effects, however, can only be detected if the temperature difference at

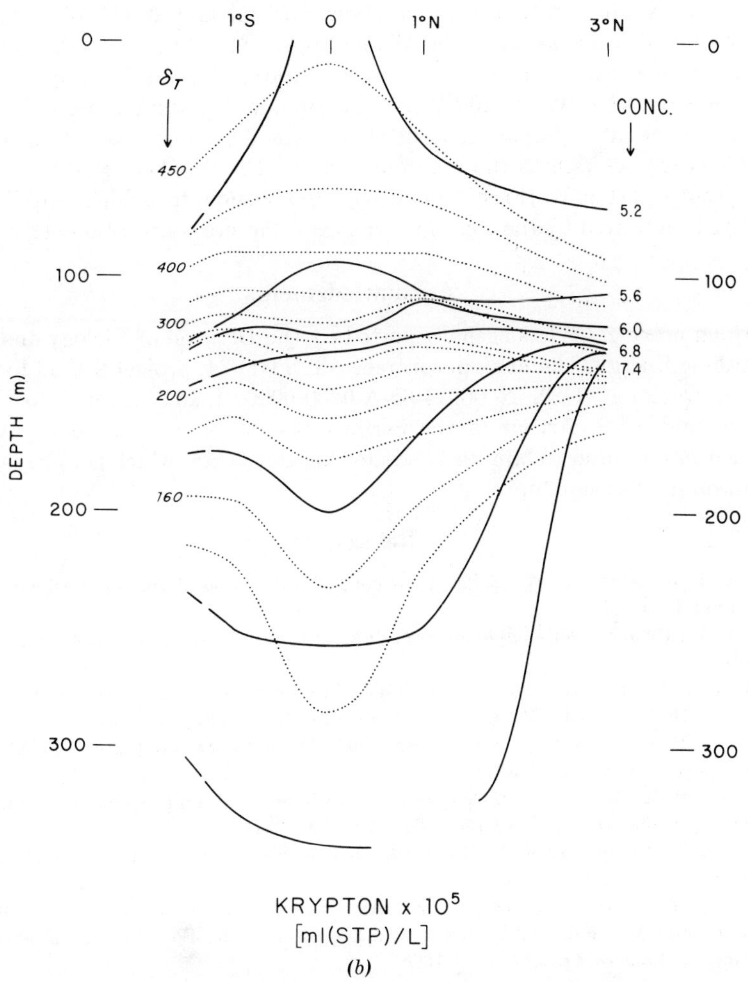

(b)

the boundaries is large. In practice this means that Δ's caused by other mechanisms will almost invariably overshadow effects of mixing. This is especially true for abyssal waters between about 1000 and 4000-m depth, where boundary temperature differences are of the order of 3°C and where the application of equation 33 for T and S for vertical diffusion and advection has met some success in the evaluation of w/κ (Munk, 1966). Bieri et al. (1966) have exercised the application of equation 34 for mean Δ's from the East Pacific and between the surface layer and 1000-m depth. While the vertical diffusion-advection model definitively does not apply to individual profiles, as was pointed out by Craig et al. (1967), there may be some cases where its application to mean values covering a large area can be justified.

B. Tracer Studies

Dissolved conservative gases can be useful as tracers in situations where supersaturation is pronounced and connected to water masses possessing other prominent features. An example is found in the Pacific Equatorial Undercurrent (for reference material about the Undercurrent, see Taft and Jones, 1972). Indications that water near the core of the Undercurrent is highly supersaturated in all gases were first found by Bieri and Koide (1972) in a profile at the equator and at 111°W. Later analyses from meridional crossings along 150°W and approximately 160°W (Bieri and Barnes, 1972) again revealed the presence of supersaturated Ar and Kr in and about 40 m below the core at 150°W. At 160°W, the maxima in Δ_{Kr} and Δ_{Ar} were both less pronounced and broader. Δ_{He} and Δ_{Ne} in all stations for reasons as yet not understood were not nearly as high as those encountered at 111°W. Concentrations from meridional profiles at 150°W (Figs. 6*a* and 6*b*) clearly show troughing and ridging, and upwelling is indicated by the concentrations and the supersaturation of Ar and Kr.

Acknowledgments

Work on noble gases has been supported by the Division of Biology and Medicine, U.S. Atomic Energy Commission, contract AT (11-1)-34, project 84 and by the Office of Naval Research, USN N 00014-65-A-0200-6006. I am indebted to Drs. E. D. Goldberg and R. S. Arthur of the Scripps Institution of Oceanography for their continued interest and to Minoru Koide for his assistance, which goes beyond normal recognition in coauthorship.

References

Aldrich, L. T. and A. O. Nier, 1948. The occurrence of He^3 in natural sources of helium. *Phys. Rev.*, **74**, 1590–1594.

Benson, B. B., 1965. Some thoughts on gases dissolved in the oceans. *Mar. Geochem. Proc. Symp.*, 91–107.

Bieri, R. H., M. Koide, and E. D. Goldberg, 1964. Noble gases in seawater. *Science*, **146**, 1035–1037.

Bieri, R. H., 1965. Hermetically-sealing seawater sampler. *J. Mar. Res.*, **23**. 33–38.

Bieri, R. H., M. Koide, and E. D. Goldberg, 1966. The noble gas contents of Pacific seawaters. *J. Geophys. Res.*, **71**, 5243–5265.

Bieri, R. H., M. Koide, and E. D. Goldberg, 1967. Geophysical implications of the excess helium found in Pacific waters. *J. Geophys. Res.*, **72**, 2497–2511.

Bieri, R. H., M. Koide, and E. D. Goldberg, 1968. Noble gas contents of marine waters. *Earth Planet. Sci. Letters* **4**, 329–340.

Bieri, R. H., 1971. Dissolved noble gases in marine waters. *Earth Planet. Sci. Letters*, **10**, 329–333.

Bieri, R. H. and M. Koide, 1972. Dissolved noble gases in the East Equatorial and Southeast Pacific. *J. Geophys. Res.*, **77**, 1667–1676.

Bieri, R. H. and M. Koide, 1972a. Noble gas concentrations in the North Pacific. To be published.

Bieri, R. H. and R. Barnes, 1972. Noble gas profiles in and near the Pacific Equatorial Undercurrent at 150°W and 160°W in April 1971. To appear in *J. Mar. Res.*

Bolin, B., 1960. On the exchange of carbon dioxide between the atmosphere and the sea. *Tellus*, **12**, 274–281.

Clarke, W. B., M. A. Beg, and H. Craig, 1969. Excess He^3 in the sea: evidence for terrestrial primordial helium. *Earth Planet. Sci. Letters*, **6**, 213–220.

Clarke, W. B., M. A. Beg, and H. Craig, 1970. Excess helium 3 at the North Pacific Geosecs Station. *J. Geophys. Res.*, **75**, 7676–7678.

Craig, H., R. F. Weiss, and W. B. Clarke, 1967. Dissolved gases in the Equatorial and South Pacific ocean. *J. Geophys. Res.*, **72**, 6165–6181.

Craig, H. and R. F. Weiss, 1968. Argon concentrations in the ocean: a discussion. *Earth Planet. Sci. Letters*, **5**, 175–183.

Craig, H. and R. F. Weiss, 1971. Dissolved gas saturation anomalies and excess helium in the ocean. *Earth Planet. Sci. Letters* 1971, **10**, 289–296.

Craig, H. and W. B. Clarke, 1971. Oceanic He^3: contribution from cosmogenic tritium. *Earth Planet. Sci. Letters*. 9, 45–48.

Dankwerts, P. V., 1951, Significance of liquid-film coefficients in gas absorption. *Ind. Eng. Chem.*, **43**, 1460–1467.

Davis, D. S. and G. S. Crandall, 1930. The role of the liquid stationary film in batch absorptions of gases. *J. Am. Chem. Soc.*, **52**, 3757–3768.

Douglas, E., 1964. Solubilities of oxygen, argon and nitrogen in distilled water. *J. Phys. Chem.*, **68**, 169–174.

Douglas, E., 1965. Solubilities of argon and nitrogen in seawater. *J. Phys. Chem.*, **69**, 2608–2610.

Ewing, G. and E. D. McAlister, 1960. On the thermal boundary layer of the ocean. *Science*, **131**, 1374–1376.

Flynn, H. G., 1964. Physics of acoustic cavitation in liquids, *Phys. Acoustics*, **1** (Part B), Academic Press, New York and London, 57–171.

Guenther, P., W. Zeil, U. Grisar, and E. Heim, 1957. Versuche über die Sonolumineszenz Wässriger Lösungen. *Z. Elektrochem*, **61**, 188–201.

Hamm, R. E. and G. T. Thompson, 1941. Dissolved nitrogen in the seawater of the Northeast Pacific, with notes on the total carbon dioxide and the dissolved oxygen. *J. Mar. Res.*, **4**, 11–26.

Higbie, R., 1935. The rate of absorption of a pure gas into a still liquid during short periods of exposure. *Am. Inst. Chem. Eng. Trans.*, **31**, 365–389.

Himmelblau, D. M., 1960. Solubilities of inert gases in water. *J. Chem. Eng. Data*, **5**, 10–15.

Hintenberger, H., H. Koenig, and L. Schultz, 1964. Krypton and xenon in the oceans. *Z. Naturforsch.*, **19**a, 1227–1228.

Kanwisher, J., 1963. On the exchange of gases between the atmosphere and the sea. *Deep-Sea Res.*, **10**, 195–207.

Klots, C. E. and B. B. Benson, 1963. Solubilities of nitrogen, oxygen and argon in distilled water. *J. Mar. Res.*, **21**, 48–57.

König, H., 1963. Ueber die Löslichkeit der Edelgase in Meerwasser. *Z. Naturforsch.*, **18**a, 363–367.

König, H., H. Wänke, G. S. Bien, N. W. Rakestraw, and H. E. Suess, 1964. Helium neon and argon in the oceans. *Deep-Sea Res.*, **11**, 243–247.

Lee, W. H. K. and G. J. F. MacDonald, 1963. Global variation of terrestrial heat flow. *J. Geophys. Res.*, **68**, 6481–6492.

Liebermann, L., 1956. Air bubbles in water. *J. Appl. Phys.*, **28**, 205–211.

Matsuo, S. and Y. Miyake, 1966. Gas composition in ice samples from Antarctica. *J. Geophys. Res.*, **71**, 5235–5241.

McAlister, E. D. and W. McLeish, 1969. Heat transfer in the top millimeter of the ocean. *J. Geophys. Res.*, **74**, 3408–3414.

Mazor, E., G. J. Wasserburg, and H. Craig, 1964. Rare gases in Pacific ocean water. *Deep-Sea Res.*, **11**, 929–932.

Metzger, I. and W. E. Dobbins, 1967. Role of fluid properties in gas transfer. *Env. Science Techn.*, **1**, 57–65.

Morrison, T. J. and N. B. Johnstone, 1954. Solubilities of the inert gases in water. *J. Chem. Soc.*, 3441–3446.

Munk, W. H., 1966. Abyssal recipes. *Deep-Sea Res.*, **13**, 707–730.

Murray, C. N., J. P. Riley, and T. R. S. Wilson, 1969. The solubility of gases in distilled water and seawater—I. Nitrogen. *Deep-Sea Res.*, **16**, 297–310.

Murray, C. N. and J. P. Riley, 1970. The solubility of gases in distilled water and seawater—III. Argon. *Deep-Sea Res.*, **17**, 203–209.

Neumann, G. and W. J. Pierson, 1966. Principles of Physical Oceanography. Englewood Cliffs, N.J., Prentice-Hall.

Rakestraw, N. W. and V. M. Emmel, 1938. The relation of dissolved oxygen to nitrogen in some Atlantic waters. *J. Mar. Res.*, **1**, 207–216.

Reid, J. L., 1972. Intermediate waters of the Northwest Pacific in winter. Johns Hopkins Oceanographic Stud., 5, 96 pp.

Revelle, R. and H. E. Suess, 1962. Interchange of properties between sea and air. In *The Sea* Vol. 1. M. N. Hill, ed. Wiley-Interscience, New York, pp. 313–321, (Chapter 7).

Strickland, J. D. H., 1965. Phytoplankton and marine primary production. *Ann. Rev. Microbiol.*, **19**, 127–162.

Suess, H. E. and H. Wänke, 1965. On the possibility of a helium flux through the ocean floor. In *Progress in Oceanography* Vol. 3. Pergamon Press, New York, 347–353.

Swinnerton, J. W. and J. P. Sullivan, 1962. Shipboard determination of dissolved gases in seawater by gas chromatography. N.R.L. Report 5806, U.S. Naval Res. Lab.

Taft, B. A. and J. H. Jones, 1972. Measurements of the Equatorial Undercurrent in the Eastern Pacific. In *Progress in Oceanography* 6 Pergamon Press, New York.

Weiss, R. F., 1970. The solubility of nitrogen, oxygen and argon in water and seawater, *Deep-Sea Res.*, **17**, 721–735.

Weiss, R. F., 1970a. Helium isotope effect in solution in water and seawater. *Science*, **168**, 247.

Weiss, R. F., 1971. The solubility of helium and neon in water and seawater. *J. Chem. Eng. Data*, **16**, 235–241.

Westlake, D. F., 1963. Comparisons of plant productivity. *Biol. Rev.*, **38**, 385–425.

Wood, D. and R. Caputti, 1966. Solubilities of Kr and Xe in fresh and seawater. USNRDL-TR-988.

7. DISSOLVED NONCONSERVATIVE GASES IN SEAWATER

W. Seiler and U. Schmidt

1. Introduction

Besides N_2 and O_2, which are the main components, atmospheric air contains a variety of trace gases. According to Henry's law, all of these gases should occur as solutes in ocean waters. Their concentrations would be expected to depend essentially on their partial pressures in the atmosphere, their solubilities, and the temperature of the water. However, the observations indicate that the concentration of many gases dissolved in the ocean water deviates from the expected equilibrium values. Apparently the concentration of these dissolved gases is influenced by other processes in the water. Accordingly, we must differentiate between the conservative gases whose concentrations in ocean water correspond to equilibrium values and the nonconservative gases whose concentrations in ocean water are determined by marine processes.

The determination of trace gases in both categories has recently generated considerable interest among marine and atmospheric scientists for several reasons. First, trace gases have been found very suitable in studies of ocean currents and turbulent mixing processes, particularly in the upper layers of the oceans as well as of the air-sea exchange processes. Second, more and more measurements are concerned with atmospheric pollutants such as PCBS, CCl_4, etc., which are brought into the oceans by a variety of processes, not only by rivers but also by washout and rainout, and may lead to changes in the marine ecosystem (Goldberg, 1971). Third, air chemistry, concerned mainly with the budget and cycle of trace gases in the atmosphere, involves interactions and exchanges with the mixed layer of the oceans because physical, chemical, and biological processes in the water can provide sources or sinks for several atmospheric trace gases and thereby effect their distribution and mixing ratios in the atmosphere. A good example of this problem is the cycle of CO_2 in the atmosphere, which is discussed elsewhere in this volume.

This chapter surveys present knowledge of dissolved carbon monoxide, molecular hydrogen, methane, and nitrous oxide concentrations in ocean waters, and a discussion of their influence on the budget of these gases in the atmosphere. A number of recent unpublished results on dissolved CO and H_2 will be presented. These data were obtained in two cruises, one with the German research vessel *F. S. Meteor* in the summer of 1971 in the Northern Atlantic, the other with the British Royal research vessel *R.R.S. Shackleton* in the winter of 1971 to 1972 in the Southern Atlantic.

2. Cruises

Table I summarizes the most important cruises of several research vessels during which measurements of dissolved CO, H_2, CH_4, and N_2O were carried out with the dates, locations, and gases investigated. The precise routes of the various cruises are shown in Fig. 1. The majority of the measurements are concentrated in the Northern Atlantic. In the Southern Atlantic measurements are available only for H_2 and CO; in the Northern Pacific measurements are available only for CH_4 and CO; in the Southern Pacific N_2O only has been determined in a few samples.

For most of the measurements, discrete samples of ocean waters were employed; exceptions are measurements of CO during the cruise with the German *F. S. Meteor* in the summer of 1970, and measurements of the H_2 and CO during the cruise with the same vessel in the summer of 1971 and with the British *R.R.S. Shackleton* in the winter

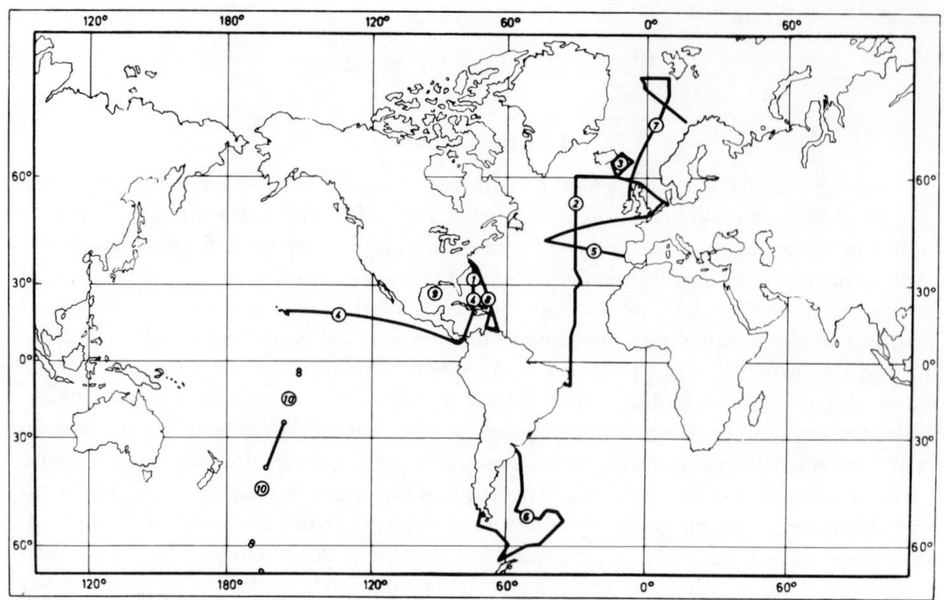

Fig. 1. Tracks of main cruises. The numbers refer to the cruise number enlisted in Table I.

of 1971 to 1972, where a continuous sampling technique was used. These methods will be described in the next section.

3. Analytical Methods

The two methods now available for detecting small amounts of the dissolved trace gases treated in this chapter are gas chromatography and a hot mercury oxide technique. Several processes are used for separating the dissolved gases from the solution, depending on their chemical and physical properties.

Nitrous oxide is purged from the heated solution by extremely pure nitrogen and adsorbed on a 5-Å molecular sieve trap. Subsequently, the trap is heated to 350°C and the sample is transferred with helium as the carrier gas into a gas chromatograph equipped with a thermal conductivity detector (Hahn, 1972a). The lower limit of detection is 10^{-10} cm^3 N_2O/liter H_2O in a 5-liter sample.

Methane is stripped from solution at normal temperature by a helium stream and concentrated in an activated charcoal trap cooled to a temperature of -80°C. Subsequently the temperature is raised to $+90$°C and the sample is swept into the gas chromatograph, again using a helium carrier. With a flame ionization detector the technique is capable of determining 10^{-8} cm^3 CH_4/liter H_2O (Swinnerton and Linnenbom, 1967a).

For carbon monoxide analysis of water samples, Swinnerton et al. (1968) used the same stripping technique, collecting carbon monoxide together with methane in the charcoal trap. For analysis, CO was converted to CH_4 by means of a nickel catalyst and determined in the same manner as CH_4 with the same limit of detection, 10^{-8} cm^3 CO/liter H_2O.

We used two sampling methods to determine the dissolved carbon monoxide and molecular hydrogen: a discontinuous method and a continuous method. The first was

TABLE I

Summary of Expeditions During Which the Gases N_2O, CH_4, CO, and H_2 Were Measured in Seawater. The Cruises of These Expeditions are Shown in Fig. 1.

Cruise Number	Time	Location	Analysis of Gases				Authors
			N_2O	CH_4	CO	H_2	
1	June, 1968	Potomac River, Coastal Water, Tropical Western Atlantic	—	×	×	—	Swinnerton et al. (1969)
2	April, 1969	Middle and Northern Atlantic	×	—	×	—	Seiler and Junge (1970); Junge et al. (1971a)
3	June–July, 1970	Norwegian Sea	×	—	×	—	Seiler and Greese [a]; Hahn (1972b)
4	May–June, 1970	Western Atlantic, Northern Pacific	—	×	×	—	Lamontagne et al. (1971)
5	May–June, 1971	Northern Atlantic	×	—	×	×	Seiler and Schmidt [a]; Hahn [a]
6	November–December, 1971	Southern Atlantic	—	—	×	×	Seiler and Schmidt [a]
7	August, 1971	Norwegian Sea, Greenland Sea	—	×	—	—	Lamontagne et al. (1972)
8	—	Caribbean Sea, Sargasso Sea	—	×	—	—	Lamontagne et al. (1972)
9	October, 1971	Gulf of Mexico	—	×	—	—	Brooks and Sackett (1972)
10	January–April, 1961	Southern Pacific	×	—	—	—	Craig and Gordon (1963)

[a] Unpublished data.

used to analyze single 5-liter water samples for the determination of vertical concentration profiles in the oceans; the second method was used for the assays of dissolved CO and H_2 in the surface water to depths of 3 m.

In the discontinuous technique, a 5-liter sample is sucked into an evacuated 10-liter glass flask. Because of the instantaneous dispersion into small water droplets during this process and the low pressure in the glass flask, an equilibrium between the gaseous and the liquid phases is rapidly obtained. Immediately afterward the flask is filled to atmospheric pressure with CO-free and H_2-free air. Subsequently the entire sample is fed into a CO and H_2 analyzer (Seiler and Junge, 1970; Schmidt and Seiler, 1970), based on the hot mercury oxide technique. The reduction of mercury oxide by CO and H_2 liberates mercury vapor, which is detected by atomic absorption. This method allows the detection of 1×10^{-6} cm^3 CO/liter H_2O and 5×10^{-6} cm^3 H_2/liter H_2O, respectively, with a relative error of about 10%.

The continuous sampling method employs an upright 1.5 m long glass cylinder into which a continuous flow of seawater is directed downward. From the bottom CO- and H_2-free air enters and is recycled with an equivalent flow rate. Both gases dissolved in the seawater are equilibrated with the air. Owing to their low solubility, more than 97% of the dissolved CO and H_2 is transferred into the gaseous phase. The mixing ratios of CO and H_2 in the air are measured continuously by the hot mercury oxide technique. The lower limit of detection is 0.5×10^{-6} cm^3 CO/liter H_2O and 2.5×10^{-6} cm^3 H_2/liter H_2O, respectively.

4. Results

In this section the available body of data concerning CO, CH_4, H_2, and N_2O in seawater will be discussed with respect to the processes by which the seawater content of these gases is governed. The concentrations of all gases are given here in units of milliliter per liter. Data published in different units were recalculated accordingly. The required solubility coefficients are summarized in Table II: for CO from Douglas (1967); for CH_4 from Atkinson and Richards (1967); and for N_2O from Junge et al. (1971a). For H_2 no solubility coefficients in seawater appear to be available. For the present purpose the data of Morrison and Billet (1952) were used to correct the solubility coefficient in a 3.5% NaCl solution compared with pure water. The density values of seawater were taken from the tables of Kalle and Thorade (1940).

As it is customary in air chemistry, the amount of a trace gas in air will be given in terms of the volume mixing ratio (ppmv). The amount of a gas C dissolved in seawater, expressed in terms of ml gas/liter H_2O depends on the solubility coefficient α from Henry's law, as well as the partial pressure p in the gaseous phase. At equilibrium the

TABLE II

Solubilities in Seawater α(ml/ml H_2O atm) in dependence on the temperature. s is the Salinity

t(°C)	0	5	10	15	20	25	30	s(‰)
α_{CO}	0.0287	0.0256	0.0232	0.0213	0.0196	0.0183	0.0172	34.3
α_{H_2}	0.0184	0.0176	0.0169	0.0164	0.0159	0.0154	0.0150	35.0
α_{N_2O}	1.4	0.89	0.75	0.63	0.53	0.50	0.48	35.0
α_{CH_4}	0.0438	0.0399	0.0362	0.0325	0.0290	0.0255	0.0221	36.0

partial pressure of a gas is the same in the liquid phase and in the gaseous phase. In this case the concentration C is given by

$$C = 10^3 \times \alpha(t, s) \times p \qquad \text{(ml/liter)} \tag{1}$$

or

$$C = 10^3 \times \alpha(t, s) \times M \times P \qquad \text{(ml/liter)} \tag{1a}$$

with α as a function of water temperature t(°C) and salinity s(‰). M is the mixing ratio of the gas in the air above the water surface, given in ppmv. P is the air pressure measured in atm, and $p = M \times P$ is the partial pressure of the gas in air.

If the concentration C of a gas dissolved in seawater is known, the above equation can be applied to determine the mixing ratio E, which the gas would assume in air, provided an equilibrium between liquid and gaseous phases is attained. In this case the so-called equilibrium value E is

$$E = 10^{-3} \times \frac{C}{\alpha \times P} \qquad \text{(ppmv)} \tag{2}$$

Equilibrium exists when E is identical with M. Otherwise the equilibrium is disturbed. The extent of the deviation from equilibrium is expressed by the saturation factor $F = E/M$. With respect to the gas under consideration, water is either supersaturated or undersaturated, depending on whether F is greater or smaller than unity. Setting aside perturbations of the equilibrium by chemical and biological processes, there are three physical effects that frequently lead to a deviation from equilibrium:

1. The exhalation of gases at the bottom of the sea by volcanic activity may lead to considerable supersaturations that, however, are restricted to specific localities.

2. More important is the bubble injection at the ocean surface produced by violent storms that, according to Bieri (1971) and Craig and Weiss (1971), may lead to supersaturations in surface water up to 20%, depending on the solubility of the gases.

3. Furthermore, supersaturation can also occur as the result of the mixing of two water bodies, equilibrated with the air at different temperatures, because of the non-linear relationship between water temperature and solubility. In extreme cases, supersaturations up to 10% may be caused in this way.

Considerably greater perturbations of the equilibrium were observed as the result of chemical or biological processes being active in seawater (e.g., respiration and photosynthesis).

A. Carbon Monoxide

CO in Surface Waters

A summary of all published results, as well as our own unpublished data, is given in Table III. The initial measurements of CO dissolved in seawater were made by Swinnerton et al. (1969) during a cruise starting in Washington, D.C. and ending in Puerto Rico. Eight samples of surface water in the open ocean were analyzed, and concentrations ranging from 2–5 $\times$ 10^{-5} m/liter were found. Since the CO mixing ratio in air is 0.10 to 0.25 ppmv, the results correspond to a supersaturation in seawater by a factor of between 10 and 30.

On similar cruises in the Western Atlantic, Swinnerton et al. (1970), as well as Lamontagne et al. (1971), found much greater variations of dissolved CO ranging from 1.0–19.0 $\times$ 10^{-5} ml/liter with an average value of 6 $\times$ 10^{-5} ml/liter. In the

Table III

Dissolved CO in Surface Waters

Author	Location	Cruise Number	CO-Content $C \times 10^{-5}$ (ml/liter)	Equilibrium Value E (ppm$_v$)	Surface Air Mixing Ratio M (ppm$_v$)	Saturation Factor $F = E/M$	Number of Samples
Swinnerton et al. (1969)	Tropical Western Atlantic	1	2–5	1–3	0.10–0.25	10–30	8
Swinnerton et al. (1970)	Western Atlantic	Stations	1–10	0.5–5.0	0.09–0.15	5–100	26
Seiler and Junge (1970)	Middle and Northern Atlantic	2	3–10	2–5	0.15–0.25	15–33	20
Seiler and Greese (1970) [a]	Norwegian Sea	3	1.5–18.5	0.8–9.0	0.13–0.30	3–56	cont [b]
Lamontagne et al. (1971)	Western Atlantic	4	6–19	3–10	0.10–0.18	20–100	11
	Northern Pacific	4	2–14	1–7	0.08–0.16	10–60	52
Seiler and Schmidt (1971) [a]	Northern Atlantic	5	0.3–15.0	0.1–7.0	0.1–0.3	0.8–70.0	cont
Seiler and Schmidt (1971) [a]	Southern Atlantic	6	0.2–21.0	0.1–10.0	0.05	1–140	cont

[a] Unpublished data.
[b] cont = continuous registration.

Northern Pacific the range of values was 2.0–14.0 × 10^{-5} ml/liter. Here the average value was 8 × 10^{-5} ml/liter.

On the GARP-Expedition in 1969 Seiler and Junge (1970) found in the Middle and Northern Atlantic CO concentrations in the range of 3.0–10.0 × 10^{-5} ml/liter. The total number of water samples taken between 5°S and 55°N along the meridian 30°W at different times of the day were limited to 20 samples.

A much larger and more detailed body of data was obtained from continuous sampling and assays of dissolved CO. Sampling was performed at a depth of 3 m during three cruises (numbers 3, 5, and 6) for the period of 1970 to 1971. Figure 2 shows the frequency distribution of values of dissolved CO averaged over time periods of half an hour, recorded over a time period of five weeks in the Norwegian Sea south of Iceland (cruise number 3).

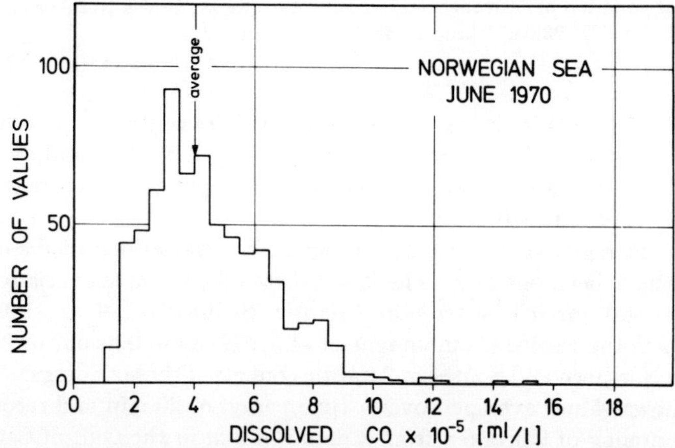

Fig. 2. Frequency distribution of 20-min-averages of CO-concentrations in surface waters from 45 days continuous registration during cruise Number 3.

The range of variation is 1.5–18.5 × 10^{-5} ml/liter with an average of 5.4 × 10^{-5} ml/liter. Values lower than 1.5 × 10^{-5} ml/liter corresponding to an equilibrium value E equal to 0.8 ppmv were not observed. Concurrently measured values of CO mixing ratio in air never exceeded 0.3 ppmv. Accordingly the seawater was supersaturated with CO by a factor of at least 3 during the entire period of observation.

On the other hand, during cruise Number 5 in the Northern Atlantic, slight undersaturations with values of 0.3 × 10^{-5} ml/liter were observed on several days while the simultaneously measured CO mixing ratio in air was 0.16–0.25 ppmv. The average value of all measurements during this cruise was 4.4. × 10^{-5} ml/liter. Similar values were observed in the Southern Atlantic south of the Falkland Islands (cruise number 6). Here the CO concentrations varied from 0.2–21.0 × 10^{-5} ml/liter. The highest values during this expedition were found in the region between the South Orkneys and South Scotland Islands. In stormy weather with winds exceeding 50 knots and corresponding rough seas, CO concentrations sometimes decrease to 0.2 × 10^{-5} ml/liter, corresponding approximately to the equilibrium of CO mixing ratios in air which were observed to be 0.05 ppmv.

The measurements made so far on CO dissolved in seawater indicate a good accord of average values in the Northern Atlantic and Southern Atlantic as well as the Northern Pacific. Hence it can be assumed that similar values will be encountered in the

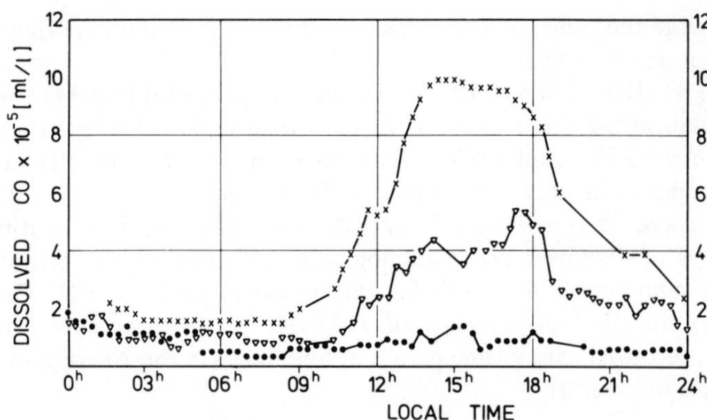

Fig. 3. Diurnal variation of CO-concentration in surface water. Cruise Number 5, Gulf of Cadiz. × 27.05.71 clear; ▽ 23.05.71 broken; ● 21.05.71 overcast.

Southern Pacific. If this is the case, the average CO concentration in seawater averaged over all oceans would amount to approximately 6×10^{-5} ml/liter. This value corresponds to an average equilibrium value of 3.0 ppmv. The average CO mixing ratio in air, by contrast, is 0.11 ppmv.

In addition to regional variations, strong diurnal variations of dissolved CO in surface water have been observed. The first indication for diurnal variations were obtained on two stations in the tropical Atlantic (Swinnerton et al., 1969). Further measurements in the Pacific (Lamontagne et al., 1972) as well as our own continuous records in the Northern and Southern Atlantic confirmed these findings.

Figure 3 shows values averaged over a time period of 20 min and recorded during continuous sampling of CO taken from a depth of 3 m in the Gulf of Cadiz on three days with differing weather conditions. These data illustrate an unambiguous correlation of CO concentrations with the intensity of sunlight.

On sunny days the diurnal variations of CO in surface water are indicated by low values during the night and the early morning and by a maximum occurring in the early afternoon at about 3.00 P.M. Afterwards, the CO concentration decreases within a few hours to the initial low concentrations. A similar diurnal variation was found also on cloudy days, but the maximum CO concentrations were always much less than those observed on sunny days. Short time fluctuations were found to be caused by the changing cloud cover. On days with an overcast sky the CO concentrations in seawater are nearly constant. On such days it is often observed to fall into the range of equilibrium values. Several times on such occasions an undersaturation of 10 to 30% was found to occur for several hours. Diurnal variations of this kind were observed on all cruises during which CO was measured. These results indicate quite strongly a biological source of CO supersaturations. In support of this conclusion are markedly higher maxima occurring in ocean regions with high nutrient supply.

We have never observed on any of the cruises that the variation of CO concentrations dissolved in surface water affected the CO mixing ratio measured in air 10 m above the water level. Figure 4 shows, as an example, a section from a record obtained during several weeks on the Southern Atlantic for CO contained in seawater on the one hand and in air on the other hand. Although CO concentrations in seawater fluctuate by ±50%, the CO mixing ratio in air remains constant at 0.05 ppmv. These results are in contrast to measurements of Lamontagne et al. (1972), who report parallel

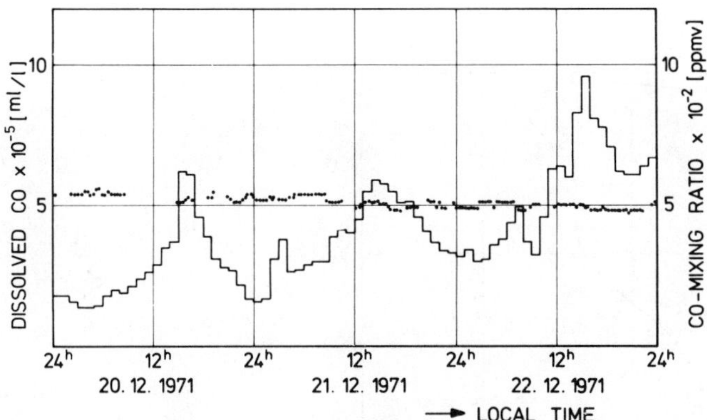

Fig. 4. Continuous registration of CO concentrations in surface water (——) and surface air (····). Cruise Number 6 Southern Atlantic 54°–58°S; 36°–45°W.

diurnal variations of CO concentrations in surface water and in air of the Atlantic and of the Pacific.

Vertical Profiles

On several cruises, dissolved CO was measured also in deep-water samples and vertical concentration profiles were determined. Two typical CO profiles are shown in Fig. 5. They were determined in the Gulf of Cadiz on a sunny and a rainy day, respectively (cruise number 5). Both profiles differ appreciably in the "euphotic" layer. There can be no doubt that the difference is caused by the different intensity of sunlight. These measurements indicate again that on sunny days during the afternoon the upper layers are well supersaturated. During the night and on rainy days the CO content of the entire euphatic layer decreases to values near equilibrium.

In water layers below 100-m depth very slight supersaturation is normally observed. An exception involved observations of vertical concentration profiles in the Northern Atlantic during cruise number 2 (Seiler and Junge, 1970) and some measurements in the Gulf of Cadiz (cruise number 5) during which separate concentration maxima were found at greater depths.

Figure 6 shows the vertical concentration profile of dissolved CO at a station located at 36°N, 6.9°W in the direct zone of influence of Mediterranean water, which enters the Atlantic Ocean near the bottom with a velocity of 1 m/sec. The upper

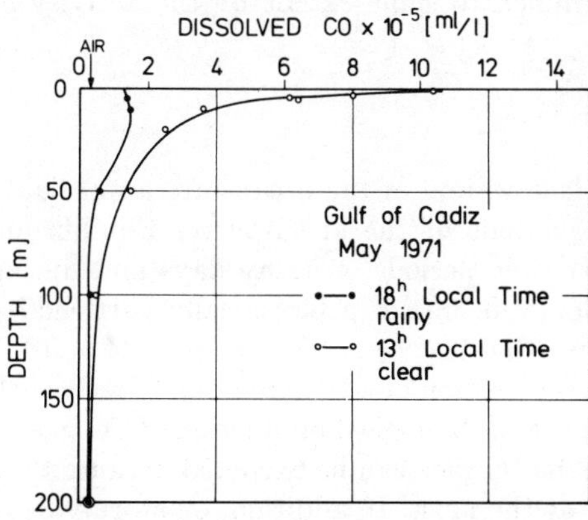

Fig. 5. Vertical CO-concentration profiles. Cruise Number 5. Position: 36°N 10°W.

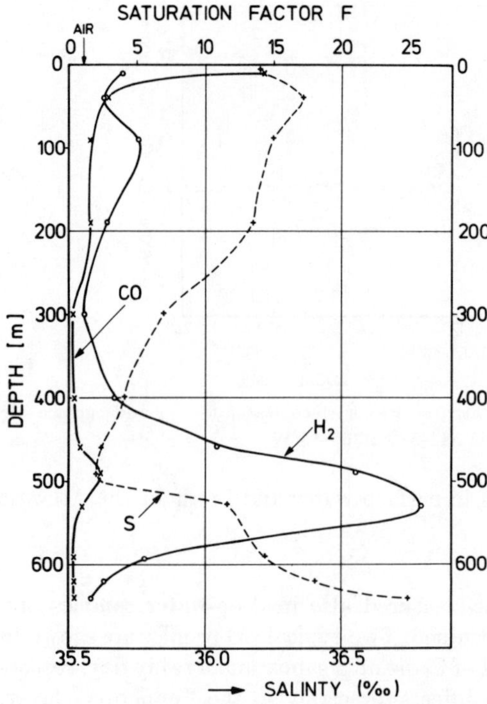

Fig. 6. Vertical profiles of salinity (+), carbon monoxide (×), and molecular hydrogen (○). Cruise Number 5, Gulf of Cadiz. Position: 36°01′N; 06°47′W.

portion of the outflow from the Mediterranean is clearly indicated by the increase of salinity in a depth of 500 m. The waters in the upper layers are of Atlantic origin.

Similar to the data shown in Fig. 5, the CO content shown in Fig. 6 decreases with depth almost exponentially toward values below the limit of detection at about 1000 m. Shortly above the upper limit of the outflow of the Mediterranean water, a renewed increase of dissolved CO is observed with a maximum, located at 500 m depth. In the main flow of the Mediterranean waters the CO concentration decreases again so that the maximum at a depth of 500 m cannot be caused by a generally higher CO concentration in the Mediterranean. The concentration of microorganisms in water samples from the depth of the CO maximum (Rüger, personal communication) also showed an increase up to values 10 times higher than in the layers immediately above or below. Apparently the CO concentration is determined to some extent by the activity of microorganisms.

Discussion

As the preceding sections show, the surface waters of the oceans are appreciably supersaturated in comparison to the CO content of the atmosphere. Equilibrium values were encountered only during short time periods on rainy days and during stormy weather. The highest concentrations were found in biologically particularly active waters of the Northern and Southern Atlantic oceans. Values up to 24×10^{-5} ml/liter were found corresponding to a supersaturation of a hundredfold. Clearly such high values can be explained only by a chemical or biological production of CO in seawater. Purely physical processes at the oceans' surface can be excluded because they can lead to supersaturations of 10 to 20%, at the most. In addition, on stormy days during which the processes should be particularly pronounced, the smallest supersaturations were encountered. The increased CO concentrations sometimes found in deeper layers of the oceans cannot be explained by physical processes.

On the other hand, several chemical or biological processes are known that lead to the formation of CO in water. Laboratory experiments of Wilson et al. (1970) demonstrated the production of CO in sterilized water enriched with organic material and subjected to UV-radiation. The amount of CO production at constant light intensity was proportional to the amount of dissolved organic substances. A small CO production was observed also in a parallel experiment carried out in the dark.

The production of CO by various algae has been known for some time (Langdon, Loewus and Delwiche, 1963; Chapman and Tocher, 1966). More recently it has been found that several species of siphonophores also generate CO. A larger part of the plankton in the oceans is composed of these species (Barham and Wilton, 1964). CO concentrations up to 20% were found in the floats of the *Physalia physalis* (Portuguese Man of War) and can be explained only by the production of CO in the float cells (Wittenberg, 1960).

Our own investigations have demonstrated CO production by algae isolated from seawater. The precise species have not been determined. The CO production of these algae depends on the amount of radiation. It was also found in laboratory investigations that a variety of heterotrophic bacteria in aqueous solution can generate carbon monoxide (Junge et al., 1971b). From water samples taken from the Gulf of Cadiz at 500-m depth where high CO concentrations occurred, Junge et al. (1972) isolated several different species of bacteria and demonstrated that some of these generate CO (Table IV).

Therefore it appears that bacteria can be responsible for the maxima of CO concentrations observed in deeper ocean layers. In surface waters the activity of phototrophic microorganism probably predominates. The distribution of both kinds of microoganism in the ocean has been discussed by Kriss et al. (1961).

At present it is difficult to explain the rapid decrease of the CO concentration in the entire euphotic zone within a few hours in the afternoon, from values of 10×10^{-5} ml/liter to 2×10^{-5} ml/liter. This rapid decrease cannot be explained by transport to and the release at the surface to the atmosphere because of the comparatively low rate of turbulent diffusion in the upper layer of about 100 m as well as the slow sea-air exchange of gases. Additional processes capable of CO consumption must exist in seawater. One possibility is the oxidation of CO by a large variety of algae and bacteria (Chapelle, 1962). Such processes can occur in the dark. This activity increases with the irradiation.

B. Molecular Hydrogen

H_2 in Surface Waters

We have made the only measurements of molecular hydrogen dissolved in seawater on two cruises (numbers 5 and 6) in the Northern and Southern Atlantic. The detailed results will be published elsewhere; a summary is presented in Table V.

In the Northern Atlantic, H_2 concentrations were found to range from 0.8×10^{-5} to 5.0×10^{-5} ml/liter with an average value of 2.2×10^{-5} ml/liter. The average mixing ratio in air obtained from continuous registrations during both cruises was 0.56 ppmv. From these data the saturation factor is calculated to be 2.4, corresponding to a supersaturation of 240% of H_2 dissolved in seawater. Similar values were found also in the Southern Atlantic (Table V). On this cruise, the average value,

TABLE IV

H_2 and CO Production by Various Species of Bacteria Isolated from a Depth of 900 m in the Gulf of Cadiz

Species	CO Test (ppmv)	CO Control (ppmv)	CO Net (ppmv)	CO Production (10^{-5} cm^3/hr)	H_2 Test (ppmv)	H_2 Control (ppmv)	H_2 Net (ppmv)	H_2 Production (10^{-5} cm^3/hr)
Alginomonas M 239	0.71	0.71	—	—	0.30	0.25	—	—
Alginomonas M 240	2.54	0.88	1.66	10	0.94	0.51	0.43	2
Alginomonas M 247	1.24	0.88	0.36	2	1.10	0.51	0.59	3
Alginomonas M 246	0.69	0.65	—	—	1.27	0.60	0.67	4
Alginomonas M 248	0.65	0.69	—	—	1.62	0.60	1.02	6
Alginomonas M 249	0.72	0.69	—	—	2.30	0.25	2.05	11
Alginomonas M 243a	0.46	0.65	—	—	0.84	0.60	0.24	1
Alginomonas M 244a	0.78	0.71	—	—	0.91	0.60	0.31	2
Brevibakterium M 243b	1.63	0.88	0.75	4	0.68	0.60	—	—
Brevibakterium M 244b	0.67	0.71	—	—	0.65	0.60	—	—
Agrobakterium M 241	0.60	0.58	—	—	0.32	0.25	—	—
Agrobakterium M 242	0.60	0.58	—	—	0.31	0.60	—	—

TABLE V

Dissolved H_2 in Surface Waters

Author	Location	Cruise Number	H_2 Content $C \times 10^{-5}$ (ml/liter)	Equilibrium Value E (ppm_v)	Surface Air Mixing Ratio M (ppm_v)	Saturation Factor $F = E/M$	Number of Samples
Schmidt and Seiler [a]	Northern Atlantic	5	0.8–5.0	0.48–3.03	0.55–0.60	0.8–5.4	cont [b]
Schmidt and Seiler [a]	Southern Atlantic	6	1.8–5.7	0.96–3.04	0.54–0.59	1.7–5.3	cont

[a] Unpublished data.

[b] cont = continuous registration.

obtained from continuous measurements of H_2 in surface water and observed over a period of five weeks, was 3.3×10^{-5} ml/liter. No diurnal variations of dissolved H_2 were observed in contrast to the observations of dissolved CO taken at the same time.

Vertical Profiles

On cruise number 5 in the Northern Atlantic, 14 vertical concentration profiles were obtained. Three of these from the open ocean are shown in Fig. 7. The individual profiles show little similarity; specifically, they exhibit no recurrent maxima and minima in preferred layers. At all depths, supersaturations by a factor of 1.4 to 3.5 were observed. Exceptions were found for concentration profiles measured in the Gulf of Cadiz in the zone under the influence of the Mediterranean waters. At the upper limit of the water of Mediterranean origin, indicated by a strong increase in salinity (Fig. 6), a very pronounced increase of dissolved H_2 was found. In the concentration profile shown in Fig. 6, a maximum value of 23×10^{-5} ml/liter was reached corresponding to a supersaturation factor of 24. Similar values were frequently found also near the bottom of the sea.

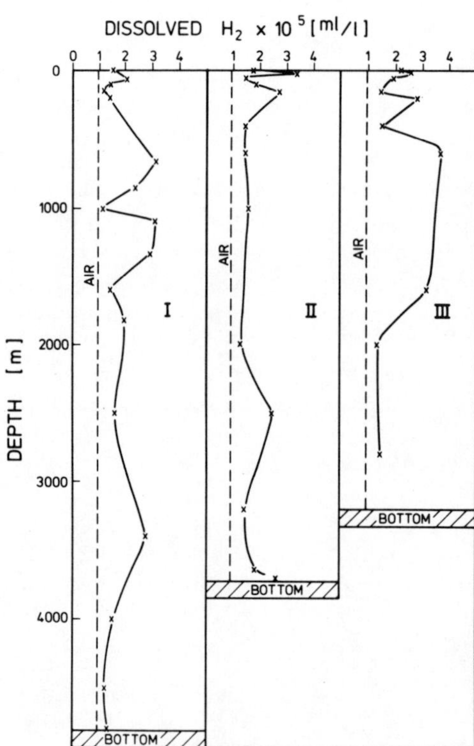

Fig. 7. Vertical H_2-concentration profiles from the Northern Atlantic; cruise Number 5. (I) 44°N; 43°W; (II) 43°N, 34°W; (III) 41°N, 26°W. Vertical dashed lines show equilibrium concentrations corresponding to surface air mixing ratios.

Discussion

At the present time the available measurements of the H_2-content in seawater are still limited. Although these data were obtained only in the region of the Atlantic Ocean, they can nevertheless give an indication of the global distribution, since the measurements of other dissolved gases (e.g., CO, CH_4) have shown that the occurrence of differences between the oceans is not probable. The surface water shows an average marked supersaturation of 300%, which cannot be explained on the basis of physical processes alone. Similar to the case of CO, it is probable that the supersaturations of H_2 originate from microbiological processes, since a large number of microorganisms, especially bacteria, are capable of producing or consuming molecular hydrogen (see, e.g., Koffler and Wilson, 1951; Gest, 1954; Healey, 1970).

It is therefore not surprising that high H_2 concentrations occur mainly in water layers with a high nutrient supply. An impressive example of this is the occurrence of the H_2 concentration maxima at the upper boundary of the Mediterranean outflow in the Gulf of Cadiz (Fig. 6). The increase of salinity and the concurrent increase in density impede the sedimentation of living and dead organic material, which thus is accumulated in the boundary layer between Atlantic and Mediterranean waters. Accordingly, both the number of bacteria and the nutrient supply for microorganisms is increased. Laboratory investigations (Junge et al., 1972) have shown that several different species of bacteria, especially the species *Alginomonas*, isolated from water samples with high H_2 concentrations, generate molecular hydrogen (Table IV). Since bacteria are abundantly distributed in ocean water (Kriss et al. 1961), it may reasonably be assumed that the supersaturation of surface waters with respect to H_2 is caused by bacterial production.

C. Methane

CH_4 in Surface Waters

The CH_4 concentrations in surface waters of the open oceans fall into the same range of values observed for CO and H_2 (Table VI). Because of the higher atmospheric mixing ratio of CH_4, the supersaturations are smaller. Swinnerton and Linnenbom (1967b) report CH_4 concentrations of 4.7×10^{-5} ml/liter in the Atlantic 500 km west of Ireland (53°N 20°W). In tropical waters (Gulf of Mexico) the concentrations of CH_4 were only a little higher, 6.8×10^{-5} ml/liter. These values correspond to an equilibrium value of 1.5 and 3.4 ppmv, respectively. They lie appreciably above the average CH_4 mixing ratio of 1.35 ppm in maritime air (Lamontagne et al., 1972).

On a cruise from Washington, D.C. to Puerto Rico (cruise number 1), Swinnerton et al. (1969) determined Atlantic CH_4 concentrations to be 4.0–5.0 $\times 10^{-5}$ ml/liter. Similar results were found on a cruise from Washington to Hawaii in the Atlantic and in the Pacific. Short-time fluctuations or diurnal variations, as observed in parallel measurements for CO, could not be detected for CH_4 (Lamontagne et al., 1972). Further measurements of the same authors in surface waters of several other regions of the Atlantic gave values between 3.7×10^{-5} and 7.8×10^{-5} ml/liter. The average value of these measurements is 4.7×10^{-5} ml/liter, corresponding to an equilibrium value of 1.8 ppmv. With an average CH_4 mixing ratio in air of 1.38 ppmv, the supersaturation of CH_4 in seawater in these regions is also slight (14 to 18%). Similar measurements in the Southern Atlantic and in the Southern Pacific are yet to be made. Since the CH_4 concentration in surface waters of the Northern Atlantic and the Northern Pacific do not show any dependence on the time of day or the seasons, and the fluctuations around the average value of 5×10^{-5} ml/liter are small, it is expected that the oceans of the southern hemisphere will contain similar CH_4 surface concentrations.

These observations refer to unpolluted areas. Different values are encountered in polluted regions. Brooks and Sackett (1972) report higher CH_4 concentrations in the Gulf of Mexico near ports, shipways, and offshore patrol drilling platforms. They

TABLE VI

Dissolved CH_4 in Surface Waters

Author	Location	Cruise Number	CH_4 Content $C \times 10^{-5}$ (ml/liter)	Equilibrium Value E (ppm_v)	Surface Air Mixing Ratio M (ppm_v)	Saturation Factor $F = E/M$	Number of Samples
Swinnerton and Linnenbom (1967)	Northern Atlantic	Stations	4.7	1.5	1.35	1.1	Unknown
	Gulf of Mexico		6.8	2.8	1.35	2.1	Unknown
Swinnerton et al. (1969)	Potomac River	1	100–850	28–240	1.24	15–170	9
	Tropical Western Atlantic	1	4–5	1.6–2.0	—	1.2–1.5 [a]	12
Lamontagne et al (1972)	Western Atlantic	4	3.7–4.9	1.5–2.0	1.27–1.31	1.2–1.5	25
	Eastern Pacific	4	4.1–5.6	1.6–2.4	1.30–1.53	1.1–1.6	50
	Norwegian and Greenland Seas	7	5.2–7.8	1.6–2.5	1.30–1.50	1.1–1.8	70
	Greenland Ice Pack	7	7.4–11.3	1.5–2.4	1.30–1.50	1.2–1.8	23
	Caribbean Sea	8	4.1–4.4	1.7–1.9	1.28–1.35	1.3–1.4	3
	Sargasso Sea	8	4.1–4.5	1.6–1.7	1.28–1.81	1.2–1.3	6
Brooks and Sackett (1972)	Gulf of Mexico	9	< 2.5–250	< 1.2–120	—	0.9–89 [a]	~ 600
	Mississippi River	9	20–90	8–36	—	6–27 [a]	> 20

[a] Due to lack of concurrent air samples $M = 1.35$ ppm_v was used to calculate F values.

observed CH_4 concentrations up to 250 × 10^{-5} ml/liter. On the other hand, in regions characterized by upwelling waters, they found values of <2.5 × 10^{-5} ml/liter, that is, undersaturation conditions. In the Potomac River, Swinnerton et al. (1969) and Lamontagne et al. (1972) found CH_4 concentrations up to 3850 × 10^{-5} ml/liter corresponding to supersaturations by a factor of 750. Abnormally high concentrations were also observed in the York River and in the Mississippi River (Brooks and Sackett, 1972; Lamontagne et al., 1972).

Vertical Profiles

In the open oceans the CH_4 concentrations decrease with increasing depth to very low values. Lamontagne et al. (1972) analyzed deep-sea samples and found CH_4 concentrations of 0.6 × 10^{-5} ml/liter in the Northern Atlantic at 5000-m depth, in the Northern Pacific of 0.2 × 10^{-5} ml/liter at 4000-m depth, and in the Gulf of Mexico of 2.0 × 10^{-5} ml/liter at 3500-m depth. This is in accord with measurements by Swinnerton and Linnenbom (1967b), who in the Atlantic (53°N 20°W) and in the Gulf of Mexico at 500-m depth found CH_4 concentrations between 2 × 10^{-5} ml/liter. Brooks and Sackett (1972) determined a CH_4 concentration of 1 × 10^{-5} ml/liter at 1300-m depth in the Gulf of Mexico.

It is of considerable interest that the CH_4 concentrations show an increase in the upper layer of the oceans with a maximum at a depth between 50 and 100 m (Fig. 8). However, measurements are available only for the Gulf of Mexico (Brooks and Sackett, 1972; Swinnerton and Linnenbom, 1967b) and outside the Cariaco Trench (Lamontagne et al., 1972). Maximum CH_4 concentrations range between 10 × 10^{-5} and 30 × 50^{-5} ml/liter, corresponding to supersaturations between 3.0 and 9.0. Extremely high CH_4 concentrations were observed in anoxic waters occurring in some fjords and lakes (Strøm, 1957; Holton, 1965; Williams et al., 1961). In Lake Nitinat, Atkinson and Richards (1967) investigated the variation of concentration with depth

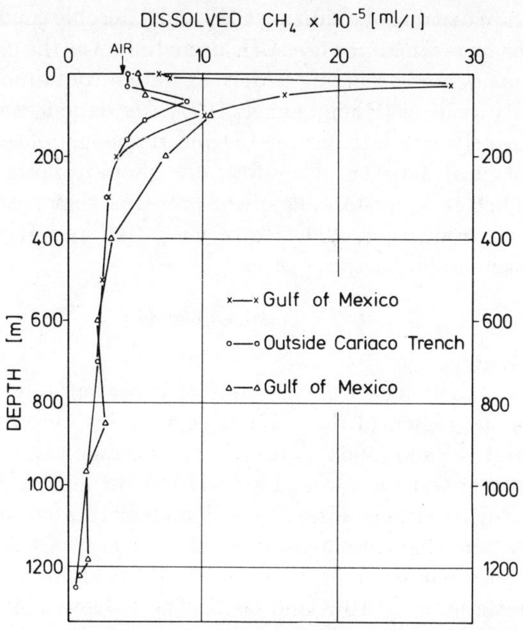

Fig. 8. Vertical CH_4-concentration profiles from the Northern Atlantic. O——O. Lamontagne et al. (1972); Δ——Δ Brooks and Sackett (1972); × —— × Swinnerton and Linnenbom (1967).

and found at depths below 20 m, an increase of CH_4 concentration from $<2.0 \times 10^{-3}$—corresponding to the lower limit of detection of their device—up to 70 μmol/liter or 1600×10^{-3} ml/liter. Such high CH_4 concentrations always occurred with an increase of H_2S concentration.

In the Cariaco Trench (12°N 65°W), Lamontagne et al. (1972) observed a maximum in CH_4 concentration of 50×10^{-5} ml/liter at a depth of 80 m. Further down to the sill depth at 300 m, the CH_4 content decreases to values of 1×10^{-5} ml/liter and increases again at greater depths to values of about 0.3 ml/liter. Atkinson and Richards (1967) report also on similarly high supersaturation in the Black Sea at depths below 200 m.

Discussion

The high supersaturations observed in the upper layer of the oceans and the extremely high supersaturations in anoxic waters of various regions, as well as in polluted rivers, clearly indicate a methane production caused by bacterial activity. Several anaerobic species of bacteria are known (*Methanobacterium*, *Methanococcus*, and *Methanosarzina*) that convert alcohols and organic acids into methane (Pine and Barker, 1956; Barker, 1956; Kojama, 1963). Organic acids are generated by anaerobic fermentation of cellulose and degradation of lipids by lipoclastic bacteria (Rheinheimer, 1971). Methane can also be produced by the complete reduction of CO_2 by *Methanobacterium omelianski* in the presence of hydrogen as an H donor. Other bacteria are known (*Methanosarzina bacteri*) that reduce CO to CH_4. Schlegel (1969) estimates that approximately 30% of naturally produced CH_4 is formed by the reduction of CO_2, and that the larger part is generated from the fermentation of organic acids and alcohols. The maximum of CH_4 concentrations at a depth of 100 m in the oceans shows that aerobic bacteria exist that form methane in waters with considerable oxygen contents.

On the other hand a variety of bacteria exist that cannot degrade long-chained hydrocarbons but are capable of oxidizing CH_4 under aerobic conditions. For example, the species *Pseudomonas methanica* uses CH_4 or methanol as the only source of carbon. The species *Actinomycetum*, occurring widely in waters containing methane, must be considered as a CH_4 oxidizer (Rheinheimer, 1971). Methane fermentation by bacteria probably is significantly correlated to the CO and H_2 budget of seawater, especially in areas of high biological activity. Therefore one should expect to get much more information and a better understanding of the processes that are effective with regard to the distribution, production, and fate of CH_4, CO, and H_2 in seawater by the simultaneous measurements of these gases.

D. Nitrous Oxide

N_2O in Surface Waters

The majority of measurements of N_2O content in seawater have been carried out in the Northern Atlantic region (Table VII). Two analyses were made in the Southern Pacific by Craig and Gordon (1963), who give the average values in two sets of water samples taken between 0° to 70°S and 150 to 170°W at depths between 10 to 2200 m. The sample from high southern latitudes was undersaturated and that from middle southern latitudes was slightly supersaturated. During the GARP-Expedition 1969 with *F.S. Meteor* (cruise number 2), Junge et al. (1971a) found supersaturations at all times in the Atlantic between 10°S and 60°N. The N_2O content in surface water exhibited only small fluctuations in the range 22–31 $\times 10^{-5}$ ml/liter. Owing to the temperature dependence of the solubility N_2O, equilibrium values decrease from a

TABLE VII

Dissolved N_2O in Surface Waters

Authors	Location	Cruise Number	N_2O Content $C \times 10^{-5}$ (ml/liter)	Equilibrium Value E (ppmv)	Average Surface Air Mixing Ratio M (ppmv)	Saturation Factor $F = E/M$	Number of Samples
Craig and Gordon (1963)	Southern Pacific						
	45°–70°S	9	18.0[b]	0.18	—	0.72[d]	9
	0°–40°S	9	27.0[c]	0.36	—	1.44[d]	10
Junge et al. (1971a)	Middle and Northern Atlantic	2	22.0–31.0	0.31–0.62	0.25	1.24–2.48	6
Hahn (1972b)	Norwegian Sea	3	20.2–29.0	0.26–0.35	0.25	1.03–1.39	19[e]
Hahn (1972c)[a]	Northern Atlantic	5	18.7–28.6	0.33–0.52	0.27	1.19–1.88	41[e]

[a] Unpublished data.
[b] Average of 9 samples from 10 to 1500 m depth (see text).
[c] Average of 10 samples from 10 to 2200 m depth (see text).
[d] Due to lack of concurrent air samples $M = 0.25$ ppmv was used to calculate F values.
[e] Samples from 2 m depth are included.

value of 0.62 ppmv in the tropical regions to 0.31 ppm_v at higher northern latitudes. The average value would be 0.5 ppm_v. The mixing ratio of N_2O in air is constant at 0.25 ppm_v. Accordingly, the saturation factor ranges from $F = 2.5$ to $F = 1.2$. In the Norwegian Sea, southwest of Iceland, Hahn (1972b) observed small supersaturations of 5 to 40%. Unpublished data by the same author obtained in the Northern Atlantic on cruise number 5 are in agreement with the measurements of Junge et al. (1971a).

Vertical Profiles

A survey of measurements of the N_2O content in deep sea samples has been given by Hahn (1972c). All measurements were made in the North Atlantic. Averaged vertical concentration profiles from several latitudes are shown in Fig. 9. In the tropics

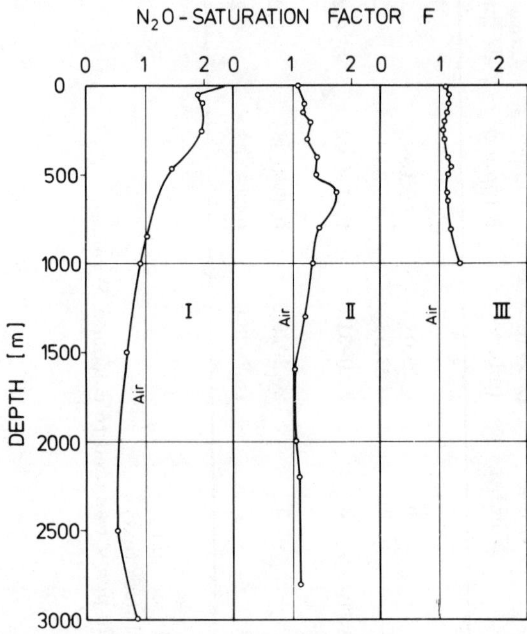

Fig. 9. Vertical N_2O-concentration profiles from Northern Atlantic After Hahn (1972c). I 0–25°N/30°W, cruise Number 2; II 41–44°N/26–43°W, cruise Number 5; III Iceland-Faroe-Ridge, cruise Number 3.

and at middle latitudes (Profiles I and II) the upper layers show supersaturation with maximum values of a factor of two or even more (Junge et al., 1971a). Parallel with surface conditions the supersaturations for the upper few hundred meters decreases northward. Below a depth of 1000 to 1800 m, equilibrium exists or there is slight undersaturation. Secondary concentration maxima at greater depths or at sea bottom were not observed. At high latitudes, as shown by Profile III (Fig. 9), the N_2O concentration is fairly evenly distributed down to depths of 100 m with a supersaturation of about 10 to 15%. There were no water samples taken in this region at greater depths.

Discussion

In general, all measurements of N_2O in seawater of the Atlantic (0 to 1000 m) display in the upper layers a supersaturation that decreases systematically from the tropical to higher latitudes. The very small supersaturations in the Icelandic region were assumed by Junge and Hahn (1971) to occur as a result of physical processes such as air injection or the mixture of water bodies of different water temperature. For rare gases these processes may result in supersaturations of about 15% (Bieri et al., 1968). The supersaturations observed in the tropics cannot be explained in this way and it appears necessary to postulate a N_2O production in the seawater. The mechanism of production is now known. We know that in soils nitrous oxide can be generated by denitrifying bacteria (Verhoeven, 1952; Wijler and Delwiche, 1954). Presumably soil bacteria can live in water, too. Junge and Hahn (1971) therefore assume that the N_2O supersaturations are caused by processes similar to those occurring in soils. Their assumption receives some support by the observation of Kriss et al. (1961), who found a large number of bacteria in the tropical regions of the Atlantic, whereas the number of bacteria decreases strongly in higher latitudes. In the deep sea (below 2000 m), the measurements of N_2O reveal undersaturations indicating that in these layers N_2O is consumed, probably by bacteria (Matsubara and Mori, 1968).

2. Trace Gas Exchange from the Oceans' Surface to the Atmosphere

The exchange of gas through the boundary layer of a two-phase system of many components is a dynamic process. This is true also for the ocean surface characterizing the boundary between seawater and air. At equilibrium, the number of molecules entering the liquid phase from the air through the boundary layer is equal to the number of molecules leaving the liquid phase in the opposite direction. Otherwise, a flux of molecules in the direction of the gradient of partial pressure will be set up. According to Bolin (1960) and Kanwisher (1963), the flux density is determined mainly by molecular diffusion through a laminar boundary layer at the water surface. The flux depends on the difference of the partial pressures in the liquid and gaseous phase and on the thickness of the boundary layer. It is assumed that the air above the water and the water below the boundary layer are well mixed, so that the partial pressure of the gas on both sides of the boundary layer are not influenced by the flux through the boundary layer.

In such a model the flux density J of a gas is given (Broecker and Peng, 1971) by:

$$J = \frac{(C - p) \times D}{z} \text{ (cm/sec}^1\text{)} \tag{3}$$

or

$$J = \frac{(E - M)\rho\alpha \times D \times P}{z} \text{ (g/cm}^2\text{/sec)} \tag{3a}$$

where C = concentration of the dissolved gas in water in ml/ml H_2O
p = partial pressure of the gas in air in atm
P = barometric pressure in atm
ρ = density of the trace gas
α = solubility of the gas in seawater ml/ml H_2O atm
D = molecular diffusion coefficient in water cm²/sec
z = thickness of the boundary layer
$E = 10^{-3}(C)/(\alpha \times P)$ is the equilibrium value of the gas in ppmv
M = surface air mixing ratio in ppmv

The annual flux of the gas through the total surface of the oceans $A = 3.6 \times 10^{18}$ cm² is then given by:

$$J^* = 11.4 \times 10^{25}\rho \times \alpha \times D \times P\frac{(E - M)}{z} \text{ (g/yr)} \tag{4}$$

TABLE VIII

Data on Trace Gases used in Calculations

Item	CO	CH_4	H_2	N_2O
Density ρ_{20}° (g/cm³)	1.165×10^{-3}	0.668×10^{-3}	0.084×10^{-3}	1.845×10^{-3}
Solubility α_{20}° (cm³/cm³H_2O atm)	0.0196	0.0290	0.0159	0.53
Diffusion constant D (cm²/sec)	2.3×10^{-5}	2.8×10^{-5}	5.8×10^{-5}	1.9×10^{-5}
Equilibrium value E[a] (ppmv)	3.0	2.0	1.6	0.5
Mixing ratio M (ppmv)	0.11	1.40	0.55	0.25
Atmosphere reservoir R (g)	5.3×10^{14}	38.9×10^{14}	1.9×10^{14}	19.1×10^{14}
Oceanic source strength J (g/yr)	0.7×10^{14}	0.16×10^{14}	0.04×10^{14}	2.1×10^{14}
Global production[b] (g/yr) (oceans not included)	19×10^{14}	2.7×10^{14}	0.3×10^{14}	0.5×10^{14}

[a] Averages.
[b] Estimated.

Table VIII summarizes the values required to calculate from equation 4 the total fluxes for the trace gases under consideration. Some uncertainties associated with parameters z and D are considered below.

The thickness of the boundary layer z depends strongly on the wind speed. Bolin (1960) estimates theoretically that the thickness is less than 2.5×10^{-3} cm for a calm sea but that it decreases by 1 to 2 orders of magnitude for rough seas. Kanwisher (1963) made laboratory experiments on the exchange rates and deduced thickness of 4×10^{-3} cm at a wind speed of 7 m/sec. Increasing the wind speed to 12 m/sec brought an increase in the exchange by a factor of 3. Broecker and Peng (1971) determined two radon profiles in the Boomex area, known for small exchange rates. They report on a layer thickness of 6.0×10^{-3} cm. In the following we shall assume an average value of 2.5×10^{-3} cm (Münnich, personal communication).

Our knowledge of the molecular diffusion coefficients is also unsatisfactory. For some gases no diffusion coefficients appear to be available at all, whereas for other gases the published values differ considerably. For the present purpose we have employed the diffusion coefficients given by Davidson and Cullen (1957) for H_2 and N_2O. We have not found diffusion coefficients for CO and CH_4 and therefore have estimated them from data for other gases of similar molecular weight. To faciliate an estimate of the individual flux it was assumed here that the average values of gas concentrations in seawater resulting from the various measurements are representative for all oceans. Furthermore, it is assumed that the average values refer to the physically dissolved gas and not to the gas liberated chemically during the measurements.

Due to the uncertainies concerning the boundary thickness z and the diffusion coefficients D, the calculation of the gas exchange through the ocean surface can only give an order of magnitude estimate. However, such a rough estimate provides valuable insights on the influence of the oceans on the budget and the cycle of trace gases in the atmosphere.

In Table VIII the oceanic source strengths calculated for the individual trace gases from equation 4 are given and compared with the total global production of the same gases from other sources.

The flux of CO from the oceans into the atmosphere is approximately 0.7×10^{14} g/yr or 4% of the total CO production from other sources, which is estimated to be 19×10^{14} g/yr. The main sources of CO are the anthropogenic production 4×10^{14} g/yr (Jaffe, 1972) and the natural CO production stemming from the CH_4 oxidation in the troposphere 15×10^{14} g/yr (Wofsy et al., 1972).

The flux of CH_4 from the oceans into the atmosphere of 1.6×10^{13} g/yr is not very significant compared with the annual global production of 27×10^{13} g/yr (Kojama, 1963) from other sources. Much more important in this respect may be the high supersaturations found in polluted waters. According to the measurements by Brooks and Sackett (1972), the Texas and Luisiana shelf in the Gulf of Mexico, having an area of 1.5×10^{11} m^2 (i.e., 0.03% of the total oceans' surface), produce 1.4×10^{11} g annually corresponding to 1% of the annual CH_4 production of all oceans.

The oceanic source strength of H_2 is 4.0×10^{12} g/yr compared with an estimated global production of 30×10^{12} g/yr from other sources. Here the contribution of the oceans to the atmospheric H_2 budget is about 15%.

Most important to the atmospheric budget is the production of N_2O in the oceans. For an average equilibrium value of 0.5 ppmv the N_2O flux into the atmosphere is 2.1×10^{14} g/yr. This must be compared with a N_2O production of 0.5×10^{14} g/yr in soils. This estimate assumes that the entire land surface of the earth provides the same rate of production of 10^{-12} g/cm^2 sec as was determined by Albrecht et al. (1970) in a variety of soils. From the rate of N_2O production and the atmospheric concentration, the residence time in the atmosphere is calculated to about 8 yr in good agreement with an estimation by Junge (1971) obtained by a different reasoning. Even if an averaged supersaturation of not more than 50% is assumed for surface waters of the oceans, the resulting source strength is much larger than any other known sources.

Acknowledgments

This work was sponsored by the Deutsche Forschungsgemeinschaft under contract SFB 73. We acknowledge the invitation by the NERC, Great Britain, to participate in the Antarctic cruise during 1971 to 1972 with the *R.R.S. Shackleton*.

References

Albrecht, B., C. Junge, and H. Zakosek, 1970. Der N_2O-Gehalt der Bodenluft in drei Bodenprofilen. *Z. Pflanzenernährung u. Bodenkunde*, **125**, 205–211.

Atkinson, L. P. and F. A. Richards, 1967. The occurrence and distribution of methane in the marine environment. *Deep-Sea Res.*, **14**, 673–684.

Barham, E. G., 1963. Siphonophores and the deep scattering layer. *Science*, **140**, 826–828.

Barham, E. G. and J. W. Wilton, 1964. Carbon monoxide production by a bathypelagic siphonophore. *Science*, **144**, 860–862.

Barker, H. A., 1956. Biological formation of methane. *Ind. and Eng. Chem.*, **48**, 1438–1442.

Bieri, R. H., 1971. Dissolved noble gases in marine waters. *Earth. Planet. Sci. Letters*, **10**, 329–333.

Bieri, R. H., M. Koide, and E. D. Goldberg, 1968. Noble gas contents of marine waters. *Earth Planet. Sci. Letters*, **4**, 329–340.

Bolin, B., 1960. On the exchange of carbon dioxide between the atmosphere and the sea. *Tellus*, **12**, 274–281.

Broecker, W. S. and T. H. Peng, 1971. The vertical distribution of radon in the Bomex area. *Earth Planet. Sci. Letters*, **11**, 99–108.

Brooks, J. M. and W. M. Sackett, 1972. Light hydrocarbon concentrations in the Gulf of Mexico. Paper presented at the meeting on *Sources, Sinks, and Concentrations of Carbon Monoxide and Methane in the Earth's Environment*, St. Petersburg, Florida.

Chapman, D. J. and R. D. Tocher, 1966. Occurrence and production of carbon monoxide in some brown algae. *Can. J. Botany*, **44**, 1438–1442.

Chappelle, E. W., 1962. Carbon monoxide oxidation by algae. *Biochim. Biophys. Acta*, **62**, 45–62.

Craig, H. and L. J. Gordon, 1963. Nitrous oxide in the ocean and the marine atmosphere. *Geochim. Cosmochim. Acta*, **27**, 949–955.

Craig, H. and R. F. Weiss, 1971. Dissolved gas saturation anomalies and excess helium in the ocean. *Earth Planet. Sci. Letters*, **10**, 289–296.

Davidson, J. F. and E. J. Cullen, 1957. The determination of diffusion coefficients for sparingly soluble gases in liquids. *Trans. Inst. Chem. Engrs.*, **35**, 51–60.

Douglas, E., 1967. Carbon monoxide solubilities in seawater. *J. Phys. Chem.*, **71**, 1931–1933.

Gest, H., 1954. Oxidation and evolution of molecular hydrogen by microorganism. *Bacteriol. Revs.*, **18**, 43–73.

Goldberg, E. D., 1971. Chemical invasion of ocean by man. In *Man's Impact on Terrestrial and Oceanic Ecosystems*. W. H. Matthew, F. E. Smith, and E. D. Goldberg, eds. MIT Press, pp. 261–274.

Hahn, J., 1972a. Improved gas chromatographic method for field measurements of nitrous oxide in air and water, using a 5 Å molecular sieve trap. *Anal. Chem.*, **44**, 1889–1892.

Hahn, J., 1972b. Nitrous oxide in air and seawater over the Iceland-Faeroe-Ridge. "*Meteor*" *Forsch. Ergebn.*, Ser. A, in preparation.

Hahn, J., 1972c. Nitrous oxide in air and seawater over the Atlantic Ocean. In *The Changing Chemistry of the Oceans*. D. Dyrssen and D. Jagner, eds. Almquist & Wiknell, Stockholm, pp. 53–69.

Healey, F. P., 1970. Hydrogen evolution by several algae. *Planta* (*Berl*), **91**, 220–226.

Holtan, H., 1965. Salt water in the bottom layer of two Norwegian lakes. *Nature*, **207**, 156–158.

Jaffe, L. S., 1972. Carbon monoxide in the biosphere: sources, distribution, and concentrations. Paper presented at the meeting on *Sources, Sinks, and Concentrations of Carbon Monoxide and Methane in the Earth's Environment*, St. Petersburg, Florida.

Junge, C., 1971. Residence time and variability of tropospheric trace gases. *Tellus*, **24**, in press.

Junge, C. and J. Hahn, 1971. N_2O measurements in the North Atlantic. *J. Geophys. Res.*, **76**, 8143–8146.

Junge, C., B. Bockholt, K. Schütz, and R. Beck., 1971a. N_2O-measurements in air and seawater over the Atlantic. "*Meteor*" *Forsch. Ergebn.* Ser. B, **6**, 1–11.

Junge, C., W. Seiler, R. Bock, K. D. Greese, and F. Radler, 1971b. Über die CO-Produktion von Mikroorganismen. *Naturwissenschaften*, **58**, 362–363.

Junge, C., W. Seiler, U. Schmidt., R. Bock, K. D. Greese, F. Radler, and H. J. Rüger, 1972. Kohlenoxid- und Wasserstoff-Produktion mariner Mikroorganismen im Nährmedium mit synthetischem Seewasser. *Naturwissenschaften*, **59**, 514–515.

Kalle, K. and H. Thorade, 1940. Tabellen und Tafeln für die Dichte des Seewassers. *Arch. Dtsch. Seewarte*, **60**.

Kanwisher, J., 1963. On the exchange of gases between the atmosphere and the sea. *Deep-Sea Res.*, **10**, 195–207.

Koffler, H. and P. W. Wilson, 1951. The comparative biochemistry of molecular hydrogen. In *Bacterial Physiology*. C. H. Weikmann and P. W. Wilson, eds. Academic Press, New York, pp. 517–530.

Kojama, T., 1963. Gaseous metabolism in lake sediments and paddy soils and the production of atmospheric methane and hydrogen. *J. Geophys. Res.*, **68**, 3971–3973.

Kriss, A. E., J. N. Mitzkevitch, J. E. Mishustina, and S. S. Abyzov, 1961. Micro-organisms as hydrological indicators in seas and oceans—IV. The hydrological structure of the Atlantic Ocean including the Norwegian and Greenland Seas, based on microbiological data. *Deep-Sea Res.*, **7**, 225–236.

Lamontagne, R. A., J. W. Swinnerton, and V. J. Linnenbom, 1971. Non-equilibrium of carbon monoxide and methane at the air-sea interface. *J. Geophys. Res.*, **76**, 5117–5121.

Lamontagne, R. A., J. W. Swinnerton, V. J. Linnenbom, and W. Smith, 1972. Methane concentrations in various marine environments. Paper presented at the meeting on *Sources, Sinks, and Concentrations of Carbon Monoxide and Methane in the Earth's Environment*, St. Petersburg, Florida.

Langdon, S. C., 1916. Carbon monoxide in the pneumatocyst of Nereocystis. *Puget Sound Marine Station Pub.*, **1**, 237–246.

Loewus, M. W. and C. C. Delwiche, 1963. Carbon monoxide production by algae. *Plant Physiol.*, **38**, 371–374.

Matsubara, T. and T. Mori, 1968. Studies on denitrification. *J. Biochem.*, **64**, 863–871.

Morrison, T. J. and F. Billett, 1952. The salting-out of non-electrolytes. Part II: The effect of variation in non-electrolytes. *J. Chem. Soc.*, **1952** 3819–3822.

Pine, M. J. and H. A. Barker, 1956. Studies on the methane fermentation. XII: The pathway of hydrogen in the acetate fermentation. *J. Bacteriol.*, **71**, 644–648.

Rheinheimer, G., 1971. *Mikrobiologie der Gewässer, Vol. I: Einführung in die Hydrobiologie*. Fischer-Verlag, Jena.

Schlegel, H. G., 1969. *Allgemeine Mikrobiologie*, 2nd ed. Thieme-Verlag, Stuttgart.

Schmidt, U. and W. Seiler, 1970. A new method for recording molecular hydrogen in atmospheric air. *J. Geophys. Res.*, **75**, 1713–1716.

Seiler, W. and C. Junge, 1970. Carbon monoxide in the atmosphere. *J. Geophys. Res.*, **75**, 2217–2226.

Strøm, K., 1957. A lake with trapped seawater? *Nature*, **180**, 982–983.

Swinnerton, J. W. and V. J. Linnenbom, 1967a. Determination of the C_1 to C_4 hydrocarbons in seawater by gas chromatography. *J. Gas Chromatog.*, **5**, 570–573.

Swinnerton, J. W. and V. J. Linnenbom, 1967b. Gaseous hydrocarbons in seawater: Determination. *Science*, **156**, 1119–1120.

Swinnerton, J. W., V. J. Linnenbom, and C. H. Cheek, 1968. A sensitive gas chromatographic method for determining carbon monoxide in seawater. *Limnol. Oceanog.*, **13**, 193–195.

Swinnerton, J. W., V. J. Linnenbom, and C. H. Cheek, 1969. Distribution of methane and carbon monoxide between the atmosphere and natural waters. *Env. Sci. Techn.*, **3**, 836–838.

Swinnerton, J. W., V. J. Linnenbom, and R. A. Lamontagne, 1970. The ocean: A natural source of carbon monoxide. *Science*, **167**, 984–986.

Verhoeven, W., 1952. Aerobic spore forming nitrate reducing bacteria. Thesis, Delft, Netherlands.

Wijler, J. and C. C. Delwiche, 1954. Investigations on the denitrifying process in soil. *Plant and Soil*, **5**, 155–169.

Williams, P. M., W. H. Mathews, and G. L. Pickard, 1961. A lake in British Columbia containing old seawater. *Nature*, **191**, 830–832.

Wilson, D. F., J. W. Swinnerton, and R. A. Lamontagne, 1970. Production of carbon monoxide and gaseous hydrocarbons in seawater: Relation to dissolved organic carbon. *Science*, **168**, 1577–1579.

Wittenberg, J. B., 1960. The source of carbon monoxide in the float of Physialia physalis, the "Portuguese Man of War." *J. Exptl. Biology*, **37**, 698–705.

Wofsy, S. C., J. C. McConnell, and M. B. McElroy, 1972. Atmospheric CH_4, CO and CO_2. *J. Geophys. Res.*, **77**, 4477–4493.

8. CHEMICAL FRACTIONATION AND SEA-SURFACE MICROLAYER PROCESSES

FERREN MACINTYRE

The transport of salts from sea to air is by no means a simple mechanical process.

C.-G. ROSSBY (1959)

Some fractionation process seems to take place at the sea surface, possibly involving organic material derived from surface films.

E. ERIKSSON (1959)

1. Prolog

A. Introduction

Long a neglected area, the chemistry of three-quarters of the world's surface—the sea-air interface—is receiving increasing attention today as its role in environmental problems becomes apparent. Perhaps nowhere else do microscopic physicochemical hydrodynamic processes exert so profound an influence over macroscopic geochemical and geophysical phenomena.

Although the transport of radiation, momentum, and gases is also affected by events in the surface microlayer, this chapter will focus on chemical fractionation at the surface during the ejection of particulate matter from sea to air. Isotopic fractionation of H/D and $^{16}O/^{18}O$ is an evaporational phenomenon unrelated to chemical fractionation and will not be treated here (see Craig and Gordon, 1965).

There is no question about the reality of gross chemical fractionation between sea and air. Skeptics need only park a car facing the ocean and examine the material deposited on the windshield, which will be most unlike dried seawater. Its predominant characteristic is not saltiness, but greasiness. Many workers feel that this separation by chemical class underlies nearly all sea-air chemical fractionation. Yet there are hints of exotic mechanisms that, if verified, would return electrolyte solutions once again to the center of physicochemical interest.

Unfortunately, there is a paucity of good data. Both laboratory and field data on chemical fractionation are more confusing than helpful if approached without a conceptual framework in which the peculiarities of the liquid surface fit. Accordingly, this chapter examines the surface microlayer and phenomena peculiar to it in some detail before proceeding to the data. By the time we reach the latter, the reader should have some feeling for the possible mechanisms, anomalies, and appropriately suspicious cast of mind.

In the long run, practical matters such as agriculture, air pollution, and weather modification relate directly to sea-air chemistry through such questions as: (1) To what extent does the sea surface contribute the plant nutrients N, K, and P to global rainfall? (2) To what extent are pollutants concentrated in the surface microlayer, and where do they go from there? and (3) Is it possible, by modifying the sea surface, to modify the rate of energy transfer through it? Can we alter the efficiency of marine raindrop nuclei in this way?

Needless to say, this chapter cannot answer questions such as these, but only raise them, and perhaps make some recommendations designed to assist in resolving these and similar questions.

B. *History*

Not surprisingly, sea-air chemical interaction was first noticed in precipitation studies. The first analysis of any chemical component of rainwater seems to have been made by Barrichins of Copenhagen in 1674 (Miller, 1913), but the earliest recognition of marine components in rainwater was evidently Dalton's measurement on the storm of December 5, 1822 (Anon., 1825), in which he found 1 part seawater to 400 parts of rain, and noted that the salt had been carried 30 to 100 mi from the sea.

The difficulty of sorting out a specifically maritime component of precipitation is still very much with us, but it was first foreshadowed by Brandes' analysis, listing as components of rainwater "resin, pyrrhin, mucus, . . . , oxide of iron and manganese," as well as various salts of Mg, Ca, K, and Na (Anon., 1829).

By 1881 the pollution of the Industrial Revolution had made obvious the anthropogenic input to atmospheric chemistry, and had so demoralized English atmospheric chemists that they already spoke of the "ordinary dirty appearance" of rainwater (Lawes et al., 1881). This same paper recognized the ocean as a possible source of atmospheric NH_3. In 1911 it was proposed that most atmospheric sulfate was not of marine origin, but arose from coal burning (Vityn, 1911; Gray, 1911), although a natural input of H_2S to rain was recognized by Eaton and Eaton (1926). Cauer (1939) concluded that the high atmospheric iodine of central Europe could not be directly marine, but was injected by seaweed burning along the coasts of northern Europe.

It is difficult to assign priority to the first recognition of what we speak of today as chemical fractionation, either during ejection from the sea surface or during the residence time of a marine particle in the atmosphere. In 1940 to 1942 Köhler and Båth investigated ejection fractionation on the hypothesis of inorganic Gibbsian surface adsorption at the sea surface. They were motivated by Lipp's (1933) report of high Mg/Cl ratios in Nebelfrost (ice crystals on rocks, growing into the wind, and deposited directly from supercooled cloud droplets) on the Zugspitze. Either they realized that their work was ahead of its time, or their results were not as definite as they had hoped, because they did not publish until 1953, and then somewhat obscurely.

In the meantine, Cauer (1941, 1942) observed that the chloride in sea spray was highly reactive and was quickly converted to gaseous chlorine compounds—an observation that unfortunately did not end the practice of using chloride as a reference ion for estimating the marine component of precipitation. Matsui (1944) and, independently, Dessens (1946) explained the variation of sea salts in rainwater by assuming a fractional crystallization and separation during drying of seawater particles, an idea picked up and extended by other Japanese workers.

As frequently happens, ideas become clearer with the passage of time, and several authors during the 1940s and 1950s are able to look back at their early work and read into it rather more than is apparent. Nevertheless, during this period the basic concepts of chemical fractionation were set forth, and at the First International Oceanographic Congress, Sugawara (1959) clearly enunciated the distinction between fractionation at the moment of ejection from the sea surface, and fractionation during the atmospheric sojourn of the sea salt particle. Unfortunately, he created something of a credibility gap by reporting extreme fractionations of I/Cl and Na/Cl on the basis of a single experiment, and the importance of his fundamental distinction was somewhat veiled. It will appear below that his iodine numbers, at least, were quite possibly good.

A convenient watershed between the historical and the modern is 1959, which also produced the epigraphs that head this chapter; we will, in general, focus on material since 1960.

C. *Dean's "Recipe"*

One of the simplest of seminal observations about maritime precipitation and chemical fractionation was made by Dean (1963), in the form of the following recipe for reproducing the rain that falls on Taita, in coastal New Zealand:

Seawater	0.5 ml
Dried algae and plankton	4 mg
Distilled water	to make 1 liter

At least part of the biological material was particulate and visible under the microscope. This mix matches the observed quantities of the major ions, as well as iodine, phosphorus, and organic nitrogen. The only serious question it raises is how to associate 4 mg of dried biological materials with 0.5 ml of seawater, for 8 g/liter of organic compounds approaches the realm of thin soup, and is a factor of 2000 above the 4 mg/liter of dissolved plus particulate organic carbon, which one expects to find (Duursma, 1960).

However, Dean's recipe poses no problem to the microlayer chemist, for surface monolayer organic coverages of 1 mg/m^2 are commonplace, and an 0.1-μm cut from such a sea surface would provide the organic-to-seawater ratio required by the recipe. This thickness is within the range of the available ejection mechanisms provided by breaking bubbles, whose known ability to concentrate and eject particulate matter from the microlayer (Kohn, 1968; Blanchard and Syzdek, 1970) can also account for the occasional bits of jetsam.

2. Physical Phenomena

A. *Geochemical Reality of the Surface Microlayer*

"Surface" means many things to many people, and to an oceanographer it has customarily meant anything he could catch in a bucket from shipboard. "Surface microlayer" is also a loosely defined term, and rather than try to make a single estimate of its thickness, its depth can be defined operationally by some particular area of interest. Roughly, it extends from 3 Å (the diameter of a water molecule, and therefore as close as one can come to pinning down the surface), to about 3 mm, which is near the extreme limit of nonturbulent kinematics with no wind, and also the penetration depth of jets from small bubbles (which are a major dynamic expression of microlayer forces).

On a logarithmic scale, it is interesting to note that these seven decades cover slightly more than half of the distance to the deepest ocean trenches. In terms of *processes* the microlayer may prove to be as rich a field of research as the deeper half of the ocean. Figure 1 attempts to indicate some of the pertinent depths and scale lengths for events in the microlayer, and also points out the division of the microlayer into two known areas: the top 10 Å, which is the domain of the classical surface chemist, and the region from 1 μm to 1 cm, which is the domain of the physicochemical hydrodynamicist. The three decades from 10 Å to 1 μm are mostly unknown territory.

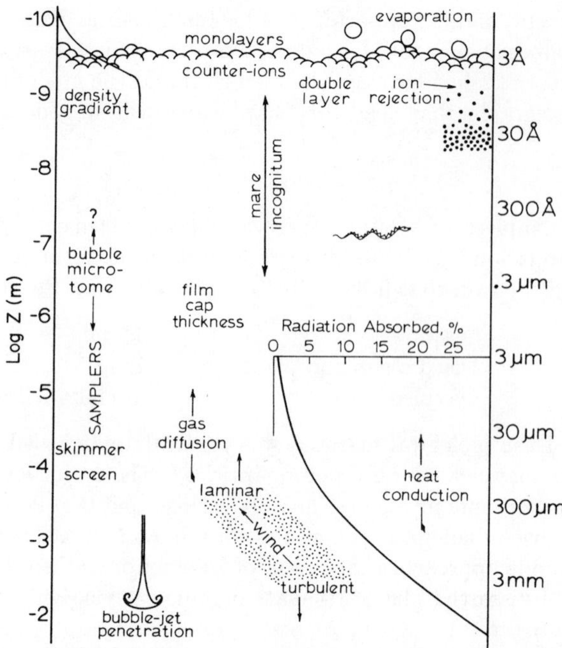

Fig. 1. Structure and events in the microlayer are best displayed on a logarithmic scale. The bottom of the microlayer is probably most appropriately taken as the transition from turbulent to laminar flow. The position of this boundary for winds from 0 to 10 m/sec lies in the dotted band.

Perhaps the first question to resolve is the reality of this microlayer as an oceanic province distinct from the classical bucket sample. The items that argue against such a distinction are common sense, bolstered by observations of wind-induced turbulence, and such known surface mixing processes as Langmuir circulation and breaking waves. The oceanographer who has seen intense sonar scatter at 200 m from bubbles carried down by a North Atlantic storm may be dubious about the geochemical significance of a 3-mm-thick "surface." (The correct rebuttal, of course, is that on occasion the microlayer extends to 200 m . . ..)

Certainly molecular transfer processes are important only when they exceed turbulent transfer, and turbulence is omnipresent in the sea. But oceanic turbulence is nonisotropic. Vertical motions are strongly damped by density stratification and at the surface they necessarily become zero (relative to the surface). Much of the observed vertical shear produced by waves and ripples is locally coherent, periodically reversible, and does not contribute to vertical flux transport.

Microlayer thicknesses at which various processes exceed turbulent transfer are related in a logical fashion. Momentum is transferred by elastic collisions, which can be felt far down a line of molecules. Heat is transferred by inelastic collision, and cannot propagate as far. Diffusion requires actual exchange of neighboring molecules, and is dominant only when convective motion is essentially absent. Given an observed distance δ_0 for one of these processes with diffusivity D_0, the distance δ_i over which another process with diffusivity D_i is effective is given by

$$\delta_i \approx \left(\frac{D_i}{D_0}\right)^{1/3} \delta_0$$

(Levich, 1962). The microlayer thicknesses shown in Table I for momentum, heat, and ordinary diffusion are correlated on this basis and chosen to encompass the usual values reported in the oceanographic literature. The microlayer thickness for thermal diffusion is similarly computed, but carries the restriction "per degree," referring to ΔT across the microlayer thickness, which is usually quite small (see below). The microlayer thickness for particulate transfer refers to the bubble microtome, also described below. Presumably only these last two entries are in any way related to chemical fractionation.

The time required to transport flux across the microlayer is taken as $t_i = \delta_i^2/2D_i$ (making δ_i correspond to the root mean square distance covered in time t_i). These times are also shown in Table I, but it should be noted that times considerably shorter than these can produce noticeable flux transfer (Davies and Rideal, 1961).

Thus the geochemical reality of the microlayer depends to some extent on the process considered. As winds increase, the momentum boundary layer decreases—but the transit times drop simultaneously, so that unless there has been actual rupture of the surface, or an upwelling eddy that sweeps new material into the surface, within the last half second, molecular processes govern flux transport. Significantly, the process we are most concerned with—bubble rupture—is unaffected by wind speed (except in the sense that wind is required to generate bubbles). The forces released by surface free energy so exceed the forces arising from wind stress that drop formation by bubbles is unaffected by winds that wipe out all other microlayer mechanisms.

B. Deformation of the Microlayer

Obviously there is continuous microscopic exchange of matter between the molecular surface (i.e., the top "layer" of molecules) and the underlying liquid, driven by Brownian motion. Davies and Rideal (1961) compute the surface lifetime $\bar{t}$ of a molecule (for exchange with subsurface molecules) from the self-diffusion coefficient D_s of water through $\bar{t} = \lambda^2/D_s$, with $D_s = 2 \times 10^{-5}$ cm^2/sec and λ, the equilibrium distance between molecules, equal to 3.5×10^{-8} cm. This makes $\bar{t}$ about 60 psec, or perhaps 1000 molecular vibrations. This rapid exchange can be ignored in both chemical and geochemical problems because it occurs at all times and in all places as a constant background activity of the microlayer, and there is no way to sort it out to study it.

Kinetically, the microlayer results from a macroscopic steady-state process: a balance between the creating force of viscous damping and the destroying force of erosion by turbulence from below. In addition, the microlayer is affected by surface dilation (local changes in area or curvature) at two grossly different scales. In contrast to Brownian exchange, dilation produces bulk hydrodynamic flows between surface and subsurface and alters surface properties by changing the number of molecular sites available. The usual macrohydrodynamic assumptions can be made about dilational motion: "particles" of fluid (containing many molecules, but below the limit of experimental spatial resolution) remain simply connected throughout all motions, and if they have corners at the surface, those corners remain at the surface. Two kinds of periodic dilation have been studied, and both have been shown to augment transport through the microlayer.

O'Brien (1967) studied large gravity waves theoretically, assuming a Gerstner profile (points-up trochoid and a reasonable approximation to real gravity waves), and found that the average exchange of heat through the microlayer could double as a result of deformation by the wave.

TABLE I

Microlayer Thickness and Transit Times for Various Processes

Flux Transported	Driving Force	Relevant Molecular Constant		Microlayer Thickness (μm)	Transit Time (sec)
Momentum	Velocity gradient	Viscosity	$\nu = 10^{-2}$ cm^2/sec	300–1500	0.05–1.1
Heat	Temperature gradient	Conductivity[a]	$\alpha = 10^{-3}$ cm^2/sec	140–700	0.10–2.5
Mass	Concentration gradient	Diffusivity	$D = 10^{-5}$ cm^2/sec	30–150	0.50–11
Mass	Temperature gradient	Thermal Diffusivity	$D' = 10^{-8}$ cm^2/sec-deg	3–15/deg	5–113
Mass particulate	Surface energy instability	Surface free energy	$\gamma = 74$ erg/cm^2	0.01–1	0.001

[a] Normally called the diffusivity of heat, or thermal diffusivity, which we reserve for D'.

MacIntyre (1971) studied capillary ripples by numerical simulation and in a preliminary experiment, found that mass transfer could increase fourfold by surface dilation accompanying Crapper ripples (essentially, points-down trochoids and a reasonable approximation to wind ripples). Both of these waveforms are exact solutions to the Navier-Stokes equations, and the results are probably applicable to the real ocean, which is, on the average, covered by both gravity waves and capillary ripples. Since the scales of these two dilations are sufficiently disparate to remain uncoupled, it appears that routine surface dilation of the microlayer may enhance transfer processes some eightfold above that found in flat-surface laboratory experiments having the same level of near-surface turbulence. This in turn suggests caution in comparing laboratory and field experiments unless attention is given to both wave and ripple regimes.

We conclude that the only effect of normal oceanic waves and ripples is to cause periodic changes in the thickness of the microlayer. Breaking waves, of course, disrupt the microlayer completely, if briefly, but whitecaps cover only 3 to 4% of the ocean surface, and over the remainder, molecular forces are dominant. However, turbulent exchange is so much faster than molecular exchange that whitecaps and other turbulent events may dominate exchange processes even though their areal percentage is small. Certainly this is true of particulate mass transfer and some kinds of chemical fractionation, which would hardly exist if it were not for bubble patches.

C. The Physical Structure of the Interface

To the oceanographer, the air-water surface seems an abrupt transition from one substance to another, but at the molecular level, it is demonstrably not a step change in properties but a smear. If the surface had no thickness, light reflected at the Brewsterian angle ($\tan \phi_B = n$, or 53° for water) would be entirely horizontally polarized. In actuality, residual ellipticity, or the ratio of vertical to horizontal polarization, is on the order of 10^{-3}, indicating a finite transition layer in which the refractive index changes smoothly from $n_1 = 1$ (air) to $n_2 = 1.333$ (water). Theory is still inadequate to deal with a smooth change, but Drude (1900) explained the residual polarization by postulating a transition layer of thickness d with an intermediate refractive index n. Choosing $n = (n_1 n_2)^{1/2}$ gives a minimum value for d. At 25°C the thickness found for pure water is about 7 Å (Kinosita and Yokota, 1965). No data seem to be available for salt solutions, but CCl_4 (a liquid about as unlike water as possible) has a transition thickness of 9 Å (Yokota, 1966), which suggests that small changes in liquid properties do not appreciably affect the nature of the transition from gas to liquid.

A theoretical examination of the density transition across the surface gives similar results. Figure 2 shows this transition for a structureless hard-sphere fluid (with simplifying assumptions that make it a rather poor model of water). The computations for Fig. 2 (Hill, 1952) were exact thermodynamically (i.e., equality of the Helmholtz free energy in gas, liquid, and interface at constant N, V, and T), but the radial distribution function $g(r)$ and the intermolecular potential $u(r)$ were approximated rather crudely as indicated in the figure. Nevertheless, this approach gives the best available semiquantitative view of the vapor-liquid transition.

The density change is essentially complete in four molecular diameters, or about 12 Å for water. Hydrogen bonding, which yields a much stronger intermolecular potential than that used by Hill, will tend to make the density transition more abrupt.

The dielectric constant K undergoes the same gradual transition as does n. With

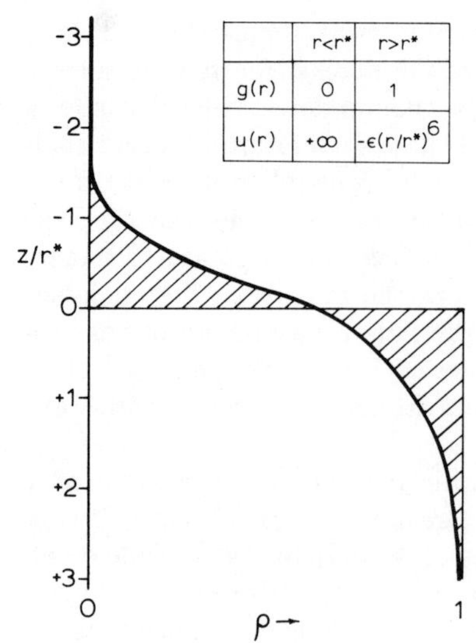

Fig. 2. Density transition at the surface of an unstructured hard-sphere fluid of molecular radius r^* at $T = \frac{1}{2}T_{\text{critical}}$ (52°C for water). After Hill (1952), who observes that this density transition may be slightly too diffuse for water because the radial distribution function $g(r)$ used underestimates hydrogen bonding.

$K = 1$ (air) and $K = 81$ (water), K in the transition layer is only 9, enough lower than the bulk water to produce significant electrostatic effects on ions in solution. [The dielectric constant for water at the critical point—also, in a sense a transition from liquid to vapor—is 7.8, close to the estimated surface value (Stillinger and Ben-Naim, 1967).]

The electrical energy E of a sphere of radius a and charge q in a continuous medium is $E = q^2/2Ka$. To the extent that this crude model applies to aqueous ions (see Gurney, 1953), we can estimate the concentration ratio between bulk solution and the interface from a Boltzmann distribution. This is done in Table II for a singly charged

TABLE II
Electrical Energy E of a Singly Charged Ion of Radius 2 Å and its Relative Concentration in Various Environments

Layer	$E(ev)$	E/kT	Relative Concentration
Air	3.6	138	$e^{-136} \approx 10^{-60}$
Transition	0.4	15.4	$e^{-13.7} \approx 10^{-6}$
Solution	0.045	1.7	1

ion at unit concentration in the bulk liquid. The high rejection factor (which is even more impressive for multiply charged ions) is the basis for the usual assumption that the top molecular layer of an electrolyte solution is composed of "pure water" (Harkins and McLaughlin, 1925). The difficulty of extracting a bare ion into the atmosphere is also made clear.

D. Molecular Architecture

The last comprehensive review of surface structure in liquids seems to have been Henniker's (1949), and the dearth of recent work may reflect some subsequent disenchantment with the idea. At that time most of the data suggestive of a special structure dealt with the solid-liquid interface, which alone would make the concept suspect, for only rarely is a solid surface smooth at the atomic level. There remains always the possibility that "anomalous behavior" in the liquid arose simply from irregularities in the solid, including such things as adherent dust and attached microorganisms.

More subtly, the crystal structure of the solid may impose its own order on the liquid, leading to a totally different sort of behavior than that found at a free surface. Nevertheless, reliable measurements of the structural peculiarities of liquids adjacent to solids are important because they put an upper limit on the thickness of liquid structure at the gas-liquid interface. As one recent example, Churayev et al. (1970) found that the viscosity of water in 500-μm quartz capillaries was high by a factor of 1.4, which they interpreted to mean that the SiO_2 surface immobilized an 80-Å layer of water. This increase in viscosity was totally absent with benzene and CCl_4 in the same capillaries. This observation may indicate a specialized interaction between water and quartz, which would perhaps be of some interest to a marine geologist, but hardly affects the surface microlayer. In any event, this is clear experimental refutation of the idea of a surface structure of water that extends as far as 100 Å into the bulk liquid.

A similar conclusion can be reached by considering the surface potential of water. Complete surface ordering would give $\Delta V = 4\pi n\mu_D = 7$ V, where $n = 10^{15}$ is the number of molecules per square centimeter and $\mu_D = 1.87 \times 10^{-18}$ esu, the dipole moment. Stillinger and Ben-Nain (1967) computed the surface potential at 320°C to be only 4 mV: by a long extrapolation one arrives at 26 mV at 25°C. But 0.026/7 is only 0.4% of the molecules that are nonrandomly oriented (oxygens out, hydrogens in). Such a low percentage does not support the idea of a highly structured surface.

There have been suggestions of inflections in the temperature dependence of the surface tension of pure water and of salt solutions (Drost-Hansen, 1965) which would be highly suggestive of "phase changes" in the surface structure. However, very careful recent work has failed to find these (Gittens, 1969).

Drost-Hansen (1972) has marshalled the evidence supporting the existence of a deep structure in water below monolayers, including results by Coster and Simons (1970), which were interpreted to indicate a change in the dielectric properties of water for a distance of 4 μm adjacent to a lipid membrane. Obviously the last word has not been heard in this debate.

E. Thin Films

A simplified model of the monolayer-covered air-water interface is a thin film with two monolayer surfaces and no bulk liquid. The thickness of the film provides a way of examining the solution at various distances from the surface. There are four important thicknesses for our discussion.

The thinnest relevant film is the so-called "second black film" ("black" because the two surfaces are so close together that they individually reflect out-of-phase light; a similar process is used to make "invisible," or nonreflecting, glass). This metastable film forms a structure some 45 Å thick, that is essentially a two-dimensional "liquid crystal" composed of two layers of surfactant with some water of hydration surrounding the hydrophilic groups and counter ions in the middle of the sandwich. The useful information that this film provides is that the water in the inner core—some 20 Å thick—is rather firmly attached to the ionized monolayer. It is apparently the work required to desorb this water that stabilizes the film at this thickness (Clunie et al., 1967).

The next relevant thickness is the "first black film." This film is about 100 Å thick and is stabilized by ionic repulsion between the diffuse (Gouy) layers of ions in the two surface double layers. At low ionic strength this film thickens (up to 2000 Å), and at high ionic strength the thickness depends somewhat on specific ion interactions with the monolayer, thus providing information about the chemical and electrical structure of the solution near the interface (Jones et al., 1966). In particular, dynamic experiments on drainage rates suggest that it is only the "water of hydration" that has a high viscosity, and that the influence of surfactants on the architecture and properties of water is limited to a layer not more than 10 Å deep (Lyklema et al., 1965). We conclude that any structure imparted to the sea surface by monolayers is likewise no more than 10 Å thick.

The third thickness of interest is the unstable freshly created film of an ordinary soap bubble. Such films customarily show interference colors (i.e., thicknesses less than 1.5 μm); they thin by drainage and evaporation until they are less than a quarter of the wavelength of light in thickness (0.1 μm or 1000 Å), at which time they show a uniform silvery sheen. The persistence of films of this thickness is hydrodynamic in origin, since viscous drainage of the interlamellar water is slow. The change from silver to black is a discontinuous step in thickness, apparently because further thinning by drainage is difficult and required the increased pressure exerted by the sharp curvature of the step. Allen et al. (1971) found that bubbles in aqueous glycerol thinned below 4000 Å before breaking (some survived to 400 Å) in a quiet system that minimized evaporation.

The fourth thickness of interest is that of ocean bubbles, which seem to be thicker than the films just described. Apparently no one has measured them directly, but they seldom show interference colors and so seem to be about 2 μm thick when they break. There is no convincing explanation of this extra thickness. Mysels (personal communication) has suggested hydrodynamic stabilization by rigid monolayers, which retard drainage more than mobile monolayers, but this does not seem to accord with the short lifetime that Garrett (1967) found that rigid monolayers imparted to bubbles.

F. Gibbs' Surface Adsorption

As mentioned above, the earliest work on fractionation hoped to explain it by Gibbsian surface adsorption. Thermodynamically, substances that lower the surface free energy (surface tension × area) accumulate at the surface; substances that raise the surface tension are rejected (negatively adsorbed) by the surface. Suppose that the curved gradient of Fig. 2 were replaced by the step change, so located that the excess of water molecules above it just balanced the deficit below (i.e., the shaded areas are equal). A second component in the solution will not be distributed in exactly the same way, and its equal-area dividing line will lie above (positive adsorption) or below (negative adsorption) that for water. The mismatch between the two lines can be equated to the "surface excess" Γ_i (mol/cm^2) of the second component. Assuming an activity coefficient of unity, Γ_i is related to the surface tension γ through Gibbs' equation

$$\Gamma_i = -\left(\frac{\partial \gamma}{RT\,\partial \ln m}\right)_{T,A}$$

and so can be predicted if the variation of surface tension with molality m is known.

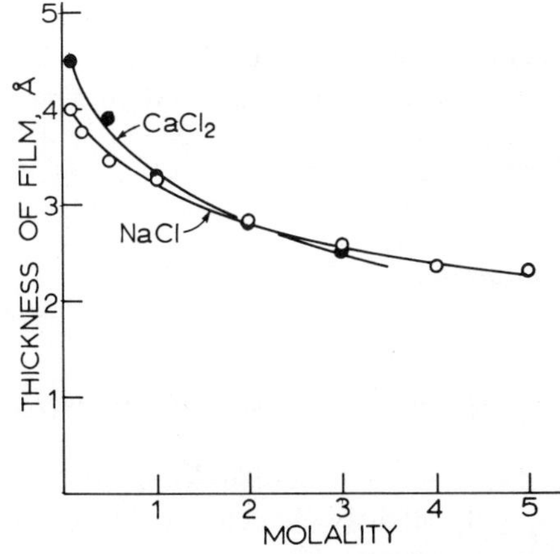

Fig. 3. Thickness of water film on NaCl and $CaCl_2$ solutions, after Harkins and McLaughlin (1935) and Harkins and Gilbert (1926). For comparison, a water molecule occupies a space roughly 2 × 3 × 5 Å.

Just as the density gradient at the interface occupies only a few angstroms, so the surface excess is accommodated in a very small distance. Assuming that the density of water in the superficial layer is unity, the thickness of ionic rejection for a negative surface excess is simply $t = 1000\Gamma_i/m_i$. Figure 3 plots this thickness versus molality for sodium and calcium chlorides (Harkins and McLaughlin, 1925).

Somewhat more sophisticated models have become available since this early work. Bell and Rangecroft (1971) have computed the distribution of ions in a $BaCl_2$ solution and after some strenuous mathematical exercise arrive at Fig. 4. Note that they succeeded in showing the structure of the double layer, with Cl^- near the interface and Ba^{2+} lying deeper. The peak appearing in the Ba curve compensates for the Cl above and maintains local electroneutrality. One additional point must be made: it is not the concentration of the particular ions that determines the depth of surface rejection, but the ionic strength of the solution. In 0.7*M* NaCl the rejection depth of 0.001*M* $BaCl_2$ will be less than 5 Å.

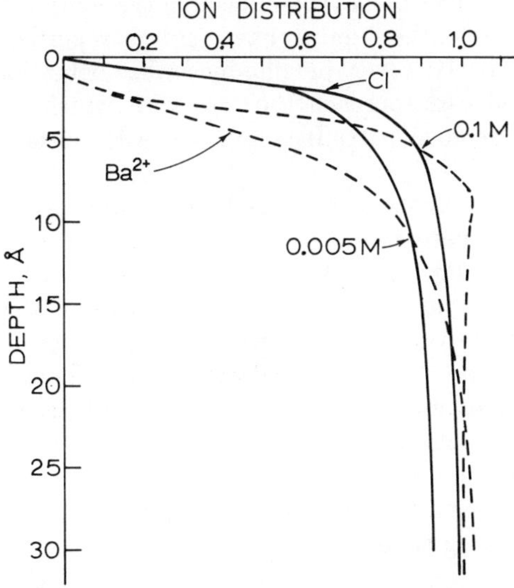

Fig. 4. Ion distribution in $BaCl_2$, after Bell and Rangecroft (1971). Note that the depth of ionic rejection is smaller at higher concentrations. The curve plotted for Cl^- is $\frac{1}{2}[Cl^-]$.

What this means to chemical fractionation is that any successful attempt to invoke Gibbsian inorganic surface adsorption as an explanation must first produce a credible mechanism for separating a film of solution whose thickness is no more than a few molecules.

3. Organic Phenomena

A. *Microlayer Sampling Techniques*

There are two standard techniques for sampling the microlayer and two novel approaches.

The surface skimmer, developed by Harvey (1966) is a hydrophilic drum rotating about a horizontal axis, dipping into the water only slightly. It collects a layer of water 60 to 100 μm thick, which is scraped off by a neoprene blade into a collecting vessel. This device can be mounted in front of a slow-moving boat and used to collect microlayer samples in moderate waves, although control over the sample thickness is lost when the depth of immersion is not constant. Several sizes of skimmers have been used, ranging from 40 cm in diameter by 60 cm long, rotating at 9 rpm, down to laboratory models 10 cm in diameter and 5 cm long, rotating at 30 rpm. Plastic, glass, and ceramic surfaces have been tried, with ceramic appearing the most suitable. The skimmer can easily collect 20-liter samples.

Harvey and Burzell (1972) have used a similar technique for smaller samples, consisting of a flat glass plate withdrawn vertically from the surface at about 20 cm/sec and wiped off with a neoprene windshield wiper blade. A liter of microlayer can be collected in about 45 min by this method.

Garrett (1965) used a 16-mesh monel screen in a frame to collect the upper 150 μm of the ocean, and Sieburth (1963, 1965) used a stainless steel version. Duce et al. (1972) used 20-mesh polyethylene. Ordinary plastic window screen will change the surface potential of a clean water surface by as much as 450 mV on contact after repeated cleanings, and cannot be recommended.

Garrett reports 75% collection efficiency at removing organic monolayers after the first pass (which covers the wires with persistent monolayer), indicating that only the open spaces are collecting samples. Efficiencies for the skimmer have not been reported, but it would appear to be nearly quantitative. However, judging by surface potential changes in the laboratory, neither method can approach the ease with which an ordinary cellulose tissue can (reversibly) remove partial monolayers with surface pressures well below 1 dyne/cm.

Surface organics will also adhere to a microscope-slide-shaped germanium prism dipped through the surface. If the ends are properly bevelled, such a prism can be used to obtain the infrared spectrum of the molecular layer adsorbed onto the surface by multiple-internal-reflection spectroscopy. Furthermore, the surface tension of the original material can also be estimated from the prism by measuring the contact angle that small clean water droplets make on the adsorbed organic (Baier, 1972). Although the spectrum and surface tension of a complex mixture contain limited information, processes such as the natural oxidation and removal of surface contaminants from lakes can be monitored elegantly by this approach.

Finally, the bubble microtome (see below) remains a promising but largely untested method of collecting small samples of surprising thinness.

B. Organic Material

The samplers just discussed are apparently unselective and collect all organic material present. Subsequent analysis has never been as comprehensive. Garrett (1964) analyzed the chloroform-soluble fraction of material collected with a screen and found it, not surprisingly, to consist chiefly of C_8 to C_{22} acids, esters, alchols, and hydrocarbons. Polypeptides and carbohydrates, being generally water soluble were observed, but only in small quantities.

The composition of the mix varies greatly from place to place. Jarvis et al. (1967) measured film pressure and surface potential of 17 assorted samples and found that at a (compressed) surface density of 10 mg/m^2 the film pressure varied from 0 to 29 dynes/cm while surface potential ranged (in roughly the same order) from 130 to 325 mV. A reasonable interpretation is that the material contains a mixture of low-surface-potential acids and high-surface-potential alcohols and esters.

Jarvis (1967) further studied the distribution of surfactants in the upper 18 m in the Bay of Panama, and the rate at which material accumulated at a cleaned surface from a 15-cm-deep container. In the absence of intentional stirring, surface concentrations were in general still increasing after 3 hr, with the film pressure showing signs of levelling out at about 0.2 dyne/cm while the surface potential had reached 50 mV and was still climbing rapidly. There was little evidence of variability with depth except that the single microlayer sample contained much more surfactant, reaching a film pressure of 2.7 dynes/cm in about 20 min and a surface potential of 70 mV somewhat faster. Neither parameter showed signs of levelling out at this time. Surprisingly vigorous stirring was required to increase the rate of surface accumulation, while bubbling, even at low rates, was relatively effective.

The work just cited seems to state that the surface monolayer is mainly composed of long-chain hydrocarbons. This is probably not entirely true, since the water-soluble components appear to have been slighted. In the remainder of this section I shall consider a probable (but still largely unquantified) polypeptide component. The rationale for assuming such a component as a major constituent is as follows.

Menzel and Ryther (1964) found that particulate detritus in the euphotic zone had the same C/N ratio (and presumably the same lipid to protein ratio) as living plankton at the same season, ranging from 12 to 1 in January to 5 to 1 in April. Parsons and Strickland (1962) found about 100 mg/m^3 of protein in particulates in the upper 1000 m. Williams (1967) found organic nitrogen to be enriched in the microlayer by factors of 2 to 15 (dissolved) and 4 to 50 (particulate). According to Degens (1970), more than 90% of the "so-called dissolved organic matter" in seawater has a molecular weight greater than 400, with the bulk falling in the range 3000 to 5000 and a C/N ratio of 2.5 to 3, which is just that of protein. Thus, there would seem to be an abundance of protein available for inclusion in the surface microlayer.

The failure of traditional methods to detect such protein may be related to an observation made by Knox and Parshall (1970), who found that gelatin does not appreciably change the surface tension of sodium decyl sulfate when they form a surface complex. This suggests that a lipid-protein complex might be equally difficult to detect by film-pressure measurements. Such a complex would prevent the high film pressure of the lipid from forcing the protein out of the monolayer. The surface potential of protein happens to lie in the observed range of potentials, which is shared by acid-ester mixtures (Jarvis, 1967). Apparently our two best detectors are blind to polypeptides.

How does protein behave at the surface? MacRitchie and Alexander (1963) note that every protein molecule that diffuses to the surface is adsorbed, and that only a small portion of the molecule needs to penetrate the surface before complete unfolding of the structure begins. Although the enthalpy of adsorption may be low because each adsorption site is loosely held, the entropy of adsorption is large because all segments of the molecule must desorb simultaneously before the molecule can leave, so that there is a large free-energy barrier keeping an adsorbed protein at the surface (cf. Gonzales and MacRitchie, 1970). However, the elasticity ($\partial\gamma/\partial A$) of a protein layer is low because desorption under pressure can occur one group at a time (MacRitchie, 1963). Murumutsu and Sabotka (1963) describe the surfactant groups as hydrophobic side chains tilted into the air phase. The picture begins to emerge of a largely denatured protein chain attached to the surface by a few hydrophobic groups, but with long hydrophilic loops dangling below into the microlayer.

Perhaps the most convincing single datum regarding the proportion of protein in the surface monolayer is Sieburth's (1971) observation that the bacteria in the microlayer have a lipolytic : proteolytic : amylolytic enzyme ratio of 93 : 92 : 24, compared to 46 : 53 : 54 for subsurface bacteria. This suggests that protein is as abundant as lipids in the microlayer, while starch is relatively scarce, as would be expected. This argument was confirmed by R. E. Baier and D. W. Goupil (Collection and identification of sea-surface films, with special attention to natural slicks and foams. Abstract A-1, International Symposium on the Chemistry of Sea/Air Particulate Exchange Processes, 4–10 October 1973, Nice; to be published in *J. Rech. Atmos.*). They report that glycoproteins and proteoglycons (also known as humic acids, Gelbstoff, and mucopolysaccharides) are major and ubiquitous components of the sea-surface film. These authors do not find lipids except in polluted areas, and suggest that the preponderance of lipids reported from "surface" samples represent material extracted from organisms present in the samples.

The consequences of a major proteinaceous component in the surface monolayer are both chemical and mechanical. Mechanically speaking, a protein of molecular weight 4000 may be a chain some 200 Å long when unwound. Such chains, if attached at relatively few points, might extend the influence of the surface on the viscosity of water by an order of magnitude beyond the reach of the lipid head groups, and might, for instance, help to account for the thickness of oceanic bubble film caps. Chemically proteins provide abundant sites for complexing of specific ions. To the extent that chemical fractionation between sea and air occurs in response to specific surface adsorption, proteins provide useful carriers for a wide variety of substances.

4. Thermal Phenomena

A. Surface Temperature Gradient

Leaving now the molecular surface for the deeper reaches of the microlayer, we inquire into thermal effects. It is difficult to describe meaningfully the "average" thermal regime at the sea surface, for the heat input is a function of latitude and season, and ranges from 0 to 4000 cal/cm^2-day. The day-to-day average heat flow over an area of a few square degrees may change by 300 cal/cm^2-day (Laevastu, 1963), and the momentary value is somewhat at the mercy of cloud shadows. However, from the point of view of chemical fractionation, it is sufficient to put a maximum value on the temperature gradient in the microlayer.

As indicated in Fig. 1, only 10% of the incoming radiation is absorbed above 1 mm, so there must be a net heat flow upward (which is carried away by evaporation) and a corresponding decrease in temperature upward throughout the conduction region Spangenberg and Rowland (1961) observed evaporation-induced gradients of $-1.8°C/cm$ at the surface in tank experiments. Measured values of the oceanic gradient range from $-3.2°C/cm$ at night (McAlister et al., 1971) to $-5°C/cm$ in the daytime (McAlister and McLeish, 1970). McAlister (1964) showed that these values are large enough to account for the entire heat flow out of the ocean. However, the reported values are averaged over 1.6 km of sea surface and 2600 individual measurements of a 25° field of view, and so may conceal occasional much larger gradients. Hill's (1970) laboratory experiments showed that the gradient decreases by a factor of 3 when waves appear, and Witting's (1972) analysis shows that capillary ripples can reduce the gradient almost an order of magnitude. The largest gradient reported was $-26°C/cm$ at a simulated sea surface (McAlister and McLeish, 1969), and all in all it seems safe to take $-30°C/cm$ as a (improbable) maximum oceanic gradient.

B. The Soret Effect

The reason for our interest in the maximum thermal gradient in the microlayer is that thermal diffusion, or the Ludwig-Soret effect (Ludwig, 1856; Soret, 1881), has been suggested as a possible mechanism for ion separation at the sea surface (Komabayasi, 1962). However, few data have been adduced to support such a mechanism. We attempt here to estimate the maximum fractionation that the Soret effect might produce in the oceans. But first, a brief introduction to the world of irreversible thermodynamics.

In a stationary solvent, the flow of mass J_i (mol/cm^2-sec) of component i across a horizontal plane is

$$J_i = -D_i \frac{\partial m_i}{\partial z} - D_i' m_i \frac{\partial T}{\partial z}$$

where m is the molality and D_i and D_i' are the ordinary and thermal diffusivity of molecules of i, respectively. At steady state, $J_i = 0$, and

$$D_i \frac{\partial m_i}{\partial z} = -D_i' m_i \frac{\partial T}{\partial z}$$

The Soret coefficient σ is defined to be

$$\sigma = -\frac{D_i'}{D_i} = \frac{\partial m_i}{m_i\, \partial T}$$

or, with a linear gradient,

$$\sigma\, \Delta T = \Delta \ln m_i$$

(Caution: σ is sometimes defined with the opposite sign convention.)

The "mechanical" origin of the Soret effect is that the entropy of transport S^* varies with the structure-making/structure-breaking ability of an ion. Structure makers bring the molecules around them to a higher degree of order than that of the water structure, and so decrease the entropy of the solvent in their hydration spheres. If a structure-making ion in a hot region were to be magically removed from its structured solvent shell, heat would flow from the surroundings into the relatively cold shell. If the structure-maker were next inserted bare into a cold region, heat would flow out of the hydration sphere into the surroundings as the water molecules assumed their (relatively) ordered positions. The net effect would have been to move the ion together with a certain amount of heat of transport Q^* down the temperature gradient. Alternatively, it is the heat of transport moving down the gradient that carries the ion with it. Another hueristic explanation regards the ion-plus-hydration sphere as a large object in a thermal gradient, subject to thermal phoresis (see Derjaguin and Yalamov, 1965) from Brownian-motion impacts on its periphery. Solvent molecules on the hot side hit harder and more often than on the cold side, creating a mechanical force that drives the structure-maker toward the cold wall. The structure-breaker gets crowded toward the hot wall.

These motions are complicated by the strong requirement for local electrical neutrality in the solution, so that strictly speaking it is possible to talk only of the Soret coefficient of a salt, not of an ion. Nevertheless, the usual attempt is made to separate out individual ion effects by assigning a conventional heat of transport of zero to the chloride ion.

The relation between the heat of transport and the Soret coefficient is

$$Q^* = TS^* = -(\nu_1 + \nu_2)\, RT^2 B\sigma$$

where ν_1 and ν_2 are the number of ions a salt forms, R is the gas constant, and B is the thermodynamic activity correction $(1 + d \ln f/d \ln m)$, where f is the activity coefficient. Numerical values of Q^* are shown in Table III. The Soret coefficient ranges from -0.1×10^{-3} to $+10 \times 10^{-3}$/deg. Neither Q^* nor S^* is predictable by present theory. KCl, for instance, normally migrates toward the cold wall, but at low temperatures in dilute solution, the data suggest that the sign of σ changes and KCl migrates toward the hot wall. Despite occasional statements to the contrary, any correlation between an ion's mass and its Soret coefficient is largely coincidental, because specific ion-solvent interactions overwhelm any gas-kinetic dependence of diffusional velocity on mass.

Redistribution of ions in a thermal gradient is fairly rapid. For a distance a between hot and cold walls, the relaxation time (not the transit time of Table I) is $\theta = a^2/\pi^2 D_i$, and in experiments in which the temperature gradient is established by suddenly changing both walls away from the mean temperature, a linear concentration gradient is established within $0.2a$ of the walls in 0.1θ (Longworth, 1959). For our purposes, it is sufficiently accurate to note that the Soret effect can redistribute ions over a 1-μm distance in 0.25 sec, and that the time is independent of the temperature gradient or the concentration. This response is conceivably fast enough to establish gradients in the surface microlayer.

But the important question remains: How large a concentration gradient can thermal diffusion create? If we take maximal values ($\sigma = 10^{-2}$, $m = 0.3M$, $\Delta T/\Delta z =$ 30°C/cm) we find

$$\frac{\Delta m}{\Delta z} = \sigma m \frac{\Delta T}{\Delta z} = 0.1M/\text{cm} = 10^{-5}M/\mu\text{m}$$

as an upper limit. We are not so much interested in the concentration gradient of a single ion as in the differential gradient for a pair of ions, and the maximum concentration-ratio gradients that can be achieved. We are probably safe in taking 1 μM/μm as a working maximum, and as a practical matter, this value is probably two orders of magnitude large.

Because of the small gradients that can be established by thermal diffusion, it is difficult to conceive of an oceanic condition in which the Soret effect could become important enough to produce measurable geochemical consequences. The possibility remains that someone will be ingenious enough to find a mechanism (such as counter-current flow) capable of multiplying the Soret effect (see below), but the unsupported

TABLE III

Conventional Single-Ion Heats of Transport Q^*, in Calories per mole at $0.01M$ and 25°C (Agar, 1959)

Li^+	Na^+	K^+	Rb^+	Cs^+	Ag^+	NMe_4^+	NEt_4^+	H^+	F^-	Cl^-	Br^-	I^-	NO_3^-	$\frac{1}{2}SO_4^{2-}$
−25	778	512	833	841	1537	2000	3112	3100	870	0	40	−547	−286	872

mention of "thermal diffusion" no longer seems legitimate as a way of explaining chemical fractionation.

5. Biological Phenomena

A. *Surface Biota*

The surface biota, or neuston, deserves notice for two reasons. First, some organisms are remarkably concentrated at the surface, just as are some compounds. Second, the neuston undoubtedly exist at the surface because it feeds them well. They must exert a profound influence on the chemical composition of the surface as they metabolize it.

We ignore the pleuston, or sailing jellyfish and their associated biocoenoses, because their role in the microlayer is obscure, and only mention the macroscopic members of the neuston such as the snail *Janthina prolongata*—which may feed directly on surface monolayers as do freshwater tadpoles (Goldacre, 1949) and snails (Cheesman, 1956)—and the sea striders (*Halobates spp*: *Gerridae*); however fascinating they may be to the biologist, their geochemical influence is slight. They are of interest to us chiefly in that they show that under some conditions there is sufficient organic matter available in the microlayer to support such large animals.

Little work has been done on the neuston. Some indication of the richness of the microlayer is given by Tables IV to VI. The authors of Table IV were not directly

TABLE IV

Obligate Psychrophiles (Bacteria Requiring Low Temperatures) at Various Stations in Arctic Waters, from Morita and Burton (1970), Who Unfortunately, Do Not Describe Their Collection Techniques for "Surface" and "Surface Film" Samples

Depth (m)	Bacteria/50 ml			
Surface film	TMC[a]			
Surface	60	TMC	12,865	10,750
20	273	550		
30	107	302		
50	140			181
75			115	

[a] TMC = "too many to count," evidently considerably more than 13,000.

TABLE V

Neuston Collected by Skimmer in La Jolla (Harvey, 1966). Dinoflagellates Are Principally *Prorocentrum micans*. Detritus Present But Not Counted

	Unidentified flagellates < 15 μm	Unidentified flagellates > 15 μm	Dinoflagellates	Ciliates	Diatoms
Skimmer	4,470	30	31,270	330	930
10 cm	0	0	3,900	370	3,770
13 m	0	0	1,100	100	16,100

TABLE VI

Neuston and Fluorescent Biological Compounds Collected in Hawaiian Waters by Skimmer and Plate Techniques (Harvey and Burzell, 1972)

	Detritus	Ciliates	Colorless Flagellates	Chain Diatoms	Tryptophan	Tyrosine	Chlorophyll a
Ceramic drum	54,400	2,210	1,700	568	31.50	22.0	2.03
Glass plate	47,600	3,140	5,250	309	29.80	19.40	2.35
10-cm depth	3,640	322	296	112	2.17	2.00	0.19

concerned with the distinction between "surface" and "surface film" in their investigation and do not comment on their collection techniques. It is a reasonable hypothesis (bolstered by the populations shown in the first column and in Tables V and VI) that some of their "surface" samples actually included a good deal of "surface film." In any event, it is clear that cold-loving bacteria in the Arctic are most abundant in or near the microlayer.

Harvey (1966) compared skimmer samples with deeper water at La Jolla and found the distribution shown in Table V. Not unexpectedly, some organisms shun the surface as avidly as others seek it. Diatoms apparently find the light too bright. No work seems to have been done on the nocturnal distribution of the neuston.

Harvey and Burzell (1972) compared the collection ability of the ceramic-drummed skimmer with that of a flat glass plate, both for identifiable neuston and for certain fluorescent compounds found in whole organisms, with the results shown in Table VI. Once again the enrichment in the microlayer is pronounced.

Some members of the neuston apparently take advantage of surface ejection mechanisms and may be adapted to aerial transport. Zobell and Mathews (1936) observed viable marine bacteria carried 30 mi inland. Schlichting (1961) found seven algae and protozoa that can be cultured from air samples, and Stevenson and Collier (1962) report three diatoms and four microflagellates from the Gulf of Mexico that are viable after impaction capture on a glass plate 2 mi inland. Blanchard and Syzdek (1970, 1972) have shown that microorganisms are routinely captured by bubbles and thence ejected into the atmosphere.

The specialization necessary for taking advantage of this free transport mechanism seem to be the ability to withstand heat, osmotic pressure, and drying, and a small size, for the bubble microtome is highly selective for small particles. These are severe requirements, and aerial transport may be an unfortunate accident rather than a mode of propagation. Just to keep things in balance, it should be pointed out that Reimann (in Delaney et al., 1967) identified benthic marine plankton, along with African and Alpine freshwater diatoms and terrestrial fungi, in particulate samples from the Barbados trade winds (but did not try to culture these). The neuston at least has no monopoly on aeolian transport.

6. Electrical Phenomena

A. Charge Fractionation

The fractionation of charge—the balloelectricity of Christiansen (1913, 1916, 1919), or electrification of particles as they separate from a solution—seems closely related to inorganic chemical fractionation. However, a difference of scale in the two processes makes them fundamentally unrelated. A pocket comb is all that is needed to observe charge fractionation on jet drops, which will be attracted to it over a distance of several centimeters. It is not difficult to detect a single unbalanced charge on a small drop in a Millikan experiment, or 1000 charges on a single drop with a transistorized impactor in the field (Takahashi, 1972). Jet drops of 40-μm from seawater normally carry a positive charge on the order of 10^{-6} esu or 2000 excess positive ions (Blanchard, 1963) out of a total of 2×10^{13} ions, for an easily detectable charge fractionation of one part in 10^{10}.

Chemical fractionation, in contrast, requires about one part in 10^3 to be detectable, and a sample volume of several thousand drops. The two types of fractionation are thus separated by about 10 orders of magnitude in detectability, so that the ubiquity of charge fractionation says nothing useful about the geochemical significance of chemical fractionation.

However, certain aspects of the underlying mechanisms are undoubtedly the same: both processes require the separation of a surface and bulk liquid of different composition by some dynamic process, and charge fractionation studies should prove a useful tool for investigating the much more difficult problem of chemical fractionation.

The work of Frumkin and Obrutcheva (1931) revealed a straightforward connection between charge fractionation and the electrical double layer in the form of the linear relation between spray-drop charge and surface potential shown in Fig. 5. Although the problem is not as simple as it first appears, the obvious conclusion is undoubtedly the correct one: charge fractionation occurs when the double layer is somehow sheared between its constituent sublayers.

But the thickness of the double layer is on the order of the Debye-Hückel length $1/\kappa$, which is about $3/c^{1/2}$ Å, where c is the molarity, and again, it is difficult to imagine a shear of this nicety.

If one were to form an oceanic droplet by "coring" the sea surface with an inert microscopic cylindrical tube (shaped like a cookie cutter) to obtain a flat cylindrical sample, no charge fractionation would occur as the circle became a sphere. Neither can one fractionate charge by cutting circles out of bubble film caps. The net charge on such samples is zero, for both the microlayer and film cap are electrically neutral across the thickness that goes into oceanic droplets, and the net charge remains zero during the transition to a sphere. However, the dynamic details of the processes that create film caps and jet drops—different though they are—manifestly provide some mechanism for separating charge. Film drops carry fewer than 10 unit charges (Blanchard, 1963). One can imagine a process by which a net positive charge of this

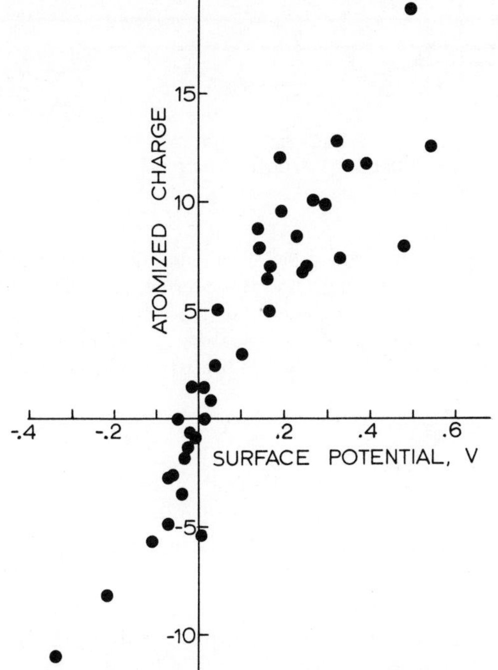

Fig. 5. Charge on atomized drops (arbitrary units) versus surface potential of mixed electrolyte-organic solutions. After Frumkin and Obrucheva (1931).

magnitude is put into small film drops while an equal negative charge remains on large film drops that do not stay airborne. In any case, the problem of charging jet drops is 200 times as severe.

Flow during jet-drop formation is complex, but the reproducibility of charge bespeaks a highly reproducible flow pattern. As presently understood, the sequence is this: the surface first shrinks from the outside in as the bubble cavity collapses. Surface energy is converted to kinetic energy in this phase. Surface flow converges on the axis, forming opposing jets. As the upward jet elongates the surface must stretch briefly, but contracts again as the jet breaks up into drops. The net result of this flow seems to be that the top jet drop is composed of material that was originally spread over most of the interior of the bubble, while succeeding drops are formed from succeeding onionlike shells surrounding the original bubble. Shear is minimized in this flow in two ways: the curvature of the cavity opposes the rotation of boundary layer flow, and a ripple very like Crapper's irrotational wave form develops (MacIntyre, 1972). If despite these features some shear still occurs, it is spread over a depth of micrometers rather than angstroms, and the components of the double layer are not appreciably separated. But as the flow climbs the upward jet, moving at speeds approaching 10^4 cm/sec, it is slowed at the surface by air friction (Blanchard, 1963) and by surface dilation, which requires the conversion of kinetic energy into surface free energy. The interior of the jet then ascends slightly faster than the outside, creating the required shear flow just before the jet breaks up into drops.

In terms of the "coring" analogy, the result is that of taking a tapered core, smaller at the top (negative ions are preferred in the top of the double layer). Crude calculations suggest that the taper needed is incredibly small, amounting to 3×10^{-6} Å

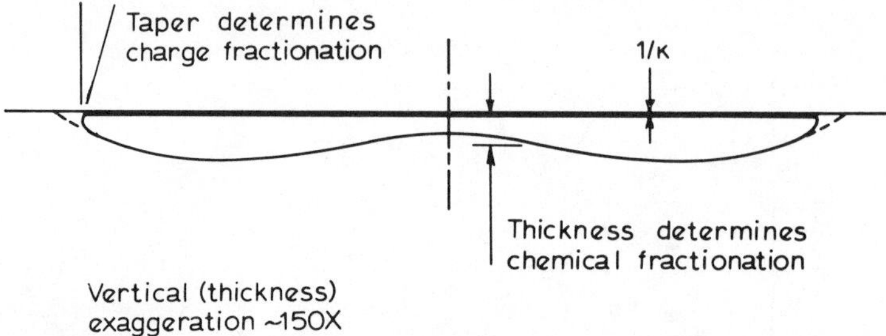

Fig. 6. Bubble-microtome cut: schematic cross section of the circular sample taken from the surface by the top jet drop. The sample should be curved around the interior of a spherical bubble, but is shown flat for artistic convenience and to emphasize the tapering edge, which arises from retardation of the surface during elongation of the upward jet. Electrical and chemical events are confined to the $1/\kappa$ thickness. The dashed tails indicate the sample in the absence of surface retardation.

over the 5 Å of the double layer, referred back to the original position of the "core" (Fig. 6). This is an increase of the bottom diameter of the core of only one part in 10^{13}—a shear so minimal that it in no way violates the general experimental impression of irrotational flow during bubble rupture.

It is obvious that such a small taper cannot account for any measurable chemical fractionation, which, as indicated in Fig. 6, must arise from a sample so thin that $1/\kappa$ is an appreciable percentage of the total thickness.

Studies currently underway, relating the surface potential of the solution to the charge distribution of the several drops that form from the ascending jet, should extend our knowledge of this process.

B. Time-Dependent Effects

An aspect of charge fractionation that may bear directly on chemical fractionation is the time dependence of bubble-related electrical processes. Alty (1924) seems to have been the first to observe the long time required for a bubble to come to equilibrium with a solution with respect to "attached charge." Currie and Alty (1929) found a 30-min equilibration time for bubbles maintained at the center of a rotating tube of water. Similar results were found by Whybrew et al. (1952), who further computed a surface charge density of 0.8 esu/cm^2, or roughly 2 unbalanced charges/10^6 surface sites.

The concept of "attached charge" requires clarification. Despite the name, it probably does not prepresent free charge occupying a few parts per million of the bubble surface. More likely, it is a dynamic effect in which the water moving by the bubble displaces the diffuse portion of the double layer slightly downstream, as in the classical picture of the eccentric ionic atmosphere surrounding a moving ion.

Blanchard (1963) measured the charge on jet drops as a function of bubble age and found rather complex behavior, at least part of which was most easily explained as contamination leaking from a rubber stopper in the system. Medrow and Chao (1972) repeated Blanchard's work and fitted the charge-to-mass ratio Q of the jet drops to a four-parameter curve:

$$Q = a(e^{bt} - 1) + c(e^{dt} - 1)$$

where t is the bubble lifetime. Equilibrium values were reached only after 200 sec. These data are compatible with the hypothesis that bubble charge is not, after all, related to the inorganic double layer (which is established in milliseconds) but to organic surfactants present at very low concentration that must reach the bubble surface by diffusion.

I have observed (but not attempted to quantify) the transition between free-slip flow and no-slip flow past a rising bubble in a 1-m water column. A bubble freshly broken loose from an orifice reaches its terminal velocity within a few centimeters, or "immediately," to the naked eye. If the water is relatively clean, the bubble will maintain this velocity for some distance, and then quite abruptly slow down. Subsequent bubbles repeat this performance, slowing at the same height—but the height itself is very much a function of the particular trace surfactant composition of the water, and not repeatable from batch to batch. If continued indefinitely, the bubbles would transfer this trace material onto the jet drops and effectively clean the solution.

The slowing was not subtle; casual passersby would notice and stop to watch. The change in velocity marks the point at which the bubble surface has collected enough surfactant to lose its mobility and begin to behave like a solid sphere. The velocity at this point drops to $\frac{2}{3}$ of the free-slip velocity (Lamb, 1932).

In the system just described, monolayer coverage was complete in about 1 sec. However, this says nothing about time to ultimate equilibrium. The original monolayer is formed on a first-come, first-seated basis. In terms of the equation above, a is related to the total concentration of surfactant contaminant present and b is related to some diffusion coefficient characteristic of the mixing regime. Equilibrium may require desorbing some of this first batch in favor of material that arrives later but is energetically favored at the interface. After the establishment of the equilibrium surface monolayer, there may still be a time lag before the diffuse portion of the double layer settles down, particularly if it, too, involves organic materials. The constant c is related to some particular components of the surfactant melange and d is related to the kinetics by which it replaces the early material. Evidently all of these parameters refer to trace contaminants, and there is little reason to believe that they convey much detailed information.

In terms of chemical fractionation, this dynamic behavior suggests that young bubbles may produce less fractionation than old ones. Such variability is undoubtedly one of the many uncontrolled variables that have plagued fractionation studies with irreproducible results.

7. Chemical Phenomena

A. Apologia

I fully intended to provide a comprehensive table of fractionation values reported in the literature, since this proof of having done one's homework is an almost sacred duty of the monograph writer. But after reexamining my first attempt (MacIntyre, 1970), I have come to feel that this approach is about as useful as a table of random numbers flawed with hidden irregularities: a sort of chimera that could be used to support anyone's favorite preconceptions regarding the reality, the sign, or the extent of fractionation of any particular ion.

Fractionation experiments are so varied, and their results so diverse, that I have thought it better to chop out some of the underbrush, making, as it were, a clearing in the jungle where someone may eventually be able to erect a useful and welcome table. I have endeavored to maintain an appropriate scientific detachment while swinging my machete, but it has sometimes seemed that workers in the field who appreciate the need for experimental precision, theoretical rigor, and reportorial completeness are in the minority. I have never seen so many papers that bring to mind Lewis and Randall's magnificent phillipic (1923) against the would-be thermodynamicists of the early days:

> We have seen "cyclic processes" limping about eccentric and not quite completed cycles, we have seen the exact laws of thermodynamics uncritically joined to assumptions comprising half-truths or no truth at all, and worst of all we have seen ill-begotten equations supported by bad data.

This scolding did its work so well that Pitzer and Brewer were able to remove it from their revision (1961); I mention it in the hope that it will have the same salutory effect on chemical fractionation studies.

B. Nomenclature

A minor but annoying aspect of fractionation is the lack of a standardized terminology among workers, and it is unfortunate that the set used herein goes counter to some published work. The notation is merely one that I find convenient, but the nomenclature has the blessing of the Working Symposium on Sea-to-Air Chemistry

(Fort Lauderdale, Florida, January 31 to February 4, 1972), and it is hoped that it will become standard. We define:

$$\text{Fractionation:} \qquad F_{\text{Na}}(X) = \frac{(X/\text{Na})_{\text{sample}}}{(X/\text{Na})_{\text{standard}}}$$

$$\text{Enrichment:} \qquad E_{\text{Na}}(X) = F(X) - 1 = \frac{(X/\text{Na})_{\text{samp}} - (X/\text{Na})_{\text{stan}}}{(X/\text{Na})_{\text{stan}}}$$

The common practice of using a simple ratio such as X/Na suffers from a dependency on the units used (moles or mass), while $F(X)$ and $E(X)$ are unit free. The reasons for preferring Na as the reference ion appear below. Fractionation referred to sodium will usually be expressed without the subscript, but when other ions such as Cl^- or Mg^{2+} are used as reference ions, they will appear explicitly.

C. Geochemical Sampling Problems

Geochemical investigation of fractionation requires a large number of carefully considered samples. Some feeling for just how many can be had by examining Fig. 7, which is perhaps the most meaningful format for displaying fractionation in gross samples that are not classified by size. In terms of Fig. 7, $k = (\text{Y/Na})_{\text{seawater}}$. Now suppose that the samples "really" lie along the line

$$\text{Y}' = \text{Y}_0 + k'(\text{Na} - \text{Na}_0)$$

where k', the fractionation that we hope to measure, is not equal to k but is a real event occurring during ejection from the sea surface. k' can only be determined if the number of samples, and their distribution, enables us to distinguish the two heavy lines in Fig. 7, so that samples falling in or close to the shaded area are ambiguous and of little value. Furthermore, in the real world there is no guarantee that Y_0 and Na_0, the nonmarine background values, are constant in time or space, even though

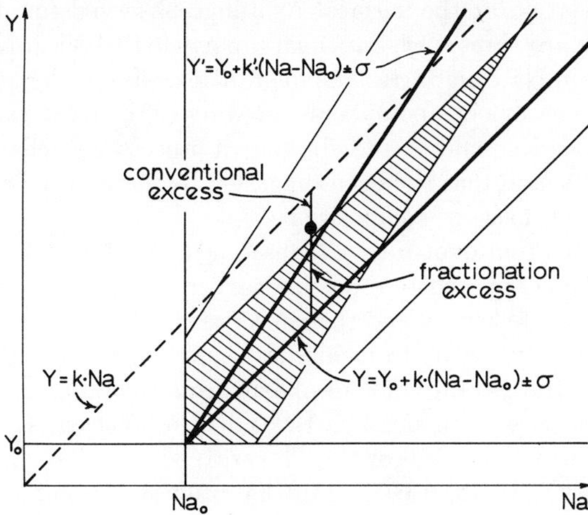

Fig. 7. Sampling considerations in geochemical investigation of fractionation. The problem is, How many samples are needed to distinguish between the two heavy lines? How many more to show that Y_0 and Na_0 are well known? Samples in the shaded area are not likely to be very helpful.

one collects samples of known volume. It becomes clear that a dozen samples of oceanic rain, for instance, collected over two months and 1000 mi, do not constitute a particularly useful test of fractionation.

Good experimental design requires a careful choice of sampling sites to minimize and stabilize Y_0 and Na_0 and an optimization between the number of samples taken (to get the maximum number of points along a line) and the size of the samples (to reduce chemical errors). After all, if the data do not warrant a statistical analysis of confidence limits, they were probably not worth taking. Incidentally, it is relatively easy to put a good line through a set of such observations if there are 2^N points, by estimating the desired line and finding the midpoint of pairs of observations taken on opposite sides of the line and as close to normal to it as possible. This reduction, performed $N - 1$ times, leaves two points determining the desired line. The number of possible lines obtainable in this way is large, but if the data are good, the useful ones lie closely clumped together. Improving the fit by regrouping and computing the confidence limits of the coefficients are somewhat more tedious, but can be done rigorously (Wald, 1940).

Figure 7 also points out the imprecision inherent in discussing the conventional "excess" of Y, by which is meant $Y_{\text{observed}} - k \cdot Na_{\text{observed}}$, and which purports to be the amount of Y in excess of that which has come from the ocean. The "fractionation excess," or difference from the real marine ejection value, may be of opposite sign, as indicated for the sample point. Still other definitions of "excess" are possible and even useful for particular studies, but it is good to think carefully about their significance in terms of Y_0, Na_0, and σ, and to explain carefully just what is meant.

D. Chlorine

Of all chemical fractionation that might occur at the sea surface, the most basic would be a change in the Cl/Na ratio of ejecta. However, since any value of F(Cl) from 0 to 64 can be observed in precipitation and air samples (Egnér and Eriksson, 1955), random collections of geochemical data are of limited value in investigating the reality of chloride fractionation at the surface. As Junge observed (quoted in Rossby and Egnér, 1955), there are three ways in which a particle's Cl/Na ratio can change after ejection. It may gain Na from terrestrial dust, it may lose Cl by atmospheric conversion to unspecified gaseous compounds (denoted by Cl*), and it may gain chlorine by adsorbing Cl*. To these should be added a fourth process that changes the ratio in an ensemble of particles, and that has been suggested by many workers: selective rainout of particles of a certain size or composition.

Cauer (1951), in an often-quoted paper, observed a rapid loss of Cl from an atomized aerosol. But here he is apparently reporting earlier results, for the description of the experiment is somewhat sketchy and the references to the original work seem to have become garbled. In any event, from his data one can derive the fractionations of Table VII, in which the distance of aerosol drift from the atomizing nozzle is taken as a measure of particle size, with small particles drifting further. The conclusion drawn from these results was that 85% of the Cl^- escaped into the gas phase, "probably predominantly as ClO_2, Cl_2, and HCl," but the rationale behind this conclusion is not entirely clear. The K deficit was not discussed, and, if fractionation of such magnitude can be routinely achieved with such ease, the theoreticians have their work cut out for them.

Oddie's (1959) analysis of precipitation from the remote Shetland Islands, where exposed land is either granite rock or wet soil, and sodium can scarcely be added to the

TABLE VII

Fractionation Reported by Cauer (1951) in Atomized Spray

	Distance from Atomizing Nozzle (cm)		
	30	150	300
$F_{Mg}(Cl)$	0.19	0.07	0.08
$F_{Mg}(K)$	0.52	0.38	0.31

atmosphere by local particles, suggests that gaseous loss might be very rapid. Oddie notes that the total salt content of his samples is tenfold higher than that found in any other European rainfall station, and that spray could be seen blowing clear across the island on windy days. The shore was nowhere more than a few miles from the sampling site, and on the assumption that most of the material collected was generated by local surf, the exposure time during flight could only have been a few minutes. As shown in Fig. 8, Cl/Na was consistently low by amounts ranging from 7 to 35%.

Rapid loss of Cl^- is supported by the laboratory work of Robbins et al. (1959), who observed a 44% conversion of particulate NaCl to volatile HCl in 5 min of exposure to an 0.004 μM/l gas-phase concentration of NO_2. (This is still rather more NO_2 than one expects in the Shetland Islands.) Other compounds that might produce Cl* are sulfuric acid (Eriksson, 1960), and oxidants such as ozone (Cauer, 1949), although Eriksson argued against oxidation to Cl_2. Junge (1957) found 50% of the atmospheric

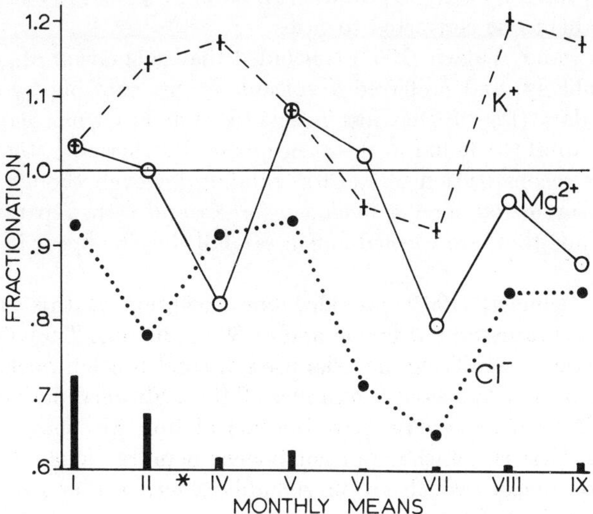

Fig. 8. Fractionation in airborne material collected during precipitation, having a terminal velocity less than 3 cm/sec, from Lerwick Observatory, Shetland Islands. Values are monthly means. Vertical extent of symbols indicates the uncertainty in $F(X)$ from the limited number of significant figures reported, and makes no allowance for sampling errors. Heavy vertical bars represent relative mass of salt collected: the January value is 36 g/m^3. Data from Odie (1957).

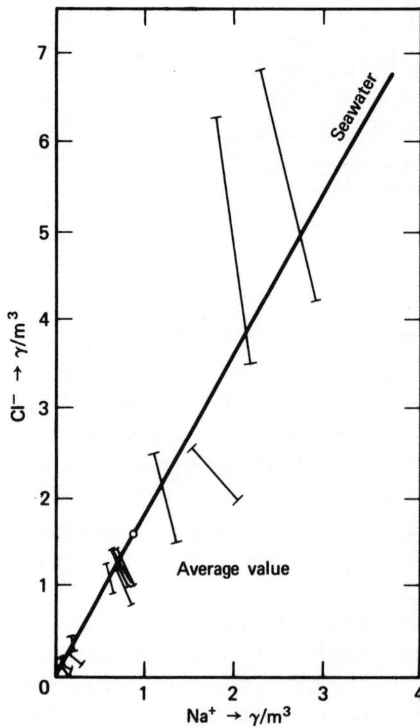

Fig. 9. Cl versus Na in 0.8- to 8-μm aerosol in Florida. The limits of accuracy are indicated by the line lengths for each sample. From Junge (1956).

Cl in Hawaiian samples to be Cl*, but did not determine its composition beyond its ability to be captured by a K_2SO_4 solution. Duce et al. (1965) found that Br^- and I^- are similarly liable to be converted to gases.

On the other hand, Valach (1967) concluded that generation of gaseous Cl* from sea salt was unlikely, and preferred a volcanic origin, showing by a Cl balance on Junge's (1956) data (Fig. 9) that insufficient Cl^- was lost from sea salt particles to account for the total Cl* found in the atmosphere. Furthermore, there would appear to be a curious reconstitution of NaCl in rainfall, for even though particulate and gaseous Cl measurements show a tendency for Na and Cl to separate in the atmosphere, by the time they are washed out in rainfall they reappear in very nearly the seawater ratio.

Miyake and Tsunogai (1965) provided one exception to this generalization by sampling the same rainstorm at 800 m and at 80 m altitude. They defined the upper sample as "rainout," signifying material used as condensation nuclei, and the lower sample as rainout plus "washout," meaning all the additional material picked up by falling drops. Their observations as a function of time are shown in Fig. 10, and strongly suggest that the washed-out component is unfractionated sea spray, while the condensation nuclei—which are presumably older, smaller particles—appear to have collected additional Cl*.

In direct contradiction to the geochemical results that suggest a loss of Cl soon after particles become airborne, Köhler and Båth (1953) found a slight Cl excess in a closed laboratory system in which a jet of air was blown over a seawater surface. They captured particles in a series of glass vessels that gave only a very crude sorting by size, and the fractionation they observed was small. Figure 11 shows their results

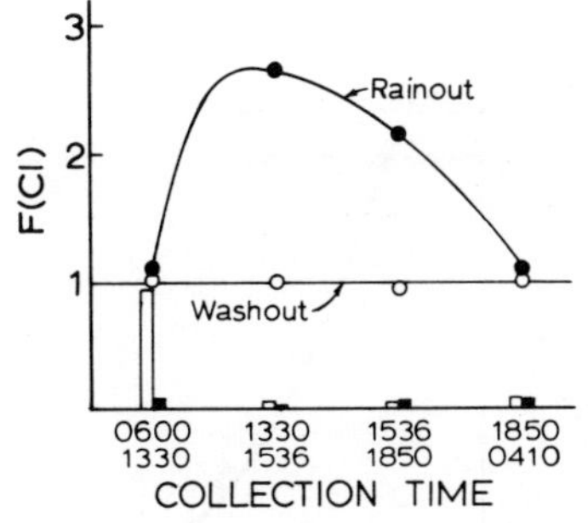

Fig. 10. Rainfall sampled at 800 m provides information on the Cl/Na ratio in condensation nuclei (rainout); the same rain sampled at 80 m includes material picked up by the falling raindrops (washout), which appears to be unfractionated sea salt. Bars at bottom show relative amounts of washout (white) and rainout (black). Only a small percentage of the total material is fractionated. Data from Miyake and Tsunogai (1965).

using Na as the reference ion; Mg as the reference gave slightly more fractionation but more scatter. In both cases fractionation occurred only for a particular range of concentrations, perhaps related in some obscure way to the size-classifying ability of their collector.

Rossby and Egnér (1955) attempted to rationalize Scandinavian Cl/Na ratios with the approach indicated in Fig. 12. This rapid oscillation of the ratio would reduce the sea-surface ejection ratio to an unimportant curiosity if it occurred universally, but Gambell (1961) did not observe such an oscillation in North American values. One explanation is that the Scandinavian results, collected somewhat downwind of the industrial centers of Europe, may show much greater conversion to Cl* by industrial effluvia.

Recent geochemical work is not much more definitive. Lazrus et al. (1970) collected eight samples of orographic cloud water from Puerto Rico and found F(Cl) = 1.04 ± 0.17 (90% confidence limits), and although this is indistinguishable from no fractionation, it still covers all potential values. The best current assessment of the

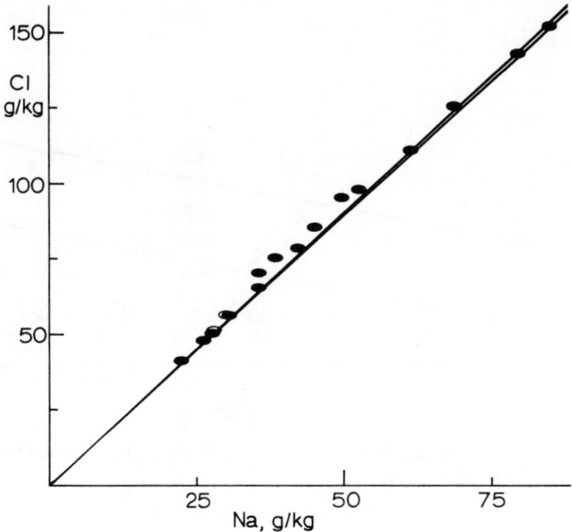

Fig. 11. Cl versus Na in droplets from seawater in a closed system, replotted from Köhler and Bath (1953), who seem to have been the first to display putative fractionation in this manner. The diverging lines are their two determinations of Cl/Na in seawater.

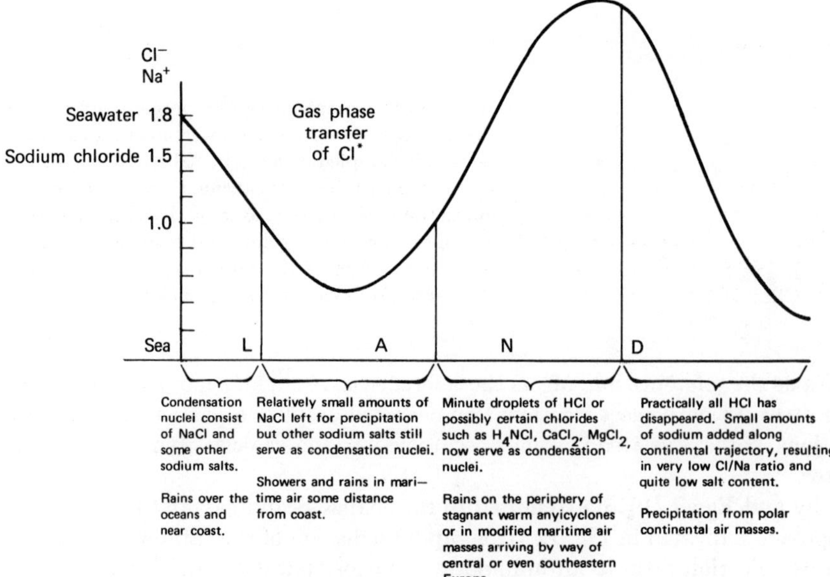

Fig. 12. Schematic representation of the variations of the Cl/Na ratio of precipitation in Scandinavia. After Rossby and Egnér (1955).

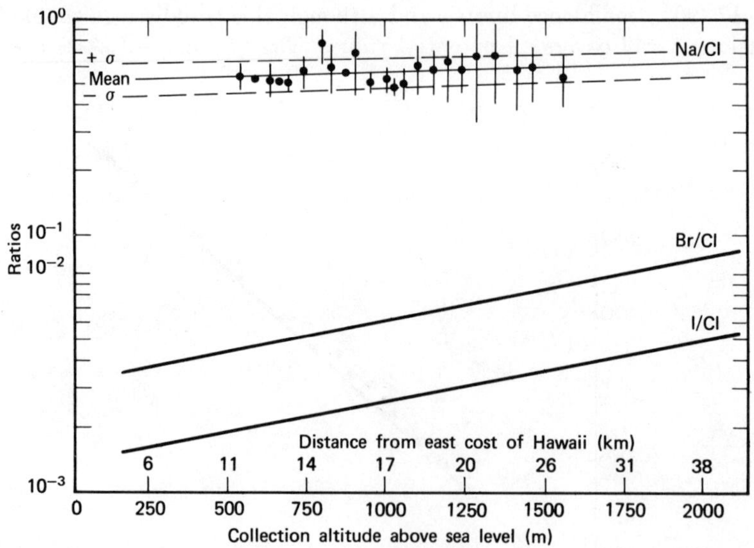

Fig. 13. Na/Cl ratio in Hawaiian rain (Seto et al., 1969). The Na/Cl line is not significantly different from the seawater value.

marine aerosol Cl/Na ratio is that of Seto et al. (1969), reproduced in Fig. 13. Once again there is neither evidence for fractionation nor a sure rejection of such data as Köhler and Båth's.

E. Bromine

The best data available for Br/Cl at ejection is the aerosol collected in the surf zone by Duce and Woodcock (1971), shown as the dashed line of Fig. 14. Br/Cl in fresh sea spray is indistinguishable from the seawater value for all drop sizes. The solid lines of Fig. 14 are old marine aerosol particles collected simultaneously with the

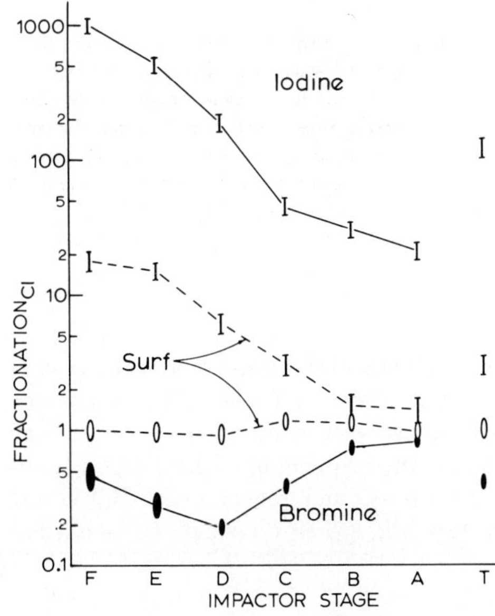

Fig. 14. Iodine and bromine fractionation with respect to Cl in fresh aerosol from surf (dashed lines) and in aged open-ocean particles (solid lines). Data from Duce and Woodcock (1971). See Table IX for interpretation of impactor stage designations.

surf-zone samples, but just high enough to be out of reach of the spray. Thus they represent either the Br/Cl ratio at ejection from a calmer environment than surf, or marine particles operated on by atmospheric chemical processes. The Br deficit in these samples is evident, but if it arises from atmospheric processes it is not clear whether it signifies a loss of Br* or a gain of Cl*. Laboratory data on the I/Na ratio within minutes of ejection show a photochemical loss of I with a profile very similar to this one (Fig. 15).

TABLE VIII

Bromine and Iodine Fractionation in Aerosol and Rain (Duce et al., 1965)

	Aerosol	Rain
$F_{Cl}(Br)$	0.7	1.6
$F_{Cl}(I)$	130	420

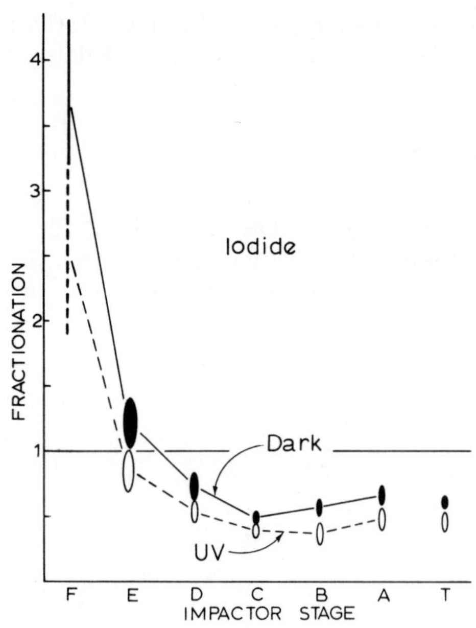

Fig. 15. Fractionation of iodide from filtered seawater with and without UV irradiation Vertical height of symbols spans three dark samples and six irradiated samples, making this the most reproducible fractionation experiment yet performed. Iodine loss appears to occur by rapid gas-phase reactions. Data from Seto (1970).

An additional complication is Duce et al.'s (1965) observation that rain is considerably richer in both Br and I than is aerosol, as shown in Table VIII. The authors note that the rain and aerosol samples are not strictly comparable because they were made in different seasons, and they discuss the problem of anthropogenic addition of Br from leaded gasoline, but the strong possibility remains that Br* is lost from seawater particles and captured by rainfall, either on small condensation nuclei or in washout.

F. Iodine

As is evident from the iodine lines of Fig. 14, fractionation of I is unequivocally important, and it has long been recognized (Heymann, 1927) that the I/Cl ratio in marine aerosol and precipitation is far greater than in seawater. The increase in $F(\mathrm{I})$ with time evident from the figure requires some source of iodine above anything available from marine particles (Moyers and Duce, 1972; Seto and Duce, 1972), and several processes have been proposed to account for this, mostly related to events in the surface microlayer.

One possibility is the photochemical oxidation of I^- to I_2, which could then evaporate from the sea surface. Miyake and Tsunogai (1963) reported that irradiation with ultraviolet (near 320 nm) led to an appreciable increase in the evaporation of radiotracer $^{131}I^-$ from seawater, probably through the reaction

$$2I^- + \tfrac{1}{2}O_2 + H_2O \xrightarrow{h\nu} I_2 + 2\,OH^-$$

This was partially confirmed by Seto (1970), who found a three-fold increase in I_2 formation and evaporation upon irradiating a model ocean with ultraviolet. However, only freshly added iodide would escape, and natural seawater did not emit I_2 upon irradiation. Seto concluded that perhaps the "iodide" in seawater was not free I^- but some less accessible form.

TABLE IX

Approximate particle-size ranges collected by the lettered stages of the Scientific Advances aerosol impactor. The collection efficiency depends on both the particle radius and its density as it approaches a collection stage, and since these are functions of the relative humidity in the complex aerodynamics inside the impactor, prudence dictates a certain reluctance to relate particle size to impactor stage. Nevertheless, for purposes of discussion we assume the following ranges. T represents the total material collected on all stages

Stage	F	E	D	C	B	A
Particle diameter, μm	0.3 0.6	0.6 1.2	1.2 2.5	2.5 5	5 10	>10

Seto also studied I/Na fractionation in bubbling. His results for I^- are shown in Fig. 15. Droplets remained above his model ocean for a maximum of 18 min before being collected, but this was time enough for appreciable amounts of I to be lost. Irradiating either the droplets and the seawater surface or only the airborne droplets increased the loss of I, which he interpreted as showing that Miyake and Tsunogai's photooxidation process takes place much more readily on particles than in the ocean itself.

Much greater enrichment occurred when I was incorporated into biological compounds. Simple addition of organics to an I-containing solution had no effect, but organic material extracted from plankton cultures fed ^{131}I produced the results of Fig. 16 when added to seawater. Ultraviolet irradiation of the particles caused a

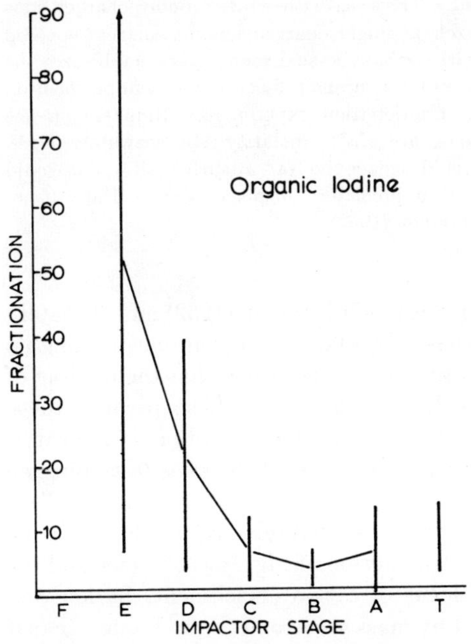

Fig. 16. Fractionation of organic iodine from filtered seawater and from 3% NaCl solutions, with and without UV irradiation. The vertical bars span the standard deviations of 14 separate runs containing various undetermined I-containing organics extracted from diatom cultures. Data from Seto (1970).

slight loss of I, but not enough to show through the experimental scatter in this figure. Comparison of Figs. 14 and 16 shows that organic enrichment is still an order of magnitude smaller than the steady-state enrichment found over the ocean.

An additional marine source of extra I may have been found by Tsunogai and Sase (1969). Investigating the processes that keep the I^-/IO_3^- system so far from equilibrium in seawater, they found that microorganisms that can reduce NO_3^- (*Achromobacter*, *Pseudomonas*, *Bacillus*, *Vibrio*, and *E. coli*, all in seawater cultures) can also reduce IO_3^- with nitrate reductase. Gozlan (1968) has reported strains of bacteria capable of oxidizing I^- to I_2, so that there is a potential biological pathway from IO_3^- to free iodine that might well be at work near the sea surface.

G. Alkali and Alkaline Earth Cations

Komabayasi (1964) reported appreciable fractionation of Mg, Ca, Sr, and Ba in drops less than 0.4 μm in diameter, as shown in Table X. The two most likely hypotheses for this enrichment are Gibbsian adsorption and organic binding to the surface. Komabayasi discounted the possibility of organic transport on the grounds that he had used water distilled from a copper vessel (presumably because copper binds fatty acids very tightly). However, this alone is an inadequate precaution and it does not seem possible to draw a clear-cut conclusion about the mechanism of this fractionation.

The reason for suspecting organic transport for these ions is shown in Figs. 17 and 18. Figure 17 plots the extent to which Ca occupies surface sites beneath a monolayer

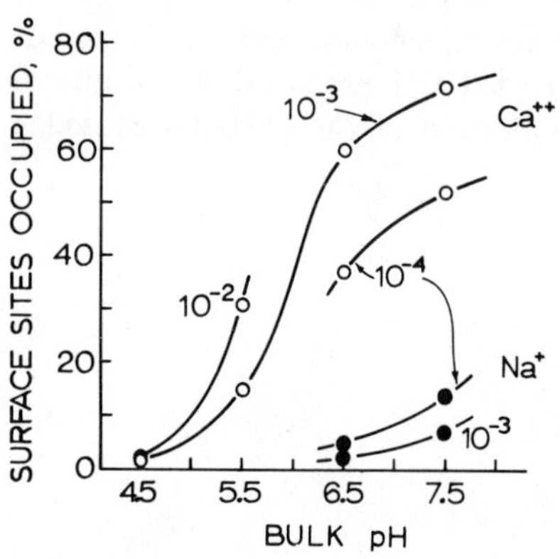

Fig. 17. The ease with which doubly charged ions exclude singly charged ions at surfaces covered with carboxylic-acid monolayers emphasizes the need for scrupulous surface-chemical purification in fractionation experiments. Numbers on the lines are Ca^{2+} molarity. In seawater, Mg^{2+} would replace the Na^+ at surface sites, but would not appreciably displace Ca^{2+}. Data from Havinga (1952).

of stearic acid in competition with H and Na. Although Havinga (1952) unfortunately neglected to state the Na concentration in these experiments (beyond mentioning its presence in the buffer), other experiments in the same paper show that the binding of Ca was unchanged as Na varied from 4×10^{-4} to $6 \times 10^{-2}M$, so perhaps these results can be extrapolated to $5 \times 10^{-1}M$ Na. It should be noted that in seawater, Mg, not Na, would compete with Ca, and occupy about $\frac{1}{12}$ of the sites (assuming no carbonate complexing).

Figure 18 shows the size distribution of organic material relative to Na in marine aerosols. The similarity to the organic iodine distribution of Fig. 16 is obvious, and the concentration on stage *F* agrees with the locus of cation enrichment. Barker and Zeitlin (1972) measured this organic material by mass spectrometry and found that it

TABLE X

Comparison of Recent Fractionation Values for Various Cations

K	Mg	Ca	Sr	Ba	Sample	Reference
—	1.37 ± 0.30	1.87 ± 0.25	2.04 ± 0.30	1.40 ± 0.10	Laboratory, $< 0.4\ \mu m$	Komabayasi (1964)
—	1.04 ± 0.01	—	—	—	Orographic cloud	Lazrus et al. (1970)
1.4	—	—	—	—	Various	Wilkniss and Bressan (1972)
1.05 ± 0.36	0.98 ± 0.03	0.97 ± 0.17	0.88 ± 0.28	—	Hawaiian aerosol	Hoffman and Duce (1972)
1.69 ± 0.958	0.997 ± 0.195	1.72 ± 0.506	0.546 ± 0.271	—	Hawaiian aerosol	Barker and Zeitlin (1972)
9.61 ± 15.9	2.40 ± 1.79	6.07 ± 7.43	1.56 ± 1.48	—	Hawaiian aerosol, stage *F* only	Barker and Zeitlin (1972)

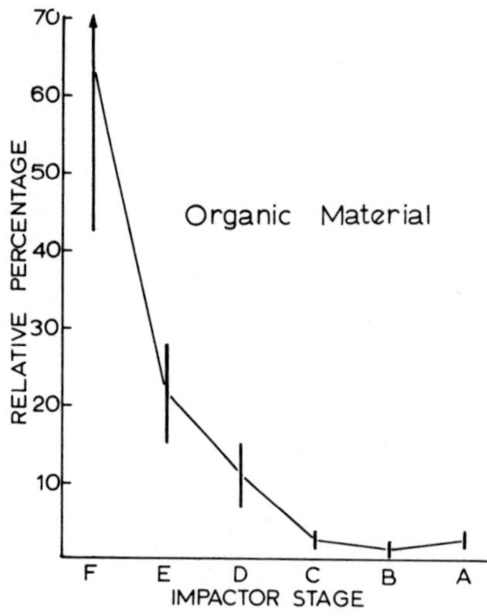

Fig. 18. Size distribution of organic material relative to sodium (i.e., $(\text{organic/Na})_i \div \sum_i (\text{organic/Na})_i \times 100$). Note the similarity to Fig. 16 and to the tendency for cation enrichment to increase on small particles. Data from Barker and Zeitlin (1972).

consisted of long-chain fatty acids and "other less discernible but relatively long-chain compounds." Certainly the ability to transport divalent cations is present.

Granting that bubbles might eject fatty acids and cations together into the atmosphere is not sufficient to establish the geochemical significance of such a process. Lazrus et al. (1970) found no evidence for fractionation of Ca in their studies of orographic Caribbean cloud water (nor did they find fractionation of Cl, Na, or SO_4). Contrary to the expectations of organic transport, which might have Mg fractionation less than Ca, these authors did find some evidence for Mg enrichment, reporting $F_{\text{Cl}}(\text{Mg}) = 1.04 \pm 0.01$ (95% confidence limits). The absence of Na fractionation argues that the apparent excess of Mg does not arise from a real deficit of Cl. Figure 19 is their plot of Mg versus Cl after removal of the unfractionated marine component, that is, the plotted line is $(\text{Mg})_{\text{obs}} - (\text{Cl})_{\text{obs}} \cdot (\text{Mg/Cl})_{\text{seawater}}$. (Zero enrichment would appear as a horizontal line on this plot.) The excellent fit at high Cl concentrations is remarkable. If it is real it indicates that Mg fractionation is not swamped by bulk sea spray during periods of maximum aerosol production, and perhaps that it is not dependent on unusual conditions at the sea surface.

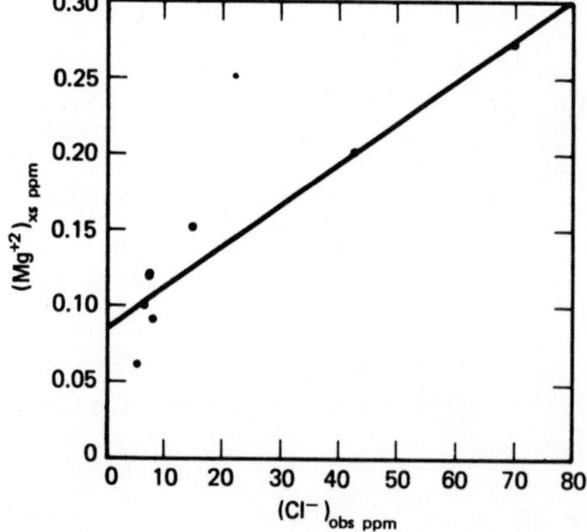

Fig. 19. Excess Mg versus Cl in orographic cloud water from Puerto Rico. The non-zero slope of the line is evidence for Mg/Cl fractionation at the sea surface. (From Lazrus et al., 1970.)

In recent work there has been a greatly increased awareness of the difficulties involved in determining meaningful fractionation values and an accompanying increase in the sophistication of the experiments and the care with which fractionation values are reported. Unfortunately, this increase in finesse has not yet brought with it any notable increase in our knowledge of what is happening out there. Table X gathers some of the recent work on cations to illustrate this point. It should be emphasized that these various experiments are not necessarily comparable, and the original works must be consulted for details. Evidently there is no such thing as "a" fractionation value for a given element, but only values appropriate to conditions that we have seldom been able to describe or control sufficiently to make our experiments repeatable.

Additional material on alkali and alkaline earth cations appears in Section 8.D.

H. *Sulfate*

There is no good reason to suspect sulfate fractionation at the sea surface at present. Since SO_4^{2-} is the equilibrium atmospheric form of sulfur, both the natural input of H_2S and the anthropogenic input of SO_2 [about 30% of the total atmospheric budget (Junge, 1960)] are converted to SO_4^{2-} quickly. Oxidation of SO_2 proceeds by two mechanisms, a direct oxidation in sunlight to SO_3, at a rate of 0.1 to 0.2%/hr (Gerhard and Johnstone, 1955), and a catalytic oxidation in cloud droplets in the presence of trace amounts of metal ions (Junge and Ryan, 1957). Against this massive input and rapid conversion, it is difficult to believe that the maximum of 0.5 mg/liter of "excess" sulfate found over the ocean (Junge and Werby, 1958) represents a marine contribution.

There are grounds for suspecting that organic material can carry sulfate from sea to air, and sulfate enrichment could probably be demonstrated in the laboratory—under conditions of no geochemical importance.

A significant aspect of atmospheric sulfate is that it comprises some 38% of the total ionic content (by weight) of fossil precipitation from Greenland (Junge, 1960; Langway, 1967). This extra SO_4^{2-} is not directly industrial in origin, for combustion nuclei are conspicuously absent. Nor does it seem to be terrigenous, although clay particles contribute measureable amounts of SiO_2, and, by leaching, some of the extra cations. The most probable source of the sulfate is $(NH_4)_2SO_4$ formed by gas-phase reaction of H_2SO_4 and NH_3 (Junge, 1972).

The northern-hemisphere anthropogenic production of SO_2 doubled from 1915–1957, but the Greenland ice shows no such increase, and cannot reflect an "average" atmospheric level of SO_4^{2-}. This discrepancy is usually explained on the basis of a short residence time for industrial input, with removal occurring before the material can reach Greenland.

I. *Boron*

The sea-air chemistry of boron may not be quite as simple as has been thought for nearly 15 yr, since Gast and Thompson (1959) described the codistillation of boric acid and water from the sea surface. Distilling both seawater and artificial solutions containing boron near the seawater concentration ($\sim$4 mg/liter), they found 100 μg/liter of boron in distillates, and no trace of Cl; working with condensates of 25°C boron-free air passed over 32°C seawater, they found up to 60 μg/liter of boron and no Cl. Although they did not provide a thermodynamic analysis of the process, it seemed as though they had shown that at least part of the high B/Cl ratio in precipitation arose by evaporative fractionation of boric acid at the sea surface.

Nishimura and Tanaka (1972), using very similar apparatus, could find no more than 1.1 ± 0.4 μg/liter boron (90% confidence level) in condensate when air and seawater were at *equilibrium* at 25°C. They further observed that the boron content of air equilibrated with seawater was only 19 ± 3 pg/liter compared to the oceanic value of 170 ± 30 pg/liter. From this they concluded that the atmosphere was probably supersaturated with boron compared to the ocean, making the sea a sink rather than a source of atmospheric boron. In this case, the extra atmospheric boron would undoubtedly be of volcanic origin.

Resolution of these conflicting data turns on the question of equilibrium. The experiments are not directly comparable, for one was at equilibrium and the other was not. Neither one, perhaps, is a particularly good model of the sea surface, where the temperature jump is, on the average, greater than zero but less than 7°C. All that can presently be said is that boric acid undeniably codistills with water, in amounts between 1 and 100 μg/liter, and that boron fractionation occurs by a mechanism that is unique among the elements.

J. Phosphate and Organic Aggregates

In contrast to the organic-iodine transport mechanism, which requires biological activity to bind the iodine to surface-active carriers, inorganic phosphate will attach to organic material sufficiently firmly to be ejected by bubbles. This observation was first made by Baylor et al. (1962), who were concerned with the role that bubbles played in maintaining a high concentration of nutrient phosphate in surface water. They found that phosphate concentration at the surface (1-m depth) on a calm day correlated well with wind speed (and therefore bubble production) on the preceeding day. They also noted that 24-hr bubbling in the laboratory would exponentially reduce phosphate by a factor of 100 if the ejecta were not allowed to fall back into the surface. Although all particles were removed by filtration prior to bubbling, and all the original phosphate was inorganic, the phosphate remaining after bubbling for a while, or captured from the air, was both organically bound and particulate. Such particles as a sole food supply enabled brine shrimp to grow, albeit slowly (Baylor and Sutcliffe, 1963), showing that bubbles provided a direct route for dissolved phosphate and organic material to enter the foodchain.

Riley (1963) suggested that such "carbon-rich aggregated particles" (by this time being referred to by acronym) were of ecological importance and a food source exploited by plankton communities. This conclusion was strengthened by the high oceanic correlation between aggregates and plankters found by Riley et al. (1964). Sutcliffe et al. (1963) observed that Langmuir circulation collected phosphate-rich surfactants at zones of convergence, and that certain organisms were concentrated in these downwelling regions of high nutrients. Sutcliffe et al. (1971) found a small but consistent increase in particulate carbon in such convergences, which increased with increasing wind, but did not identify its source or composition. It is possible that surface convergence is capable of converting monolayers into micellar particles or into the platelike marine "snow" observed in calm subsurface water by Nishizawa et al. (1954).

Menzel (1966) raised some doubts about the reality of particle production by bubbles, showing that simple filtration could also produce particles, and that not all bubble experiments produced aggregates. Barber (1966) suggested that bacterial activity was an essential ingredient. The problem has been restudied (Batoosingh et al., 1969) and largely resolved by the finding that particles 0.2 to 1.2 μm in diameter (including bacteria and particles that can pass the customary 0.45-μm filters) are necessary as nuclei for the formation of larger aggregates by bubbles.

In the meantime, MacIntyre (1965) had confirmed the ability of bubbles in sea-water to transport phosphate into the air phase in a decreasing exponential fashion, and showed that either exhaustion of phosphate or exhaustion of the surfactant carrier would lead to an exponential decrease of transport. He also noted the efficient conversion of dissolved inorganic phosphate in a particle-free system to particulate organic phosphate upon bubbling. The actual binding sites of phosphate to organic matter remains unresolved, but a charge dependence was shown with negative surfactants decreasing phosphate enrichment on aerosol particles (MacIntyre and

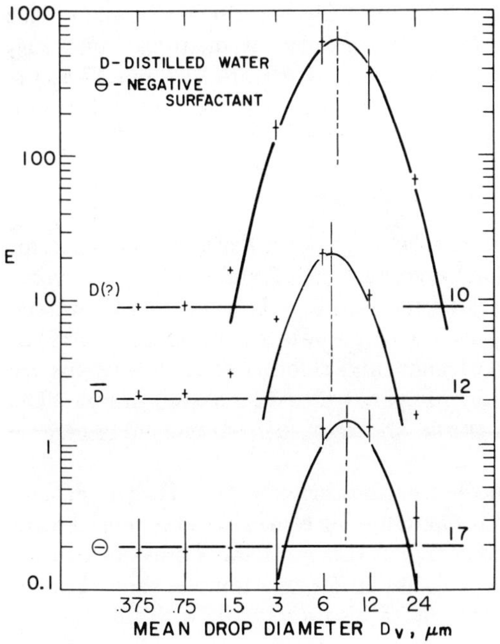

Fig. 20. Phosphate enrichment from bubbled "distilled" water with radio-tracer Na^+ and PO_4^{3-} added. Enrichment apparently occurs only because phosphate is carried by a positively charged surfactant, and is depressed by the addition of a negative surfactant (MacIntyre and Winchester, 1969).

Winchester, 1969), as shown in Fig. 20. Despite much hypothesizing, the size dependence of the phosphate enrichment curves of this figure remains a mystery. The parabolic hump is Gaussian in Cartesian coordinates and appears to represent a mechanical process separate from the one that gives rise to the horizontal component of the curve, as it is not always present. The small volume of the sample in this region and a certain correlation with film-drop production suggest that the hump might be film material and the background jet drops.

Phosphate enrichment does not proceed in the absence of surfactant carriers, but it is very difficult to purify water sufficiently to remove all possible carriers. The "distilled water" mentioned in Fig. 20 was distilled from alkaline permanganate, followed by an immediate redistillation from 50% phosphoric acid in a closed system under clean N_2, and yet the difference between runs 10 and 12 was simply the gradual removal of some trace phosphate-carrying organic material. The only time that no enrichment was observed (MacIntyre, 1965) was when a flocculent precipitate ("stainless-steel hydroxide"), inadvertently generated *in situ* in the reaction vessel, adsorbed the organic material present without changing the phosphate concentration.

The mechanism whereby small "nucleation particles" grow during bubbling remains unknown, but it may be related to the intrinsic solubility of the organic material. Soluble surfactants collected by a rising bubble and compressed by the surface flows as the bubble breaks (MacIntyre, 1972) may form a very transitory clump that can be easily dispersed and redissolved, while the same material folded onto a preexisting small particle also collected by the bubble might be sufficiently stabilized by the contact to remain particulate.

This process is closely related to the formation of acid-resisting carbonate particles on bubbling CO_2-free gas through seawater. As dissolved CO_2 is purged, carbonate must precipitate to maintain equilibrium, and the water sometimes becomes clouded with small particles. Centrifuged, these are dirty grey, insoluble in HCl for several days, char slightly on heating, and are soluble in HCl after further heating. This behavior is consistent with an adherent organic coating on carbonate particles, suggesting that the particles nucleate at the bubble surface and are "wrapped" as the bubble breaks. Chave (1965) has observed similar protective organic coatings on carbonates in surface seawater.

K. Pollution of the Microlayer

As might have been anticipated, the microlayer shows a distinct preference for pollutants when it can get them. Seba and Corcoran (1969) found chlorinated hydrocarbon pesticides enriched some 250-fold in slicks on inshore Florida Atlantic waters. Duce et al. (1972) have reported samples from inshore waters (Narragansett Bay) in which Pb, Fe, Ni, Cu, fatty acids, hydrocarbons, and chlorinated hydrocarbons are enriched 1.5- to 50-fold in the top 150 μm compared to a 20-cm deep sample. The metals appear in biogenic particulate material and in a chloroform-soluble organic phase instead of as inorganic ions.

Piotrowicz et al. (1972) extended these observations into the New York Bight and the open ocean between Nova Scotia and Iceland, finding somewhat lower enrichment far from shore, confirming the land-based source of this material. Visible slicks were not present when these samples were collected, but 70% of the samples showed pollutant enrichment. Manganese and aluminum were also analyzed, with Al showing moderate enrichments up to 7.5 (again in the organic phase, exclusing aluminosilicate dusts). Manganese is not enriched in the microlayer.

Szekielda et al. (1972) collected gram quantities of surface slicks from convergences in Delaware Bay and found 10,000-fold enrichment of Cr, Cu, Fe, Hg, Pb, and Zn in the chloroform-extracted fraction of the slick.

Duce et al. (1972) pointed out that the metals and the pollutant organics are undoubtedly present in a monomolecular layer, and that enrichments calculated on this basis are nearly 10^5 higher than those calculated on the basis of a 150-μm thick, screen-collected sample. This high enrichment is biologically significant, since organisms consume only the organic material.

No estimate is yet available for the efficiency with which the microlayer retains airborne pollutants that fall on it, but it is not unreasonable to suppose that a large proportion of such things as DDT and Pb are retained at the surface and never go through a period of gross dilution in seawater before reaching the biosphere. Some such direct route seems necessary to explain the prompt appearance of DDT in

Antarctic crabeater seals (Sladen et al., 1966), and the pathway appears to have been: crop dust → codistillation with water → aeolian transport → oceanic fallout → reconcentration in microlayer → assimilation by neuston → biological amplification up the food chain → accumulation in body fat of Wilson's petrel in the North Atlantic → migration of petrel to antarctic → dissemination of DDT → reconcentration by scavenging crustacean → crabeater seal. Unlikely as this seems, no other route has been proposed to account for the rapid transport and the repeated reconcentrations after apparent dilution.

8. Exotic Phenomena

Any subject as complicated and elusive as sea-air chemical fractionation is bound to generate attempts to explain it, and some of these will seem exotic and controversial, if not downright bizarre, to other workers. Some explanations display no little ingenuity and imagination on the part of their creators, and they are all entertaining, thought provoking, and perhaps contain varying degrees of truth. We will look briefly at some of these.

A. Fractional Crystallization

Dessens (1946) captured 1- to 10-μm airborne particles on 0.01-μm spider web and held them at various relative humidities below 78% (the vapor pressure of saturated sea salt). The droplets were metastable for varying periods, depending on the degree of supersaturation, but would eventually nucleate. Nucleation, in Dessens' words,

> . . . resembles a minuscule explosion: as soon as the crystals form, the solution becomes just saturated; its vapor pressure then exceeds that of the water in the surrounding air, and vaporization is instantaneous. If crystals have formed, their complete separation is facilitated by this abrupt vaporization.
>
> The best crystals retained by the filament are pure sodium chloride and not sea salt: the abrupt transition from supersaturated drop to crystal explains the natural separation of the various dissolved salts in the ocean.

He continued, to describe the production of 0.3- to 0.5-μm condensation nuclei (measured at 60% relative humidity) in quantities of some 100/cm^3 by this mechanism. The idea was further explored by Sugawara et al. (1948) and Koyama and Sugawara (1952), who credit Matsui (1944) with earlier work. Sugawara et al. speculated that crystallization in a supersaturated droplet would follow the classical course of precipitation in evaporating seawater, with the less-soluble compounds such as $CaCO_3$, $CaSO_4$, and $MgCO_3$ appearing first. Twomey and McMaster (1955) observed the production of many nuclei on slowly drying (<70% RH) and rehumidifying (90% RH) air containing salt particles, lending indirect support to the fractional crystallization theory. However, not all investigators have hit upon experimental conditions that produce this result, for Twomey (1954), Lodge and Baer (1954), Junge (1963), and Blanchard (1963) failed to find such an effect. Junge felt that the remaining hygroscopic salts such as $MgSO_4$ would preserve a tenacious film of liquid around the crystal whose surface tension should prevent any particulate separation.

Electron-microscope photographs by Frank et al. (1972) suggest that while some separation may occur on drying, it is very incomplete. Their pictures show NaCl particles surrounded by spattered drops of sulfuric acid, but the NaCl crystals themselves are often entangled among long needles of ammonium bisulfate and ammonium sulfate, testifying to the gradual neutralization of sulfuric acid by ammonia. Samples collected in the Santa Barbara Channel were, numerically, 40% sulfuric acid, 20% other sulfates, 7% chloride, 2.5% phosphate, and about 25% featureless and unidentifiable tiny particles. No mention was made of carbonates, but the observed distribution seems quite at variance with that expected from the above discussion.

Dessens' initial observation of "explosive" nucleation has apparently been ignored. No one seems to have repeated it, or, which is more curious, has anyone even mentioned it. The possibility of periodically releasing a pulse of heat of crystallization during humidification cycles in the atmosphere has implications for particle chemistry that extend well beyond the realm of sea-air chemical fractionation.

B. "Evaporation" of Ions from Aqueous Solution

A number of Russian papers discuss a phenomenon called "mechanical evaporation" (Zubov, 1938), and further explained as "physicochemical co-entrainment of the molecules [of dissolved salt] with the water vapor" (Bruyevich and Korzh, 1969). I have not been able to obtain copies of other relevant papers (Nemeryuk, 1964, 1966, 1968, 1969).

It is obviously impossible to evaluate properly work known only at second hand. Nevertheless, the assurance with which oceanographic fractionation data are explained in terms of "mechanical evaporation" makes some attempt at assessment necessary. The only possible test one can apply would seem to be that of self-consistency, and even this raises serious doubts. The laboratory data are discussed as though the underlying processes were thermodynamic, and treated as though they belonged in the established tradition of unequivocal high-precision electrolyte chemistry. However, data that are presented without comment (Bruyevich and Korzh, 1969) as replicate experimental values for ratios of "evaporated" ions include: Na/Cl = 0.56 and 1.46; Mg/Cl = 0.20 and 0.40—which does little to establish confidence.

Levitskiy (1950) has proposed that the hydration energy enters strongly into the fractionation of mechanically "evaporated" ions, but it is not made clear whether a high energy aids or opposes "evaporation."

One might expect this effect to appear whenever water is distilled. Certainly it is difficult to produce ion-free water, but the essential precautions are concerned with the prevention of mechanical entrainment of macroscopic drops, the elimination of a continuous liquid film along the walls of the apparatus, the use of condensers and receivers that do not leak ions into the product, and the chemical trapping of volatile compounds. There has been little reason to suspect the *gaseous* movement of 0.5 mg of ions/liter of distillate, and the theoretical expectations of Table II make the energetics extraordinarily unfavorable.

Korzh (1971) has carried this concept further. On the kinetic assumption that ions should "evaporate" in proportion to their surface concentration ratios instead of their bulk ratios, he computed "surface concentrations" of surface-inactive ions as the $\frac{2}{3}$ power of the volume concentration C. Mechanistically, this is equivalent to requiring that the depth from which ion j evaporates be proportional to $C_i^{-1/3}$, which is a most peculiar restraint and one seemingly very difficult to justify.

Korzh equates an "expected fractionation" α to the surface concentration:

$$\alpha = \frac{(X/\mathrm{Cl})_{\mathrm{surface}}}{(X/\mathrm{Cl})_{\mathrm{volume}}} = \frac{(X/\mathrm{Cl})_{\mathrm{vol}}^{2/3}}{(X/\mathrm{Cl})_{\mathrm{vol}}} = \left\{\frac{(\mathrm{Cl})}{(X)}\right\}_{\mathrm{vol}}^{1/3}$$

His data for oceanic rains (and for rains plus condensed water vapor) appear in

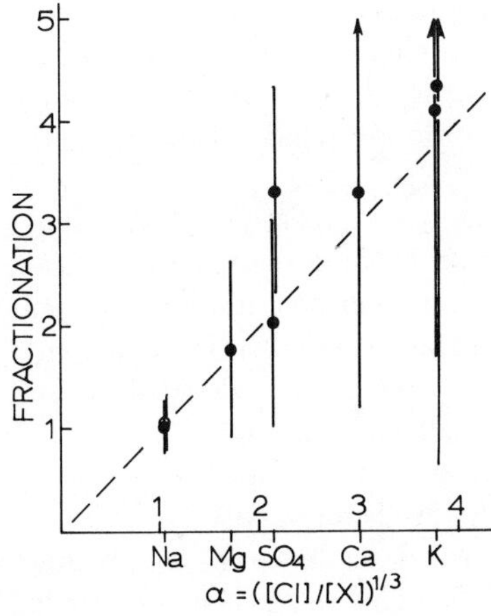

Fig. 21. Observed fractionation in rain and condensed water vapor from the Pacific and Indian Oceans, plotted against the "surface concentration" discussed in the text. Error bars are ± 1 standard deviation, computed from Tables 2 and 3 of Korzh (1971).

Fig. 21, in which the error bars are $\pm 1\sigma$ based in each case on seven to nine samples. The agreement between his hypothesis and the sample means is better than one might expect, but the standard deviations are large enough to render the agreement statistically fortuitous.

Fortunately, both ionic "evaporation" and the $C^{2/3}$ fractionation hypothesis are easily checked in the laboratory.

C. Film-Centrifuge Data

The report of Koske and Martin (1972) contains not so much an exotic mechanism as exotic data: inexplicably high fractionation from what seems a very straightforward experiment. They allowed a solution to overflow the edge of a centrifuge rotor at 2400 g (an acceleration too small to cause ionic sedimentation), skimming off a 1-μm-thick layer at 0.5 μl/sec for analysis by gamma-ray spectroscopy. The fractionations obtained are compared with those expected in Table XI.

TABLE XI

Film-centrifuge fractionation from Koske and Martin (1972). The sample is a nominal 1-μm-thick surface layer, and the "expected" fractionation computed from Onsager and Samaras' (1934) equation for surface concentration

	Concentration (Each Ion)	Fractionation Expected	Fractionation Found
F(Cs)	0.005	1.0000	1.013
F(Ba)	0.005	0.9995	1.07
F_{Cs}(Ba)	0.0005	0.9995	1.06
F_{Cs}(Sr)	0.25	—	1.032

The "expected" fractionations are computed on the basis of Debye-Hückel theory from the equation of Onsager and Samaras (1934), which distinguishes ions principally on the basis of valence. As expected from our earlier discussion, the computed fractionation over a 1-μm cut is small and rejects the doubly charged ion from the surface.

The observed fractionations range up to 7%, 140 times the expected value, and are in the opposite sense, favoring the doubly charged ions. If these results are verified, electrolyte theory is in for some revisions. The authors' only suggestion is equivalent to noting that Gibbs' law says nothing at all about surface concentrations, but only about activities, a subject on which we have very little data indeed. This is fair, and yet one would like to see impeccable technique that resolves all doubts.

Unfortunately, the report of the experiment leaves several questions unanswered. Surface tensions were measured, and the inorganic salts used were heated to 500°C to oxidize organic surfactants, and these are essential precautions. Nevertheless, it must be remembered that surface concentrations 100 times smaller than those detectable by surface tension changes (detectable by surface potentiometry) can lead to fractionation. There was apparently no replication of the runs, and therefore no indication of the significance of the difference between the various salts.

The implications of these results are fascinating, and further work is sorely needed!

D. Humidity

Bloch and Luecke (1968) observed that Gibbs' equation for surface excess is applicable only at equilibrium, and in particular, only at 100% relative humidity. Citing the Eötvös equation (the rate of change of molar surface energy with temperature is constant and independent of composition) and experimental results as justification for ignoring temperature effects, they worked with bubbles made by boiling, and controlled the relative humidity by heating or cooling the vapor phase. They obtained F(K) values ranging from 1.6 to 4.1, and reported similar results with the ion pairs Na–NH_3, Mg–Ca, SO_4–Cl, and Cl–NO_3. In each case the ion with the least surface desorption seems to have been enriched, strongly suggesting that Gibbsian adsorption is at work.

Earlier work by Bloch et al. (1966) gave similar F(K) values (1.6 to 4.7), and they also reported Br–Cl, Mg–Pb, and Ca–Na fractionation.

Figure 22 shows the striking dependence of F(K) on humidity, replotted from about 100 experiments of Bloch and Luecke (1972). The material collected in these experiments came from film drops, and in seeking a way around the difficult point that Gibbsian adsorption cannot appreciably affect the composition of a 1-μm-thick film, the authors suggest that "an internal circulation stream is induced that multiplies the differentially ion-depleted layer, bringing increasingly larger amounts of this differentially depleted or enriched solution to the apex of the bubble. In this way the thickness of the layer affected by differential adsorption can become quite considerable." Such a model is difficult to envisage. Certainly surface tension gradients in soap films can induce unpredictable swirling motions at several centimeters per second, but here both sides of the film cap move together. In the present case, the "internal circulation" apparently requires a counterflow within the film thickness, as it is difficult to imagine any motion up one side of the cap and down the other that would result in increased enrichment at the top. The diffusion path from apex to bulk solution is far too great for tangential diffusion to be important.

The simplest model that I have been able to construct seems inordinately complex

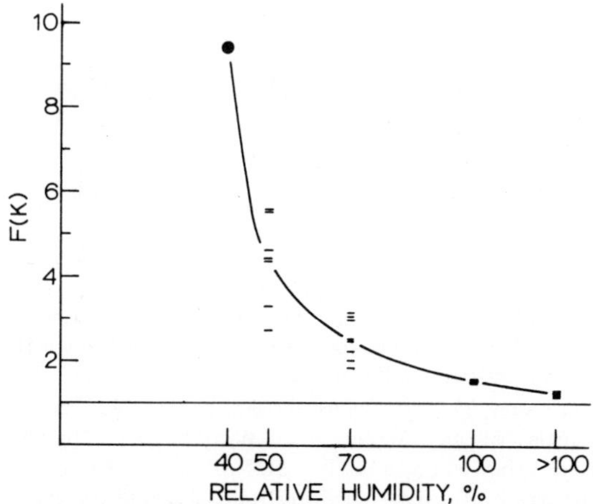

Fig. 22. Potassium fractionation from film caps of vapor bubbles as a function of relative humidity in the gas phase, after Bloch and Luecke (1972). Some of the spread in values may arise from differences in composition of the feed, which ranged from tap water to Dead Sea water at 37‰ salinity, but the agreement of all runs at 100% humidity suggests that most of the scatter arises from the difficulty of controlling humidity in a dynamic situation. Nearly 100 experiments are summarized here, but the extreme value at 40% R.H. is from a single measurement.

and eminently attackable. But if a model is to invite simplifications and improvements, perhaps it should be vulnerable. Because I get nowhere with a model in which the film cap configuration is static, it seems useful to consider the processes that occur while the film cap is being formed, although our knowledge of this is limited. I know of no hydrodynamic studies of the events lying between the moment when a large bubble is just tangent to the surface—or better, first raises a "blister" of solution above itself—and the moment when it is a nearly hemispherical film cap resting on a more-or-less plane surface. This can hardly take longer than 100 msec, but it appears that this is the only period available in which fractionation might develop.

During the thinning of the "blister" the two surfaces of the incipient film cap form a wedge, as shown in Fig. 23. If no surfactants are present, the surfaces of the wedge are free-slip surfaces (ignoring tangential viscous stress from the gas phase) and move with the velocity of the liquid adjacent to them. (If surfactants are present, surface viscosity will retard the surface flow, but the qualitative details should remain much the same.) There is a continuous removal of surface material tangential to the surface combined with an increasing surface area. This combination requires dilational flow of subsurface liquid into the surface. The velocity field must look something like the left half of Fig. 23 (in which, however, the converging flow required by the decreasing thickness obscures the fact that the surface overtakes the interior, thus incorporating subsurface liquid into itself).

The consequence of such a flow regime is that the film cap is entirely composed of material that was at the original point of tangency. The motion of this material is that of deforming a cylinder into a curved plate. We now ask, "What effect can nonequilibrium have on ion distribution during such a motion?"

Where there is nonequilibrium there is heat flow and an associated Soret redistribution of ions across the film thickness. There is also a mass flow of water through the

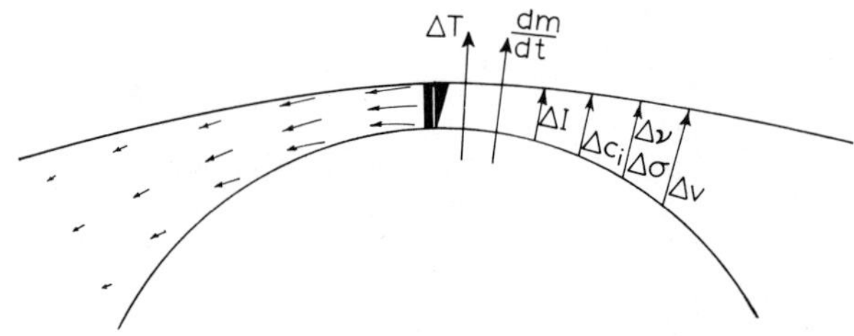

Fig. 23. "Blister" stage, between submerged bubble and completed film cap, in nonequilibrium. On the left is a possible velocity vector field; on the right, known thermal gradient ΔT and mass flux dm/dt, and putative radial gradients of ionic strength ΔI, concentrations of particular ions Δc_i, viscosity $\Delta \nu$, and surface tension $\Delta \sigma$. The last two gradients may lead to a gradient in tangential velocity Δv across the film thickness. In black at the center of the blister is the material that will ultimately make up the entire film cap: on the left, a cylinder, on the right, a frustrum of a cone resulting from the velocity gradient. In the presence of Δc_i of the right sign, this conical shape might produce appreciable chemical fractionation in the film drops.

film, directed inward for supersaturation and outward for undersaturation, so that the solution is more concentrated on one side of the film than on the other. Thus there is opportunity for differential ionic diffusivity to become manifest—but again, only across the film. Gradients of temperature, concentration, and composition will cause a gradient of viscosity across the film and a difference of surface tension on its two sides. Then, and this is the point of the exercise, there is the possibility of a gradient in the tangential velocity of material flowing out of the film, so that the "cylinder" mentioned above is deformed into the frustrum of a cone. In essence, the film drops are no longer made up of uniform circles cut out of the film with a cookie cutter, but contain a perhaps appreciable excess of one side of the film, which, if all gradients have conspired to work together, might be enriched in potassium.

This model contains more than its share of imagination. Before putting much effort into pursuing a theoretical Lorelei to comb out such a tangle of second-order effects, one would like more data such as Fig. 22, and a better understanding of the hydrodynamics of film-cap formation.

This model leaves fractionation at thermal equilibrium somewhat in limbo. Perhaps differential ionic diffusion near the surface in dilational flow needs more attention. Luecke and Nielson (1972) have found sulfur isotope fractionation in sprayed SO_4^{2-} solutions, which also suggests that differential diffusion is important.

Before we close this interesting and somewhat frustrating section, one possibly relevant report should be mentioned. This is Hoover and Berkshire's (1969) study of CO_2 transfer across the interface, in which they remark in passing, "condensation on the surface of the water could effectively stop gaseous exchange." We have already mentioned the importance of humidity in the problem of boric acid codistillation.

Whatever is going on in the sea-surface microlayer, it appears to be strongly affected by water vapor in the air immediately above the interface, which is seldom at equilibrium over the ocean, even in a microscopic layer (Craig and Gordon, 1965). Humidity is a variable that has seldom been measured or controlled in fractionation experiments, but it is evidently one to which meticulous attention must be paid in the future.

E. The Bubble Microtome

We have stressed throughout that any mechanism that produces drops of liquid with a composition measurably different from bulk seawater must slice a sample from very near the surface. Evidence is accumulating that jet drops are made by just such a process (MacIntyre, 1968, 1972; Iribarne and Mason, 1967) and that the breaking bubble is a very effective surface microtome.

Briefly, the process is seen as a sharply localized pressure gradient arising from rapid changes in surface curvature as the bubble breaks. The gradient is greatest at the surface and at the inner edge of the toroidal bead around the opening bubble cavity, which forms a travelling impulse converging on the axis. The acceleration caused by this pressure gradient is tangential to the bubble surface and for small bubbles rises to $10^6\,g$. Material on the bubble surface is accelerated inward and constitutes the entire volume of the top jet drop.

Figure 24 is an attempt to relate the average depth of microtome cut to bubble diameter. We start from Blanchard's (1963) data for jet drop diameter versus bubble diameter, and extrapolate his curve toward smaller diameters (although there is some doubt about whether a 10-μm bubble disappears by rupture or by solution!). Next we assume that jet drops dry to NaCl particles, shrinking to almost exactly 1/4 of their original diameter. Finally—and this is the uncertain step—we take MacIntyre's (1972) estimate that top jet drops come from a slice of the bubble interior that is 0.05% of the bubble diameter, and assume that this relationship (which has some

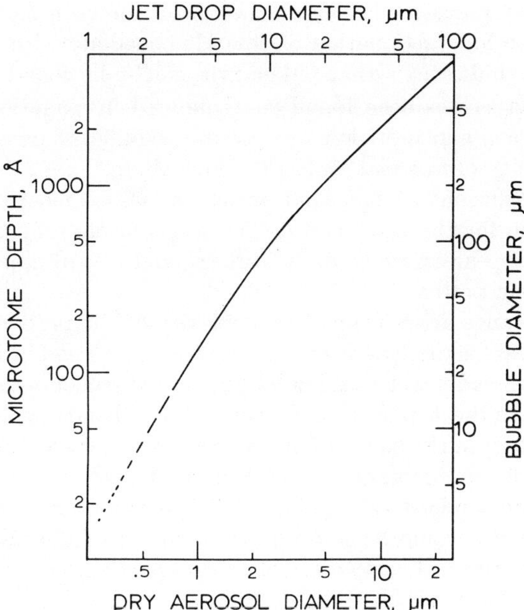

Fig. 24. Microtome-cut depth on jet drops. The curve and axes at top and right are taken from the data of Blanchard (1963), extrapolated where dashed. The bottom axis is the particle size for relative humidity $<78\%$. The left-hand axis assumes the validity of MacIntyre's (1972) estimate that the top jet drop is composed of material from the interior bubble surface to a depth of 0.05% of the bubble diameter, and that this relationship holds for all sizes.

experimental support for 2-mm bubbles) holds for all sizes. This leads to the relationship between wet and dry aerosol diameters and microtome depth of Fig. 24.

It is unreasonable to believe that the depth of cut should be much less than shown in Fig. 24, but it is probably not as much as an order of magnitude thicker. On electrical grounds, Iribarne and Mason (1967) estimated a surface cut of 0.17% for *all* jet drops from bubbles 80 to 200 μm in diameter. Two to four jet drops normally escape from such bubbles, bringing their estimate into excellent agreement with Fig. 24.

It is a curious reversal of intuitive expectations that jet drops should cut the sea surface as finely as film drops, but even a 1-μm film (which seems thin for an ocean bubble) is two 5000-Å layers back to back. The only way in which film drops can rival jet drops as microtomes is by peculiarities in the flow pattern during breakup of the film. The overall composition of film drops must be that of the original film, so only if "bulk" solution flows out of the interior of incipient small drops into incipient large drops can appreciable inorganic fractionation occur on the small drops.

F. Summary

Some forms of fractionation during ejection from sea to air are firmly established. Among these are phosphate bound to organic material (which is not geochemically significant), and organic iodine, which is a dominant source of atmospheric iodine. Cation fractionation is less well established; if it is real, it occurs most markedly on small drops, and we cannot yet distinguish between organic transport and inorganic Gibbsian adsorption sampled by a thin slice from the bubble microtome. The geochemical importance of cation fractionation is questionable. Evaporation and codistillation from the sea surface occur with iodine and with boric acid, but again, the importance of these processes has been questioned for both elements. There is no compelling evidence for fractionation of chloride or sulfate with respect to sodium, although there are indications that either type might be found in the laboratory. The surface microlayer has been found contaminated by pollution products (heavy metals, hydrocarbons, and pesticides) in possibly significant quantities, considering the direct availability of this material to the food chain.

This crop of conclusions is somewhat anticlimactic, for most of these have been assumed to be true for the last decade. The mechanisms proposed to account for fractionation still appear exotic to most workers, and it is disappointing that we do not understand them better.

Part of our ignorance arises from the complexity of the problem. There has been encouraging progress in the last few years toward better definition and control of experiments, but it is sadly true that few laboratory experiments have been performed that are repeatable to the degree one expects of "real" chemistry. Even those that are more or less consistent in the hands of one man seem to behave differently for others.

The remainder of our ignorance stems from a limited knowledge of correlative events. We have some understanding of geochemical conditions in one or two selected locations, but little that could be called a sure understanding of which is the marine and which is the continental component of aerosol particles.

References

Agar, J. N., 1959. Thermal diffusion and related effects in solutions of electrolytes. In *The Structure of Electrolyte Solutions.* W. J. Hamer, ed. Wiley, New York, pp. 200–223.

Allen, R. S., G. E. Charles, and S. G. Mason, 1961. The approach of gas bubbles to a gas/liquid interface. *J. Coll. Sci.*, **16**, 150–165.

Alty, T., 1924. The cataphoresis of gas bubbles in water. *Roy. Soc. London Proc.*, **106**, 315–340.

Anonymous, 1825. Saline impregnation of rain. *Edinburgh J. Sci.*, **2**, 176.

Anonymous, 1829. Impurity of rain water. *Am. J. Sci. and Arts*, **14**, 185.

Baier, R. E., 1972. Organic films on natural waters: Their retrieval, identification, and modes of elimination. *J. Geophys. Res.*, **77**, 5062–5075.

Barber, R. T., 1966. Interaction of bubbles and bacteria in the formation of organic aggregates in seawater. *Nature*, **211**, 257–258.

Barker, D. R. and H. Zeitlin, 1972. Metal-ion concentrations in sea-surface microlayer and size-separated atmospheric aerosol samples in Hawaii. *J. Geophys. Res.* **77**, 5076–5086.

Batoosingh, E., G. A. Riley, and B. Keshwar, 1969. An analysis of experimental methods for producing particulate organic matter in seawater by bubbling. *Deep-Sea Res.*, **16**, 213–219.

Baylor, E. R. and W. H. Sutcliffe, 1963. Dissolved organic matter in seawater as a source of particulate food. *Limnol. Oceanog.*, **8**, 369–371.

Baylor, E. R., W. H. Sutcliffe, and D. S. Hirschfeld, 1962. Adsorption of phosphate onto bubbles. *Deep-Sea Res.*, **9**, 120–124.

Bell, G. M. and P. D. Rangecroft, 1971. Theory of surface tension for a 2-1 electrolyte solution. *Faraday Soc. Trans.*, **67**, 649–659.

Blanchard, D. C., 1963. Electrification of the atmosphere by particles from bubbles in the sea. *Prog. Oceanog.*, **1**, 73–202.

Blanchard, D. C. and L. D. Syzdek, 1970. Mechanism for the water-to-air transfer and concentration of bacteria. *Science*, **170**, 626–628.

Blanchard, D. C. and L. D. Syzdek, 1972. Concentration of bacteria in jet drops from bursting bubbles. *J. Geophys. Res.*, **77**, 5087–5099.

Bloch, M. R., D. Kaplan, V. Kertes, and J. Schnerb, 1966. Ion separation in bursting air bubbles: An explanation for the irregular ion ratios in atmospheric precipitations. *Nature*, **209**, 802–803.

Bloch, M. R. and W. Luecke, 1968. Uneinheitliche Verschiebungen der Ionenverhältnisse zwischen Meereswasser und Niederschlägen durch Gischtbildung. *Naturwiss.*, **55**, 441.

Bloch, M. R. and W. Luecke, 1972. Geochemistry of ocean water bubble spray. *J. Geophys. Res.*, **77**, 5100–5105.

Bruyevich, S. V. and V. D. Korzh, 1969. Salt exchange between the ocean and the atmosphere. *Oceanology* (Ak. nauk USSR, Doklady), **9**, 465–475.

Cauer, H., 1939. *Schwankungen der Jodmenge der Luft in Mitteleuropa*. Verlag Chemie, Berlin.

Cauer, H., 1941. Studien über den Chemismus der Nebelkerne in Ober Schreibau. *Der Balneologie*, **8**, 345–353.

Cauer, H., 1942. Das Magnesiumchlorid der Nebelkerne. *Der Balneologie* **9**, 301–309.

Cauer, H., 1949. Ergebnisse chemisch-meteorologischer Forschung. *Archiv für Meteor. Geophys. Bioklim. Wien*, Ser. B, **1**, 221–256.

Cauer, H., 1951. Some problems of atmospheric chemistry. In *Compendium of Meteorology*, Am. Met. Soc., Boston, pp. 1126–1136.

Chave, K. E., 1965. Carbonates: Association with organic matter in surface seawater. *Science*, **148**, 1723–1724.

Cheeseman, D. H., 1956. The snail's foot as a Langmuir trough. *Nature*, **178**, 987–988.

Churayev, N. V., V. D. Sobolev, and Z. M. Zorin, 1970. Viscosity of liquids in capillaries. *Faraday Soc. Spec. Disc.*, **1**, 213–220.

Clunie, J. S., J. F. Goodman, and J. R. Tate, 1968. Adsorption of inorganic ions in black foam films. *Faraday Soc. Trans.*, **64**, 1336–1348.

Coster, H. G. L. and R. Simons, 1970. Anomalous dielectric dispersions in bimolecular lipid membranes. *Biochim. Biophys. Acta*, **203**, 17–27.

Craig, H. and L. I. Gordon, 1965. Deuterium and Oxygen-18 variations in the ocean and the marine atmosphere. In *Stable Isotopes in Oceanographic Studies and Paleotemperatures*, Consiglio Nazionale delle Ricerche, Pisa, pp. 9–130.

Christiansen, C., 1913, 1916, 1919. Elektrizitätserregung biem Zerspritzen von Flüssigkeiten (Balloelektrizität). *Ann. Physik*, Ser. 4, **40**, 107–137, 233–248; **51**, 530–548; **59**, 95–100, 280–292.

Currie, B. W. and T. Alty, 1929. Absorption at a water surface. *Roy. Soc. London Proc.*, **122**, 622–633.

Davies, J. T. and E. K. Rideal, 1961. *Interfacial Phenomena.* Academic Press, New York, pp. 6, 316.

Dean, G. A., 1963. The iodine content of some New Zealand drinking waters with a note on the contribution from sea spray to the iodine in rain. *New Zea. J. Sci.*, **6**, 208–214.

Degens, E. T., 1970. Molecular nature of nitrogenous compounds in seawater and recent marine sediments. In *Symposium on Organic Matter in Natural Waters.* D. W. Hood, ed. Inst. Mar. Sci. (U. Alaska) Occ. Pub. #1.

Delaney, A. C., A. C. Delaney, D. W. Parkin, J. J. Griffin, E. D. Goldberg, and B. E. F. Reimann, 1967. Airborne dust collected at Barbados. *Geochim. Cosmochim. Acta*, **31**, 885–909.

Derjaguin, B. V. and Yu. Yalamov, 1965. Theory of thermophoresis of large aerosol particles. *J. Coll. Sci.*, **20**, 555–570.

Dessens, H., 1946. Les noyaux de condensation de l'atmosphere. *Acad. Sci. Paris C.R.*, **223**, 915–917.

Drost-Hansen, W., 1965. Aqueous interfaces—Methods of study and structural properties, Part 2. *Ind. Eng. Chem.*, **57** (4), 18–37.

Drost-Hansen, W., 1972. Molecular aspects of aqueous interfacial structures. *J. Geophys. Res.*, **77**, 5132–5146.

Drude, P., 1900. *The Theory of Optics*, Dover, New York, p. 295. Reprint of the C. R. Mann and R. A. Millikan translation of the Leipzig edition.

Duce, R. A., J. G. Quinn, C. E. Olney, S. T. Piotrowicz, B. J. Ray, and T. L. Wake, 1972. Enrichment of heavy metals and organic compounds in the surface microlayer of Narragansett Bay, Rhode Island. *Science*, **176**, 161–163.

Duce, R. A., J. T. Wasson, J. W. Winchester, and F. Burns, 1963. Atmospheric iodine, bromine, and chlorine. *J. Geophys. Res.*, **68**, 3943–3947.

Duce, R. A., J. W. Winchester, and T. W. Van Nahl, 1965. Iodine, bromine, and chlorine in the Hawaiian marine atmosphere. *J. Geophys. Res.*, **70**, 1775–1799.

Duce, R. A. and A. H. Woodcock, 1971. Difference in chemical composition of atmospheric sea salt particles produced in the surf zone and on the open sea in Hawaii. *Tellus*, **23**, 427–435.

Duursma, E. K., 1960. Dissolved organic carbon, nitrogen, and phosphorus in the sea. *Neth. J. Sea Res.*, **1**, 1–148.

Eaton, S. V. and J. H. Eaton, 1926. Sulphur in rain water. *Plant Physiology*, **1**, 77–87.

Egnér, H. and E. Eriksson, 1955. Current data on the chemical composition of air and precipitation. *Tellus*, **7**, 135–139 et seq.

Eriksson, E., 1959, 1960. The yearly circulation of chloride and sulfur in nature: meteorological, geochemical, and pedological implications. *Tellus*, **11**, 375–403; **12**, 63–109.

Frank, E. R., J. P. Lodge, Jr., and A. Goetz, 1972. Experimental sea salt profiles. *J. Geophys. Res.*, **77**, 5147–5151.

Frumkin, A. and A. Obrucheva, 1931. Zusammenhang zwischend en balloelektrischen Erscheinungen und der Potenzialdifferenz an der Trenningsfläche Gas/Losung. *Kolloid Z.*, **54**, 2–7.

Gambell, A. W. J., 1962. Indirect evidence of the importance of water-soluble continentally derived aerosol. *Tellus*, **14**, 91–94.

Garrett, W. D., 1964. The organic chemical composition of the ocean surface. U.S. Naval. Res. Lab. Rep. 6201, 12 pp.

Garrett, W. D., 1965. Collection of slick-forming materials from the sea surface. *Limnol Oceanog.* **10**, 602–605.

Garrett, W. D., 1967. Stabilization of air bubbles at the air/sea interface by surface-active material. *Deep-Sea Res.*, **14**, 661–672.

Gast, J. A. and T. G. Thompson, 1959. Evaporation of boric acid from seawater. *Tellus*, **11**, 344–347.

Gerhard, E. R. and H. F. Johnstone, 1955. Physicochemical oxidation of sulfur dioxide in air. *Ind. Eng. Chem.*, **47**, 972–976.

Gittens, G. J., 1969. Variations of surface tension of water with temperature. *J. Coll. Interf. Sci.*, **30**, 406–412.

Goldacre, R. J., 1949. Surface films on natural bodies of water. *J. Animal Ecology*, **18**, 36–39.

Gonzales, G. and F. MacRitchie, 1970. Equilibrium adsorption of proteins. *J. Coll. Interf. Sci.*, **32**, 55–61.

Gozlan, R. S., 1968. Isolation of iodine-producing bacteria from aquaria. *Antonie van Leeuenhoek*, **34**, 226.

Gray, G., 1911. Dissolved matter contained in rain water collected at Lincoln, N.Z. *Chem. Soc. London J.*, **100**, 327–328.

Gurney, R. W., 1953. *Ionic Processes in Solution*, Dover, New York, 1962 reprint of McGraw-Hill, New York.

Harkins, W. D. and E. C. Gilbert, 1926. The structure of films of water on salt solutions. II. The surface tension of calcium chloride solutions at 25°. *Am. Chem. Soc. J.*, **48**, 604–607.

Harkins, W. D. and H. M. McLaughlin, 1925. The structure of films of water on salt solutions. I. Surface tension and adsorption for aqueous solutions of sodium chloride. *Am. Chem. Soc. J.*, **47**, 2083–2089.

Harvey, G. W., 1966. Microlayer collection from the sea surface: A new method and initial results. *Limnol. Oceanog.*, **11**, 608–613.

Harvey, G. W. and L. A. Burzell, 1972. A simple microlayer method for small samples. *Limnol Oceanog.*, **17**, **156–157.**

Havinga, E., 1952. Properties and reactions of molecules at interfaces II. *Rec. Trav. Chim. Pais-Bas*, **71**, 72–79.

Henniker, J. C., 1949. The depth of the surface zone of a liquid. *Rev. Mod. Phys.*, **21**, 322–341.

Heymann, J. A., 1927. Het Jodiumgehalte van duin-en regenwater. *Nederland Tijdschr. Geneeskunde*, **71**, 640–646.

Hill, T. L., 1952. Statistical thermodynamics of the transition region between two phases. II. One-component system with a plane interface. *J. Chem. Phys.*, **20**, 141–144.

Hoffman, G. L. and R. A. Duce, 1972. Consideration of the chemical fractionation of alkali and alkaline earth metals in the Hawaiian marine atmosphere. *J. Geophys. Res.* **77**, 5161–5169.

Hoover, T. E. and D. C. Berkshire, 1969. Effects of hydration on carbon-dioxide exchange across an air-water interface. *J. Geophys. Res.*, **74**, 456–465.

Hill, R. H., 1970. Laboratory measurements of heat transfer, wind-velocity profiles, and temperature structure at an air-water interface. U.S. Naval Res. Lab. Rep. 7212, 31 pp.

Iribarne, J. V. and B. J. Mason, 1967. Electrification accompanying the bursting of bubbles in water and dilute aqueous solutions. *Faraday Soc. Trans.*, **63**, 2234–2245.

Jarvis, N. L., 1967. Adsorption of surface-active material at the sea-air interface. *Limnol. Oceanog.*, **12**, 213–221.

Jarvis, N. L., W. D. Garrett, M. A. Scheimann, and C. O. Timmons, 1967. Surface-chemical characterization of surface-active material in seawater. *Limnol. Oceanog.*, **12**, 88–96.

Jones, M. N., K. J. Mysels, and P. C. Scholten, 1966. Stability and properties of the second black film. *Faraday Soc. Trans.*, **62**, 1336–1348.

Junge, C. E., 1956. Recent investigations in air chemistry. *Tellus*, **8**, 127–139.

Junge, C. E., 1957. Chemical analysis of aerosol particles and of gas traces on the island of Hawaii. *Tellus*, **9**, 528–537.

Junge, C. E., 1960. Sulfur in the atmosphere. *J. Geophys. Res.*, **65**, 227–237.

Junge, C. E., 1963. *Air Chemistry and Radioactivity*. Academic Press, New York.

Junge, C. E., 1972. Our knowledge of the physico-chemistry of aerosols in the undisturbed marine environment. *J. Geophys. Res.*, **77**, 5183–5200.

Junge, C. E. and T. Ryan, 1957. The oxidation of sulfur dioxide in dilute solutions. *Roy. Met. Soc. Quart. J.*, **84**, 46–55.

Junge, C. E. and R. T. Werby, 1958. The concentration of chloride, sodium, potassium, calcium, and sulfate. *J. Meteor.*, **15**, 417–425.

Kinosita, K. and H. Yokota, 1965. Temperature dependence of the optical surface thickness of water. *Phys. Soc. Japan J.*, **20**, 1086.

Köhler, H. and M. Båth, 1953. Quantitative chemical analysis of condensation nuclei from seawater. *Nova Acta Reg. Soc. Sci. Upsaliensis*, Ser. 4, **15**, 1–24.

Komabayasi, M., 1962. Enrichment of inorganic ions with increasing atomic weight in aerosol, rainwater, and snow in comparison with seawater. *Met. Soc. Japan J.*, **40**, 25–38.

Komabayasi, M., 1964. Primary fractionation of chemical components in the formation of submicron spray drops from seasalt solution. *Met. Soc. Japan J.*, **42**, 309–316.

Kohn, H. W., 1968. Bubbles, drops, and entrainment in molten salts, ORNL-TM-2373, 19 pp.

Korzh, V. D., 1971. Computation of the ratios of the chemical components of seawater that migrate from the ocean to the atmosphere during evaporation. *Oceanology* (Ak. nauk USSR, Doklady), **11**, 727–733.

Koske, P. H. and H. Marin, 1972. Ion fractionation at the surface of aqueous inorganic salt solutions by means of a "film centrifuge." *J. Geophys. Res.*, **77**, 5201–5203.

Koyama, T. and K. Sugawara, 1953. Separation of the components of atmospheric salt and their distribution (cont'd). *Chem. Soc. Japan Bull.*, **26**, 123–126.

Knox, W. J., Jr., and T. O. Parshall, 1970. The interaction of sodium dodecyl sulfate with gelatin. *J. Coll. Interf. Sci.*, **33**, 16–23.

Laevastu, T., 1963. Energy exchange in the North Pacific; its relation to weather and its oceanographic consequences. Hawaii Inst. Geophys., University of Hawaii, Rept. #30, 11 pp.

Lamb, H., 1932. *Hydrodynamics*, 6th ed., Sec. 338. Dover, New York.

Langway, C. C., Jr., 1967. Stratigraphic analysis of a deep ice core from Greenland, USA CRREL Res. Rept. #77.

Lawes, J. B., J. H. Gilbert, and R. Warrington, 1881. On the amount and composition of the rain and drainagle waters collected at Rothamstead. *Roy. Agric. Soc. Engl. J.*, **17**, 241–279, 311–350.

Lazrus, A. L., H. W. Baynton, and J. P. Lodge, Jr., 1970. Trace constituents in oceanic cloud water and their origin. *Tellus*, **22**, 106–113.

Levich, V. G., 1962. *Physicochemical Hydrodynamics*. Prentice-Hall, Englewood Cliffs, N.J., p. 59.

Levitskiy, M. V., 1950. Investigation of the physico-chemical factors of electrolyte transport with water vapor (on the hydration theory of electrolyte transport). Tr. Sev.-Kavkzsk. gorno-metallurg. inst., Gos. Izd. Sev.-Osetinsk, ASSR, Dzaudzhikau.

Lewis, G. N. and M. Randall, 1923. *Thermodynamics*. McGraw-Hill, New York.

Lewis, G. N., M. Randall, K. S. Pitzer, and L. Brewer, 1961. *Thermodynamics*, 2nd ed., McGraw-Hill, New York.

Lipp, H., 1921. Uber die chemische Zusammensetzung des Nebelfrotses auf der Zugspitze. Jahresbericht des Sonnenblickveriens 1931, p. 32, Wien.

Lodge, J. P., Jr., and F. Baer, 1955. An experimental investigation of the shatter of salt particles on crystallization. *J. Met.*, **11**, 420–421.

Longworth, L. G., 1959. The concentration and temperature dependence of the Soret coefficient of some aqueous electrolytes. In *The Structure of Electrolyte Solutions*. W. H. Hamer, ed. Wiley, New York, pp. 183–199.

Ludwig, C., 1856. Diffusion zwischen ungleich erwärmten Orten gleich Zusammengesetzten Lösungen. *Wien. Akad. Ber.*, **20**, 539.

Luecke, W. and H. Nielsen, 1972. Isotopen fractionierung des Schwefels in Blasensprüh. *Fortschr. Mineral.*, **50** (3), 36–38.

Lyklema, J., P. C. Scholten, and K. J. Mysels, 1965. Flow in thin liquid films. *J. Phys. Chem.*, **69**, 116–123.

MacIntyre, F., 1965. Ion fractionation in drops from breaking bubbles. Thesis, Mass. Inst. Tech., 272 pp.

MacIntyre, F., 1968. Bubbles: A boundary-layer "microtome" for micron-thick samples of a liquid surface. *J. Phys. Chem.*, **72**, 589–592.

MacIntyre, F., 1970. Geochemical fractionation during mass transfer from sea to air by breaking bubbles. *Tellus*, **22**, 451–462.

MacIntyre, F., 1971. Enhancement of gas transfer by interfacial ripples. *Phys. Fluids*, **14**, 1596–1604.

MacIntyre, F., 1972. Flow patterns in breaking bubbles. *J. Geophys. Res.*, **77**, 5211–5228.

MacIntyre, F. and J. W. Winchester, 1969. Phosphate ion enrichment in drops from breaking bubbles. *J. Phys. Chem.*, **73**, 2163–2169.

MacRitchie, F., 1963. Collapse of protein monolayers. *J. Coll. Interf. Sci.*, **18**, 555–561.

MacRitchie, F. and A. E. Alexander, 1963. Kinetics of adsorption of proteins at interfaces. *J. Coll. Interf. Sci.*, **18**, 453–457, 458–463.

McAlister, E. D., 1964. Infrared-optical techniques applied to oceanography. *Appl. Optics*, **3** 609–612.

McAlister, E. D. and W. McLeish, 1969. Heat transfer in the top millimeter of the ocean. *J. Geophys. Res.*, **74**, 3408–3414.

McAlister, E. D. and W. McLeish, 1970. A radiometric system for airborne measurement of the total heat flow from the sea. *Appl. Optics*, **9**, 2697–2705.

McAlister, E. D., W. McLeish, and E. A. Corduan, 1971. Airborne measurements of the total heat flux from the sea during Bomex. *J. Geophys. Res.*, **76**, 4172–4180.

Matsui, H., 1944, 1948. Chemical studies of condensation and sublimation nuclei. *Metor. Soc. Japan J.*, **22**, 2–72; **26**, 169–171.

Medrow, R. A. and B. T. Chao, 1971. Charges on jet drops produced by bursting bubbles. *J. Coll. Interf. Sci.*, **35**, 683–687.

Menzel, D. W., 1966. Bubbling of seawater and the production of organic particles: a re-evaluation. *Deep-Sea Res.*, **13**, 963–966.

Menzel, D. W. and J. H. Ryther, 1964. The composition of particulate organic matter in the Western North Atlantic. *Limnol. Oceanog.*, **9**, 179–186.

Miller, N. H. J., 1913. Composition of rain-water collected in the Hebrides and in Iceland. *Scottish Meteor. Soc. J. Ser.*, **3**, **16**, 141–158.

Miyake, Y. and S. Tsunogai, 1965. Chemical composition of oceanic rain. *Proc. Internat. Conf. Cloud Physics, Tokyo and Sapporo*, 73–78.

Miyake, Y. and S. Tsunogai, 1963. Evaporation of iodine from the ocean. *J. Geophys. Res.*, **68**, 3989–3994.

Morita, R. Y. and S. D. Burton, 1970. Occurrence, possible significance, and metabolism of obligate psychrophiles in marine waters. In *Symposium on Organic Matter in Natural Waters*, D. W. Hood, ed. Inst. Mar. Sci., University of Alaska, Occ. Pub. #1, pp. 275–285.

Moyers, J. L. and R. A. Duce, 1972. Gaseous and particulate iodine in the marine atmosphere. *J. Geophys. Res.*, **77**, 5229–5238.

Murumutsu, M. and H. Sobotka, 1963. Studies of modified protein. *J. Coll. Interf. Sci.*, **18**, 625–646.

Nemeryuk, G. Ye., 1964. On the study of the aerochemistry of the main hydrochemical ions. *Tr. Sev.-Osetinsk. sel.-khoz. inst.*, **22**

Nemeryuk, G. Ye., 1966. The migration of salts from soils into the atmosphere. *Pochvovedeniye*, **1**.

Nemeryuk, G. Ye., 1968. Migration of salts into the atmosphere on evaporation from soil and from plants. Thesis, Ordzhonikidze.

Nemeryuk, G. Ye., 1969. Role of evaporation during salt migration into the atmosphere. *Gidrokhimicheskiye Materialy*, **50**.

Nishimura, M. and K. Tanaka, 1972. Seawater may not be a source of boron in the atmosphere. *J. Geophys. Res.*, **77**, 5239–5242.

Nishizawa, S., M. Fukuda, and N. Inoue, 1954. Photographic study of suspended matter and plankton in the sea. *Fish. Fac. Hokkaido U. Bull.*, **5**, 36–40.

O'Brien, E. E., 1967. On the flux of heat through laminar wavy liquid layers. *J. Fl. Mech.*, **28**, 295–303.

Oddie, B. C. V., 1959. The composition of precipitation at Lerwick, Scotland. *Roy. Met. Soc. Quart. J.*, **85**, 163–165.

Onsager, L. and N. N. T. Samaras, 1934. The surface tension of Debye-Hückel electrolytes. *J. Chem. Phys.*, **2**, 528–536.

Parsons, T. R. and J. D. H. Strickland, 1962. Oceanic detritus. *Science*, **136**, 313–314.

Piotrowicz, S. T., B. J. Ray, G. L. Hoffman, and R. A. Duce, 1972. Trace metal enrichment in sea-surface microlayer. *J. Geophys. Res.*, **77**, 5243–5254.

Riley, G. A., 1963. Organic aggregates in seawater and the dynamics of their formation and utilization. *Limnol. Oceanog.*, **8**, 372–381.

Riley, B. A., P. J. Wangersky, and D. Van Hemert, 1964. Organic aggregates in tropical and subtropical surface waters of the North Atlantic Ocean. *Limnol. Oceanog.*, **9**, 546–550.

Robbins, R. C., R. D. Cadle, and D. L. Eckhardt, 1959. The conversion of sodium chloride to hydrochloric acid in the atmosphere. *J. Met.*, **16**, 53–56.

Rossby, C.-G., 1959. Current problems in meteorology. In *The Atmosphere and Sea in Motion.* B. Bolin, ed. Rockefeller Inst. Press, New York, p. 44.

Rossby, C.-G. and H. Egner, 1955. Chemical climate and its variation with the atmospheric circulation pattern. *Tellus*, **7**, 118–133.

Schlichting, H. E., Jr., 1961. Viable species of algae and protozoa in the atmosphere. *Lloydia*, **24**, 81–88.

Seba, D. B. and E. F. Corcoran, 1969. Surface slicks as concentrators of pesticides in the marine environment. *Pestic. Monit. J.*, **3**, 190–193.

Seto, F. Y. B., 1970. The ratio of iodine to chlorine on sea-salt particles from bursting bubbles compared to that ratio in seawater. Thesis, University of Hawaii, 163 pp.

Seto, F. Y. B. and R. A. Duce, 1972. A laboratory study of iodine enrichment on atmospheric sea-salt particles produced by bubbles. *J. Geophys. Res.*, **77**, 5339–5349.

Seto, F. Y. B., R. A. Duce, and A. H. Woodcock, 1969. Sodium-to-chlorine ratio in Hawaiian rains as a function of distance inland and of elevation. *J. Geophys. Res.*, **74**, 1101–1103.

Sieburth, J. McN., 1963. Abundance of bacteria in oceanic surface films. Am. Soc. Microbiol., 63rd Ann. Meeting, Cleveland, Abstract A8.

Sieburth, J. McN., 1965. Bacteriological samplers for air-water and water-sediment interfaces. Trans. Joint Conf. Ocean Sci. Eng. MTS-ASLO, Washington, D.C., pp. 1064–1068.

Sieburth, J. McN. 1971. Distribution and activity of oceanic bacteria. *Deep-Sea Res.*, **18**, 1111–1121.

Sladen, W. J. L., C. M. Menzie, and W. L. Reichel, 1966. DDT residues in Adelie penguins and a crabeater seal from Antarctica: ecological implications. *Nature*, **210**, 670–673.

Soret, C., 1881. Sur l'état d'équilibre que prend en point de vue de sa concentration saline primitivement homogène dont deux parties sont portées à des températures differentes. *Ann. Chim. Phys.*, **22**, 293–297.

Spangenberg, W. G. and W. R. Rowland, 1961. Convective circulation in water induced by evaporative cooling. *Phys. Fluids*, **4**, 743–750.

Stillinger, F. H., Jr., and A. Ben-Naim, 1967. Liquid-vapor interface potential for water. *J. Chem. Phys.*, **47**, 4431–4437.

Stevenson, R. E. and A. Collier, 1962. Preliminary observations on the occurrence of airborne marine phytoplankton. *Lloydia*, **25**, 89–93.

Sugawara, K., 1959. Syn-bubble-bursting fractionation of sea salt. Preprints First International Oceanographic Congress, New York. AAAS, New York.

Sugawara, K., S. Oana, and T. Koyama, 1949. Separation of the components of atmospheric salt and their distribution. *Chem. Soc. Japan Bull.*, **22**, 47–52.

Sugiura, Y., 1965. Effect of organic matter on composition of sea salt in seawater bubbles. *Proc. Internat. Conf. Cloud Phys., Tokyo and Sapporo*, 47–51.

Sutcliffe, W. H., E. R. Baylor, and D. W. Menzel, 1963. Sea-surface chemistry and Langmuir calculation. *Deep-Sea Res.*, **10**, 233–243.

Sutcliffe, W. H., R. W. Sheldon, A. Prakesh, and D. C. Gordon, 1971; Relation between wind speed, Langmuir circulation, and particle concentration in the ocean. *Deep-Sea Res.*, **18**, 639–643.

Szekielda, K.-H., S. L. Kupferman, V. Klemas, and D. F. Polis, 1972. Element enrichment in organic films and foam associated with aquatic frontal systems. *J. Geophys. Res.*, **77**, 5278–5282.

Takahashi, T., 1972. Electrical charge of cloud droplets and drizzle drops. *J. Geophys. Res.*, **77**, 3869–3878.

Tsunogai, S. and T. Sase, 1969. Formation of iodine-iodine in the ocean. *Deep-Sea Res.*, **16**, 489–496.

Twomey, S., 1954. The composition of hygroscopic particles in the atmosphere. *J. Met.*, **11**, 334–338.

Twomey, S., 1969. The oceanic production of cloud nuclei. *J. Rech. Atmos.*, **4**, 179–181.

Twomey, S. and K. N. McMaster, 1955. The production of condensation nuclei by crystallizing salt particles. *Tellus*, **7**, 458–461.

Valach, R., 1967. The origin of the gaseous form of natural atmospheric chlorine. *Tellus*, **19**, 509–516.

Vityn, I., 1911. Amounts of chlorine and sulphuric acids in rainwater. *Chem. Soc., London J.*, **100**, 432.

Wald, A., 1940. The fitting of straight lines if both variables are subject to error. *Ann. Math. Stat.*, **11**, 284–300.

Whybrew, W. E., G. D. Kinzer, and R. Gunn, 1952. Electrification of small air bubbles in water. *J. Geophys. Res.*, **57**, 459–471.

Wilkniss, P. E. and D. J. Bressan, 1972. Fractionation of the elements F, Cl, Na, and K at the sea-air interface. *J. Geophys. Res.*, **77**, 5307–5315.

Williams, P. M., 1967. Sea-surface chemistry: organic carbon and organic and inorganic nitrogen and phosphorus in surface films and subsurface waters. *Deep-Sea Res.*, **14**, 791–800.

Witting, J., 1972. Effect of plane progressive waves on thermal boundary layers in air-water interfaces. *J. Fl. Mech.*, in press.

Yokota, H., 1966. Temperature dependence of the optical surface thickness of α-methylnaphthalene and carbon tetrachloride. *Phys. Soc. Japan J.*, **21**, 200.

Zobell, C. E. and H. M. Mathews, 1936. A qualitative study of the bacterial flora of the sea and land breezes. *Nat. Acad. Sci. U.S. Proc.*, **22**, 567–572.

Zubov, N. N., 1938. Morskiye vody i l'dy (Seawater and ice). Moscow, Gidrometeoizdat.

III. THE SEDIMENTARY CYCLE

9. CYCLING OF CARBON, SULFUR, AND OXYGEN THROUGH GEOLOGIC TIME

ROBERT M. GARRELS AND EDWARD A. PERRY, JR.

The importance of Lars Gunnar Sillén's 1961 article on the equilibrium model for the oceans is particularly appreciated by the first author of this article. I spent a day with him shortly after it was published, and because of the article and that conversation, the whole direction of my research was changed toward the development and testing of his concepts: "Chemical Mass Balance Between Rivers and Oceans" (Mackenzie and Garrels, 1966) was the first result of the Sillén influence; eventually a book resulted on *Evolution of Sedimentary Rocks* (Garrels and Mackenzie, 1971), in which the steady-state ocean model led us toward a nearly equivalent model of a steady-state sedimentary rock mass and focussed our attention on the total cycles of the elements from land to sea and back to land again.

1. Introduction

Here steady-state models for the geologic cycling of the major elements are developed; then an overall model illustrating the interconnections among their reservoirs is presented, and, finally, the evolution of atmosphere as a product of transfer of materials between reservoirs is discussed. Particular emphasis is placed on the cycling and interrelations among carbon, oxygen, and sulfur. Finally, an hypothesis for the origin of atmospheric oxygen and its subsequent maintenance at levels suitable for the existence of a complex of organisms through eras of geologic time is presented.

2. Steady-State Models for the Major Elements

A convenient first step in developing a realistic scheme for the cycling of the major elements is to construct a model for the sedimentary cycles in which the material fluxes and reservoir masses are treated as constants through time. We emphasize, just as Sillén did for his model, that this construction is merely a first step in interpreting reality, and chiefly gives a feel for the sizes of the material reservoirs and the rates of transfer and interconnections between them.

For this purpose the present reservoirs are assessed and the fluxes between them are based on average values for the last 600 million years estimated by Garrels and Mackenzie (1972). The total average annual flux of material from land to sea is taken to be 61×10^{14} g/yr, and the total sedimentary rock mass, $25{,}000 \times 10^{20}$ g. This rock mass includes metamorphic rock of sedimentary composition. The stream fluxes used to develop the individual chemical cycles are given in Table I. Concern is mainly with the dissolved fluxes, because they reflect material gained and lost from the solids.

TABLE I

Geologic Stream Fluxes[a]
(Units of 10^{14} mol/yr)

Element	Dissolved Load[b]	Suspended Load
Na	0.0365	0.0156
K	0.0184	0.0148
Mg	0.0550	0.0116
Ca	0.1260	0.0152
Si	0.0900	0.3985
Al	—	0.1114
Fe	—	0.0357
S	0.0189	0.0015
Cl	0.0270	—
$C_{inorganic}$	0.3729[c]	0.0166
$C_{organic}$	—	0.0583

Source: Garrels and Mackenzie (1972).

[a] For purposes of modeling, it is necessary to assign significant figures to the fluxes (and reservoirs) that suggest an accuracy of the actual values that is fictitious. Like free energy values used in mineral stability calculations, even though the values may be erroneous, they must be internally consistent.

[b] Corrected for atmospheric cycling.

[c] Includes C from atmospheric CO_2 used in rock weathering.

Because an overall steady-state system requires that all components of the system also are in a steady state, it is convenient to develop the overall system by subdividing it into seven individual subcycles. As shown in Table II, these are the subcycles of organic matter, of calcium minerals, of magnesium minerals, of pyrite (reduced sulfur), of the ferrous iron component of silicates, and of the sodium and potassium components of silicates. Residence times have been calculated according to the relation: total moles of element or compound in a reservoir/annual moles imput flux = residence time.

A given element may be associated with several subcycles; it is important to note that the residence time for such an element, as listed in the subcycles of Table II, is its residence time only for its participation in that subcycle, and can be thought of as its residence time if the given subcycle were the only one in operation. For example, the atmospheric residence time of the carbon associated with CO_2 in the cycling of organic matter is given as 0.022 million years, whereas the integrated residence time of CO_2 in the atmosphere, when all cycles are considered, is 0.0019 million years.

Integrated, or total residence times, are given in Table III. Comparison of the residence times of elements for subcycles with the total residence time is a quick way of assessing the influence of the subcycle on the overall behavior of the element.

A. Organic Carbon Cycle

The average organic carbon content of sediments is about 0.5% C by weight and corresponds to a sedimentary reservoir mass of (5×10^{-3}) $(25{,}000 \times 10^{20}$ g) =

Table II
Reservoir Sizes and Residence Times for Individual Subcycles

	Reservoir (Units of 10^{20} mol)	Residence Time (Units of 10^6 yr)
Organic subcycle		
Ocean	0.033 HCO_3^-	1.3
Atmosphere	0.00054 CO_2	0.022
	0.38 O_2	15
Biosphere	0.0042 CH_2O	0.17
Sedimentary rocks	10.42 CH_2O	417
Calcium subcycle		
Ocean	0.15 Ca^{2+}	1.2
	0.42 SO_4^{2-}	55
	0.033 HCO_3^-	0.14
	0.0014 SiO_2	0.17
Atmosphere	0.00054 CO_2	0.0043
Sedimentary rocks	1.98 $CaSO_4$	261
	42.11 $CaCO_3$	356
Magnesium subcycle		
Ocean	0.82 Mg^{2+}	15
	0.033 HCO_3^-	0.30
	0.0014 SiO_2	0.025
Atmosphere	0.00054 CO_2	0.0049
Sedimentary rocks	16.69 $MgSiO_3$	304
	8.73 $MgCO_3$	198a
Pyrite subcycle		
Ocean	0.42 SO_4^{2-}	38
	0.033 HCO_3^-	1.6
Atmosphere	0.00054 CO_2	0.026
	0.38 O_2	18
Biosphere	0.0042 CH_2O	0.20
Sedimentary rocks	1.47 FeS_2	263
$FeSiO_3$ subcycle		
Ocean	0.0014 SiO_2	0.046
	0.033 HCO_3^-	4.3
Atmosphere	0.00054 CO_2	0.070
	0.38 O_2	49
Biosphere	0.0042 CH_2O	0.55
	10.42 CH_2O	1353
Sodium subcycle		
Ocean	7.06 Na^+	193
	8.24 Cl^-	305
	0.0014 SiO_2	0.29
	0.033 HCO_3^-	3.5
Atmosphere	0.00054 CO_2	0.057
Sedimentary rocks	5.90 NaCl	219
	4.55 Na_2SiO_3	479
Potassium subcycle		
Ocean	0.15 K^+	8.2
	0.033 HCO_3^-	1.8
	0.0014 SiO_2	0.15
Atmosphere	0.00054 CO_2	0.029
Sedimentary rocks	6.49 K_2SiO_3	705

[a] Calculated from flux to ocean.

TABLE III

Reservoir Sizes and Residence Times of the Elements
(Units of 10^{20} mol and 10^{6} yr)

	Oceans		Sedimentary Rocks		Atmosphere			Biosphere	
Element	Reservoir	Residence Time[a]	Reservoir	Residence Time[c]	Element	Reservoir	Residence Time	Reservoir	Residence Time
Na	7.06	193	15.00	288	N	2.72	Not determined	$C_{organic}$ 0.0042	0.078
K	0.15	8.2	12.97	399	O_2	0.38	7	(Living and dead organisms)	
Mg	0.82	15	25.42	381	$C_{inorganic}$	0.00054	0.0019		
Ca	0.15	1.2	49.66	351					
Si	0.0014	0.016	220.03	450					
Al	—	—	56.58	504					
Fe	—	—	17.17	481					
S	0.42	22	4.91	242					
Cl	8.24	305	5.90	218					
$C_{inorganic}$	0.033	0.088[b]	50.84	381					
$C_{organic}$	—	—	10.42	417					

Source: Garrels and Mackenzie (1972).

[a] Corrected for atmospheric cycling.

[b] Includes C input from atmospheric CO_2 used in weathering.

[c] Includes input flux of both dissolved and suspended stream loads (Table I).

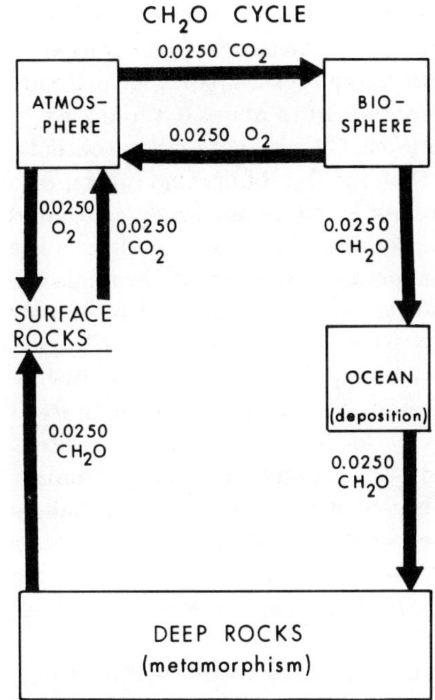

Fig. 1. Steady-state organic carbon subcycle. Material fluxes are in units of 10^{14} mol/yr for all of the steady-state diagrams.

125×10^{20} g or 10.42×10^{20} mol. This figure represents the organic carbon compounds preserved in sedimentary rocks and requires an annual depositional flux of $(61 \times 10^{14}$ g/yr$) \times (5 \times 10^{-3}) = 0.305 \times 10^{14}$ g/yr or 0.025×10^{14} mol/yr. In fact, the total organic carbon flux to the oceans is higher owing to its involvement and destruction in diagenetic reactions such as the formation of pyrite. The above flux represents only those organics preserved in sedimentary rocks.

The steady-state cycle is illustrated in Fig. 1. Four reservoirs are shown: the atmosphere, the biosphere, the ocean, and the rock reservoir called "Deep Rocks." Because there are fluxes caused by reactions after burial but before surface exposure to weathering, it is advisable to show the rock weathering site after the rocks have been buried, altered, and uplifted as a shallow box called "Surface Rocks." It is not considered a reservoir. The number of moles of carbon in each of the four reservoirs and their residence times are given in terms of the flux of organic material (Table II). As mentioned before, the residence time numbers are not the integrated turnover times of carbon in the reservoirs, but the residence times in terms of the cycling of organic material alone.

The problem of assigning those changes that take place as a result of interaction of bottom waters with deposited sediments to depositional effects or to diagenesis and metamorphism could not be entirely resolved. In general, the top few meters of sediment have been considered to be a part of the ocean reservoir, and any materials buried beyond that depth assigned to the Deep Rocks reservoir.

The flux relations can be followed by starting with the weathering of surface rocks. During weathering, fossil organic material (here represented as CH_2O) is "burned" by consuming atmospheric oxygen and releasing carbon dioxide, according to the equation: $CH_2O + O_2 = CO_2 + H_2O$. This reaction creates an O_2 deficiency and a CO_2 excess in the atmosphere, which are restored by photosynthesis: $CO_2 + H_2O =$

$CH_2O + O_2$. To keep the balance, the net CH_2O synthesized must pass into the oceans and be buried in sediments. Eventually it is returned to surface rocks and oxidized.

The average content of organic matter in sedimentary rocks, according to Ronov (1971) ranges from about 0.3 wt % in the late Precambian to about 0.8 to 0.9 wt % today. Even though these numbers may not represent the original carbon contents, because of postdepositional losses, they indicate that the flux of organic carbon into sediments probably has not been more than twice our steady-state value (calculated assuming 0.5 wt% organic C), nor less than half. Because this organic carbon is the residual from photosynthesis minus respiration and decay, it shows that the miniscule difference between these two large numbers has been closely maintained for a very long time. Photosynthesis today is estimated to fix 54×10^{14} mol C/yr (Deevey, 1970; Bolin, 1970), so the buried residual is only about $0.025 \times 10^{14}/54 \times 10^{14} =$ 0.05% of the total carbon fixed annually. Furthermore, the annual oxidation of fossil organic carbon exposed to weathering, even allowing for variation in carbon content with age, must be almost equal to the new carbon buried. Consequently, the true net of photosynthesis minus respiration and decay must be new carbon deposited minus old carbon oxidized. If so, the net is diminished to as little as 0.005×10^{14} mol/yr, or $0.005/54 = 0.01\%$ or so. It seems to us that this remarkably delicate balance is strong evidence for atmosphere-biosphere-ocean carbon exchange relations similar to those of today for much of the last 600 million years.

Many researchers (cf. Cloud and Gibor, 1970) have pointed to the burial of new organics in sediments as a continuous source of oxygen to the atmosphere, without considering the drain required by the weathering of old organics. There are 0.38×10^{20} mol of O_2 in the atmosphere. If the production of oxygen by burial of new organics represented net oxygen production, it would take 0.38×10^{20} mol/0.025×10^{14} mol/yr $= 15.4 \times 10^6$ yr to double the amount of atmospheric oxygen.

B. Calcium Mineral Cycle[1]

The annual dissolved calcium flux is estimated at 0.1260×10^{14} mol/yr, and has been divided into $CaSiO_3$ (to represent all Ca-bearing silicates), $CaSO_4$ (gypsum and anhydrite), and $CaCO_3$ (calcite, aragonite and the $CaCO_3$ component of magnesium calcites and dolomites), which become dissolved in streams and reprecipitated in the oceans (Fig. 2). The relative proportions of the various calcium species weathered have been estimated from the reconstruction of the sources of the dissolved constituents in streams by Garrels and Mackenzie (1971). During weathering, $CaSO_4$ simply dissolves to give Ca^{2+} and $SO_4{}^{2-}$ ions, whereas the weathering of both $CaCO_3$ and $CaSiO_3$ requires CO_2 to yield dissolved Ca^{2+}, $HCO_3{}^-$, and SiO_2. The demand on the atmosphere is 0.1266 mol CO_2/yr. The weathering of calcium minerals alone creates a CO_2 flux much greater than the CO_2 fluxes involved in the cycle of organic materials (Fig. 1).

Deposition of $CaCO_3$ in the oceans is the reverse of its weathering process, but calcium derived by the weathering of silicates is deposited as $CaCO_3$ with the silica released during weathering deposited as silica in the tests of organisms. Consequently, the weathering and deposition of calcium compounds causes a net CO_2 demand of 0.0082×10^{14} mol/yr. For the restoration of this CO_2, there must be a reconversion

[1] In the discussion of the calcium cycle, and in the following discussions that involve silicates of other elements, no attempt has been made to get an accurate balance of silica. All the silicates have been represented as metasilicates. On the other hand, uptake or release of silica is qualitatively in the same direction as for the real minerals.

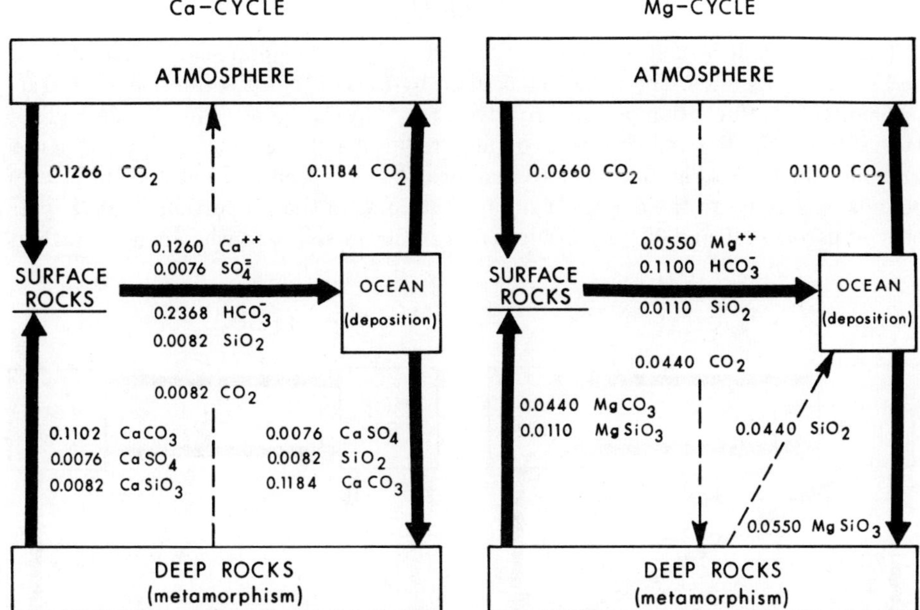

Fig. 2. Steady-state calcium and magnesium mineral subcycles. Dashed lines indicate fluxes resulting from postdepositional reactions.

of part of the deposited $CaCO_3$ to $CaSiO_3$ by metamorphism in the Deep Rocks reservoir. $CaSO_4$, except for its period of dissolution in waters of rivers and seas, travels as solid $CaSO_4$ through the cycle. In the steady-state model, $CaSO_4$ makes no demands on the atmosphere.

C. *Magnesium Mineral Cycle*

The total annual magnesium flux is about 0.07×10^{14} mol/yr, but as with calcium, only the dissolved stream flux of 0.055×10^{14} mol/yr is considered (Fig. 2). Approximately 80% of the dissolved magnesium flux is derived from the weathering of the $MgCO_3$ component of carbonate rocks, with the remaining portion coming from magnesium silicates ($MgSiO_3$), such as chlorite. However, essentially all of the magnesium delivered to the ocean must be removed by deposition as a silicate because newly deposited marine carbonates average only 6 mol% $MgCO_3$ or less (Chave, 1954). The mineralogy of initial deposition of magnesium as a silicate remains problematical. Authigenic Mg-bearing silicates such as montmorillonite, sepiolite, palygorskite, and various zeolites have been identified in recent oceanic sediments, but their importance in the total magnesium balance needed for a steady-state ocean composition cannot yet be assessed (cf. Drever, 1971).

The calcium and magnesium cycles are complementary. Calcium mineral deposition releases less CO_2 than is required for weathering while magnesium mineral deposition releases an excess of 0.0440×10^{14} mol/yr of CO_2. During metamorphism the situation is reversed, with calcium releasing CO_2 and magnesium taking up CO_2, as in the formation of dolomites. Some dolomites may represent a transfer of magnesium from shales to carbonate rocks (Garrels and Mackenzie, 1971).

D. *Pyrite Cycle*

The pyrite cycle is of special interest in that it shows the interrelation between CO_2 and sulfur compounds. The value of 0.55 used by Li (1972) for the fraction of total sulfur compounds (including oceanic dissolved SO_4^{2-}) existing as reduced sulfur (Table II) has been adopted and the most common reduced sulfur compound, pyrite, is used to depict the cycle (Fig. 3). It is also assumed that oxidized and reduced sulfur compounds contribute to the dissolved sulfur of streams in the proportions that they are present in rocks (40 and 60%). Both iron and sulfur are oxidized when pyrite weathers.

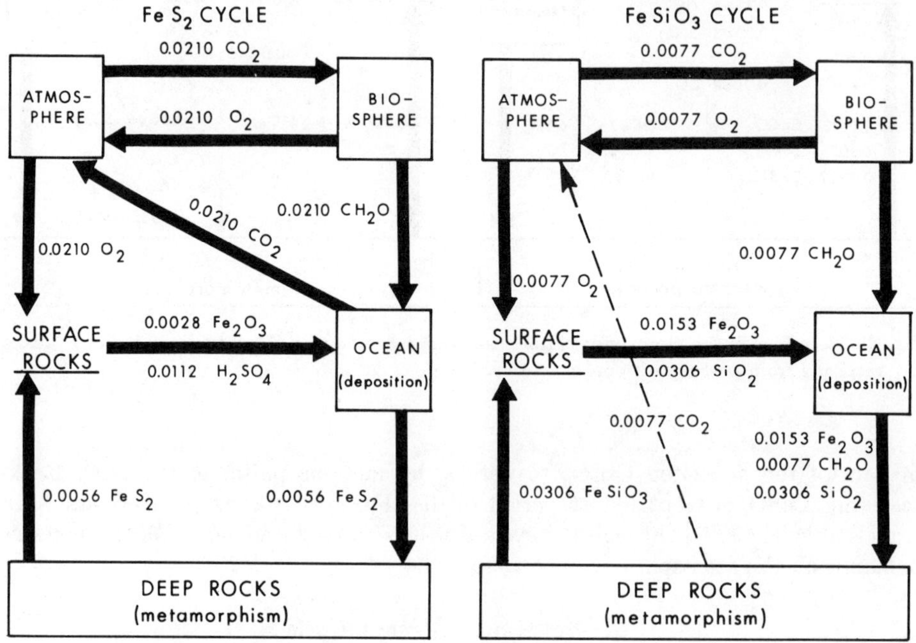

Fig. 3. Steady-state pyrite and ferrous silicate subcycles.

Much of the present SO_2 pollution of the atmosphere and continental waters results from man's utilization of fossil fuels that contain reduced sulfur. In Fig. 3 several intermediate steps involving SO_2 emission to the atmosphere, oxidation of SO_2 to sulfuric acid, and "rain out" of the acid to the earth's surface are omitted, and the pyrite is shown as being oxidized directly to sulfuric acid and ferric oxide, which are then delivered to the oceans.

Oxygen from the atmosphere is required for the weathering of sulfides. When the oxidized compounds are deposited in the sea, they combine with organic material derived from photosynthesis and are reduced back again to iron sulfide. CO_2 is released during the reduction, and through photosynthesis, can restore oxygen to the atmosphere.

This particular cycle is of special interest because we know from sulfur isotope studies of evaporite deposits (Thode and Monster, 1964; Holser and Kaplan, 1966) that the ratio of oxidized to reduced sulfur compounds has varied markedly with time. The implication is that the oxygen drain on the atmosphere, when reduced sulfur minerals are oxidized during weathering and then deposited in oxidized form, might also cause an increase in photosynthesis to return the atmospheric oxygen. This feedback mechanism involves transferring calcium from the carbonate to the sulfate reservoir and will be explored further in the following discussion on reservoir exchange.

E. $FeSiO_3$ Cycle

Figure 3 illustrates the iron silicate cycle. $FeSiO_3$ is used to represent a variety of common minerals containing reduced iron. Weathering of these minerals requires oxygen to form the ferric iron oxides and silicates abundant in soils. Their reduction again to complete the cycle takes place in euxinic environments and buried rocks. The reductant is organic matter, and the reaction releases CO_2. As in the sulfur cycle, there is an interplay between weathering and photosynthesis. The CO_2 released during iron reduction presumably stimulates photosynthesis to restore the atmospheric oxygen used in the initial weathering of the reduced iron silicates.

F. Sodium and Potassium Mineral Cycles

Halite simply dissolves to give Na^+ and Cl^- ions, but the weathering of sodium and potassium silicates involves a CO_2 drain on the atmosphere. In the steady-state system (Fig. 4), the same amount of halite, 0.270×10^{14} mol/yr, is again precipitated in evaporite basins and then travels through the cycle unchanged. The remaining sodium (0.0096×10^{14} mol/yr) and all of the potassium (0.184×10^{14} mol/yr) are deposited as silicates and release an amount of CO_2 equal to the amount consumed in the initial weathering.

As with magnesium silicate deposition, the actual mechanisms involved in the removal of sodium and potassium from the ocean have not been demonstrated to be of

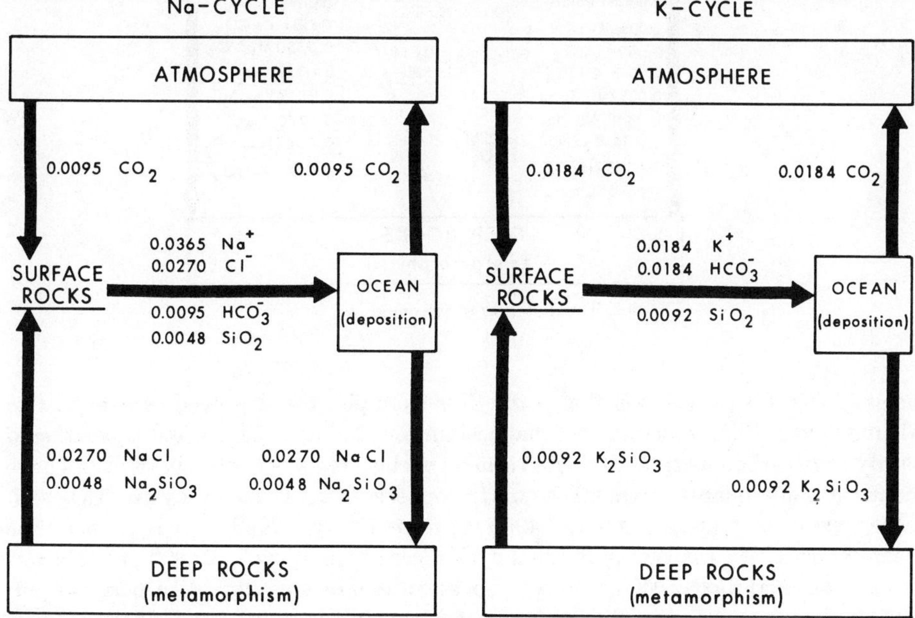

Fig. 4. Steady-state sodium and potassium mineral subcycles.

sufficient magnitude to account for a steady-state ocean composition. Authigenic zeolites precipitate a portion of the potassium and sodium, and clay mineral exchange sites can adsorb these ions to be later fixed in micaceous minerals during diagenesis (Perry and Hower, 1970) or form diagenetic feldspars (Kastner, 1971). Also, sodium may exchange for calcium in the alteration of submarine basalts.

G. The Total Cycle

Figure 5 summarizes all the preceding cycles and shows the net fluxes of O_2 and CO_2 into and out of the atmosphere. The major point illustrated is the large number of processes involved that have the same order of magnitude of importance. A comparison of the residence times of the total cycle (Table III) with those of individual

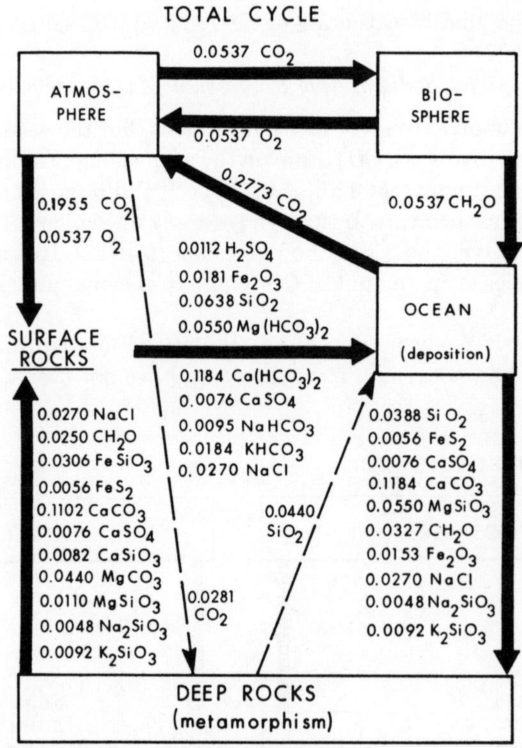

Fig. 5. Total steady-state cycle.

cycles (Table II) emphasizes this point. For example, the dissolved stream flux of calcium is more than twice that of magnesium, but because magnesium is weathered mainly from carbonates and deposited almost exclusively as silicates, both cycles have about the same quantitative effect on atmospheric CO_2, as shown by the CO_2 residence time in each cycle (4300 and 4900 yr, respectively). The longer residence time of atmospheric CO_2 in other individual cycles (e.g., $FeSiO_3$ cycle, 70,000 yr) indicates a smaller annual flux of CO_2 in these geochemical processes, but even here the differences average out to be only one order of magnitude less.

The flow net of the chemical reactions used to construct the preceding cycles is

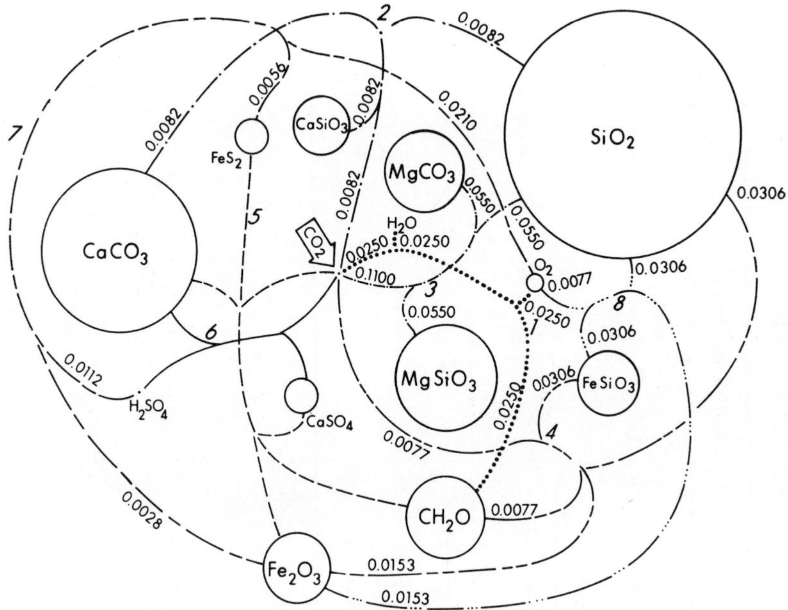

Fig. 6. Steady-state flow net. The circled numbers refer to reactions given in Table IV. Reactions 5 and 6 involve reservoir transfers so that steady-state fluxes are not given. Reservoir areas are proportional to the number of moles contained.

shown in Fig. 6. From the steady-state conditions for the subcycles, the fluxes along the flow lines are available. The area of the circle representing each reservoir is proportional to the number of moles in the reservoir.

The chemical cycles of almost any major crustal element involve CO_2, and this CO_2 may be coupled in reactions with sulfur and oxygen. The atmospheric reservoirs of O_2 and especially CO_2 are vanishingly small relative to the related masses in the sedimentary rock reservoirs. It is known that there have been variations in the individual fluxes through time (e.g., sulfur). It is, therefore, truly remarkable that the composition of the atmosphere and oceans has supported life for at least the past 600 million years. Given these considerations, the steady-state model appears to be a useful first approximation for illustrating the interconnections and integrated mean rates of transfer among the various reservoirs of the real system (Table IV).

3. Reservoir Exchange

A. Introduction

In the preceding section a steady-state model was constructed for the cycling of the major elements. From this model the complex interplay between material reservoirs is evident.

A steady-state model for all aspects of the sedimentary cycle is a gross oversimplification. What should be the next step in altering the model towards reality? There are four major conditions to be fulfilled if the model is to represent the last 600 million years.

First, the composition of the ocean must remain approximately constant. Biologists

Table IV

Partial List of Reactions Involved in Steady-State Net of Reservoirs and Fluxes

<table>
<tr><th rowspan="2">Reservoir Reactions</th><th colspan="4">Direction of Reaction</th></tr>
<tr><th>Weathering</th><th>Deposition</th><th>Short and Long Diagenesis</th><th>Metamorphism</th></tr>
<tr><td>A. CO_2 Involved</td><td></td><td></td><td></td><td></td></tr>
<tr><td>1. $CH_2O + O_2 = H_2O + CO_2$ [a]</td><td>→</td><td>←</td><td></td><td></td></tr>
<tr><td>2. $CaCO_3 + SiO_2 = CaSiO_3 + CO_2$</td><td colspan="2">←――――――――</td><td></td><td>→</td></tr>
<tr><td>3. $MgCO_3 + SiO_2 = MgSiO_3 + CO_2$</td><td colspan="2">――――――――→</td><td>←</td><td>?</td></tr>
<tr><td>4. $2\ Fe_2O_3 + 4\ SiO_2 + CH_2O = 4\ FeSiO_3 + H_2O + CO_2$</td><td colspan="2">←――――――――</td><td>→</td><td>→</td></tr>
<tr><td>5. $2\ Fe_2O_3 + 15\ CH_2O + 8\ CaSO_4 =$
$8\ CaCO_3 + 4\ FeS_2 + 7\ CO_2 + 15\ H_2O$</td><td colspan="2">←――――――――</td><td>→</td><td>→</td></tr>
<tr><td>6. $CaCO_3 + H_2SO_4 = CaSO_4 + H_2O + CO_2$</td><td colspan="2">――――――――→</td><td>←?</td><td>←?</td></tr>
<tr><td>B. Oxygen Involved, No CO_2</td><td></td><td></td><td></td><td></td></tr>
<tr><td>7. $4\ FeS_2 + 8\ H_2O + 15\ O_2 = 2\ Fe_2O_3 + 8\ H_2SO_4$</td><td>→</td><td></td><td></td><td></td></tr>
<tr><td>8. $4\ FeSiO_3 + O_2 = 2\ Fe_2O_3 + 4\ SiO_2$</td><td colspan="2">――――――――→</td><td>?</td><td></td></tr>
</table>

[a] Oxygen also involved.

insist that large excursions in the concentrations of dissolved species in the oceans are not consistent with the evolutionary record of organisms. Their general interpretation is that the times of flowering and extinction of marine species may indeed reflect compositional changes in the global seas, but that these alterations could have exceeded only trivially those established as being lethal for the organic assemblages of today. To document the permissible ranges of individual chemical species in the oceans in terms of the extinctions they would cause is not possible here, but it is doubtful if any of the near-infinite combinations of chemistry representing acceptable oceans would fail to be categorized as seawater by a geochemist classifying natural water types.

Second, it is unlikely that the mass of the oceans has changed more than a few percent in the last 600 million years. Although there is uncertainty about the possibility of major increase in oceanic mass over a time span of 3 or 4 billion years, there seem to be no proponents of significant growth during the past 600 million years (cf. Fanale, 1971). Consequently, the oceanic reservoir, if masses and compositions have changed little, can be regarded as in an approximate steady state.

Third, the restrictions on oceanic change can be extended to the atmosphere. The atmosphere, like the oceans, has continuously supported a variety of organisms, attesting to the lack of extreme ranges of O_2 and CO_2.

The steady-state flux of CO_2 is 5 times that of O_2, even though the O_2 reservoir is approximately 700 times as large as the CO_2 reservoir, so it is apparent that CO_2 is far more likely to depart from steady state than is O_2. The residence time of CO_2 in the atmosphere in terms of a steady-state cycle, is only 2000 yr, so that in 600 million years it would be turned over 300,000 times. Most land plants stop photosynthesizing at a CO_2 level about 1/3 that of the present atmosphere, so that the tolerable CO_2 minimum is uncomfortably close to the current level (Leopold, 1964). The upper limit is not well defined, although if about 0.1 atm were reached, there are a number of probable consequences that make this value a reasonable extreme. If CO_2 became an important atmospheric component (0.3 atm or more), the "greenhouse effect" of tropospheric heat storage might become so marked that earth surface temperatures would be impossibly high (Rasool and Schneider, 1971). A number of investigators (cf. Holland, 1968, 1972a, b), basing their arguments on oceanic compositions and mineral reactions, conclude that a CO_2 pressure 100 times as large as that today is a probable upper limit. This pressure is still only 0.3 atm.

In summary of the atmospheric gas relations, increases or decreases of the masses of O_2 or CO_2 in the atmosphere have been insignificant relative to the total flux of those gases through the atmosphere. As Rubey (1951) writes, following a detailed examination of the problem, "From several lines of evidence, it seems difficult to escape the conclusion that, for a large part of geologic time, carbon dioxide has been supplied to the atmosphere and ocean gradually and at about the same rate that it has been subtracted by sedimentation."

Fourth, despite the approximate constancy of ocean and atmosphere, there has been major interchange of material between some of the rock reservoirs. The exchanges involve amounts of both O_2 and CO_2 far in excess of these gases. Therefore the transfers must take place with essentially no net demands for CO_2 and O_2; the principle can be described as reservoir exchange without gas consumption.

The most striking evidence for reservoir exchange comes from the geologic record of the reduced and oxidized sulfur reservoirs. Geologists have long recognized the unusually large global accumulations of gypsum in the rocks of the Permo-Triassic Period. These observations on the variation in mass of the sulfate reservoir are reinforced by studies of the secular change of δS^{34} of the evaporites, first studied by Thode

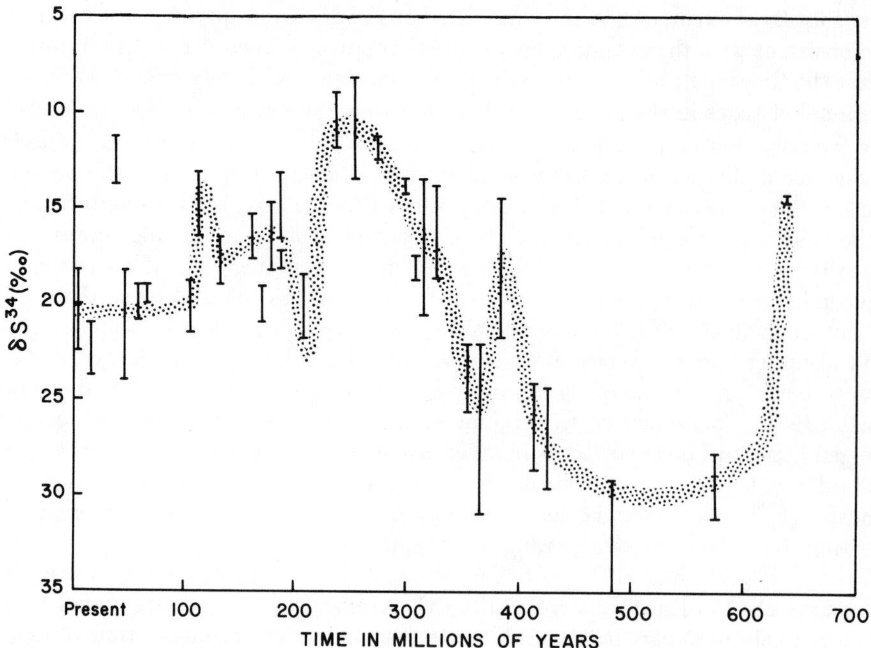

Fig. 7. Variation in the δS^{34} of evaporites as a function of their geologic age. After Holser and Kaplan (1966).

and Monster (1964). The results of the classic study of Holser and Kaplan (1966) on the variation of δS^{34} with time are summarized here by Fig. 7, adapted from their work. The δS^{34} of evaporites shows large fluctuations, from a maximum of about +30 during the Devonian to a minimum of +10 in the Permian. This depletion of δS^{34} in evaporites, and hence in the seas from which they precipitated, required precipitation of most of the sulfur flux from streams as gypsum (McKenzie, 1972). Because the sulfur in streams is weathered from both the reduced and oxidized sulfur in rocks, the formation of extensive evaporite deposits causes a transfer of sulfur from the reduced reservoir to the oxidized reservoir. As pointed out by Holster and Kaplan (op. cit.), this transfer makes an apparently intolerable demand on atmospheric oxygen. For example, if $\frac{1}{2}$ of the reduced sulfur steady-state flux (0.0056×10^{14} mol S/yr) were transferred to the sulfate reservoir (in addition to the oxidized flux) over a period of 100 million years the oxidized sulfur reservoir would be increased by 23%, and the reduced sulfur reservoir diminished by almost as much. The oxygen stored by this process would be more than three times that currently in the atmosphere.

B. Reservoir Exchange with Constant Ocean and Atmosphere

The network of fluxes shown in Fig. 6 demonstrates that a change in size of any given reservoir must be accompanied by changes in others. The pathways and the reservoirs involved in these processes are not completely defined, but with the restriction of constant ocean and atmosphere, reasonable reconstructions can be made as illustrated by the following examples.

Reservoir shifts from calcium and magnesium carbonates to silicates involve the release of CO_2. The CO_2 flux can be compensated by a complementary shift in another pair of carbonate–silicate reservoirs:

$$CaCO_3 + SiO_2 = CaSiO_3 + CO_2 \qquad \text{(1) } CO_2 \text{ release}$$

$$CaCO_3 + CO_2 + MgSiO_3 = CaMg(CO_3)_2 + SiO_2 \qquad \text{(2) } CO_2 \text{ uptake}$$

$$2\,CaCO_3 + MgSiO_3 = CaSiO_3 + CaMg(CO_3)_2 \qquad \text{(3) no atmospheric change}$$

Reaction (1) represents the metamorphism of calcite to a calcium silicate, releasing CO_2. This CO_2 is used up in converting more calcite and magnesium silicate to dolomite.

In another type of transfer between calcium and magnesium carbonate and silicate reservoirs, oxygen may also become involved in the oxidation of ferrous silicate to ferric oxide:

$$CaMg(CO_3)_2 + 2\,H_2O + 2\,CO_2 = Ca^{2+} + Mg^{2+} + 4\,HCO_3^- \qquad \text{(4) weathering}$$

$$4\,FeSiO_3 + O_2 = 2\,Fe_2O_3 + 4\,SiO_2 \qquad \text{(5) weathering}$$

$$Ca^{2+} + Mg^{2+} + 4\,HCO_3^- + 4\,SiO_2 = CaCO_3 + MgSiO_3 + 3\,SiO_2 + 3\,CO_2 + 2\,H_2O \qquad \text{(6) deposition}$$

$$CaMg(CO_3)_2 + 4\,FeSiO_3 + O_2 = CaCO_3 + MgSiO_3 + 3\,SiO_2 + 2\,Fe_2O_3 + CO_2 \qquad \text{(7) net of 4–6}$$

$$CO_2 + H_2O = CH_2O + O_2 \qquad \text{(8) photosynthesis}$$

$$CaMg(CO_3)_2 + 4\,FeSiO_3 + H_2O = CaCO_3 + MgSiO_3 + 3\,SiO_2 + 2\,Fe_2O_3 + CH_2O \qquad \text{(9) net of 7 and 8}$$

This kind of compensation might represent the weathering and depositional aspects of the magnesium cycle (Fig. 2), in which most magnesium weathered comes from dolomite, and is deposited in the oceans as magnesium silicate. This process increases the CO_2 in the oceans and eventually that in the atmosphere, with CO_2 removal taking place through increased photosynthesis. The O_2 thus produced restores the atmospheric O_2 used for the oxidation of the reduced iron compounds, such as in the $FeSiO_3$ cycle (Fig. 3) where iron is transferred from the ferrous silicate to the ferric oxide reservoir. The coupling of the two cycles through photosynthesis allows reservoir transfers in the sedimentary cycle, but makes no net demand on CO_2 or O_2.

As mentioned earlier, the geologic importance of such reservoir shifts in terms of major mass exchange is most clearly illustrated by the formation of large evaporite deposits. Their formation during restricted intervals of time implies the deposition of gypsum at rates in excess of that for steady-state conditions and therefore also requires calcium and sulfur to be transferred from the calcium mineral and pyrite reservoirs.

We shall first assume that tectonic events, which cause the formation of suitable evaporite basins and climates, initiate the deposition of large amounts of gypsum.

The initial step would then be:

$$8\,Ca^{2+} + 16\,HCO_3^- + 8\,SO_4^{2-} + 16\,H^+ = 8\,CaSO_4\cdot 2\,H_2O + 16\,CO_2$$

(10) deposition

$$16\,CO_2 + 16\,H_2O = 16\,CH_2O + 16\,O_2$$

(11) photosynthesis removes CO_2

$$8\,Ca^2 + 16\,HCO_3^- + 8\,SO_4^{2-} + 16\,H^+ + 16\,H_2O = 8\,CaSO_4\cdot 2\,H_2O + 16\,CH_2O + 16\,O_2$$

(12) net of 10 and 11

$$4\,FeS_2 + 15\,O_2 + 8\,H_2O = 16\,H^+ + 8\,SO_4^{2-} + 2\,Fe_2O_3$$

(13) weathering of pyrite

$$8\,CaCO_3 + 8\,CO_2 + 8\,H_2O = 8\,Ca^{2+} + 16\,HCO_3^-$$

(14) weathering of calcite

$$4\,FeS_2 + 8\,CaCO_3 + 8\,CO_2 + 32\,H_2O = 8\,CaSO_4\cdot 2\,H_2O + 16\,CH_2O + 2\,Fe_2O_3 + O_2$$

(15) net of 12–14

$$O_2 + CH_2O = CO_2 + H_2O$$

(16) excess O_2 removed

$$7\,MgCO_3 + 7\,SiO_2 = 7\,MgSiO_3 + 7\,CO_2$$

(17) CO_2 restored

$$4\,FeS_2 + 8\,CaCO_3 + 7\,MgCO_3 + 7\,SiO_2 + 31\,H_2O = 8\,CaSO_4\cdot 2\,H_2O + 2\,Fe_2O_3 + 15\,CH_2O + 7\,MgSiO_3$$

(18) reservoir transfer without gas consumption

The initial deposition of gypsum releases CO_2, owing to the transfer of calcium from the carbonate to the sulfate reservoir. Photosynthesis then removes the excess CO_2, which results in the net depositional reaction (12) giving an excess of O_2. The excess O_2 is used to restore sulfate to the ocean through the weathering of sulfur from the pyrite reservoir, and calcium must also be restored by weathering of the calcium carbonate reservoir.

The net result of the reservoir transfers (15) supplies Ca^{2+} and SO_4^{2-} for continued evaporite deposition, but also creates a CO_2 deficiency and a slight O_2 excess. The CO_2 may be restored by transferring magnesium from the carbonate to the silicate reservoir, and the excess O_2 balanced by the oxidation of organic matter.

The final result of these processes involves no net demands on CO_2 and O_2, but does permit the formation of excess gypsum through mass transfers from the calcium carbonate and pyrite reservoirs. The removal of the excess O_2 by the oxidation of organic material follows the concept of a kinetic maximum in atmospheric O_2 content as developed by Broecker (1970), and the ubiquitous role of photosynthesis in countering gas demands on the atmosphere is again illustrated.

The preceding sets of reactions demonstrate the ways in which various parts of the web of fluxes and reservoirs might interact to permit mass transfer on a grand scale without changing the atmosphere so much that life would be destroyed.

C. Energy Relations

The energetics of the reactions deduced for excess gypsum accumulation reinforce the important role that has been ascribed to photosynthesis in the regulation of the atmosphere. The same reactions are given below, but are slightly rearranged to show the standard free energies involved in each successive step.

$$8\,Ca^{2+} + 16\,HCO_3^- + 8\,SO_4^{2-} + 16\,H^+ = 8\,CaSO_4 \cdot 2\,H_2O + 16\,CO_2$$

(19) deposition of gypsum $\Delta G_r^\circ = -221$ kcal

$$15\,CO_2 + 15\,H_2O = 15\,CH_2O + 15\,O_2$$

(20) net of photosynthesis over oxidation $\Delta G_r^\circ = +1710$ kcal

$$4\,FeS_2 + 15\,O_2 + 16\,H_2O + 8\,CO_2 + 8\,CaCO_3 = 16\,H^+ + 8\,SO_4^{2-} + 2\,Fe_2O_3 + 8\,Ca^{2+} + 16\,HCO_3^-$$

(21) weathering of pyrite and calcite $\Delta G_r^\circ = -1103$ kcal

$$7\,MgCO_3 + 7\,SiO_2 = 7\,MgSiO_3 + 7\,CO_2$$

(22) $\Delta G_r^\circ = +50$ kcal

$$4\,FeS_2 + 8\,CaCO_3 + 7\,MgCO_3 + 7\,SiO_2 + 31\,H_2O = 8\,CaSO_4 \cdot 2\,H_2O + 2\,F2_2O_3 + 7\,MgSiO_3 + 15\,CH_2O$$

(23) $\Delta G_r^\circ = +436$ kcal

The deposition of gypsum from the oceans is driven to the right by evaporation and releases a large excess of CO_2. This stimulates photosynthesis, which releases O_2 for the oxidation of pyrite, but the photosynthetic reaction runs spontaneously strongly to the left. The actual course of the reaction, formation of organic matter, and liberation of O_2 can only take place as a result of the consumption of large amounts of solar energy. The weathering of calcite and pyrite run spontaneously strongly to the right to supply calcium and sulfur to the ocean for gypsum deposition. Conversion of magnesium carbonate to silicate is also accompanied by the consumption of energy under standard state conditions, and goes to the right spontaneously for the reaction shown only at CO_2 pressures less than $10^{-5.7}$ atm. The CO_2 pressure depends on the particular magnesium carbonate and silicate chosen, and may range over several orders of magnitude. In any case, the energy involved is relatively small. The overall reaction for reservoir transfer without gas consumption goes to the right only with major consumption of solar energy. To put it another way, if photosynthesis were halted, excess gypsum storage could not take place without entirely displacing the O_2 of the atmosphere with CO_2 by the time significant increase in the sulfate reservoir had taken place. Formation of gypsum deposits in excess of the steady-state amounts requires storage of solar energy, which takes place through photosynthesis and results in an increase of the organic carbon reservoir.

If tectonic and climatic conditions changed so that a deficiency of gypsum, relative to steady state, were formed, the events described previously would be more or less reversed. Gypsum would be transferred to the pyrite reservoir, as the flux of reduced sulfur out of the oceans increased and the flux to sulfate reservoir decreased. The transfer reaction would be the sum of reactions (19) and (21), $8\,CaSO_4 \cdot 2\,H_2O + 16\,CO_2 +$

$2\ Fe_2O_3 = 4\ FeS_2 + 15\ O_2 + 16\ H_2O + 8\ CaCO_3$. Photosynthetic rates would decrease, and the rate of deposition of organics would also diminish. The rate of oxidation of fossil organic material would exceed the rate of deposition of new material, creating an oxygen demand and CO_2 release to compensate for the effects of the increased rate of pyrite deposition. The δS^{34} of the ocean and evaporite deposits would then become more positive.

D. Stable Isotopes and Excess Sulfate Storage

The formation of extensive gypsum deposits, although accompanied by an increased rate of organic deposition according to the reservoir transfer indicated by equation (23), need not cause drastic changes in the reservoir size of organic carbon. If, for instance, half of the reduced sulfur oxidized by weathering were continuously transferred to gypsum deposits, the net deposition of organic carbon, estimated at 0.0250×10^{14} mol/yr for a steady-state system, would be increased only to 0.0355×10^{14} mol/yr. To increase the total organic carbon reservoir by 10% would require 100 million years. On the other hand, the oxidized sulfur would increase by 23%. The question now arises as to whether or not these shifts in reservoir sizes have been reflected by secular variations in the δC^{13} and δS^{34} values of sediments.

One way of testing the proposed model for reservoir transfer is to assess the pyrite and sulfate depositional rates needed to account for an observed δS^{34} shift in evaporites deposited in successive time intervals. Such a predictive model has been developed by McKenzie (1972) and may be summarized as follows:

$$F_2 = \frac{F}{A}\left(\frac{(\delta S_1{}^{34} - \delta S_F{}^{34}) - (\delta^\circ S_1{}^{34} - \delta S_F{}^{34}) \exp(-tF/M)}{[1 - \exp(-tF/M)]}\right) \tag{24}$$

where F = river input flux of S having $\delta S_F{}^{34}$
F_2 = rate of pyrite formation
t = length of time under consideration
M = mass of S in the oceans
$\delta S_1{}^{34}$ = δS^{34} of ocean S = δS^{34} of evaporites (Holser and Kaplan, 1966)
A = δS^{34} of evaporite S minus δS^{34} of pyrite S

The model is designed for steady-state oceanic conditions with the input flux (F) remaining constant at 0.0189×10^{14} mol S/yr and its $\delta S_F{}^{34}$ equal to the average crustal sulfur value of +1‰. It is also assumed that the oceanic sulfur reservoir (M) remains constant at 0.42×10^{20} mol S, and that the difference between pyrite and sulfate δS^{32} (A) equals 29‰, using the respective average values of −12 and +17‰ (relative to standard troilite, Canyon Diablo Meteorite) given by Holser and Kaplan (1966). A time period (t) of 100 million years is used to go from $\delta^\circ S_1{}^{34} = +25$ to $\delta S_1{}^{34} = +10$‰, which corresponds to the observed change from Carboniferous to the Permo-Triassic evaporites on the δS^{34} age curve (Fig. 7). The equation is solved for the rate of pyrite deposition that would cause the change in evaporite δS^{34} values during this time period.

To account for the observed δS^{34} change, it is calculated that the pyrite deposition rate would be 0.0058×10^{14} mol S/yr compared to a steady-state flux of 0.0112×10^{14}. Therefore, a shift of approximately one-half of the reduced sulfur flux to evaporite deposition for 100 million years could cause the δS^{34} of the ocean to change from +25 to +10. A comparable shift from sulfate deposition to pyrite deposition could cause the δS^{34} of the oceans to again increase.

In modeling sulfur transfer from the reduced to the oxidized sulfur reservoir, we have again oversimplified reality. Other factors involved in the δS^{34} shift from Devonian to Permo-Triassic time may have included variation in the sulfur fluxes into the oceans from the reduced and oxidized reservoirs and changes in the sulfur concentration of the oceans. But the changes in δS^{34} do not *require* major changes in the total sulfur flux into or out of the oceans. Thus we look on times of major evaporite accumulation as times during which tectonic conditions changed the emphasis on accumulating oxidized or reduced sulfur, rather than times when they drastically changed total sulfur fluxes.

A δC^{13} mass balance for sediments is useful in estimating the relative importance of increasing the organic carbon depositional flux in terms of the mean isotopic composition of the carbon reservoirs. The approximate average δC^{13} values (relative to PDB) of carbonates and organic carbon in sediments are 0 and $-26‰$ (Craig, 1953; Degens, 1969). The fraction of carbon in the organic carbon reservoir (f), according to our estimates (Table III) is given by:

$$f = \frac{\text{organic C in sediments}}{\text{total C in sediments}} = \frac{10.42 \times 10^{20}\ \text{mol}}{61.25 \times 10^{20}\ \text{mol}} = 0.170$$

This value is within the range of estimates reported in the literature (0.13 to 0.27) as summarized by Li (1972).

By knowing the amounts of reduced and oxidized carbon that have been incorporated into sedimentary rocks and their mean isotopic composition, we can estimate the δC^{13} value for mean crustal carbon. Craig (1953, 1963), using earlier estimates of sedimentary rock proportions, calculated this value to be about $-12‰$. Our revised estimates for the sedimentary abundances of reduced and oxidized carbon can now be used in the isotopic mass balance equation:

$$(\delta C^{13}\ \text{mean crustal carbon}) = f(\delta C^{13}\ \text{reduced C}) + (1 - f)(\delta C^{13}\ \text{oxidized C}) \qquad (25)$$

Solving for the δC^{13} of mean crustal carbon, a value of $-4.4‰$ is obtained that is similar to the value calculated by Broecker (1970) using the average sedimentary carbon estimates of Ronov (1964).

The McKenzie sulfur isotope model, as we have applied it, represents a sudden change from a ready-state system to one in which 50% of the steady-state reduced sulfur flux into the oceans is transferred into the sulfate reservoir continuously over a period of 100 million years. According to our calculations (p. 224), this would also increase organic carbon storage from the steady-state value to one 50% higher, representing a transfer of 0.0105×10^{14} mol/yr from the carbonate carbon feed of the oceans to the organic carbon reservoir. This change, using the McKenzie model, would increase δC^{13} of both deposited carbonate and organic carbon by about 1.9‰ in a period of about 1×10^6 yr, after which the values for δC^{13} for the deposited organic and inorganic carbon would remain constant at the new elevated value for the rest of the 100×10^6 yr. Such a change of $+1.9‰$ is about equal to observed range of fluctuations of δC^{13} of carbonate rocks (Fig. 8) and also shows that the reservoir exchange reactions postulated are broadly consistent with both the δS^{34} and δC^{13} secular variations in rocks. However, a detailed interpretation of these data may not be warranted in the older samples for the following reasons.

Keith and Weber (1964) reported both δC^{13} and δO^{18} for carbonate rocks as a function of their geologic age (Fig. 8). In Triassic and older samples, δO^{18} ranges of freshwater and marine samples overlap, but Jurassic and younger freshwater carbonates

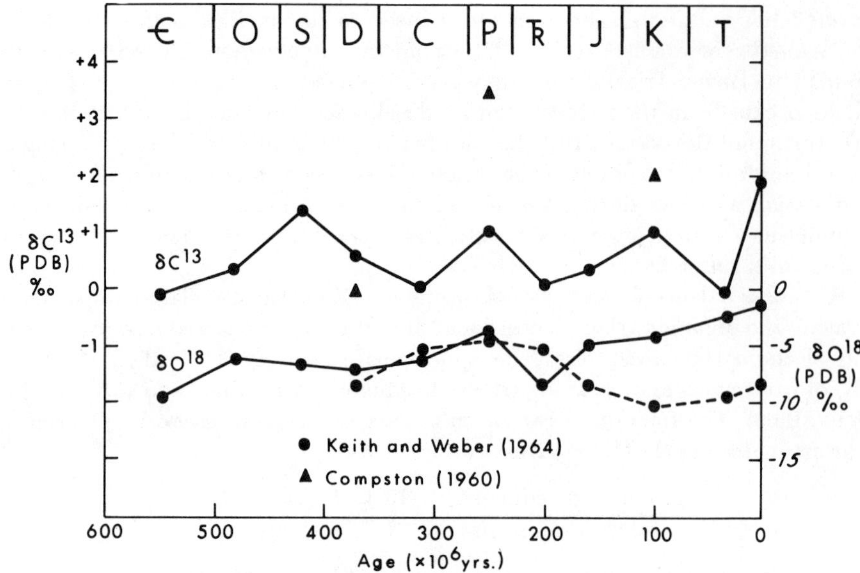

Fig. 8. Variation in the δC^{13} and δO^{18} of carbonates as a function of their geologic age. The solid lines represent marine samples, the dashed line, freshwater samples. After Keith and Weber (1964).

exhibit the usual much less positive δO^{18} values relative to marine carbonates deposited in the same time period. Keith and Weber attribute the probable cause of the overlap in older samples to postdepositional recrystallization and isotope exchange with continental waters. These processes would alter the carbon isotope values, but to a lesser degree. Because the δC^{13} age curve has a total variation of less than 3‰, it appears unwise to make a detailed interpretation of carbon isotope ratios from rocks older than Jurassic.

Similar problems are not to be expected for the δS^{34} age curve. The secular variations are of a much larger magnitude (+30 to +10‰), and evaporite beds are not apt to be exposed to dissolved sulfur with a markedly different δS^{34} composition during postdepositional recrystallization. Holser and Kaplan (1966) found that successive alterations of gypsum to anhydrite and anhydrite to gypsum do not significantly change their sulfur isotope compositions.

E. The Importance of Photosynthesis

In 1951 Rubey discussed the importance of CO_2 concentration as a regulator of photosynthesis and hence of the storage rate of organic materials. From the relations discussed here, we agree that it seems inescapable that an increase in atmospheric CO_2 causes an increase in the net of photosynthesis over oxidation. Given adequate nutrients and constancy of other variables, many terrestrial plants show a nearly linear increase in photosynthetic net with increasing CO_2 content of their environment (Leopold, 1964). This increase continues until an optimum content of CO_2 is reached, a value about three, four, or five times that of the present atmospheric CO_2 (op. cit.).

The argument is commonly given that CO_2 is not the most important limiting nutrient, and that increase of CO_2 in the atmosphere would not cause an increase in the photosynthetic rate. We suggest that CO_2 increase *does* cause increase in photosynthetic rate, perhaps as a result of the following mechanisms. Two-thirds to one-half of the world's total photosynthesis is attributed to terrestrial plants (Hutchinson, 1954; Bolin, 1970). On land, the necessary increase of nutrients can be released from the soil as a direct result of increased photosynthetic activity. The compensation for higher CO_2 could be accounted for mainly by the increased net photosynthesis of terrestrial plants, or increased terrestrial activity may supply more nutrients to the ocean, and thus allow marine algae to increase their net photosynthesis. Also, addition of CO_2 to the atmosphere, with eventual lowering of oceanic pH, would tend to increase the concentration of dissolved inorganic phosphorus in the oceans (Krumbein and Garrels, 1952; Stumm and Morgan, 1970) and thus might permit phosphorus-limited systems to respond to increased CO_2.

In summary, our interpretation is that the constancy of the atmosphere depends on response of the rate of photosynthesis to additions or subtractions of atmospheric constituents caused by changes in the masses of mineral reservoirs. Percentage fluctuations of CO_2 in the atmosphere would be far greater than O_2 variations. For the pre-man atmosphere-ocean-sedimentary rock system, variations in the rates of CO_2 addition or withdrawal from the atmosphere, in terms of moles per year more or less than the overall average, have probably been within a factor of two or three of the average. The required compensatory rate changes in photosynthesis are trivial in terms of the total photosynthetic rate. To double the average amount of new organics deposited and hence compensate for a doubling of steady-state oxygen demand would require only that photosynthesis minus oxidation change from 0.04 to 0.09% of photosynthesis. Because of the nearly linear dependence of photosynthetic rate on CO_2 content of the atmosphere, it seems unlikely that even the greatest rates of natural addition of CO_2 would change the atmospheric level by more than a fraction of the increase in the natural rate of subtraction or addition. This argument suggests that during Phanerozoic time the CO_2 content of the atmosphere ranged less from 0.01 to 0.09%.

4. Ancient Reservoirs

A. Introduction

The discussion so far has emphasized the role of photosynthesis in the maintenance of a nearly constant atmosphere. But in the early stages of the earth the atmosphere was probably strongly reducing. Most investigators (cf. Holland, 1964; French, 1966) consider that hydrogen and methane were important initial gases. If so, the Phanerozoic near-steady state must have been preceded by major chemical evolution. The present system can be conceived as derived from the initial one by a slow titration of the system by oxygen, and that the current situation is maintained energetically only by continuous addition of solar energy through the medium of photosynthesis. If photosynthesis were halted, there would be a tendency for the system to return to the initial conditions, more or less reversing the evolutionary processes. With cessation of photosynthesis, existing organic matter would play the role of reductant. Oxygen from photolytic reduction of atmospheric water will be ignored.

B. Evolution of Reservoirs

The predicted sequence of events after cessation of photosynthesis is illustrated in Fig. 9. The assumption is made, in deriving the relations shown, that there are no

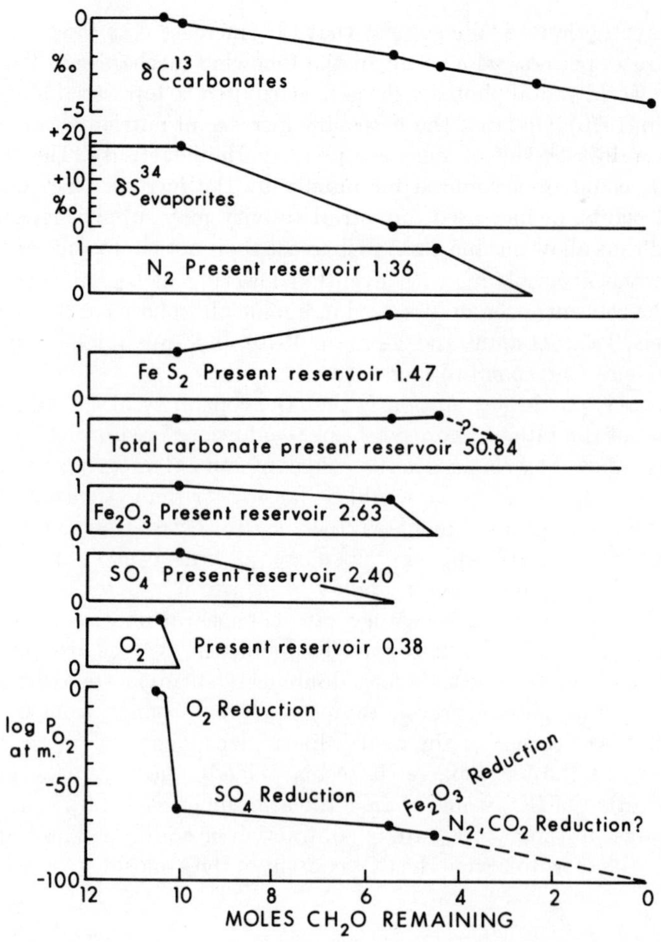

Fig. 9. Titration of the oxidized system by sedimentary organics. Reservoir sizes are in units of 10^{20} mol and their change in size is shown on a relative scale of 1 to 0.

kinetic barriers, nor any caused by poor mixing of the materials; reactions take place in the sequence predicted by thermodynamics. The model is nearly equivalent to an "equilibrium titration" of an oxidized system by small increments of a reducing agent, pausing after each addition until the reductant reacts completely.

The following discussion is keyed to Fig. 9 and Table V. With cessation of the photosynthesis, no new organic materials would be buried, and the fossil organics would be oxidized as they became successively exposed by erosion. This would create an oxygen drain on the atmosphere and CO_2 addition. As free oxygen diminished, an equivalent amount of CO_2 would take its place. The addition of CO_2 would be buffered by the oceans and by an increased solution of carbonates in the ocean. A crude calculation indicates that instantaneous conversion of the 0.38×10^{20} mol of O_2 to CO_2, followed by equilibrium of the CO_2 between atmosphere and a carbonate-saturated ocean, woud give a CO_2 pressure in the atmosphere between 0.01 and 0.1 atm, although the ocean-atmosphere system would have had its total inorganic carbon species increased eightfold. This high CO_2 pressure would tend to convert silicate minerals to carbonates, lowering the CO_2 pressure and increasing slightly the carbonate mineral reservoir.

TABLE V

Titration of the Existing Sedimentary System by Organic Matter

Reservoir To Be Reduced	CH_2O Consumed
1. 0.38×10^{20} mol O_2	0.38×10^{20} mol
2. 2.40×10^{20} mol SO_4^{2-} + $CaSO_4$ (requires 0.60×10^{20} mol Fe_2O_3)	4.50×10^{20} mol
3. 2.03×10^{20} mol Fe_2O_3	1.02×10^{20} mol
Total CH_2O reservoir = 10.42×10^{20} mol	
Amount CH_2O used above = 5.90×10^{20} mol	
Remaining CH_2O = 4.52×10^{20} mol	

Only about 4% of the total organic carbon reservoir would be used in consuming all the free O_2. Oxygen pressure would plummet as the last of the O_2 was consumed. Organic material would then begin converting sulfate to reduced sulfur, but not until O_2 pressure had dropped to about 10^{-64} atm. Conversion of all sulfate to pyrite would take place within an order of magnitude decrease of O_2 pressure, keeping the system buffered near 10^{-65} atm. Almost half (4.5/10.42) of the original organic reservoir would be required; its decrease would be accompanied by decrease in ferric iron, and increases in ferrous iron and reduced sulfur. Nitrogen would remain as N_2.

The next major reduction process would take place at about 10^{-69}–10^{-70} atm. Within the limits of error of the thermodynamic data, hematite is in equilibrium simultaneously with respect to magnetite (Fe_3O_4), siderite ($FeCO_3$), and ferrous silicate ($FeSiO_3$) (assuming 10^{-1} atm CO_2 and saturation of the system with amorphous silica) at 10^{-69} atm O_2. Thus the ferric oxide reservoir would be removed by a decrease of oxygen pressure to about 10^{-70} atm. This third stage of the reduction process, which might be called the "iron mineral" stage, would use up 1.02×10^{20} mol of organic material or 10% of the total.

After reduction of ferric oxide to magnetite, siderite, and ferrous silicate by organic matter, the system becomes too complex for us to analyze in more than the most general terms. Most of the elements in the solids are in the lowest valence states that occur in rocks. The important exception is the sulfur in pyrite, which has a formal valence of -1. A reaction can be written,

$$2\,FeS_2 + CH_2O + 3\,FeSiO_3 = 4\,FeS + 4\,FeCO_3 + 3\,SiO_{2\,amorp} + H_2O \qquad (26)$$

that involves only solid phases and water. The calculated free energy is -2.45 kcal, suggesting that CH_2O is capable of reducing pyrite to ferrous sulfide. The equilibrium O_2 pressure would be about 10^{-80} atm. On the other hand, at values of P_{O_2} less than about 10^{-75} atm, CO_2 becomes unstable with respect to methane, carbonates would tend to be destroyed, and we are unable to follow the fate of the various reservoirs.

The preceding description of the "degradation" of the present system can now be used as a guide to speculation about the evolutionary process. In that process, the initial atmosphere-ocean-sedimentary rock system has undergone an "oxidation titration," and the general pattern of evolution should more or less reverse the sequence of events predicted for reduction.

Most interpretations of the nature of the initial atmosphere are based on calculations of the compositions and relative concentrations of the gases in equilibrium with a high-temperature mafic crust (Holland, 1964; French, 1966). Such calculations yield high percentages of H_2, CO, and CH_4. This assemblage would not be stable with respect to a cooled crust. Just as the acid gases, such as HCl and CO_2, which are in equilibrium at high pressures with molten rocks, attack the rocks vigorously when they are cold, so the reduced gases emitted by a hot crust should react with cooled material to reduce the crust and oxidize the gases. Reaction with partly ferric compounds such as magnetite could theoretically destroy H_2, NH_3, CO, and CH_4. A typical reaction is:

$$2\,Fe_3O_4 + CH_4 + 4\,SiO_2 = 4\,FeSiO_3 + CO_2 + 2\,H_2O \qquad (27)\quad \Delta G_r^\circ = -30 \text{ kcal}$$

The equilibrium ratio CO_2/CH_4 is 10^{22}.

We shall bypass the events prior to the oxidation of the reduced iron reservoir, except to note that our estimated present-day organic reservoir of 10.42×10^{20} mol seems to be almost twice as big as it would need to be to supply the 5.9×10^{20} mol of oxygen to fill the ferric iron, the sulfate, and the free oxygen sinks (Table V). The 4.5×10^{20} mol remaining presumably were applied to the oxidation of primitive reduced gases. According to Holland (1964), 4.4×10^{20} mol were required just to oxidize H_2 to H_2O so that the total oxygen demand by reduced gases may have exceeded by several times the oxygen equivalent of our residual 4.5×10^{20} mol of organic material. Photosynthesis and accumulation of organic materials may have been only one of three important processes producing oxygen in the preferrous iron oxidation stage. The others are oxygen production in the upper atmosphere by photodissociation of water, with concomitant H_2 escape to space, and reaction of reduced gases with the crust itself, and with each other toward internal equilibrium at low temperature.

Table VI shows a sequence of equilibria, and lists the oxygen pressures for them,

TABLE VI

Oxygen Pressures for Some Gas and Mineral Equilibria

Reaction	P_{O_2} at 25°C for Unit Activity of Other Components
$2\,CO_g + O_{2g} = 2\,CO_{2g}$	$10^{-90.15}$
$CH_2O_s + O_{2g} = CO_{2g} + H_2O_l$	$10^{-83.6}$
$2\,H_{2g} + O_{2g} = 2\,H_2O_l$	$10^{-83.12}$
$4\,FeS_c + O_{2g} + 2\,SiO_{2\,amorp} = 2\,FeS_{2c} + 2\,FeSiO_{3c}$	$10^{-80.59}$
$\frac{4}{3}\,NH_{3g} + O_{2g} = \frac{2}{3}\,N_{2g} + 2\,H_2O_l$	$10^{-79.27}$
$\frac{1}{2}\,CaSiO_{3c} + O_{2g} + \frac{1}{2}\,CH_{4g} = \frac{1}{2}\,CaCO_{3c} + \frac{1}{2}\,SiO_{2\,amorp} + H_2O_l$	$10^{-74.83}$
$\frac{1}{2}\,CH_{4g} + O_{2g} = \frac{1}{2}\,CO_{2g} + H_2O_l$	$10^{-71.67}$
$6\,FeSiO_{3c} + O_{2g} = 2\,Fe_3O_{4c} + 6\,SiO_{2\,amorp}$	$10^{-70.07}$
$4\,Fe_3O_{4c} + O_{2g} = 6\,Fe_2O_{3c}$	$10^{-68.93}$
$\frac{4}{15}\,FeS_{2c} + \frac{8}{15}\,CaCO_{3c} + O_{2g} = \frac{2}{15}\,Fe_2O_{3c} + \frac{8}{15}\,CaSO_{4c} + \frac{8}{15}\,CO_{2g}$	$10^{-64.93}$
$\frac{2}{3}\,H_2S_g + O_{2g} = \frac{2}{3}\,SO_{2g} + \frac{2}{3}\,H_2O_l$	$10^{-58.89}$
$4\,Mn_3O_{4c} + O_{2g} = 6\,Mn_2O_{3c}$	$10^{-35.9}$
$2\,SO_{2g} + O_{2g} = 2\,SO_{3g}$	$10^{-24.84}$

Key. g = gas; l = liquid; amorp = amorphous; c = crystalline; and s = solid.

assuming unit activity of other reactants. The major conclusion that can be drawn from the table is that by the time oxidation of reduced iron minerals could begin (at about 10^{-70} atm O_2), CO, H_2, NH_3, and CH_4 would have been destroyed in an equilibrium system. This stage apparently was reached early in earth history, judging by the mineralogy of 3 billion or more year old sedimentary rocks, with their abundant pyrite, siderite, magnetite, calcite, and dolomite. The first primary sedimentary hematite must also have begun to form at about that oxygen pressure. Oxidation of sulfides would occur over a range of oxygen pressures, but a pressure of 10^{-67} atm would be required to produce more than a trace of dissolved sulfate in the ocean. On the assumption that atmospheric composition was controlled by the abundant Fe_3O_4, $FeSiO_3$, $FeCO_3$, and amorphous SiO_2, the gaseous composition of the atmosphere can be calculated. The results are given in Table VII, and show the dominance of N_2 and CO_2 at this stage of development, with H_2S, CH_4, NH_3, and H_2 having become minor or trace components. This is tantamount to saying that primordial CO and CH_4 were transferred into the CO_2 and carbonate rock reservoirs, and that NH_3 had been transferred into the N_2 reservoir.

The oceans, at this stage, would have contained no dissolved sulfate; the cations would have been balanced by Cl^- and HCO_3^-. Rubey (1951) made many calculations pertaining to ancient oceans; we add one more here, with the plea that the numbers be treated as qualitative guides to any real ocean. The calculation is made on the basis of the numbers in Table VII, plus the assumption that the Cl^- concentration was the same as today, and that equilibrium was reached with respect to calcite and dolomite, as well as the iron minerals already mentioned. The results are shown in

TABLE VII

Gas Pressures in Equilibrium with Reduced Iron Minerals

Reaction	Gas Pressures
$6\,FeSiO_{3c} + O_{2g} = 2\,Fe_3O_{4c} + 6\,SiO_{2\,amorp}$	$P_{O_2} = 10^{-70.07}$
$FeSiO_{3c} + CO_{2g} = FeCO_{3c} + SiO_{2\,amorp}$	$P_{CO_2} = 10^{-1.202}$
$2\,FeCO_{3c} + O_{2g} + 4\,H_2S_g = 2\,FeS_{2c} + 2\,CO_{2g} + 4\,H_2O_l$	$P_{H_2S} = 10^{-8.34}$
$2\,H_2O_l + 12\,FeSiO_{3c} + CO_{2g} = CH_{4g} + 4\,Fe_3O_{4c} + 12\,SiO_{2\,amorp}$	$P_{CH_4} = 10^{-4.39}$
	$P_{N_2}{}^{a} = 10^{-1.108}$
$6\,H_2O_l + 18\,FeSiO_{3c} + 2\,N_{2g} = 6\,Fe_3O_{4c} + 4\,NH_{3g} + 18\,SiO_{2\,amorp}$	$P_{NH_3} = 10^{-6.95}$
$2\,H_2O_l = 2\,H_{2g} + O_{2g}$	$P_{H_2} = 10^{-6.5}$

Key. g = gas; l = liquid; amorp = amorphous; and c = crystalline.
[a] Total $N_2 + NH_3$ assumed to be 0.78 atmospheres.

Table VIII. The major differences from modern seawater are: absence of dissolved O_2, absence of SO_4^{2-}, increase of HCO_3^{2-} by a factor of four, presence of significant soluble iron (4 ppm), lowering of pH by one unit. In this model there is little difference in Ca^{2+} and Mg^{2+} from the modern seas.

In terms of reservoirs, this ocean-atmosphere system would differ markedly in the larger amount of carbon in the oceanic and atmospheric reservoirs. The oceanic reservoir would be increased from today's 0.03×10^{20} mol to 0.135×10^{20} mol (calculated from the HCO_3^- concentration in Table VIII). In the change to present-day conditions, the ocean and atmosphere would be depleted of C by a total of

TABLE VIII

Reconstruction of Ancient Seawater[a]

P_{O_2}	$= 10^{-70.07}$ atm	$Ca_{aq}{}^{2+}$	$= 10^{-1.95}$ (0.011 m)
P_{CO_2}	$= 10^{-1.20}$ atm	$Mg_{aq}{}^{2+}$	$= 10^{-1.52}$ (0.030 m)
P_{CH_4}	$= 10^{-4.39}$ atm	$Fe_{aq}{}^{2+}$	$= 10^{-4.13}$ (0.000074 m)
P_{H_2}	$= 10^{-0.11}$ atm	$K_{aq}{}^{+}$	$= 10^{-2}$ (0.01 m)
P_{NH_3}	$= 10^{-6.95}$ atm	$Na_{aq}{}^{+}$	$= 10^{-0.330}$ (0.47 m)
P_{H_2S}	$= 10^{-8.34}$ atm	$Cl_{aq}{}^{-}$	$= 10^{-0.26}$ (0.55 m)
$HS_{aq}{}^{-}$	$= 10^{-5.41}$ m	$SiO_{2\,aq}$	$= 10^{-2.7}$ (0.002 m)
$SO_{4\,aq}$	$= 10^{-10.4}$ m	pH	$= 10^{-6.68}$
$HCO_{3\,aq}{}^{-}$	$= 10^{-2.02}$ (0.0094m)		

Key. aq = dissolved species.

[a] Assumptions: Equilibrium at 25°C with $FeSiO_3$, FeS_2, $FeCO_3$, $CaCO_3$, $CaMg(CO_3)_2$, amorphous SiO_2. Also that Na^+, K^+, and Cl^- were the same as present ocean, and that activity coefficients of ions were same as present ocean.

0.214×10^{20} mol, which must have moved into the organic carbon or carbonate rock reservoirs.

Again we emphasize the unreliability of the specific numbers given, and emphasize only that in the change from conditions some 3 billion or more years ago to the present there has been significant transfer of C from atmosphere and ocean to the rock reservoirs (including CH_2O).

In continuing the discussion of evolution of the system from a time some 3-plus billion years ago with an oxygen pressure of 10^{-70} atm, following the reduction curve in reverse, there is a long stretch of curve representing the buffering of the system by the oxygen requirements of the reduced iron and sulfur minerals. It seems probable that the oceanic and atmospheric oxidation state was continuously much higher than that indicated by contemporary sediments. The slightest restriction on a sedimentary system tends to deplete oxygen and to yield minerals indicative of anaerobic conditions, even today when atmospheric and oceanic oxygen are high. At lower but still finite levels of free oxygen, the effect of restriction would be magnified, and in all except high-energy depositional environments, the sediments would reflect the local oxygen depletion instead of the actual oceanic and atmospheric compositions (Broecker, 1970).

The cherty iron formations, which reached their maximum development about 2 billion years ago, give evidence for this suggested oxidation gap between sediments and the ocean and atmosphere. James (1966), in his classic monograph on the iron-rich rocks, describes the situation clearly. In brief, he points out that the pyritic facies has a high organic content, and that the sulfur in the pyrite must have been derived from reduction of seawater sulfate. The siderite facies also contains appreciable organic material, and demonstrates, from the continuous undisturbed thin layering, that deposition was in relatively quiet water. The hematite facies, on the other hand, is a shallow water facies, gives evidence of mechanical disturbance during deposition, and is free of organic material. The picture emerges that all the facies except the hematite facies are products of restricted conditions, and that only the hematite facies was near equilibrium with a mildly oxygenated atmosphere.

The overall picture, 2 billion years ago, is that there was already sulfate in the oceans and enough oxygen in the atmosphere to oxidize simultaneously ferric iron and to remove organic material if the sediment was deposited in shallow waters so that atmosphere, water, and sediment could interact.

Consequently, oxidation of ferrous carbonates and silicates, followed by oxidation of sulfides to sulfates, followed by development of free oxygen, as would be expected from strict adherence to consecutive equilibria, probably did not occur. Instead, the development of the oxygen, sulfate, and ferric iron reservoirs probably took place contemporaneously. Such a picture is consistent with Ronov's concept of the evolution of the ocean and atmosphere (1971). The relative rates of development, however, may have been highly variable with time. The work of Rhodes and Morse (1971), who showed an interesting parallelism between the oxygen content of present-day sedimentary environments and related faunas to the emergence of faunas in geologic time, at least suggests that the current level of free oxygen was not reached until late Precambrian time. If so, most of the sulfate and ferric iron reservoirs may have been filled before the free oxygen reservoir grew significantly.

C. Isotopic Evidence

This same sequence of events is also consistent with the data provided by carbon isotope studies on Precambrian organic matter. Oehler et al. (1972) determined the δC^{13} of the organics from the Swaziland sequence ($3.0 - 3.4 \times 10^9$ yr) as well as from other Precambrian series of Africa, Australia, and North America. Figure 10 illustrates their results, as well as the mean δC^{13} value for Paleozoic sedimentary organic matter (Degens, 1969). It must be emphasized that the δC^{13} values cover a

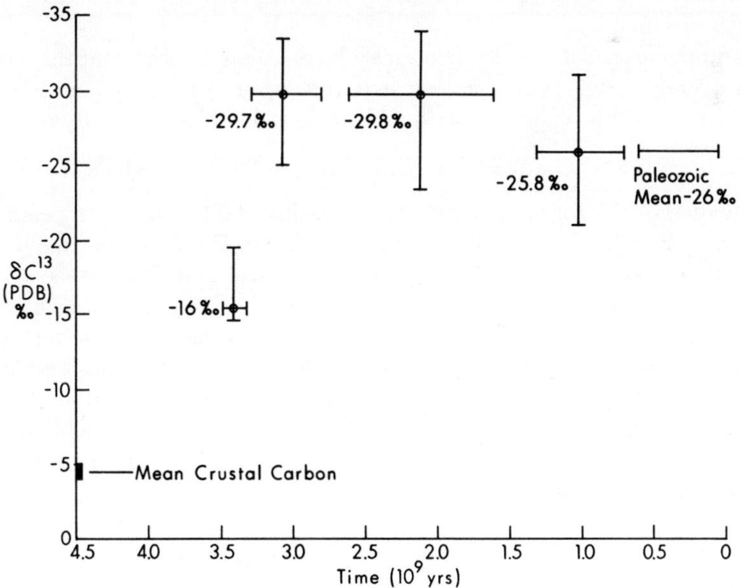

Fig. 10. Variation of δC^{13} of sedimentary organics as a function of their geologic age. After Oehler et al. (1972). The vertical bars represent the range of δC^{13} values averaged, the horizontal, the time range averaged.

very large range for any given time period and that the following discussion represents highly tentative generalizations.

The most important additions to our knowledge of Precambrian δC^{13} values of sedimentary organic matter may be the δC^{13} values of samples from the oldest portion of the Swaziland sequence. Their average δC^{13} is $-16‰$, which falls outside the normal range for preserved reduced carbon of established biological origin but which is roughly comparable to values characteristic of primordial organic matter in carbonaceous chondrites (Oehler et al., 1972). The δC^{13} value of younger rocks then decreases to an average of -29 to $-30‰$, and at about 1.5 billion years increases to about $-26‰$, the average value for Paleozoic samples.

The break between the oldest, $-16‰$ samples, and younger samples may reflect a geologic event that altered the distribution of isotopes in the carbon reservoirs, or, it may mark the time of origin of biochemical mechanism (e.g., photosynthesis) capable of fractionating carbon isotopes in a manner similar to that of modern autotrophs (Oehler et al., 1972). Organic matter from rocks 3.0 to 1.6 billion years old has an average δC^{13} more negative (-29 to $-30‰$) than that of younger sediments ($-26‰$). This may mean that the reservoir of organic carbon was perhaps half its present size, and/or higher CO_2 levels caused a greater isotope fractionation between reduced and oxidized carbon (Epstein, 1968).

A simple mass balance calculation illustrates these effects. In our model the mass of organic material stored during this time interval would equal the amount to produce enough O_2 for the oxidation of reduced iron (1.02×10^{20} mol) plus the "remaining" CH_2O (Table V) that may have had a role in oxidizing reduced gases (4.52×10^{20} mol). As mentioned before, this would mark the end of ferrous iron control on the atmosphere. Epstein (1968) found that plants grown under CO_2 concentrations 50 times that of present levels produced reduced carbon showing a 28‰ depletion. Therefore, the fraction (f) of the total sedimentary carbon reservoir occurring as organic carbon would be $5.54/61.26 = 0.09$ and it could have a δC^{13} value 28‰ lower than carbonate carbon.

The isotopic mass balance equation may be calculated because of the lengthy time interval averaged (1.4 billion years), and the mean crustal carbon δC^{13} (-4.4%) derived earlier in this chapter is used. The mass balance equation becomes:

$$(f)(\delta C^{13}_{\text{organics}}) + (1 - f)(\delta C^{13}_{\text{organics}} + 28‰) = -4.4‰ \qquad (28)$$

The predicted δC^{13} for organic material deposited 3.0 to 1.6 billion years ago is calculated to be 29.8‰, the same value shown in Fig. 10 for the same time period. Once the organic carbon reservoir grew to its present size and CO_2 levels were lowered preserved organic matter would have δC^{13} values of $-26‰$. This may have occurred 1 to 2 billion years ago as also deduced in a similar manner by Epstein (1968).

Because of the large variations in observed δC^{13} values of reduced carbon in sedimentary rocks, it must again be emphasized that this interpretation of the data of Oehler et al. (1972) is very speculative and by no means in itself conclusive. However, the data do not contradict the model proposed here for the early evolution of ocean and atmosphere compositions.

D. Transition to the Steady-State

Because of the various complications that have been discussed, we have been unable to model the evolutionary system of atmosphere, ocean, and sediments to show convincingly the transition from evolving ocean and atmosphere into steady-state conditions. Photosynthesis would have the most important role in producing free atmospheric oxygen (Gregor, 1971), but the problem is to produce an excess of oxygen above that needed to oxidize the reduced sinks so that free oxygen could then accumulate in the atmosphere (Van Valen, 1971a, b). Very broadly it can be said that so long as photosynthetic oxygen was used in a manner that produced more CO_2 than O_2 consumed, organic material would be stored and the atmosphere would remain high in CO_2 and low in oxygen. Our tendency is to put the blame (or credit) on the gradual elimination of most of the $FeCO_3$ reservoir. When it became converted largely to iron oxide, photosynthesis had won the battle with the sinks; atmospheric CO_2 dropped to low levels, and became the control on photosynthesis; atmospheric oxygen took its place. Ferrous carbonate was eliminated as an important sedimentary precipitate; with the drop in atmospheric CO_2 the Mg silicates and carbonates became the minerals that interchanged during the cycles of erosion and deposition. The reduction-oxidation parts of the sedimentary cycle today involve chiefly sulfur compounds and organic matter.

E. Atmospheric Oxygen

The origin of the present atmosphere can be regarded as a case of reservoir transfer without the restriction of atmospheric constancy. The problem becomes one of transferring from the FeS_2, $FeCO_3$, and $FeSiO_3$ reservoirs in such a way as to create 2.63×10^{20} mol of Fe_2O_3 [2], 2.40×10^{20} mol of sulfate, and 0.38×10^{20} mol of O_2 (Table V).

This can be accomplished as follows:

First, enough pyrite is oxidized to produce 2.40×10^{20} mol of sulfate

$$1.20\ FeS_2 + 2.40\ CaCO_3 + 4.50\ O_2 = 2.40\ CaSO_4 + 0.60\ Fe_2O_3 + 2.40\ CO_2 \quad (29)$$

Only 0.6×10^{20} mol of Fe_2O_3 are produced. The remainder, 2.03×10^{20} mol, must come from the oxidation of $FeCO_3$ and $FeSiO_3$, as well as the 0.38 mol of free O_2. This requirement is fulfilled by the next reaction:

$$3.50\ FeCO_3 + 0.56\ FeSiO_3 + 1.02\ O_2 = 2.03\ Fe_2O_3 + 3.50\ CO_2 + 0.56\ SiO_2 \quad (30)$$

Adding (29) and (30):

$$\begin{aligned} 1.20\ FeS_2 + 3.40\ FeCO_3 + 0.56\ FeSiO_3 + 2.4\ CaCO_3 + 5.52\ O_2 &= \\ 2.4\ CaSO_4 + 2.63\ Fe_2O_3 + 0.56\ SiO_2 + 5.90\ CO_2 & \quad (31) \end{aligned}$$

Finally, CO_2 is removed by photosynthesis:

$$5.90\ CO_2 + 5.90\ H_2O = 5.90\ CH_2O + 5.90\ O_2 \quad (32)$$

Adding (31) and (32):

$$\begin{aligned} 1.20\ FeS_2 + 3.50\ FeCO_3 + 0.56\ FeSiO_3 + 2.40\ CaCO_3 + 5.90\ H_2O &= \\ 2.40\ CaSO_4 + 2.63\ Fe_2O_3 + 0.38\ O_2 + 5.90\ CH_2O + 0.56\ SiO_2 & \quad (33) \end{aligned}$$

Reaction (33) shows that the estimated reservoirs of sulfate, ferric oxide, and free oxygen can be obtained by a judicious choice of the ratios of FeS_2, $FeSiO_3$, and $FeCO_3$, which are oxidized.

The role of the oxidation of $FeCO_3$ in creating free oxygen should be emphasized.

[2] Excess crustal Fe_2O_3 was calculated by assuming the average sedimentary rock to now have 3.50% Fe_2O_3 (Garrels and Mackenzie, 1971), but prior to the presence of free oxygen, to have had a Fe_2O_2/FeO ratio of 0.44, which equals that of an average igneous rock (Wickman, 1954).

Oxidation of FeS_2 and $FeSiO_3$ in any combination requires more oxygen than there is CO_2 released, hence photosynthesis cannot produce free oxygen by consuming CO_2. On the other hand, $FeCO_3$ produces 4 mol of CO_2 for each O_2 utilized in its oxidation to Fe_2O_3, so that ensuing photosynthesis produces free oxygen. The level of free oxygen in the present steady-state atmosphere would seem to be fortuitous, in that it apparently was controlled by the relative amount of siderite in the preoxygen rocks. If there had been more siderite, the Phanerozoic steady state might have operated at a somewhat higher level.

As stated before, the time relations between the development of free oxygen pressure and the oxidation of pyrite, siderite, and ferrous silicate cannot be predicted because of uncertainties about the rates of the various reactions involved. The problems

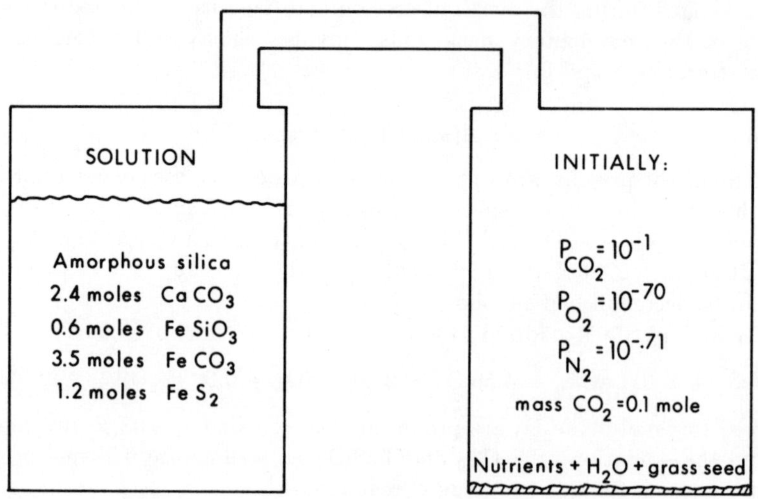

Fig. 11. Experiment for the evolution of atmospheric oxygen.

can be illustrated by an hypothetical laboratory experiment (Fig. 11). Container 1 contains 1.2 mol of pyrite, 3.5 mol of siderite, 0.6 mol of ferrous silicate, 2.4 mol of calcite, and a small amount of amorphous silica, powdered and put into a container filled with water. This container could then be connected to a 22.4-liter second container, initially containing only N_2. After a time, gas pressures in the two would equalize, as shown. But the second container also contains grass seed and a little fertilizer.

The initial oxygen pressure in the system would be 10^{-70} atm, and the CO_2 pressure would be about 10^{-1} atm. The O_2 pressure would be controlled by equilibrium between the iron compounds and Fe_2O_3 (or Fe_3O_4), the CO_2 pressure by equilibrium between $FeCO_3$, $FeSiO_3$, and amorphous silica.

The grass would sprout and grow (with light available). Conditions would be ideal for a high photosynthetic rate—high CO_2 and low O_2 (Gibbs, 1970). The grass would quickly drop the CO_2 pressure to about 10^{-4} atm, the approximate cut-off value for photosynthesis, simultaneously raising the O_2 pressure to 10^{-1} atm. Then growth would stop. But all three iron minerals are unstable at 10^{-1} atm O_2. The next events would depend on the relative reactivity of $FeCO_3$, $FeSiO_3$, and FeS_2.

If it is assumed that $FeSiO_3$ is rapidly reactive, and the other two minerals are inert, $FeSiO_3$ would consume the oxygen produced, and again lower the oxygen pressure to about 10^{-70} atm. No CO_2 would be produced, so CO_2 pressure would remain at 10^{-4} atm, and the plants would not grow.

If FeS_2 is assumed to be the only reactive mineral, and the other two are inert, it would oxidize to Fe_2O_3 put H_2SO_4 in solution, and eventually make gypsum by conversion of $CaCO_3$. As shown by reaction (29), oxidation of FeS_2 would produce about half as much CO_2 as O_2 consumed. Therefore, there would be a brief flurry of grass growth, as the CO_2 was released during O_2 consumption, but the system would run down quickly. Reaction would stop after about 0.2 mol of grass had grown, with CO_2 again at 10^{-4} atm and O_2 at 10^{-70}.

But if $FeCO_3$ is reactive and FeS_2 and $FeSiO_3$ are inert, a remarkable series of events would take place. First the grass would grow to 0.1 mol, dropping CO_2 to 10^{-4} atm, while raising O_2 to 10^{-1}. The O_2 would react with the siderite to produce 0.4 mol of CO_2 (and some Fe_2O_3). This 0.4 mol of CO_2 would be used in turn by the grass to increase the moles of grass to 0.5, and to raise the O_2 pressure to 0.4 atm. Consumption of this oxygen by siderite would then increase CO_2 to 1.6 atm. If it is assumed that grass growth is much faster than siderite oxidation, the atmosphere in the container would be maintained at a CO_2 pressure slightly higher than the cut-off pressure for the plant, while oxygen pressure would rise continuously. If the grass did not die of oxygen poisoning, the final oxygen pressure would be 3.6 atm when all the siderite was consumed.

These three sequences of events, with markedly different effects on the atmosphere of the container, show the extremes of behavior possible as a result of differing reaction rates and degrees of exposure to the atmosphere of the reduced iron minerals. One general conclusion is that as the rate of photosynthesis approaches modern global rates, atmospheric CO_2 would be diminished to levels near the compensation point (0.01%).

4. Summary and Conclusion

1. A steady-state model was constructed for the sediment-ocean-atmosphere system, based on the current reservoirs of the major components of sedimentary rocks and estimates of the average fluxes for the most recent several hundreds of millions of years. The model served to show the complex chemical interconnections between the major mineral reservoirs, and that they all have an important influence on the atmosphere and demonstrated that the mass transfer of CO_2 and O_2 through the atmosphere through geologic time has been many, many times the current content of that reservoir.

2. The model was then modified to describe the more realistic conditions of constant ocean and atmosphere during Phanerozoic time, but with provision for mass transfer between mineral reservoirs. A number of examples were given of hypothetical transfer reactions that would permit major changes in the mass of mineral reservoirs. From this analysis the importance of variation in the rate of photosynthesis in maintaining constant atmosphere and ocean was deduced, and it was postulated that increase in photosynthetic rate with increasing atmospheric CO_2, and vice versa, is the basic mechanism maintaining the constancy of oceans and atmosphere.

3. The evolution of the atmosphere-ocean-sediment system prior to achievement of a new steady-state ocean and atmosphere at some time near the beginning of the Phanerozoic was then attempted. First a model was presented for the degradation of

the present system based on the consequences of eliminating photosynthesis and permitting spontaneous reduction of the existing system to take place. The deduced sequence of events was then used as a guide to discussion of evolution of the system in terms of a reversal of the reduction process. From this discussion emerged the concept of concomitant growth of the ferric iron, the sulfate, the organic matter, and the free oxygen reservoirs at the expense of reduced iron minerals. General predictions were also made as to the changes with time of the average δC^{13} and δS^{34} values for the carbon (both carbonate and organic carbon) and sulfate reservoirs.

4. The origin of free oxygen in the atmosphere was tied to the ratio of O_2 consumption to CO_2 release for the oxidation of the reduced iron mineral reservoirs. It was pointed out that if CO_2 release exceeds O_2 consumption, the response of photosynthesis is to produce net free oxygen. The mass of free oxygen in the atmosphere today was correlated with the ratios of FeS_2, $FeSiO_3$, and $FeCO_3$ that have been oxidized since about 2 billion years ago. The achievement of a steady-state system some 600 plus million years ago was correlated with destruction of most of the early $FeCO_3$ reservoir, followed by a drop of CO_2 in the atmosphere to near-present levels, and limitation of photosynthesis by atmospheric CO_2 level.

5. Acknowledgments

This work was supported by the Petroleum Research Fund administered by the American Chemical Society, NSF Grant No. GA-32058 and funds from the University of Hawaii. The original manuscript was read by Ian Kaplan and some of his colleagues at the University of California at Los Angeles, by Heinrich Holland of Harvard University, by Bryan Gregor of Wright State University, by Harmon Craig of Scripps Institute of Oceanography, by Peter Kroopnick of the University of Hawaii, and by Fred Mackenzie of Northwestern University. As a result of these readings, as well as suggestions by still others of our colleagues, we have made many changes; we have altered some of our views, and we have clung to others that were questioned. In particular both Kaplan and Holland challenged the emphasis we have placed on photosynthesis as the dominant CO_2 regulator. None of our reviewers was entirely convinced by the postulation that the oxidation of sediments, coupled with photosynthesis, is responsible for atmospheric oxygen, although they did seem willing to entertain the possibility. There were numerous other points of controversy that could not be resolved. We are deeply grateful to all of them; they will not be satisfied, but the chapter is at least greatly improved over the original version.

We are indebted to R. Oldnall for the calculations, including a great many not presented here, to Cynthia Garrels and Jean Kartchner for typing the manuscript and for help in editing and bibliographic search. The work of W. E. Rubey and Lars Gunnar Sillén are the foundation of this chapter.

References

Broecker, W. S., 1970. A boundary condition on the evolution of atmospheric oxygen. *J. Geophys. Res.*, **75**, 3553–3557.

Bolin, B., 1970. The carbon cycle. *Sci. Am.*, **233**, 124–132.

Chave, K. E., 1954. Aspects of the biogeochemistry of magnesium. I. Calcareous marine organisms. *J. Geol.*, **62**, 587–599.

Cloud, P. and A. Gibor, 1970. The oxygen cycle. *Sci. Am.*, **223**, 110–123.

Compston, W., 1960. The carbon isotopic compositions of certain marine invertebrates and coals from the Australian Permian. *Geochim. Cosmochim. Acta*, **18**, 1–22.

Craig, H., 1953. The geochemistry of the stable carbon isotopes. *Geochem. Cosmochim. Acta*, **3**, 53–92.

Craig, H., 1963. The isotopic geochemistry of water and carbon in geothermal areas. *Proc. First Spoleto Nuclear Geology Conference;* Nuclear Geology on Geothermal Areas, Consiglio Nazionale Delle Ricerche, Laboratorio di Geologia Nucleare, Pisa, 17–53.

Deevey, E. S., 1970. Mineral cycles. *Sci. Am.*, **233**, 148–158.

Degens, E. T., 1969. Biogeochemistry of stable isotopes. In *Organic Geochemistry*. G. Eglinton and M. T. J. Murphy, eds. Springer-Verlag, New York, pp. 304–329.

Drever, J. I., 1971. Early diagenesis of clay minerals, Rio Ameca Basin, Mexico. *Sediment, Petrol.*, **41**, 982–994.

Epstein, S., 1968. Distribution of carbon isotopes and their biochemical and geochemical significance. In CO_2: *Chemical, Biochemical and Physiological Aspects*. Symposium at Haverford College, August 20–21, 1968. R. Forster, J. Edsall, A. Otis, and F. Roughton, eds. N.A.S.A. Office of Technology Utilization, pp. 5–14.

Fanale, F. P., 1971. A case for catastrophic early degassing of the earth. *Chem. Geol.*, **8**, 79–105.

French, B. V., 1966. Some geologic implications of equilibrium between graphics and a C–H–O gas phase at high temperatures and pressures. *Rev. Geophys.*, **4**, 223–253.

Garrels, R. M. and F. T. Mackenzie, 1971. *Evolution of Sedimentary Rocks*. W. W. Norton, New York, 397 pp.

Garrels, R. M. and F. T. Mackenzie, 1972. A quantitative model for the sedimentary rock cycle. *Marine Chemistry*, **1**, 27–41.

Gibbs, Martin, 1970. The inhibition of photosynthesis by oxygen. *Amer. Sci.*, **58**, 634–640.

Gregor, B., 1971. Carbon and atmospheric oxygen. *Science*, **174**, 316–317.

Holland, H. D., 1964. On the chemical evolution of the terrestrial and cytherean atmosphere. In *The Origin and Evolution of Atmosphere and Oceans*. P. J. Brancazio and A. G. W. Cameron, eds. J. Wiley, New York, pp. 86–101.

Holland, H. D., 1968. The abundance of CO_2 in the earth's atmosphere through geologic time. In *Origin and Distribution of the Elements*. L. H. Ahrens, ed., Pergamon Press, New York, pp. 951–954.

Holland, H. D., 1972a. The geologic history of seawater—an attempt to solve the problem. *Geochim. Cosmochim. Acta*, **36**, 637–651.

Holland, H. D., 1972b. Ocean water, nutrients, and atmospheric oxygen. preprint, 21 pp.

Holser, W. T. and I. R. Kaplan, 1966. Isotope geochemistry of sedimentary sulfates. *Chem. Geol.*, **1**, 93–135.

Hutchinson, G. E., 1954. The biochemistry of the terrestrial atmosphere. In *The Earth as a Plant*. G. P. Kuiper, ed. University of Chicago Press, Chicago, pp. 371–433.

James, H. L., 1954. Sedimentary facies of iron formation. *Econ. Geol.*, **49**, 235–293.

James, H. L., 1966. Chemistry of the iron-rich sedimentary rocks. In *Data of Geochemistry*, 6th ed. M. Fleischer, eds. U.S. Geol. Survey Prof. Paper 440W, W1–W60.

Kastner, M., 1971. Authigenic feldspars in carbonate rocks. *Am. Min.*, **56**, 1403–1442.

Keith, M. L. and J. N. Weber, 1964. Carbon and oxygen isotopic composition of selected limestones and fossils. *Geochim. Cosmochim. Acta*, **28**, 1787–1816.

Krumbein, W. C. and R. M. Garrels, 1952. Origin and classification of chemical sediments in terms of pH and oxidation-reduction potentials. *J. Geol.*, **60**, 1–33.

Leopold, A. C., 1964. *Plant Growth and Development*. McGraw-Hill, New York, 466 pp.

Li, Y. H., 1972. Geochemical mass balance among lithosphere, hydrosphere, and atmosphere. *Am. J. Sci.*, **272**, 119–137.

Mackenzie, F. T. and R. M. Garrels, 1966. Chemical mass balance between rivers and oceans. *Am. J. Sci.*, **264**, 507–525.

Mackenzie, J. A., 1972. A mathematical model for the isotopic balance of sulfur in the oceans. Abstr. with Programs, **4** (3), Geol. Soc. Am., 197.

McKenzie, J. A., 1972. A mathematical model for the isotopic balance of sulfur in the oceans. In preparation.

Oehler, D. Z., J. W. Schopf, and K. A. Kvenvolden, 1972. Carbon isotopic studies of organic matter in Precambrian rocks. *Science*, **172**, 1246–1248.

Perry, E. A., Jr. and J. Hower, 1970. Burial diagenesis in Gulf Coast pelitic sediments. *Clays and Clay Min.*, **18**, 165–177.

Rasool, S. I. and S. H. Schneider, 1971. Atmospheric carbon dioxide and aerosols: effects of large increases on global climate. *Science*, **173**, 138–141.

Rhoads, D. C. and J. W. Morse, 1971. Evolutionary and ecologic significance of oxygen-deficient marine basins. *Lethaia*, **4**, 413–428.

Ronov, A. B., 1958. Organic carbon in sedimentary rocks (in relation to the presence of petroleum). *Geochemistry*, **5**, 510–536.

Ronov, A. B., 1964. Common tendencies in the chemical evolution of the earth's crust, ocean and atmosphere. *Geochemistry*, **8**, 715–743.

Ronov, A. B., 1971. Allgemeine entwicklungstendenzen in der zusammensetzung der ausseren Erdhulle, Ber. deutsch. *Ges. Geol. Wiss. A. Geol. Palaont.*, **16**, 331–350.

Rubey, W. W., 1951. Geologic history of seawater: An attempt to state the problem. *Bull. G.S.A.*, **62**, 1111–1147.

Sagan, C. and G. Mullen, 1972. Earth and Mars: Evolution of atmospheres and surface temperatures. *Science*, **177**, 52–56.

Sillén, L. G., 1961. The physical chemistry of seawater. In *Oceanography*. M. Sears, ed. A.A.A.S., Washington, D.C., pp. 549–581.

Sillén, L. G., 1967. The ocean as a chemical system. *Science*, **156**, 1189–1197.

Sillén, L. G., 1967. Gibbs phase rule and marine sediments. In *Equilibrium Concepts in Natural Water System*. Advances in Chemistry Series 67, Am. Chem. Soc., Washington, D.C., pp. 57–69.

Stumm, W. and J. J. Morgan, 1970. *Aquatic Chemistry*. J. Wiley, New York, 583 pp.

Thode, H. G. and J. Monster, 1964. The sulfur-isotope abundances in evaporites and in ancient oceans. In *Khimiia Zemloi Kori*. A. V. Vinogradov, ed. Izv. Akad. Nauk S.S.S.R., Moscow, pp. 589–600.

Thorstenson, D. C., 1970. Equilibrium distribution of small organic molecules in natural waters. *Geochim. Cosmochim. Acta.*, **34**, 745–770.

Van Valen, L., 1971a. The history and stability of atmospheric oxygen. *Science*, **171**, 439–443.

Van Valen, L., 1971b. Carbon and atmospheric oxygen (discussion). *Science*, **174**, 317.

Vinogradov, V. I., I. B. Ivanov, M. A. Litsarev, N. N. Pertsev, and L. L. Shanin, 1969. Age of the oxygen atmosphere of the earth. *Doklady, Akad. Nauk. S.S.S.R.*, **188**, 196–198.

Weber, J. N., 1967. Possible changes in the isotopic composition of the oceanic and atmospheric carbon reservoir over geologic time. *Geochim. Cosmochim. Acta.*, **31**, 2343–2351.

Wickman, F. E., 1954. The total amount of sediments and the composition of the "average igneous rock." *Geochim Cosmochim. Acta*, **5**, 97–110.

Yeremenko, N. A. and R. G. Pankina, 1971. Variation of δS^{34} in the sulfates of modern and ancient marine basins of the Soviet Union. *Geochemistry International*, **8**, 45–53.

10. THE MAGNESIUM PROBLEM

JAMES I. DREVER

1. Introduction

The magnesium problem can be summarized very simply. We estimate that dissolved magnesium is being brought to the oceans at a rate of approximately 1.3×10^{14} g/yr (Garrels and Mackenzie, 1971a); we assume that the ocean is in a steady state chemically, impling that Mg is removed from the ocean at the same rate as it is supplied by rivers and other sources, but the known processes by which Mg is removed do not appear to be quantitatively sufficient to balance the known input. Also, an understanding of the Mg cycle is essential to an understanding of the CO_2 cycle. Mg occurs in rocks as a carbonate, most commonly dolomite ($CaMg(CO_3)_2$), and as a variety of silicates (olivine, pyroxene, biotite, chlorite, etc.). Weathering of a carbonate removes 1 mol of CO_2 from the atmosphere per mole of Mg:

$$MgCO_3 + H_2O + CO_2 = Mg^{2+} + 2\,HCO_3^- \tag{1}$$

whereas weathering of a magnesium silicate removes 2 mol of CO_2 per mole of Mg:

$$MgSiO_3 + H_2O + 2\,CO_2 = Mg^{2+} + 2\,HCO_3^- + SiO_2 \tag{2}$$

[For the present discussion it is adequate to use simple molecules ($MgCO_3$, $MgSiO_3$) rather than the more complicated mineral formulas (dolomite, chlorite, etc.).]

Mg^{2+} may also be removed from the oceans as a carbonate or as a silicate, in effect reversing equations 1 and 2. If the ratio of Mg carbonate to Mg silicate formation in the oceans and during diagenesis is the same as the ratio of Mg carbonate to Mg silicate consumed during weathering, there will be no net addition or removal of CO_2 from the ocean-atmosphere system. If these ratios are not equal, however, there will be a net addition of CO_2 to, or removal of CO_2 from, the ocean-atmosphere system. If atmospheric CO_2 pressure is to remain constant, there must be a relationship between atmospheric P_{CO_2} and the ratio of Mg carbonate to Mg silicate formed in sediments. This relationship can be explained on an equilibrium model (Holland, 1965), or on a feedback model (Broecker, 1971).

The great impetus for the study of removal mechanisms of ions from seawater was the publication of Sillén's (1961) equilibrium model. The basic postulate of this model was that the cationic ratios in seawater were controlled by equilibria among the major solid phases present in marine sediments; thus, for example, the $[Mg^{2+}]/[H^+]^2$ ratio would be determined by equilibrium between chlorite and quartz (a similar reaction can be written for an aluminous chlorite, with kaolinite as a product on the right-hand side):

$$\underset{\text{chlorite}}{Mg_3(OH)_6Mg_3Si_4O_{10}(OH)_2} + 12\,H^+ = \underset{\text{quartz}}{4\,SiO_2} + 6\,Mg^{2+} + 10\,H_2O$$

$$K_{\text{equilibrium}} = \frac{[Mg^{2+}]^6}{[H^+]^{12}}$$

$$K^{1/6}_{\text{equilibrium}} = \frac{[Mg^{2+}]}{[H^+]^2}$$

All cation ratios were determined by similar reactions involving mica, kaolinite, montmorillonite, and phillipsite, and total cation content was determined by $[Cl^-]$, which did not participate in silicate reactions. Sillén himself was careful to point out that complete equilibrium was not to be expected in marine sediments; instead he proposed the equilibrium model as an abstraction against which the real ocean could be compared. The equilibrium model was amplified by Holland (1965), who added the concept that atmospheric P_{CO_2} was buffered by the coexistence of chlorite, calcite, dolomite, and quartz. In an equilibrium model, the problem of ion removal is automatically taken care of by transformation of a low-cation clay mineral (e.g., kaolinite) into a clay mineral of higher cationic content (e.g., illite, chlorite, or montmorillonite).

Distributional and isotopic studies, however (Biscaye, 1965; Hurley, 1966; Dasch, 1969; Savin and Epstein, 1970), have tended to show that clay minerals are chemically unreactive in the deep oceans, and have undergone little change since formation in the zone of weathering. More recent models have, therefore, tended to stress non-equilibrium processes. Mackenzie and Garrels (1966) proposed synthesis of clay minerals from an amorphous starting material as an important cation-removal process, and Broecker (1971) stressed the importance of kinetic rather than thermodynamic factors in controlling the composition of seawater.

In this chapter we shall follow more of a kinetic approach. We shall examine various processes that have been proposed as mechanisms for the removal of Mg^{2+} from seawater and attempt to assess the quantitative significance of each. In these calculations several numbers recur frequently, and for convenience they are tabulated in Table I. They are taken largely from Garrels' and Mackenzie's (1971a) book, which gives the most reliable estimates of present-day fluxes of earth materials currently available. In a later section we shall discuss possible modifications of these numbers.

TABLE I

Numbers Used in Mg Flux Calculations

		Reference[a]
Total river flux of H_2O	0.32×10^{20} g/yr	1, 2
Flux of dissolved Mg^{2+} in rivers	1.31×10^{14} g/yr	1, 2
Atmospherically cycled Mg^{2+}	0.08×10^{14} g/yr	1
Mg^{2+} flux from rock weathering	1.23×10^{14} g/yr	
Total suspended sediment from rivers	183×10^{14} g/yr	1, 3
Ratio shale: sandstone in average sediment	87:13	1
Clay mineral content of average shale	61%	4
Assuming river suspended sediment = average shale + sandstone		
Clay mineral content of suspended load	53%	
Clay mineral flux from streams	97×10^{14} g/yr	

[a] 1—Garrels and Mackenzie (1971a); 2—Livingstone (1963); 3—Holeman (1968); and 4—Shaw and Weaver (1965).

2. Sources of Mg

The principal source of dissolved Mg^{2+} for the oceans is subaerial weathering on the continents. Average river water contains 4.1 mg/liter Mg^{2+} (Livingstone, 1963) of which approximately 0.27 mg/liter is attributable to atmospheric cycling (Garrels and Mackenzie, 1971a). Assuming a total river discharge of 0.32×10^{20} g/yr (Livingstone, 1963; Garrels and Mackenzie, 1971a), the total flux of dissolved Mg^{2+} to the oceans from rock weathering is 1.23×10^{14} g/yr. This value will be referred to as the net river flux of Mg^{2+}. It is very difficult to calculate the proportion of dissolved Mg^{2+} that comes from carbonate weathering, as Mg^{2+} makes up only a small fraction of the total dissolved solids in river water. An order of magnitude calculation can be made in the following way. If we accept Garrels and Mackenzie's (1971a, p. 171) estimate that 70% of the Ca^{2+} in river water comes from carbonate weathering (the remainder coming from gypsum and atmospheric cycling), and that limestone weathering contributes Ca^{2+} and Mg^{2+} in the same ratio as they occur in the average limestone of Clark (1924), then 1.64 ppm of the Mg^{2+} in average river water (40% of the total Mg^{2+}) is derived from carbonate weathering. This value should be a maximum, as Garrels and Mackenzie assumed that no Ca^{2+} whatsoever was derived from silicate weathering. Waters from igneous terrains have an average Ca^{2+}/SiO_2 ratio (wt) of approximately 0.6. Thus the 13.1 ppm SiO_2 in average river (Livingstone, 1963) should be accompanied by 7.9 ppm Ca^{2+} from silicate weathering. If the remaining Ca^{2+} in average river water is assumed to come from weathering average limestone, the corresponding Mg^{2+} from limestone weathering would be 1.08 ppm, or 26% of the total in average river water. Thus the amount of Mg^{2+} in river water that is derived from the weathering of carbonates is probably between 20 and 40% of the total Mg^{2+}.

Submarine Alteration of Volcanic Detritus

When volcanic rock comes in contact with sea water it characteristically loses Ca^{2+} and Mg^{2+} to the water, and gains alkalis. Mass balance calculations by Garrels and Mackenzie (1971a) and Garrels, Mackenzie and Siever (1972) suggest that approximately half the Ca present in limestones must have been derived originally from submarine alteration of volcanic material. If the total mass of limestone in sedimentary rocks is $3{,}500 \times 10^{20}$g (Garrels and Mackenzie, 1971a, p. 249), the total Ca^{++} supplied to the oceans over geological time from submarine alteration of volcanics would be 550×10^{20}g. If this Ca^{++} had been released to the oceans uniformly over geological time, the annual Ca^{++} flux from this source would be 0.18×10^{14} g/yr. The ratio of Mg loss to Ca loss during submarine alteration of basalt in 0.34:1 (Muehlenbachs and Clayton, 1972, table 4), so that the corresponding Mg^{2+} flux would be $.07 \times 10^{14}$ g/yr, or 6% of the Mg^{2+} flux from continental weathering. Muehlenbachs and Clayton (1972) show that the present-day rate of submarine alteration of basalt would generate an Mg^{2+} flux at least an order of magnitude smaller than this. Thus the Mg^{2+} flux from the alteration of submarine volcanics to the present-day oceans appears to be negligible compared to the flux from continental weathering, but alteration of submarine volcanics may have been quantitatively more important in the geological past than it is today.

3. Removal Mechanisms for Mg

Carbonate Formation

Organisms that secrete carbonate skeletons incorporate varying amounts of Mg into the skeleton as high-magnesium calcite, low magnesium calcite and aragonite. The amount of Mg incorporated varies from species to species, and also varies as a function of the temperature to which the organism is exposed (Chave, 1954a). Skeletal aragonite generally contains approximately 0.1% Mg; benthonic organisms with calcite skeletons typically form skeletons containing high concentrations of Mg (1 to 30% $MgCO_3$, Chave, 1954a) while skeletons of pelagic organisms generally contain less than 1% $MgCO_3$. Shallow water ("shelf") carbonate sediments are composed predominantly of skeletal debris from benthonic organisms, and typically contain 5% $MgCO_3$ by weight (Chave, 1954b). Pelagic oozes, on the other hand, typically contain approximately 0.5% $MgCO_3$ (datum from Chester, 1965, corrected for detrital contribution).

To a first approximation, we may assume that the amount of calcium carbonate formed per year is equivalent to the river flux of dissolved Ca^{2+}, plus the Ca^{2+} released by ion exchange. Clay minerals in fresh waters generally have Ca^{2+} ions occupying the majority of the ion exchange sites. When the clays encounter sea water, most of this Ca^{2+} is replaced by Mg^{2+}, Na^+ and K^+ (see Table II). Assuming a Ca^{2+} content of average river water of 15 mg/liter (Livingstone, 1963), a clay mineral flux of 97×10^{14} g/yr (Table I) and a Ca^{2+} contribution from ion exchange of 0.0058 g/g clay (Russell, 1970), the total Ca^{2+} flux from the continents is 5.36×10^{14} g/yr.

If all the Ca^{2+} is removed as "shelf-type" carbonates, carbonate formation will remove 0.27×10^{14} g/yr Mg^{2+} (22% of the river flux) from the oceans. If, on the other hand, all the Ca^{2+} is removed as pelagic carbonates, the total Mg^{2+} removed by carbonate formation will be only 0.027×10^{14} g/yr (2.2% of the river flux). Turekian (1964) estimated that in the present-day oceans pelagic ooze formation can account for all the Ca^{2+} brought to the sea by rivers, and hence shelf carbonate formation must be of minor importance. This cannot have been true in the past, since the bulk of the Ca^{2+} in the river water comes from the weathering of shelf carbonates and not pelagic oozes or their metamorphosed equivalents (including igneous rocks). The discrepancy is presumably related to a change in the principal locus of carbonate sedimentation from the shelves to the deep oceans as a consequence of the widespread development of pelagic calcareous organisms in the late Jurassic/early Cretaceous.

If we assume that 20% of river Ca^{2+} flux is removed as shelf carbonate (a reasonable upper limit), and 80% as pelagic ooze, the corresponding Mg^{2+} removal will be 0.075×10^{14} g/yr, or 6% of the net dissolved Mg^{2+} flux in rivers. We previously estimated that 40% of river Mg^{2+} flux came from the weathering of carbonates, which indicates the importance of pre-Cretaceous limestones, and of dolomites formed by diagenesis out of contact with seawater. Dolomite forming is today in supratidal environments in the subtropics (Bathurst, 1972). The amount of dolomite formed in this way is quantitatively unimportant in comparison to the Mg^{2+} incorporated into skeletal calcite.

Ion Exchange

Clay minerals in the suspended load of rivers have Ca^{2+} as the principal cation occupying exchange sites. When the clays enter seawater, the Ca^{2+} is largely replaced by Mg^{2+}, K^+, and Na^+. The process has been studied in detail by Russell (1970), from whom the data in Table II are taken. These results show that, for the clays of the Rio Ameca: (*a*) the total uptake of Mg^{2+}, K^+, and Na^+ is exactly balanced by loss of Ca^{2+} (within the uncertainty of the data), and (*b*) the measured cation exchange capacity of the clays decreases as the clays pass from fresh water to the oceans. Thus some of the ions that replace calcium are no longer exchangeable, and might be regarded as "fixed."

If we assume that world average clay behaves as Rio Ameca clay, and a clay flux of 97×10^{14} g/yr (Table I), the net removal of Mg^{2+} from the oceans by ion exchange will be 0.097×10^{14} g/yr, or 8% of the net dissolved Mg^{2+} flux from rivers. This value is, if anything, slightly high, as the montmorillonite content and hence cation exchange capacity of Rio Ameca clay is probably higher than that of world average clay. The clay mineral content of Rio Ameca sediment is approximately 60% montmorillonite, 30% kaolinite, 10% illite (Drever, 1968).

TABLE II

Cation Exchange of Clay Fraction of Rio Ameca Sediment (Data from Russell, 1970). (Units are Milliequivalents per gram of Clay.)

	River (1)		Sea (2)		Difference (2 − 1)	
	Total	Exchange	Total	Exchange	Total	Exchange
Na	0.19	0.06	0.27	0.06	0.08	0
K	0.31	0.12	0.42	0.03	0.11	−0.09
Ca	0.51	0.48	0.22	0.06	−0.29	−0.42
Mg	1.41	0.10	1.49	0.31	0.08	0.21
Sum	2.42	0.76	2.40	0.46	−0.02 (±0.07)	−0.30

Authigenic clays with high cation exchange capacities (nontronite) are presently being formed in the oceans by alteration of volcanic material. The net effect of the alteration process will be to add Mg^{2+} to the oceans, and the Mg^{2+} on the exchange sites of nontronite will be minor in comparison with the overall Mg^{2+} loss during alteration, and with the Mg^{2+} taken up on land-derived clays.

"Upgrading of Degraded Lattices"

The term "upgrading of degraded lattices" has been used extensively in the literature (e.g. Grim, 1968, pp. 536–537, Holland, 1965, Porrenga, 1967, p. 60), but the precise chemical mechanism implied by the term, especially in the context of Mg^{2+} fixation, has never been clearly stated. The overall concept is, that during weathering, illites, chlorites, and vermiculites become "stripped" of K^+ and Mg^{2+}; when the "stripped" clays enter the ocean, they take up K^+ and Mg^{2+} from seawater to regenerate the original structure (Weaver, 1958). The process has been shown to affect the X-ray diffraction properties of the clays (Weaver, 1958), but the question of cation balance in the "stripped" clays has not been investigated in detail. If the negative charges generated by the loss of Mg^{2+} and K^+ are balanced by exchangeable Ca^{2+} (as suggested by Weaver), the process is chemically indistinguishable from the ion exchange/fixation process discussed in the preceding section. If the charges are balanced by H^+ (or H_3O^+), we have a different process that could lead to an additional removal of Mg^{2+} from seawater. The data of Potts (quoted by Keller, 1963) and of Russell (1970) show that there is no significant exchange of K^+ or Mg^{2+} for H^+ when clays from river sediment are exposed to seawater. Thus the process of upgrading stripped clays is chemically equivalent to ion exchange/fixation, the quantitative significance of which has already been discussed. The "upgrading" of montmorillonite to chlorite by formation of brucite ($Mg(OH)_2$) islands between the silicate layers will be discussed in the next section.

Clay Mineral Transformation and Synthesis

The transformation of one clay-type mineral into another has been proposed by many authors as a mechanism for removing ions from seawater. During the years 1949–1958 several studies (Grim, Dietz, and Bradley, 1949; Grim and Johns, 1954; Johns and Grim, 1958; Griffin and Ingram, 1955; Powers, 1957; Pinsak and Murray, 1960; Nelson, 1960) showed systematic changes in the relative abundance of clay minerals as a function of distance from the inferred source, and these changes were commonly interpreted as evidence for the transformation of one clay mineral into another. Weaver (1959) argued, however, that the variations in abundance of different clay minerals could be explained equally well by differential flocculation and differences in source. Weaver's conclusions were strongly supported by the studies on differential settling by Whitehouse, Jeffrey, and Debbrecht (1960), and Biscaye's (1965) study of clay mineral distribution in the Atlantic Ocean provided strong evidence against any large-scale clay mineral transformation occurring in the ocean.

Possible transformation reactions can be divided into several groups: (*a*) transformations involving major changes in the clay lattice, for example, the conversion of kaolinite to montmorillonite or chlorite; (*b*) transformations involving only the interlayer positions in phyllosilicates, for example, the formation of brucite interlayers in montmorillonite; (*c*) synthesis of clay minerals from an amorphous starting material; (*d*) glauconite formation; and (*e*) conversion of gibbsite to chlorite.

Major structural transformations

Conversion of kaolinite to a chloritic phase according to the equation

$$Al_2Si_2O_5(OH_4) + SiO_2 + 5\,Mg^{2+} + 7\,H_2O = Mg_5Al_2Si_3O_{10}(OH)_8 + 10H^+ \quad (3)$$

would, if it occurred, be a highly effective mechanism for the removal of Mg^{2+} from seawater. Sillén (1961) originally proposed that equilibrium among the species of equation 3 controlled the $[Mg^{2+}]/[H^+]^2$ ratio of seawater. Calculations (e.g., Helgeson and Mackenzie, 1970) have tended to show that kaolinite is unstable relative to a more magnesian phase in seawater, although uncertainties in the thermochemical data make this conclusion tentative.

Experimental and field observations, however, suggest that kaolinite is chemically inert in the marine environment. Whitehouse and McCarter (1958) exposed kaolinite to seawater for periods of up to 5 yr in the laboratory, and saw no evidence of reaction. Biscaye's (1965) study indicates that no large-scale conversion of kaolinite to another phase occurs, although he would not have detected transformation of a small fraction of the kaolinite. The results of Perry and Hower (1970) indicate that kaolinite in Gulf Coast sediment remains inert even after burial to 12,000 ft (4 km), while other phases (mixed-layer illite-montmorillonite, mica, K-feldspar) are reacting extensively.

Mackenzie et al. (1967) and Siever (1968) have shown that kaolinite will take up silica rapidly from silica-enriched seawater and release silica rapidly to low-silica seawater. These results have been interpreted as indicating that kaolinite is highly reactive in the marine environment. Wollast and De Broeu (1971) suggest that transformation of disordered kaolinite to a more siliceous clay (illite, montmorillonite, or chlorite) controls the silica content of interstitial water of sediments from the estuary of the Scheldt, but no data for Mg^{2+} or other cations were reported. A rather sensitive test of whether the silica data of Mackenzie et al. (1967) and Siever (1968) do, in fact, indicate that kaolinite transform rapidly to illite or montmorillonite in marine sediments would be to examine the Mg^{2+} and K^+ content of interstitial waters from sediments containing kaolinite and biogenic silica. Biogenic silica will maintain a high silica activity in the interstitial water. The conversion of kaolinite to illite or montmorillonite can be described by the equations:

$$1.1\,Al_2Si_2O_5(OH)_4 + 0.8\,K^+ + 0.5\,Mg^{2+} + 1.2\,SiO_2 = \underset{\text{Illite}^1}{K_{0.8}Mg_{0.5}Al_{2.2}Si_{3.4}O_{10}(OH)_2} + 1.8\,H^+ + 0.3\,H_2O$$

[1] Formula modified from Mackenzie and Garrels (1972) to exclude iron.

$$1.67\ Al_2Si_2O_5(OH)_4 + 0.84\ Mg^{2+} + 0.2\ Na^+ + 0.1\ K^+ + 4.66\ SiO_2 =$$
$$\underset{\text{Montmorillonite}^2}{(Na_{0.2}K_{0.1}Mg_{0.1}Mg_{0.18)})Mg_{0.66}Al_{3.34}Si_8O_{20}(OH)_4} + 1.98\ H^+ + 0.35\ H_2O$$

Any conversion of kaolinite to montmorillonite or illite in the sediment should cause depletions in interstitial Mg^{2+} and K^+. Pore waters from oxidizing sediments in the Atlantic Ocean, which contain biogenic silica, and presumably kaolinite from comparison with Biscaye's (1965) maps, do show depletions in Mg^{2+}; however, the Mg^{2+} depletions are matched by corresponding K^+ enrichments, suggesting that kaolinite transformation is not the controlling process (Bischoff and Ku, 1970). More striking evidence is provided by core 13, section 3 (middle Eocene) of the Deep Sea Drilling Project (Maxwell et al., 1970). The two most abundant constituents of the sediment of this section are radiolaria and kaolinite (Pimm, 1970; Rex, 1970). Neither illite nor montmorillonite was detected (Rex, 1970), although interstitial Mg^{2+} was high (1.24/mg/g), and interstitial silica relatively high (29 mg/kg) (Manheim et al., 1970). Unless some argument can be made that the pH of these sediments was anomalously low, the persistence of the assemblage kaolinite + opal + seawater since the middle Eocene without any sign of reaction is strong evidence against the conversion of kaolinite to illite or montmorillonite being a significant process in marine sediments.

Interlayer transformations

Reactions involving only the interlayer atoms of phyllosilicates may occur rapidly at low temperatures, since the activation energies for such processes should be very much less than for processes involving the lattice as a whole. The reaction of greatest interest for the magnesium problem is the formation of $Mg(OH)_2$ (brucite) layers between the silicate layers of montmorillonite. If carried to completion, the result will be to convert the montmorillonite to a chlorite. Caillère and Hénin (1949), Slaughter and Milne (1960), Youell (1960), and Carstea, Harward, and Knox (1970) have all demonstrated this reaction at low temperature in the laboratory. The experiments of Whitehouse and McCarter (1958) suggested that montmorillonite may convert to chlorite on prolonged exposure to seawater, however, their results can be interpreted in other ways (Perry, 1971).

Deffeyes (1965, and quoted by Russell, 1970) has shown that a similar reaction occurs when natural sediments are maintained in contact with the seawater at a sufficiently high pH. The Deffeyes experiment was simple and elegant. Soil clay was mixed with seawater, the pH of the mixture was raised to a predetermined value by addition of Na(OH) solution, then maintained at that value for five weeks by continuous addition of more Na(OH) solution. When the predetermined pH value was 8.0 or lower, no significant addition of Na(OH) was required during the five-week period. At pH 8.5 and 9.0, however, continuous addition of Na(OH) was required to maintain the pH value, and there was no sign of levelling off even after five weeks. If the experiment was repeated using either Mg-free seawater or montmorillonite-free clay, the effect was not observed. The conclusion is that a reaction of the type $Mg^{2+} + 2(OH)^- +$ montmorillonite = $Mg(OH)_2$-montmorillonite complex will occur whenever montmorillonite is in contact with seawater at a pH value of approximately 8.5 (There are no data for pH values between 8.0 and 8.5.)

The question is whether the pH of seawater in contact with sediments is ever sufficiently high for this reaction to proceed. Although surface seawater commonly has a pH of approximately 8.2, deep water pH values are generally lower, and pH

[2] Idealized formula with exchangeable cation ratios from Drever (1971a).

values of interstitial waters in sediments are generally below 8.0. Russell (1970) showed that a reaction of this type did not occur when the clay of the Rio Ameca encountered seawater, and available data on interstitial waters of sediments show no obvious correlation between high pH values and Mg^{2+} depletions. In summary, formation of $Mg(OH)_2$ interlayers in montmorillonite would become an important buffer for the pH and Mg^{2+} content of seawater, should the pH of the oceans ever rise. The apparent closeness of seawater composition to the equilibrium value is striking, but there is no direct evidence that the process is actively removing Mg^{2+} from the ocean today.

Transformation of amorphous material

Mackenzie and Garrels (1966) suggested that X-ray amorphous aluminosilicate material of approximately kaolinitic composition was formed in abundance during weathering, and that this material was rapidly transformed in the marine environment to illite, montmorillonite, and chlorite. These reactions were postulated as important mechanisms for the removal of Mg^{2+}, K^+, and Na^+ from seawater. Such reactions have not, however, been shown to occur in nature. Russell (1970) showed that ion exchange was the only chemical reaction affecting the major ion composition of the clay fraction of the sediments of the Rio Ameca during the first year or so of contact with seawater. [Drever (1968) originally selected the Rio Ameca basin as an area likely to contribute a large amount of amorphous material to the sediment.] The "amorphous material" content [measured by the alkali solubility technique of Hashimoto and Jackson (1960)] of Rio Ameca sediment does, in fact, decrease on prolonged contact with seawater (Drever, 1971a), but Drever's data suggest that there is no uptake of K^+ of Mg^{2+} that can be related to the disappearance of the "amorphous material." Moberly, Kimura, and McCoy (1968) reported that amorphous material produced by weathering of basalt on Hawaii was transformed to illite and montmorillonite in the ocean. It is possible, however that their results could be explained by a combination of differential settling and admixture of clays from the continents.

Glauconite formation

Glauconite is an authigenic silicate forming in the marine environment. Glauconites typically contain 2 to 5% MgO by weight; whether their formation represents a net gain or loss of Mg^{2+} depends on the Mg content of the starting material from which the glauconite is formed. Transformation of biotite to glauconite, for example, will result in a net loss of Mg from the sediment. Porrenga (1967) showed that glauconite off the Niger Delta formed from fecal pellets composed of mixed detrital clays. During the transformation the MgO content of the pellets increased from 1.03 to 2.18%. This is the only direct measurement of Mg^{2+} uptake by glauconite formation known to the author. Using this value and the numbers in Table I, formation of glauconite equal to 1% of the total river sediment flux would remove 0.013×10^{14} g/yr of Mg^{2+} from the oceans, or 1.0% of the net river Mg^{2+} flux. Although the mean glauconite content of Recent sediments is not known, it is probably not greater than 3%, so that the Mg^{2+} removed from seawater by glauconite formation is probably not greater than 3% of the net river Mg^{2+} flux.

Conversion of gibbsite to chlorite

Swindale and Fan (1967) described gibbsite grains rimmed by chlorite from Waimea Bay, Hawaii, which they interpreted as diagenetic transformation of gibbsite formed in the weathering environment. A similar alteration of "desert varnish" to chlorite was described by Bonatti and Arrhenius (1965), although this transformation may have occurred well below the sediment-water interface.

From the optical properties listed by Swindale and Fan (1967), it appears that the chlorite they observed is a low-iron sheridanite, with an approximate formula $Mg_9Al_6Si_5O_{20}(OH)_{16}$. The overall reaction can thus be represented by the equation:

$$6\,Al(OH)_3 + 9\,Mg^{2+} + 5\,SiO_2 + 8\,H_2O = Mg_9Al_6Si_5O_{20}(OH)_{16} + 18\,H^+$$

If average sediment contained 1% authigenic chlorite formed by this reaction, the process would remove 0.36×10^{14} g/yr of Mg^{2+} from seawater, or 29% of the net river Mg^{2+} flux. Thus, if widespread conversion of gibbsite to chlorite does occur in the oceans, the process will be an important removal mechanism for Mg^{2+}. How wide spread is the phenomenon? Gibbsite is almost certainly unstable with respect to a more magnesian phase in surface marine sediments (cf. Helgeson and Mackenzie, 1970), but the reaction is likely to be kinetically slow. The only observation of gibbsite rimmed by chlorite in marine sediments are those of Swindale and Fan, and their data does not prove unequivocally that the grains formed in a normal marine environment. Porrenga, (1967), in his detailed study of the sediments of the Niger Delta, the Orinoco Shelf and the Sarawak Shelf, saw no evidence of a similar phenomenon, and specifically concluded that authigenic chlorite was not forming in these sediments. Biscaye's (1965) data show no indication that the gibbsite in Atlantic Ocean sediments is being destroyed, and chlorite abundances are lowest in areas where gibbsite is present in the sediment. In the Pacific Ocean, on the other hand, chlorite abundances are relatively high around Hawaii (Griffin, Windom, and Goldberg, 1968), which is consistent with the Swindale-Fan mechanism. Chlorite is also formed as a minor constituent during the submarine alteration of volcanic debris (Griffin et al., 1972), which may explain the distribution of chlorite in the Pacific Ocean.

Magnesium-Iron Exchange in Anaerobic Sediments

Drever (1971a, b) proposed that in the presence of free hydrogen sulfide (or HS^-), iron is extracted from clay minerals to form a sulfide, and Mg^{2+} from the surrounding water enters the clay mineral structure to occupy the sites vacated by Fe. The reaction can be described by the generalized equation

$$2\,Fe_{(clay)} + 3\,Mg_{(soln)} + 4[S] = 3\,Mg_{(clay)} + 2\,FeS_{2(pyrite)}$$

where [S] represents some form of reduced sulfur and $Fe_{(clay)}$ represents ferric iron in a nonexchange site in the clay mineral. The conclusion was based on the observation that (*a*) the Mg content of clays from anoxic sediments in Banderas Bay, Mexico,was significantly higher than the Mg content of similar clays from oxidizing environments in the same area and (*b*) interstitial waters from anoxic marine sediments are generally depleted in Mg^{2+}, and the depletions often cannot be explained by formation of a carbonate phase. Mg^{2+} and $SO_4{}^{2-}$ depletions in interstitial waters of cores from Deep Sea Drilling Project Legs IV and V show a relationship which is also consistent with this mechanism (Drever, 1971b).

If we write the reaction for the conversion of the nontronite component of a montmorillonite to a saponite component (equation 4), we can predict the relationship between $SO_4{}^{2-}$ and Mg^{2+} depletions and carbonate alkalinity increases. The relationship is independent of the mineral in which the Fe^{3+} occurs; it will be somewhat different if Fe^{2+} is involved. The relationship will also be different for other possible Mg-consuming reactions (e.g., carbonate formation).

$$(X)_{0.66}Fe_4^{3+}Al_{0.66}Si_{7.34}O_{20}(OH)_4 + 6\,Mg^{2+} + 8SO_4^{2-} + 15[C] + 13\,H_2O = (X)_{0.66}Mg_6Al_{0.66}Si_{7.34}O_{20}(OH)_4 + 4\,FeS_2 + 15\,HCO_3^- + 11\,H^+ \quad (4)$$

(X) represents exchangeable cations, [C] reduced carbon.

Sayles, Manheim, and Waterman (1972) studied in detail the relationships between SO_4^{2-} depletions and changes in alkalinity and Mg^{2+}, Ca^{2+}, K^+, and NH_4^+ concentrations in interstitial waters from cores taken on Leg XV of the Deep Sea Drilling Project. They concluded that in the core dominated by terrigenous sediment, a reaction of the type indicated by equation 4 was an important process. Berner, Scott, and Thomlinson (1970), however, found no evidence for such a reaction in an intertidal mud from Long Island Sound and an organic-rich sediment from a Maine fjord. It is possible that these sediments did not contain suitable clay minerals, or that they were so recently deposited that the reaction did not have time to proceed appreciably. In general, it appears that anoxic, terrigenous, marine sediments do take up Mg^{2+}, although the precise mechanism has not yet been established.

The significance of this reaction to the overall magnesium problem will depend on what fraction of the terrigenous clay flux encounters anaerobic conditions while still in diffusional contact with seawater. For this reaction to be effective, anaerobic conditions need not exist at the sediment-water interface. Mg^{2+} uptake by clays in the top few meters of sediment can be balanced by a diffusional flux of Mg^{2+} into the interstitial water of the sediment from the overlying seawater, provided the sedimentation rate is not too rapid. An upper limit to the amount of Mg^{2+} that could be fixed in this way can be calculated from considerations of sulfate balance. If all the river sulfate flux were consumed by the reaction of equation 4, the process would remove 0.64×10^{14} g/yr of Mg^{2+}, or 52% of the net river Mg^{2+} flux. Obviously this reaction is not the only process by which sulfur is removed from seawater; some goes to form gypsum in evaporites, some to form pyrite from iron oxides, and some is "buried" in interstitial water of nonreducing sediments. An upper limit would be to assume that 50% of river sulfate could be removed by a reaction of the type discussed here. The corresponding Mg^{2+} uptake would then be 0.32×10^{14} g/yr, or 26% of the river flux of dissolved Mg^{2+}.

Alternatively, we can try to estimate the fraction of the river clay flux that encounters reducing conditions prior to the final burial, and use Drever's (1971a) data to calculate the corresponding Mg^{2+} uptake. The uncertainties here are enormous, particularly as Drever's data show considerable scatter, and there is no evidence that all clays behave identically to those in Banderas Bay. If all the clays in river sediment (Table I) encountered reducing conditions while still in contact with seawater, and the Mg^{2+} uptake is 0.005 g/g clay (cf. Drever, 1971a, Fig. 3), the total Mg^{2+} uptake would be 0.49×10^{14} g/yr, or 40% of the river flux of dissolved Mg^{2+}. Obviously the figure of 100% for clays encountering reducing conditions is unreasonable, however, the bulk of sedimentation takes place around continental margins, where reducing conditions are normally encountered near the sediment-water interface. If 60% of the terrigenous clay supply encounters reducing conditions, the corresponding Mg^{2+} uptake will be 0.29×10^{14} g/yr, or 24% of the river flux, which is essentially the same as the upper limit value estimated from consideration of the sulfur flux.

Magnesium Silicate Precipitation

Seawater and interstitial water in marine sediments are supersaturated with respect to a number of magnesium silicates (Fig. 1), but only members of the sepiolite-

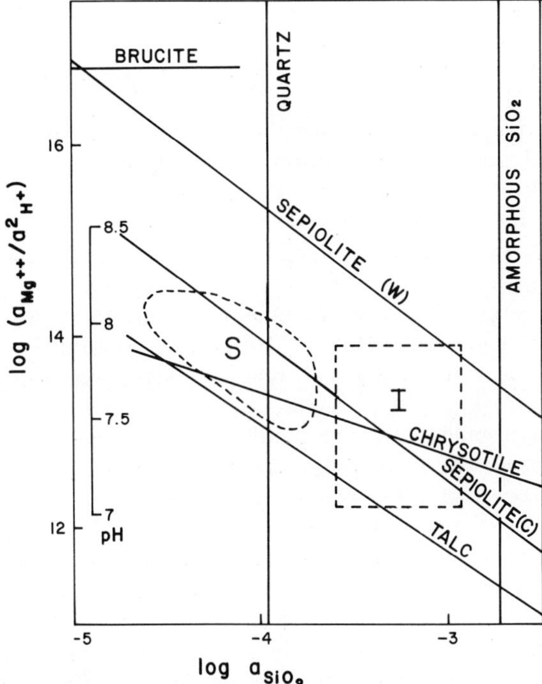

Fig. 1. Equilibrium solubilities of some phases in the system $MgO–SiO_2–H_2O$ at 25°C and 1 atm pressure. Data for chrysotile and talc from Hostetler et al. (1971); data for sepiolite (*C*) from Christ, Hostetler, and Siebert (1973); data for sepiolite (*W*) from Wollast, Mackenzie, and Bricker (1968). *S* is normal range for seawater, *I* for interstitial water. pH scale assumes a Mg^{2+} activity in seawater of $10^{-1.87}$. From Garrels and Thompson (1962).

palygorskite group appear to have kinetic barriers low enough to allow them to precipitate under conditions approximating those present in seawater. In their experiments on silica uptake by clays, Mackenzie et al. (1967) noted that silica concentrations greater than 26 ppm in surface seawater (pH 8.2) caused rapid precipitation of a sepiolite-like phase.

Sepiolite is a hydrated magnesium silicate with a fibrous structure, commonly represented by the formula $Mg_8(H_2O)_4Si_{12}O_{30}(OH)_4 \cdot 8\,H_2O$. Palygorskite (synonymous with attapulgite) is a closely related fibrous magnesium silicate. Analyzed palygorskites have contained aluminum (Caillère and Hénin, 1961; Bowles et al., 1971), but it is not known if aluminum is essential in the palygorskite structure. The difference in the solubility of sepiolite reported by Wollast, Mackenzie, and Bricker, (1968), and Christ, Hostetler, and Siebert, (1973) represents the difference in free energy between a disordered, freshly precipitated phase and well-ordered crystals of natural sepiolite.

Most reported occurrences of sepiolite in deep-sea sediments have been associated with active spreading centers or sediments originally deposited near active spreading centers (Hathaway and Sachs, 1965; Bonatti and Joensuu, 1968; Bowles et al., 1971; Drever, 1971c). Bowles et al. (1971) and Drever (1971c) have presented strong evidence that the palygorskite examined by them was a primary precipitate and not an alteration product of volcanic ash or other material. The most probable explanation is that it is the product of interaction between hydrothermal solutions related to volcanism and normal seawater. Solutions which have been in contact with basaltic material at slightly elevated temperatures are likely to have higher silica activities and higher pH values than normal seawater. Both factors will favor the precipitation of sepiolite (see Fig. 1).

Overall, it is not possible to say whether the whole process of hydrothermal exhalation and sepiolite/palygorskite precipitation adds or substracts Mg^{2+} from seawater. As an order of magnitude calculation, if sufficient sepiolite were formed at spreading centers, deriving all its Mg^{2+} from seawater, to balance the net river Mg^{2+} flux, a layer of sepiolite 150 to 200 m thick would have to be formed continuously at all spreading centers, assuming a rate of production of new sea floor of 4×10^{10} cm^2/yr. Although sepiolite group minerals are abundant in some Deep Sea Drilling Project Cores (e.g., Peterson et al., 1970; Drever, 1971c), their overall abundance does not appear to approach the value required to remove a significant fraction of the river dissolved Mg^{2+} flux.

There are other environments where sepiolite group minerals might be expected to form. An example (originally suggested to the author by G. Arrhenius) would be in surface water or shallow-water sediments following a diatom bloom. Dissolution of diatoms would provide local high-silica activities that, combined with normal surface pH values of around 8.2 could easily cause local precipitation of sepiolite (see Fig. 1). In this context, the reports of sepiolite group minerals in recent carbonate muds (Manley, 1972; Isphroding, 1972) are highly significant.

Can sepiolite/palygorskite precipitation in surface waters be an important mechanism for transferring Mg^{2+} from seawater into sediments? Small amounts of these minerals are very difficult to detect by conventional X-ray diffraction techniques, and it could be argued that once in the sediment they are converted rapidly to chlorite or dolomite plus quartz, so that the paucity of reported occurrences is not really significant. Sepiolite/palygorskite burial in shallow-water carbonate rocks cannot be an important removal mechanism for Mg^{2+}, as shallow-water carbonate formation itself accounts for only a small fraction of the river Ca^{2+} flux (Turekian, 1964). As an absolute upper limit, if shallow-water carbonates contained 5% sepiolite, and shallow-water carbonates accounted for 20% of the river Ca^{2+} flux, the amount of Mg^{2+} that would be removed by the process is 0.08×10^{14} g/yr, or 7% of the river Mg^{2+} flux. This number represents an upper limit; there is no evidence that the actual value even approaches it.

Sepiolite/palygorskite minerals do not appear to be significant constituents of biogenic oozes. Although traces of these minerals are hard to detect by X-ray diffraction, their characteristic morphology shows up very clearly under electron microscopy. There has been sufficient electron microscope study of biogenic oozes by micropaleontologists that the presence of abundant sepiolite or palygorskite would surely have been noticed. Also, the low MgO contents of biogenic oozes (El Wakeel and Riley, 1961; Chester, 1965) indicated that oozes cannot be an important sink for Mg, regardless of what phases are present.

Data on the occurrence of authigenic sepiolite and palygorskite in terrigenous sediments unrelated or volcanic or hydrothermal activity are scant. Rex and Murray (1970) report sepiolite in sediments of the Venezuelan Basin, which presumably precipitated from interstitial water as part of a complicated series of diagenetic reactions taking place well below the sediment-water interface. Overall, there has not been sufficient electron microscope study of terrigenous sediments to prove that sepiolite/palygorskite minerals are not common minor constituents (4 to 5% sepiolite in all terrigenous sediments would account for the entire river Mg^{2+} flux). Drever

(1971a) found no evidence for these minerals by electron microscopic examination of sediments from Banderas Bay, an area of high biological productivity, and, in general, chemical conditions at the sediment-water interface of terrigenous sediments (low pH, moderate silica activity) would favor dissolution rather than preservation of sepiolite. Thus it is possible that incorporation of authigenic sepiolite into terrigenous sediments is an important sink for Mg^{2+}, but it is not probable.

Burial of Interstitial Water

Reactions in interstitial waters of sediments can affect the composition of seawater in two ways. Reactions in the top few meters of sediment can cause diffusional fluxes for various species into or out of the sediment, and reactions at depth may change the composition of the water so that when it finally returns to the ocean-atmosphere system its ionic composition is quite different from that of the original seawater.

Near-surface reactions

Possible reactions that might affect the distribution of Mg in the top few meters of the sediment column have been discussed in the preceding sections of this article. Mg^{2+} is commonly depleted in interstitial waters (Siever, Beck, and Berner, 1965; Bischoff and Ku, 1970, 1971; Drever, 1971a). If sufficient data were available on concentration gradients of Mg^{2+} in interstitial waters, it would be possible to calculate an Mg^{2+} flux into the sediment without any knowledge of the controlling chemical reactions. Assuming a value of 5×10^{-6} cm^2/sec for the diffusion coefficient of Mg^{2+} in interstitial water (Manheim, 1970), and ignoring advection effects, a negative concentration gradient of 0.2 mg/liter/cm in Mg^{2+} at the sediment-water interface over the entire ocean floor would cause a diffusional flux of Mg^{2+} into the sediment equal to the river flux of dissolved Mg^{2+}. Measured concentration gradients for Mg^{2+} are commonly greater than this, particularly in terrigenous sediments where reducing conditions are present. The data are, however, too few and too perturbed by temperature of squeezing effects (Mangelsdorf, Wilson, and Daniell, 1969; Bischoff, Greer, and Luistro, 1970) to allow any reliable calculation of the overall diffusional flux.

Reactions at Depth

Interstitial water that is trapped in sediment may interact with solid phases either chemically or by membrane filtration in such a way that certain ions are retrained in the sediment when the interstitial water is ultimately returned to the ocean-atmosphere system. From studies of formation waters it appears that Mg^{2+} initially present in interstitial water does become incorporated into the solid phases of sediments (White, 1965; Hitchon, Billings, and Klovan, 1971; Russell, 1971). Assuming that Mg^{2+} is retained quantitatively in the sediment, the overall effectiveness of this process in removing Mg^{2+} from seawater will depend on the total amount of seawater trapped in the sediment at the depth at which the Mg^{2+} uptake reaction is effective. This, in turn, will be a function of the total sedimentation rate and the porosity of the sediments at the depth at which the Mg^{2+} reaction is effective. There is obviously no one depth at which the uptake reaction takes place. Results from the Deep-Sea Drilling Project indicate that Mg^{2+} is frequently taken up more or less continuously, and Russell's data (1971) suggests that the reaction is more or less complete by a depth of 8000 ft (2,500 m). On this basis, an effective porosity of 50% by volume (30% H_2O by weight) is a reasonable estimate. Assuming an annual sedimentation rate of 200×10^{14} g (183×10^{14} g terrigenous sediment, 17×10^{14} g carbonate), the rate of Mg^{2+} removal by this process would be 0.11×10^{14} g/yr, or 9% of the net river dissolved Mg^{2+} flux. It is possible that the assumed porosity value is too low in view of the high porosities commonly encountered in Deep Sea Drilling Project cores. As an upper limit, a porosity of 70% by volume (50% H_2O by weight) would result in Mg^{2+} removal equivalent to 0.26×10^{14} g/yr or 21% of the river dissolved Mg^{2+} flux.

4. Discussion

The most probable processes by which Mg^{2+} is removed from seawater are listed in Table III. It is obvious that if the assumptions underlying the calculations are accepted, the Mg^{2+} flux into the oceans from rivers is significantly greater than Mg^{2+} removal from the oceans into sediments. This means that (*a*) we have overlooked or underestimated some removal process, (*b*) one or more of the assumptions or numbers used in the calculations are wrong, or (*c*) the oceans are currently accumulating Mg^{2+}.

TABLE III

Mg^{2+} Removal from the Oceans

Process	Estimated Mg^{2+} Removal ($\times 10^{14}$g)	(% of River Flux)
Carbonate formation	0.075	6
Ion exchange	0.097	8
Glauconite formation[a]	0.039	3
Mg–Fe exchange[a]	0.29	24
Burial of interstitial water	0.11	9
	0.61	50

[a] Upper limits; actual value may be much lower.

Is explanation (*a*) reasonable? Let us investigate the hypothesis that the entire river Mg^{2+} flux, excluding the atmospherically cycled contribution and the Mg^{2+} incorporated into carbonates (Table III), is incorporated uniformly into terrigenous sediments in general, or into the clay fraction of terrigenous sediments. If the Mg^{2+} is incorporated into the sediment as a whole, the MgO content of marine sediment should be 1.1% greater than that of river sediment; if the Mg^{2+} is incorporated into the clay fraction only, the clay fraction of marine sediment should be 2.0% greater than that of river sediment. Some measured values are reported in Table IV.

Although the data are few, especially for river sediment, they do not support the hypothesis that marine clays contain 2.0% more MgO than clays in river sediment. The data for the sediment as a whole are not conclusive, but the analyses of Perry and Hower (1970) and van Moort (1971) suggest that Mississippi sediment does not pick up much Mg^{2+} during its contact with seawater. The high values for deep sea clay and red clay are not significant for the overall problem, as much of the red clay is volcanic in origin, and the rate of deposition of red clay is so slow. Broecker (1971) pointed out that the *total* Mg deposited in pelagic clays per year was only one-fifth of the river dissolved Mg^{2+} flux. The apparent low Mg content of clay minerals in marine sediments suggests that the search for further mechanisms by which Mg^{2+} is incorporated into the bulk of land-derived clay minerals is unlikely to solve the overall problem. Also, if the analyses of Table IV are meaningful, neither authigenic chlorite

TABLE IV

MgO Contents of Sediments

River	Marine
	Total Sediment
2.64 Nile[a]	1.44–0.98 Gulf Coast[b]
1.41 Mississippi[a]	1.92 Gulf Coats[c]
	2.4 terrigenous mud[d]
	2.2 average blue mud[d]
	2.3 average terrigenous mud[a]
	2.18 average pelagic sediment[e]
	2.62 DSDP Leg IV[f]
	3.48 deep sea clay[g]
	4.35 red clay[h]
	Clay Fraction Only
2.83 Rio Ameca[i]	3.01 Rio Ameca[k]
1.14 Niger[j]	1.40 Niger Delta[j]
	1.74 Orinoco Shelf[j]

[a] Clarke (1924).
[b] Perry and Hower (1970) range is top to bottom of section analyzed.
[c] Van Moort (1971)
[d] Poldervaart (1955).
[e] Chester (1965).
[f] Kuykendall et al. (1970) average terrigenous sediment excluding samples with significant biogenic or zeolitic material.
[g] Turekian and Wedepohl (1961).
[h] El Wakeel and Riley (1961).
[i] Russell (1970).
[j] Porrenga (1967).
[k] Drever (1971a).

formation nor sepiolite formation is a significant process in modifying the composition of detrital sediments. Thus, either the Mg^{2+} removal process must be highly localized, or, again, one or more of the assumptions is wrong. Postulating that Mg^{2+} is currently accumulating in the oceans does not solve any problems directly, as the MgO contents of marine sediments in the Tertiary do not appear to be higher than those in the Recent. Perry and Hower's (1970) analyses of bulk sediment samples from oil wells on the Gulf Coast show a decrease in MgO content with increasing sediment age. The decrease may be attributable to diagenetic effects (Garrels and Mackenzie, 1972), but there is certainly no evidence of any increase. The widespread development of calcareous pelagic organisms in the late Jurassic-early Cretaceous (approximately 135×10^6 yr b.p.) may have affected the Mg^{2+} distribution in the oceans and sediments, but since the residence time of Mg^{2+} in the oceans is approximately 15×10^6 yr, a new steady state should have been established since that time.

The most critical number in all the preceding discussion is the ratio of sedimentation rate (or river sediment load) to river dissolved Mg^{2+} flux. If the ratio were higher than Garrels and Mackenzie's (1971a) value, which has been used so far, Mg^{2+} removal by ion exchange, burial of interstitial water, and perhaps exchange for Fe in anaerobic sediments would be proportionally greater, and the required increase in the MgO content of sediments would be proportionately less. Drever (1971a, table III) calculated that steady-state weathering of an andesitic terrain would result in a suspended clay load to dissolved Mg^{2+} load ratio of 80 to 1. Steady-state weathering in this context means transportation of clay by streams at the same rate as it is formed by weathering. If we again use Shaw and Weaver's (1965) value for the clay content of average shale, and Garrels and Mackenzie's (1971a) value for the percentage of clastic rocks that are shale (Table I), the total sediment load to dissolved Mg^{2+} load ratio would be 150 to 1. This value is slightly, but not significantly, higher than Garrels and Mackenzie's value of 130 to 1. The major part of the surfaces of the continents are underlain by sedimentary and not igneous rocks. Intuitively, one might expect that weathering of sedimentary rocks would produce a higher total sediment to dissolved Mg^{2+} ratio than weathering of igneous rocks. Chemical weathering of silicates in sedimentary rocks should be less rapid, as the minerals are closer to equilibrium under earth surface conditions, and physical weathering should be more rapid, as sedimentary rocks are generally less well consolidated than igneous rocks. The principal uncertainty in this argument is the significance of Mg^{2+} from carbonate weathering. If our previous calculation is valid that at most, 40% of river Mg^{2+} flux comes from the weathering of carbonate rocks, the general conclusion should not be affected. From this argument, steady-state weathering of a sedimentary terrain, and hence of the continents as a whole, should generate higher total suspended sediment to dissolved Mg^{2+} ratios in streams than steady-state weathering of igneous rocks, assuming other factors (climate, relief, etc.) are constant.

Why then is the present-day value of the total sediment to dissolved Mg^{2+} flux ratio so low? Either our estimate of the present-day sediment flux is wrong, or the steady-state model does not fit the world's weathering processes today. Garrels and Mackenzie's (1971a) sediment flux value may be too low (for a discussion, see Garrels and Mackenzie, 1971a, p. 104), but it is unlikely that the error is sufficiently great to account for the discrepancies in the mass balance calculation. Judson (1968) estimated that in the absence of man's activities, the suspended sediment flux would be only half the present-day value. It is highly probable, however, that weathering today does not even approximate the steady-state model as a result of the large fluctuations in climate, sea level, and erosion patterns associated with the Pleistocene glaciations.

I wish to propose the hypothesis that over a sufficiently long interval of time, or in the absence of perturbations due to glacial cycles, global weathering approaches the steady-state model; there is a concomitant increase in the ratio of suspended sediment to dissolved Mg^{2+}, so that the magnesium problem can be "solved" by presently known reactions. Available evidence indicates that sedimentation rates were no higher in the Mesozoic and Tertiary than at present (Gregor, 1970; Garrels and Mackenzie, 1971b), which implies that the dissolved Mg^{2+} flux must have been lower. I have no specific mechanism to explain why past Mg^{2+} fluxes should have been lower; the conclusion is a consequence of the low MgO content of terrigenous marine sediments, and of the qualitative arguments concerning steady-state weathering.

If this hypothesis is not valid, what are some alternatives?

1. The present-day pH of the oceans may be anomalously low; during "normal" times the pH is higher, and Mg^{2+} incorporation by formation of brucite layers in montmorillonite is an important process. This is possible, but we have no supporting

evidence, and no external reason for suggesting that the present-day (meaning post-Pleistocene) pH of the oceans is anomalous.

2. The Mg^{2+} removal process is localized and we have not studied the correct location. This is certainly possible, but what could be the location? Broecker's (1971) calculation shows that it cannot be in pelagic sediments; the analyses of Drever (1971a) and Porrenga (1967) suggest that relatively near-shore sediments off the mouths of rivers are not the place. There is perhaps a region around the continental margins where sedimentation is rapid, and in which no detailed studies have been carried out, which could logically be a sink for Mg^{2+}, but there is no direct evidence to support this hypothesis. It is most unlikely that the transformation of gibbsite to chlorite is sufficiently widespread to be quantitatively significant. In general, if we hypothesize that a quantitatively important Mg^{2+} removal reaction is to occur over a relatively small area, the net change in Mg within that area must be very large, simply because the annual Mg^{2+} flux is so large.

3. The sediments of the Rio Ameca (Drever, 1971a) and the Niger (Porrenga, 1967) are, for some reason, atypical in their Mg^{2+} uptake behavior. It could thus be argued that certain clays that are absent in Ameca and Niger sediment are present in the sediment of other rivers (e.g., the Mississippi), and these clays react with seawater to take up large quantities of Mg^{2+}. Support for this would be the reports of authigenic chlorite in Gulf of Mexico sediment, but there is no direct chemical evidence.

4. Igneous rocks react with seawater at some depth below the sea floor, and take up Mg^{2+} to form chlorite. It is necessary to postulate reaction at depth because alteration of basalt on the sea floor involves a loss of Mg from the basalt to seawater (Muehlenbachs and Clayton, 1972). Support for this hypothesis is the observation that rocks exposed on land that have been interpreted as fragments of ancient ocean floor are commonly rich in chlorite (e.g., the Karmutsen Group, British Columbia, Surdam, 1973). Objections are that the required reaction has not been demonstrated to occur, and that there is no obvious mechanism by which large volumes of seawater can be circulated through the deeper layers of the oceanic crust.

5. Summary and Conclusions

The principal mechanisms by which magnesium is removed from seawater are exchange for iron in anaerobic sediments, burial of interstitial water, ion exchange, and carbonate formation. At present it appears that these processes can account for at most 50% of the dissolved Mg^{2+} flux from rivers.

The low MgO content of the clay fraction of terrigenous marine sediments appears to indicate that the river Mg^{2+} flux is not being incorporated uniformly into land-derived clay minerals.

The problem can be resolved either by postulating that the present-day Mg^{2+} flux is anomalously high, that the present-day oceanic pH value value is anomalously low, or that the Mg^{2+} removal process is localized in a region that has not yet been studied intensively. I prefer the first explanation.

Acknowledgments

I thank R. M. Garrels for reading the manuscript and making several suggestions for its improvement.

This work was supported by N.S.F. grant GA-33503.

References

Bathurst, R. G. C., 1972. *Carbonate Sediments and Their Diagenesis*. Elsevier, New York, 620 pp.

Berner, R. A., M. R. Scott, and C. Thomlinson, 1970. Carbonate alkalinity in the pore waters of anoxic marine sediments. *Limnol. and Oceanog.*, **15**, 544–549.

Biscaye, P. E., 1965. Mineralogy and sedimentation of Recent deep-sea clay in the Atlantic Ocean and adjacent seas and oceans. *Bull. Geol. Soc. of Amer.*, **76**, 803–832.

Bischoff, J. L., R. E. Greer, and A. O. Luistro, 1970. Composition of interstitial waters of marine sediments: Temperature of squeezing effect. *Science*, **167**, 1245–1246.

Bischoff, J. L. and T. Ku, 1970. Pore fluids of Recent marine sediments: I. Oxidizing sediments of 20°N, continental rise to Mid-Atlantic Ridge. *J. Sediment. Petrol.*, **40**, 960–972.

Bischoff, J. L. and T. Ku, 1971. Pore fluids of Recent marine sediments: II. Anoxic sediments of 35° to 45°N, Gibralter to Mid-Atlantic Ridge. *J. Sediment. Petrol.*, **41**, 1008–1017.

Bonatti, E. and G. Arrhenius, 1965. Eolian sedimentation in the Pacific off Northern Mexico. *Marine Geol.*, **3**, 337–348.

Bonatti, E. and O. Joensuu, 1968. Palygorskite from Atlantic deep-sea sediments. *Am. Mineralogist*, **53**, 975–983.

Bowles, F. A., E. A. Angino, J. W. Hosterman, and O. K. Galle, 1971. Precipitation of deep-sea palygorskite and sepiolite. *Earth and Planet. Sci. Letters*, **11**, 324–332.

Broecker, W. S. 1971. A kinetic model for the chemical composition of seawater. *Quaternary Res.*, **1**, 188–207.

Caillère, S. and S. Hénin, 1949. Experimental formation of chlorites from montmorillonite. *Min. Mag.*, **28**, 612–620.

Caillère, S. and S. Hénin, 1961. Palygorskite. In *The X-ray Identification and Crystal Structures of Clay Minerals*. G. Brown, ed. Min. Soc. London, pp. 343–353.

Carstea, D. D., M. E. Harward, and E. G. Knox, 1970. Formation and stability of hydroxy-Mg interlayers in phyllosilicates. *Clays and Clay Minerals*, **18**, 213–222.

Chave, K. E., 1954a. Aspects of the biogeochemistry of magnesium: 1. Calcareous marine organisms. *J. Geol.*, **62**, 266–283.

Chave, K. E., 1954b. Aspects of the biogeochemistry of magnesium: 2. Calcareous sediments and rocks. *J. Geol.*, **62**, 587–599.

Chester, R., 1965. Elemental geochemistry of marine sediments. In *Chemical Oceanography*. Vol. 2. J. P. Riley and G. Skirrow, eds. pp. 23–80.

Christ, C. L., P. B. Hostetler, and R. M. Siebert, 1973. Studies in the system $MgO–SiO_2–CO_2–H_2O$ (III): The activity-product constant of sepiolite. *Am. J. Sci.*, **273**, 507–525.

Clarke, F. W., 1924. The data of geochemistry. *U.S. Geol. Survey Bull.*, **770**.

Dasch, E. J., 1969. Strontium isotopes in weathering profiles, deep-sea sediments, and sedimentary rocks. *Geochim. Cosmochim. Acta*, **33**, 1521–1552.

Deffeyes, K. S., 1965. The Columbia River flood and the history of the oceans. Pacific NW Oceanographers Annual Meeting, Corvallis, Oregon.

Drever, J. I., 1968. Electrophoresis and the study of clay minerals in Recent sediments. Unpublished Ph.D. dissertation, Princeton University.

Drever, J. I., 1971a. Early diagenesis of clay minerals, Rio Ameca Basin, Mexico. *J. Sediment. Petrol.*, **41**, 982–994.

Drever, J. I., 1971b. Magnesium-iron replacements in clay minerals in anoxic marine sediments. *Science*, **172**, 1334–1336.

Drever, J. I., 1971c. Chemical and mineralogical studies, site 66. In 1971, *Initial Reports of the Deep Sea Drilling Project*. Vol. VII. E. L. Winterer, et al., eds. U.S. Government Printing Office, Washington, D.C., 965–975.

El Wakeel, S. K. and J. P. Riley, 1961. Chemical and mineralogical studies of deep-sea sediments. *Geochim. Cosmochim. Acta*, **25**, 110–146.

Garrels, R. M. and F. T. Mackenzie, 1971a. *Evolution of Sedimentary Rocks*. Norton, New York, 397 pp.

Garrels, R. M. and F. T. Mackenzie, 1971b. Gregor's denudation of the continents. *Nature*, **231**, 382–383.

Garrels, R. M. and F. T. Mackenzie, 1972. Chemical history of the oceans deduced from post-depositional changes in sedimentary rocks. In press.

Garrels, R. M., F. T. Mackenzie, and R. Siever, 1972. Sedimentary cycling in relation to the history of the continents and oceans. In *The Nature of the Solid Earth.* E. C. Robertson, ed. McGraw-Hill, New York, pp. 93–121.

Garrels, R. M. and M. E. Thompson, 1962. A chemical model for seawater at 25°C and one atmosphere total pressure. *Amer. J. Sci.*, **260**, 57–66.

Gregor, B., 1970. Denudation of the continents. *Nature*, **228**, 273.

Griffin, G. M. and R. L. Ingram, 1955. Clay minerals of the Neuse river estuary. *J. Sediment. Petrol.*, **25**, 194–200.

Griffin, J. J., M. Koide, A. Hohndorf, J. W. Hawkins and E. D. Goldberg, 1972. Sediments of the Lau Basin—rapidly accumulating volcanic deposits. *Deep Sea Res.*, **19**, 139–148.

Griffin, J. J., H. Windom, and E. D. Goldberg, 1968. The distribution of clay minerals in the World Ocean. *Deep-Sea Res.*, **15**, 433–459.

Grim, R. E., 1968. *Clay Mineralogy* (second edition). McGraw-Hill, New York, 596 p.

Grim, R. E., R. S. Dietz, and W. F. Bradley, 1949. Clay mineral composition of some sediments from the Pacific Ocean off the California Coast and the Gulf of California. *Bull. Geol. Soc. of Amer.*, **60**, 1785–1808.

Grim, R. E. and W. D. Johns, 1954. Clay mineral investigations of sediments in the northern Gulf of Mexico. *Clays and Clay Minerals*, Natl. Acad. Sci.-Natl. Res. Council pub. 327, 81–103.

Hashimoto, I. and M. L. Jackson, 1960. Rapid dissolution of allophane and kaolinite-halloysite after dehydration. *Clays and Clay Minerals*, Proc. Nat. Conf. 7, 102–113.

Hathaway, J. C. and P. L. Sachs, 1965. Sepiolite and clinoptilolite from the Mid-Atlantic Ridge. *Am. Mineralogist*, **50**, 852–867.

Helgeson, H. C. and F. T. Mackenzie, 1970. Silicate-sea water equilibria in the ocean system. *Deep-Sea Res.*, **17**, 877–892.

Hitchon, B., G. K. Billings, and J. E. Klovan, 1971. Geochemistry and origin of formation waters in the western Canada sedimentary basin-III. Factors controlling chemical composition. *Geochim. Cosmochim. Acta*, **35**, 567–598.

Holeman, J. N., 1968. The sediment yield of major rivers of the world. *Water Resources Res.*, **4**, 737–747.

Holland, H. D., 1965. The history of ocean water and its effect on the chemistry of the atmosphere. *Proc. Nat. Acad. Sci.*, **53**, 1173–1183.

Hostetler, P. B., J. J. Hemley, C. L. Christ, and J. E. Montoya, 1971. Talc-chrysotile equilibrium in aqueous solutions. Geol. Soc. of Amer. Abstracts with Programs for Annual Meetings, Washington, D.C., 605.

Hurley, P. M., 1966. K-Ar dating of sediments: In *Potassium-Argon Dating.* O. A. Schaeffer and J. Zahringer, eds. Springer-Verlag, New York, pp. 134–150.

Isphroding, W. C., 1972. Primary marine attapulgite clays of the Yucatan Platform and Southeastern United States. Paper presented at 21st Clay Minerals Conf., Woods Hole, Mass.

Johns, W. D. and R. E. Grim, 1958. Clay mineral composition of Recent sediments from the Mississippi River delta. *J. Sediment. Petrol.*, **28**, 186–199.

Judson, S., 1968. Erosion of the land. *Am. Scientist*, **56**, 356–374.

Keller, W. D., 1963. Diagenesis of clay minerals—a review. *Clays and Clay Minerals*, Proc. Nat. Conf. 11, 136–157.

Kuykendall, W. E., Jr., B. W. Hoffman, and R. E. Wainerdi, 1970. 14 MeV Neutron activation analysis of selected Leg 4 core samples. In *Initial Reports of the Deep Sea Drilling Project.* Vol. IV. R. G. Bader, et al. eds. U.S. Government Printing Office, Washington, D.C., pp. 371–374.

Livingstone, D. A., 1963. Chemical composition of rivers and lakes. In *Data of Geochemistry.* M. Fleischer, ed. U.S. Geol. Survey Prof. Paper, 440G.

Mackenzie, F. T. and R. M. Garrels, 1966. Chemical mass balance between rivers and oceans. *Am. J. Sci.*, **264**, 507–525.

Mackenzie, F. T., R. M. Garrels, O. P. Bricker, and F. Bickley, 1967. Silica in seawater: Control by silica minerals. *Science*, **155**, 1404–1405.

Mangelsdorf, P. C., Jr., T. R. S. Wilson, and E. Daniell, 1969. Potassium enrichments in interstitial waters of Recent marine sediments. *Science*, **165**, 171–174.

Manheim, F. T., 1970. The diffusion of ions in unconsolidated sediments. *Earth and Planet. Sci. Letters*, **9**, 307–309.

Manheim, F. T., K. M. Chan, D. Kerr, and W. Sunda, 1970. Interstitial water studies on small core samples, Deep Sea Drilling Project, Leg 3. In *Initial Reports of the Deep Sea Drilling Project.* Vol. III. A. E. Maxwell, et al., eds. U.S. Government Printing Office, Washington, D.C., pp. 663–666.

Manley, F. H., 1972. Paper presented at A.A.P.G. National Meetings, Denver, Colorado.

Maxwell, A. E. et al., 1970. *Initial Reports of the Deep Sea Drilling Project,* Vol. III. U.S. Government Printing Office, Washington, D.C.

Moberly, R., H. S. Kimura, and F. W. McCoy, 1968. Authigenic marine phyllosilicates near Hawaii. *Geol. Soc. of Amer. Bull.,* **79**, 1449–1460.

Muehlenbachs, K. and R. N. Clayton, 1972. Oxygen isotope studies of fresh and weathered submarine basalts. *Canadian. Jour. of Earth Sci.,* **9**, 172–184.

Nelson, B. W., 1960. Clay mineralogy of the bottom sediments, Rappahannock River, Virginia. *Clays and Clay Minerals,* Proc. Nat. Conf. 7, 135–148.

Perry, E. A., Jr., 1971. Silicate-sea water equilibria in the ocean system: a discussion. *Deep-Sea Res.,* **18**, 921–924.

Perry, E. and J. Hower, 1970. Burial diagenesis in Gulf Coast pelitic sediments. *Clays and Clay Minerals,* **18**, 167–177.

Peterson, M. N. A. et al., 1970. *Initial Reports of the Deep Sea Drilling Project,* Vol. II, U.S. Government Printing Office, Washington, D.C.

Pimm, A. C., 1970. Grain size analysis, Leg 3. In 1970, *Initial Reports of the Deep Sea Drilling Project,* Vol. III. A. E. Maxwell, et al., eds. U.S. Government Printing Office, Washington, D.C., pp. 475–494.

Pinsak, A. P. and H. H. Murray, 1960. Regional clay mineral patterns in the Gulf of Mexico. *Clays and Clay Minerals,* Proc. Nat. Conf., 7, 162–178.

Poldervaart, A., 1955. Chemistry of the Earth's Crust. In *Crust of the Earth.* A. Poldervaart, ed. Geol. Soc. of Amer. Special Paper 62, pp. 119–144.

Porrenga, D. H., 1967. *Clay mineralogy and geochemistry of Recent sediments in tropical areas.* Stolk-Dort, Dordrecht, Netherlands, 145 pp.

Powers, M. C., 1957. Adjustment of land derived clay to the marine environment. *J. Sediment. Petrol.,* **27**, 355–372.

Rex, R. W., 1970. X-ray mineralogy results, Leg 3, Deep Sea Drilling Project. In 1970, *Initial Reports of the Deep Sea Drilling Project,* Vol. III. A. E. Maxwell, et al., eds. U.S. Government Printing Office, Washington, D.C., pp. 509–581.

Rex, R. W. and B. Murray, 1970. X-ray mineralogy studies, Leg 4. In *Initial Reports of the Deep Sea Drilling Project,* Vol. IV. R. G. Bader, et al., eds. U.S. Government Printing Office, Washington, D.C., pp. 325–369.

Russell, K. L., 1970. Geochemistry and halmyrolysis of clay minerals, Rio Ameca, Mexico. *Geochim. Cosmochim. Acta,* **34**, 893–907.

Russell, K. L., 1971. Fresher interstitial waters from normal marine shales. Paper presented at 1971 Fall Annual Meeting of the Amer. Geophys. Union. E.O.S. 52, 929.

Savin, S. M. and S. Epstein, 1970. The oxygen and hydrogen isotope geochemistry of ocean sediments and shales. *Geochim. Cosmochim. Acta,* **34**, 43–63.

Sayles, F. L., F. T. Manheim, and L. S. Waterman, 1972. Interstitial water studies on small core samples: Leg 15. *Initial Reports of the Deep Sea Drilling Project,* Vol. XV. In press.

Shaw, D. B. and C. E. Weaver, 1965. The mineralogical composition of shales. *J. Sediment. Petrol.,* **35**, 213–222.

Siever, R., 1968. Establishment of equilibrium between clays and seawater. *Earth and Planet. Sci. Letters,* **5**, 106–110.

Siever, R., K. C. Beck, and R. A. Berner, 1965. Composition of interstitial waters of modern sediments. *J. Geol.,* **73**, 39–73.

Sillén, L. G., 1961. The physical chemistry of seawater. In *Oceanography.* Mary Sears, ed. AAAS, Washington, D.C.

Slaughter, M. and I. H. Milne, 1960. The formation of chlorite-like structures from montmorillonite. *Clays and Clay Minerals,* Proc. Nat. Conf. 7, 114–125.

Surdam, R. C., 1972. The low-grade metamorphism of tuffaceous rocks in the Karmutsen Group, Vancouver Island, British Columbia. *Bull. Geol. Soc. of Amer.* 84, 1911–1922.

Swindale, L. D. and Pow-Foong Pan, 1967. Transformation of gibbsite to chlorite in ocean bottom sediments. *Science,* **157**, 799–800.

Turekian, K. K., 1964. The geochemistry of the Atlantic Ocean. *Trans. N.Y. Acad. Sci.*, **26**, 312–330.

Turekian, K. K. and L. H. Wedepohl, 1961. Distribution of elements in some major units of the Earth's crust. *Bull. Geol. Soc. of Amer.*, **72**, 175–192.

van Moort, J. C., 1971. A comparative study of the diagenetic alteration of clay minerals in Mesozoic shales from Papua, New Guinea, and in Tertiary shales from Louisiana, U.S.A., *Clays and Clay Minerals*, **19**, 1–20.

Weaver, C. E., 1958. The effects and geologic significance of potassium "fixation" by expandable clay minerals derived from muscovite, biotite, chlorite, and volcanic material. *Am. Mineralogist*, **43**, 839–861.

Weaver, C. E., 1959. The clay petrology of sediments. *Clays and Clay Minerals*, Proc. Nat. Conf. 6, 154–187.

White, D. E., 1965. Saline waters in sedimentary rocks. In *Fluids in Subsurface Environments.* Young and Galley, eds. A.A.P.G. Memoir 4, pp. 342–366.

Whitehouse, U. G., L. M. Jeffrey, and J. D. Debrecht, 1960. Differential settling tendencies of clay minerals in saline waters. *Clays and Clay Minerals*, Proc. Nat. Conf. 7, 1–79.

Whitehouse, U. G. and R. S. McCarter, 1968. Diagenetic modification of clay minerals in artificial seawater. Clays and Clay Minerals, Natl. Acad. Sci. Natl. Res. Council. pub. 556, 81–119.

Wollast, R. and F. De Broeu, 1971. Study of the behavior of dissolved silica in the estuary of the Scheldt. *Geochim. Cosmochim. Acta*, **35**, 613–620.

Wollast, R., F. T. Mackenzie, and O. P. Bricker, 1968. Experimental precipitation and genesis of sepiolite at earth-surface conditions. *Am. Mineralogist*, **35**, 1645–1662.

Youell, R. F., 1960. An electrolyte method for producing chlorite-like substances from montmorillonite. *Clay Min. Bull.*, **4**, 191–195.

11. THE SILICA PROBLEM

R. WOLLAST

1. Introduction

The chemical model of the ocean proposed by Sillén (1961), based on the equilibrium of a series of chemical reactions, gave rise to a new interest in the study of dissolved and particulate silica in the ocean. It was generally assumed until then that the behavior of silica was essentially controlled by the biological activity of certain species. From this point of view it was assumed that the input of dissolved silica by rivers into the ocean was rapidly taken up by organisms and precipitated as the opal of which their skeletons are made.

This latter assumption conformed poorly to the model of Sillén and could not explain the mean value of the concentration of dissolved silica in the ocean. There was, however, insufficient data available to Sillén for him to define the chemical reactions able to control the concentration of dissolved silica in seawater. In 1966 Mackenzie and Garrels proposed reactions between dissolved silica and suspended clay minerals of continental origin to support the model of Sillén. These reactions require high concentrations of alkali or alkaline earth ions to produce new clay minerals, and are therefore favored in the marine environment. Furthermore, the clay minerals synthesized during these reactions are typical of those in marine sediments. This hypothesis was very attractive because it allowed the authors to explain the mean concentration of dissolved silica in the ocean on the basis of the chemical equilibria involved in their proposed reactions. It was, moreover, in agreement with the requirements of other constituents in the geochemical cycle.

The theory of Garrels and Mackenzie was, however, criticized not only by biologists but also by geologists in regard to the mass balance of silica in the ocean, the distribution of diatoms and radiolarians in the sediments, and observations or experimental studies on the behavior of dissolved silica in seawater.

This chapter will establish the relative importance of chemical reactions and biological processes in the control of the cycle and in the distribution of dissolved silica. A great deal of this chapter will be devoted to the chemical properties of silica and silicates in seawater. Certain properties are reasonably well known but we have attempted to describe them in a more rigorous manner in order to resolve contradictions often present in the literature. They will then be used to propose a tentative cycle for silica within the ocean.

2. Chemical Properties of Dissolved Silica in Seawater

A. Soluble Forms of Silica

The soluble form of silica in seawater is silicic acid, the formula of which is probably $Si(OH)_4$. The degree of hydration of this acid is, in fact, not well known and numerous authors prefer to write it as $SiO_2(aq)$, implying that this molecule is hydrated. Silicic acid is a very weak acid ($pK_a = 9.41$) and is not appreciably dissociated below pH 9 (Ingrie, 1959). It may be regarded as essentially nondissociated in seawater.

Silicic acid tends to form polymers in the following type of reaction:

$$4\,Si(OH)_4 \rightleftharpoons Si_4O_8(OH)_2^{2-} + 2\,H^+ + 6\,H_2O$$

The equilibrium constant of this reaction is $10^{-13.5}$ at 25°C (Sillén, personal communication). A quick calculation shows that at pH 8, for the mean concentration of silica in seawater (10^{-4} mol/liter), the concentration of this polymeric form should be only $10^{-13.5}$ mol/liter. Burton et al. (1970) have shown elsewhere that the polymeric forms of silicic acid depolymerize rapidly in seawater.

B. Solubility of Silica in Seawater

There is often confusion in the literature about the concept of the degree of saturation of silica in seawater because of a failure to distinguish the metastable states, which can be maintained indefinitely, from the more thermodynamically stable states.

Other sources of confusion are the precipitation reactions of dissolved silica due to reactions with dissolved species or suspended matter in seawater. These will be discussed separately in Sections 2.C and 2.D.

The simplest reaction controlling the solubility of silica can be considered as the dissolution of one of the various polymorphic forms of solid silica:

$$SiO_2(s) \rightleftharpoons SiO_2(aq)$$

This reaction depends only on the temperature, pressure, and the nature of the solid phase. The solubility is also influenced by the pH since one must take into account the contribution of dissociated silicic acid $SiO_2(aq)$. This effect is important only above pH 9 and does not normally occur to any appreciable extent in seawater.

The nature of the solid phase has the most influence on the solubility of silica in seawater. Table I gives some reliable values of the solubilities of the various polymorphic forms of silica at 25°C and 1 atm, taken from recent literature. It is important to notice the large differences that are given for the solubility of a particular polymorphic form, especially quartz. These differences are essentially due to the degree of perfection of the crystal structure. Thus, in the case of freshly ground quartz, it is now well established (Van Lier et al., 1960; Henderson et al., 1970) that on the surface of the grains, there is a highly disturbed layer with a solubility nearly that of amorphous silica. In addition, one may also distinguish various types of amorphous silica ranging from silica glass to the finely divided silica gel, which has a more disordered structure and, consequently, a higher solubility. The excess of free energy of

TABLE I

Solubility of Silica in Seawater at 25°C and 1 atm (Millimoles/liter)

Form	Experimental Data	
Quartz	0.086	Mackenzie (1971)[a]
Quartz	0.10	Morey et al. (1962)
Tridymite	0.63	Stöber (1967)[b]
Cristobalite	1.00	Stöber (1967)
Amorphous silica	1.84	Stöber (1967)
Amorphous silica	1.75	Krauskopf (1956)
Finely divided silica gel	2.34	Siever (1962)

[a] Measured at 20°C, recalculated at 25°C.
[b] Solution NaCl 1%, pH 8.4.

these solid silicas compared to that of quartz is a direct measure of the degree of disorder in the silica.

From a thermodynamical point of view, if one considers only the equilibria of the solution with the polymorphic forms of solid silica, the solubility of silica in seawater at 25°C and 1 atm pressure is close to 100 μM/liter corresponding to the dissolution equilibrium of quartz, the most stable form.

On the other hand it is possible to observe values as high as 1800 μM/liter if, for example, amorphous silica is present in the form of skeletons of biological organisms. However, the above system is in a metastable state and, theoretically, quartz should then precipitate until the complete disappearance of amorphous silica.

From the point of view of kinetics such a reaction is highly unlikely. In the absence of a solid phase favorable to the nucleation of quartz, it is possible to maintain indefinitely an aqueous solution saturated with amorphous silica. It may easily be shown (Wollast, 1971) that the processes of homogeneous nucleation require a degree of supersaturation that may attain several orders of magnitude. We shall demonstrate in the next chapter that even in the presence of quartz acting as a nucleating agent a certain degree of supersaturation is required.

The influence of temperature on the solubility of quartz has been studied by Kennedy (1950), Van Lier et al. (1960), Morey et al. (1962), and Siever (1962). Their results agree very well if one neglects the results of Kennedy (1950) at temperatures below 200°C. The mean standard heat of dissolution has a value of 5.25 $\pm$ 0.07 kcal/mol.

If the solubility of quartz at 25°C is taken as 100 μM/liter the following relation is then obtained:

$$\log c = -0.151 - 1.147 \frac{10^3}{T}$$

where c is the solubility in moles per liter at any temperature T°K. From this relation the solubility of quartz at 5°C is equal to 53 μM/liter. The data concerning amorphous silica have been reviewed by Iler (1955), Krauskopf (1959), and Siever (1962). The mean heat of dissolution calculated from the collected values of the above authors is equal to 3.30 $\pm$ 0.03 kcal/mol.

The variation of the solubility of amorphous silica as a function of the temperature may be expressed by

$$\log c = -0.309 - 0.723 \frac{10^3}{T}$$

The solubility of amorphous silica at 5°C from this relation is 1230 μM/liter.

The influence of pressure on the solubility of amorphous silica in seawater was measured recently by Jones and Pytkowicz (1973). The solubility at 2°C increases slightly with pressure ranging from 56 to 70 ppm at one and 1000 atmospheres respectively.

C. Precipitation Reactions of Dissolved Silica with Ions Present in Seawater

The maximum possible solubility of amorphous silica in seawater may be limited by precipitation reactions of dissolved silica with other ions present in seawater. The only reaction of this type that is actually known to occur is the formation of sepiolite (Wollast et al., 1968), which involves only the ions Mg^{2+} and OH^- in the reaction:

$$2\,Mg^{2+} + 3\,SiO_2(aq) + 4\,OH^- = Mg_2Si_3O_8$$

The experimental value of the equilibrium constant of this reaction is equal to $10^{-37.2}$ at normal temperature and pressure. In other words, for the mean composition of seawater containing 58.8 mM/liter of Mg^{2+} at pH 8.2, the maximum value of the concentration of dissolved silica, above which spontaneous and rapid precipitation occurs, is equal to 280 μM/liter. This reaction is, however, very sensitive to changes of pH so that the maximum value of the dissolved silica concentration at pH 8.5 is reduced to 112 μM/liter, whereas at pH 7.8 it attains 1000 μM/liter. In fact, the first product resulting from the experimental precipitation of magnesium silicate is a relatively disordered hydrated sepiolite ($\sim$1.5 mol H_2O/mol sepiolite). Christ et al.(1971) have shown that the equilibrium constant for this reaction is highly sensitive to the degree of crystallinity of the sepiolite. For a well-crystallized sample these authors obtained a value of $10^{-40.1}$. Using this value for seawater at pH 8.2, the maximum concentration of dissolved silica should be 30 μM/liter, which is about one-third that for quartz in equilibrium with seawater. However, we encounter the same limitation for sepiolite as that for quartz, that is, the possibility of the spontaneous precipitation of a well-crystallized sepiolite. These studies on sepiolite show that the synthesis of this product in seawater is thermodynamically highly favored, to at least the same extent as the precipitation of quartz.

As a result of the spontaneous precipitation of sepiolite the maximum level of dissolved silica in seawater above pH 7.5 is greatly reduced by comparison with the maximum possible value from amorphous silica. Figure 1 represents the above behavior and shows the maximum concentration of dissolved silica in seawater that may occur in the absence of an active solid phase in suspension.

It is interesting to note from the work of Christ et al. (1971) that the precipitation

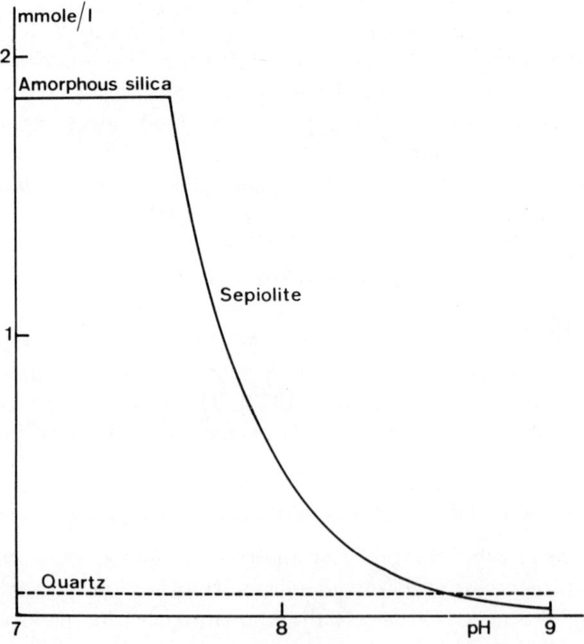

Fig. 1. Maximum concentration of dissolved silica in seawater in the absence of an active solid phase in suspension. The dashed line corresponds to the theoretical solubility of quartz.

reaction for magnesium silicate is favored at low temperature and the equilibrium constant of the reaction is reduced to $10^{-41.8}$ at 0°C for well-crystallized sepiolite.

Dissolved silica may also react with other ions such as Al^{3+}, Fe^{3+}, and Cr^{3+} to produce various disordered silicates. We shall not consider here these reactions discussed in detail by Iler (1955), since they only affect the solubility of silica when the ions are in high concentration at levels that do not occur in normal seawater.

D. Reaction of Dissolved Silica with Suspended Matter

In order that the conditions of the stationary state model of the ocean described by Sillén (1961) be satisfied, Mackenzie and Garrels (1966) proposed that *particular* constituents of seawater, such as silica, should react with degraded aluminosilicates, transported by rivers into the ocean, to form the typical clay minerals in lutites. These reactions may be represented by:

$$\text{silicate} + \text{cations} + \text{dissolved } SiO_2 + HCO_3^- = \text{more siliceous silicate} + CO_2$$

The mass balances established by the authors using these reactions are in accordance with the model of Sillén (1961) and also explain the removal of alkali and alkaline earth ions from seawater, the ions then being incorporated in the marine clay deposits. Furthermore, these reactions generate the CO_2 necessary to maintain the atmospheric level and account for some of the buffering capacity of seawater.

Mackenzie et al. (1967) conducted laboratory experiments on the reactions between clay minerals, dissolved silica, and cations in seawater. Figure 2 shows the result of experiments where various clay minerals were suspended in seawater deficient in or enriched with dissolved silica. In both cases one observes rapid changes in the concentration of dissolved silica. In the silica-deficient seawater the clay minerals release silica to form less siliceous compounds, and the reverse occurs in the enriched seawater.

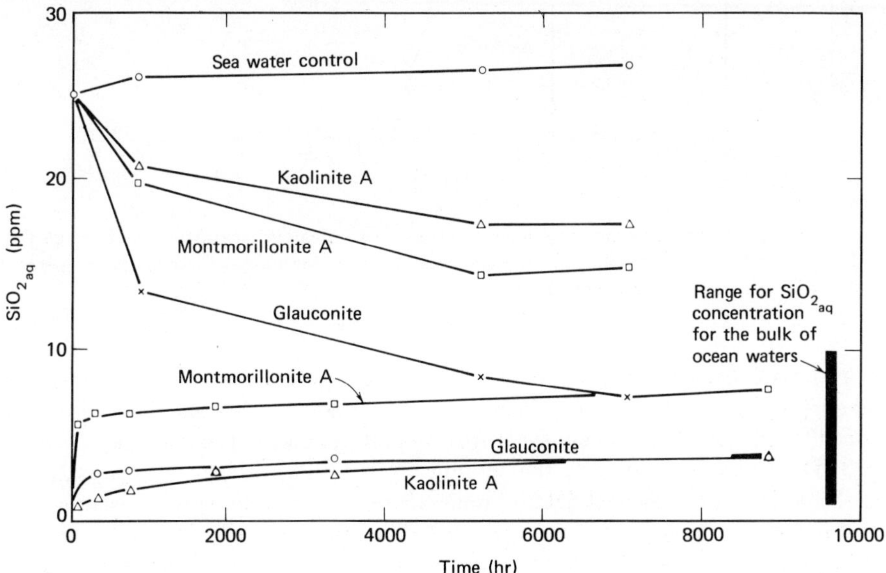

Fig. 2. Concentration of dissolved silica as a function of time for seawater-clay suspensions. The clays were added to seawater initially containing 0.03 and 25 ppm silica. After Mackenzie et al. (1967).

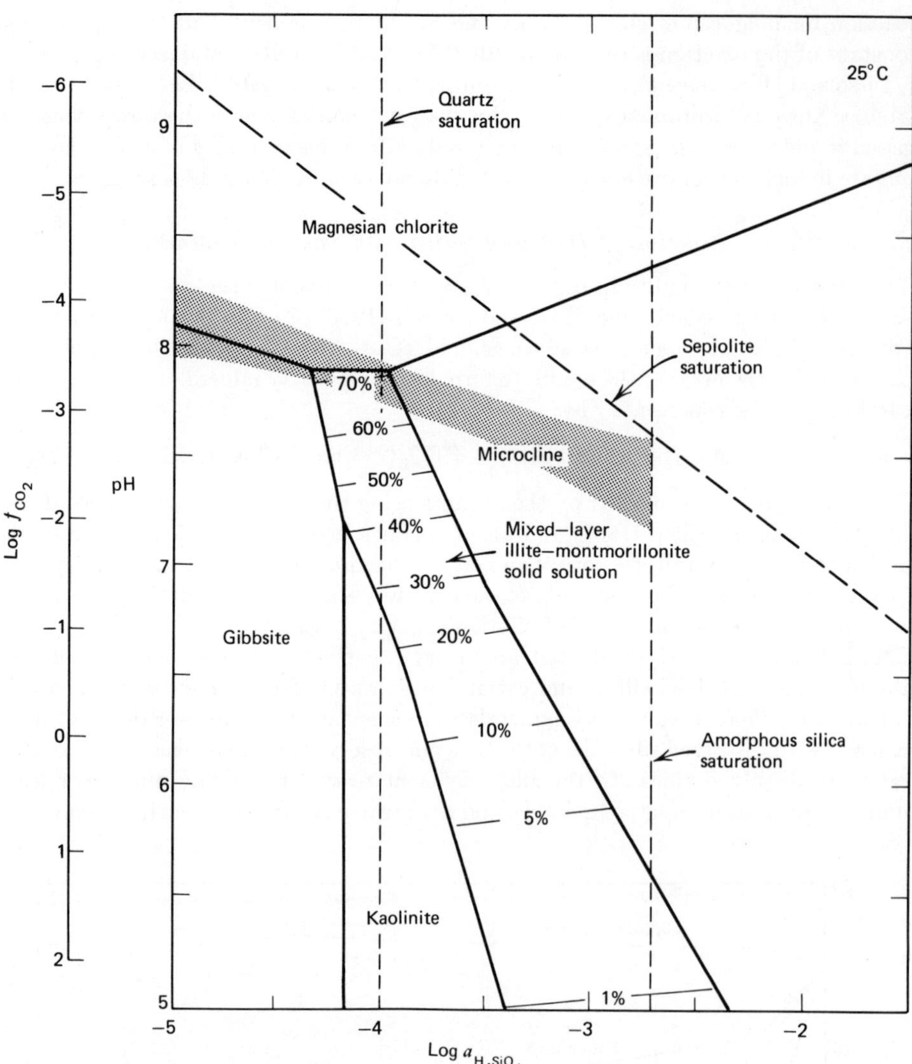

Fig. 3. Activity diagram illustrating phase relations in an idealized seawater system at 25°C and 1 atm. The shaded area is the approximate range of seawater composition at this temperature. After Helgeson and Mackenzie (1970).

The authors concluded that the final values of dissolved silica concentrations are in good agreement with the mean value observed for seawater. Thermodynamical calculations by Helgeson and Mackenzie (1970) support this conclusion, as may be seen in Fig. 3. This figure, representing the equilibrium between stable solid phases and seawater, shows that the typical detrital minerals in the ocean (e.g., magnesian chlorite, mixed-layer illite-montmorillonite solid solutions) are virtually in equilibrium with seawater. Although Siever (1968) recognizes the usefulness of this model in regard to CO_2 equilibrium in the atmosphere, he notes that these reactions are more probably postdepositional or postburial.

We performed similar experiments (Wollast and De Broeu, 1971) to those of Mackenzie et al. (1967) with highly disordered kaolinite similar to the suspended clay in estuarine waters. In an experiment with silica-enriched seawater the system attained, after 2500 hr, an equilibrium value for the concentration of dissolved silica equal to 19 ppm. This result agrees fairly well with those of Mackenzie et al. (1967).

It is significant that the experimental equilibrium values are always much larger than the concentrations of dissolved silica encountered in seawater, even in coastal or estuarine regions, which are rich in dissolved silica. The uptake of silica by clay minerals is, consequently, even more unlikely to occur in the ocean. Moreover, in the case of the ocean, it is probable that the clay minerals release silica as they sink to the ocean floor. The reactions between dissolved silica and clay minerals should, however, be highly favored after deposition of the clay minerals because of the high values of the concentration of dissolved silica, which often exceed the experimentally determined values in the interstitial waters.

3. Kinetic Behavior of Silica in Seawater

A. Introduction

It is well known that the thermodynamical approach is insufficient to explain the dissolution and precipitation reactions of silica in seawater because metastable states of the system may be maintained indefinitely if the rate of transformation toward the most stable phase is extremely slow. We will show in the next section that the dynamical behavior of dissolved silica plays an important role. Even if one admits that the biological activity has a considerable influence on the concentration of dissolved silica in surface seawater, the rate of dissolution of skeletons of organisms in the deep seawaters may be one of the controlling processes in producing the concentration profile of dissolved silica. Also, in the interstitial waters of the sediments, the rate of mass transfer of silica from one phase to another can lead to stationary states and control the level of dissolved silica in these waters.

We will next discuss the rate of dissolution and precipitation of the pure solid silica phases and then the reactions of dissolved silica with other solid phases.

B. Rate of Dissolution and Precipitation of Various Polymorphic Forms of Solid Silica

There is a considerable body of work concerning the dissolution kinetics of the various forms of silica prompted by interest in the causes of silicosis.

The results often appear contradictory at first sight. However, these contradictions are only apparent and result mainly from an insufficient control of the experimental parameters governing the rate of the reactions: pH, temperature, chlorinity, specific surface area of the solid, disturbance of the superficial layer of the grains, agitation of the solutions, etc.

The following discussion is essentially based on the analysis of the dissolution kinetics of quartz due to Van Lier et al. (1960). These authors have, in particular, clearly defined the influence of the parameters controlling the rate of dissolution of quartz and established the mechanism of the reaction. We have successfully applied their approach to the experimental results in the literature obtained at normal temperature for seawater or for solutions of chlorinity near to that of seawater.

Van Lier et al. (1960) first demonstrated that the rate of dissolution of quartz was not controlled by diffusion of dissolved silica from the surface of the grains into the solution. A simple calculation shows that such a mechanism would require a diffusion layer of several hundred metres which is, of course, absurd. Their experimental results suggest that the rate is controlled by a reaction at the surface which obeys the relation:

$$\left(\frac{dc}{dt}\right)_1 = k_1 \frac{\Omega}{V} \tag{1}$$

where Ω represents the surface area of the solid and V the volume of the solution. The constant k_1 is not the real kinetic constant, since it depends on the pH and the chlorinity.

At high concentrations of dissolved silica, this reaction competes with the reprecipitation of dissolved silica onto the quartz surface. The rate of the latter reaction is directly proportional to the number of molecules of dissolved silica in the surrounding solution per unit surface area of the solid and may be represented by

$$\left(\frac{dc}{dt}\right)_2 = -k_2 \frac{\Omega}{V} c \tag{2}$$

The overall equation representing the rate of dissolution and precipitation of silica is:

$$\frac{dc}{dt} = \frac{\Omega}{V}(k_1 - k_2 c) \tag{3}$$

At equilibrium

$$\left(\frac{dc}{dt}\right)_1 = -\left(\frac{dc}{dt}\right)_2 \quad \text{and} \quad c_{eq} = \frac{k_1}{k_2} = K_{eq} \tag{4}$$

Relation 3 then becomes

$$\frac{dc}{dt} = \frac{\Omega}{V} k_2(c_{eq} - c) \tag{5}$$

Equation 5 is identical to the one obtained if the assumption is made that the *reaction* rate is controlled by diffusion and k_2 is replaced in equation 5 by the diffusion coefficient of dissolved silica in the solution. This similarity explains certain differences in interpretation of the experimental observations.

Integrating relation 5 one finally obtains

$$\ln\left(\frac{c_{eq} - c}{c_{eq} - c_0}\right) = k_2 \frac{\Omega}{V} t \tag{6}$$

where c_0 represents the concentration of dissolved silica at $t = 0$.

Recently, Hurd (1972) verified that equation 6 also applies very well to the dissolution of amorphous silica (radiolarians tests) in seawater. On the other hand, Stöber (1967) concluded from a detailed study of the dissolution kinetics of various polymorphic forms of silica that the above mechanism was too simple. He therefore took into account the existence of the adsorption isotherm for dissolved silica on the surface of the solid. We do not think that this extension of the theory is justified; the values of the solubility of quartz and the trends of the experimental curves suggest that the slight discrepancies between equation 6 and the experimental results are because the samples used did not have their disturbed surface layers completely removed. For all practical purposes equation 6 is sufficient to describe the results. We recalculated Stöber's (1967) results using only equations 1, 2, and 6. The results then appear to be self-consistent, when one considers the various polymorphic forms of silica, and they are in very good agreement with those recalculated from the studies of other authors. Table II summarizes the results of these calculations. The values of the constants

TABLE II

Rate Constants for Dissolution of Silica in Seawater Calculated at 25°C—pH 8.0–8.4

Form	k_1 (mol/cm^2 sec)	k_2 (cm/sec)	e_{equ} (mol/liter)	Experimental Data from
Quartz	2.5×10^{-15}	1.25×10^{-8}	0.20×10^{-3}	Stöber (1967)
Quartz	2.1×10^{-15}	1.15×10^{-8}	0.18×10^{-3}	Henderson, Syers, and Jackson (1970)
Quartz	8.5×10^{-15}	1.45×10^{-8}	0.58×10^{-3}	Lucas et al. (1939)
Tridymite	7.2×10^{-15}	1.14×10^{-8}	0.63×10^{-3}	Stöber (1967)
Cristobalite	13.5×10^{-15}	1.35×10^{-8}	1.00×10^{-3}	Stöber (1967)
Amorphous silica	37.6×10^{-15}	2.04×10^{-8}	1.84×10^{-3}	Stöber (1967)
Diatoms	42.1×10^{-15}	2.47×10^{-8}	1.7×10^{-3}	Grill et al. (1964)
Radiolarians	67.0×10^{-15}	4.30×10^{-8}	1.55×10^{-3}	Hurd (1972)

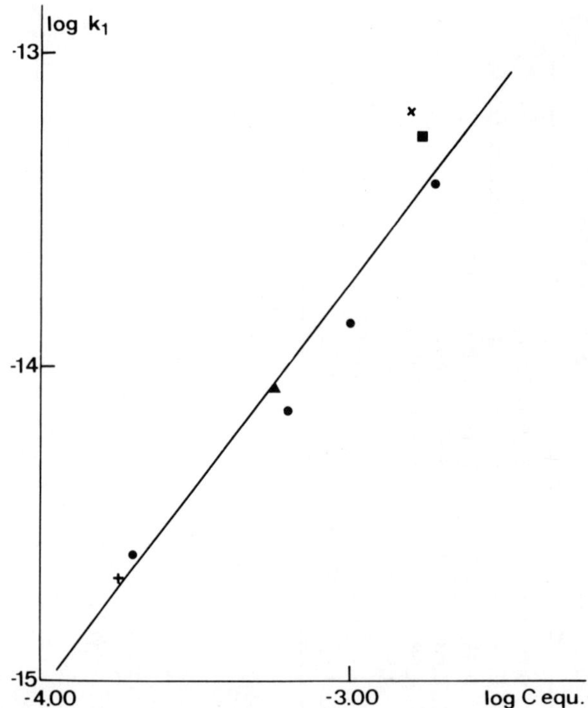

Fig. 4. Relation between the rate of dissolution of various solid silica phases and their solubility. After ● Stoeber (1967); + Henderson et al. (1970); ▲ Lucas et al. (1939); ■ Hurd (1972).

have been corrected by applying the relation $k_1 = k(\mathrm{Cl})^{0.7}$, deduced from the experiments of Van Lier (1960), so that they are expressed for a chlorinity equal to that of the mean composition of seawater.

Some interesting conclusions may be deduced from these calculations. The rate of dissolution k_1 is mainly influenced by the nature of the solid phase, whereas the rate of reprecipitation k_2 is rather insensitive to this parameter. More remarkable is the fact that log k_1 is nearly proportional to log c_{eq} (Fig. 4), which means that the activation energy of the dissolution reaction is directly proportional to the free energy of formation of the solid phase. This confirms a hypothetical reaction mechanism in which the rate is controlled by a surface chemical reaction involving the rupture of ionic bonds in the solid.

The relative rates of dissolution of amorphous silica and of quartz indicate that in the production of the concentration profile of silica in seawater the importance one could attribute to quartz as the controlling solid phase, because of its dissolution equilibrium value, is overestimated when one considers the abundance of diatoms and radiolarians skeletons suspended in seawater. The comparatively small changes in the rate of reprecipitation of silica as a function of the nature of the solid phase are perhaps surprising in view of the large energy differences possible between the solution and the various solid phases. This behavior may, however, be explained if one examines the specific experiments of Stöber (1967), who followed reactions of solid quartz in various solutions supersaturated with respect to the appropriate equilibrium concentration of dissolved silica. An analysis of the experimental data of this author was made using equation 5.

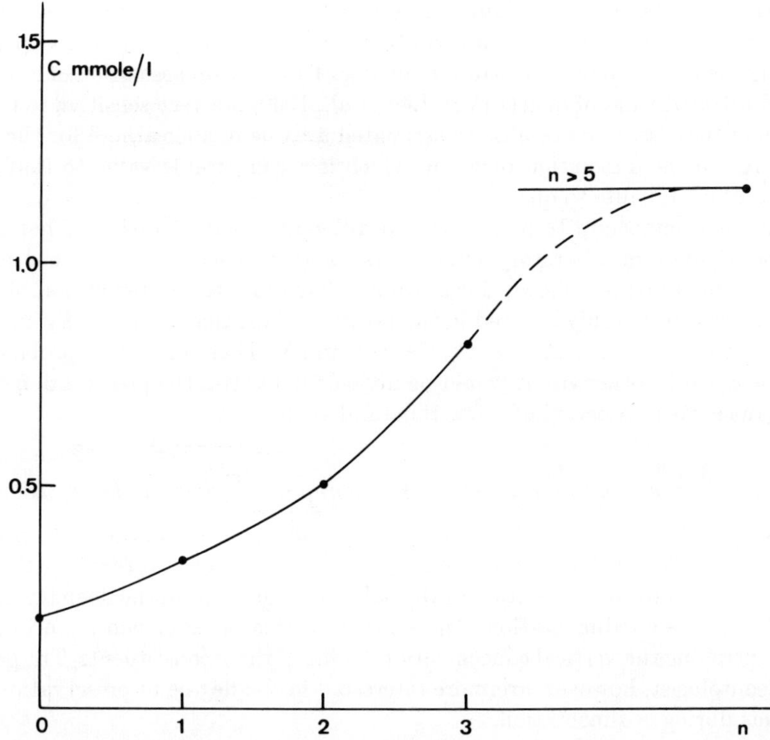

Fig. 5. Concentration of dissolved silica in equilibrium with the newly deposited phase as a function of the number of layers deposited on the surface of quartz during precipitation of dissolved silica.

The calculated values of dissolved silica concentration as a function of time agree well with the experimental data if one takes the constant value for k_2 of 1.40×10^{-8} cm/sec and increasing values for the concentration of dissolved silica in equilibrium with the new deposited phase as a function of the number of layers formed. Figure 5 represents the equilibrium values as a function of the thickness of the silica layer deposited on quartz. This curve indicates that the solid deposited has a tendency to attain a more and more disordered structure approaching that of cristobalite, in accordance with the rate of precipitation and the value of c_{eq}, as the layer increases in depth. If, from a kinetical point of view, the presence of quartz favors the nucleation of new silica layers the precipitation of dissolved silica requires higher degrees of supersaturation as the number of deposited layers increases.

Reprecipitation of dissolved silica on quartz must thus be considered to be rapidly inhibited for low degrees of supersaturation. Such a process, however, may occur on the geological time scale in marine sediments, with a slow reorganization of the deposited layers leading to the formation of relatively well-crystallized quartz. This mechanism has been experimentally demonstrated (Harder and Flehming, 1970; Mackenzie, 1971) and proposed by Heath and Moberly (1971) as the explanation for the occurrence of authigenic quartz in marine sediments. It also explains the diagenetic evolution of opal as recently reviewed by Laurent and Scheere (1972), who concluded that the amorphous silica is progressively transformed into quartz by a mechanism of dissolution and reprecipitation during which cristobalite appears as an intermediate phase.

Additional evidence for the importance of this process is the activation energy of 23 kcal/mol obtained by Ernst and Calvert (1969) for hydrothermal experiments involving the inversion of cristobalite to quartz. The rates of dissolution of amorphous silica (Hurd, 1972) and of quartz (Van Lier et al., 1960) are very sensitive to temperature. From these author's results we estimated a value of 20 kcal/mol for the activation energy of the dissolution reaction, which is a comparable value to that for the inversion of cristobalite to quartz.

Finally, it is important to point out that differences may be observed between the behavior of silica in laboratory experiments and its behavior in natural environments. Lewin (1961) has shown, for example, that the rates of dissolution of diatom skeletons are considerably lowered in the presence of organic matter or by adsorption of cations such as those of Al, Be, Fe, Ga, Gd, and Y. These inhibitors probably play an important role, otherwise it would be difficult to explain the preservation of silicified organisms over a period of a few thousand years.

C. Sedimentation of Particles Undergoing the Process of Dissolution

The sedimentation of particles undergoing dissolution is of considerable interest in oceanography. The cycling of numerous constituents in seawater (e.g., nutrients and $CaCO_3$) is related to the dissolution of the debris of organisms in the deep layers of the ocean during their sedimentation. The kinetics of this phenomenon is an important factor controlling the vertical concentration profile of these constituents. The geologist and paleontologist, however, are more interested in the degree of preservation of the organisms during sedimentation.

One may distinguish two models describing the process of dissolution of particles undergoing sedimentation. In one the kinetics of dissolution is controlled by the diffusion of the chemical species from the surface of the particle. In this case the vertical movement of the solid in water generates a convection current that accelerates the mass transfer and thus the rate of dissolution. This behavior has been described by Pond et al. (1971) who have established a model based on dimensional analysis. The model does not apply to silica as the dissolution reaction is controlled by a surface reaction (the second model) and thus is insensitive to movement of the solid. Of course, the rate of sedimentation varies continuously, since the weights and dimensions of the particles diminish with time. This problem may be easily solved by introducing the relation for the dissolution rate of the solid, expressed as a function of the particle radius, into the Stokes equation.

Let us consider, for example, the problem of the diatom skeletons. As seawater is always largely undersaturated with respect to amorphous silica, the rate of dissolution of the skeletons may be simply described by equation 1.

Equation 1 may be rewritten as,

$$\frac{dq}{dt} = -k_1\Omega_r = -4\pi\alpha r^2 k_1 \tag{7}$$

where q = amount (moles) of silica that has been dissolved
r = Stokes radius of the particle
α = shape factor relating the Stokes radius of the particle to the apparent radius deduced from measurements of specific surface area
Ω_r = surface area of the particle

Also,

$$q = \tfrac{4}{3}\pi r^3 \frac{\rho_s}{M} \tag{8}$$

where ρ_s = specific gravity of the solid
M = molecular weight of the solid

Differentiating equation 8 with respect to time and substituting into equation 7 we obtain:

$$\frac{dr}{dt} = -\alpha \frac{M}{\rho_s} k_1 = k_1' \tag{9}$$

The radius r at any time t is given by

$$r = r_0 - k_1' t \tag{10}$$

Substituting equation 10 into the Stokes relation one obtains:

$$v = \frac{dx}{dt} = \tfrac{2}{9} g \frac{\rho_s - \rho_l}{\eta} (r_0 - k_1' t)^2 \tag{11}$$

By integration,

$$x = \tfrac{2}{9} g \frac{\rho_s - \rho_l}{\eta} \left(r_0{}^2 t - r_0 k_1' t^2 + \frac{k_1'{}^2 t^3}{3} \right) \tag{12}$$

One may express, similarly, the change in the radius of the solid particle as a function of the depth x:

$$x = \frac{1}{k_1'} \left(\tfrac{2}{27} g \frac{\rho_s - \rho_l}{\eta} \right) (r_0{}^3 - r^3) \tag{13}$$

Equation 13 allows us to calculate the change in mass of particle (m) as a function of the depth x:

$$m_0 - m = \pi k_1' \rho_s \times \left(\frac{18}{9} \frac{\eta}{\rho_s - \rho_l} \right) \tag{14}$$

The lifetime (t^*) of a dissolving particle is determined by putting $r = 0$ into equation 10, which leads to

$$t^* = r_0 / k_1' \tag{15}$$

The maximum depth (x^*) that the particle may reach is given by:

$$x^* = \tfrac{2}{27} g \left(\frac{\rho_s - \rho_l}{\eta} \right) \left(\frac{r_0{}^3}{k_1'} \right) \tag{16}$$

We have used these equations to describe the behavior of diatom skeleton debris during its sedimentation. We have assumed, of course, that the skeletons were free of their original organic coating. Experiments of Grill et al. (1964) showed that the removal of the organic membrane is complete for a few days after the death of the diatoms. The mean Stokes radius of the diatom debris particles was estimated to be 7 μ from experimental measurements of the rate of sedimentation due to Margalef (1961) and Calvert (1966). The low values for the apparent radii of the diatom skeletons are due to the grazing of diatoms by copepods (Lisitzin, 1972). The shape factor α was

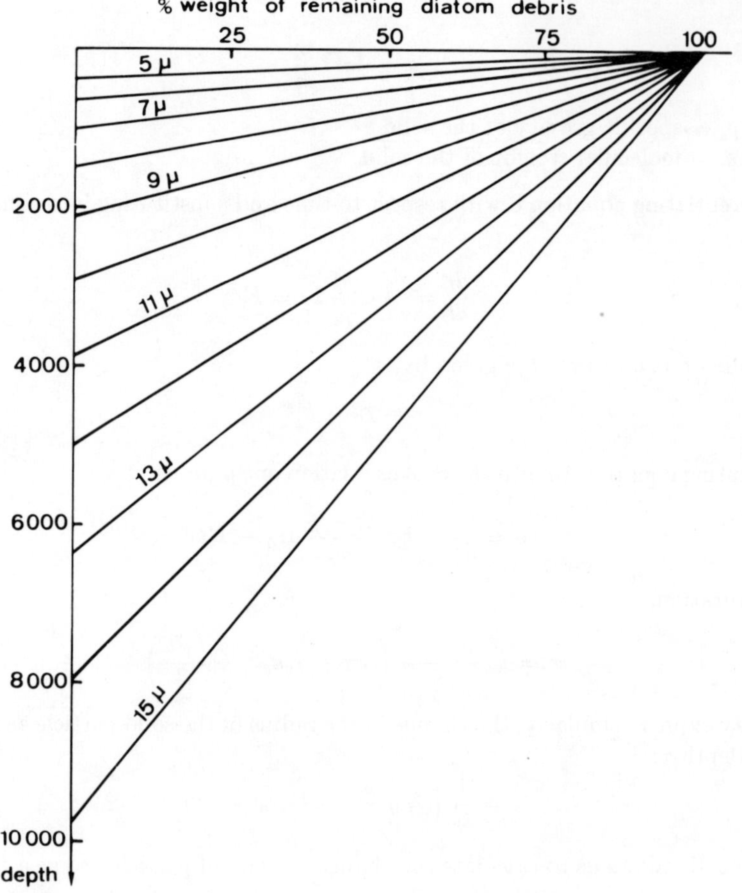

Fig. 6. Weight fraction of diatom debris remaining at particular depths for various initial radii of the particles.

computed using an estimate of 60 m^2/g for the surface area of the solid. All the physical constants for seawater and the rate of dissolution were taken for a constant temperature of 5°C.

Figure 6 represents the weights of diatom debris particles that remain at particular depths for various initial radii of the particles. Considering that the mean value of the radius for these particles is about 7 μ, Fig. 6 shows that only a few particles of this dimension remain below 1000 m. The data of Kozlova (1964) are in good agreement with these calculations. We have represented in Fig. 7 the frequency of occurrence of diatom skeletons counted by Kozlova (1964) at 30 stations in the Antarctic Sea as a function of depth. It appears from the data that only about 2% of diatom skeletons remain at 1000 m. Lisitzin (1972) supports this conclusion but points out that skeletons of silicoflagellates and radiolarians are more robust and settle more rapidly.

The above observation also confirms our theoretical calculations. Assuming a Stokes equivalent radius of 15 μ for a particle one can show that 50% of the weight of the debris remains at a depth of 5000 m, which agrees well with the estimations made by Lisitzin (1972) for the preservation of radiolarians skeletons. The influence of the

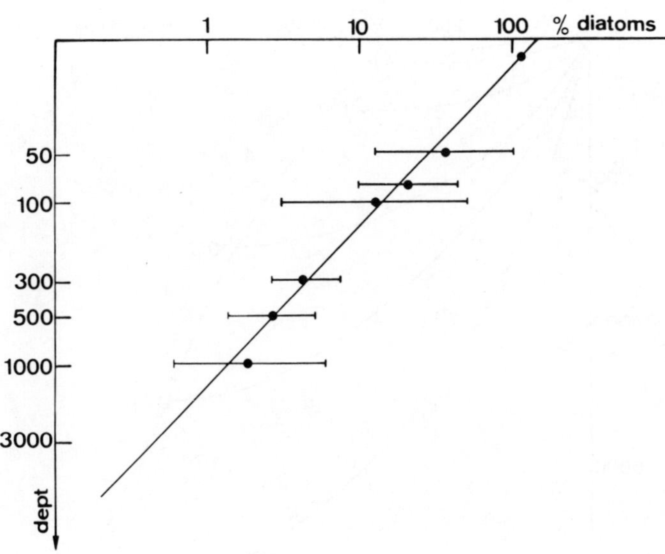

Fig. 7. Frequency of occurrence of diatom skeletons at 30 stations of the Antarctic Sea as a function of depth. Data from Kozlova (1964).

radius of amorphous silica particles on the ultimate depth reached by the particles is given in Table III. Figure 8 represents the paths taken by particles of selected radii.

An interesting feature of these theoretical considerations is that, from equation 14, the amount of silica that goes into solution as a function of depth is independent of the particle radius. In other words, each debris particle releases an equivalent amount of silica at every depth until its final dissolution. If we assume that the distribution of the particle radii obeys the Gaussian law, then with a mean diameter of 7 μ and a

TABLE III

Ultimate Depth Reached by Particles of Amorphous Silica as a Function of the Initial Radius

Initial Radius r_0 (μmeters)	Ultimate Depth x^* (meters)
5	360
6	625
7	990
8	1480
9	2110
10	2900
11	3850
12	5000
13	6360
14	7950
15	9770

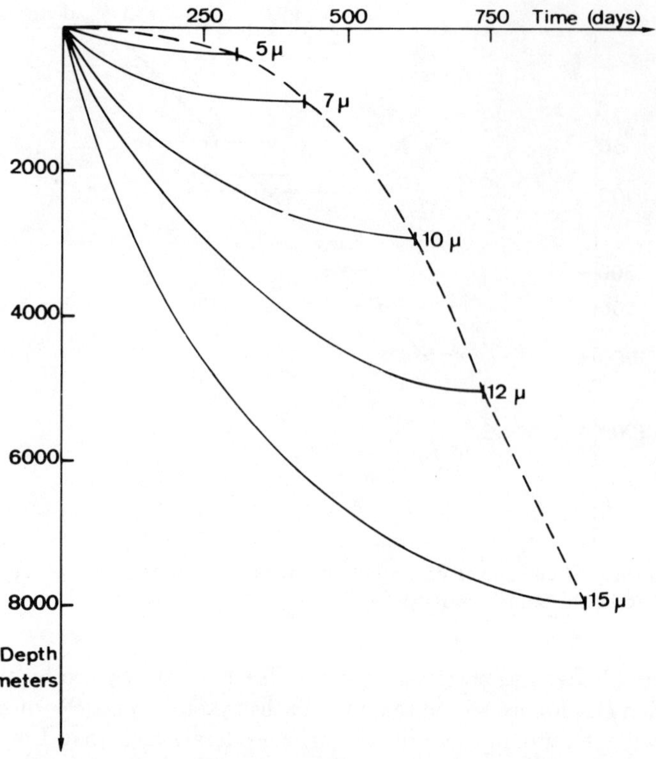

Fig. 8. Time for various-sized particles to reach ultimate depth. The curves represent the paths taken by particles of selected radii.

standard deviation of 2 μ, calculation shows that 45% of the weight of silica debris is dissolved between 0 and 1000 m.

It is also interesting to estimate the influence of upwelling on the dissolution process of settling particles. It is sufficient, therefore, to introduce into equation 13 a constant term of convection. We shall not discuss the modified calculations here because they show that for normal rates of upwelling (1 to 50 m/yr) the behavior of the particles is appreciably affected only if their diameters are less than 0.5 μ, and the paths taken by the particles are only affected during the last few meters of their settling.

D. *Kinetics of Reactions Involving Silicates*

The experiments of Mackenzie and Garrels (1967) discussed in Section 2.D showed that suspended silicates in seawater react rapidly to release silica in seawater deficient in dissolved silica or to take up dissolved silica in silica-enriched waters. Although the equilibrium values of dissolved silica obtained by these authors indicate that such reactions are probably unimportant in the open ocean, they may be predominant in the interstitial waters of marine sediments. The mechanism and the kinetics of this type of reaction have been studied for a potassium feldspar (Wollast, 1967). The rate of release of silica in this particular case is controlled by the diffusion of the chemical species involved through the reaction layer, which forms on the surface of the grain and increases with time. At the interface between this layer and the initial feldspar the concentration of dissolved silica is determined by the equilibrium relation between the two phases. This model may be used also for the uptake of dissolved silica, but is limited to the case of thin reaction layers and cannot be used to describe the transformation of solids during diagenesis. We will describe an extension of this model to a complex reaction where one phase releases silica into solution, the silica then being consumed by another solid phase to form a more siliceous compound. Both dissolution and precipitation kinetics may be controlled by a surface reaction or by a diffusion process. Let us consider here that the first phase is amorphous silica, or any other phase for which the rate of dissolution is controlled by a surface reaction. According to equation 5, if n_1 is the number of particles of radius r_1 per unit volume of seawater V at time t, the rate (v_1) of this reaction may be written

$$v_1 = 4\pi K(c_1 - c)\frac{n_1 r_1^2}{V} \tag{17}$$

where c_1 = equilibrium concentration for the dissolution of amorphous silica
c = concentration at time t.

If we assume that the subsequent reaction involving the uptake of silica by the clay mineral is controlled by the rate of diffusion of silica through the reaction layer composed of the new phase, the rate of this reaction v_2 will be given by,

$$v_2 = 4\pi D\left(\frac{c - c_2}{R_2 - r_2}\right)\frac{n^2 r_2^2}{V} \tag{18}$$

where c_2 = concentration of dissolved silica for the equilibrium between the two phases
R_2 = initial radius of the clay particle
r_2 = radius at time t of the unreacted clay particle
n_2 = number of clay particles per unit volume V of seawater
D = diffusion coefficient for silica passing through the reaction layer.

Figure 9 shows schematically the model used to derive these equations. The overall change in the concentration of dissolved silica is described by combining equations 17 and 18:

$$\frac{dc}{dt} = \frac{4\pi}{V}\left\{K(c_1 - c)n_1 r_1^2 - D\left(\frac{c - c_2}{R_2 - r_2}\right)n_2 r_2^2\right\} \tag{19}$$

The radii r_1 and r_2 appearing in equation 19 vary with time but can be expressed as

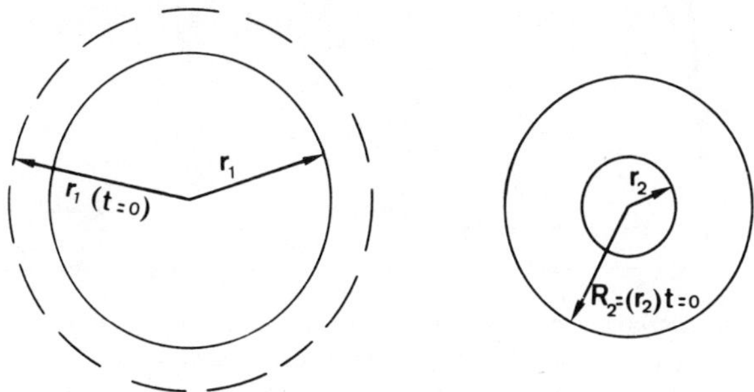

Fig. 9. Schematic model of a complex reaction where phase 1 releases silica into solution, the silica being consumed by phase 2 to form a more siliceous compound. The first reaction is controlled by a surface reaction and the second by a diffusion process.

a function of c and t. For amorphous silica, we may write, in a similar form to equation 9, that the rate of dissolution is related to the changes in the radius r_1 by the expression

$$-K(c_1 - c)r_1\Omega_1 = r_1\Omega_1 \frac{dr_1}{dt}\frac{\rho_s}{M} \tag{20}$$

Equation 20 reduces to

$$\frac{dr_1}{dt} = -\frac{KM}{\rho_s}(c_1 - c) \tag{21}$$

Similarly, the change in the thickness of the reaction layer may be written as

$$-D\left(\frac{c - c_2}{R_2 - r_2}\right) r_2\Omega_2 = r_2\Omega_2 \frac{dr_2}{dt} c_0 \tag{22}$$

where c_0 = number of moles of silica necessary to transform one unit volume of the initial clay into the more siliceous clay

Equation 21 reduces to

$$\frac{dr_2}{dt} = -\frac{D}{c_0}\left(\frac{c - c_2}{R_2 - r_2}\right) \tag{23}$$

We solved the system of differential equations 19, 21, and 23 using an analog computer, and the most significant results are represented in Figs. 10 and 11.

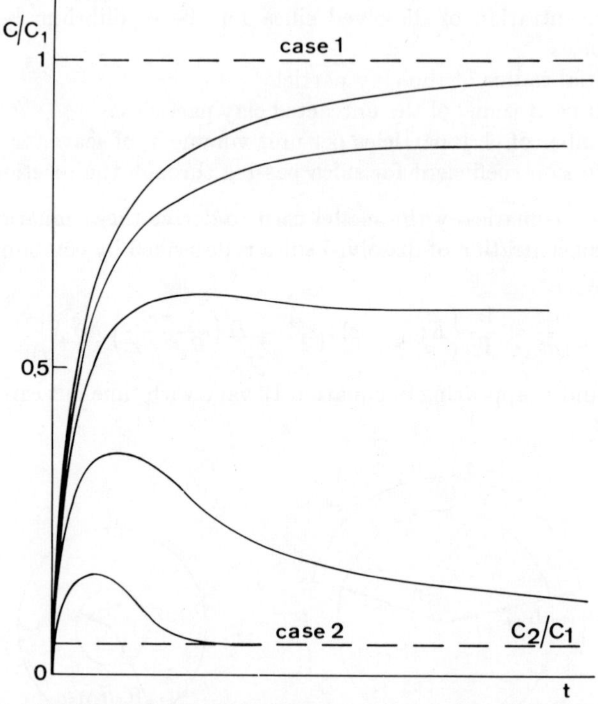

Fig. 10. Calculated dissolved silica change with time for a reaction between amorphous silica and clay minerals. Case 1 represents the change when the dissolution process is *predominant* and Case 2 when the uptake of dissolved silica by clay minerals is *predominant*. Intermediate curves show the evolution of dissolved silica when both processes control the kinetics. The upper dashed line corresponds to the saturation with respect to amorphous silica and the lower line to the dissolved silica concentration in equilibrium with the clay system.

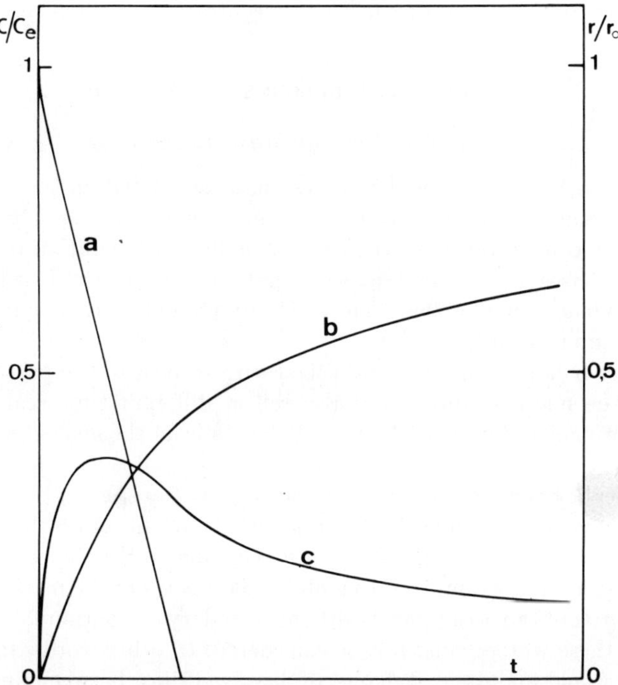

Fig. 11. Theoretical variation of (a) the relative radius of the amorphous silica particles, (b) the layer of the reacted clay, and (c) the concentration of dissolved silica in the interstitial waters.

The kinetic behavior of such a system is, of course, mainly controlled by the relative numbers of dimensions of the particles of amorphous silica and clay minerals on the one hand and by the ratio of the constants k and D on the other hand.

If the dissolution process for amorphous silica is predominant the equilibrium concentration for this phase in the solution is rapidly attained (Fig. 10, case 1). Alternatively, if the uptake of dissolved silica by the clay mineral is predominant, the concentration of dissolved silica increases briefly and then decreases rapidly toward the equilibrium value for the reaction with the clay mineral (Fig. 10, case 2). The most interesting feature of these theoretical results lies in the fact that the concentrations of dissolved silica reach a series of quasistationary states at various levels between the maximum and minimum values given by cases 1 and 2, respectively, in Fig. 10.

These results show, unfortunately, that the concentration of dissolved silica in a solution, even if it is relatively independent of time, is not a sufficiently sensitive parameter, in many cases, to distinguish between the reactions that may occur in the system. Strictly speaking, it is also necessary to determine quantitatively the various phases present and their physicochemical properties. We shall further show that the behavior of other dissolved species may often provide important information.

The mechanism described above represents only one of the multiple combinations possible between the various elementary processes that describe the kinetics of such reactions. In this discussion we have restricted ourselves to an analysis of the mechanism most likely to occur in the marine environment. Similar results may, however, be obtained for other combinations and, for instance, the alternative control mechanisms of diffusion for dissolution and of surface reaction for reprecipitation lead to the same kind of variation as above in the concentration of dissolved silica (Wollast 1967).

4. Silica Mass Balances in the Ocean

A. Geochemical Mass Balance

The mass balance of an element in a system is calculated on the assumption that the system has reached a steady state at a given moment. The steady-state condition implies that the concentration of the element under consideration remains constant in the various phases due to equal rates of input for every phase. It is then possible to calculate a residence time for that element in any phase by dividing its concentration by the rate of input or output.

Various mass balances may be established with respect to the particular phases in the system. The mass balances may also reflect different time scales so that it is possible to distinguish, for example, mass balances from the geological and biological points of view.

The geological system comprises three parts: the atmosphere, the oceans, and the upper crustal layers of the mantle. If we focus our attention on the oceans, various sources of silica may be taken into account, depending on the choice of boundaries for the oceanic system. For example, if the interstitial waters of the marine sediments are regarded as a part of the ocean phase without boundary discontinuity, then the release of silica from these waters must not be considered. In other words, this definition of the boundary would make the exchange of dissolved silica between interstitial waters and the ocean a subsystem within the oceanic reservoir. Also, redissolution during settling of the silica skeletons produced by biological activity, mainly in the upper layers of the ocean, would not be considered as an external source affecting the silica budget, but represents only one of the numerous possible steps of the transformations undergone by silica during its residence time in the ocean.

Mass balances for silica have been extensively discussed recently (Harris, 1966; Calvert, 1968; Heath, 1973). The best quantitative estimations of the sources and sinks of dissolved silica are summarized in Table IV. Rivers supply the major portion of the dissolved silica in the ocean and, although there is not yet enough quantitative information on submarine weathering and volcanism it is clear that these cannot be a major source of dissolved silica in the present ocean. The rate of accumulation of amorphous silica in marine sediments has been estimated by Calvert (1968) from the data of Bezrukov (1955), Baranov et al. (1958), Goldberg et al. (1962), Calvert (1966), and Lisitzin (1967). According to Heath (1973), it is necessary to take into account the experimentally observed removal of 10% of the dissolved silica from river input by organic adsorption involving detrital particles to explain the data of Bien et al. (1959) and Liss et al. (1970). The latter authors discovered that there was a removal of soluble silica in the estuaries, presumably because of abiological reactions. However, these observations are inconsistent with other observations (Stephanson and Richards, 1963; Burton et al., 1970b; Wollast and Debroeu, 1971), and seem related to the nature of the suspended matter in the estuarine region. The estimation given by Heath (1973) is therefore somewhat arbitrary but does not change the conclusions very much. If one assumes that the total weight of dissolved silica in the ocean is 5.5×10^{18} g (Strakhov, 1963), then its mean residence time in the ocean is about 1.310^4 yr.

The values are close to those from the first attempted calculations based on the data of Livingstone (1963), who estimated the supply of dissolved silica by rivers, and those of Goldberg (1965) who estimated the silica accumulated in marine sediments.

TABLE IV

Geological Mass Balance of Silica in the Ocean[a]

	10^{14} g $SiO_{2/y}$
Supply	
Rivers	4.27
Submarine weathering	0.03
Submarine volcanism	0.0003
	4.30
Removal	
Siliceous sediments	3.60
Inorganic uptake	0.43
	4.03

[a] Revised figures from the data collected by Harris (1966), Calvert (1968), and Heath 1973).

B. Biological Mass Balance

A comparison of the geochemical mass balance with that of the biological subsystem is of considerable interest because it clearly demonstrates the importance of biological activity to the behavior of dissolved silica in the ocean. The approach that we will consider here is a classical one based on the amount of dissolved silica precipitated from seawater by organisms during the primary productivity process. The data for this process are difficult to establish at the present time, but there is sufficient agreement on the orders of magnitude involved to approach an understanding of the role of biological activity in the silica cycle.

Table V gives the estimated values, taken from the literature, of the annual uptake of silica by organisms, based on the corresponding uptake of carbon during the primary productivity process and the ratio of Si/C in marine organisms. Despite the imprecision of the data it is clear that the biological activity requires an amount of dissolved silica of an order of magnitude higher than that supplied by rivers and submarine activities. A remarkable implication of these figures is that the mean residence time for dissolved silica in seawater may be reduced to only 200 to 300 yr if one considers the biological subsystem.

TABLE V

Biological Uptake of Silica Within the Ocean

Author	Estimation
Harris (1966)	0.77×10^{16} g/yr
Lisitzin (1967)	$8 - 16 \times 10^{16}$ g/yr
Heath (1973)	$1.7 - 3.2 \times 10^{16}$ g/yr

It is evident from these data that the dynamical behavior imposed on the ocean system by the living organisms will be a determining factor in the control of the distribution of dissolved silica in the oceans. Geochemical factors and the influence of external sources such as the river input of dissolved silica will only play secondary roles in the distribution of this constituent in the ocean.

We shall show that the chemical dissolution of silicified organism tests in the water column is almost entirely sufficient to meet the nutritional requirements of the living organisms for dissolved silica. We have seen in Section 3.C that, due to grazing, an important dissolution of the skeleton debris already occurs in the upper few thousand meters of the ocean, and that only a very small fraction of the skeletons are preserved in the sediments.

On the other hand, the important uptake of dissolved silica by organisms in surface waters creates a concentration gradient, which becomes more marked as biological activity increases. This concentration gradient (dc/dz) causes, by eddy diffusion, a vertical mass transfer of dissolved silica toward the surface, given by:

$$J = K_e \frac{dc}{dz} \tag{24}$$

where J is the flux of silica (mol/cm^2/sec) and K_e is the eddy diffusion coefficient. According to Stommel (1958) and Munk (1966), K_e varies between 0.1 and 10 cm^2/sec. Craig (1970) estimated the value of this coefficient for the South Pacific Ocean from measurements of the C^{13} distribution and found a mean value of 2 cm^2/sec. We adopted this value to calculate the amount of dissolved silica transported by eddy diffusion toward the surface of various oceans, taking into account their respective concentration gradients of dissolved silica. Table VI summarizes these estimations.

On the basis of the total surface area of the oceans the total amount of dissolved

TABLE VI

Estimation of the Contribution of Eddy Diffusion and Advection in the Vertical Transport of Dissolved silica

Ocean[a]	dc/dx 10^{-13} mol/cm$^3\cdot$cm	J Diffusion 10^5 mol/km$^2\cdot$y	J Advection 10^5 mol/km$^2\cdot$y
Atlantic (1)	2	1.3	3.5
North Pacific (2)	17	11	15
South Pacific (3)	12	7.6	10
Indian (4)	16	10	12.5
Antarctic (5)	18	11	13

[a] Concentrations and concentration gradients were estimated from:

(1) Woods Hole Institute of Oceanography. Ref. 58–30 (1958), *Discovery II*, IGY, Cruise 2.

(2) Scripps Institution of Oceanography. Oceanic observations of the Pacific, University of California Press, Berkeley and Los Angeles. OOP 1958 (1965) POG, P-58-1; uw, BB-199; OOP 1959 (1965) POG, P-59-1; OOP 1957 (1965) SIO, MUKLUK.

(3) OOP 1957 (1965) SIO, Downwind.

(4) Rozanov, A. G. 1964, Distribution of phosphorus and silica in the north Indian Ocean. Academia NAUK SSSR—Trudy Instituta Okeanologii TOM LXIV.

(5) IGY World Data Center A: IGY Oceanography Rpt no. 2 (1961), Ob, Cruises 1, 2, 3.

silica that diffuses to the surface is 1.2×10^{16} g/yr. This value is in rather good agreement with the previous estimations of the amount of silica necessary for the annual biological activity (Table V). It is necessary to point out that eddy diffusion is not the only mechanism in operation for the mass transfer of dissolved silica toward the ocean surface and that upwelling may provide an important contribution in certain regions. The rate of upwelling (w) varies from 0.3 to 30 m/yr (Stommel, 1958; Munk, 1966). Craig (1970) obtained a mean value of 7 m/yr for upwelling in the South Pacific Ocean, which we also adopted as a good estimate. In the case of upwelling the vertical mass transfer due to diffusion and convection may be estimated by using the relation

$$J = K_e \frac{dc}{dz} + wc \tag{25}$$

From the values of Craig (1970) for K_e and w we obtain, for the South Pacific,

$$J = \underset{\text{Diffusion}}{1.2 \times 10^{-12}\ \text{mol/cm}^2\text{/sec}} + \underset{\text{Convection}}{2 \times 10^{-12}\ \text{mol/cm}^2\text{/sec}}$$

We have indicated in Table VI, as an example, the fluxes of dissolved silica due to advection for the various oceans taking a value for w of about 10 m/yr. It thus appears that mass transfer by advection is of the same order of magnitude as that by diffusion.

It is, of course, difficult to appreciate the quantitative importance of upwelling for the total oceanic system, because this phenomenon is generally of a local nature. Our calculations show, however, that mass transfer by upwelling is comparable to that of eddy confusion.

If we take this contribution into account, the calculated amount of dissolved silica transported to the ocean surface by physical processes is very close to that recently estimated by Heath (1973) to be required for uptake by organisms at the surface. These calculations demonstrate that the biological subsystem acts as a quasiclosed cycle. The activity of silica-secreting microplankton is essentially maintained by the rapid turnover of silica in this system. The debris of silicified skeletons dissolves rapidly during settling and continuously supplies the water column with dissolved silica. The dissolved silica is taken up by the organisms practically at the rate at which it becomes available in the surface layers, where it maintains in this manner a nearly zero concentration. The input of dissolved silica in these layers is largely controlled by eddy diffusion and upwelling. These two factors are mainly influenced by the concentration of dissolved silica in the deep seawaters which depends on the number of settling skeletons, which, in turn, depends on the surface biological activity. It is easy to understand that, in such a case, the concentration profile of dissolved silica in a water column tends toward a stationary state, the surface biological activity being mainly controlled by the equal contributions of eddy diffusion and upwelling.

This conclusion agrees with the earlier observations of Calvert (1966), Berger (1970), Scheere and Laurent (1970), and Lisitzin (1972). Figure 12 represents the annual production of silica in the World Ocean, as mapped by Lisitzin (1972). One can see in this figure the high productivity zone associated with the Antarctic divergence, where upwelling is considerable, which extends along the Occidentical coast of South America owing to the prevailing trade winds. We have represented in Fig. 13 a longitudinal section of the North Pacific Ocean, which clearly indicates that the vertical mass transfer process for dissolved silica increases with increasing latitude along this section. It explains the high productivity zone in this region (see Fig. 12).

If one compares, on the other hand, the values given in Table VI for the fluxes of

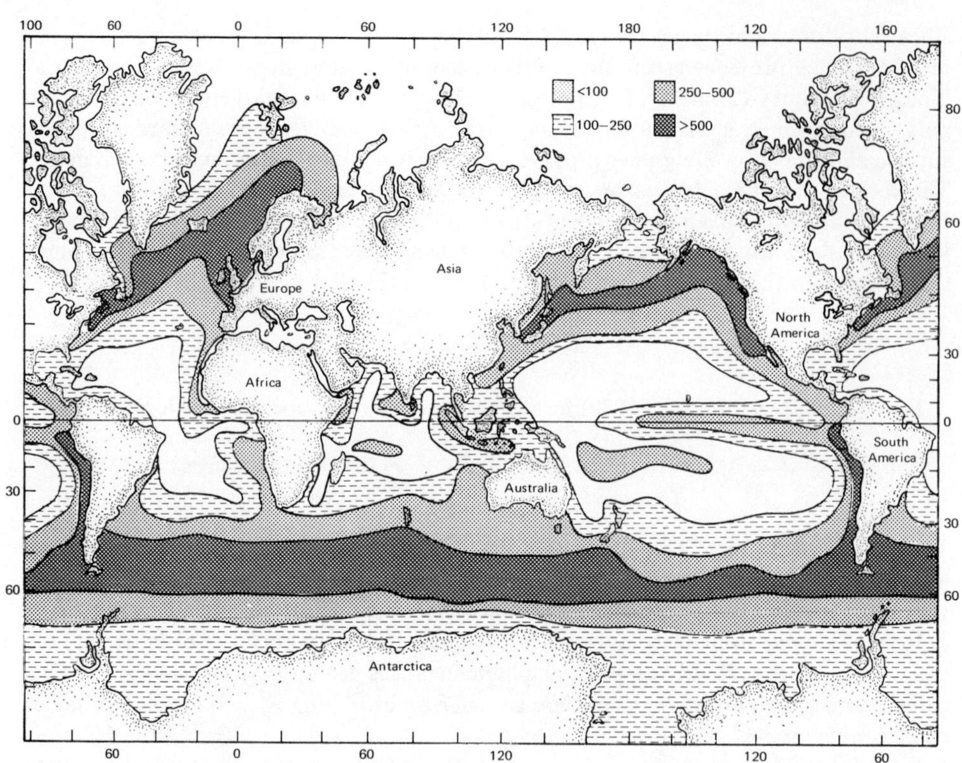

Fig. 12. Annual production of silica by marine organisms in the world ocean constructed from primary production data. From Lisitzin (1972).

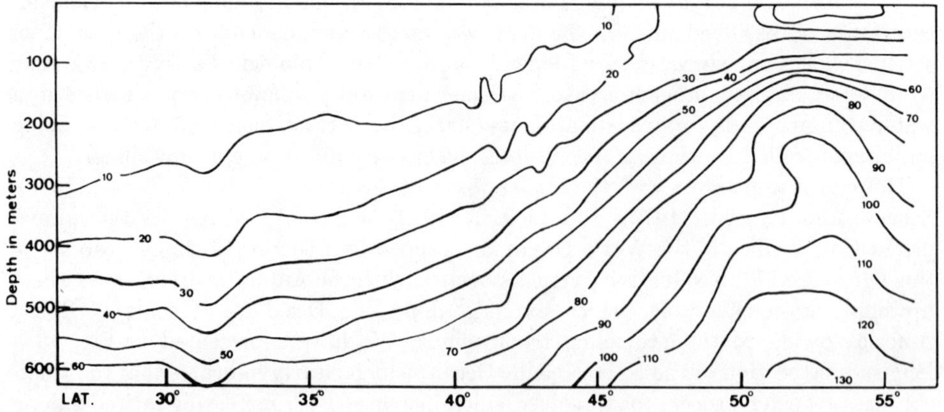

Fig. 13. Meridional section of the North Pacific Ocean for dissolved silica at 155°W longitude. After University of California Scripps, 1965. URSA Major Exp., data report, SI 0 Rep. 67–5.

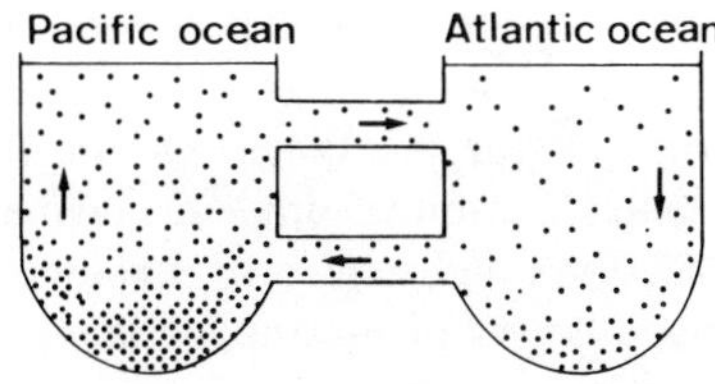

Fig. 14. Model of transfer of dissolved silica from the Atlantic to the Pacific Ocean. After Berger (1970).

dissolved silica in the Atlantic and Pacific Oceans one obtains excellent confirmation of the basin-basin fractionation model presented by Berger (1970). In this model, shown schematically in Fig. 14, Berger (1970) explains, with reference to their deep circulation patterns, the relative fertilities of the oceans and, in turn, the relative abundance of siliceous microfossils. The Pacific Ocean has relatively nutrient-rich waters because it collects deep waters, whereas the reverse occurs in the Atlantic Ocean.

C. *Interactions Between the Geochemical and Biochemical Cycles of Silica*

The calculations of the preceding section provide evidence that the biological cycle plays a predominant role in the control of the distribution of dissolved silica in the open ocean. This factor will, of course, influence the geochemical cycle of this constituent and we shall analyze the implications here. From these considerations we shall attempt to estimate more closely the values involved in the various stages used to calculate the geochemical mass balance.

The first aspect we shall consider is the relationship between the cycle of SiO_2 and CO_2, the importance of which was emphasized by Sillén (1961), Mackenzie et al. (1966), and Siever (1968). The origin of dissolved silica in riverwater is, in fact, mainly due to the chemical leaching of continental silicate rocks and soils. The weathering of feldspar may be considered as a typical example. This process requires the action of an acid, which can only be provided by atmospheric CO_2:

$$2\,NaAlSi_3O_8 + 2\,CO_2 + 11\,H_2O = Al_2Si_2O_5(OH)_4 + 2\,Na^+ + 2\,HCO_3^- + 4\,H_2SiO_4 \quad (26)$$

If one takes into account the annual amount of silica dissolved by this process (4.27×10^{14} g/yr), this requires (equation 26) a consumption of 3.5×10^{12} mol CO_2/yr from the atmosphere. This estimate also agrees with the mean composition for HCO_3^- in the rivers (Garrels and Mackenzie, 1966). If the dissolved silica introduced by rivers into the ocean is precipitated as opal, as is suggested by the biological activity, this reaction may be written simply as

$$SiO_2(aq) \rightarrow SiO_2(opal) \quad (27)$$

and does not involve CO_2. In other words, if we assume that reactions 26 and 27 control the geochemical cycle of silica, this implies an uptake of 3.5×10^{12} mol CO_2/yr from the atmosphere. If we make the reasonable assumption that the activity of marine organisms had controlled the accumulation of silica in marine sediments for 400×10^6 yr, the total consumption of CO_2 would have been 1.4×10^{21} mol CO_2. The total amount of CO_2 in the atmosphere being 5.4×10^{16} mol, this would imply that 20,000 times the CO_2 in the present atmosphere had been consumed, which is, of course, difficult to imagine. There must exist, therefore, some other reactions associated with this cycle to compensate for the consumption of CO_2 from the atmosphere. These reactions may be due either to early diagenesis of opal or to metamorphic processes in the marine sediments.

In the same way, if we take a mean sedimentation rate for the World Ocean of 50×10^{14} g/yr (Garrels and Mackenzie, 1971), the concentration of opal in marine sediments would be 4.27×10^{14} g/50×10^{14}g $= 8.5\%$ by weight. If one considers the map of amorphous silica distribution in the surface layers of marine sediments (Lisitzin, 1972), this estimate corresponds fairly well with the mean value for opal in these layers. This value, however, is much higher than that observed for the deeper layers of the sediments. Measurements of the amounts of amorphous silica in sediments, made by Lisitzin et al. (1971) on cores from the Deep Sea Drilling Project, show that the mean value for opal concentration in 243 samples is only 1.9% by weight. This mean value is also in good agreement with an earlier estimation of the rate of accumulation in marine sedimentary rocks (Calvert, 1968). One may conclude that approximately 80% of the amorphous silica accumulated in the surface layers of the sediments undergoes a rapid diagenesis.

D. Behavior of Dissolved Silica in Marine Sediments

The behavior of dissolved silica in the marine sediment environment differs greatly with respect to that in the open ocean. These differences are explained by the absence of a significant biological activity involving silica, the presence of a practically immobile aqueous phase, and an extremely high solid/solution ratio. As a result, the distribution of dissolved silica in interstitial waters essentially reflects the physicochemical properties of the sediments.

Siever et al. (1965) had already shown that, as a general rule, the concentration of dissolved silica in the interstitial waters was somewhat higher than in the open ocean. More recently, Heath (1973) has calculated a mean concentration of 0.4 m mol/liter from about 800 of these determinations available in the literature. There may be some imprecision in certain data due to the experimental techniques used (Fanning and Pilson, 1971), but, nevertheless, the mean values obtained agree sufficiently well to be used here.

One of the most interesting sources of data is the set of results obtained during the Deep Sea Drilling Project for which one has not only the concentrations of dissolved silica but also the concentration of other ions, and, in particular, the mineralogical composition of the sediments. It is not possible to give here a detailed analysis of all these results and we shall therefore restrict ourselves to a consideration of the most important trends. We will attempt to illustrate these by examining the analytical data from Hole 149 (Gieskes, 1973).

An important trend in the composition of interstitial waters was first pointed out by Presley and Kaplan (1970), who noted that the deep interstitial waters show generally a decrease of Mg^{2+} and K^+, and an increase in HCO_3^- and Ca^{2+} with respect to normal seawater. They supposed that this behavior was mainly due to the reaction

$$Mg^{2+} + 2\,CaCO_3 = MgCa(CO_3)_2 + Ca^{2+} \tag{28}$$

although they pointed out that there is more Ca^{2+} liberated than predicted by the mass balance based on equation 28. They attributed the uptake of K^+ to the neoformation of illite. It must be emphasized that the most important decrease in Mg^{2+} discussed by these authors was observed in Hole 27 where, from the mineralogical data of Rex and Murray (1970), dolomite is absent, but kaolinite, micas, chlorites, and montmorillonites are abundant. The decrease in Mg^{2+} is even more marked in the later analyzed Hole 35 (Manheim et al., 1970) where the concentration of Mg^{2+} drops

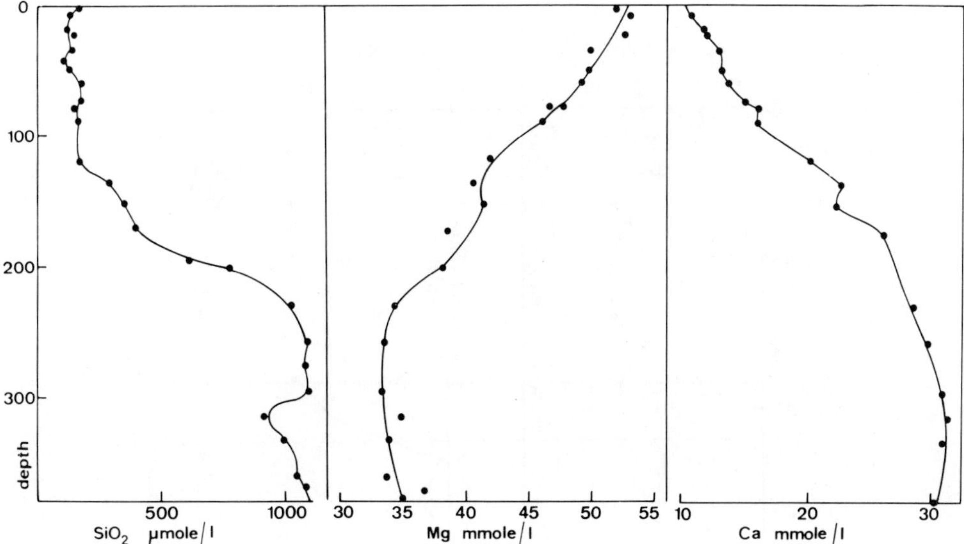

Fig. 15. Vertical concentration profile of dissolved silica, magnesium, and calcium in the interstitial waters of Hole 149. Data from Deep Sea Drilling Project (Gieskes, 1973).

from 1.4% in seawater above the sediments to 0.22% in the interstitial waters at −360 m. The dominant mineralogical phase is zeolitic clay and, again, dolomite is absent. It is also interesting to observe that there are generally smaller values for dissolved silica in the interstitial waters when important amounts of clay minerals are present.

We will now make a more detailed analysis of the concentration profiles of Hole 149 (Gieskes, 1973) for which we have a more complete set of data and the core of which is the useful example of a radiolarian ooze overlaid by a clay-rich deposit. These types of deposit represent the two extreme cases encountered in marine sediments that control the concentration of dissolved silica in the interstitial waters. Figure 15 gives the concentration profiles of dissolved silica, magnesium, and calcium in the interstitial waters of Hole 149. They are representative of the types of profile described by Presley (1970) and Manheim (1970), showing a decrease of magnesium and increase of calcium with depth. The large increase of dissolved silica observed in the deep layers may favor the reactions of dissolved silica with clay minerals and even initiate the precipitation of sepiolite (see Sections 2.C and 2.D).

The precipitation of sepiolite is the reaction most likely to occur in radiolarians oozes where clay minerals are absent. This reaction implies, however, the uptake of OH^- or the release of H^+. The observed replacement of Mg^{2+} by Ca^{2-} in the waters where sepiolite is formed may be explained by taking into account the buffering action of calcite.

The overall mechanism may be described by the combination of the following consecutive reactions:

$$6\ SiO_2(am) = 6\ SiO_2(aq) \tag{29}$$

$$6\ SiO_2(aq) + 3\ H_2O + 4\ Mg^{2+} + 8\ HCO_3^- = 2\ Mg_2Si_3O_6(OH)_4(1.5\ H_2O) + 8\ CO_2 \tag{30}$$

$$4\ CO_2 + 4\ H_2O + 4\ CaCO_3 = 8\ HCO_3^- + 4\ Ca^{2+} \tag{31}$$

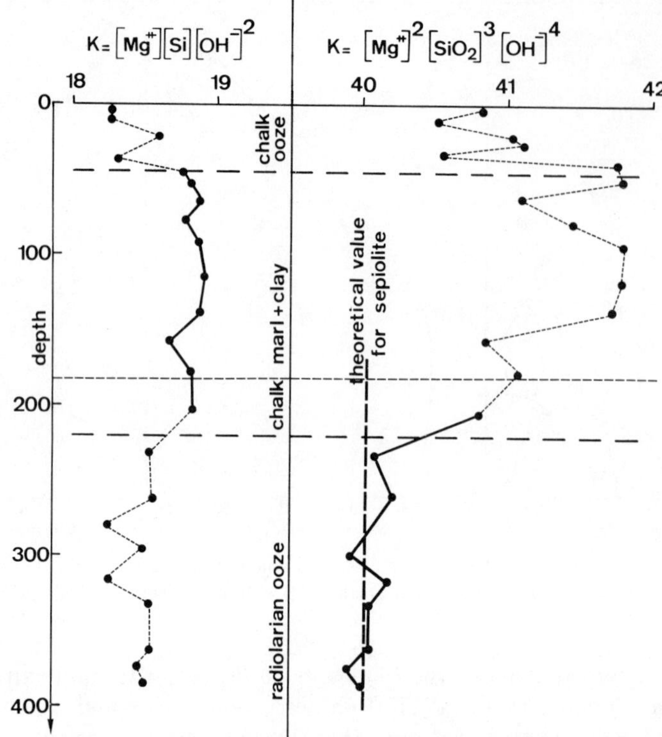

Fig. 16. Equilibrium products, assuming an uptake of dissolved silica by clay minerals, in the upper layers and the synthesis of sepiolite in the radiolarian ooze.

The overall reaction is

$$6\,SiO_2(am) + 4\,CaCO_3 + 4\,Mg^{2+} + 7\,H_2O = 2\,Mg_2Si_3O_6(OH)_4(1.5\,H_2O) + 4\,CO_2 + 4\,Ca^{2+} \quad (32)$$

Confirmation of this hypothetical mechanism may be obtained by calculating the product $(Mg^{2+})^2(SiO_2(aq))^3(OH^-)^4$ corresponding to the equilibrium of the ions involved in the synthesis of sepiolite. The variation in this product as a function of depth is shown in Fig. 16. It can be seen that this product is remarkably constant between -220 and -400 m and corresponds exactly to the equilibrium value for sepiolite precipitation determined by Christ et al. (1971) (see Section 2.C). Since the product is less in the layers above -200 m than the equilibrium constant for sepiolite precipitation one may suppose that another reaction takes place that decreases the concentration of dissolved silica in these upper layers. This change corresponds exactly to the depth where the radiolarian ooze is first replaced by marls. In this case, one may assume that, according to Section 3.D, the dissolved silica released by amorphous silica is taken up by the clay minerals and that these reactions control the concentration of dissolved silica in interstitial waters. Another useful indication is given by the fact $(Mg^{2+})(SiO_2(aq))(OH^-)^2$, which may correspond to a reaction of the type

$$\text{Clay I} + Mg^{2+} + 2\,OH^- + SiO_2(aq) = \text{Clay II} \quad (33)$$

which is also remarkably constant between -220 and -45 m. We have, however, shown in Section 3.D that it is quite impossible to identify the *particular* clays in equation 33 solely on the basis of the concentration of dissolved silica.

We have only considered above the reactions of clay minerals with Mg^{2+}. Potassium also exhibits a great affinity toward clay minerals and, to a lesser degree, sodium and calcium. The uptake of potassium from interstitial waters is a confirmation of the importance of such reactions in marine sediments. It is therefore impossible to establish a mass balance between Ca^{2+} and Mg^{2+}, the mass balance being actually more complicated.

The X-ray diffraction analyses made by Rex and his collaborators during the Deep Sea Drilling Project confirm the reactions of dissolved silica with clay minerals discussed above. They have provided evidence of the frequent occurrence of authigenic sepiolite, palygorskite, clinoptilotite, and phillipsite in marine sediments (see, e.g., Rex, 1970; Cook, 1971).

Another consequence of the high concentration of dissolved silica in interstitial waters is the diffusion of this species to the ocean. Hurd (1973) has measured the silica concentration gradient in the surface layers of the sediments of the Central Pacific. This gradient is extremely steep for about the first 30 cm of the sediment and we estimate it to be about 20 μM/liter cm at the sediment-ocean interface. The flux of dissolved silica from interstitial waters to the ocean may then be described (Berner, 1971) by

$$J = -\frac{D\phi}{\theta^2}\frac{\partial c}{\partial x} \tag{34}$$

where D = diffusion coefficient for silica in seawater
ϕ = porosity
θ = tortuosity of the sediment

The value of D, determined by Wollast and Garrels (1971), is equal to 1.0×10^{-5} cm^2/sec at 25° and is estimated to be 5×10^{-6} cm^2/sec at 5°. Considering that the combined effects of the tortuosity and porosity of the sediment may decrease the rate of diffusion by a factor of 2 one finally obtains a flux $J = 10^{-4}$ g/cm^2 yr. For the total surface area of the World Ocean the estimated annual transfer of dissolved silica from interstitial waters to the ocean is 3.2×10^{14} g/yr. This input is nearly equal to that of rivers but we must emphasize that this transfer does not take part in the geochemical mass balance since it is a part of another subsystem. Indeed, a portion of the silica deposited as opal is dissolved in the sediments and retransferred to the surface waters of the ocean where it is reprecipitated. As in the case of river input, the amount of silica released by interstitial waters is negligible with respect to the requirements of biological activity for dissolved silica.

5. Conclusions: Tentative Cycle for Silica Within the Ocean

The biological activity in the ocean generates an extremely high chemical mobility of silica, which is exhibited by a mean residence time for dissolved silica in the ocean of only 250 yr. The rate of dissolution of amorphous silica precipitated by the organisms insures, moreover, a rapid recycling of silica. These two processes mainly control the vertical concentration profile of dissolved silica in the ocean. The geographical distribution is, on the other hand, related to the hydrodynamical properties of the ocean (upwelling, eddy diffusion) which, in fact, control the biological activity. The river input, the release of dissolved silica from interstitial waters, and the underwater volcanic activity play only minor roles in the distribution of dissolved silica in the ocean. Uptake of dissolved silica by any chemical reaction is highly improbable with respect to this high biological activity. The hypothesis of Sillén, developed by Garrels and Mackenzie, in which the concentration of dissolved silica in seawater is controlled by a chemical equilibrium, may not be valid under these conditions.

The uptake of silica by chemical reactions is, on the other hand, extremely important in the interstitial waters of marine sediments and is one of the principal factors controlling the geochemical cycle of silica. These chemical reactions also take into account the requirements for CO_2 in the geochemical cycle.

In the preceding sections we have attempted to analyze as quantitatively as possible the various steps of the biochemical and geochemical cycles. We will now use these estimations in order to establish a hypothetical overall cycle for silica in the ocean based on a stationary state model.

The figures given here have only an illustrative value. Much of the available fundamental data, for example, the value for the total primary productivity of the oceans, are only known approximately at the present time. It is therefore difficult to justify a rigorous proof of a model based on a mass balance. We have thus preferred to use reasonable values for the various steps in our mass balance calculations, with the requirement that the mass balance must be self-consistent.

The first basic figure in the calculation of our mass balance is the amount of silica taken up annually by marine organisms (Table V), which we estimated to be 250×10^{14} g SiO_2/yr. In agreement with the calculations and experimental results described in Section 3.C we have assumed for convenience that 97% of the opal precipitated by living organisms was dissolved during settling. As a result, 7.5×10^{14} g SiO_2/yr is deposited in the surface layers of the marine sediments. This amount also corresponds to a rate of deposition of approximately 0.25 g SiO_2/cm^2/1000 yr. We have shown in Sections 4.C and 4.D that only a small fraction of the deposited opal is preserved. The skeleton debris is, for the most part, dissolved after burial in the marine sediments. A portion of the dissolved silica (3.2×10^{14} g SiO_2/yr) (Section 4.D) in the interstitial waters diffuses to the ocean. Another portion reacts with the clay minerals present, or with Mg^{2+}, to form more siliceous clays or sepiolite. These reactions produced the CO_2 necessary for the continental weathering of silicates. Finally, a small fraction of the opal is preserved or diagenetically transformed into cristobalite or quartz. The present steady-state condition of the ocean implies that the input of dissolved silica, equal to 4.3×10^{14} g SiO_2/yr (Table IV), must accumulate in the sediments by one of the above processes. From the data discussed in Section 4.C we estimate that 20% of the silica input is preserved as opal in the sediments.

This therefore represents a rate of accumulation for opal of 0.8×10^{14} g SiO_2/yr, while 3.5×10^{14} g SiO_2/yr of dissolved silica reacts to form authigenic minerals. The rate of accumulation for opal may also be expressed as 0.025 g SiO_2/cm^2/1000 yr, which corresponds within a factor of 2 to the estimate of Heath (1973). The dissolved silica necessary for the biological activity in the photic zone is essentially provided (Section 4.B) equally by upwelling and eddy diffusion from the deep sea layers of the dissolved silica resulting from dissolution of settling organism tests. The flux of dissolved silica due to upwelling and eddy diffusion may be estimated from Table VI to be, respectively, 125×10^{14} g SiO_2/yr and 120×10^{14} g SiO_2/yr. The river input provides the complementary amount of dissolved silica that compensates exactly for the amount of silica accumulated in the sediments.

Figure 17 summarizes the overall cycle proposed here. We believe that this cycle resolves the apparent contradictions in the relevant data from geologists and biolo-

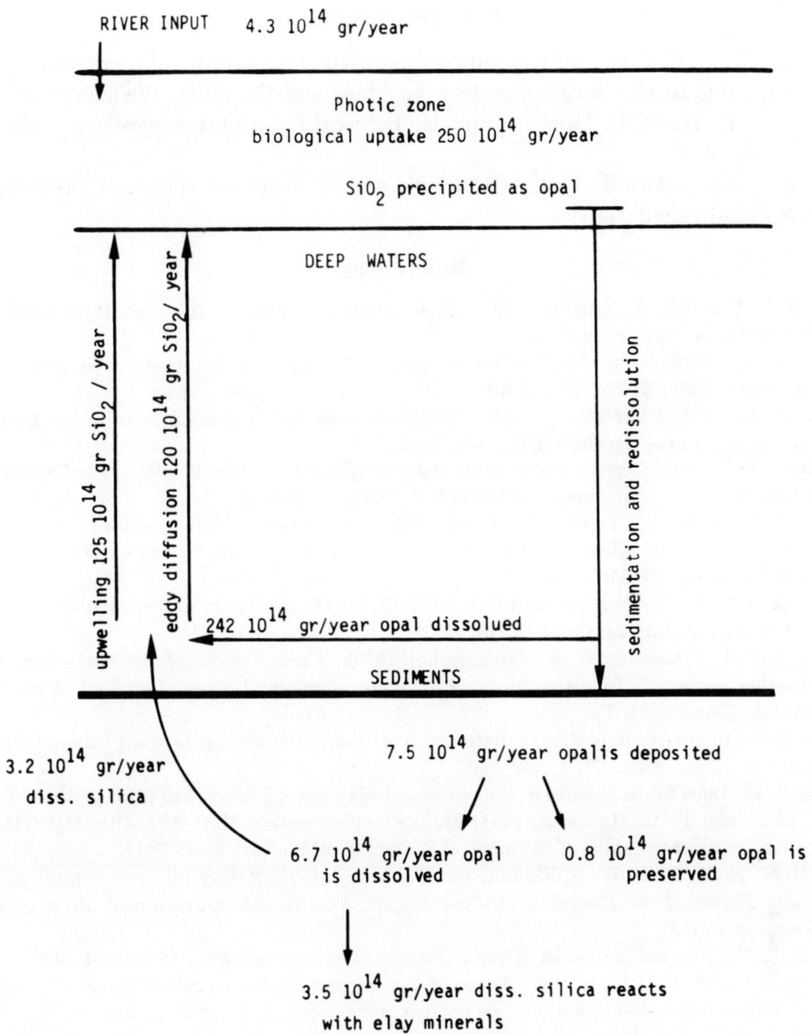

Fig. 17. Tentative cycle for silica within the ocean.

gists, but further work is needed to determine more precisely certain parameters. The information accumulated during the Deep Sea Drilling Project is an extremely important source of data for the geochemical cycle of silica, which has not yet been sufficiently exploited for this purpose.

This cycle reveals, on the other hand, an interesting problem concerning the history of the ocean. Bearing in mind the present importance of biological activity in the ocean, the question arises as to what the state of the ocean was in pre-Cambrian times when this activity was nonexistent.

Some light has been thrown on this problem by the work of Garrels discussed in a previous chapter where it can be seen that ancient seawater was presumably saturated with respect to amorphous silica and had a pH of 6.68, too low to favor the precipitation of sepiolite.

Acknowledgments

We thank R. M. Garrels for innumerable discussions and helpful criticisms, which were invaluable to the development of our ideas and thoughts. We also thank F. T. Mackenzie, D. Hurd, C. Laurent, and H. Percival for useful suggestions to improve the manuscript.

We are indebted to J. P. Vanderborght and S. Wacj for computer programming and numerical calculations.

References

Baranov, V. I. and L. A. Kuzmina, 1958. *Radioisotopes in Scientific Research.* R. C. Extermann, ed. Pergamon, New York, p. 60.

Berger, W. H., 1970. Biogenous deep-sea sediments: fractionation by deep-sea circulation. *Geol. Soc. Amer. Bull.*, **81** (5), 1385–1401.

Berner, R. A., 1971. *Principles of Chemical Sedimentology.* International Series in the Earth and Planetary Sciences. McGraw-Hill, New York.

Bezrukov, P. L., 1955. *On the distribution and rate of sedimentation of siliceous sediments in the Okhotsk Sea.* Vol. 103. Akad. Nauk. S.S.S.R. Doklady, p. 473.

Bien, G. S., D. E. Contois, and W. H. Thomas, 1959. The removal of soluble silica from fresh water entering the sea, in silica in sediments. Tulsa, Okla., Soc. Econ. Paleontol. Mineralog. Spec. Publ. No. 7, pp. 20–35.

Burton, J. D., T. M. Leatherland, and P. S. Liss, 1970a. The reactivity of dissolved silicon in some natural waters. *Limnol. Oceanog.*, **15**, 473.

Burton, J. D., P. S. Liss, and V. K. Venugopalan, 1970b. The behaviour of dissolved silicon during estuarine mixing. I. Investigation in Southampton water. *J. Cons. Int. Eopl. Mer.*, **33** (2), 134–140, (Chapter IV 1).

Calvert, S. E. (1966). Accumulation of diatomaceous silica in the sediments of the Gulf of California. *Geol. Soc. Amer. Bull.*, **77**, p. 569–596.

Calvert, S. E., 1968. Silica balance in the ocean and diagenesis. *Nature*, **219** (5157), 919–920

Christ, C. L. and P. B. Hostetler, 1971. Studies in the system $MgO–SiO_2–CO_2–H_2O$(III). The activity-product constant of Sepiolite. U.S. Geological Survey. Spec. Publ.

Cook, H. E., R. W. Rex., W. A. Eklund, and B. Murray, 1971. X-Ray mineralogy studies, leg. 7. *Initial Report of the Deep Sea Drilling Project.* Vol. 7. U.S. Government Printing Office, Washington, D.C.

Craig, H., 1970. Abyssal carbon 13 in South Pacific. *J. of Geophys. Res.*, **75** (3), 691–695.

Ernst, W. G. and S. E. Calvert, 1969. An experimental study of the recrystallization of porcelanite and its bearing on the origin of some bedded cheets. *Am. J. Sci.*, **267-A**, 114.

Fanning, K. A. and M. E. A. Pilson, 1971. Interstitial silica and pH in marine sediments: some effects of sampling procedures. *Science*, **173**, 1228–1231.

Garrels, R. M. and F. T. Mackenzie, 1971. *Evolution of Sedimentary Rocks.* W. W. Norton, New York.

Gieskes, J. M., 1973. Interstitial water studies, Leg. 15. In : Edgard, N. T., J. B. Saunders, et al : *Initial reports of the Deep Sea Drilling Project.* Vol. 15, in press.

Golberg, E. D. and G. O. S. Arrhenius, 1958. Chemistry of Pacific Pelagic sediments. *Geochim. Cosmoch. Acta*, **13**, 153.

Golberg, E. D. and M. Koide, 1962. Geochronological studies of deep sea sediments by the ionium/thorium method. *Geochim. Cosmochim. Acta*, **26**, 417.

Goldberg, E. D., 1965. In *Chemical Oceanography.* Vol. 1. J. P. Riley and G. Skirrow, eds. Academic Press, London.

Grill, E. V. and F. A. Richards, 1964. Nutrient regeneration from phytoplankton decomposing in seawater. *J. Mor. Res.*, **22**, 51.

Harder, A. and W. Flehmig, 1970. Quartz synthese by thiefen temperatures. *Geochim. Cosmochim. Acta*, **34**, 295.

Harris, R. C., (1966). Biological buffering of oceanic silica. *Nature*, **212**, 275–276.

Heath, G. R. and R. Moberly, 1971. In *Initial Reports of the Deep-Sea Drilling Project.* Vol. VII. U.S. Government Printing Office, Washington, D.C., pp. 991–1007.

Heath, G. R., 1973. Dissolved silica and deep-sea sediments. *Geologic History of the Ocean.* W. W. Hay, ed. S.E.P.M. Spec Publ. In press.

Helgeson, J. C. and F. T. Mackenzie, 1970. Silicate-sea water equilibrium in the ocean system. *Deep-Sea res.* In press.

Henderson, J. H., J. K. Syers, and M. L. Jackson, 1970. Quartz dissolution as influenced by pH and the presence of a disturbed surface layer. *Israel J. Chem.*, **8**, 357.

Hurd, D. C., 1972. Factors affecting solution rate of biogenic opal in seawater. *Earth and Planet Sci. Letters.* In press.

Hurd, D. C., 1973. *Biogenic Opal-Seawater Interaction in Deep-Sea Sediments.* In press.

Iler, R. K., 1955. *The Colloid Chemistry of Silica and Silicates.* Ithaca, Cornell University Press. 324 pp.

Ingri, N., 1959. Equilibrium studies of Polyanions. IV. Silicate Ions in NaCl medium. *Acta Chem. Scand.*, **13**, 758.

Jones M. M. and R. M. Pytkowicz (1973). Solubility of silica in seawater at high pressures. In press.

Kennedy, G. C., 1950. A fraction of the system silica-water. *Econ. Geology*, **45**, 629.

Kozlova, O. G., 1964. *Diatoms of the Indian and Pacific Sectors of the Antarctic.* Moscow. Publ. House Akad. Nauk. S.S.S.R.

Krauskopf, K. B., 1956. Dissolution and precipitation of silica at low temperatures. *Geochim. Cosmochim. Acta*, **10**, 1.

Krauskopf, K. B., 1959. In *Silica in Sediments.* Soc. Econ. Paleontologists and Mineralogists. Spec. Publ. 7. pp. 4–19.

Laurent, E. and J. Scheere, 1972. Les silicites: Evolution de la silice. *Bull. Soc. Belge Geol., Paleont., Hydrol.* (in Press).

Lewin, J. C., 1961. The dissolution of silica from diatom walls. *Geochim. Cosmochim. Acta*, **21**, 182–198.

Lisitzin, A. P., 1967. Basic relationship in distribution of modern siliceous sediments and their connection climatic zonation. *Inter. Geol. Rev.*, **9** (5), 631–652.

Lisitzin, A. P. et al., 1971. Geochimical, mineralogical and paleontological studies, leg. 6. *Initial Report of the Deep Sea Drilling Project.* Vol. 6. U.S. Government Printing Office, p. 922, Washington, D.C.

Lisitzin, A. P., 1972. Sedimentation in the world ocean. Soc. of Econ. Paleont. and Min. Special Publ. No. 17.

Liss, P. S. and C. P. Spencer, 1970. Abiological processes in the removal of silicate from seawater. *Geochim. Cosmochim. Acta*, **34** (10), 1073–1088.

Livingstone, D. A., 1963. Chemical composition of rivers and lakes. U.S. Geol. Survey Prof. Paper 440-G, 64 p.

Lucas, C. C. and M. E. Dolan, 1939. *Can. Med. Assoc. J.*, **40**, 125.

Mackenzie, F. T. and R. M. Garrels, 1966. Chemical mass balance between rivers and oceans. *Am. J. Sci.*, **264**, 507–525.

Mackenzie, F. T., R. M. Garrels, O. P. Bricker, and F. Bickley, 1967. Silica in seawater: control by silica minerals. *Science*, **155**, 1404–1405.

Mackenzie, F. T., 1971. Synthesis of quartz at earth-surface conditions. *Science*, **173**, 533–35.

Manheim, F. T., K. M. Chou, and F. L. Sayles, 1970. Interstitial water studies on small core samples, leg. 5. *Inital Report of the Deep Sea Drilling Project.* Vol. 5. U.S. Government Printing Office, Washington, D.C.

Margalef, R., 1961. Velocidad de sedimentacion de organismos passivos de fitoplancton. Barcelona, *Inv. Pesqueros*, **18**.

Morey, G. W., R. O. Fournier, and J. J. Rowe, 1962. The solubility of quartz in water in the temperature interval from 25° to 300°C. *Geochim. Cosmochim. Acta.*, **26**, 1029.

Munk, W. H., 1966. Abyssal recipes. *Deep-Sea Res.*, **13**, 707–730.

Pond, S., R. M. Pytkowicz, and J. E. Hawley, 1971. Particle dissolution during settling in the oceans. *Deep-Sea Res.*, **18**, 1135–1139.

Presley, B. J. and Kaplan, I. R., 1970. Interstitial water chemistry. *Deep Sea Drilling Project, Leg. 4. Initial Reports of the Deep Sea Drilling Project.* Vol. 4. U.S. Government Printing Office, Washington, D.C., p. 415.

Rex, R. W. and B. Murray, 1970. X-ray mineralogy studies, leg. 7. *Initial Reports of the Deep Sea Drilling Project.* Vol. 4. U.S. Government Printing Office, Washington, D.C., pp. 325–370).

Rozanov, A. G., 1964. Distribution of phosphorus and silica in the north Indian Ocean (in Russian) Academia Nauk S.S.S.R. Trudy Instituta Okeanologii, Tom LXIV.

Scheere, J. and E. Laurent, 1970. Silicites litées de Blaton (Belgique) et de l'Inzecca (Corse): comparaison et considérations. *Bull. Soc. Belge. Géol. Paléont., Hydrol.*, **79**, fasc. 3–4, 225–246.

Siever, R., 1962. Silica solubility, 0°–200°C, and the diagenesis of silicous sediments. *J. Geol.*, **70**, 127.

Siever, R., K. C. Beck, and R. A. Berner, 1965. Composition of interstitial waters of modern sediments. *J. Geol.*, **73** (1), 39–73.

Siever, R., 1968. Sedimentological consequence of a steady-state ocean-atmosphere. *Sedimental.*, **11** ($\frac{1}{2}$), 5–29.

Sillén, L. G., 1961. The physical chemistry of seawater. In *Oceanography*, M. Sears, ed. *Am. Assoc. Adv. Sci. Publ.*, **67**, 549–581.

Stefansson, V. and F. A. Richards, 1963. Processes contributing to the nutrient distribution of the Columbia River and Strait of Juan de Fuca. *Limnol. Oceanog.*, **8** (4), 394–410.

Stöber, W., 1967. In *Equilibrium Concepts in Natural Water Systems*. Werner Stumm, ed. American Chemical Society, Washington, D.C.

Stommel, H., 1958. The abyssal circulation. *Deep-Sea Res.*, **5**, 80.

Strakhov, N. M., 1963. Types of lithogenesis and their evolution in the earth. Gosgeoltekhizdat Moscow.

van Lier, J. A., P. L. De Bruyn, and J. Th. G. Overbeek, 1960. The solubility of quartz. *J. Phys. Chem.*, **64**, 1675.

Wollast, R., 1967. Kinetics of the alterations of K-feldspar in buffered solutions at low temperature. *Geochim. Cosmochim. Acta*, **31**, 635–648.

Wollast, R., F. T. Mackenzie, and O. P. Bricker, 1968. Experimental precipitation of sepiolite at earth surface conditions. *Am. Min.*, **53**, 1945–1962.

Wollast, R. and F. De Broeu, 1971. Study of the behaviour of dissolved silica in the estuary of the Scheldt. *Geochim. Cosmochim. Acta*, **35**, 613–620.

Wollast, R. and R. M. Garrels, 1971. Diffusion coefficient of silica in seawater. *Nature Phys. Sci.*, **229** (3), 94.

Wollast, R., 1971. Kinetic aspects of the nucleation and growth of calcite from aqueous solution. In *Carbonate Cements*. O. P. Bricker, ed. J. Hopkins Press. pp. 264–273.

12. THE STABLE ISOTOPES OF OXYGEN, CARBON, AND HYDROGEN IN THE MARINE ENVIRONMENT

G. DONALD GARLICK

1. Introduction

Stable isotope geochemistry has flourished during the past two decades since the pioneering paleotemperature work of Urey et al. (1951), and it continues to provide unique information concerning both the history of the marine environment and the geochemical processes that take place in the modern ocean system. The most important and interesting isotopes are those of hydrogen, oxygen, carbon, and sulfur. The sulfur isotopes are discussed in Chapter 17.

This chapter considers a number of diverse stable isotope phenomena that need not be read in their given sequence.

2. Notation

The isotopic fractionation between two substances (a and b) is described in terms of the following convenient notation (using hydrogen as an example):

$$\alpha_{ab} = \frac{(D/H)_a}{(D/H)_b} = 1 + \frac{\epsilon}{1000}$$

$$\delta_a = \left[\frac{(D/H)_a}{(D/H)_{Std}} - 1\right] 1000$$

and

$$\delta_a - \delta_b \approx 1000 \ln \alpha_{ab} \approx \epsilon_{ab}$$

where δ and ϵ values are in per mil (‰). The usage of α and ϵ often implies isotopic equilibrium, whereas δ is purely descriptive.

3. Standards

The most commonly used standards for reporting analyses are Standard Mean Ocean Water, abbreviated to SMOW, and PDB, the CO_2 prepared from the rostrum of a particular belemnite from the PD formation by reaction with 100% H_3PO_4 at 25.2°C. PDB has a δO^{18} value of +41‰ on the SMOW scale (O'Neil and Epstein, 1966a). To state that calcite has a δ value of x‰ relative to PDB means that the CO_2 derived from that calcite is x‰ relative to CO_2 from PDB. The PDB calcite actually has a δ value of about +30.5‰ on the SMOW scale. Oxygen isotope compositions reported in this chapter are relative to SMOW, unless PDB is specified.

The absolute isotopic ratios of the standards have been given by Craig (1957, 1961):

$$\begin{aligned} D/H\ (SMOW) &= 0.16 \times 10^{-3} \\ O^{18}/O^{16}\ (SMOW) &= 2.00 \times 10^{-3} \\ C^{13}/C^{12}\ (PDB) &= 11.23 \times 10^{-3} \end{aligned}$$

4. Analytical Considerations

Weber and Deines (1971) have provided a review of stable isotope mass spectrometry as well as the techniques employed in converting samples into CO_2, the gas commonly introduced into spectrometers determining both carbon and oxygen isotope ratios. Craig (1957) and Deines (1970) have discussed the mass-spectrometric corrections required in the analysis of carbon dioxide.

The precisions achieved with mass spectrometers having dual sample inlets and double ion-collectors are compared below to the isotopic ranges reported in the marine environment:

	High	Low	Approximate Range (‰)	Approximate Precision (‰)
δO^{18}	+41‰ atmospheric CO_2[a]	−30‰ Arctic iceberg[b]	70	0.02
δC^{13}	+21‰ dolomite (Oceanographer Canyon)[c]	−64‰ dolomite (Hudson Canyon)[c]	85	0.02
δD	(+30‰) hypersaline waters[d]	−250‰ average Arctic meteoric water[e]	280	0.1

[a] Keeling (1961).
[b] Dansgaard (1964).
[c] Deuser (1970a).
[d] Estimated from δO^{18} of hypersalines (Lloyd, 1966) and the Red Sea relationship. $\delta D = 6\ \delta O^{18}$ (Craig, 1966).
[e] Redfield and Friedman (1969).

5. The Causes of Isotopic Variation

The quantum-statistical effects of isotopic substitution lead to a temperature-dependent partitioning of isotopes between phases in equilibrium. The theory developed by Urey (1947) and Bigeleisen and Mayer (1947) has been applied to the calculation (from spectroscopic data) of partition function ratios and hence isotopic fractionations in a few natural systems. For example, Bottinga (1968) calculated fractionations in the system $CaCO_3$–CO_2–H_2O and obtained results that agree rather well with experimentally determined fractionations (O'Neil et al., 1969):

Calcite-Water	Calculated	Experimental
1000 ln α at 0°C	33.7	33.9
1000 ln α at 25°C	28.0	28.0

As no adequate theory has been developed for liquids, Bottinga used experimental values for $\alpha_{\text{watervapor}}$. Theoretical calculations, isotope exchange experiments, and the analyses of natural systems constitute three sources of information on equilibrium isotope fractionations.

Pressure effects on equilibrium isotope fractionations are probably insignificant.

Hoering (1961) observed no pressure effect at low temperature in the system HCO_3^-–H_2O within a 4 kb range; Clayton et al. (1972) found no effect in the system $CaCO_3$–H_2O at 500°C in the range 1 to 20 kb. On the other hand, Garlick et al. (1971) invoked a pressure effect in silicate magmas to explain the isotopic trends observed in mantle-derived eclogites.

Isotopes may also be fractionated by kinetic effects resulting directly from vibration or velocity differences between isotopic species, or indirectly from differences in bonding energies. For example, $C^{13}O_2$ molecules not only strike a leaf surface less often than predicted from their relative abundance alone (equipartition of kinetic energy), but are also less reactive than $C^{12}O_2$ molecules (molecular energy levels are related to vibrational frequencies and are thus affected by mass substitutions). Both effects contribute to the concentration of C^{12} in vascular plants during photosynthesis (Park and Epstein, 1960).

Isotopic variations in nature often exceed those caused by single-stage equilibrium or kinetic fractionations. For example, because water condensed from atmospheric vapor is enriched in O^{18} by 9.2‰ at 25°C (an equilibrium effect), the residual vapor is depleted in O^{18}, subsequent precipitation is consequently lighter than the initial precipitation, and the final result is that some Antarctic snow is as much as 60‰ depleted in O^{18} relative to tropical rain or SMOW (Dansgaard, 1964). Rayleigh's equation is useful in describing such processes:

$$\delta - \delta_0 \approx 1000(\alpha - 1) \ln f,$$

where δ_0 and δ are the initial and instantaneous compositions of a reservoir, α is the isotopic fractionation between the reservoir and material being removed from it, and f is the fraction of reservoir remaining.

Hydrogen is likewise fractionated during condensation (by 74‰ at 25°C) and meteoric waters obey the linear relationship:

$$\delta D = 8\ \delta O^{18} + 10‰$$

The 10‰ intercept is due to the choice of SMOW as the standard and a kinetic effect accompanying the evaporation of water from the oceans (Craig and Gordon, 1965).

6. Ocean Water

D/H and O^{18}/O^{16} variations in the oceans originate almost entirely through interaction with the meteoric cycle, and have been described in detail by Craig and Gordon (1965). Figure 1 depicts the isotopic relationship between ocean water and the world-average meteoric cycle. Figure 2 indicates the isotopic and salinity variations of ocean waters due to evaporation, precipitation, and freezing, and is an introduction to Fig. 3.

The δO^{18}-salinity data in Fig. 3 are compatible with the derivation of North Atlantic deep water from Atlantic surface waters enriched in O^{16} by high-latitude precipitation ($\delta O^{18} \approx -21‰$; Epstein and Mayeda, 1953); the derivation of Antarctic bottom water from Weddell Sea surface waters enriched in salt by freezing ($\alpha_{\text{icewater}} = 1.003$; O'Neil, 1968); and the derivation of Pacific and Indian deep water by the mixing of roughly equal portions of Antarctic bottom water and Atlantic deep water. The manner in which the cycle is completed probably deserves further study.

Evaporation into unsaturated air, accompanied by diffusion-related fractionations,

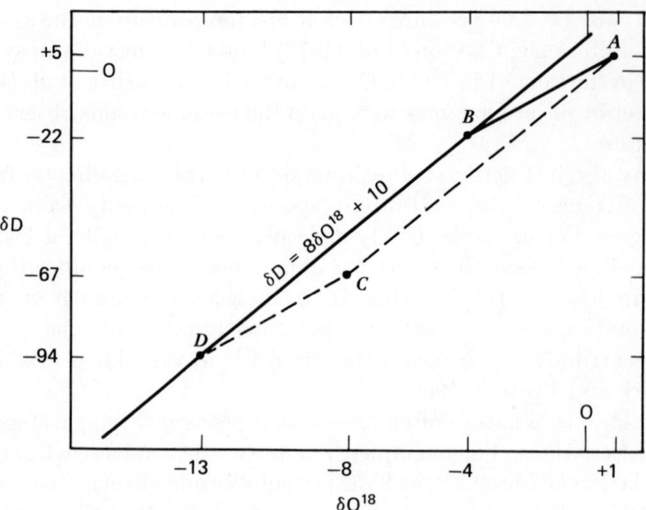

Fig. 1. The world average isotopic compositions of surface ocean water (*A*), net evaporation and net precipitation (*B*), hypothetical vapor in equilibrium with ocean surface (*C*), and actual vapor (*D*). The line passing through *B* and *D* is the meteoric water line. Craig and Gordon (1965).

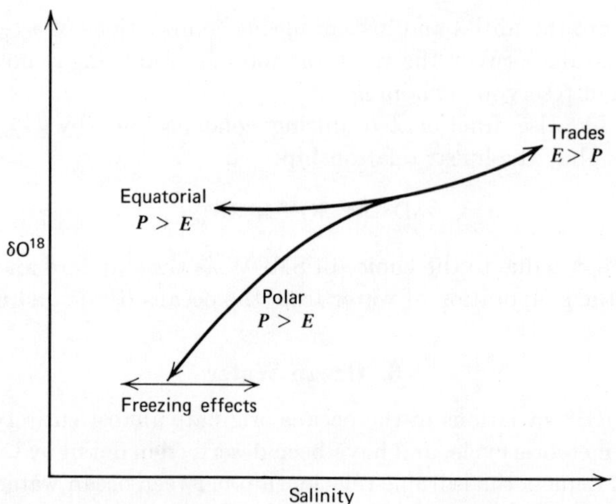

Fig. 2. Schematic δO^{18}-salinity diagram for surface ocean waters. E = evaporation; P = precipitation. Craig and Gordon (1965).

causes the δD value of the residual water to increase about five or six times more rapidly than its δO^{18} value, both reaching steady-state maxima determined by molecular exchange with isotopically lighter atmospheric vapor (Craig et al., 1963). The maximum δO^{18} values attained by evaporating brines in humid coastal regions are less than $+6‰$ (Lloyd, 1966). Heavier brines may be found in arid regions; $\delta O^{18} = 31‰$ and $\delta D = 129‰$ have been observed in the Sahara (Fontes and Gonfiantini, 1967).

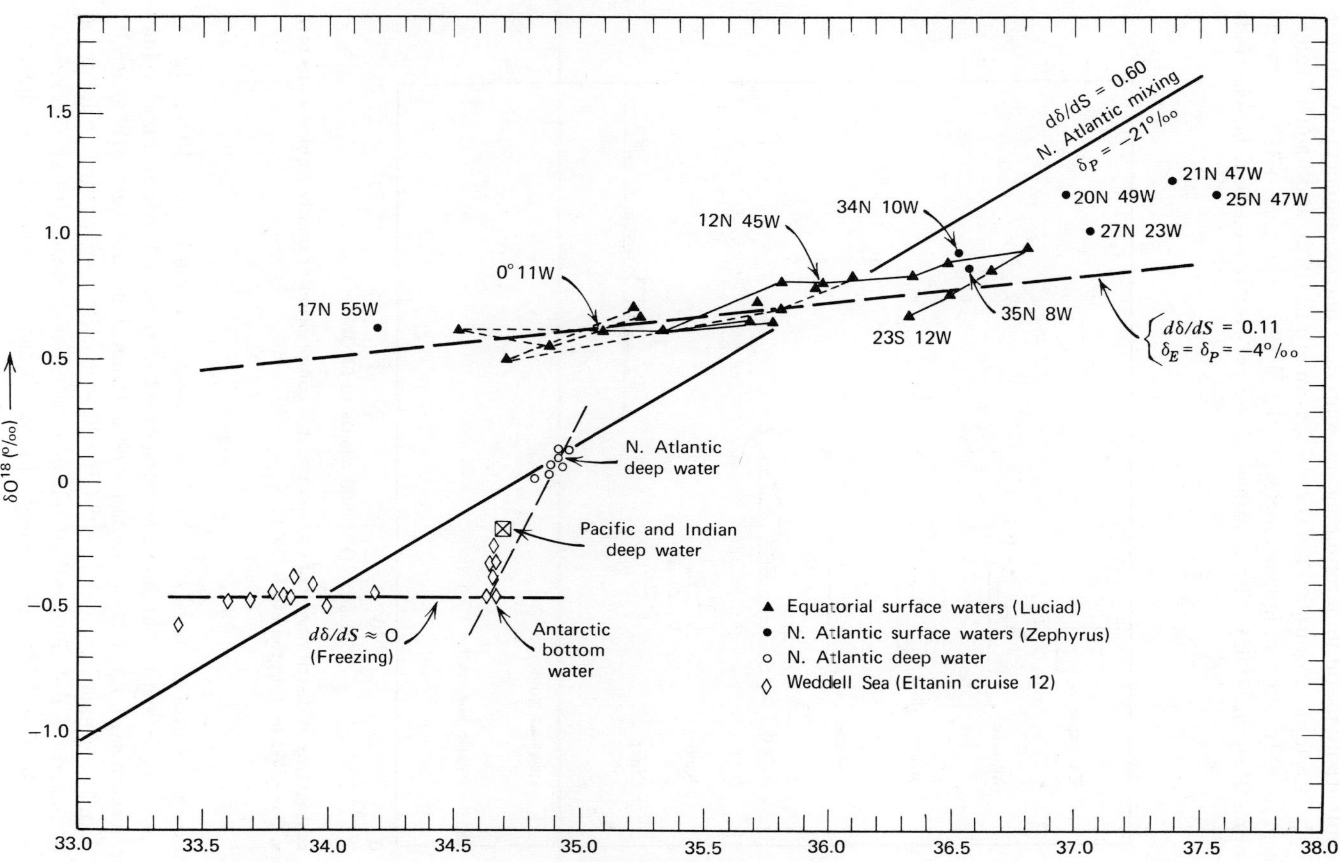

Fig. 3. δO^{18}-salinity relationships in the Atlantic. δ_E and δ_P refer to the isotopic composition of evaporating vapor and precipitation, respectively. Craig and Gordon (1965).

7. Coarse Detrital Minerals

Minerals that are resistant to weathering retain their initial isotopic compositions and are potentially useful in determining the sources of detrital sediments. Quartz is particularly resistant to isotopic alteration (Clayton et al., 1972), and its δO^{18} values range from roughly $+9‰$ in igneous rocks (Taylor, 1968) to roughly $+34‰$ in cherts (Degens and Epstein, 1962). The δ values of several North American beach sands

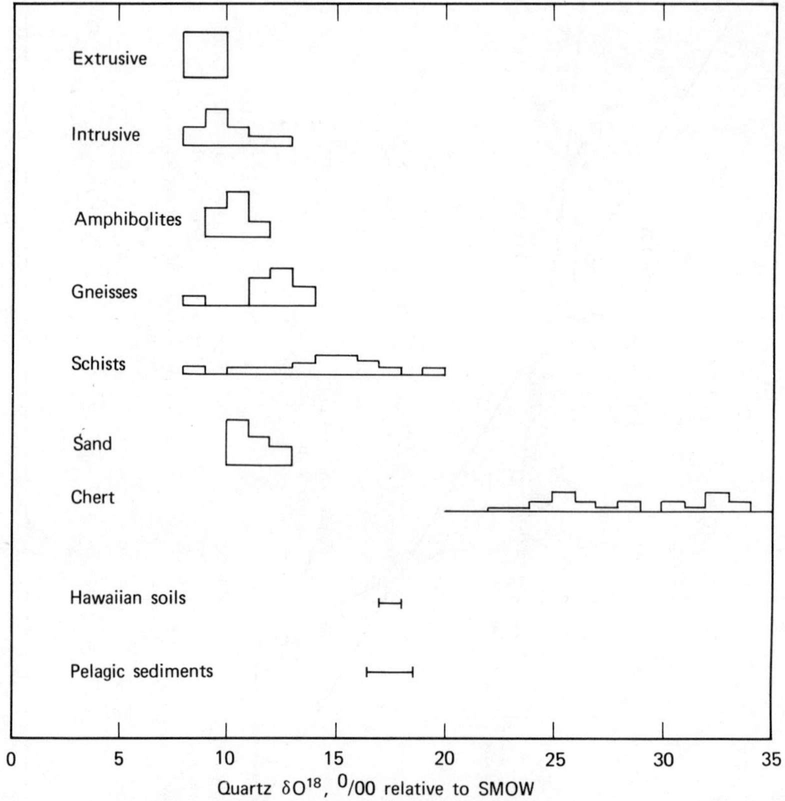

Fig. 4. Histograms of distributions of oxygen isotopic composition of quartz from various rock types. Compiled by Clayton et al. (1972).

reported by Savin and Epstein (1970c) exhibit a relatively small range, 10.3 to 12.5‰ (Fig. 4), possibly reflecting the homogenizing effect of repeated sedimentary cycling.

Other minerals in igneous or metamorphic mineral assemblages are generally lighter than the coexisting quartz. O^{18}/O^{16} ratios usually decrease in the following sequence: quartz or dolomite; alkali feldspar or calcite; muscovite or plagioclase; garnet or inosilicates; biotite; olivine; chlorite; ilmenite; magnetite or hematite (Garlick, 1969).

Unfortunately, very few stable isotope studies have been made of coarse detrital sediments.

8. Eolian Components

Micron-sized quartz can be isolated unaltered from soils and sediments by fusion with $Na_2S_2O_7$ followed by treatment with dilute HCl, NaOH, and 30% H_2SiF_6 (Syers et al., 1968). Using this technique, Clayton et al. (1972) found that the oxygen isotope compositions of quartz isolated from each of several North Pacific deep-sea core samples vary systematically with grain size, increasing from +16 to +19‰ as grain size decreases from 25 μm to 1 μm (Fig. 5). Quartz fractions from Hawaiian soils and northern hemisphere tropospheric dusts are isotopically similar to the deep-sea quartz. Quartz isolated from southern hemisphere pelagic sediments and soils ranges from about +12 to +15.5‰, suggesting that there is a difference in the O^{18}/O^{16} ratios of northern and southern tropospheric dusts. It was estimated that the atmosphere transports quartz to pelagic sediments at the rate of 40 μg/cm^2/yr (0.2 m/10^6 yr). Furthermore, since mica, vermiculite, and kaolinite are also abundant in tropospheric dusts, most of the noncarbonate portion of pelagic sediments is probably Eolian in origin.

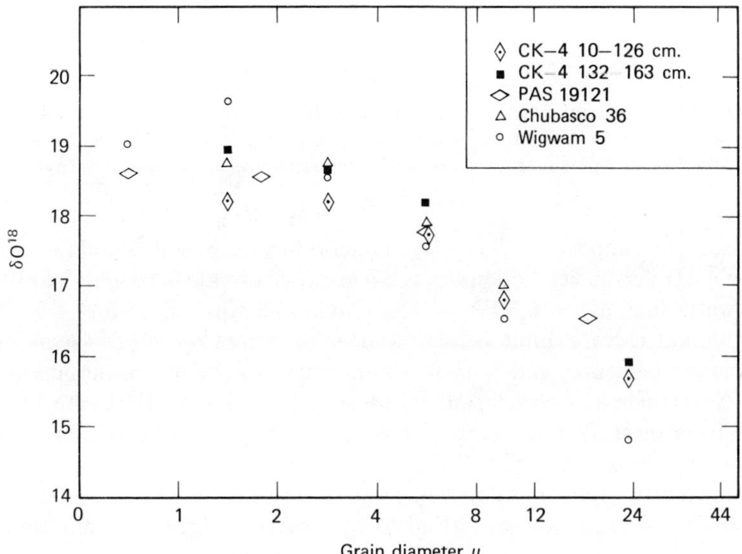

Fig. 5. Variation of oxygen isotopic composition of quartz with grain size for five North Pacific pelagic clays. Clayton et al. (1972).

9. Clay Minerals

The major processes that produce clays are the low-temperature weathering of rocks in contact with meteoric or ocean waters, the diagenesis of sediments, and the alteration of country rocks by hydrothermal fluids at elevated temperatures. The investigations of Savin and Epstein (1970a), Lawrence and Taylor (1971), and Sheppard et al. (1971) have shown that clays from these sources are usually isotopically distinguishable. The regularities revealed by these investigations suggest that clays attain approximate isotopic equilibrium with the waters in which they form. A particular clay mineral formed in the deep-sea environment should have a relatively

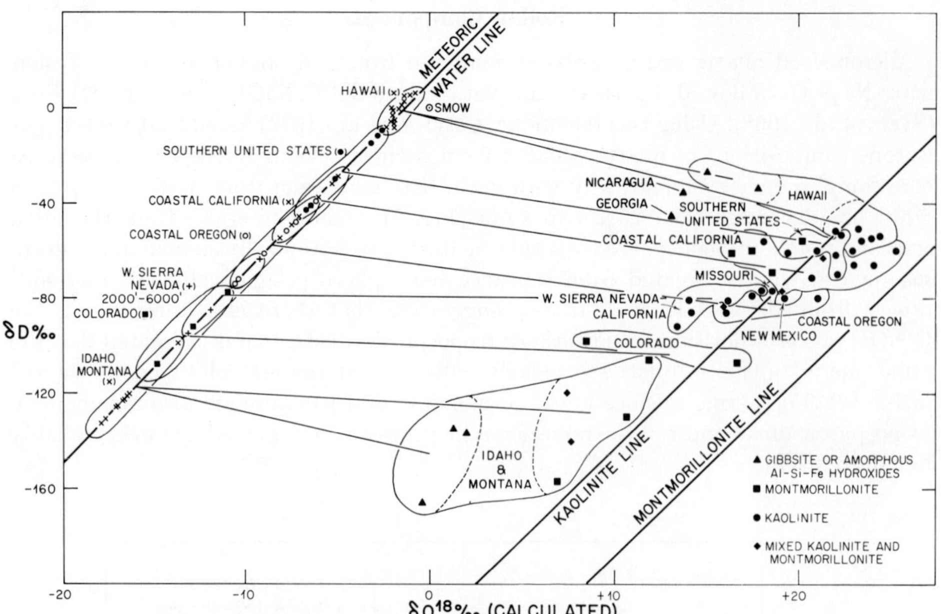

Fig. 6. δD–δO[18] plot of clay minerals and hydroxides from Quaternary soils of the United States. Tie lines are drawn to their corresponding meteoric waters. The kaolinite and montmorillonite lines of Savin and Epstein (1970a) are shown for reference. Lawrence and Taylor (1971).

constant isotopic composition. The same mineral formed in soils should exhibit, when plotted on a δD versus δO^{18} diagram, a linear array of values roughly parallel to the meteoric water line, $\delta D = 8\ \delta O^{18} + 10\%$ (Savin and Epstein, 1970a).

Hydrothermal clays exhibit a large scatter of points on a δD versus δO^{18} plot because the temperatures and isotopic compositions of the hydrothermal fluids were variable. Nevertheless, a correlation is observed between the D/H ratios of sericites and clays from most Tertiary porphyry copper deposits and those of local meteoric ground waters (Sheppard et al., 1971).

The following isotopic fractionation factors between clays and water have been deduced from the study of soils (Fig. 6) and marine authigenic montmorillonites (Fig. 7):

Mineral	$\alpha^{ox}_{\text{Min-H}_2\text{O}}$	$\alpha^{hy}_{\text{Min-H}_2\text{O}}$	Source	Reference
Kaolinite	1.027	0.97	Soils	Savin and Epstein (1970a)
	1.026	0.968	Soils	Lawrence and Taylor (in press)
Montmorillonite	1.027	0.94	Marine	Savin and Epstein (1970a)
Brown	1.025	[a]	Soils	Lawrence and Taylor (in press)
Gray	1.028	[a]	Soils	Lawrence and Taylor (in press)

[a] Not determinable with precision because hydroxyl and interlayer water exchange during extraction procedure.

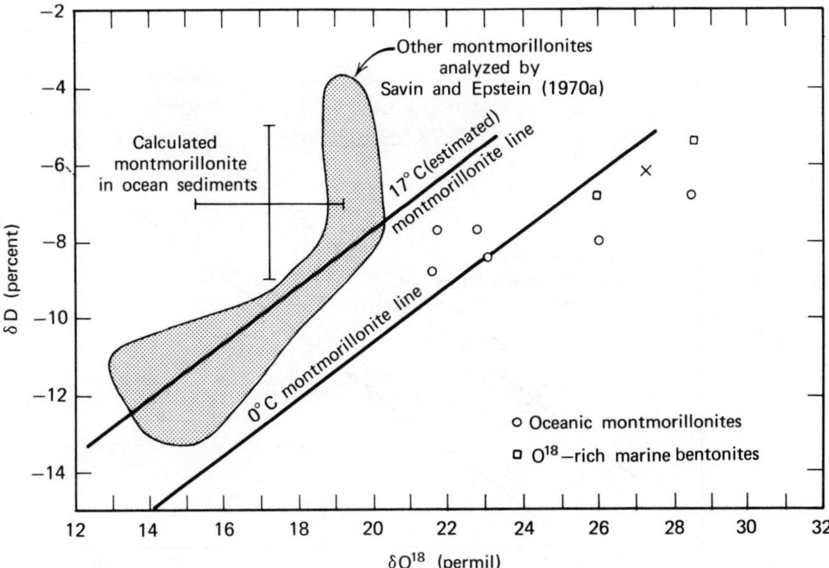

Fig. 7. Calculated isotopic composition of montmorillonite in ocean sediments and analyzed compositions of selected montmorillonites. Small cross denotes the approximate composition of montmorillonite in equilibrium with seawater at 0°C. The lines represent the expected compositions of montmorillonites in equilibrium with meteoric waters at 0 and 17°C. After Savin and Epstein (1970a,b).

The analyses of modern deep-sea clay minerals shown in Figs. 7 to 9 were obtained by Savin and Epstein (1970b) on the carbonate-free fraction of core samples sieved through a 44-μ screen. Samples for oxygen analyses were dried in a box containing P_2O_5 for 24 hr prior to loading into a fluorination vacuum system. In the routine analysis of hydrogen, interlayer water was removed and discarded by heating the clays at 100–250°C for 2 hr under vacuum. The δO^{18} values were corrected for the presence of minor amounts of quartz on the assumption that the quartz has a δO^{18} value of +18‰ (see section on eolian components).

Utilizing correlations between the bulk isotopic compositions and natural variations in the abundances of the various clay minerals, and assuming each clay mineral to be regionally homogeneous, Savin and Epstein obtained the following least-squares solutions for the isotopic compositions of deep-sea clays:

Phase	δO^{18}‰	δD‰
Montmorillonite	17.2	−70
Kaolinite	24.9	−32
Illite	15.4	−60
Chlorite	14.9	−145

It appears that the clay minerals in these deep-sea cores are predominantly detrital. The isotopic composition of the montmorillonite is very different from that of authigenic montmorillonite (Fig. 7). The isotopic composition of kaolinite in the deep-sea

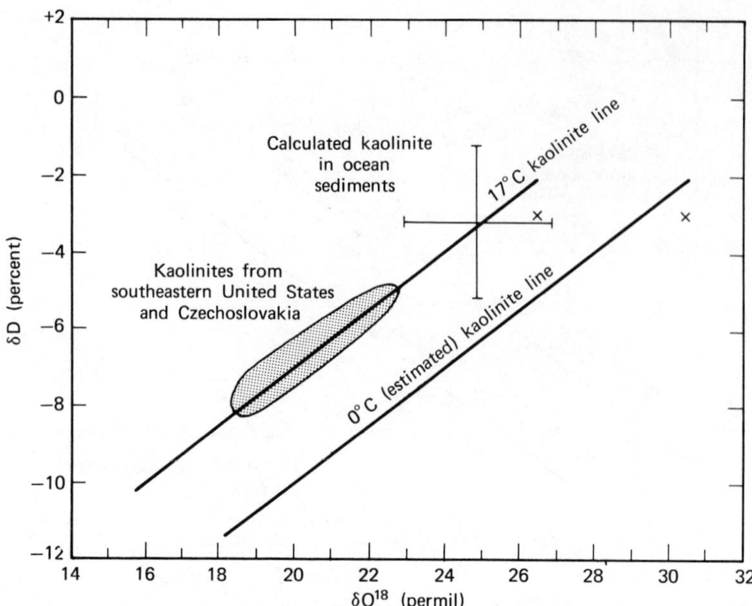

Fig. 8. Calculated isotopic composition of kaolinite in ocean sediments and its relationship to the 17°C kaolinite line and an estimated 0°C kaolinite line. Small crosses denote estimated compositions of kaolinites in equilibrium with seawater at the two temperatures. After Savin and Epstein (1970a,b).

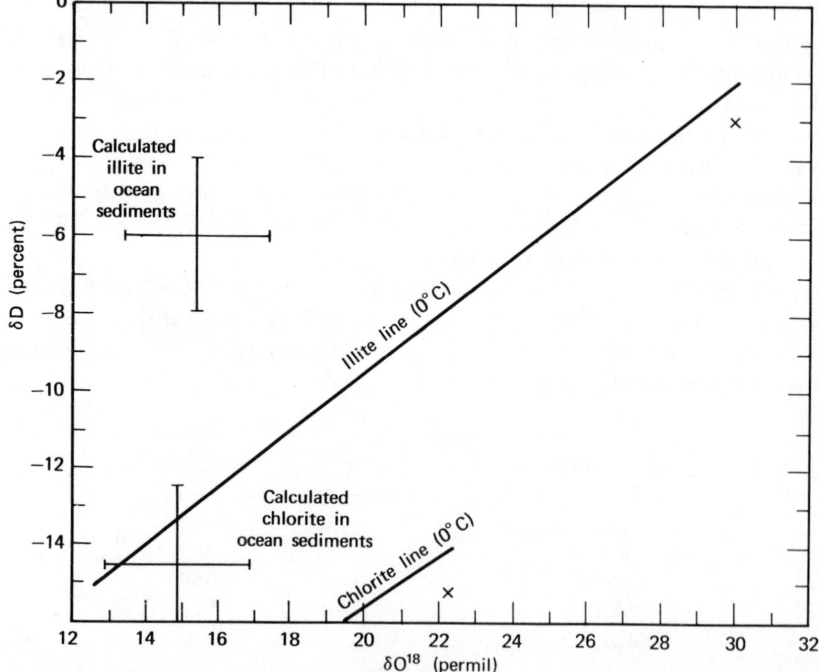

Fig. 9. Calculated isotopic compositions of illite and chlorite in ocean sediments and their relationship to estimated illite and chlorite lines and the estimated compositions (small crosses) of illite and chlorite in equilibrium with seawater. After Savin and Epstein (1970b).

cores (Fig. 8) suggests an origin either in contact with low-latitude meteoric waters or ocean waters. In fact, the consensus of other workers is that most kaolinite originates in tropical weathering processes (Biscaye, 1965). The isotopic compositions of the illite and chlorite (Fig. 9) are compatible with their possible origins in diagenetic environments.

Yeh and Savin (1972) demonstrated that the exchange of oxygen isotopes between illite and seawater is extremely slow. Only 13% exchange was determined for the 0.2 to 0.4-μ size fraction of an illite-dominated sediment about 350,000 yr old.

The potential value of oxygen and hydrogen isotopes in deciphering the origins of deep-sea clays has been demonstrated.

10. Authigenic Phases

Of the authigenic, nonbiogenic phases that have been recognized in deep-sea sediments, montmorillonite, phillipsite, and ferromanganese oxides are the most abundant. Published analyses of these and a few other minerals that were possibly in approximate equilibrium with seawater are listed below:

Phase	Sample	δO^{18}‰	δD‰	Reference
Montmorillonite	RIS 81	+26.1	−78	Savin and Epstein (1970a)
	EM7-RUN 1	+28.5	−68	Savin and Epstein (1970a)
Sepiolite	CH35 Drll	+32.5		Savin (in press)
Phillipsite	MSN 130	+33.6		Savin and Epstein (1970b)
	RIS 79	+34.1		Savin and Epstein (1970b)
	Tet 23	+33.6		Savin and Epstein (1970b)
Clinoptilolite	CH35 Drll	+27		Savin (in press)
Manganese nodule	Blake Plateau	+15.0	−77	Savin and Epstein (1970b)
Glauconite	Blake Plateau	+26.3	−74	Savin and Epstein (1970a)
Quartz	Henderson Sea Mount	+36		Garlick (1969)
	CH35 Drll	+36		Savin (in press)
Phosphate from phosphorite	five Pliocene marine sediments	+18 to +23		Longinelli and Nuti (1968); see Kolodny and Kaplan (1970)

On a plot of δO^{18} versus Fe + Mn content (Fig. 10), deep-sea sediments with abundant authigenic components can be readily distinguished from those derived predominantly from terrigenous sources (Savin and Epstein, 1970b).

Crystals of calcite up to 90 μm in size have been found in South Pacific pelagic red clays (Bonatti, 1966). Their δO^{18} values range, in three cores, from −1.2 to −0.5‰ relative to PDB, indicating nonequilibrium with Pacific waters at present bottom temperatures. Equilibrium would require temperatures near 20°C or waters near −5‰ relative to SMOW. Bonatti suggests that the carbonates, including dolomite in one core, were probably precipitated from hydrothermal solutions related to deep-sea volcanic activity.

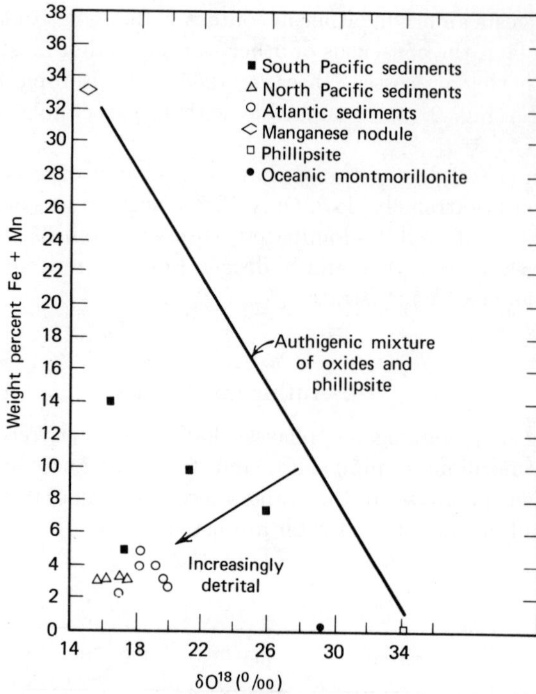

Fig. 10. Iron and manganese contents in ocean sediments and some authigenic minerals plotted against δO^{18}. All ocean sediments cluster together except three East Pacific Rise samples with large authigenic contents. Savin and Epstein (1970b).

11. Sulfates

The oxygen isotope exchange rate between dissolved sulfate and water is very slow in nonacidic solutions (Lloyd, 1968). The half-time of exchange in the oceanic environment (pH $\approx$ 8.2, $T \approx 4°C$) is possibly between 10^4 and 10^5 yr. As the residence time of sulfate in ocean water is roughly 10^7 years (Longinelli and Craig, 1967), oceanic sulfate should be in approximate isotopic equilibrium with ocean water. An extrapolation of Lloyd's (1968) experimentally determined fractionations ($\ln \alpha = 3241/T^2 - 0.0056$) to 4°C suggests that dissolved sulfate should be 38‰ enriched in O^{18} relative to ocean water (see also Mizutani and Rafter, 1969a). However, the δO^{18} of marine SO_4^{2-} is uniformly near +9.7‰. Lloyd interprets the discrepancy as due to a rapid biochemical cycling of sulfate that causes the sulfate to attain a steady-state isotopic composition, whereby the sulfate destroyed by bacterial reduction (involving a kinetic fractionation of −4.5‰) has the same composition as the sulfate produced by oxidation of H_2S (+4.6‰ when H_2O = 0‰ and O_2 = 23‰, the atmospheric value). Although the oxidation process is poorly understood, it appears that water exerts a greater influence than molecular oxygen on the isotopic composition of the sulfate produced. The above deductions are also compatible with the experiments of Mizutani and Rafter (1969b). Lloyd's model would require very rapid cycling of oxygen, equivalent to the amount in the atmosphere every 10^5 yr or less, in order to prevent significant drift toward isotopic equilibrium.

It should be noted that the O^{18}/O^{16} ratio of oxygen dissolved in ocean water increases with decreasing oxygen concentration due to the preferential consumption of O^{16} during respiration (see Fig. 13). Therefore, it is quite possible that the oxidation of H_2S in the oceans produces sulfate more enriched in O^{18} than allowed by Lloyd's model. Additional uncertainties arise from the results of interstitial water analyses from two Deep Sea Drilling Project cores which suggest that kinetic fractionations of -9 and $-39‰$ accompanied the reduction of sulfate (Lloyd, 1972). A third core demonstrated the sluggishness of inorganic isotopic exchange in the sulfate-water system by yielding δO^{18} values near 10‰ for SO_4^{2-} at depths as great as 370 m in sediments as old as 10^7 yr.

Experimental exchange data in the range 100–500°C yielded the following relationship for the fractionation between anhydrite and water (Lloyd, 1968): $\ln \alpha = 3878/T^2 - 0.0034$. Anhydrite—$SO_4^{2-}$ fractionation at 25°C is thus predicted to be roughly 9‰. Sulfate in gypsum derived from evaporating marine waters is observed to have δO^{18} values near 13 or 14‰ relative to SMOW, only 4‰ heavier than the dissolved sulfate.

Gypsum from lacustrine environments is more variable (16–20‰ relative to SMOW) than gypsum derived from modern seawater. It is on this basis that gypsum and anhydrite from Upper Miocene Mediterranean evaporites, which range from $+9$ to $+17‰$ in three samples from DSDP leg XIII, are interpreted as having been deposited in dessicated inland lakes after the Strait of Gibralter was closed in the Late Miocene (Lloyd and Hsu, 1971). The O^{18} and C^{13} contents of limestone and dolomite from the Mediterranean evaporites are also more variable than marine-derived carbonates (Fontes et al., 1971).

Claypool et al. (1972) report the following variation with age of the δO^{18} values of evaporite sulfates; Proterozoic 14–17, Cambrian 13, Devonian 12, Mississippian 17, Permian 10, Mesozoic 11, Lower Tertiary 15, and Present 13‰. They attribute this variation to changes in the ratio of sulfate reduction (fractionation $= -11‰$) to evaporite deposition (fractionation $= +4‰$). However, our understanding of the isotopic geochemistry of sulfate is still in a state of flux.

12. Biogenic Silica and Cherts

Oxygen isotope analyses of radiolarian skeletons from a few antarctic and equatorial deep-sea cores yielded a mean δO^{18} of $+38‰$ with a mean deviation of 0.5‰ (Mopper and Garlick, 1971). The large deviation from the mean is undoubtedly caused by variations in the amount and isotopic composition of easily exchanged water of hydration in the opal, even after storage in a dry box for 24 hr prior to oxygen extraction. Although the top few centimeters of equatorial cores yielded δO^{18} values of about $+36‰$, no latitudinal dependence was observed in sediments older than few thousand years, possibly because of isotopic exchange with cold bottom waters. Siliceous spicules from warm-water sponges yielded values of about $+34‰$. Labeyrie (1972) found that the reproducibility of biogenic opal analyses improved after treatment in 10% NaOCl solution for three days and dehydration at 1000°C under vacuum. He reports a lacustrine diatom-water fractionation of $+38.7‰$ at 10°C and a marine sponge-water fractionation of $+40.2‰$ at 5°C.

Chert is microcrystalline quartz, possibly derived from the diagenesis of opaline silica. Knauth (1972) estimates the oxygen isotope fractionation between chert and water to follow the relationship $1000 \ln \alpha = 3.09(10^6/T^2) - 3.29$. Cherts are further discussed near the end of this chapter in reference to the history of ocean water.

13. Carbonates

In contrast to the sulfate system, the carbonate system is frequently observed to be in approximate isotopic equilibrium. Departures from equilibrium are commonly related to biological activity.

The most pertinent experimentally derived fractionation factors in the carbonate system are listed below and plotted in Figs. 11 and 12.

Oxygen	1000 ln α	Reference
Calcite-water 0 to 500°C	$2.78\ (10^6/T^2) - 3.39$	O'Neil et al. (1969)
Dolomite-water	$3.20\ (10^6/T^2) - 2.00$	Northrop and Clayton (1966)
Dolomite-calcite 350 to 400°C	$0.56\ (10^6/T^2) + 0.45$	O'Neil and Epstein (1966)
CO_2-water −2 to 85°C	$16.60\ (10^3/T) - 15.69$	O'Neil and Adami (1969)
Protodolomite-water 25 to 80°C	$2.62\ (10^6/T^2) + 2.2$	Fritz and Smith (1970)
Aragonite-calcite 25°C	0.6	Tarutani et al. (1969)

Carbon	ϵ(‰) at 20°C	$d\epsilon/dT$(‰/°C) at 20°C	Reference
$CaCO_3$–CO_2(gas)	$+10.17 \pm 0.18$	-0.063 ± 0.008	Emrich et al. (1970)
$CaCO_3$–HCO_3^-	$+1.85 \pm 0.23$	$+0.035 \pm 0.013$	Emrich et al. (1970)
HCO_3^-–CO_2(gas)	$+8.38 \pm 0.12$	-0.109 ± 0.005	Emrich et al. (1970)
CO_2(ag)–CO_2(gas)	+1.1		Vogel et al. (1970)
HCO_3^-–CO_3^{2-}	+3		Mook quoted by Craig (1970)
Aragonite–calcite	+1.8 (25°C)		Rubinson and Clayton (1969)
Calcite–HCO_3^-	+0.9 (25°C)		Rubinson and Clayton (1969)

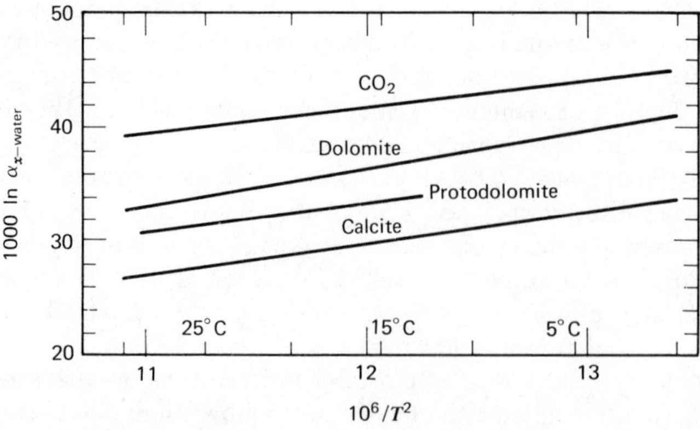

Fig. 11. Experimental oxygen isotope fractionations between carbonates and water. Fritz and Smith (1970); Northrop and Clayton (1966); O'Neil and Adami (1969); O'Neil and Epstein (1966); and O'Neil et al. (1969).

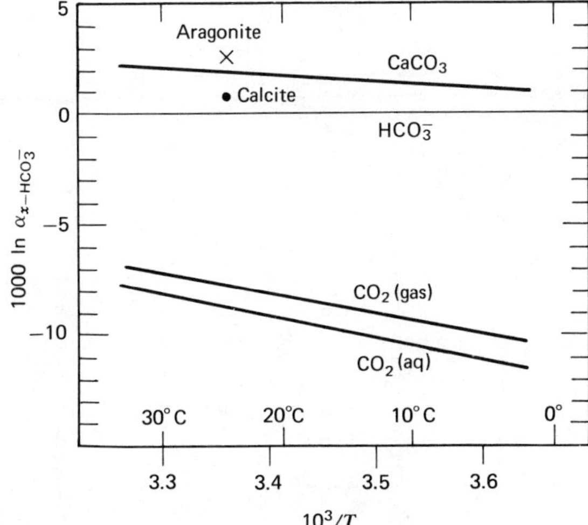

Fig. 12. Experimental carbon isotope fractionations among carbonates, carbon dioxide, and bicarbonate ion. Emrich et al. (1970); Rubinson and Clayton (1969); and Vogel et al. (1970).

The mean O^{18} and C^{13} contents of Quaternary marine limestones have been given by Keith and Weber (1964):

$$\delta O^{18} = -1‰ \text{ (PDB)} = +29.4‰ \text{ (SMOW)} \quad \text{and} \quad \delta C^{13} = +2‰ \text{ (PDB)}$$

If these are assumed to be equilibrium values, one could deduce that the δO^{18} of warm surface ocean waters should average +1‰ (SMOW) and that the mean δC^{13} of bicarbonate in surface waters should be roughly +1‰ (PDB). The former value is a good approximation to the mean δO^{18} value of surface waters (Craig and Gordon, 1965), but δC_{13} values in surface waters are closer to +2‰. Craig (1970) reports the following carbon isotope values in South Pacific waters:

	δC^{13}‰
Total dissolved inorganic carbon	
At surface	+2.2
At 2.5 km (CO_2 maximum and O_2 minimum)	+0.27
In bottom water	+0.5
Foraminiferal tests	+2
Surface HCO_3^- (87%)	+2.5[a]
Surface CO_3^{2-} (13%)	−0.5[a]
Atmospheric CO_2	−6.5[b]

[a] Assuming $\epsilon_{HCO_3^- - CO_3^{2-}} = 3$.
[b] The $\epsilon_{HCO_3^- - CO_2(G)}$ of 9‰ corresponds to equilibrium at about 15°C.

A δC^{13} profile for total dissolved carbonate in the North Atlantic is shown in Fig. 13 (Kroopnick et al., 1972). The decrease in δC^{13} toward the oxygen minimum in both oceans is due to the addition of carbon having a δC^{13} of about −16‰:70% from the oxidation of the organic particulate flux (−23‰) and 30% from the solution of carbonate foraminiferal tests (+2‰).

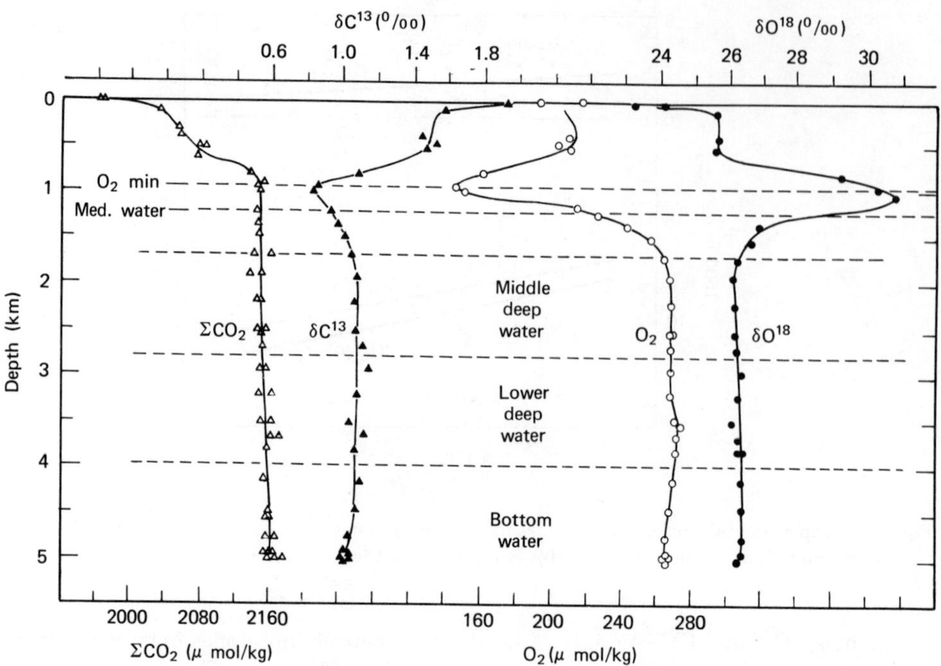

Fig. 13. Vertical profiles of ΣCO_2, δC^{13}, dissolved O_2, and the δO^{18} of dissolved O_2 at Geosecs II in the North Atlantic. Kroopnick et al. (1972).

Weber and Woodhead (1971) observed diurnal variations in the carbon isotope composition of dissolved inorganic carbon in coral reef environments, and attributed the variations to photosynthesis and respiration. δC^{13} values of +2.6 and 0.0‰ were obtained on a reef flat at 13:25 and 00:30 hr, respectively.

Other manifestations of the interdependence of the carbonate and reduced carbon cycles are the decreases in δC^{13} values, amounting to several per mil, observed both in carbonates (Lloyd, 1964; Keith and Parker, 1965; Mook and Vogel, 1968) and in reduced carbon (Sackett and Thompson, 1963; Fredericks and Sackett, 1970), as land is approached from the open ocean. More extreme cases of C^{13} depletion in carbonates include aragonite and high-magnesium calcite at −60‰ (Hathaway and Degens, 1969) and dolomite at −64‰ (Deuser, 1970a), all from the continental shelf of the northeastern United States. As organic material is known to decompose into CH_4 of lower C^{13}/C^{12} ratio and CO_2 of higher C^{13}/C^{12} ratio (Oana and Deevey, 1960), these extremely light carbonates are possibly due to the incorporation of CO_2 derived from the oxidation of C^{13}-poor methane. A continental shelf dolomite extremely enriched in C^{13} (+21‰) may have formed from CO_2 or CH_4 derived from residual material enriched in C^{13} by previous loss of CH_4 (Deuser, 1970a).

The mutual interaction of the oxidized and reduced branches of the geochemical cycle of carbon, from the point of view of its stable isotopes, is depicted schematically in Fig. 14.

Some organisms precipitate calcite or aragonite with oxygen and carbon isotope ratios similar to those of inorganically precipitated carbonates. Such carbonates are considered to be in isotopic equilibrium with their surrounding waters, although the possibility that equilibrium does not extend deeper than a few molecular layers into

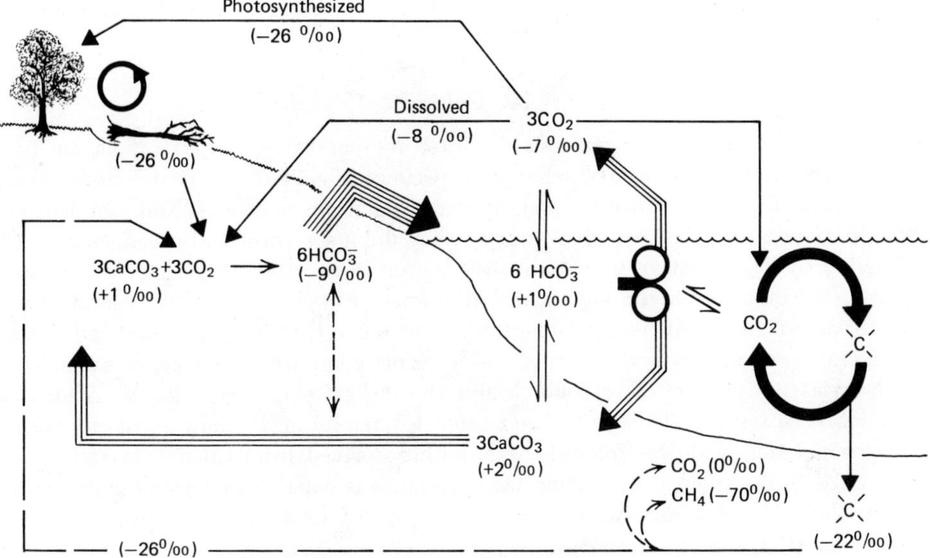

Fig. 14. Schematic depiction of the oxidized and reduced carbon cycles and their isotopic interactions. δC^{13} values in parentheses. Heavy circles denote rapid cycling in the biosphere. Two-way arrows indicate isotopic exchange leading toward isotopic equilibrium. Based on data compiled by Degens (1969) and Schwarcz (1969).

the solid carbonates cannot be discounted (Hamza, 1972). Other organisms exhibit "vital effects," depositing carbonates not in isotopic equilibrium with their environments. There remain some uncertainties regarding the assignment of organisms into these categories:

Equilibrium	Reference	Nonequilibrium	Reference
Belemnites	Urey et al. (1951); Stevens and Clayton (1971)	Algae (red)	Keith and Weber (1965);
		Belemnites	Spaeth et al. (1971)
Brachiopods	Lowenstam (1961)	Corals	Keith and Weber (1965);
Fish otoliths	Devereux (1967); Degens et al. (1969)	Echinoderms	Weber and Woodhead (1972)
Foraminifera	Emiliani (1954); Smith and Emiliani (1968)	Foraminifera	Weber and Raup (1968); Weber (1968)
Molluscs	Epstein et al., 1953		Duplessy et al. (1970)

Keith and Weber (1965) found a maximum difference in δC^{13} of over 8‰ between green and red algae (C^{13}-deficient) from the same reef complex. The average δC^{13} values of aragonite precipitated by lagoonal algae and the high-magnesium calcite of coralline algae are +3.4 and −2.5‰, respectively (Weber and Woodhead, 1969).

Some of the most striking effects have been reported in echinoderms (Weber and Raup, 1968). Although the isotopic compositions of echinoid spines are similar to those of molluscs and foraminifera, their test and lantern parts exhibit large variations of several per mil in oxygen and carbon. In several species, the tooth, pyramid, rotula, and epiphysis form linear arrays with positive slopes when δO^{18} is plotted against

δC^{13}. In another species, the various lantern parts plot in the same sequence along a straight line, but with a negative slope.

14. Dolomites

Dolomite has not been synthesized at low temperatures, but extrapolation from the results of hydrothermal exchange experiments suggests that dolomite should concentrate O^{18} by roughly 6‰ relative to syngenetic calcite (O'Neil and Epstein, 1966b). Several lines of evidence suggest that dolomite should also concentrate C^{13} (possibly by 2‰) relative to calcite (see Clayton et al., 1968b). Degens and Epstein (1964), however, found no significant difference between coexisting dolomites and calcites in recent and ancient sediments and concluded that the dolomites had formed by metasomatism and had inherited the isotopic compositions of precursor calcium carbonates. Clayton et al. (1968b) found the dolomite in recent South Australian lagoons to be 1 or 2‰ richer in O^{18} and about 1‰ poorer in C^{13} than coexisting calcite. They concluded that the dolomite was neither derived from calcite nor strictly co-genetic with it. Another indication that dolomite is capable of crystallizing directly from solution is a dolomite-water fractionation of 35‰ observed in Deep Springs Lake, California (Clayton et al., 1968a).

Fritz and Smith (1970) determined the oxygen isotope fractionations between water and protodolomite (poorly ordered dolomite) synthesized at temperatures as low as 25°C, and found the isotopic behavior of protodolomite to be intermediate between that of dolomite and that of calcite (see Fig. 11). Fritz and Smith suggest that the small isotopic differences commonly observed between dolomites and associated limestones are due to the initial deposition of the dolomites as metastable proto-dolomite.

15. Paleotemperatures

The precipitation of calcium carbonate in oxygen-isotope equilibrium with water, as occurs inorganically or by the action of some organisms, allows the determination of paleotemperatures, provided the isotopic compositions of the waters are known. Epstein et al. (1953) determined the following empirical relationship for this purpose (slightly modified by Craig, 1965):

$$t°C = 16.9 - 4.2\Delta + 0.13\Delta^2$$

where Δ is the per mil difference between CO_2 derived from the calcium carbonate, by reaction with H_3PO_4 at 25°C, and CO_2 equilibrated at 25°C with the water in which the carbonate was precipitated.

Variations in the isotopic composition of the planktonic foraminifera, *Globigerinoides sacculifer*, separated from several Caribbean and equatorial Atlantic cores, have enabled Emiliani (1966, 1972) to construct a paleotemperature curve showing about eight major climatic cycles within the past 400,000 yr (Fig. 15). The observed isotopic variation, amounting to 1.7‰, reflects changes in both the temperature and isotopic composition of seawater, but the relative magnitudes of these two effects is disputed. Estimating the mean δO^{18} of continental ice during the last glacial maximum to be −30‰, Dansgaard and Tauber (1969) claim that the glacial-interglacial δO^{18} variation of ocean water approximated 1.2‰. This is roughly the variation noted in benthonic foraminifera (Shackleton, 1967). If Dansgaard and Tauber are correct, temperature fluctuations in the Caribbean and equatorial Atlantic were 2°C, or less, rather than the 6°C estimated by Emiliani.

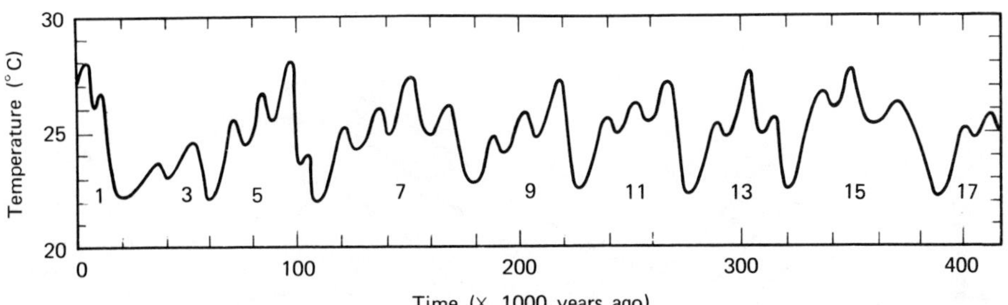

Fig. 15. Generalized temperature curve for Caribbean surface waters based on δO^{18} variations in planktonic foraminifera. The numbers above the horizontal axis refer to stages. Emiliani (1972).

Duplessy et al. (1970) reported that three different species of benthic foraminifera taken at the same level in an Atlantic core yielded δO^{18} values differing by 1‰, possibly because of the incorporation of varying amounts of metabolic CO_2 (vital effects are discussed in the section on carbonates). Furthermore, these benthic species and three pelagic species exhibited similar isotopic variations with depth in the core, providing strong evidence that the time-dependent variations of isotopic composition were not caused by temperature fluctuations confined to surface waters.

We can look forward to a wealth of isotopic data on older sediments from the Deep Sea Drilling Project cores, but they will require meticulous scrutiny before yielding reliable paleotemperatures. Different species of planktonic foraminifera simultaneously occupying various depth habitats have yielded temperatures that differ by as much as 15°C (Savin and Douglas, in press), and no single species has persisted throughout the Cenozoic. Douglas and Savin (1971) may therefore be commended for not attempting to draw a Cenozoic paleotemperature curve through their analyses of nonspecific foraminifera from three Pacific cores. My curves drawn through their data in Fig. 16 may be interpreted, with caution, as representing relative temperature variations. Better interpretations will evolve from recent progress in relating species morphology to depth habitat (Douglas and Savin, 1972).

O^{18} enrichment due to evaporation and depletion due to dilution with meteoric waters are additional uncertainties confronting paleothermometers dependent on the isotopic compositions of coastal ocean waters. Even if the extent of dilution with meteoric water were constant with time in a particular locality, the indicated temperature trends could be reversed. With increasing mean annual temperature, the δO^{18} of meteoric water increases three times faster (+0.7‰/°C) than the fractionation between calcite and water decreases (−0.23‰/°C). Moreover, although the O^{18} content of seawater in coastal areas commonly decreases with decreasing salinity, Lloyd (1964) has shown that the opposite trend occurs in Florida Bay.

Mook and Vogel (1968) observed linear relationships between the C^{13} and O^{18} contents of shell carbonates in estuarine environments. They suggest that the paleotemperature for such an environment could be deduced by extrapolating the δC^{13} versus δO^{18} regression lines to the δC^{13} value of normal marine carbonate, thereby obtaining an estimate of the δO^{18} of carbonate that would have grown in equilibrium with normal ocean water at the temperature of the estuary.

A major difficulty encountered when applying the paleotemperature technique to pre-Cenozoic fossils is the frequent lack of isotopic preservation in such old samples. Belemnites are regarded as one of the best preserved fossil types, but even they have

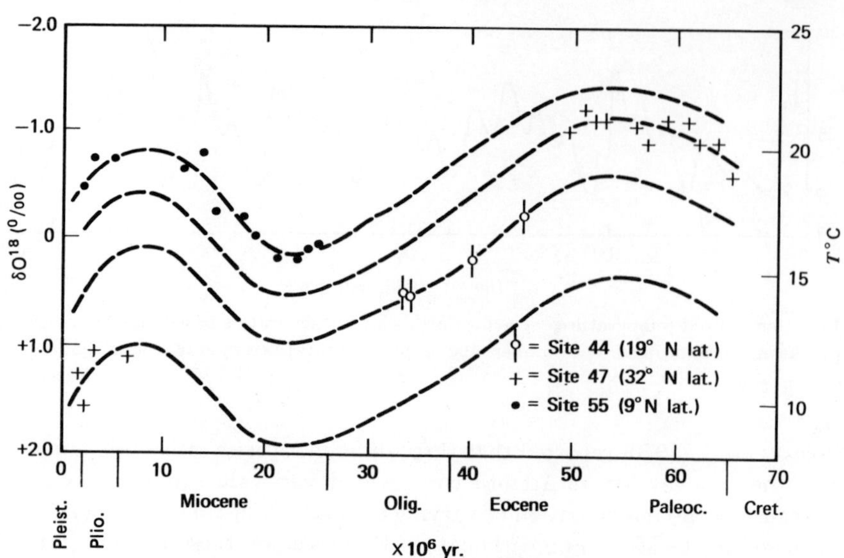

Fig. 16. Oxygen isotope compositions and apparent growth temperatures of planktonic foraminifera in three Deep Sea Drilling Project cores from the Northwest Pacific. Douglas and Savin (1971).

yielded confusing results because of postdepositional alteration (Longinelli, 1969; Stevens and Clayton, 1971). Alteration usually results in lower C^{13}/C^{12} ratios (because of exchange with biogenic sources of carbon), and lower O^{18}/O^{16} ratios (because of exchange with oceanic waters at elevated temperatures or with light meteoric waters). Fossils encased in contemporaneous calcareous concretions (Tourtelot and Rye, 1969) or chert nodules (Knauth, 1972) may provide the most suitable material for isotopic analyses. The preservation of metastable aragonite in a fossil is commonly considered to be an indication that recrystallization and isotopic alteration have not occurred. Therefore, the 5‰ range observed in the δO^{18} of aragonite within single belemnite specimens (Spaeth et al., 1971) is evidence of a vital effect.

In an effort to develop an additional isotopic thermometer, Longinelli (1966) analyzed phosphate (PO_4^{3-}) from the shells of several orders of marine organisms, compared these with coprecipitated calcium carbonate, and derived an indirect calibration of the phosphate-water fractionation. Unfortunately, the temperature coefficient of the calcite-phosphate fractionation is too small to be useful in paleothermometry, so the phosphate calibration does not eliminate the need to know the isotopic composition of the environmental waters.

The possibility of using biogenic opal as a paleothermometer has been explored by Mopper and Garlick (1971), Labeyrie (1972), and Knauth (1972). Labeyrie improved analytical reproducibility by removing organic matter with NaOCl solution and by dehydrating at 1000°C under vacuum. He reported a lucustrine diatom-water fractionation of +38.7‰ at 10°C and a marine sponge-water fractionation of +40.2‰ at 5°C.

Matsuo et al. (1972) found that the hydrogen isotope fractionation between trona and water exhibits a marked temperature dependence. However, the prospects of obtaining marine paleotemperatures from the hydrogen of hydrated authigenic phases is not good, because such hydrogen is probably too exchangeable. Hydroxyl hydrogen may be more suitable for paleotemperature studies (Knauth, 1972).

16. Organic Carbon

Photosynthesis in the marine environment utilizes dissolved carbon dioxide, the isotopic composition of which is determined chiefly by equilibration with the large reservoir of bicarbonate. The dissolved CO_2 is 6 to 10‰ depleted in C^{13} relative to oceanic bicarbonate and PDB (see Fig. 11).

The HCO_3^- reservoir itself is not isotopically uniform. In shallow coral reef environments diurnal variations exceeding 2‰ have been observed (Weber and Woodhead, 1971), due chiefly to photosynthesis and respiration. Sackett and Thompson (1963) found that the C^{13} content of organic carbon in Recent Gulf Coast sediments decreases with decreasing distance from shore. The variation is attributable directly to the influence of organic detritus derived from land plants having δC^{13} values of roughly -26‰ (Craig, 1953; Smith and Epstein, 1971), and indirectly to the influence of bicarbonate containing light carbon derived from the decarboxylation of organic materials (see Fig. 13).

Although chemical equilibrium among the dissolved carbon species is attained within a matter of minutes, isotopic equilibration is much slower. Deuser (1970b) reports that a Black Sea diatom bloom was enriched in C^{13} by 1.5‰ compared with normal plankton (-23‰), presumably because it upset the CO_2–HCO_3^- isotopic equilibrium by consuming CO_2 more rapidly than it could be isotopically equilibrated. Degens et al. (1968a) observed similar effects in laboratory-cultured marine plankton. Compared with a maximum C^{13} depletion of 28‰ obtained at 10°C in the presence of abundant CO_2, plankton grown rapidly at 30°C, and at higher pH were only 12‰ depleted in C^{13} relative to bicarbonate. Sackett et al. (1965) observed that the δC^{13} values of plankton are correlated with temperature, varying from roughly -28‰ at 0°C to roughly -22‰ at 25°C. This variation may be understood in light of the abovementioned experiments (Deuser et al., 1968).

The experiments of Degens et al. (1968a) also revealed isotopic fractionations accompanying respiration. The δC^{13} value of cultured phytoplankton decreased exponentially from about -16 to -22‰ during 12 days of dark respiration.

The carbon isotope distribution among the various organic compounds comprising plankton have been investigated by Degens et al. (1968b). Whereas the total organic matter in their samples of marine plankton averaged -20‰, pectin and proteins showed δC^{13} values near -17 and -18‰, carbohydrates had δC^{13} values near -19‰, and $CHCl_3$-extractable lipids had a mean value of -29‰. Recent marine sediments contain organic material with a mean δC^{13} value near -22‰; pre-Cenozoic sediments have values near -26‰; and the majority of crude oils fall within the range -25 to -30‰ (Degens, 1969). It appears that the diagenesis of organic matter destroys C^{13} enriched carbohydrates and proteins and converts the residual lipid-rich fraction into hydrocarbons (Silverman and Epstein, 1958). However, the process is not simple, as large fractionations are involved in the decay of organic matter into CO_2 and CH_4. Oana and Deevey (1960) and Deevey et al. (1963) reported the mean δC^{13} values of CO_2 and CH_4 in five bottom muds from Lindsey Pond, Connecticut, to be -5 and -77‰, respectively. These gases were derived from an organic substrate having a δ value of about -30‰. The mean $\epsilon_{CO_2-CH_4}$ of 78‰ corresponds to the equilibrium fractionation calculated for 6°C by Bottinga (1968). The measured bottom temperature was in agreement with the theoretical calculation. On the other hand, the discovery of δC^{13} values as low as -89‰ in nonvolatile organic material associated with sulfur in Pleistocene sediments (Kaplan and Nissenbaum, 1966) reveals a complexity of diagenetic processes beyond our present understanding.

17. Ocean-Crust Interactions

The weathering and erosion of igneous rocks and the subsequent deposition, diagenesis, and metamorphism of their components involves extensive exchange of oxygen isotopes with the hydrosphere. The participation of the continental crust in this process is well recognized (Perry and Tan, 1972a), but there is little information concerning the extent of isotopic interaction between ocean water and the oceanic crust. Evidence of chemical exchange, however, is accumulating rapidly (Hart, 1970), and it is known that isotopic exchange usually accompanies chemical alteration. Garlick and Dymond (1970) report an increase in the δO^{18} of siliceous glass shards accompanying their hydration, from +8 to +20‰, over a time period of about 50 million years. They also show that the isotopic alteration accompanying the weathering of submarine basalts can be roughly described by the following equation: $\delta O^{18} = 5.4 + 1.2$ (% H_2O total) permil. Palagonites, the products of extreme weathering of basaltic glass, yield δO^{18} values as high as +25‰. Muehlenbachs and Clayton (1972a) suggest that basalts weathered in the deep sea may be considered as binary mixtures of fresh basalt (δO^{18} = 5.7‰, H_2O^+ = 0.1%) and iron-rich montmorillonite (δO^{18} = 27‰, H_2O^+ = 10%). They estimate that $10^{14\text{-}15}$ g of submarine pyroclastic basalts are weathered per year. This would amount to $10^{23\text{-}24}$ g in 10^9 yr, which is comparable to the mass of the hydrosphere (1.4×10^{24} g).

Oxygen isotope exchange between rocks and water may be expected to be less dramatic at higher temperatures, because equilibrium fractionations between most rock-forming minerals and water decrease with temperature and typically become slightly negative at igneous temperatures. For example, the mineral-water fractionation curves for anorthite, albite, muscovite, and calcite all pass through zero within the range 450–700°C (O'Neil and Taylor, 1967 and 1969; O'Neil et al., 1969). On the basis of such data, it is possible to estimate that basalt or gabbro should be in oxygen-isotope equilibrium with ocean water at roughly 500°C.

Disregarding one possible ice-rafted rock and a few weathered samples, Muehlenbachs and Clayton (1972b) report 14 submarine greenstones ranging from 2.8 to 6.8‰ and having a mean value of 5.2‰, which is slightly lower than that of fresh basalts. As isotopic fractionations between coexisting minerals indicate metamorphic temperatures of 200–300°C, the metamorphic water may be estimated to have ranged from −2 to +2‰. In contrast, the δO^{18} of "juvenile" water in equilibrium with the mantle at igneous temperatures should be about +7 to +8‰ (Epstein and Taylor, 1967). Muehlenbachs and Clayton (1971) report eight submarine diorites ranging from 5.2 to 6.9‰ and having a mean value of 6.1‰, which is close to the value expected of igneous diorites. Thus, although there is ample evidence of exchange between rocks and fluids during metamorphism, the net effect on the mean oxygen isotopic compositions of the oceanic crust and seawater may not be significant. On the other hand, one may argue that the isotopic similarity between ocean water and the average metamorphic water is not a coincidence, but means that the dominant control on the oxygen isotope composition of ocean water is the process of isotopic equilibration with oceanic crust during metamorphism.

Wenner and Taylor (in press) provide data on both the oxygen and hydrogen isotopic compositions of oceanic serpentinites:

$$\delta O^{18} = +0.5 \text{ to } +6.5‰ \qquad \delta D = -30 \text{ to } -70‰.$$

These values can be reconciled with the presence of oceanic water during metamorphism, but the δO^{18} and δD values are lower and higher, respectively, than would be expected if "juvenile" water were dominant. Wenner and Taylor show that the waters responsible for the serpentinization of the Vourinos and other ophiolite complexes were meteoric in origin.

18. Isotopic Evolution of the Oceans

Degens and Epstein (1962) and Keith and Weber (1964) observed that the O^{18}/O^{16} ratios of marine cherts and limestones are correlated with age, Cambrian samples being on the average roughly 8‰ lighter than Tertiary samples. This correlation is possibly a result of progressive isotopic exchange with warm and/or isotopically light waters. However, Perry and Tan (1972a) contend that the more gradual δO^{18} variation noted in more massive cherts records a progressive increase in the δO^{18} of ocean water amounting to 15‰ during the past 3 billion years (Fig. 17). Their interpretation is in direct conflict with the proposal made by Silverman (1951) that "juvenile" water, outgassed from the mantle at igneous temperatures, was lightened by about 7‰ during the process of converting isotopically light igneous rocks into isotopically heavy sedimentary rocks. As crustal igneous rocks are themselves enriched in O^{18} with respect to mantle-derived rocks of equivalent chemical composition (Garlick, 1966), the conflict with Silverman's model is even more severe. Perry and Tan (1972a) and Chase and Perry (1972) conclude that the major factor responsible for the apparent progressive concentration of O^{18} into both crust and hydrosphere is the recycling of water through the mantle. There remain the possibilities, however, that even the heaviest ancient massive cherts have been lightened by postdepositional exchange with ground waters, or that the temperatures of formation of the cherts were higher

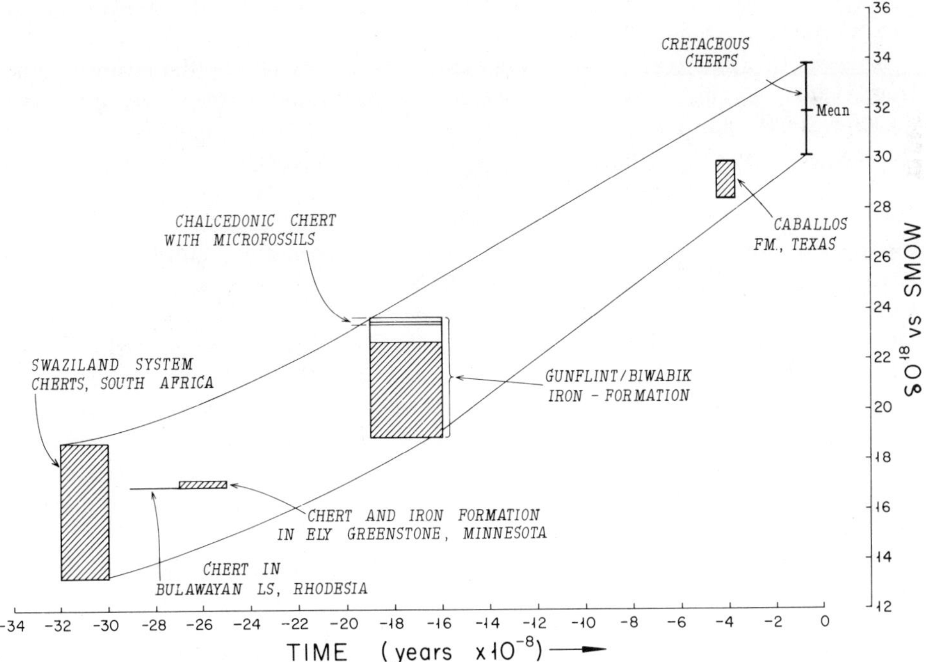

Fig. 17. Values of δO^{18} for cherts of various ages. Mean of Cretaceous cherts from Degens and Epstein (1962); older cherts from Perry and Tan (1972a).

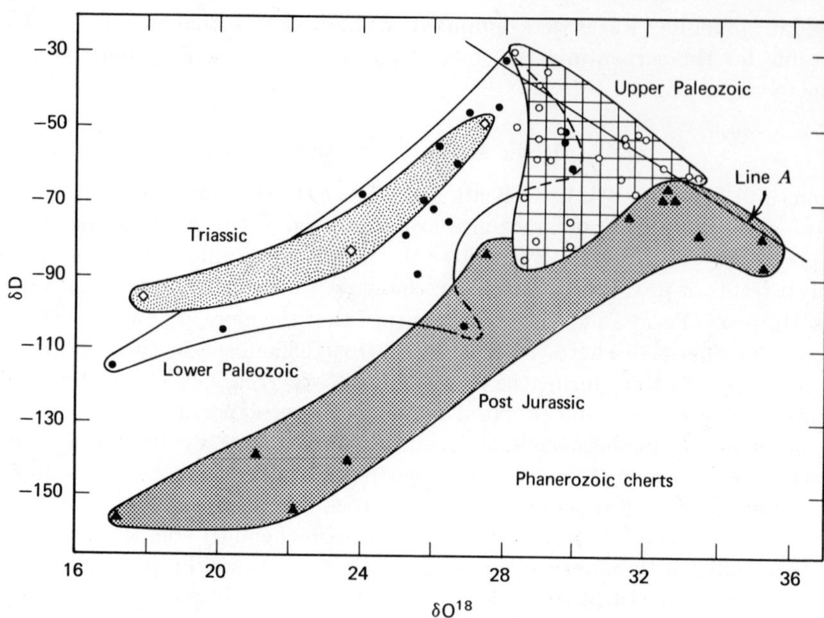

Fig. 18. Isotopic compositions of Phanerozoic cherts. The domains are elongated in a direction parallel to the meteoric water line. The three highest δO^{18} values represent Cretaceous and Tertiary Deep Sea Drilling Project cherts. Line A is intended to represent cherts in equilibrium with ocean water at various temperatures. Knauth (1972).

in ancient times. A 15‰ change in fractionation between chert and water corresponds to a temperature change of about 70°C.

Knauth (1972) analyzed both oxygen and hydrogen in cherts, the latter obtained from hydroxyl groups within the cherts. He observed that cherts of a given age yield an approximate linear relationship between δD and δO^{18}, approximately parallel to the meteoric water line (Fig. 18), suggesting that many cherts formed diagenetically in the presence of meteoric waters, and that their temperatures of formation were fairly uniform within each age group. The displacements with time of the δD-δO^{18} relationship were interpreted as being caused by climatic temperature changes. Estimating the oxygen isotope fractionation between chert and water at equilibrium to be $1000 \ln \alpha = 3.09(10^6/T^2) - 3.29$, Knauth deduced that climatic temperatures for the central and western United States decreased from 34 to 20°C through the Paleozoic, increased to 35 to 40°C in the Triassic, and then decreased to the present value of 13 to 15°C. The isotopic compositions of a few Precambrian cherts are shown in Fig. 19. However, more work will be required before these data can be deciphered in terms of isotopic history of ocean water, the thermal histories of the diagenetic environments of chert formation, and the effects of subsequent alteration of the cherts.

On the basis of D/H ratios in phlogopites of possible mantle origin (−58‰ ± 18‰) and the experimental fractionation factors of Suzuoki and Epstein (1970), Sheppard and Epstein (1970) estimate that the δD value of "juvenile" water should be −48 ± 20‰. The δD of the hydrosphere is about −6 or −7‰ (cf. Kokubu et al., 1961). The processes that could possibly account for the derivation of the modern D/H ratio of the hydrosphere from that of "juvenile" water are the preferential escape of

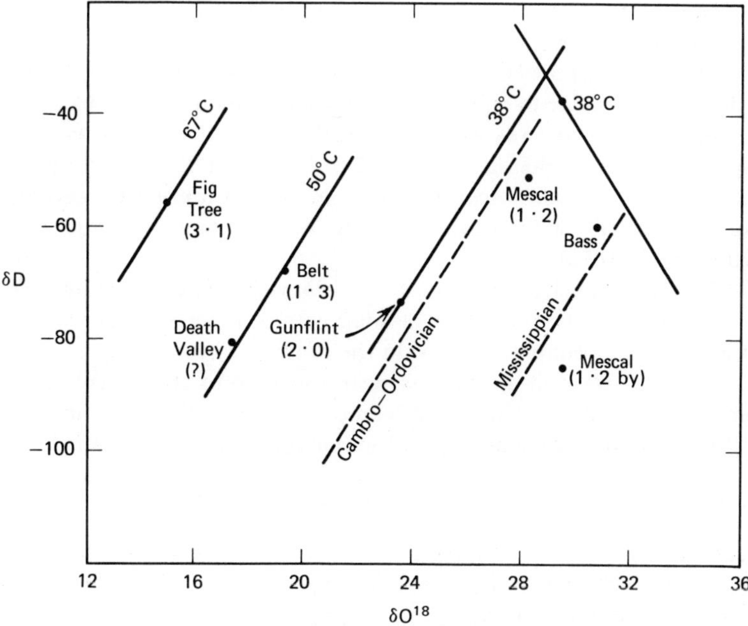

Fig. 19. Isotopic compositions of Precambrian cherts. Approximate ages (by) in parentheses. Lines are intended to represent cherts in equilibrium with modern ocean and meteoric waters at various temperatures. Dashed lines from Fig. 18. Knauth (1972).

protium into space and the preferential consumption of protium by serpentinization and other hydration reactions. If the first process were dominant and if only protium had escaped, about 4% of the total surface hydrogen would have disappeared. If the second process were dominant and if the mean δD of hydroxyl (and hydration) water in crustal rocks is tentatively estimated to be −80‰, as much hydrogen would be bound in crustal rocks as is present in the oceans. It is probable that both processes have played a role, but the available isotopic data do not permit a more specific statement.

The dominant influence on the distribution of carbon isotopes on earth is the process of photosynthesis. Assuming the isotopic fractionation between carbonate and organic carbon to be 25‰, and the exchange system to be recycled but closed, the photosynthetic conversion of 20% of the available carbon into reduced form should have been accompanied by a 5‰ increase in the δC^{13} of both carbonate and reduced carbon. The relative uniformity of marine limestone δC^{13} values through Phanerozoic time (Keith and Weber, 1964) prompted Broecker (1970) to argue that the size of the reduced carbon reservoir has remained fairly constant since Cambrian times at a level controlled by a feedback mechanism involving the partial pressure of atmospheric oxygen. On the other hand, Garrels and Perry (Chapter 9 in this volume) suggest that the deposition of unusual quantities of gypsum during the Permo-Triassic Period was accompanied by a considerable transfer of carbon from the carbonate to organic reservoirs: $4\,FeS_2 + 8\,CaCO_3 + 7\,MgCO_3 + 7\,SiO_3 + 31\,H_2O = 8\,CaSO_4 \cdot 2\,H_2O + 2\,Fe_2O_3 + 15\,CH_2O + 7\,MgSiO_3$. The mean δC^{13} values of carbonates as determined by Keith and Weber (1964) do exhibit small fluctuations, ranging from −1‰ in the Pennsylvanian to +2‰ in the Quaternary, and the Permian mean of +1‰ is about

2‰ higher than the Pennsylvanian mean as expected by Garrels and Perry, but it is no higher than the Silurian, Mississippian, Cretaceous, and Quaternary means. Perry and Tan (1972a) report δC^{13} values ranging from −1.0 to +1.8‰ in Swaziland Sequence dolomites, similar to those of Phanerozoic dolomites. It thus appears that the reduced carbon reservoir was well established over 3 billion years ago, long before the atmosphere became oxidizing (Cloud, 1972). Perry and Tan (1972b) feel that the lower C^{13}/C^{12} ratios observed in carbonates from banded iron-formations are caused by reaction of hematite with organic carbon to yield magnetite and siderite (cf. Becker and Clayton, 1972).

The C^{13}/C^{12} ratios in ancient organic materials have been examined by Oehler et al. (1972). Whereas most Phanerozoic samples fall within the range −20 to −30‰, and almost all Precambrian samples fall within the range −20 to −40‰, the very oldest samples from the Theespruit Formation near the base of the Swaziland Sequence range from −14 to −20‰. These 3.3-billion-year-old δC^{13} values may represent abiologically produced organic matter or the remains of preautotrophic life.

19. The Red Sea

The great utility of stable isotope geochemistry is clearly demonstrated by the major role it played in elucidating the Quaternary history, of the Red Sea and the origin of its intriguing hot brines.

The D/H and O^{18}/O^{16} ratios in the brines (Fig. 20) showed that the source water is postglacial seawater of 38.2/mil mean salinity, which occurs on a shallow sill near the

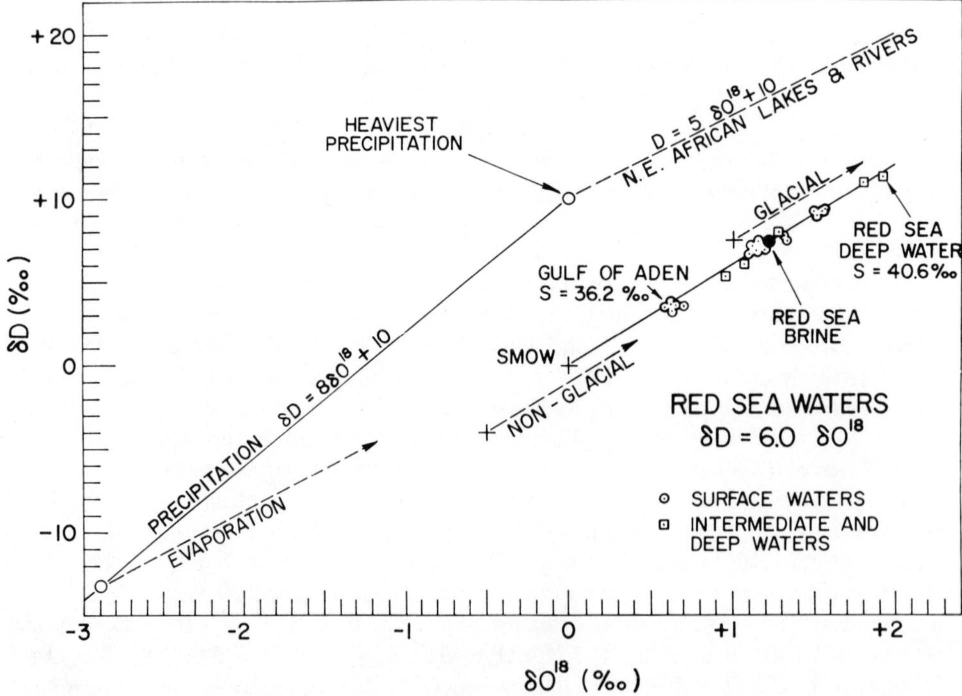

Fig. 20. Isotopic diagram for waters of the Red Sea Region. $S =$ salinity. The dashed lines above and below the Red Sea points begin at crosses marking the isotopic compositions to which SMOW would move at maximum glacial and completely nonglacial times. Craig (1966).

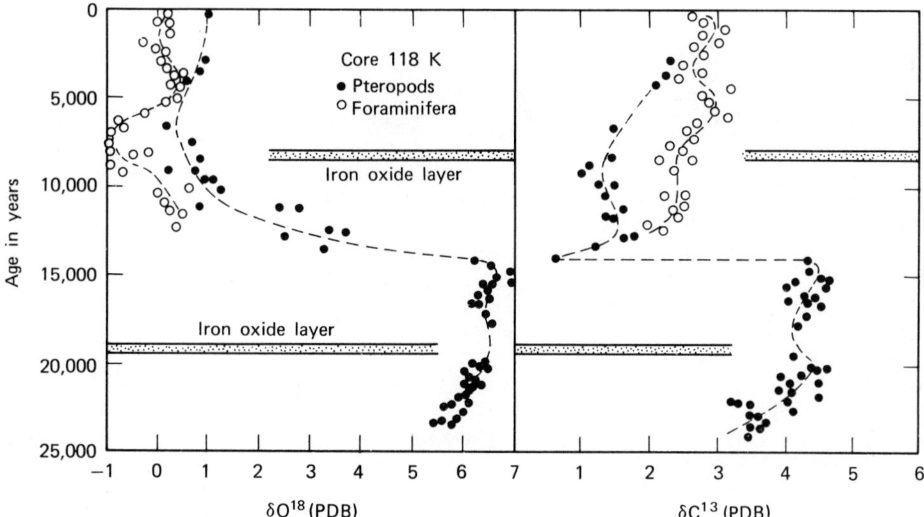

Fig. 21. δO^{18} and δC^{13} distributions in foraminifera and pteropods and in aragonite-incrusted pteropods (older than 14,000 yr) from a core taken 5 km southeast of the Discovery Deep brine pool, Red Sea. C^{14} chronology from Ku et al. (1969); isotopic data from Deuser and Degens (1969).

southern end of the Red Sea (Craig, 1966). The water acquired salt from buried evaporites, but did not experience oxygen isotope exchange with surrounding sediments as did the Salton Sea geothermal brines.

The O^{18}/O^{16} and C^{13}/C^{12} ratios in carbonates from a few cores, one of which is shown in Fig. 21, revealed the following scenario (Deuser and Degens, 1969). Four periods of marked evaporation, probably related to times of glacially lowered sea level, occurred during the past 80,000 yr. Each period of evaporation caused a progressive increase in the δO^{18} of the Red Sea and its carbonate products, which continued until abruptly terminated by the influx of normal seawater. Pteropods were incrusted with inorganically precipitated aragonite during the periods of increased salinity, and the high C^{13}/C^{12} ratios of this aragonite account for the high δC^{13} values plotted in Fig. 21. Unincrusted pteropod shells have relatively low C^{13}/C^{12} ratios possibly due to the incorporation of metabolic CO_2 during their growth.

The pteropods in Fig. 21 are slightly depleted in C^{13} and enriched in O^{18} relative to contemporaneous foraminifera, indicating a deeper depth habitat for the pteropods (see Figs. 11 to 13). The δO^{18} fluctuations observed in the foraminifera probably record surface-water temperature changes amounting to 6°C within the past 10,000 yr. Recent foraminifera deposited within a 44°C brine pool have experienced some postdepositional isotopic exchange with the hot brines and are consequently about 0.9‰ lower in δO^{18} than those deposited outside the hot brine pools.

The δC^{13} values of foraminifera in one core exhibit minima correlated with δO^{18} maxima at about 45,000 and 25,000 yr ago. It appears that extensive precipitation of inorganic aragonite at times of maximum salinity depleted the C^{13} content of the bicarbonate reservoir to the extent of 1 or 2‰.

Acknowledgments

I am greatly indebted to Drs. W. G. Deuser, E. D. Goldberg, L. P. Knauth, R. M. Lloyd, J. R. O'Neil, and especially S. M. Savin for their many valuable suggestions.

References

Becker, R. H. and R. N. Clayton, 1972. Carbon isotopic evidence for the origin of a branded iron-formation in Western Australia. *Geochim. Cosmochim. Acta*, **36**, 577–595.

Bigeleisen, J. and M. G. Mayer, 1947. Calculation of equilibrium constants for isotopic exchange reactions. *J. Chem. Phys.*, **15**, 261–271.

Biscaye, P. E., 1965. Mineralogy and sedimentation of recent deep sea clay in the Atlantic Ocean and adjacent seas and oceans. *Bull. Geol. Soc. Amer.*, **76**, 803–832.

Bonatti, E., 1966. Deep-sea authigenic calcite and dolomite. *Science*, **153**, 534–537.

Bottinga, Y., 1968. Calculation of fractionation factors for carbon and oxygen isotopic exchange in the system calcite-carbon dioxide-water. *J. Phys. Chem.*, **72**, 800–808.

Bottinga, Y., 1969. Calculated fractionation factors for carbon and hydrogen isotope exchange in the system calcite-carbon dioxide-graphite-methane-hydrogen-water vapor. *Geochim. Cosmochim. Acta*, **33**, 49–64.

Broecker, W. S., 1970. A boundary condition on the evolution of atmospheric oxygen. *J. Geophys. Res.*, **75**, 3553–3557.

Chase, C. G. and E. C. Perry, 1972. The oceans: Growth and oxygen isotope evolution. *Science*, **177**, 992–994.

Claypool, G. E., W. T. Holser, I. R. Kaplan, H. Sakai, and I. Zak, 1972. Sulfur and oxygen isotope geochemistry of evaporite sulfates. *Abs. Geol. Soc. Am. Annual Meet.*, **4**, 473.

Clayton, R. N., J. R. Goldsmith, K. J. Johnson, and R. C. Newton, 1972. Pressure effect on stable isotope fractionation. *Abs. Trans. Am. Geophys. Union*, **53**, 555.

Clayton, R. N., B. F. Jones, and R. A. Berner, 1968a. Isotope studies of dolomite formation under sedimentary conditions. *Geochim. Cosmochim. Acta*, **32**, 415–432.

Clayton, R. N., H. C. W. Skinner, R. A. Berner, and M. Rubinson, 1968b. Isotopic compositions of recent South Australian lagoonal carbonates. *Geochim. Cosmochim. Acta*, **32**, 983–988.

Cloud, P., 1972. A working model of the primitive earth. *Am. J. Sci.*, **272**, 537–548.

Craig, H., 1953. The geochemistry of the stable carbon isotopes. *Geochim. Cosmochim. Acta*, **3**, 53–92.

Craig, H., 1957. Isotopic standards for carbon and oxygen and correction factors for mass spectrometric analysis of carbon dioxide. *Geochim. Cosmochim. Acta*, **12**, 133–149.

Craig, H., 1961. Standard for reporting concentrations of deuterium and oxygen-18 in natural waters. *Science*, **133**, 1833.

Craig, H., 1965. The measurement of oxygen isotope paleotemperatures. *Proc. Spoleto Conf. on Stable Isotopes in Oceanographic Studies and Paleotemp.*, **3**, 1–24.

Craig, H., 1966. Isotopic composition and origin of the Red Sea and Salton Sea geothermal brines. *Science*, **154**, 1544–1548.

Craig, H., 1970. Abyssal carbon 13 in the South Pacific. *J. Geophys. Res.*, **75**, 691–695.

Craig, H. and L. I. Gordon, 1965. Isotopic oceanography: Deuterium and oxygen 18 variations in the ocean and the marine atmosphere. *Proc. Symp. Mar. Geochem.*, University of Rhode Island Occ. Publ. **3**, 1965, 277–374.

Craig, H., L. I. Gordon, and Y. Horibe, 1963. Isotopic exchange effects in the evaporation of water. *J. Geophys. Res.*, **68**, 5079–5087.

Dansgaard, W., 1964. Stable isotopes in precipitation. *Tellus*, **16**, 436.

Dansgaard, W. and H. Tauber, 1969. Glaicer oxygen-18 content and Pleistocene ocean temperatures. *Science*, **166**, 499–502.

Deevey, E. S., N. Nakai, and M. Stuiver, 1963. Fractionation of sulfur and carbon isotopes in a meromictic lake. *Science*, **139**, 407–408.

Degens, E. T., 1969. Biogeochemistry of stable carbon isotopes. In *Organic Geochemistry*. Eglinton and Murphy, eds. Springer-Verlag, New York, pp. 304–329.

Degens, E. T., M. Behrendt, B. Gottlardt, and E. Reppmann, 1968b. Metabolic fractionation of carbon isotopes in marine plankton, part II. *Deep-Sea Res.*, **15**, 11–20.

Degens, E. T., W. G. Deuser, and R. L. Haedrich, 1969. Molecular structure and composition of fish otoliths. *Marine Biology*, **2**, 105–113.

Degens, E. T. and S. Epstein, 1962. Relationship between O^{18}/O^{16} ratios in coexisting carbonates, cherts and diatomites. *Bull. Amer. Assoc. Petrol. Geol.*, **46**, 534–542.

Degens, E. T. and S. Epstein, 1964. Oxygen and carbon isotope ratios in coexisting calcites and dolomites from recent and ancient sediments. *Geochim. Cosmochim. Acta*, **28**, 23–44.

Degens, E. T., R. L. Guillard, W. M. Sackett, and J. A. Hellebust, 1968a. Metabolic fractionation of carbon isotopes in marine plankton, part 1. *Deep-Sea Res.*, **15**, 1–9.

Deines, P., 1970. Mass spectrometer correction factors for the determination of small isotopic composition variations of carbon and oxygen. *Int. J. Mass Spectrom. Ion Phys.*, **4**, 283–295.

Deuser, W. G., 1970a. Extreme $^{13}C/^{12}C$ variations in Quaternary dolomites from the continental shelf. *Earth Planet. Sci. Letters*, **8**, 118–124.

Deuser, W. G., 1970b. Isotopic evidence for diminishing supply of available carbon during diatom bloom in the Black Sea. *Nature*, **225**, 1069–1070.

Deuser, W. G. and E. T. Degens, 1969. O^{18}/O^{16} and C^{13}/C^{12} ratios of fossils from the hot-brine deep area of the Red Sea. In *Hot Brines and Recent Heavy Metal Deposits in the Red Sea*. E. T. Degens and D. A. Ross, eds. Springer-Verlag, New York, pp. 336–347.

Deuser, W. G., E. T. Degens, and R. R. L. Guillard, 1968. Carbon isotope relationships between plankton and seawater. *Geochim. Cosmochim. Acta*, **32**, 657–660.

Devereux, I., 1967. Temperature measurements from oxygen isotope ratios of fish otoliths. *Science*, **155**, 1684–1685.

Douglas, R. G. and S. M. Savin, 1971. Isotopic analyses of planktonic foraminifera from the Cenozoic of the Northwest Pacific, Leg 6. *Deep Sea Drilling Project Initial Reports*. Vol. 6, Washington, D.C., U.S. Government Printing Office, pp. 1123–1127.

Douglas, R. G. and S. M. Savin, 1972. Depth stratification in Tertiary and Cretaceous planktonic foraminifera. *Abs. Geol. Soc. Am. Annual Meet.*, **4**, 491.

Duplessy, J. C., C. Lalou, and A. C. Vinot, 1970. Differential isotopic fractionation in benthic foraminifera and paleotemperatures reassessed. *Science*, **168**, 250–251.

Emiliani, C., 1954. Depth habitats of some species of pelagic foraminifera as indicated by oxygen isotope ratios. *Am. J. Sci.*, **252**, 149–158.

Emiliani, C., 1966. Isotopic paleotemperatures. *Science*, **154**, 851–857.

Emiliani, C., 1972. Quaternary paleotemperatures and the duration of the high-temperature intervals. *Science*, **178**, 398–401.

Emrich, K., E. H. Ehhalt, and J. C. Vogel, 1970. Carbon isotope fractionation during the precipitation of calcium carbonate. *Earth Planet. Sci. Lett. Letters*, **8**, 363–371.

Epstein, S., R. Buchsbaum, H. A. Lowenstam, and H. C. Urey, 1953. Revised carbonate-water temperature scale. *Bull. Geol. Soc. Am.*, **64**, 1315–1326.

Epstein, S. and T. K. Mayeda, 1953. Variation of O^{18} content of waters from natural sources. *Geochim. Cosmochim. Acta*, **4**,, 213–224.

Epstein, S. and H. P. Taylor, 1967. Variation of O^{18}/O^{16} in minerals and rocks. In *Researches in Geochemistry*. Vol. 2. P. H. Abelson, ed. Wiley, New York, pp. 29–62.

Fontes, J. C. and R. Gonfiantini, 1967. Comportement isotopique au cours de l'evaporation de deux bassins Sahariens. *Earth Planet. Sci. Letters*, **3**, 258–266.

Fontes, C., R. Letolle, and W. D. Nesteroff, 1971. Las forages D.S.D.P. Mediterranee (Leg 13); Reconnaissance isotopique. International Sed. Congress, 1971.

Fredericks, A. D. and W. M. Sackett, 1970. Organic carbon in the Gulf of Mexico. *J. Geophys. Res.*, **75**, 2199–2206.

Fritz, P. and D. G. W. Smith, 1970. The isotopic composition of secondary dolomites. *Geochim. Cosmochim. Acta*, **34**, 1161–1173.

Garlick, G. D., 1966. Oxygen isotope fractionation in igneous rocks. *Earth Planet. Sci. Letters*, **1**, 361–365.

Garlick, G. D., 1969. The stable isotopes of oxygen. In *Handbook of Geochemistry*. 2. K. H. Wedepohl, ed. Springer-Verlag, Berlin, 8B1–27.

Garlick, G. D. and J. R. Dymond, 1970. Oxygen isotope exchange between volcanic materials and ocean water. *Geol. Soc. Amer. Bull.*, **81**, 2137–2142.

Garlick, G. D., I. D. MacGregor, and D. E. Vogel, 1971. Oxigen isotope ratios in eclogites from kimberlites. *Science*, **172**, 1025–1027.

Garrels, R. M. and E. A. Perry, Jr., 1973. Cycling of carbon, sulfur, and oxygen through geologic time. In *The Sea: Ideas and Observations*. Vol. 5. Edward G. Goldberg, ed. Wiley, New York (Chapter 9).

Hamza, M. S. A., 1972. Isotope fractionation studies between CO_2, water vapor and the outermost molecular layers of the carbonate minerals, and oxygen diffusion in calcite. Ph.D. thesis, Columbia University, New York, pp. 1–100.

Hart, R. A., 1970. Chemical exchange between sea water and deep-ocean basalts. *Earth Planet. Sci. Letters*, **9**, 269–279.

Hathaway, J. C. and E. T. Degens, 1969. Methane-derived marine carbonates of Pleistocene age. *Science*, **165**, 690–692.

Hoering, T. C., 1961. The physical chemistry of isotopic substances. Annual Report of the Geophys. Lab., Carnegie Institute, 201.

Kaplan, I. R. and A. Nissenbaum, 1966. Anomalous carbon-isotope ratios in nonvolatile organic material. *Science*, **153**, 744–745.

Keeling, C. D., 1961. Concentration and isotopic abundances of carbon dioxide in rural and marine air. *Geochim. Cosmochim. Acta*, **24**, 277.

Keith, M. L. and R. H. Parker, 1965. Local variation of ^{13}C and ^{18}O content of mollusk shells and the relatively minor temperature effect in marginal marine environments. *Marine Geol.*, **3**, 115–129.

Keith, M. L. and J. N. Weber, 1964. Carbon and oxygen isotopic composition of selected limestones and fossils. *Geochim. Cosmochim. Acta*, **28**, 1787–1816.

Keith, M. L. and J. N. Weber, 1965. Systematic relationships between carbon and oxygen isotopes in carbonates deposited by modern corals and algae. *Science*, **150**, 498–501.

Knauth, L. P., 1972. Oxygen and hydrogen isotope ratios in cherts and related rocks. Ph.D. thesis, Cal. Inst. of Technology, pp. 1–369.

Kokubu, N., T. Mayeda, and H. C. Urey, 1961. Deuterium content of minerals, rocks and liquid inclusions from rocks. *Geochim. Cosmochim. Acta*, **21**, 247–256.

Kolodny, Y. and I. R. Kaplan, 1970. Carbon and oxygen isotopes in apatite and coexisting calcite from sedimentary phosphorite. *J. Sediment. Petrol.*, **40**, 954–959.

Kroopnick, P., R. F. Weiss, and H. Craig, 1972. Total CO_2, ^{13}C, and dissolved oxygen–^{18}O at Geosecs II in the north Atlantic. *Earth Planet. Sci. Letters*, **16**, 103–110.

Ku, T. L., D. L. Thurber, and G. Mathieu, 1969. Radiocarbon chronology of Red Sea sediments. In *Hot Brines and Recent Heavy Metal Deposits in the Red Sea*. E. T. Degens and D. A. Ross, eds. Springer-Verlag, New York, pp. 348–359.

Labeyrie, M. L., 1972. Composition isotopique de l'oxygene de la silice biogenique. *C.R. Acad. Sc. Paris*, **274**, 1605–1608.

Lawrence, J. R. and H. P. Taylor, 1971. Deuterium and oxygen-18 correlation: Clay minerals and hydroxides in Quaternary soils. *Geochim. Cosmochim. Acta*, **35**, 993–1003.

Lawrence, J. R. and H. P. Taylor. Hydrogen and oxygen isotope systemics in weathering profiles. *Geochim. Cosmochim. Acta*. In press.

Lloyd, R. M., 1964. Variations in the oxygen and carbon isotope ratios of Florida Bay mollusks and their environmental significance. *J. Geol.*, **72**, 84–111.

Lloyd, R. M., 1966. Oxygen isotope enrichment of sea water by evaporation. *Geochim. Cosmochim. Acta*, **30**, 801–814.

Lloyd, R. M., 1968. Oxygen isotope behavior in the sulfate-water system. *J. Geophys. Res.*, **73**, 6099–6110.

Lloyd, R. M., 1972. Interstitial water studies from leg 15, D.S.D.P. *D.S.D.P. Prelim. Rept.*, **15**.

Lloyd, R. M. and K. J. Hsu, 1971. Preliminary isotopic investigations of samples from deep-sea drilling cruise to the Mediterranean. Symp. on Sed. in Mediterranean Sea; Int. Sed. Congress, 1971.

Longinelli, A., 1966. Ratios of oxygen-18: oxygen-16 in phosphate and carbonate from living and fossil marine organisms. *Nature*, **211**, 923–927.

Longinelli, A., 1969. Oxygen-18 variations in belemnite guards. *Earth Planet. Sci. Letters*, **7**, 209–212.

Longinelli, A. and H. Craig, 1967. Oxygen-18 variations in sulfate ions in sea water and saline lakes. *Science*, **156**, 56–59.

Longinelli, A. and S. Nuti, 1968. Oxygen isotopic composition of phosphorites from marine formations. *Earth Planet. Sci. Letters*, **5**, 13–16.

Lowenstam, H. A., 1961. Mineralogy, O^{18}/O^{16} ratios, and strontium and magnesium contents of

Recent and fossil Brachiopods and their bearing on the history of the oceans. *J. Geol.*, **69**, 241–260.

Matsuo, S., I. Friedman, and G. I. Smith, 1972. Studies of Quaternary saline lakes—I. Hydrogen isotope fractionation in saline minerals. *Geochim. Cosmochim. Acta*, **36**, 427–435.

Mizutani, Y. and T. A. Rafter, 1969a. Oxygen isotope composition of sulphates—Part III. Oxygen isotopic fractionation in bisulphate-water system. *N.Z.J. Sci.*, **12**, 54–59.

Mizutani, Y. and T. A. Rafter, 1969b. Oxygen isotopic composition of sulphates—Part IV. Bacterial fractionation of oxygen isotopes in the reduction of sulphate and in the oxidation of sulphur. *N.Z.J. Sci.*, **12**, 60–68.

Mook, W. G. and J. C. Vogel, 1968. Isotopic equilibrium between shells and their environment. *Science*, **159**, 874–875.

Mopper, K. and G. D. Garlick, 1971. Oxygen isotope fractionation between biogenic silica and ocean water. *Geochim. Cosmochim. Acta*, **35**, 1185–1187.

Muehlenbachs, K. and R. N. Clayton, 1971. Oxygen isotope ratios of submarine diorites and their constituent minerals. *Can. J. Earth Sci.*, **8**, 1591–1595.

Muehlenbachs, K. and R. N. Clayton, 1972a. Oxygen isotope studies of fresh and weathered submarine basalts. *Can. J. Earth Sci.*, **9**, 172–184.

Muehlenbachs, K. and R. N. Clayton, 1972b. Oxygen isotope geochemistry of submarine greenstones. *Can. J. Earth Sci.*, **9**, 471–478.

Northrop, D. A. and R. N. Clayton, 1966. Oxygen-isotope fractionations in systems containing dolomite. *J. Geol.*, **74**, 174–196.

Oana, S. and E. S. Deevey, 1960. C^{13} in lake waters and its possible bearing on paleolimnology. *Amer. J. Sci.*, **258A**, 253–272.

Oehler, D. Z., J. W. Schopf, and K. A. Kvenvolden, 1972. Carbon isotopic studies of organic matter in Precambrian rocks. *Science*, **175**, 1246–1248.

O'Neil, J. R., 1968. Hydrogen and oxygen isotope fractionation between ice and water. *J. Phys. Chem.*, **72**, 3683–3684.

O'Neil, J. R. and L. H. Adami, 1969. The oxygen isotope partition function ratio of water and the structure of liquid water. *J. Phys. Chem.*, **73**, 1553–1558.

O'Neil, J. R., R. N. Clayton, and T. K. Mayeda, 1969. Oxygen isotope fractionation on divalent metal carbonates. *J. Chem. Phys.*, **51**, 5547–5558.

O'Neil, J. R. and S. Epstein, 1966a. A method for oxygen isotope analysis of milligram quantities of water and some of its applications. *J. Geophys. Res.*, **71**, 4955–4961.

O'Neil, J. R. and S. Epstein, 1966b. Oxygen isotope fractionation in the system dolomite-calcite-carbon dioxide. *Science*, **152**, 198–201.

O'Neil, J. R. and H. P. Taylor, 1967. The oxygen isotope and cation exchange chemistry of feldspars. *Am. Mineral.*, **52**, 1414–1437.

O'Neil, J. R. and H. P. Taylor, 1969. Oxygen isotope equilibrium between muscovite and water. *J. Geophys. Res.*, **74**, 6012–6022.

Park, R. and S. Epstein, 1960. Carbon isotope fractionation during photosynthesis. *Geochim. Cosmochim. Acta*, 21, 110–126.

Perry, E. C. and F. C. Tan, 1972a. Significance of oxygen and carbon isotope variations in early Precambrian cherts and carbonate rocks of southern Africa. *Bull. Geol. Soc. Amer.*, **83**, 647–664.

Perry, E. C. and F. C. Tan, 1972b. Significance of carbon isotope variations in carbonates from the Biwabik iron-formation. *Proc. Soc. Ec. Geol.*, November 1972.

Redfield, A. C. and I. Friedman, 1969. The effect of meteoric water, melt water and brine on the composition of polar sea water and of the deep waters of the ocean. *Deep-Sea Res.*, **16**, 197–214.

Rubinson, M. and R. N. Clayton, 1969. Carbon-13 fractionation between aragonite and calcite. *Geochim. Cosmochim. Acta*, **33**, 997–1002.

Sackett, W. M., W. R. Eckelmann, M. L. Bender, and A. W. H. Be, 1965. Temperature dependence of carbon isotope composition in marine plankton and sediments. *Science*, **148**, 235–237.

Sackett, W. M. and R. R. Thompson, 1963. Isotopic organic carbon composition of Recent continental derived clastic sediments of eastern gulf coast, Gulf of Mexico. *Bull. Am. Assoc. Petrol. Geologists*, **47**, 525–531.

Savin, S. M. Oxygen and hydrogen isotope studies of minerals in ocean sediments. *Proceedings of Int. Symp. Hydrogeochem. and Biogeochem.*, Tokyo, 1970. In press.

Savin, S. M. and R. G. Douglas. Stable isotope and magnesium geochemistry of Recent planktonic foraminifera from the South Pacific. *Bull. Geol. Soc. Am.* In press.

Savin, S. M. and S. Epstein, 1970a. The oxygen and hydrogen isotope geochemistry of clay minerals. *Geochim. Cosmochim. Acta*, **34**, 25–42.

Savin, S. M. and S. Epstein, 1970b. The oxygen and hydrogen isotope geochemistry of ocean sediments and shales. *Geochim. Cosmochim. Acta*, **34**, 43–63.

Savin, S. M. and S. Epstein, 1970c. The oxygen isotopic compositions of coarse grained sedimentary rocks and minerals. *Geochim. Cosmochim. Acta*, **34**, 323–329.

Schwarcz, H. P., 1969. The stable isotopes of carbon. In *Handbook of Geochemistry*. Vol. 2. K. H. Wedepohl, ed. Springer-Verlag, Berlin, GB1-15.

Shackleton, N., 1967. Oxygen isotope analyses and Pleistocene temperatures reassessed. *Nature*, **215**, 15–17.

Sheppard, S. M. F. and S. Epstein, 1970. D/H and $^{18}O/^{16}O$ ratios of minerals of possible mantle or lower crustal origin. *Earth Planet. Sci. Letters*, **9**, 232–239.

Sheppard, S. M. F., R. L. Nielsen, and H. P. Taylor, 1971. Hydrogen and oxygen isotope ratios in minerals from porphyry copper deposits. *Econ. Geol.*, **66**, 515–542.

Silverman, S. R., 1951. The isotopic geology of oxygen. *Geochim. Cosmochim. Acta*, **2**, 26–42.

Silverman, S. R. and S. Epstein, 1958. Carbon isotopic compositions of petroleums and other sedimentary organic materials. *Bull. Amer. Ass. Petrol. Geol.*, **42**, 998–1012.

Smith, B. N. and S. Epstein, 1971. Two categories of $^{13}C/^{12}C$ ratios for higher plants. *Plant Physiol.*, **47**, 380–384.

Smith, P. B. and C. Emiliani, 1968. Oxygen-isotope analysis of Recent tropical Pacific benthonic foraminifera. *Science*, **160**, 1335–1336.

Spaeth, C., J. Hoefs, and U. Vetter, 1971. Some aspects of isotopic composition of belemnites and related paleotemperatures. *Geol. Soc. Am. Bull.*, **82**, 3139–3150.

Stevens, G. R. and R. N. Clayton, 1971. Oxygen isotope studies on Jurassic and Cretaceous belemnites from New Zealand and their biogeographic significance. *N.Z.J. Geol. Geophys.*, **14**, 829–897.

Suzuoki, T. and S. Epstein, 1970. Hydrogen isotope fractionation factors between muscovite, biotite, hornblende and water. *Trans. Amer. Geophys. Union*, **51**, 451.

Syers, J. K., S. L. Chapman, M. L. Jackson, R. W. Rex, and R. N. Clayton, 1968. Quartz isolation from rocks, sediments and soils for determination of oxygen isotopic composition. *Geochim. Cosmochim. Acta*, **32**, 1022–1025.

Tarutani, T., R. N. Clayton, and T. K. Mayeda, 1969. The effect of polymorphism and magnesium substitution on oxygen isotope fractionation between calcium carbonate and water. *Geochim. Cosmochim. Acta*, **33**, 987–996.

Taylor, H. P., 1968. The oxygen isotope geochemistry of igneous rocks. *Contr. Mineral. and Petrol.*, **19**, 1–71.

Tourtelot, H. A. and R. O. Rye, 1969. Distribution of oxygen and carbon isotopes in fossils of late Cretaceous age, western interior region of North America. *Bull. Geol. Soc. Am.*, **80**, 1903–1922.

Urey, H. C., 1947. The thermodynamic properties of isotopic substances. *J. Chem. Soc.*, 562–581.

Urey, H. C., H. A. Lowenstam, S. Epstein, and C. R. McKinney, 1951. Measurement of paleotemperatures of the upper Cretaceous of England, Denmark, and the southeastern United States. *Bull. Geol. Soc. Am.*, **62**, 399–416.

Vogel, J. C., P. M. Grootes, and W. G. Mook, 1970. Isotopic fractionation between gaseous and dissolved carbon dioxide. *Z. Phys.*, **230**, 225.

Weber, J. N., 1968. Fractionation of the stable isotopes of carbon and oxygen in calcareous marine invertebrates—the Asteroidea, Ophiuroidea and Crinoidea. *Geochim. Cosmochim. Acta*, 32, 33–70.

Weber, J. N. and P. Deines, 1971. Mass spectrometry. In *Modern Methods of Geochemical Analysis*. R. E. Wainerdi and E. A. Uken, eds. Plenum Press, New York, pp. 351–397.

Weber, J. N. and D. M. Raup, 1968. Comparison of $^{13}C/^{12}C$ and $^{18}O/^{16}O$ in the skeletal calcite of Recent and fossil echinoids. *J. Paleotol.*, **42**, 37–50.

Weber, J. N. and P. M. J. Woodhead, 1969. Factors affecting the carbon and oxygen isotopic composition of marine sediments—II. Heron Island, Great Garrier Reef, Australia. *Geochim. Cosmochim. Acta*, **33**, 19–38.

Weber, J. N. and P. M. J. Woodhead, 1971. Diurnal variations in the isotopic composition of dissolved inorganic carbon in seawater from coral reef environments. *Geochim. Cosmochim. Acta*, **35**, 891–902.

Weber, J. N. and P. M. J. Woodhead, 1972. Temperature dependence of oxygen-18 concentration in reef coral carbonates. *J. Geophys. Res.*, **77**, 463–473.

Wenner, D. B. and H. P. Taylor. Oxygen and hydrogen isotope studies of the serpentinization of ultramafic rocks in oceanic environments and continental ophiolite complexes. *Contrib. Mineral. and Petrol.* In press.

Yeh, H. and S. M. Savin, 1972. Rate of oxygen isotope exchange between clay minerals and sea water. *Abs. 21st Annual Clay Minerals Conference.*

13. KINETIC MODELS FOR THE EARLY DIAGENESIS OF NITROGEN, SULFUR, PHOSPHORUS, AND SILICON IN ANOXIC MARINE SEDIMENTS*

Robert A. Berner

1. Introduction

The ratio of particle mass and surface area to solution volume in natural marine sediments is large. As a consequence the composition of sediment pore solutions is a sensitive indicator of the reactions of minerals and organic matter (through microbial activity) with seawater. In a sense, the interstitial water of sediments is an idealized ocean where reaction rates are maximized. If equilibrium between seawater and solid constituents coming into contact with it can be achieved as predicted by the Sillén model (Sillén, 1961), then the "ocean" within sediments should be an equilibrium one. One of the major purposes of this chapter is to show that for several biogenic elements, that is, those contained in biological tissue (including hard parts), an equilibrium model is occasionally a very good approximation, but in most situations is insufficient. Equilibrium models predict in what direction reactions are proceeding, but what is needed, in addition, are kinetic models actually describing the reactions. In this way the assumption of equilibrium can be checked and nonequilibrium situations explained.

Of the major elements, some of the greatest concentration changes in marine interstitial waters during burial to depths of a few meters are exhibited by nitrogen, sulfur, phosphorus, and silicon, each of which is at least partly biogenic. The changes, except in the case of silicon, are due primarily to the decomposition of organic matter by microorganisms, and as a result, the greatest effects are found in sediments rich in organic matter, that is, anoxic sediments. The large changes are well beyond anyone's estimate of measurement error, and since depth in sediments is proportional to time, the data are amenable to kinetic interpretation. In this chapter theoretical kinetic models are presented for chemical reactions involving nitrogen, sulfur, phosphorus, and silicon, which take place within anoxic marine sediments during burial to depths of a few meters (i.e., early diagenesis). This chapter will indicate the usefulness of studying natural chemical reactions from a kinetic, rather than an a priori, equilibrium standpoint, and also point to the need for better models and for much more data by which to check them.

2. Theory

A. General

Because vertical gradients in porewater composition are in general much greater than lateral gradients, one can treat early diagenesis in terms of one-dimensional depth models (Berner, 1971). Thus, concentration is a function only of depth and time, which leads to the general expression:

$$\left(\frac{\partial C}{\partial t}\right)_x = \frac{dC}{dt} - \omega \frac{\partial C}{\partial x} \tag{1}$$

* Research supported at various stages by the John Simon Guggenheim Memorial Foundation, the Swiss Federal Institute for Water Resources and Water Pollution Control (EAWAG), and N.S.F. Grants GA-1441 and GA-30288x. I thank D. Thorstenson, A. Katz, and the Bermuda Biological Station for aid in data collection and W. Stumm, R. Siever, and L. K. Benninger for review of the manuscript. Additional helpful discussions were supplied by K. Wuhrmann and E. Sholkovitz.

where C = concentration of dissolved species (or solid species involved in reactions) in terms of mass per unit volume of porewater

x = depth measured positively downward from the sediment-water interface

t = time

$\omega = dx/dt$ = the net rate of sediment deposition (deposition minus compaction)

Strictly speaking, an additional advective term should be included in equation 1 for water velocity due to compaction. If compaction is included, equation 1 is modified to:

$$\left(\frac{\partial C}{\partial t}\right)_x = \frac{dC}{dt} - \left(\frac{\phi_x}{\phi}\right)\omega_x \frac{\partial C}{\partial x} \tag{1a}$$

where ϕ is sediment porosity and x refers to the shallowest depth where continuous upward flow of water from compaction is interrupted due to encountering bedrock, permeable sand layers, and so on. However, the term $(\phi_x/\phi)\omega_x$ is (except for the uppermost ~10 cm) generally within a factor of two of the average value of ω for the top few meters. For the purposes of the present study the average measured value of ω will be sufficiently accurate and equation 1 rather than equation 1a will be used.

The total derivative dC/dt as used here contains all processes affecting the concentration of a substance undergoing diagenesis except convection. Here, four processes will be considered. They are (1) diffusion, (2) rapid (equilibrium) adsorption and ion exchange, (3) organic matter decomposition by microorganisms, and (4) mineral precipitation and dissolution. Mathematically:

$$\frac{dC}{dt} = D\frac{\partial^2 C}{\partial x^2} - \frac{d\bar{C}}{dt} + \frac{dC}{dt_{\mathrm{biol}}} + \frac{dC}{dt_{\mathrm{min}}} \tag{2}$$

where D = diffusion coefficient for dissolved species *in the sediment*. This includes the effects of tortuosity and similar phenomena but *excludes* effects due to ion exchange or adsorption

$\bar{C}$ = concentration (in mass per unit volume of porewater) of species on the surfaces of solids that can interact rapidly with porewater through adsorption, desorption, and ion exchange

At ion exchange or adsorption equilibrium

$$\bar{C} = KC \tag{3}$$

where K = equilibrium constant times the ratio of concentrations (assumed constant) of major species undergoing ion exchange with the species under study (for further details, consult Berner, 1971, pp. 99–100).

From equation 3:

$$\frac{d\bar{C}}{dt} = K\frac{dC}{dt} \tag{4}$$

Substituting equation 4 into equation 2 and rearranging:

$$\frac{dC}{dt} = \frac{1}{(1+K)}\left[D\frac{\partial^2 C}{\partial x^2} + \frac{dC}{dt_{\mathrm{biol}}} + \frac{dC}{dt_{\mathrm{min}}}\right] \tag{5}$$

Finally, substitution of equation 5 into equation 1 yields:

$$(1+K)\left(\frac{dC}{dt}\right)_x = D\frac{\partial^2 C}{\partial x^2} - (1+K)\omega\frac{\partial C}{\partial x} + \frac{dC}{dt_{\mathrm{biol}}} + \frac{dC}{dt_{\mathrm{min}}} \tag{6}$$

For the general situation of fluctuating conditions at the sediment-water interface with time, solution of equation 6 is mathematically difficult so that for the purposes of this chapter only steady-state diagenesis, where $(\partial C/\partial t)_x = 0$, will be considered. This assumes a constant chemical environment at $x = 0$ over the time of deposition of the thickness of sediment under study. Since we are concerned here only with early diagenesis involving sediment thicknesses on the scale of tens of centimeters to a few meters, it is appropriate in many localities to assume steady state because of the relatively short period of time represented by the sediment. Thus, for steady state:

$$D\frac{\partial^2 C}{\partial x^2} - (1 + K)\omega\frac{\partial C}{\partial x} + \frac{dC}{dt_{\text{biol}}} + \frac{dC}{dt_{\text{min}}} = 0 \tag{7}$$

To greatly simplify solution of equation 7 it will be assumed throughout this chapter that K and D (as well as ω) are constant with depth. This is equivalent to assuming that there is no porosity change (compaction). Although, during early diagenesis some change in porosity does occur, the use of average values for K and D, over the depth interval studied, introduces negligible errors compared to errors resulting from other assumptions.

One factor ignored by the diagenetic equations is the phenomenon of sediment mixing by burrowing benthonic organisms (bioturbation). No attempt is made here to correct for this. Thus, equations 6 and 7 apply strictly only to areas and depths where bottom benthos are sparse or absent. This is the situation for anoxic sediments deposited in poorly aerated bottom waters where benthonic activity is severely restricted by the lack of dissolved oxygen in the overlying water. In anoxic sediments overlain by oxygenated waters the diagenetic equations apply only to sediment depths below the deepest level of effective bioturbation, that is, $x = 0$ only at this level. In addition bacterial decomposition is probably too rapid in the uppermost layers to be described by a simple one-stage decomposition model (Berner, 1972), so that, strictly speaking, the level where $x = 0$ should be located a few millimeters to a few centimeters (depending on the rate of deposition) below the sediment-water interface. This is true whether or not bioturbation is present.

B. *Organic Matter Decomposition*

The kinetics of organic matter decomposition in anoxic sediments by bacteria and other microorganisms is poorly understood. Nevertheless, in general the number of bacterial cells decrease rapidly with sediment depth (Kaplan and Rittenberg, 1963), and (at least for sulfate reduction) rates of decomposition correspondingly also decrease (Sorokin, 1962). Sorokin has demonstrated that in the case of sulfate reduction the rate decrease is caused by the depletion of metabolizable organic compounds. On this basis, and in the absence of more refined data such as Michaelis-Menten parameters (Dixon and Webb, 1964), a reasonable first approximation can be made. That is, that the overall rate of decomposition is first order with respect to the material undergoing decomposition:

$$\frac{dG}{dt} = -kG \tag{8}$$

where k = first-order rate constant

G = concentration (in mass per unit volume of porewater) of organic carbon that can be decomposed by the reaction or set of reactions under study. This material is referred to as potentially metabolizable organic carbon, or more briefly, G

G is not to be confused with either total organic carbon (including biologically refractory substances), total organic carbon undergoing decomposition through all reactions, or the actual compounds directly used by the individual microorganisms. Instead, it is the originally deposited organic carbon that, through various breakdown pathways, furnishes the actual compounds used by the bacteria. For the sake of clarification, consider the example of simultaneous sulfate reduction and ammonia formation in sediments. Assume that the sulfate-reducing bacteria use amino acids and simple sugars (this is not at all necessarily the true case) furnished to them by the breakdown of long chain polysaccharides and proteins by other microorganisms. As a result they produce both H_2S and ammonia. Also assume that a separate set of bacteria reduce amino acids to ammonia with the amino acids having been furnished to them by the breakdown of proteins. Thus, the overall situation is:

$$\text{proteins } (A) \longrightarrow \text{amino acids } (A) \longrightarrow NH_3$$
$$\text{proteins } (B) \longrightarrow \text{amino acids } (B) \xrightarrow[+SO_4^{2-}]{} H_2S + NH_3 + HCO_3^-$$
$$\text{polysaccharides} \longrightarrow \text{sugars} \xrightarrow[+SO_4^{2-}]{} H_2S + HCO_3^-$$

G for ammonia formation is simply the concentration of total decomposable protein carbon at any given time (protein A + protein B) whereas G for sulfate reduction is total decomposable polysaccharides plus that fraction of protein (protein B) that upon breakdown furnishes amino acids that are used by the sulfate-reducing bacteria to form H_2S and ammonia. Thus, the two processes are represented as:

$$\frac{dG_S}{dt} = -k_S G_S \tag{9}$$

$$\frac{dG_N}{dt} = -k_N G_N \tag{10}$$

where the subscripts S and N refer to sulfate reduction and ammonia formation respectively. Note that each reaction has a different value of k as well as G.

As can be seen, even by the simplified hypothetical decomposition scheme above, the assumption of simple first-order kinetics is crude. Mechanistically one is dealing with many different simultaneous reactions, many of which are probably not first order. In addition, sequential reactions undoubtedly occur as a result of changing organic source materials, changing redox potentials, and such processes as catabolic repression and inhibition (Stumm-Zollinger, 1966). Nevertheless, Wuhrmann (1964), for one, has demonstrated that although individual dissolved organic species may be decomposed by sewage bacteria according to zero-order kinetics, the decomposition of total organic carbon, as a result of *sequential zero-order reactions*, is essentially exponential, that is, first order. Also, as will be shown in this chapter, the assumption of first-order kinetics leads to useful and internally consistent results when more than one element is considered.

In order to describe the formation of dissolved phosphate and ammonia by organic matter decomposition, two additional parameters must be defined. They are the mole ratio (to carbon) of nitrogen (α_N) and phosphorus (α_P) associated with G. The resulting kinetic expressions for ammonia and phosphate formation are:

$$\frac{dC}{dt_{\text{biol }(NH_3)}} = -\alpha_N \frac{dG_N}{dt} = \alpha_N k_N G_N \tag{11}$$

$$\frac{dC}{dt_{\text{biol }(PO_4)}} = -\alpha_P \frac{dG_P}{dt} = \alpha_P k_P G_P \tag{12}$$

C. Mineral Precipitation and Dissolution

For mineral precipitation or dissolution in a sediment an appropriate expression (Munk and Riley, 1952; Nielsen, 1964; Berner, 1971) is:

$$\frac{dC}{dt_{\text{min}}} = \frac{\phi N \bar{A} D(C_s - C)}{d} \tag{13}$$

where d = average size (cube edge length, disc diameter, sphere diameter) of precipitating or dissolving particles

$\bar{A}$ = surface area of precipitating or dissolving particles per unit volume of porewater

C_s = concentration of the dissolved species in the pore solution layer adjacent to the surface of the particles

C = concentration out in the pore solution

ϕ = sediment porosity expressed as a fraction

N = the Nusselt number, a dimensionless parameter that is a function of the geometry, size, and flow characteristics of water past the particles

To simplify calculation and enable application of laboratory results to sediment studies, the parameter E is defined as

$$E = \frac{\phi N \bar{A} D}{d}$$

Equation 13 is strictly valid for a sediment only if the particles undergoing reaction are equal sized and greater than about 10 diameters apart (Nielsen, 1964). However, for the purposes of the present chapter acceptable errors result if sizes vary within one order of magnitude and if the particles are greater than five diameters apart. For a surficial sediment with a typical water content of 75% by wet weight ($\phi = 0.85$), this corresponds to roughly 6% reacting particles by dry weight.

In fine-grained sediments water flow rates are sufficiently slow that the value for N corresponding to zero flow (resting Nusselt number) can be used. Resting values of N are from Munk and Riley (1952): $N = 2$ for spheres; $N = 8/\pi$ for flat circular discs. The value of C_s depends on whether the mineral dissolves or precipitates rapidly. If precipitation or dissolution are sufficiently rapid, the rate limiting step is simply diffusion of material toward or away from the particles. In this case $C_s = C_{\text{eq}}$, the value for saturation equilibrium, and the process is referred to as being diffusion controlled. If the rate limiting step is the attachment or detachment of ions and molecules at the particle surface, as is the case in slow growth or dissolution, C_s must be intermediate between C and C_{eq} and must change at some stage during reaction and approach C_{eq} as equilibrium is achieved. In this case the process is referred to as being surface reaction controlled. By way of clarification the two mechanisms are illustrated and compared in Fig. 1.

A special case of surface reaction controlled dissolution is the situation where a mineral dissolves incongruently, leaving a layer of solid decomposition product on the surface of the mineral. Here the rate of dissolution is controlled by solid-state diffusion through the layer. The layer may show a discontinuous change in composition at its interface with the host mineral or may continually grade in composition from the interface with the mineral to the interface with the solution (Luce et al., 1971). In either case a different expression from equation 13 results. In its place we have for

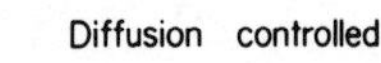

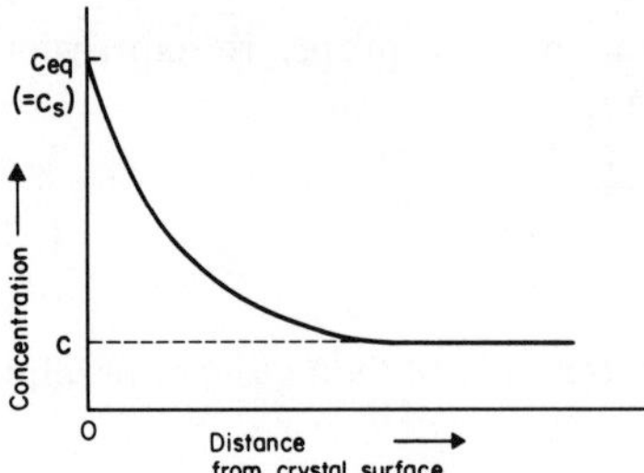

Surface reaction controlled

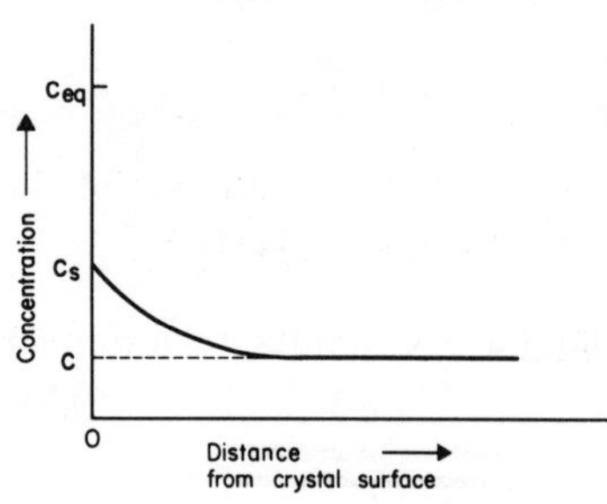

Fig. 1. Comparison of diffusion-controlled and surface reaction-controlled dissolution. In diffusion-controlled dissolution, detachment of ions from the crystal surface is rapid enough to maintain saturation C_{eq} at the surface of the solid, whereas in surface reaction-controlled dissolution the surface concentration C_s is less than C_{eq} because of slow detachment of ions from the surface. Analogous reasoning applies to precipitation.

incongruent dissolution with the formation of a protective surface layer:

$$\frac{dC}{dt_{\min}} = \bar{A}Lt^{-1/2} \tag{14}$$

where L = a constant characteristic of the mineral including terms for the solid-state diffusion coefficient within and the chemical potential difference across the surface layer (for details see Luce et al., 1972)

Equation 14 is based on a one-dimensional model that is valid only if the surface layer is very thin relative to the dimensions of the host grain.

3. Specific Models

A. Nitrogen

Nitrogen exhibits a number of different oxidation states in natural waters. The principal ones are +5 (NO_3^-), +3 (NO_2^-), 0 (N_2), and −3 ($NH_3 + NH_4^+$). Under the conditions existing in the porewaters of fully anoxic marine sediments the principle species are N_2 and NH_4^+ (Thorstenson, 1970; Rittenberg et al., 1955). The lack of nitrate and nitrite is due to rapid bacterial reduction to N_2 and NH_4^+. Unfortunately, little is known about the distribution of dissolved N_2 in porewaters because of difficulties in extraction (Reeburgh, 1967). Therefore, the discussion here will be confined to a discussion of dissolved ammonia.

Ammonia is produced in anoxic sediments for the most part by the decomposition of organic nitrogen compounds (a very minor amount can also come from nitrate reduction). It is not precipitated to form discrete minerals, as is phosphate, nor is there any firm evidence that it is oxidized to N_2, nitrate, or nitrite in the absence of dissolved oxygen. Thus, the steady-state diagenetic equation for ammonia includes terms only for diffusion, adsorption and ion exchange (as NH_4^+), convection, and organic matter decomposition. From equations 7 and 11:

$$D\frac{\partial^2 C}{\partial x^2} - (1 + K)\omega\frac{\partial C}{\partial x} + \alpha_N k_N G_N = 0 \tag{15}$$

where C represents the total concentration of all ammonia species (mainly NH_4^+). If G_N (which represents mainly proteinaceous matter) is nondiffusable, we also have at steady state:

$$-\omega\frac{\partial G_N}{\partial x} - k_N G_N = 0 \tag{16}$$

Solution of equations 15 and 16 for the boundary conditions:

$$\begin{array}{ll} x = 0 & x \to \infty \\ C \approx 0 & C \to C_\infty \\ G_N = G_{N,0} & G_N \to 0 \end{array}$$

for constant ω and D yields:

$$G_N = G_{N,0}\exp\left(-\frac{k_N}{\omega}x\right) \tag{17}$$

$$C = \frac{\alpha_N G_{N,0}\omega^2}{Dk_N + (1 + K)\omega^2}\left[1 - \exp\left(-\frac{k_N}{\omega}x\right)\right] \tag{18}$$

A plot of dissolved ammonia versus depth is shown in Fig. 2 for a core taken from the black, polluted, highly reducing sediments of a small, deep depression in Somes Sound, Maine. For comparison, the distribution of sulfate with depth is included. Equation 18 can be fitted to the ammonia data, as shown in Fig. 2, and as a result:

$$\frac{k_N}{\omega} = 2 \times 10^{-2}/\text{cm} \tag{19}$$

$$\frac{\alpha_N G_{N,0}\omega^2}{Dk_N + (1 + K)\omega^2} = C_\infty = 1.5 \times 10^{-5}\ \text{mol/cm}^3 \tag{20}$$

Unfortunately, the values for α_N, $G_{N,0}$, K, and ω are not known for this sediment, but reasonable estimates can be made. For a rapidly filling depression located in a polluted estuary into which flows no major streams, a reasonable order of magnitude value for ω is 2 cm/yr or 7×10^{-8} cm/sec. This relatively high value is reflected in the low degree of compaction of the sediment, which contains about 80% water (wet weight) from top to bottom, and is verified by the sulfate and sulfide data discussed in the following section.

The concentration of total organic carbon at the top of the sediment column is about 4% by dry weight. At 80% water this is equivalent to 8.3×10^{-4} mol of total organic carbon per cubic centimeter of porewater. Emery (1960) indicates that the ratio of total organic nitrogen to total organic carbon in the uppermost portions of anoxic marine sediments is about 0.12. Therefore, the concentration of total organic nitrogen at the top of the Somes Sound core should be about 10^{-4} mol/cm^3. Data for organic nitrogen in a core from the Santa Barbara Basin (see Table I) indicate that at least one-third of the originally deposited organic nitrogen is destroyed by microorganisms during burial. On this basis, let us assume as a reasonable rough estimate

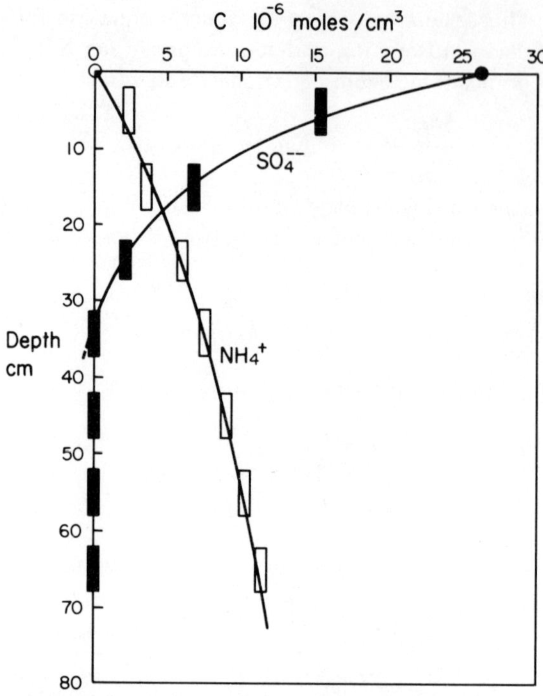

Fig. 2. Concentrations of dissolved sulfate and ammonia in a sediment core from a small depression in Somes Sound, Maine. Data from Berner et al. (1970). Data are fitted by the expressions SO_4^{2-}: $C = 28 \times 10^{-6} \exp(-0.10x) - 2 \times 10^{-6}$ and NH_4^+: $C = 15 \times 10^{-6}[1 - \exp(-0.02x)]$, where C is in moles/cm³.

that two-thirds of the total organic nitrogen in the Somes Sound sediment is metabolizable. On this basis:

$$\alpha_N G_{N,0} = 6.7 \times 10^{-5} \text{ mol/cm}^3$$

TABLE I

Organic nitrogen in a core taken from the sediments of the Santa Barbara Basin, California. Metabolizable organic nitrogen is assumed to be two-thirds of total organic nitrogen at $x = 0$. Data from Rittenberg et al. (1955)

Depth (cm)	Total N (% Dry Weight)	Metabolizable N (% Dry Weight)	Water (% Dry Weight)	$\alpha_N G_N$ (10^{-6} mol/cm³)
1–15	0.344	0.234	328	51
15–30	0.336	0.228	206	82
30–46	0.347	0.237	182	93
61–76	0.317	0.207	177	84
91–107	0.314	0.204	155	94
122–137	0.290	0.180	151	85
153–168	0.271	0.161	132	87
183–198	0.218	0.108	112	69

Severe limits on the value of K can be placed. From equation 20:

$$D = \frac{\omega^2}{k_N}\left[\frac{\alpha_N G_{N,0}}{C_\infty} - (1 + K)\right] \tag{21}$$

For D to be a positive number:

$$(1 + K) < \frac{\alpha_N G_{N,0}}{C_\infty} \tag{22}$$

This is equivalent to saying that the dissolved plus adsorbed ammonia nitrogen cannot exceed the originally deposited organic nitrogen. From the above values:

$$K < 3.5 \tag{23}$$

Here, a reasonable value, $K = 2.5$, is assumed.

Substitution of the above estimation for $\alpha_N G_{N,0}$, K, and ω into equations 19 and 20 yields:

$$k_N = 1.4 \times 10^{-9}\ \text{sec} \tag{24}$$

$$D = 3.5 \times 10^{-6}\ \text{cm}^2/\text{sec} \tag{25}$$

The value calculated for D is very reasonable for the diffusion coefficient of a singly charged ion (NH_4^+) diffusing in a sediment containing 80% water (Duursma, 1966). (Remember that retardation due to ion exchange is not included in D.) Therefore, considering all the crude estimates, the model predicts a diffusion coefficient that is of the correct order of magnitude.

A core taken from the anoxic sediments of the Santa Barbara Basin, California, by Rittenberg et al. (1955) provides additional data for the use and testing of equation 15.[1] Data are shown in Fig. 3 and Table I. From these data it can be demonstrated that organic nitrogen shows essentially no change with depth when expressed in terms of mass per unit volume of porewater. This does not mean that organic nitrogen is not being destroyed, but only that the decrease in organic nitrogen is matched by a decrease in water content due to compaction. About one-third of the originally deposited organic nitrogen has been decomposed during burial to 200 cm. Thus, $\alpha_N G_{N,0}$ is at least one-third the value for total organic nitrogen at the sediment surface. A reasonable estimate is that $\alpha_N G_{N,0}$ equals two-thirds the surface value. On this basis values of $\alpha_N G_N$ are plotted in the last column of Table I. Note that except for the top and bottom samples, values of $\alpha_N G_N$ are also essentially constant with depth. Since the rate of ammonia formation through equation 11 is directly proportional to $\alpha_N G_N$, these data suggest that the rate of formation is constant over the depth interval sampled. In this case we are dealing with pseudozero-order kinetics, and as a result we obtain a different solution of equation 15. It is:

$$C = A\left[\exp\left(\frac{(1 + K)\omega}{D}x\right) - 1\right] + \frac{\alpha_N k_N G_N}{(1 + K)\omega}x \tag{26}$$

The parameter A is a constant of integration that can be evaluated by curve fitting. For the Santa Barbara Basin core the data for dissolved ammonia are fitted well by a straight line, as shown in Fig. 3. If the data are truly linear, then $A = 0$, so that

$$C = \frac{\alpha_N k_N G_N}{(1 + K)\omega}x \tag{27}$$

[1] This core is not assumed to be necessarily representative of all of Santa Barbara Basin sediments and is probably not (E. Sholkovitz, personal communication).

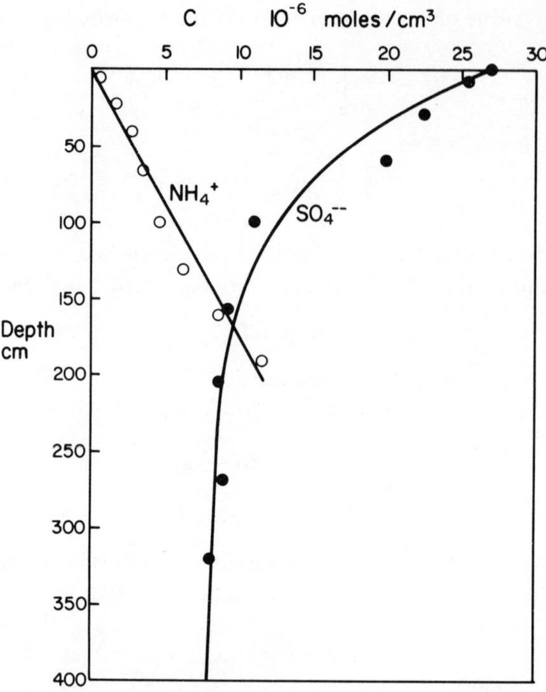

Fig. 3. Concentrations of dissolved sulfate and ammonia in sediment cores from the deeper portion of the Santa Barbara Basin. Data from Rittenberg et al. (1955) and Kaplan et al. (1963). Data are fitted by the expressions $SO_4^{2-}: C = 19 \times 10^{-6} \exp(-0.015x) + 8 \times 10^{-6}$ and $NH_4^+: C = 5.7 \times 10^{-8}x$, where C is in moles/cm³.

Thus, equation 27 can be easily fitted to the data that further supports the suggestion of pseudozero-order kinetics. From the data of Fig. 3

$$\frac{\alpha_N k_N G_N}{(1 + K)\omega} = 5.7 \times 10^{-8}\ \text{mol/cm}^4 \tag{28}$$

From Table 1, $\alpha_N G_N = 8.5 \times 10^{-5}$ mol/cm³. Using this value and $K = 3$ and $\omega = 5 \times 10^{-9}$ cm/sec (based on radiocarbon dating and varve counts cited by Emery, 1960), substitution into equation 28 yields

$$k_N = 1.3 \times 10^{-11}\ \text{sec} \tag{29}$$

This is about 100 times lower than the value obtained for Somes Sound, which demands an explanation.

The sediment core from the Santa Barbara Basin was deposited about one-tenth as slowly as the sediment core from the small depression in Somes Sound. Considerable differences in rate of deposition show up as considerable differences in degree of compaction. Water is uniform at about 80% in the Somes Sound sediment whereas over the same depth interval it changes from 80 to 60% in the Santa Barbara Basin sediment. In addition, the Maine sediments show evidence of organic pollution due to discharge of sewage from nearby large campgrounds. Both situations should cause the *type* of organic nitrogen compounds buried below the sediment-water interface to differ. Organic pollution plus rapid deposition should enable more compounds that are easily decomposed to ammonia to be buried without destruction in the overlying water. This should cause the value of k_N for the Somes Sound sediment to be much higher than that for the Santa Barbara Basin where Emery (1960) has shown that much of the organic nitrogen is destroyed prior to burial. Furthermore, the finding of a much smaller k_N value for the Santa Barbara Basin is in qualitative agreement with the results of the next section, where k_S for sulfate reduction in sediments of the Santa Barbara Basin is ~75 times lower than k_S for Somes Sound sediment.

B. Sulfur

Like nitrogen, sulfur occurs in a number of oxidation states in natural waters although only two are of major importance. They are +6 (SO_4^{2-}) and −2 (HS^-, H_2S). In the waters of anoxic sediments all three are present, with sulfate usually the most abundant. This is partly because dissolved sulfide species are to a large extent precipitated to form iron sulfide minerals, mainly pyrite. The sulfide species, which are absent in oxic waters, are produced in anoxic marine sediments almost entirely by the bacterial reduction of sulfate ion (e.g., Berner, 1972). A very generalized reaction exemplifying the overall stoichiometry (i.e., including all individual fermentation steps) is:

$$2\,CH_2O + SO_4^{2-} \rightarrow H_2S + 2\,HCO_3^-$$

In this reaction two atoms of organic carbon are utilized to reduce one atom of sulfate. If organic sources other than carbohydrate are used, the stoichiometry can vary somewhat, but the overall reaction does not differ greatly from two carbon atoms to one sulfur atom. As pointed out earlier (Sorokin, 1962), the sulfate reducers do not directly use long chain molecules such as polysaccharides, but instead metabolize small molecules produced by other microorganisms. Thus, k_S and G_S for sulfate reduction include the activity of other microorganisms and cannot be directly compared with results obtained in the laboratory for pure bacterial cultures and simple growth media.

Sulfate ion in sediments of normal salinity is not involved in quantitatively important precipitation or dissolution reactions, nor does it undergo appreciable ion exchange. Thus, the processes affecting its concentration in anoxic sediments are diffusion, convection, and bacterial sulfate reduction. The steady-state diagenetic equation from equation 7 with $K = 0$ is, accordingly:

$$D\frac{\partial^2 C}{\partial x^2} - \omega\frac{\partial C}{\partial x} + \frac{dC}{dt_{\text{biol}}} = 0 \tag{30}$$

where C now represents the concentration of dissolved sulfate present both as free ions and ion pairs. Now, from the above discussion and equation 8:

$$\frac{dC}{dt_{\text{biol}}} = \frac{1}{2}\frac{dG_S}{dt} = \frac{-k_S G_S}{2} \tag{31}$$

where G_S stands for organic carbon that can be ultimately used for sulfate reduction. If G_S is nondiffusible we have, as in the case of nitrogen:

$$-\omega\frac{\partial G_S}{\partial x} - k_S G_S = 0 \tag{32}$$

Solution of equations 30 to 32 for the boundary conditions:

$x = 0$	$x \rightarrow \infty$
$C = C_0$ (concentration in overlying water)	$C \rightarrow C_\infty$
$G_S = G_{S,0}$	$G_S \rightarrow 0$

yields:

$$C = (C_0 - C_\infty) \exp\left(\frac{-k_S}{\omega} x\right) + C_\infty \tag{33}$$

$$C_0 - C_\infty = \frac{\omega^2 G_{S,0}}{2(\omega^2 + Dk_S)} \tag{34}$$

$$G_S = G_{S,0} \exp\left(\frac{-k_S}{\omega} x\right) \tag{35}$$

Tests of the above equations have already been made (Berner, 1972) for a sediment core from the Santa Barbara Basin and for several cores from the Black Sea. For the Santa Barbara Basin, using (as with ammonia) $\omega = 5 \times 10^{-9}$ cm/sec and $G_{S,0} = 2.5 \times 10^{-4}$ mol/cm^3 and fitting equations 33 and 34 to the sulfate data of Fig. 3, we obtain:

$$k_S = 7.5 \times 10^{-11}/\text{sec} \tag{36}$$

$$D = 2 \times 10^{-6}\ \text{cm}^2/\text{sec} \tag{37}$$

The calculated value for D is in good agreement with recent laboratory measurements of the diffusion of sulfate in natural sediments (Y. H. Li, personal communication). In addition, the model, when applied to the sediments of the Black Sea deep basin, correctly predicts the approximate rate of sulfate reduction and its change with depth, as measured by Sorokin (1962).

From Fig. 2 and the ω value previously used for the Somes Sound sediment, further applications of the sulfate model can be made. Assuming that D for sulfate is the same as in the Santa Barbara Basin sediments, one obtains, by fitting equations 33 and 34 to the sulfate data for Somes Sound (Fig. 2):

$$k_S = 5.6 \times 10^{-9}/\text{sec} \tag{38}$$

$$G_{S,0} = 1.8 \times 10^{-4}\ \text{mol/cm}^3\ (0.8\%\ \text{C by dry weight}) \tag{39}$$

The calculated value for $G_{S,0}$ is reasonable and less than the value for total carbon as it must be. A check on it is provided by the iron sulfide content of the sediments. Here, due to precipitation as iron sulfide, very little dissolved sulfide has accumulated in solution, as indicated by sulfide electrode measurements. This means that little has diffused out of the sediments and that the concentration of sulfur present as iron sulfide at the depth where sulfate disappears represents the total sulfate reduced since deposition. This, in turn, according to the model, is equal to one-half the value of $G_{S,0}$. The measured value for sulfide sulfur is $1.25 \pm 0.1\%$ by dry weight, which corresponds to $G_{S,0} = 2.0 \times 10^{-4}$ mol/cm^3. This value agrees very well with the value calculated above. In fact, this agreement supports the validity of the value assumed for the rate of deposition ω of the Somes Sound sediment both in the models for sulfate and for ammonia.

One might argue that sulfate reduction in the Somes Sound sediment is limited by the concentration of sulfate (and, therefore, a function of it) because all sulfate disappears at a shallow depth. In this case an organic matter controlled rate model as used here would be incorrect. However, recent work by L. K. Benninger (personal communication) has shown that in organic-rich sediments the rate of reduction of sulfate is independent of the concentration of sulfate, at least down to 1.2×10^{-6} mol/cm^3. Thus, equation 33 can be justifiably fitted to the sulfate curve of Fig. 2 down to the point where sulfate disappears.

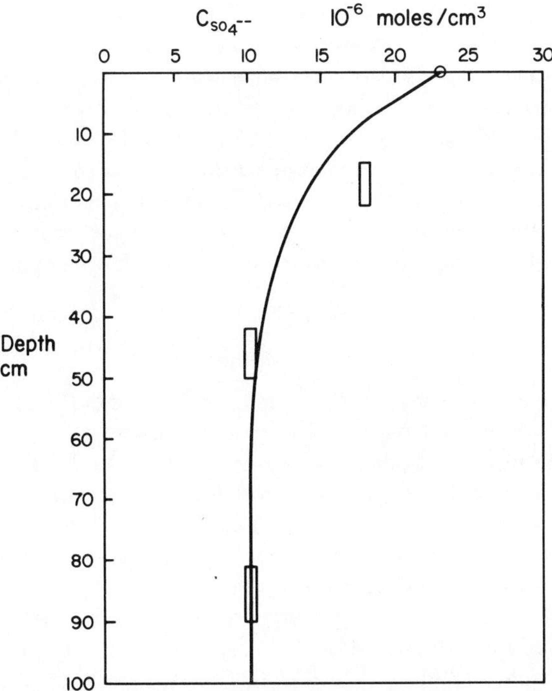

Fig. 4. Concentration of dissolved sulfate in a sediment core from a depression near the central Connecticut coast of Long Island Sound. Data are fitted by the expression $C = 13 \times 10^{-6} \exp(-0.06x) + 10 \times 10^{-6}$ where C is in moles/cm^3.

A third sediment core from the central Connecticut coast of Long Island Sound (Fig. 4) can also be used to obtain values for k_S and $G_{S,0}$. The sediment has a high, uniform water content ($\sim 75\%$) and is located in a near-shore, rapidly filling depression. For this area a reasonable estimate for ω is 1 cm/yr or 3×10^{-8} cm/sec (K. K. Turekian, personal communication). From this value and the sulfate data of Fig. 4:

$$k_S = 1.8 \times 10^{-9}/\text{sec} \tag{40}$$

$$G_{S,0} = 1.3 \times 10^{-4}\ \text{mol/cm}^3\ (0.62\%\ \text{C by dry weight}) \tag{41}$$

As in the Somes Sound sediment, these values appear to be reasonable.

Constructing a model for dissolved sulfide is very difficult for two reasons. First, the kinetics of the precipitation of sulfide as iron sulfide are exceedingly complicated (Berner, 1970) and certainly not a simple diffusion-controlled mechanism. Second, there is no existing data for sulfide versus depth that is entirely trustworthy. This is because acidification is necessary to convert HS^- to H_2S so that all dissolved sulfide can be removed from the sediment (as H_2S gas) for analysis. During acidification ferric compounds that definitely persist in anoxic sediments (e.g., Strakhov, 1958) are partly dissolved and the liberated ferric ion immediately reacts with H_2S to form elemental sulfur, thus immobilizing it. This results in incorrectly low measured values for dissolved sulfide and accounts for the correlation of excess elemental sulfur with acidification (e.g., Nriagu, 1968; Berner, 1973). Acidification also causes the dissolution of black iron monosulfides, if present, which in the absence of ferric ion oxidation gives incorrectly high values for dissolved sulfide. One way around this problem is to use a sulfide ion electrode that is directly inserted into the sediment, but it is my experience that sulfide electrodes are only good for rough, order of magnitude work and do not give sufficiently stable readings necessary for more exact analytical determinations. Perhaps the best way around these problems would be to study sulfide formation in carbonate sediments that are sufficiently low in iron that ferric oxidation and iron sulfide formation are unimportant. In this case the model for sulfide formation would be simply the same as that for sulfate reduction, the only difference being the slight difference in the diffusion coefficients for sulfate and sulfide. This points to the need for data on dissolved sulfide, as well as sulfate, from low-iron carbonate sediments.

C. Phosphorus

At the redox conditions encountered in marine sediments the most stable and predominant form of dissolved phosphorus is orthophosphate, which is present mainly as ion pairs with the major cations of seawater (Kester and Pytkowicz, 1967). Phosphorus in oxidation states other than +5 is practically unknown in sediments. Therefore, unlike nitrogen and sulfur, it is not involved directly in redox reactions. Dissolved orthophosphate (hereafter referred to as phosphate) in oxic sediments shows little change from values for the overlying water (e.g., Fanning and Pilson, 1971). By contrast, in anoxic sediments large increases in phosphate occur (Rittenberg et al., 1955; Brooks et al., 1968) and the increases correlate with increases in ammonia and, to a lesser extent, sulfide.

Phosphate is released to anoxic porewaters by the decomposition of phosphorus-containing organic matter and by the reduction of hydrous ferric oxides that, under oxic conditions, bind phosphate onto their surfaces (Mackereth, 1966; Stumm and Leckie, 1971). Phosphate released by organic matter decomposition or iron reduction may be subsequently rapidly adsorbed on clay minerals (Chen, 1972) and precipitated as calcium phosphate once the solubility product of apatite, the least soluble form of calcium phosphate (Stumm and Morgan, 1970) is exceeded. If it is assumed that release of phosphate due to the reduction of ferric oxides is rapid and essentially complete prior to burial (W. Stumm, personal communication), the appropriate steady-state equation for anaerobic phosphate diagenesis from equations 7, 12, and 13 is:

$$D\frac{\partial^2 C}{\partial x^2} - (1 + K)\omega\frac{\partial C}{\partial x} + \alpha_P k_P G_P + E(C_s - C) = 0 \tag{42}$$

where C here represents the total concentration of all dissolved orthophosphate species. Also, for steady state, analogous to the models for nitrogen and sulfur:

$$-\omega\frac{\partial G_P}{\partial x} - k_P G_P = 0 \tag{43}$$

Solution of equations 42 and 43 for the boundary conditions:

$$\begin{array}{ll} x = 0 & x \to \infty \\ G_P = G_{P,0} & G_P \to 0 \\ C = C_0 \sim 0 & C \to C_s \end{array}$$

and for constant E and C_s (diffusion controlled precipitation) yields:

$$G_P = G_{P,0}\exp\left(\frac{-k_P}{\omega}x\right) \tag{44}$$

$$C = C_s + \left[\frac{\alpha_P k_P G_{P,0}\omega^2}{Dk_P^2 + (1 + K)\omega^2 k_P - E\omega^2} - C_s\right]$$
$$\times \exp\left\{\frac{(1 + K)\omega - [(1 + K)^2\omega^2 + 4ED]^{1/2}}{2D} x\right\}$$
$$- \left\{\frac{\alpha_P k_P G_{P,0}\omega^2}{Dk_P^2 + (1 + K)\omega^2 k_P - E\omega^2}\right\} \exp\left(\frac{-k_P}{\omega} x\right) \quad (45)$$

If all the parameters in equation 45 were known for a given sediment core, the model could be tested. Unfortunately, this is not the case. The major problem is the value of E. Independent laboratory measurements of E under simulated sedimentary conditions are not available and the value cannot be obtained by curve fitting because all the rest of the parameters are not known independently. To avoid this problem only two extreme situations are considered. They are (1) very rapid phosphate precipitation (high E) and (2) no phosphate precipitation ($E = 0$). In case 1 as $E \rightarrow \infty$, equation 45 reduces to

$$C = C_s \quad (46)$$

In other words, saturation with apatite is present at all depths. In case 2, as $E \rightarrow 0$, equation 45 reduces to:

$$C = \frac{\alpha_P \omega^2 G_{P,0}}{Dk_P + (1 + K)\omega^2}\left[1 - \exp\left(\frac{-k_P}{\omega} x\right)\right] \quad (47)$$

Leckie (1969) and Stumm and Leckie (1971) have demonstrated that the precipitation of calcium phosphate as apatite at marine pH values is greatly accelerated by calcium carbonate, the surface of which acts as a nucleating agent for crystallization. In the absence of calcium carbonate, high degrees of supersaturation can be maintained indefinitely. Thus, sediments high in calcium carbonate, especially when it is fine grained with a large specific surface area, should represent the most favorable situation for the achievement of case 1. I have found this to be true. Fine-grained sediments from Bermuda and South Florida, most of which contain greater than 95% $CaCO_3$, exhibit equilibrium with apatite at all depths. This is shown in Table II and Fig. 5. The solubility of apatite on the surface of the $CaCO_3$ grains is assumed to be the same as that measured by Roberson (1966) for natural marine phosphorite in seawater. Because of the variability in composition of natural apatite and the strong dependency of solubility upon composition, much of the scatter shown in Fig. 5 may be due to changes in composition.

Case 2, where no precipitation of calcium phosphate occurs, is best favored by sediments with low calcium carbonate content and/or low $CaCO_3$ specific surface area, where extensive supersaturation with respect to apatite can be maintained. The core of anoxic sediment from Long Island Sound to which the sulfate model was applied contains only a few percent $CaCO_3$ as coarse shell debris and, thus, may be a good example of this situation. A plot of dissolved phosphate concentration versus depth as I measured it, is shown in Fig. 6. Fitting equation 47 to the curve of Fig. 6 results in:

$$\frac{k_P}{\omega} = 0.3 \text{ cm}^{-1} \quad (48)$$

$$\frac{\alpha_P \omega^2 G_{P,0}}{Dk_P + (1 + K)\omega^2} = 6 \times 10^{-7} \text{ mol/cm}^3 \quad (49)$$

The value for ω used in the sulfate calculation, is 3×10^{-8} cm/sec. From the results

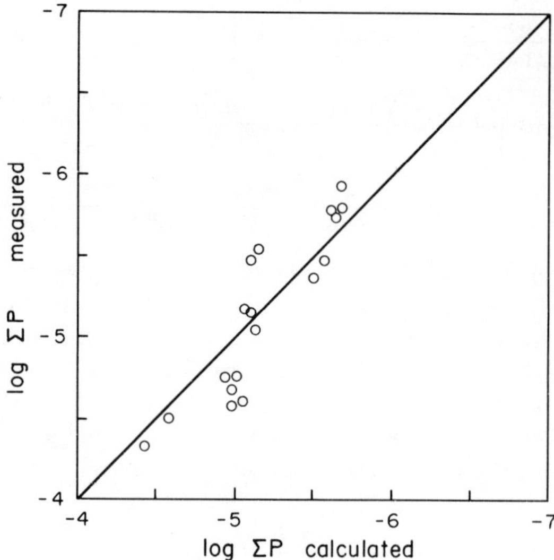

Fig. 5. Plot of logarithm of the molality of measured total dissolved (ortho) phosphate, $\sum P$, versus $\sum P$ calculated for equilibrium with apatite of marine phosphorite composition. Data from fine-grained carbonate sediments of Bermuda and Florida Bay. The straight line represents perfect agreement.

of Chen (1972), a reasonable value for the diffusion coefficient of orthophosphate species in a clay-rich marine sediment is $D = 1 \times 10^{-6}$ cm²/sec. From Chen's data also for marine clay an approximate value for the adsorption constant K for phosphate is (at 75% water content) $K = 8$. From the work of Burns and Ross (1972) a rough value for the mole ratio of phosphorus to carbon in organic matter undergoing anoxic decomposition is $\alpha_P = 0.014$. Using these values from equations 48 and 49 we obtain:

$$k_P = 9.5 \times 10^{-9}/\text{sec} \tag{50}$$

$$G_{P,0} = 7.9 \times 10^{-4}\ \text{mol/cm}^3\ (2.8\%\ \text{C by dry weight}) \tag{51}$$

The value of $G_{P,0}$ is not at all an unreasonable value for the topmost centimeters of rapidly depositing near-shore sediments of this area, as shown by the data of Berner (1970). Thus, considering all the rough assumptions of the model, it is amazing that the calculated value for $G_{P,0}$ is of the right order of magnitude.

The anoxic sediments of the Santa Barbara Basin contain ~10% $CaCO_3$ (Emery, 1960) and may represent another example of case 2. If so, the data of Rittenberg et al. (1955) shown in Fig. 6 can be fitted by a diagenetic equation to obtain values of k_P and $G_{P,0}$. Note that the phosphate curve is essentially linear with depth. This is reminiscent of the ammonia curve shown in Fig. 3. If the concentration of potentially metabolizable organic phosphorus $\alpha_P G_P$ is constant with depth, as is potentially metabolizable organic nitrogen, then phosphate production may also be pseudozero-order. On this assumption, the solution of equation 45 with $E = 0$ is:

$$C = A\left[\exp\left(\frac{(1+K)\omega}{D}x\right) - 1\right] + \frac{\alpha_P G_P k_P}{(1+K)\omega}x \tag{52}$$

If the curve is truly linear, then $A = 0$ so that:

$$C = \frac{\alpha_P G_P k_P}{(1+K)\omega}x \tag{53}$$

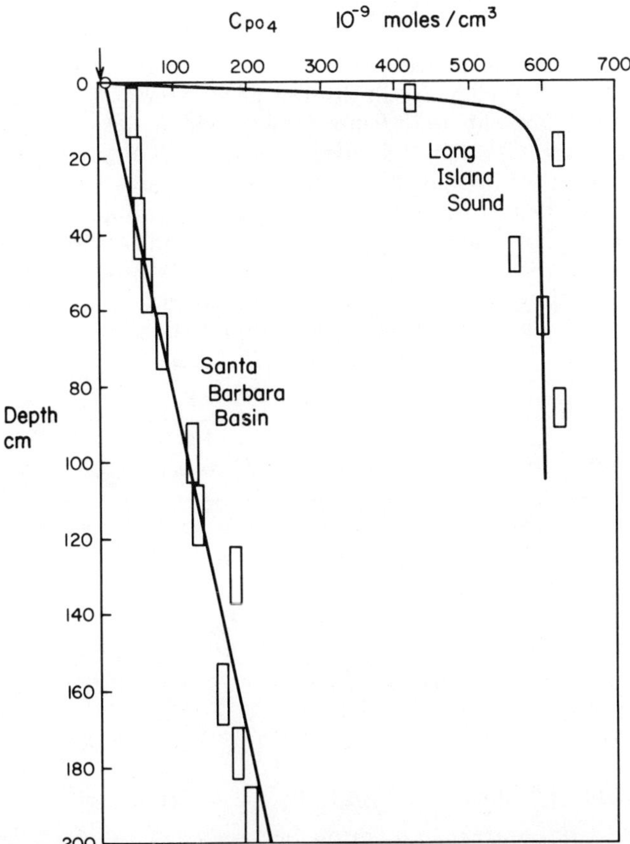

Fig. 6. Concentration of dissolved phosphate in sediment cores taken from the Santa Barbara Basin and Long Island Sound nearshore depression. Santa Barbara Basin data from Rittenberg et al. (1955). Data are fitted by the expressions S. B. Basin: $C = 1 \times 10^{-9}x$ and L. I. Sound: $C = 6 \times 10^{-7}[1 - \exp(-0.3x)]$, where C is in moles/cm³. The approximate value for apatite saturation is shown by the arrow.

Thus, from Fig. 6:

$$\frac{\alpha_P G_P k_P}{(1 + K)\omega} = 1 \times 10^{-9}\ \mathrm{mol/cm^4} \tag{54}$$

For the Santa Barbara Basin core, neither G_P nor k_P are known independently, but a reasonable first approximation is that the organic phosphorus/nitrogen ratio is the same as that for metabolizable organic matter undergoing decomposition in anoxic seawater, 0.06 (Redfield et al., 1963). If so:

$$\alpha_P G_P = 0.06\ \alpha_N G_N \tag{55}$$

As shown earlier in the discussion of nitrogen, $\alpha_N G_N = 8.5 \times 10^{-5}$ mol/cm³. Also, $\omega = 5 \times 10^{-9}$ cm/sec, and a reasonable value for K for phosphate adsorption from the data of Chen (1972) is $K = 8$. Substituting these values into equations 54 and 55 yields:

$$k_P = 9 \times 10^{-12}/\mathrm{sec} \tag{56}$$

This value is about 1000 times lower than the value obtained for the Long Island

TABLE II

Total dissolved orthophosphate ($\sum$ P) in fine-grained, anoxic, shallow water carbonate sediments. Phosphate in filtered porewater ($< 0.45\ \mu$m) determined by the method of Murphy and Riley (1962), which detects only "inorganic reactive" phosphate. Calculated saturation values ($\sum P_{calc}$) are based on solubility determinations for phosphorite nodules in seawater (Roberson, 1966), temperature dependence of K for hydroxyapatite (Kramer, 1964), dissociation constants for phosphoric acid in seawater (Kester and Pytkowicz, 1967) and in the standard state (Sillén, 1964), and measurements of chlorinity, *in situ* pH calcium concentration (EDTA titration), and fluoride concentration (specific ion electrode spike technique) (Berner)

		Molality			
Depth (cm)	pH	$100 \times Ca^{2+}$	$10^5 \times F^-$	$10^6 \times \sum P$ (calculated)	$10^6 \times \sum P$ (measured)
Bermuda, Ferry Reach mudflat (T = 25°C, S = 38‰)					
7–18	7.45	1.15	7.3	2.0	1.2
18–28	7.40	1.15	8.1	2.3	1.8
28–38	7.38	1.15	7.5	2.5	1.7
38–48	7.42	1.12	7.8	2.3	1.7
Bermuda, Devil's Hole (T = 21°C, S = 36‰)					
6–17	7.53	1.09	—	2.7	3.4
24–42	7.48	1.09	7.2	3.2	4.2
42–57	7.21	1.07	—	7.9	9.1
57–73	7.19	1.05	6.1	8.3	6.7
Bermuda, Mangrove Lake (T = 20°C, S = 29‰)					
440–450	6.85	0.80	—	26	32
707–715	6.73	0.82	—	38	48
Florida Bay, Florida (T = 23°C, S = 44‰)					
2–17	7.25	1.32	7.3	8.0	6.1
23–33	7.28	1.28	7.8	8.0	3.3
38–51	7.29	1.27	7.5	7.4	3.0
Florida Bay, Florida (T = 23°C, S = 40‰)					
2–10	7.19	1.30	7.9	10	18
17–30	7.13	1.29	8.1	12	19
42–51	7.15	1.22	8.3	11	21
55–65	7.16	1.20	8.1	11	26
70–80	7.18	1.18	7.5	9	25

Sound sediment core, but as in the case of ammonia, the explanation probably rests at least partly with the nature of the organic phosphorus compounds that become buried in the sediment. Much more easily decomposed compounds should be deposited in the Long Island Sound sediment due to a much higher depositional rate and the close proximity of the sediment to a heavily populated shoreline, which may result in a pollutive contribution to the sediment. (In a high polluted sediment from nearby New Haven Harbor, I have encountered porewater concentrations of phosphate exceeding 10^{-5} mol/cm^3 or 1000 ppm PO_4 in the top few centimeters.)

If the lower value for k_P in the Santa Barbara Basin core is not due to differences in phosphate-containing organic compounds, it may be the result of calcium phosphate precipitation, which means that equation 47 is incorrect and that the general equation 45 must be used. It is instructive that in the Tanner Basin located seaward from the Santa Barabara Basin, the sediments contain considerably more $CaCO_3$, $\sim 35\%$ (Emery, 1960), and the dissolved phosphate in a core from the anoxic sediments shows an even gentler slope with depth than in the Santa Barbara Basin core (Brooks et al., 1968). This suggests calcium phosphate precipitation, but phosphate data from greater depths are required before the precipitation hypothesis can be accepted. Equation 45 predicts the existence of a phosphate maximum that is not encountered over the depth range sampled.

D. Silicon

Silicon is not a quantitatively important component of organic matter, is present in only one oxidation state (+4), and is not appreciably affected by anaerobic bacterial metabolism; so only interactions with minerals will be considered here. Silicon in surficial sediments occurs in five fundamental mineral groups, all of which are of quantitative importance. They are (1) detrital quartz, (2) detrital aluminosilicates, principally clay minerals and feldspars, (3) opaline silica in the form of diatom, radiolarian, and sponge skeletal debris, (4) volcanic glass in various stages of hydration and devitrification, and (5) authigenic quartz and aluminosilicates such as montmorillonite and phillipsite. Since this chapter is concerned chiefly with anoxic sediments, which are often rich in diatom debris, emphasis will be placed on biogenic opaline silica and its reaction with seawater.

Opaline silica is much more rapidly reactive with seawater (at pH 7–8) than clay minerals, which in turn are much more rapidly reactive than quartz (e.g., compare the results of Hurd, 1972 with those of Mackenzie and Garrels, 1965). At the pH of marine sediments, dissolved silica occurs almost entirely as monomeric silicic acid H_4SiO_4, and its concentration invariably is higher in porewaters than in seawater (for a summary of earlier studies, see Fanning and Pilson, 1971). This means that the dominant reaction in sediments is silica dissolution, and because of its reactivity and high degree of undersaturation in seawater, opaline silica is a probable major contributor of the dissolved silica.[2] However, the fact that saturation with opaline silica is often not attained in the presence of excess dissolving solid means that reprecipitation must occur simultaneously with dissolution. The process of reprecipitation is not well understood, but the experiments of Mackenzie et al. (1967) and Siever (1968) strongly suggest adsorption on clay minerals. Because of a lack of rate data applicable to natural sediments, models involving adsorption will not be considered here. Nevertheless, it can be stated with some assurance that adsorption of silica on clays is slow (e.g., Mackenzie et al., 1967) so that fast equilibrium adsorption can be ignored in diagenetic models, which is equivalent to setting $K = 0$.

If silica in porewaters results solely from the dissolution of opaline silica, the appropriate steady-state diagenetic equation from equations 7 and 13 is, if $K = 0$:

$$D\frac{\partial^2 C}{\partial x^2} - \omega\frac{\partial C}{\partial x} + E(C_s - C) = 0 \tag{57}$$

[2] In sediments containing high concentrations of volcanic glass, which is also very reactive, the main source of dissolved silica may be the glass rather than opaline silica.

Solution for the boundary conditions:

$$\begin{array}{ll} x = 0 & x \to \infty \\ C = C_0 & C \to C_s \end{array}$$

yields for constant E and C_s (diffusion controlled dissolution):

$$C = C_s - (C_s - C_0) \exp \left\{ \left[\frac{\omega - (\omega^2 + 4ED)^{1/2}}{2D} \right] x \right\} \tag{58}$$

Equation 58 is valid only for sediments that contain enough opaline silica that dissolution involves loss of only a small proportion of the total amount (i.e., silica-rich sediments). Otherwise the surface $\bar{A}$ and size d will vary with depth, which negates the assumption of constant E.

The laboratory experiments of Hurd (1972) have demonstrated that during the dissolution of biogenic opaline silica in seawater $C_s = C_{eq}$; in other words the reaction is diffusion controlled. Comparison of calculated and measured surface areas, however, indicate that only a small proportion of the total external surface area (excluding perforations, shell interiors, etc.) is reactive. In general the rates were not affected by gentle stirring providing that unstirred particles did not pile up too close to one another. Thus, Hurd's results can be applied to natural sediments (unstirred) and used to calculated the value of E in equation 58. From Hurd's curves for 3°C (correcting for the change from common to natural logarithms), the writer obtained the relation:

$$E = 10^{-6} \phi \left(\frac{W}{10^{-4}} \right) \tag{59}$$

where W = grams of opaline silica per cubic centimeter of seawater. (In Hurd's experiments W varied from 1×10^{-4} to 8×10^{-4})

In a sediment containing 6% opaline silica by dry weight (the maximum value for which equation 13 is strictly valid) and with a porosity of $\phi = 0.75$, $W = 4 \times 10^{-2}$, so that use of equation 59 gives:

$$E = 3.0 \times 10^{-4}/\text{sec} \tag{60}$$

Now a reasonable value for the diffusion coefficient of dissolved silica (an uncharged species, H_4SiO_4) in a fine-grained sediment is:

$$D = 3 \times 10^{-6} \text{ cm}^2/\text{sec} \tag{61}$$

Values of ω for sediments range from about 10^{-12} to 10^{-7} cm/sec. Thus, $4ED \gg \omega^2$ and equation 58 can be simplified to:

$$C = C_s - (C_s - C_0) \exp \left[- \left(\frac{E}{D} \right)^{1/2} x \right] \tag{62}$$

Substituting values for E and D into equation 62:

$$C = C_s - (C_s - C_0) \exp(-10x) \tag{63}$$

This means that equilibrium ($C = C_s$) is achieved practically right up to the sediment-water interface. This calculation might be criticized for the extrapolation of Hurd's results to a much greater silica/water ratio than those studied by him. For this reason a value close to the maximum ratio studied by Hurd ($W = 10^{-3}$ gm/cm^3) is used, which gives $E = 7.5 \times 10^{-6}$/sec and the resulting expression:

$$C = C_s - (C_s - C_0) \exp(-2.7x) \tag{64}$$

Again, $C \approx C_s$ almost right up to the sediment-water interface. Therefore, it is concluded that in sediments containing appreciable opaline silica, which dissolves to saturation at the rates found by Hurd, the porewater at very shallow depths should exhibit the saturation or equilibrium value. In fact this has been found to be the case for the anoxic, diatom-rich sediments of the Gulf of California (Siever et al., 1965) and the basins off the coast of southern California (Rittenberg et al., 1955). In both areas saturation values are encountered in the top 10 cm as well as at greater depths. This indicates the overall qualitative validity of equation 58 for opaline silica-rich sediments.

Deep-sea sediments (most of which are not anoxic) often contain small amounts of opaline silica, yet show a much more gradual change of dissolved silica with depth and a leveling-off value considerably less than that predicted for opaline silica saturation (e.g., Fanning and Pilson, 1971). In these sediments reprecipitation of silica undoubtedly occurs and the leveling-off value probably represents a steady-state balance between the dissolution of opaline silica, the adsorption on clays, and diffusion.[3] In addition, silica surface area should change with depth due to dissolution (i.e., E is not constant), and preliminary calculations indicate that neither dissolution nor reprecipitation are controlled by diffusion through the interstitial water. Thus, for this situation, models much more complex than that represented by equation 58 must be used.

4. General Discussion and Conclusions

In Table III results are summarized for k and G_0 derived from the steady-state models for nitrogen, sulfur, and phosphorus. Note the close similarity between the values of k_N, k_P, and $G_{N,0}$ and $G_{P,0}$ for the Santa Barbara Basin core. Because of this similarity and because both ammonia and phosphate show linear gradients with depth, it is probable that they are released from essentially the same compounds by essentially the same microorganisms. Whether or not this is a general phenomenon, however, cannot be decided in this chapter because for the other two sediment cores there are no data for both nitrogen and phosphorus. Nevertheless, it is tentatively concluded

TABLE III

Values of k and G_0 for three sediment cores based on the theoretical models of the present study. In calculating $G_{N,0}$ and $G_{P,0}$ the following values were assumed $\alpha_N = 0.2$; $\alpha_P = 0.014$

	(10^{-10}/sec)			(10^{-4} mol/cm³)		
Location of Core	k_S	k_N	k_P	$G_{S,0}$	$G_{N,0}$	$G_{P,0}$
Santa Barbara Basin	0.75	0.13	0.09	2.5	4.3	3.6
Somes Sound, Maine	56	14	—	2.2	3.4	—
Long Island Sound	18	—	95	1.3	—	7.9

[3] The value may in some sediments correspond to saturation with the mineral sepiolite (Hurd; Wollast, personal communication).

that anoxic ammonia and phosphate formation are directly coupled. By contrast, it can be readily seen from the curve shapes and k values that for the cores studied there is no direct coupling between sulfate reduction and either ammonia or phosphate formation. Also, the value of $G_{S,0}$ is always less than that for $G_{N,0}$ or $G_{P,0}$. This indicates that phosphate and ammonia must be produced by microorganisms in addition to sulfate-reducing bacteria. This result contrasts with observations of anoxic basin waters where a simple stoichiometric correlation between sulfide, ammonia, and phosphate occurs (e.g., Redfield et al., 1963).

Much higher rate constants for all three elements are encountered in the Somes Sound and Long Island Sound sediments. This is in keeping with the contention, made above, that pollution and high rates of deposition in these areas result in the burial of more rapidly decomposable compounds, which become available to microorganisms living in the sediments. The fact that G_0 values for these sediments are not consistently higher than those for the Santa Barbara Basin core indicates that the *type* of organic matter is much more important in influencing metabolic rates than the total amount deposited in the sediment.

Values of diffusion coefficients derived from the models for fine-grained, clay-rich sediments are:

$$D_{NH_4^+} = 3.5 \times 10^{-6} \text{ cm}^2/\text{sec}$$
$$D_{SO_4^{2-}} = 2 \times 10^{-6} \text{ cm}^2/\text{sec}$$

The value for sulfate ion is in good agreement with the recent laboratory measurements of Li (personal communication), although direct comparison is impossible since sulfate diffusion in sediments is coupled with bicarbonate countercurrent diffusion whereas in laboratory experiments only the simultaneous diffusion of sulfate and accompanying cations is studied. However, because of the similar mobilities of ions, the differences should not be large compared to errors in calculating diffusion coefficients by means of the models of the present study. The value for NH_4^+ is in essentially the same ratio with that for SO_4^{2-} as occurs in infinitely dilute solution. This is demonstrable by calculation from limiting equivalent conductivities of the ions. Thus, D for ammonium ion in fine-grained clayey sediments should be on the order of 3 to 4×10^{-6} cm^2/sec. This, of course, assumes that tortuosity, dead-end pore volume, and so on, affect both ions equally. Ion exchange and adsorption do not affect both ions equally; however, the effects of these processes are not included in D, but rather in the adsorption equilibrium constant K.

In conclusion it can be stated with some assurance that:

1. Steady-state diagenetic models based on the assumption of organic matter decomposition through first-order kinetics provide results that are internally consistent and that predict reasonably accurate diffusion coefficients.

2. In anoxic sediments dissolved ammonia and phosphate appear to originate from the same overall organic decomposition process that is accomplished by microorganisms in addition to those that reduce sulfate. There is not always a simple direct stoichiometric coupling between ammonia plus phosphate formation and sulfate reduction.

3. Organic matter decomposition in sediments that are deposited rapidly and affected by pollution is much more rapid than decomposition in less polluted, more slowly deposited sediments.

4. Pseudozero-order kinetics for organic matter decomposition can result if decreases in organic matter are matched by similar decreases in water content, due to

compaction. In this case the concentration of metabolizable organic matter in terms of mass per unit volume of porewater remains constant with depth.

5. In sediments containing concentrations of fine-grained calcium carbonate, precipitation of dissolved phosphate occurs on the surfaces of carbonate particles, which act as nucleating agents. As a result, phosphate concentrations in the interstitial water of such sediments show equilibrium with an apatite of composition similar to that of marine phosphorite.

6. In sediments rich in biogenic silica, saturation with opaline silica occurs up to shallow depths due to rapid dissolution of the silica.

References

Berner, R. A., 1970. Sedimentary pyrite formation. *Am. J. Sci.*, **268**, 1–23.

Berner, R. A., 1971. *Principles of Chemical Sedimentology*. McGraw-Hill, New York, 240 pp.

Berner, R. A., 1972. Sulfate reduction, pyrite formation, and the oceanic sulfur budget. In *Nobel Symposium 20, The Changing Chemistry of the Oceans*. D. Dyrssen and D. Jagner, eds. Almqvist and Wiksell, Stockholm. 347–361.

Berner, R. A., 1973. Iron sulfides in the Pleistocene deep Black Sea sediments and their paleooceanographic significance. In *Am. Assn. Petrol. Geol. Memoir*. In press.

Berner, R. A., M. R. Scott, and C. Thomlinson, 1970. Carbonate alkalinity in the pore waters of anoxic marine sediments. *Limnol. and Oceanog.*, **15**, 544–549.

Brooks, R. R., B. J. Presley, and I. R. Kaplan, 1968. Trace elements in the interstitial waters of marine sediments. *Geochim. Cosmochim. Acta*, **32**, 397–414.

Burns, N. M. and Curtis Ross, 1972. Project Hypo; an intensive study of the Lake Erie central basin hypolimnion and related surface water phenomena. *Canada Center for Inland Waters Paper No. 6*, 119 pp.

Chen, Yi-shon, 1972. Phosphate interaction with aluminium oxide, kaolinite, and sediments. Doctoral dissertation in engineering (unpublished), Harvard University (Chapter 3).

Dixon, M. and E. C. Webb, 1964. *Enzymes*. Academic Press, New York, 950 pp.

Duursma, E. K., 1966. Molecular diffusion of radioisotopes in interstitial water of sediments. In *Disposal of Radioactive Wastes*. Intern. Atomic Energy Agency, pp. 355–371.

Emery, K. O., 1960. *The Sea Off Southern California*. Wiley, New York, 366 pp.

Fanning, K. A. and M. E. Q. Pilson, 1971. Interstitial silica and pH in marine sediments: some effects of sampling procedures. *Science*, **173**, 1228–1231.

Hurd, D. C., 1972. Factors affecting solution rates of biogenic opal in seawater. *Earth and Planet. Sci. Letters*, **15**, 411–417.

Kaplan, I. R., K. O. Emery, and S. C. Rittenberg, 1963. The distribution and isotopic abundance of sulphur in recent marine sediments off southern California. *Geochim. Cosmochim. Acta*, **27**, 297–331.

Kaplan, I. R. and S. C. Rittenberg, 1963. Basin sedimentation and diagenesis. In *The Sea: The Earth Beneath the Sea, History*. Vol. 3. Wiley, New York, pp. 583–619.

Kester, D. R. and R. M. Pytkowicz, 1967. Determination of the apparent dissociation constants of phosphoric acid acid in seawater. *Limnol. and Oceanog.*, **12**, 243–252.

Kramer, J. R., 1964. Seawater: saturation with apatites and carbonates. *Science*, **146**, 637–638.

Leckie, J. O., 1969. Interaction of calcium and phosphate at calcite surfaces. Doctoral dissertation in engineering (unpublished), Harvard University.

Luce, R. W., R. W. Bartlett, and G. A. Parks, 1972. Dissolution kinetics of magnesium silicates. *Geochim. Cosmochim. Acta*, **36**, 35–50.

Mackenzie, F. T. and R. M. Garrels, 1965. Silicates: reactivity with seawater. *Science*, **150**, 57–58.

Mackenzie, F. T., R. M. Garrels, O. P. Bricker, and F. Bickley, 1967. Silica in seawater: control by silica minerals. *Science*, **155**, 1404–1405.

Mackereth, F. J. H., 1966. Some chemical observations on post-glacial lake sediments. *Phil. Trans. Roy. Soc.*, Sect. B, No. 250, 165–220.

Munk, W. H. and G. A. Riley, 1952. Absorption of nutrients by aquatic plants. *J. Marine Res.*, **11**, 215–240.

Murphy, J. and J. P. Riley, 1962. A modified single solution method for the determination of phosphate in natural waters. *Anal. Chim. Acta*, **27**, 31–36.

Nielsen, A. E., 1964. *Kinetics of Precipitation*. Macmillan, New York, 151 pp.

Nriagu, J. O., 1968. Sulfur metabolism and sedimentary environment: Lake Mendota, Wisconsin. *Limnol. and Oceanog.*, **13**, 430–439.

Redfield, A. C., 1958. The biological control of chemical factors in the environment. *Amer. Scientist*, **46**, 205–222.

Redfield, A. C., B. H. Ketchum, and F. A. Richards, 1963. The influence of organisms on the composition of seawater. In *The Sea: Composition of Sea-water, Comparative and Descriptive Oceanography*. Vol. 2. Wiley, New York, 26–77.

Reeburgh, W. S., 1967. Measurement of gases in sediments. Doctoral dissertations in oceanography (unpublished), Johns Hopkins University, 93 pp.

Rittenburg, S. C., K. O. Emery, and W. L. Orr, 1955. Regeneration of nutrients in sediments of marine basins. *Deep-Sea Res.*, **3**, 23–45.

Roberson, C. E., 1966. Solubility implications of apatite in seawater. *U.S. Geol. Survey Prof. Paper 550-D*, 178–185.

Siever, R., 1968. Establishment of equilibrium between clays and seawater. *Earth and Planet. Sci. Letters*, **5**, 106–110.

Siever, R., K. C. Beck, and R. A. Berner, 1965. Composition of interstitial waters of modern sediments. *J. Geol.*, **73**, 39.73.

Sillén, L. G., 1961. The physical chemistry of seawater. In *Oceanography*. Amer. Assoc. Adv. Sci., pp. 549–582.

Sillén, L. G., 1964. *Stability Constants of Metal-Ion Complexes, Section I. Inorganic Ligands*, London, the Chemical Society, 356 pp.

Sorokin, Y. I., 1962. Experimental investigation of bacterial sulfate reduction in the Black Sea using S^{35}. *Mikrobiologiya*, **31**, 402–410.

Strakhov, N. M., 1958. The forms of iron in Black Sea sediments. *Dokl. Akad. Nauk. S.S.S.R.*, **118**, 803–806.

Stumm, W. and J. O. Leckie, 1970. Phosphate exchange with sediments; its role in the productivity of surface waters. *Adv. in Water Pollution Research*. Vol. 2. Pergamon Press, New York, III 26/1–26/16.

Stumm, W. and J. J. Morgan, 1970. *Aquatic Chemistry*. Wiley, New York, 583 pp.

Stumm-Zollinger, E., 1966. Effects of inhibition and repression on the utilization of substrates by heterogeneous bacterial communities. *Applied. Microbiol.*, **14**, 654–664.

Thorstenson, D. C., 1970, Equilibrium distribution of small organic molecules in natural waters. *Geochim. Cosmochim. Acta*, **34**, 745–770.

Wuhrmann, K., 1964. Microbial aspects of water pollution control. *Advances in Applied Microbiol.*, **6**, 119–151.

14. RADIOACTIVE GEOCHRONOLOGIES

EDWARD GOLDBERG AND KEN BRULAND

1. Introduction

Radioactive species involved in the major sedimentary cycle have proven especially useful for the introduction of time parameters as well as for understanding the chemical behaviors of a wide spectrum of elements. It is convenient to classify these radionuclides into three groups on the basis of their times of formation: (1) those naturally occurring radioactive nuclides that were present during the formative stages of the earth; (2) radioactive nuclides continuously produced through cosmic-ray fragmentation of atmospheric gases; and (3) man-made radioactive nuclides introduced within the last several decades into the marine environment through nuclear weapon detonations or as wastes from nuclear reactors.

The half-lives of the first group's parent isotopes are of the order of billions of years, long enough to persist on earth since its formation 4.5 billion years ago. In addition to such species as K–40 and Rb–87, which decay to stable nuclides, there are the long-lived decay chains of U–238, U–235, and Th–232 that give rise to a host of daughters of varying chemical and physical properties and half-lives. Differences in the characteristics of a daughter compared to its parent sometimes result in the separation of the former from the latter's environment and the initiation of a subseries of decays. For example, thorium isotopes are rapidly removed from solution in seawater, whereas their parent radium or uranium isotopes remain in solution for a much longer time period. Several dating techniques such as the Th–230/Th–232 or the Th–228/Th–232 methods have evolved from this situation. Radioactive radon isotopes may escape from the milieu of their parents due to their gaseous states and can introduce a radioactive subseries into a different geosphere. Thus, lead-210 is removed in precipitation from the atmosphere where it was formed from the decay of radon-222, which had entered after its formation in crustal rocks.

The cosmogenous radionuclides identified so far (Table I) have half-lives ranging from 32 min to 2.5 million years. The utilization of a specific nuclide clearly depends both on its chemistry and on its half-life. The two species most employed in earth science problems, C–14 and H–3, are especially attractive because of the former's involvement in living processes and the latter's incorporation into water molecules. In the first case, the cessation of life processes can be used to start the C–14 clock. In the second case, the H–3 in H_2O molecules can introduce a time parameter to a water body.

The artificial radioisotopes in the environment have been produced primarily by the detonation of nuclear bombs. In 1954, with the Castle Test in the Pacific conducted by the United States, the amounts of artificial radioactive species in the atmosphere exceeded those of their natural counterparts. Additional tests by the United States and Russia continued through the early 1960s. Most of this radioactive debris entered the stratosphere from blasts taking place in the air or at the earth's surface. The nuclides have residence times in the stratosphere of the order of a year or so. The stratospheric fallout went through a maximum in 1963, an event that, when recorded in the sediments, can serve as a time mark.

This chapter considers the use of radionuclides as the basis of geochronologies in the marine sedimentary column. Not all radionuclides in the oceans may be used, since some never reach measurable concentrations in marine deposits because of

TABLE I

Half-lives of Cosmic-Ray Produced Isotopes (Lal and Suess, 1968)

Radioisotope	Half-Life
Be^{10}	2.5×10^6 yr
Al^{26}	7.4×10^5 yr
Cl^{36}	3.1×10^5 yr
Kr^{81}	2.0×10^5 yr
C^{14}	5730 yr
Si^{32}	500 yr
Ar^{39}	270 yr
H^3	12.5 yr
Na^{22}	2.6 yr
S^{35}	87 days
Be^7	53 days
P^{33}	25 days
P^{32}	14.3 days
Mg^{28}	21.2 hr
Na^{24}	15.0 hr
S^{38}	2.9 hr
Si^{31}	2.6 hr
Cl^{39}	55.5 min
Cl^{38}	37.3 min
Cl^{34m}	32.0 min

short half-lives or long residence times in the water, while others are inapplicable because of their mobility within the sediment.

Radioactive geochronologies are all based on the decay equations involving pairs of nuclides or a series of decays. In the former case where an unstable parent decays to a stable daughter, the relationship is given by

$$N_p = N_p{}^0(e^{-\lambda t}) \tag{1}$$

where N_p is the number of parent atoms at time t, $N_p{}^0$ is the number of parent atoms at time zero, and λ is the decay constant of the parent. This equation can be rewritten as

$$N_p = (N_p + N_d)e^{-\lambda t} \tag{2}$$

where N_d is the number of daughter atoms at time t, or

$$A_p = A_p{}^0 e^{-\lambda t} \tag{3}$$

where A_p and $A_p{}^0$ are the activities ($A = \lambda N$) of the parent at time t and at time zero, respectively.

The radioactive decay series members, when used in dating schemes, often require the use of Bateman equations. Their application to specific methods will be treated in subsequent sections.

There are two general assumptions that must be met in the application of any geochronological technique:

1. Over the time interval considered there must be no gain or loss of parent or

daughter nuclides (or intermediate members of a radioactive series between daughter and parent)—the "*closed system assumption.*"

2. The number of atoms of the daughter nuclide relative to that of the parent at time zero must be known. Alternatively, where equation 3 is used, the activity at time zero is required. This is the "*inheritance assumption.*"

In addition, there are assumptions specific to a given method that are necessary to maintain its validity.

The unconsolidated marine sediments may have their radioactive time clocks disturbed by a number of physical or biological processes. The activities of burrowing organisms can homogenize the upper levels of the sedimentary column, destroying recent chronologies. On the basis of studies with Th–230, Goldberg and Koide (1962) conclude that such mixing can take place to depths of 5 or 10 cm in open ocean sediments. It is conceivable that near bottom currents can disturb the solids at the sediment water interface with similar effects. Slumping, erosion, and the consequential mixing of solid phases deposited at different times can give erroneous sedimentation rates.

Perhaps the greatest uncertainties involve the disturbance of the deposit during the coring operation. The integrity of both open barrel and piston cores has been questioned with respect to collecting an undisturbed sample of the sedimentary column. Ross and Reidel (1967) have indicated a shortening of piston cores relative to open barrel cores. The possible shortening of open barrel cores has been recognized and corrections to account for this have been suggested (Goldberg et al., 1964).

Large-volume box cores and liquid air coring devices apparently overcome such difficulties and appear to recover both the upper and lower portions of the deposit without loss or distortion (Soutar, personal communication).

The strategy in this presentation will be to emphasize those techniques that have given reliable ages in the marine sedimentary records. The various methods will be grouped under categories of the time periods that they cover.

Usually the criterion for the inclusion of a technique is that it shows agreement with at least one other method for age determination. In addition to radiometric methods, there are those based on paleomagnetic sequences, stratigraphy (varving), and paleontology. The first two have been especially useful for comparisons extending through the Pleistocene.

The magnetic reversal sequences observed in oceanic sediments (Opdike et al. 1966; Harrison, 1966), through their correlation with the reversal records of continental rocks (Cox et al., 1964), can provide an absolute age index extending beyond the Pleistocene. Using this method it is possible to obtain an absolute chronology for ocean sediments that can be compared with directly measured or extrapolated ages from radioactive methods. The latest Brunhes normal polarity epoch of 0.7 million years provides a convenient boundary level for the interpolation of the important Pleistocene events that occurred between it and the present.

Varved sediments that occur in anoxic environments or under waters containing very little dissolved oxygen have provided a benchmark for dating techniques extending over the past century or even millennia.

2. Geochronologies of Millions of Years

There are a number of radiometric techniques that have been utilized, with varying degrees of success, to extend radiometric geochronologies of marine sediments back millions of years. The potassium-argon method has been utilized by Dymond (1966, 1969) to determine ages for components of volcanic ash layers 0.5 to 11.4 million years old. Fission track dating of volcanic glass shards (Macdougall, 1971) and deep-sea microtektites (Gentner et al., 1970) in marine sediments have determined ages of sedimentary strata in the range of 0.7 to 11.2 million years. Amin et al. (1966) used Be–10 to determine accumulation rates of pelagic sediments. Although Be–10 is applicable for samples 5 to 10 million years old, the large amounts of material required and the low activities have not encouraged further work with unconsolidated sediments. Bhat et al. (1973) have used Be–10 to ascertain rates of accumulation for ferromanganese minerals. Finally, the uranium-helium method has been applied to determine the age of Pleistocene and Tertiary fossil aragonites (Fanale and Schaeffer, 1965). The two methods that appear to have the widest applicability to marine deposits are the K–Ar and fission track dating.

A. Potassium-Argon

Potassium-argon age determinations on mineral separates have extended the geochronological range applicable to marine sediments into the million and through the billion year levels. K–40 decays in two ways: (1) 89% by beta decay to Ca–40, and (2) 11% to Ar–40 by electron capture. Since 97% of stable calcium consists of the isotope Ca–40, beta decay of K–40 is unpracticable for a dating technique. However, the formation of the inert gas, Ar–40, when retained in the lattice structure of minerals, provides the basis for an age indicator. Potassium may be analyzed by flame photometry or atomic absorption, and a high sensitivity mass spectrometer is employed for the analysis of argon.

In addition to the usual assumption of a closed system and no inherited argon in the solidifying material, two other limitations must be maintained where volcanic materials are utilized to date marine sediments:

1. The volcanic materials are deposited soon after their formation.
2. Lithogenous phases from other volcanic events of different time periods, erosional debris, or authigenic minerals must not be present in the analyzed material.

Dymond (1966) applied this technique to volcanic minerals and glasses that had been shown by other workers in the field to have the property of being argon retentive. An obvious advantage of this technique in the marine sedimentary column is the low temperatures of the upper strata (around 0°C) which minimize the possibility of argon loss by diffusion.

Dymond's initial studies involved volcanic ash layers chosen specifically to reduce the possibility of detrital contamination and to represent short-term geological events. Two lines of evidence indicate that the obtained ages are valid: (1) an increasing age with increasing depth in the column and (2) age agreement between minerals coexisting in the strata under investigation (Table II).

Dymond (1969) compared the measured K–Ar ages of ash layers with other radiometric and paleomagnetic reversal ages. In two cores the K–Ar ages agreed with the ages for the ashes interpolated from magnetic data. A third core had potassium argon ages slightly younger than the paleomagnetic ages, although Dymond considered them compatible. The top few meters of one core were dated by Th^{230}/Th^{232} with a sedimentation rate of 4.6 mm/10^3 yr compared to 4.3 mm/10^3 yr by K–Ar. Macdougall (1971) dated the same ash layers by fission track analysis and the ages determined were identical to the K–Ar ages within experimental error (Table III).

TABLE II

Potassium-argon Ages of Minerals Extracted from Pacific Deep-Sea Sediments (Dymond, 1966)

Sample Depth	Material Dated	K (%)	Ar^{40} Radiogenic (%)	Age (10^6 yr)
(Ris 114P, 21°33′N; 134°W, 5040 m)				
554 cm	Anorthoclase	2.68	42	28.3 ± 1.0
	Biotite and Amphibole	3.66	46	28.9 ± 1.5
(Ris 120P, 120P, 28°19′N; 133°12′W, 4420 m)				
218 cm	Plagioclase	0.78	20	17.5 ± 0.6
	Sanidine	8.13	64	18.2 ± 0.7

TABLE III

Comparison of Fission Track, Magnetic Reversal, and K-Ar Ages; in million years (Macdougall, 1971)

Sample	K-Ar Age (Dymond, 1969)	Magnetic Reversal Age (Dymond, 1969)	Fission Track Age (Macdougall, 1971)
V21–145, 815 cm	1.45(±0.08)	1.4	1.47(±0.16)
V21–173, 725 cm	1.62(±0.08)	1.6	1.62(±0.17)
EM8–13[a]	11.4(±0.6)	—	10.5(±0.6)

[a] No magnetic reversal age is available for this sample, paleontologic age is early Miocene (Dymond, 1969).

Hurley et al. (1963) and Krilov et al. (1961) obtained potassium-argon ages of bulk ocean sediments and found them to reflect weathering provenances rather than ages of deposition. Krilov and Silin (1963) attempted to delineate the dispersion zones of terrigenous materials in the world oceans by the K–Ar ages of the lithogenous components. For example, the younger K–Ar age of the terrigenous sediments of the Pacific appear reasonable since the basin is fringed by comparatively young Meso-Cenozoic mountain structures. A general agreement was found to exist between the ages of the oozes and sands and those of the crystalline rocks of the source province. With similar lines of reasoning Dasch (1969) found that the isotopic composition of strontium (Sr-87/Sr-86) in the aluminosilicate fraction of marine sediments may also be used as an indicator of geologic provenance. While these studies do not use the K–Ar method as a geochronometer, they demonstrate its application to sediment provenance problems. Using K–Ar ages in conjunction with strontium isotope analysis may prove to be a powerful tool in determining origins and dispersion of lithogenous components in marine sediments.

Potassium-argon geochronologies were sought in the marine zeolite phillipsite by Bernat et al. (1970). These authigenic minerals were separated from surface sediments far removed from one another and yielded apparent K–Ar ages greater than a million years. This was attributed to the introduction of argon from relict minerals about which the phillipsites may have nucleated or which they had occluded during growth. The method has not as yet been applied to very old zeolites (greater than 10 million years) where such an inheritance of argon may not be of great significance.

Barnes and Dymond (1967) determined maximum accumulation rates of three manganese nodules by obtaining a K–Ar age on the basaltic volcanic fragments forming the nuclei. Rates of 0.5 to 4 mm/10^6 yr were found and are of the same order of magnitude as those obtained by uranium series disequilibrium studies (Ku and Broecker, 1969; Bender et al., 1970).

The potassium-argon method has also been attempted on the igneous rocks underlying the sediments from the recent deep-sea drilling program. However, excess radiogenic argon found in geologically young submarine basalts dredged from the East Pacific rise and other areas, giving anomalously high ages in some cases (Funkhouser et al., 1968; Noble and Naughton, 1968), has limited the validity of this technique. Dymond (1970) has demonstrated argon gradients in deep-sea basalt pillows with the highest concentrations of radiogenic argon occurring in the pillow margins. At depths of 5 to 8 cm within the pillows no radiogenic argon was measured, suggesting that K–Ar ages from submarine rocks may be valid if the samples are selected properly.

B. *Fission-Track Dating*

The fission track technique is applicable from approximately 0.5 million years through the billion year range. The minimum and maximum ages datable are dependent primarily on the uranium content of the sample and its resistance to alteration.

The principles in fission track dating are similar to those of other radiometric methods. Each spontaneous fission of U-238 creates a disorder in the crystal structure of its matrix. The preferential etching of such disordered zones by chemical reagents produces channels or tracks. The age of a sample can thus be expressed in terms of the measured U-238 concentration in the sample, the number of tracks per unit volume, and the spontaneous fission rate of U-238.

The number of tracks, N_t, produced by spontaneous fission of U-238 over a time t is given by

$$N_t = C^{238} \frac{\lambda_F}{\lambda_D} (e^{\lambda_D t} - 1) \tag{4}$$

where C^{238} = measured concentration of U-238
λ_D = alpha decay constant for U-238
λ_F = spontaneous fission disintegration constant for U-238

Fission track dating has two advantages over the K–Ar method: (1) much smaller samples (<5 mg) are required, and (2) since the sample grains are microscopically examined individually, contaminants can be easily distinguished and discarded.

Similar to the K–Ar dating method, fission track age determinations must be made on components of marine sediments that record the time of deposition. Glass shards present in volcanic ash layers appear to provide such samples. They are apparently windblown, originating in explosive continental or continental margin areas (Horn et al., 1969), and are often widespread enough to be useful as stratigraphic markers.

Macdougall (1971) compared fission track age determinations of volcanic glass shards with K–Ar results obtained by Dymond (1966 and 1969) and with paleomagnetic results (Table III) and found that the fission track ages are in agreement within the error limits. Macdougall attempted but was unable to date such authigenic components of sediments as barite, phillipsite, and fish teeth. The barite crystals are either too small in size or too low in uranium content. Most phillipsite crystals contain numerous inclusions that interfere by producing tracks. Fish debris are polycrystalline and porous, properties that make fission track dating difficult or impossible.

Gentner et al. (1970) analyzed microtektites associated near the Matuyama-Brunhes geomagnetic boundary and found that for each microtektite group the measured fission track ages and their stratigraphic ages agree within their limits of error. The fission track ages of the microtektites agreed well with K-Ar and fission track ages of continental tektite fields to which they were linked, indicating that the age of deposition coincides with the age of formation.

C. Beryllium-10 and Aluminium-26

These two long-lived, cosmic ray-produced nuclides were sought in some South Pacific pelagic sediments for use as possible geochronometers (Amin, Kharkar, and Lal, 1966). The observed activity ratio Al-26/Be-10 appeared to be considerably larger than that expected from the cosmic ray fragmentation of atmospheric gases. They propose that the principal source of Al-26 is cosmic dust, where it is produced by cosmic ray bombardment. The very low activity of the Al-26 in the sediments precluded its use as a dating tool.

A South Pacific core was found to have a nearly uniform concentration of Be-10 to 100 cm depth. By assuming a uniform rate of sedimentation of Be-10 with a knowledge of its atmospheric production rate, a sedimentation rate for the deposit may be found. The assumption is made that the global production rate is equal to its precipitation rate. On such a basis then, the rate of sedimentation, S, may be found with

$$C_x = (P/S) \times e^{-\lambda t} \tag{5}$$

where C_x is the concentration at any depth x in the deposit, λ is the decay constant for Be-10, and P is the global production rate of Be-10 (4.5×10^{-2} atoms/cm^2 yr). A sedimentation rate of 3.8 mm/1000 yr was found.

Amin (1970) has subsequently extended this work and made an intercomparison of Be-10 rates with results based on excess Th-230, Th-230/Th-232, and magnetic reversal methods. Amin looked at three large-diameter (12.7 cm) cores taken from the pelagic areas of the North, South, and equatorial Pacific Ocean. The three methods (Table IV) are generally in good agreement, within a factor of two of each other.

TABLE IV

Intercomparison of Be^{10} Sedimentation Rates with Independent Dating Methods in mm/10^3 yr (Amin, 1970)

Core	Latitude	Longitude	Be^{10}	Th^{230}_{excess}	$Th^{230}_{excess}/Th^{232}$	Magnetic Reversal
MSN 96	57°35′S	175°15′W	3.6	2.3	2.9	NM[a]
MSN 147G	8°20′N	145°24′W	3.9	1.9	1.9	≥2.0*[b]
NOVA III-16	0°14.1′N	179°W	2.2	1.5	1.7	1.7

[a] NM = not measured.

[b] Based on nondetection of the boundary of the Matuyama-Brunhes reversal epoch at 0.7 million years B.P.

The very low levels of Be-10 in the sediments, coupled with the difficulties in measurement, have discouraged serious involvements with the method in unconsolidated sediments. On the other hand, it has been successfully used with manganese nodules (Somayajulu, 1967; Bhat et al., 1973). Be-10 accumulation rates were in agreement with those determined by the excess Th-230 and Th-230/Th-232 methods. The Be-10 method has the advantage that it can be applied over greater depths in the rock than the disequilibrium techniques involving thorium isotopes. The latter methods can often be used to depths of only the outer few hundred microns and hence are subject to severe sampling problems.

D. Uranium-Helium

This technique is based on the production of eight helium atoms for each set of decays in the uranium-238 series. So far it has been successfully applied to the determination of the age of Pleistocene and Tertiary fossil aragonites (Fanale and Schaeffer, 1965). Uranium and helium measurements were made to an accuracy of 10% and a 15% analytical error was assigned to all of the ages.

The validity of the "closed system" assumption was sought by performing U-He age determination on samples of fossil shells and corals for which several types of independent estimates of age were available. Pleistocene coral samples gave concordant ages with those based on Th-230/U-234 measurements, except in those discordant instances in which the U-234/U-238 values indicate an exchange of uranium with the environment. Tertiary corals from the same cores gave ages in agreement with estimations based on the stratigraphic position.

The "inheritance" assumption may not be entirely valid. Modern samples of aragonites, especially corals, contain very small amounts of helium, whose origin is not as yet understood. These small amounts of helium do not seriously affect the Pleistocene and Tertiary ages reported on by Fanale and Schaeffer but could influence analyses made on younger samples. The investigators suggest that this helium may be associated with the detrital phases of the sediments. If such is the case, this inherited helium could be greatly reduced by mild dissolutions of the shells.

Shells of varying uranium contents, but presumably identical ages, gave U-238/He ages that fell on the uranium-helium isochrons (Fig. 1). If any uranium were added

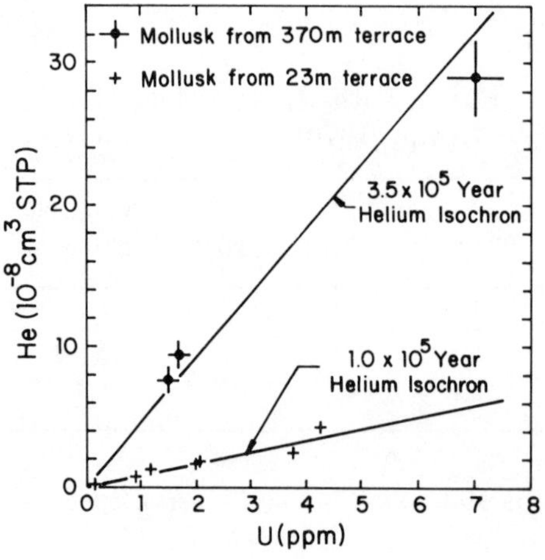

Fig. 1. Helium contents of mollusc shells as a function of uranium contents. Shells deposited at the same time but varying in uranium contents have near constant U/He ratios. Fanale and Schaeffer (1965).

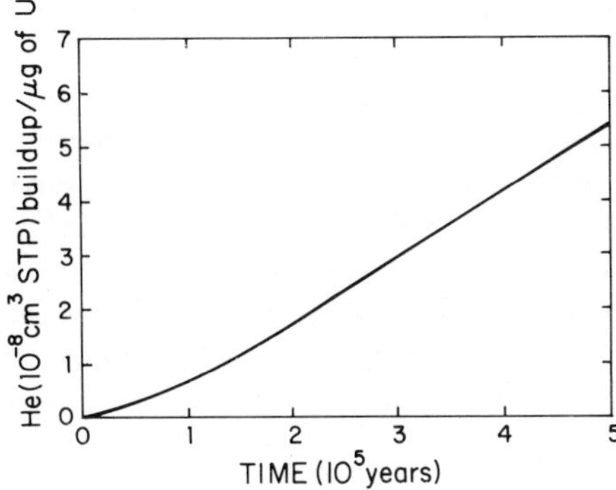

Fig. 2. Helium growth in closed systems containing uranium. Fanale and Schaeffer (1965). An initial U-234/U-238 ratio of 1.15 is assumed.

to the shells after formation, it clearly must have been added during their early history. This isochron check is especially valuable for a single suite of samples of a given age.

If the age of the sample is less than 10^6 yr, it is necessary to take into account the initial radioactive disequilibrium conditions preceding the attainment of secular equilibrium. Figure 2 illustrates the buildup of helium in a system where an initial U-234/U-238 ratio of 1.15 is taken. (See discussion of the U-234/U-238 disequilibria in a subsequent section.) For samples whose ages lie between 10^4 and 10^6 yr the initial activity ratio of U-234/U-238 is quite significant. As times greater than a million years are approached, the age becomes solely a function of the U/He ratio. The contribution of U-235 and its alpha-emitting daughters is of minor importance.

On the basis of a comparison of uranium/helium ages with those based on Th-230/U-234 for corals within the Pleistocene, there appears to be no evidence of significant loss of helium in the samples. Such studies have been extended into the Tertiary and it appears that in the absence of any recrystallization of the sample, the U-He ages are essentially equivalent to the Th-230/U-234 ages.

The U-He method is apparently not applicable to fossil bones or other deposits of apatite on the basis of some preliminary work by Turekian et al. (1970). Bones of oligocene age were shown to have lost substantial amounts of their radiogenic helium. The ages of the bones as determined stratigraphically were much older than the apparent U-He ones.

3. Geochronologies of Hundreds of Thousands of Years

Radioactive disequilibrium of the uranium series isotopes has provided a variety of means of dating oceanic sediments for periods encompassing the last several hundred thousand years. The relatively chemically unreactive uranium isotopes present in seawater generate $Th^{230}(\tau_{1/2} = 75{,}200$ yr) and $Pa^{231}(\tau_{1/2} = 34{,}300$ yr), which rapidly are removed to the sedimentary column. There is less than 1% of the equilibrium amounts of these nuclides in seawater, resulting in large amounts of unsupported Th^{230} and Pa^{231} in surface sediments. These latter nuclides often show an exponential decrease with depth below the sediment-water interface.

A second set of methods involves the growth of daughters of uranium isotopes into solids that accommodate the parent only. Corals and oolites, aragonitic forms of calcium carbonate, accumulate uranium from seawater at the part per million level in the absence of measurable quantities of thorium or protactinium isotopes. The growth of these daughter products with time has formed the basis of dating schemes.

The following geochronological methods have been used with varying degrees of success: U-234/U-238, Th-230/Th-232 and unsupported Th-230, excess Pa^{231}, Th-230/Pa-231, Th-230/U-234, and Pa-231/U-235.

The Th-230/Th-232 and the unsupported Th-230 methods have given concordant results with other radiometric and with nonradiometric dating techniques and have been utilized to a much larger extent than the unsupported protactinium techniques. Similarly, the growth of Th-230 from uranium in oolites and corals has provided a method for obtaining reliable ages. Although the U-234/U-238 technique lacks the precision of the Th-230/Th-232 and Th-230 methods, it has been most valuable to distinguish between solids formed within the last million years and those formed over a million years ago.

A. U-234/U-238 Method

The U-234/U-238 activity ratio in terrestrial waters is highly variable and usually contains an excess of U-234 relative to its long-lived parent U-238, while the weathered phases often show a deficiency in U-234 compared with U-238 (Cherdyntsev, 1955; Cherdyntsev et al., 1961).

This fractionation or disequilibrium between uranium isotopes in nature has been explained by (1) α-recoil dislocations resulting in U-234 atoms occupying metastable lattice positions (Cherdyntsev et al., 1961; Starik et al., 1958), and (2) oxidation during decay (Rosholt et al., 1963, 1966; Dooley et al., 1966). Both processes would take place in terrestrial solids where U-238 exists predominantly in the tetravalent state. In the first case, U-234 is presumed to be more readily oxidized and mobilized because of selective exposure. On the other hand, Rosholt et al., offer a mechanism that assumes the daughter U-234 is actually more oxidized from the time of its formation. In either case, weathering solutions preferentially take up the oxidized (VI) form of uranium, most probably as a result of the strong complexes formed between carbonate or sulfate ions and uranyl ion.

An excess of U-234 relative to U-238 has also been found in seawater. The U-234/U-238 activity ratios were determined indirectly by measurement of modern marine corals (Table V) and directly by measurements of samples from oceanic and near-shore waters (Table VI). From analysis of modern marine corals and oolites (where uranium is presumably derived from seawater), Thurber (1962, 1963) arrived at a value of 1.15 ± 0.01 for the activity ratio of U-234/U-238 for seawater. Subsequently, Koide and Goldberg (1965) measured the activity ratio in surface and deep waters from the Atlantic and Pacific Oceans and the Mediterranean Sea and found it to be 1.14 ± 0.014. Thus uniformity is due to the unreactivity of uranium in aqueous solution—a situation that results in its long residence time.

The excess of U-234 relative to U-238 in biogenous or hydrogenous minerals may be used as a measure of the age of the material with the assumption of an initial U-234/U-238 ratio. Since U-234 has a half-life of 250,000 yr, it can be applied to dating of samples over the period of the last million years. The age is given by the equation

$$\left[\frac{A_{\mathrm{U-234}}}{A_{\mathrm{U-238}}}\right]_t - 1 = \left(\left[\frac{A_{\mathrm{U-234}}}{A_{\mathrm{U-238}}}\right]_{t=0} - 1\right) e^{-\lambda_{\mathrm{U-234}} t} \qquad (6)$$

where

$$\left[\frac{A_{\mathrm{U-234}}}{A_{\mathrm{U-238}}}\right]_{t=0}$$

Table V

U^{234}/U^{238} Activity Ratios in Modern Corals and Oolites

Location	U^{234}/U^{238} Activity Ratio	Species	Reference
		Corals	
Eniwetok Atoll, Marshall Islands	1.13 ± 0.03	Species undetermined	Thurber (1962)
Florida Keys	1.19 ± 0.02	Species undetermined	Broecker and Thurber (1965)
	1.17 ± 0.01	Species undetermined	Broecker and Thurber (1965)
	1.14 ± 0.03	*Acropora*	Broecker and Thurber (1965)
	1.13 ± 0.04	*Acropora*	Broecker and Thurber (1965)
	1.14 ± 0.03	Mussa	Osmond et al. (1965)
	1.12 ± 0.04	*Porites*	Osmond et al. (1965)
Hawaii, Hawaii	1.15 ± 0.01	Species undetermined	Koide and Goldberg (1965)
Oahu, Hawaii	1.15 ± 0.02	*Pocillopora*	Veeh (1966)
Tahiti, Windward Island	1.16 ± 0.02	*Acropora*	Veeh (1966)
Tutuila Island, American Samoa	1.16 ± 0.02	*Acropora*	Veeh (1966)
Barbados, West Indies	1.14 ± 0.01	*Acropora*	Ku (1968)
Red Sea (off coast of Egypt)	1.15 ± 0.01	Species undetermined	Veeh (1968)
		Oolites	
Bahamas	1.16 ± 0.04		Thurber (1962)
	1.15 ± 0.02		Thurber (1962)
Bahamas	1.09 ± 0.03		Osmond et al. (1965)
	1.09 ± 0.04		Osmond et al. (1965)

TABLE VI

U^{234}/U^{238} Activity Ratios in Seawater

Location	U^{234}/U^{238} Activity Ratio	Reference
Coastal marine waters, United States	$1.13 - 1.16(1.15)^b$	Blanchard (1965)
Pacific and Atlantic Oceans and Mediterranean Sea[a]	1.14 ± 0.014	Koide and Goldberg (1965)
Red Sea	1.18 ± 0.01	
Sagami Sea, Japan	1.18 ± 0.01	Umemoto (1965)
Western North Pacific Ocean	$1.02 - 1.20(1.09)^b$	Miyake and Sugimura (1966)
Pacific Ocean[a]	1.15 ± 0.01	Somayajulu and Goldberg (1966)
Antarctic Ocean[a]	1.14 ± 0.03	Veeh (1968)
Indian Ocean coastal waters[a]	1.16 ± 0.03	Sarma and Krishnamoorthy (1968)

[a] Average.
[b] Value is an average.

represents the activity ratio at time zero and

$$\left[\frac{A_{U-234}}{A_{U-238}}\right]_t$$

represents the value of the ratio at time *t*.

This method has been applied successfully by Veeh (1966) to the age determinations of unrecrystallized fossil corals. The ages were in agreement with those determined by the Th-230/U-238 technique (see following sections). Thurber et al. (1965) obtained on fossil corals an agreement between U-234/U-238 and U-He ages. Both the closed-system assumption and the assumption that the U-234/U-238 ratio in the seawater at the time the corals deposited their shells is that of modern-day seawater seem to be valid in the samples that had undergone no alteration of their crystal structure.

Kaufman et al. (1971) point out that the above assumptions may not be upheld in mollusc shell dating. When mollusc analyses are compared with coral analyses, (1) U-234/U-238 values for a given Th-230/U-234 value are higher for molluscs, and (2) the spread in the U-234/U-238 activity ratio increases as the Th-230/U-234 activity ratio increases. This indicates that the closed-system assumption is invalid in fossil mollusc shells due to uranium incorporation after the death of the molluscs. Also, the large variation in the U-234/U-238 activity ratio observed in modern molluscan shells prevents a reasonable estimate of the initial U-234/U-238 ratio.

Ku (1965) attempted to date pelagic sediments with the U-234/U-238 method and found that the sediments do not form a closed system. Postdepositional migration of U-234 in the sedimentary column takes place. Ku proposed a diffusion model for U-234 in deep-sea sediments based on its measured concentrations. His model (Fig. 3) involved three parameters: sedimentation rate (obtained by Th-230), diffusion coefficient for U-234, and the fraction of the U-234 subject to mobility.

Kolodny and Kaplan (1970) submitted a novel use of U-234/U-238 activity ratio of tetravalent uranium for geochronological purposes in apatite or organic rich muds.

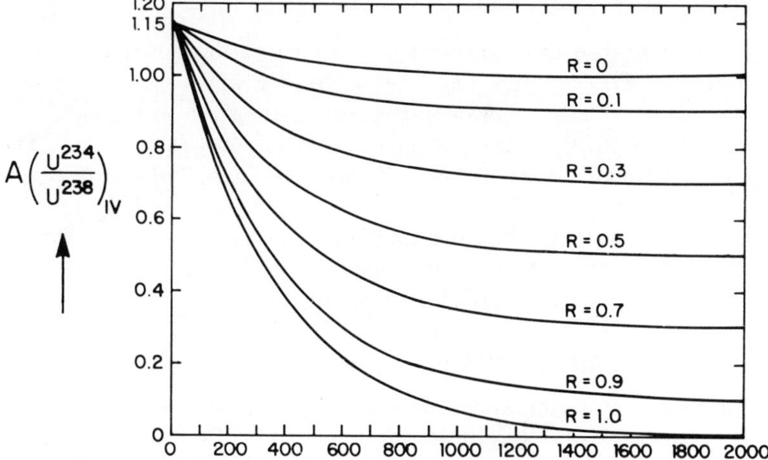

Fig. 3. U-234/U-238 ratios as a function of depth in a North Atlantic sediment and the distributional pattern (curve) based on a model with a sedimentation rate of 0.3 cm/1000 yr and a diffusion coefficient of 3.0×10^{-8} cm²/sec. F_m is the fraction of U-234 subject to mobility. Ku (1965).

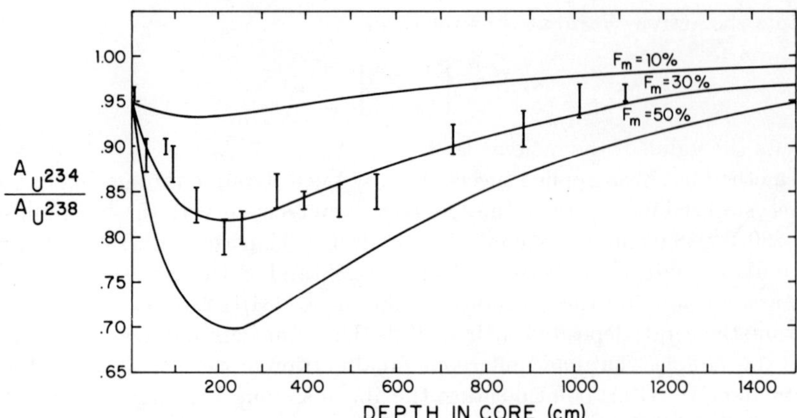

Fig. 4. Change of the U-234/U-238 activity ratio with time in U(IV). R is the fraction of the U-234 that is continually being oxidized from the tetravalent to the hexavalent state following formation from the decay of U-238. Kolodny and Kaplan (1970).

Instead of analyzing the total uranium and assuming a closed system, they analyzed for $(\text{U-234/U-238})_{\text{U(IV)}}$ and developed a quantitative model for variation of the ratio with time based on the following assumptions:

1. A fraction of the radiogenic U-234 in the tetravalent uranium in apatite is oxidized to hexavalent uranium.
2. This fraction remains constant with time.
3. Any oxidation process that is not related to radioactive decay does not distinguish between U-234 and U-238.

If R is the fraction of radiogenic U-234 that is oxidized, then

$$\left(\frac{A_{\text{U-234}}}{A_{\text{U-238}}}\right)_{\text{IV}} \approx (1 - R)[1 - e^{-(\lambda_{238} - \lambda_{234})t}] + \left[\left(\frac{A_{\text{U-234}}}{A_{\text{U-238}}}\right)_{\text{IV}}\right]_0 \cdot e^{-(\lambda_{238} - \lambda_{234})t} \tag{7}$$

This equation described the change of the activity ratio with time in Kolodny and Kaplan's system. The equation has been solved for various values of R, assuming $[(A_{\text{U-234}}/A_{\text{U-238}})_{\text{IV}}]_0 = 1.15$ (seawater); the results are given in Fig. 4.

R was calculated to be equal to 0.3, from $(A_{\text{U-234}}/A_{\text{U-238}})_{\text{IV},\infty} = 0.7$. The derived ages for the phosphorites studied were beyond the range of the dating technique (>800,000 yr).

It is interesting to note that the fraction of radiogenic U-234 that is oxidized ($R = 0.3$) as determined in this study on phosphorites is the same value that provides the best fit in Ku's studies of pelagic sediments.

B. Th-230/Th-232 and Unsupported Ionium Methods

Radioactive disequilibrium in the uranium series in marine sediments was initially indicated in the work of Joly (1908) who found unusually high radium contents in deep-sea sediments from the Challenger expedition. Pettersson (1937) suggested that this excess radium resulted from the decay of Th-230 (parent of Ra-226), which had been incorporated in the sediments unsupported by its parent U-238. Thus, the basis for Th-230 dating of sediments was established.

The ionium/thorium (Th-230/Th-232) technique, originally proposed by Picciotto and Wilgain (1954), is based on the rapid removal of dissolved thorium isotopes in seawater to hydrogenous or biogenous phases. Naturally occurring Th-232 has a half-life of 1.4×10^{10} yr, while Th-230, with a half-life of 7.52×10^4 yr, is generated in the U-238 series. The technique has been extensively applied to unconsolidated recent sediments for time periods up to 300,000 yr. The assumptions of the method include:

1. There is no migration of thorium isotopes in the sedimentary column (closed-system assumption).

2. The Th-230/Th-232 ratio in the waters furnishing these isotopes to the sedimentary solids has remained constant over the interval to be dated (inheritance assumption).

3. Th-230 and Th-232 exist in the same chemical forms in seawater, that is, there is no fractionation of isotopes between seawater and the precipitating phases accumulating thorium.

4. The analyzed materials do not contain lithogenous contributions of these two isotopes of thorium.

If the assumptions are valid, the Th-230/Th-232 ratio should decrease with depth in the sediments. The rate of falloff in the value of the ratio is determined by the half-life of Th-230 and by the rate of sedimentation.

Ages at various levels in the core can, in principle, be assigned through the solution of

$$\frac{A_{\text{Th-230}}}{A_{\text{Th-232}}} = \left[\frac{A_{\text{Th-230}}}{A_{\text{Th-232}}}\right]_{t=0} e^{-\lambda_{\text{Th-230}}t} - \frac{A_{\text{U-238}}}{A_{\text{Th-232}}}(1 - e^{-\lambda_{\text{Th-230}}t}) \tag{8}$$

where the A's refer to the activities of the subscripted nuclides, the first term on the right-hand side accounts for the decay of the unsupported ionium, and the second term accounts for the growth of ionium from the uranium in the authigenic phases. This equation assumes that the uranium that enters the authigenic phases is unaccompanied by its daughter, Th-230.

The reliability of this method depends in part on the technique used to isolate the authigenic thorium isotopes, which may be accommodated on the sorption sites of the detrital solids or located within the authigenic minerals. Goldberg and Koide (1962) found experimentally that a concentrated hydrochloric acid leaching of marine sediments did not significantly attack the primary detrital minerals (such as quartz and feldspars) but did extract thorium from the remaining phases. About two-thirds of the thorium in the noncalcareous phases could be extracted and appears to be derived from a dissolved state in seawater. Moore and Sackett (1964) found that the Th-230/Th-232 ratios were the same within experimental error for water, suspended material, and the HCl leach of sediment core tops in the North Atlantic. The assumption that Th-230 and Th-232 behave in a chemically similar manner is also supported by the work of Holmes (1965), who measured the Th-230/Th-232 ratios in pelagic foraminifera and minimized the possibility of incorporating detrital thorium.

Four general types of depth distributions of the Th-230/Th-232 ratio in sediments have been found (Fig. 5):

1. A constant exponential decrease in the ratio with depth. This type represents those cases in which there is a uniform accumulation of the sediment with time.

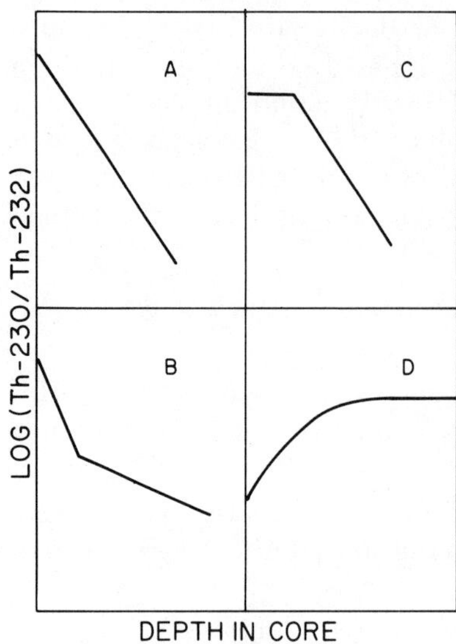

Fig. 5. Depth distributions of Th-230/Th-232 following four models, described in text. From Goldberg and Koide (1962).

2. A constant exponential decrease to a certain level followed by one or more changes in slope but with subsequent levels showing exponential decreases. Curves of this type are sensible on the basis of changes in rates of sedimentation over the time interval being studied.

3. A constant value of the ratio near the surface followed by an exponential decrease with depth. The uniform surface values may result from homogenization of the solid phases by biological activity, near-bottom water currents, or perhaps during the retrieval of the core. The point of the break in the curve is the effective depth to which such disturbances take place (Goldberg and Koide, 1962).

4. An increase in the ratio with depth to a maximum, followed by a near constancy in the value of the ratio. Such curves are indicative of a high uranium content in the authigenic phases, with the initial rise in the curves due to the growth of Th-230 from its parent U-234.

The surfaces values of the Th-230/Th-232 ratio appear to be a function of (1) differences in the inputs of Th-232 to the water masses that furnish the isotopes to the solid phases, and (2) the $CaCO_3$ content of the deposit. The North Atlantic, a relatively small oceanic area with a large number of rivers draining into it, possesses the lowest values of the surface ratio (1.5 to 6). This reflects the entry to the sedimentary solid phases of substantial quantities of dissolved Th-232 relative to those of Th-230 produced by the decay of U-234 in the seawater. One expects then for smaller relative inputs of Th-232, higher surface values of the ratio. The South Pacific, a large oceanic area receiving little river drainage, has the highest Th-230/Th-232 values (143–158). The intermediate values in the North Pacific, South Atlantic, and Indian Oceans are reasonable as they lie between the North Atlantic and South Pacific with respect to the value of the drainage area per unit of oceanic area.

A second parameter that governs the surface values of the Th-230/Th-232 in sediments involves their $CaCO_3$ contents. Goldberg et al. (1964) found an unexpected relationship between the surface values of the Th-230/Th-232 ratios and the calcium carbonate contents in the North Atlantic. Increasing values of the ratio from the same

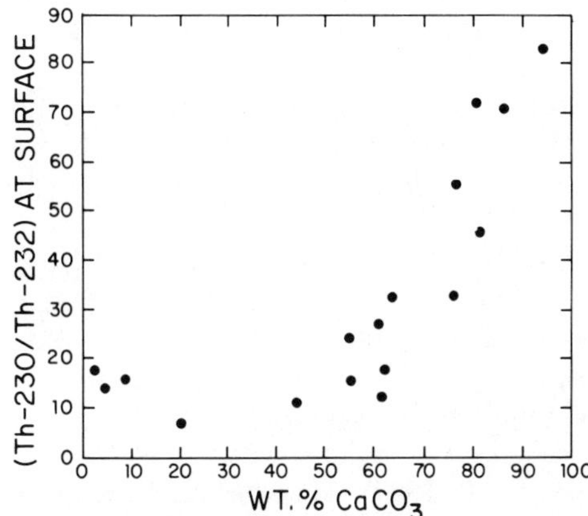

Fig. 6. The surface values of the Th-230/Th-232 ratio as a function of calcium carbonate concentration in Atlantic Ocean sediments. Goldberg and Griffin (1964).

area were complemented by increased calcium carbonate contents. This work was extended by Goldberg and Griffin (1964) to the South Atlantic and the combined data are shown in Fig. 6.

An explanation of these data may be found in the concept that there are differences in the Th–230/Th-232 ratio between surface and deep waters and that the foraminifera and other organisms amass thorium isotopes with the higher surface values. The production of ionium in both surface and deep waters will be nearly the same inasmuch as the uranium concentrations in the oceans show little, if any, variation with depth. The heights of the overlying waters are the same for these sediments within about a factor of two. If we assume that Th-232 primarily enters the coastal surface waters of the ocean, a rapid transfer to deep waters will result in ionium/thorium ratios higher in surface waters.

An alternate method for the determination of accumulation rates of marine sediments based on the decay of Th-230 is the unsupported Th-230 method (Piggot and Urry, 1939 and 1942; Ku et al., 1966, 1968, 1972). Here, there is the additional assumption that the ratio of the rates of deposition of Th-230 and bulk sediment are constant. If each sample in a given core had the same Th-230 excess at the time of deposition and if the sedimentation rate for the core were uniform, then a plot of the logarithm of the excess Th-230 activity versus depth in the core should be a straight line.

In many cores the Th-232 concentration remains constant. In such cases the character of Th-230/Th-232 and excess Th-230 plots is nearly identical.

Fluctuations in bulk sediment fluxes would cause nonlinearity in plots of the logarithm of excess Th-230 versus depth. Attempts made to assign average rates over the last 200,000 to 300,000 yr (based on the slopes of the straight lines best fitting the Th-230 distribution) are often consistent to within $\pm 20\%$ with the average rates for the past 700,000 yr determined by paleomagnetic data (Ku, Broecker, and Opdyke 1968).

Some of the methods that have been used to ascertain the compatibility of the Th-230 and Th-230/Th-232 derived rates are magnetic stratigraphy (Harrison and Somayajulu, 1966; Ku et al., 1968; Goldberg, 1968; Amin, 1970), C-14 and Pa-231 (Ku et al., 1968; Ku et al., 1972), biostratigraphic zone boundaries (Broecker and Van Donk, 1970; Ku et al., 1972), and K-Ar dating (Dymond, 1969). In general, where one finds a general exponential decrease with depth of the Th-230 or Th-230/Th-232 rate, the sedimentation rates have compared favorably with other methods.

In certain cases, cores with large, highly fluctuating $CaCO_3$ contents have given anomalous Th-230/Th-232 ages. Minor discrepancies remain to be resolved concerning both interpretation of data and sediment disturbances during sampling by piston and gravity cores. Differences in compaction of the two coring methods by as much as a factor of two have been proposed and discussed (Kuetal, 1968; Goldberg, 1968). Depending on the coring apparatus or technique, shortening of open barrel boxes with respect to piston cores, and the opposite effect have both been observed (Ross and Riedel, 1967; Emery and Dietz, 1941; Richards, 1961). Because of these differences, no simple correction factors can be used to convert measured core distances to *in situ* distances below the sediment surface.

The excess Th-230 and Th-230/Th-232 techniques have also been applied to the determination of accumulation rates for the ferromanganese minerals (Ku and Broecker, 1967, 1969; Barnes and Dymond, 1967; Bhat et al., 1973). The work of Bhat et al. (1970) indicated a concord in the results of the thorium disequilibrium techniques and Be-10 geochronologies.

C. *Protactinium Method*

Sackett (1965) proposed that the amount of unsupported Pa-231 in sediments would provide a time index. He contended that "the ionium methods may be giving erroneous results" and "the best explanation for the discrepancies between rates determined by the ionium/thorium and radiocarbon methods . . . is apparently that unsupported ionium is migrating to the sediment water interface in marine sediments." He argued that the advantage of the protactinium method over that involving unsupported ionium rests in the concept that protactinium is held more tightly by the sediment components and hence is less likely to migrate.

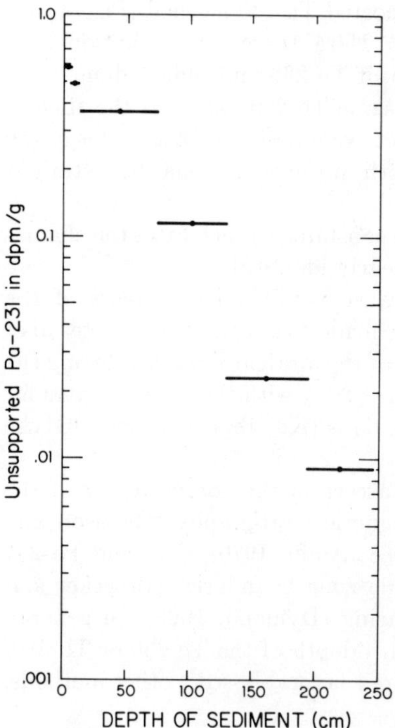

Fig. 7. Unsupported Pa-231 in a North Atlantic sediment as a function of depth. Sackett (1965).

In addition to the closed-system assumption and the inheritance assumption (this is taken into account by a measurement of the uranium in the sediment), the method demands that the deposition rate of Pa-231 be uniform. This method can be used to assign ages up to 100,000 yr or so.

Sackett analyzed five cores from the Atlantic, Pacific, and Indian Oceans and the Caribbean Sea. In general there is a decrease of unsupported Pa-231 (Fig. 7). The rates from Pa-231 were in general about 30% lower than those obtained by radiocarbon. This technique has proven useful as an alternate and complement to other age determination methods in sediments (Ku et al., 1968; Ku et al., 1972). Its use has been limited in part by experimental difficulties. The specific activity of Pa-231 is relatively low in the sediments and the separation and purification of this isotope is both painstaking and time consuming.

D. Pa-231/Th-230 Method

The protactinium-ionium method was independently proposed by Sackett (1960) and Rosholt et al. (1961). The two long-lived isotopes of naturally occurring uranium, U-238 and U-235, give rise to the daughter nuclides Th-230 and Pa-231 with half-lives of 75,200 and 34,300 yr, respectively. Thorium and protactinium have been shown to have very short residence times in the ocean (Moore and Sackett, 1964) and thus virtually all Th-230 and Pa-231 should be found unsupported in the uppermost portions of marine sediments. An expression for the ratio of the unsupported Pa-231 and Th-230 is:

$$\frac{A^U_{\text{Pa-231}}}{A^U_{\text{Th-230}}} = \frac{A^T_{\text{Pa-231}} - A_{\text{U-235}}(1 - e^{-\lambda_{\text{Pa-231}}t})}{A^T_{\text{Th-230}} - A_{\text{U-238}}(1 - e^{-\lambda_{\text{Th-230}}t})} = \left(\frac{A^U_{\text{Pa-231}}}{A^U_{\text{Th-230}}}\right)_{t=0} e^{(\lambda_{\text{Th-230}} - \lambda_{\text{Pa-231}})t} \tag{9}$$

A^U is the unsupported activity of Pa-231 and Th-230 while A^T is the total activity of the extracted isotopes. Here we have assumed that the uranium that enters the authigenic minerals is not accompanied by its thorium and protactinium daughters. Thus, the activity ratio of unsupported Pa-231/Th-230 at $t = 0$ is assumed to be $(A^T_{\text{Pa-231}}/A^T_{\text{Th-230}})_{t=0}$ and this ratio of extractable isotopes at the top of the core should equal the ratio of the instantaneous production rates of Pa-231 and Th-230 from the uranium in the overlying water column. Its theoretical value is 1/11.

The ratio of these two isotopes should decrease with a half-life of 58,000 yr and be applicable over the last 120,000 yr. Its use is usually limited by the detectability of unsupported protactinium.

The additional assumptions that must be valid for the technique include:

1. The analyzed materials do not contain contributions of these two isotopes of thorium and protactinium from lithogenous substances of continental or volcanic origin.

2. The geochemical behaviors of protactinium and ionium must be such that the ratio of the rate of deposition of protactinium to that of ionium has been constant over the time interval dated.

Rosholt et al. (1961) utilized a modification of this method to date three deep-sea cores, two from the Caribbean and one from the North Atlantic. They assumed the uranium in the cores entered with equilibrium amounts of ionium and protactinium, and hence the last equation takes the form:

$$\frac{A^U_{\text{Pa-231}}}{A^U_{\text{Th-230}}} = \frac{A^T_{\text{Pa-231}} - A_{\text{U-235}}}{A^T_{\text{Th-230}} - A_{\text{U-238}}} = \left(\frac{A^U_{\text{Pa-231}}}{A^U_{\text{Th-230}}}\right)_{t=0} e^{(\lambda_{\text{Th-230}} - \lambda_{\text{Pa-231}})t} \tag{10}$$

where $(A^{U}_{\text{Pa-231}}/A^{U}_{\text{Th-230}})_{t=0} = 0.091$ is the ratio of the instantaneous production rates of Pa-231 and Th-230 from the uranium in seawater based on an initial U-234/U-238 ratio of 1.

Thus, further restrictions are placed on the use of the method. In addition to Pa-231 and Th-230, the uranium isotopes cannot be chemically fractionated relative to their daughters during assimilation by the sediments from seawater. In addition, the initial Pa-231/Th-230 ratio should be the production ratio from uranium isotopes in seawater, as there must be no significant fractionation of thorium and protactinium between sediment types or between the sediment components whose contents can vary from one level of the deposit to another. In this work, the total sample was assayed in spite of the known existence of such lithogenous phases as volcanic ash, quartz, and feldspars whose contents of uranium, protactinium, and thorium, although unknown, were considered to be insignificant.

In spite of these apparent limitations, Rosholt and co-workers submit a set of internally consistent results on the two Caribbean cores that gave identical dates in stratigraphically equivalent levels and that were concordant with the C-14 chronology within the limits of error of the methods.

It is not certain, however, that thorium and protactinium behave exactly the same as far as mode of removal in different types of marine deposits is concerned. Rosholt et al. (1961) made the assumption of no fractionation, and although their surface ratios in the Caribbean approached that predicted by secular equilibrium, it is clear that it is by no means generally true. Work by Sackett (1964), Ku (1965b), Ku and Broecker (1967), and Ku et al. (1972) has revealed that low values for the initial ratio $A^{U}_{\text{Pa-231}}/A^{U}_{\text{Th-230}}$ are observed in sediments in many parts of the ocean, whereas Sackett (1966) has shown that the total Pa-231/total Th-230 ratio in manganese nodules is markedly higher than the theoretical ratio. Turekian and Chan (1971) conclude that Th-230 is enriched relative to Pa-231 in deep-sea sediments, particularly in the Pacific, perhaps related to an enrichment of Pa-231 over Th-230 in the manganese nodules.

The ages determined by Pa-231 and Th-230 measurements should therefore be derived from a straight line fit through the logarithmic decrease of the Pa-231/Th-230 activity ratio instead of on the basis of the unsupported Pa-231/Th-230 ratios as suggested by Rosholt et al. (1961). Those core tops with low Pa-231/Th-230 ratios yielding ages of up to 100,000 yr were attributed by Rosholt et al. (1962) to the introduction of reworked sediment, while Sackett (1965) proposes an explanation of preferential concentration of Th-230 toward the core top through migration of thorium isotopes. The explanation of the variance of Pa-231/Th-230 ratios given by Turekian and Chan (1971) due to a fractionation of ionium and protactinium between sediments and manganese nodules seems preferable.

E. The Th-230/U-234 and Pa-231/U-235 Growth Methods

The principle underlying the application of this technique is the incorporation of dissolved U-234 and U-235 from seawater into authigenic minerals in the absence of their daughters Th-230 and Pa-231, respectively. The buildup of the Th-230 and Pa-231 toward a state of radioactive equilibrium with their parents can then be used as a measure of the age of the mineral. In addition to the "closed-system" and "inheritance" assumptions, the method demands a knowledge of the U-234/U-238 ratio in the system at the time of precipitation of the solid phases. A value of the ratio of 1.14 or 1.15 is usually taken. The following equations allow the calculation of the age of the mineral for the Th-230/U-234 method where the A's and λ's refer to the activities and decay constants of the subscripted nuclides:

$$\frac{A_{\text{Th-230}}}{A_{\text{U-238}}} = (1 - e^{-\lambda_{\text{Th-230}}t}) + \left[\frac{(A_{\text{U-234}}) - (A_{\text{U-238}})}{(A_{\text{U-238}})}\right]_{t=0} \left[\frac{\lambda_{\text{Th-230}}}{\lambda_{\text{Th-230}} - \lambda_{\text{U-234}}}\right][e^{-\lambda_{\text{U-234}}t} - e^{-\lambda_{\text{Th-230}}t}] \quad (11)$$

Reef-building corals and oolites have been successfully dated by this technique (Barnes et al., 1956; Tatsumoto and Goldberg, 1959; Broecker and Thurber, 1965; Thurber et al., 1965; and Veeh, 1967). These two groups of substances are aragonitic forms of calcium carbonate and contain of the order of several parts per million by weight of uranium. Inasmuch as aragonites can convert to calcite, the thermodynamically stable phase, a check on the validity of the closed-system assumption, is the absence of calcite in such samples.

However, as carbonates with smaller amounts of uranium in their lattices are considered, certain difficulties are evident. Broecker (1963) has questioned the validity of the "closed-system" assumption in many of his samples where uranium and radium isotopes appear to have entered the carbonates from the environment subsequent to the death of the organism. Detailed critiques of this technique as applied to molluscs whose living forms usually contain less than a part per million of uranium, have been made by Blanchard et al. (1967) and Kaufman et al. (1971). A series of criteria were formulated to satisfy the inheritance and closed-system assumptions.

1. *Mineral integrity.* The sample should show no evidence of recrystallization from its original form, whether calcite, aragonite, or a mixture of the two.
2. *Uranium content.* The uranium content of the fossil carbonate should be close to that of its modern counterpart.
3. *U-234/U-238 ratio.* This ratio should be in concord with the U-238/Th-230 age. Higher or lower values of this ratio are indicative of gains or losses of uranium.
4. *Thorium-232 content.* The thorium content of the fossil carbonate should be close to that of its modern counterpart.
5. *Th-228/Th-232 activity ratio.* Values of this ratio, which indicate the state of equilibrium in the Th-232 series, differing from one suggest gains or losses of thorium and/or radium.
6. *Ra-226/Th-230 activity ratio.* The ratio should be 1.0 for specimens older than 7000 yr. Values differing from this are indicative of a gain or loss of either thorium or radium.

The growth of Pa-231 from U-235 in corals was successfully used to obtain their times of formation by Sakanoue et al. (1967) and Ku (1968). Initial attempts with the Pa-231/U-235 method, first proposed by Sackett (1958), were unrewarding as the samples were severely altered (Rosholt and Antal, 1962) and the calculated ages, as well as those based on Pa-231/Th-230 ratios, seemed to have little meaning due to violation of the closed-system assumption.

The fossil molluscs studied by Blanchard and his associates have considerably higher average uranium contents than do modern shells. Broecker (1963) observed this situation in his samples and concluded that the excess uranium is added shortly after the death of the organism, while the exoskeletal phases are still in the marine environment. Blanchard et al. (1967) disagree with this conclusion, inasmuch as the U-234/U-238 ratios are far above the value found in present-day seawater and in recent marine shells. Additional evidence of open-system conditions in the fossils appear in their thorium isotopic compositions. The fossil marine molluscs, unlike their modern counterparts, contain such a considerable amount of Th-232 that its activity approaches that of Th-230 in some specimens. It seems reasonable to assume that this Th-232 must have entered the shell after death of the organism. The Th-228/Th-232 ratios also indicate open-system conditions with values far in excess of one. Whether the excess Th-228 in the fossil shells entered directly or whether it had subsequently been produced by the decay of Ra-228 is not known, although the second alternative appears more reasonable.

It is evident that fossil mollusc shells have failed generally to satisfy the criteria for closed-system conditions. The thorium and uranium concentrations, and perhaps those of radium, have been altered, most probably by contact with weathering solutions on the continents. One can place little, if any, confidence in an age derived from a Th-230/U-238 ratio in a single fossil specimen collected from a particular locality.

Rosholt (1967), Szabo and Rosholt (1969), and Szabo and Vedder (1971) found that the closed-system assumption was not valid for the fossil shells they investigated, and they concluded that both Th-230 and Pa-231 activities must be obtained for reliable dating. Rosholt (1967) proposed that shells that do not yield concordant Th-230 and Pa-231 dates can be dated provided that the samples remained closed with respect to thorium and protactinium whereas uranium remained free to migrate. A method for this "open-system" dating was proposed in detail by Szabo and Rosholt (1969) and utilized later by Szabo and Vedder (1971).

4. Geochronologies of Tens of Thousands of Years

Only one method for dating sedimentary components through a time interval of tens of thousands of years has received attention—carbon-14. Although the literature abounds in C-14 ages of calcareous phases from both the coastal and open ocean environments, they still must be considered with caution. The old "C-14 ages" of surface sediment components remain to be explained. Until our understanding of the marine geochemistry of C-14 is more thoroughly understood, the utilization of the technique will be limited.

A. C-14

The radiocarbon method of dating marine sediments was initially applied by Arrhenius, Kjellberg, and Libby (1951). C-14 (half-life = 5570 yr) is produced in the atmosphere through the fragmentation of atmospheric gases by cosmic rays. The C-14 so produced is rapidly converted to CO_2, the form in which it enters the carbon cycle. It is found in nearly uniform relationship to stable C-12 in all living organisms. The measured C-14 in fossil materials can thus be used to estimate their age provided that the closed-system and inheritance assumptions are valid. Due to the approximately 40,000-yr range of C-14 dating the technique is mainly applicable to areas with relatively high sedimentation rates with suitable organic carbon or carbonate content.

Emery (1960) made a detailed study of sedimentation rates in the California basins utilizing C-14 in both the organic and carbonate fractions and found large differences in some of the derived ages (Table VII). Except for the Santa Barbara Basin, the greatest difference in age determined for these two components occur in the near-shore basins (Santa Monica, San Diego, Santa Catalina) where they are attributed to the introduction of relict calcium carbonate from shallow water areas to the basin floors. Such a process would have a greater influence on the near-shore basins that have steep side slopes and submarine canyons in contrast to the more isolated basins (East Cortez, San Clemente) that show similar organic carbon and carbonate ages.

Emery also examined the radiocarbon ages of the organic matter (assumed to be less subject to error from reworking than the carbonate ages) now being deposited at the sediment-water interface (Table VIII). The surface C-14 ages in the California basins as well as the Gulf of California basins (Van Andel, 1964) were found to be

TABLE VII

Apparent Radiocarbon Ages of Sedimentary Strata in Basins Off the Coast of California (Emery, 1960)

Basin	Depth (cm)	Age	
		Organic Carbon	$CaCO_3$
Santa Barbara	0–19	3,000 ± 700	2,260 ± 250
Santa Monica	386–396	4,900 ± 140	6,260 ± 250
San Diego	343–356	21,900 ± 700	27,300 ± 1500
Santa Catalina	3–13	1,970 ± 150	2,320 ± 130
	13–25	2,820 ± 140	4,270 ± 130
	406–419	18,400 ± 600	23,100 ± 1000
San Clemente	305–318	12,500 ± 250	12,400 ± 300
East Cortez	441–454	21,000 ± 550	21,200 ± 500

thousands of years old. Radiocarbon dates from the deep Atlantic Ocean (Broecker and Kulp, 1957; Suess, 1954; Turekian and Stuiver, 1964) also yield extrapolated zero ages of 1000 to about 6000 yr. These old C-14 ages have been related to sediment mixing by burrowing organisms or a loss of the top during the coring operation (Broecker, Turekian, and Heezen, 1958). This is an improbable explanation for the near-shore basin deposits due to their high sedimentation rates, since the absence or mixing of several meters of sediment would be required to make the surface sediment so old. The presence of laminated varves in the Santa Barbara Basin rules out mixing processes. The significance of these high surface ages has been discussed by Emery and Bray (1962) but an explanation is yet to be found for them. In order to obtain sedimentation rates from these radiocarbon ages, it is necessary to assume that the discrepancy between real age and surface age has been the same throughout the period of sedimentation concerned.

Radiocarbon ages on suitable cores from the deep sea seem to be reliable. Agreement of the ages of coexisting carbonate and organic phases as well as on the fine and coarse fractions of the carbonate material demonstrate that contamination is negligible in the cores observed (Table IX). The sedimentation rates based on radiocarbon compare favorably with the excess Th-230 rates obtained on the same cores (Ku, Broecker, and Opdyke, 1968).

TABLE VIII

Extrapolated Radiocarbon Ages of Surface Sediments

California Basins (Emery, 1960)	Surface "Age" (yr)	Gulf of California Basins (Van Andel, 1964)	Surface "Age" (yr)
Santa Barbara	2900	Guaymas	3500
San Pedro	2200	Farallon	1975
Santa Catalina	1800	Sal si Puedes	2650
East Cortez	2800	Western slope	1700
West Cortez	4200	Eastern slope, Mazatlan	4000

TABLE IX

Comparison of Radiocarbon Ages on Types of Coexisting Material in Deep-Sea Cores

Core Number	Latitude	Longitude	Depth (m)	Sediment type	Material	Age	Material	Age	Reference
V12–97	10°35′N	65°04′W	—	Green lutite	$CaCO_3$	7,350 ± 200	Organic	7,930 ± 150	Olson and Broecker (1961)
V10–LDC64	34°24′N	24°06′E	2300	Organic-rich *Glob.* ooze	Forams	8,700 ± 1000	Organic	8,400 ± 250	Olson and Broecker (1959)
A254–BR–C	15°57′N	72°54′W	2968	*Glob.* ooze	Forams	12,500 ± 200	Coccolith	12,800 ± 250	Rosholt et al. (1962)
A180–76	00°46′S	26°02′W	3510	*Glob.* ooze	Forams	9,800 ± 200	Coccolith	10,300 ± 350	Ericson et al. (1956)
A172–2	16°12′N	72°19′W	3070	*Glob.* ooze	Forams	11,500 ± 250	Coccolith	14,400 ± 400	Rubin and Suess (1955)
A179–4	16°36′N	74°48′W	2965	*Glob.* ooze	Forams	11,800 ± 300	Coccolith	13,500 ± 400	Rubin and Suess (1955)

5. Geochronologies of Thousands of Years

Only one radiometric geochronology for periods of millennia has been proposed for the unconsolidated marine sedimentary columns, Si-32. It suffers from a number of inadequacies. First of all, its half-life is yet to be accurately determined. Second, it has failed so far to yield concordant ages with other methods.

A. Si-32

Si^{32}, produced in the atmosphere from the cosmic-ray spallation of argon, was detected in marine sponges by Lal, Goldberg, and Koide (1960). Subsequently Kharkar et al. (1962, 1969) have dated biogenic silica-rich sediments from the Pacific and Antarctic Oceans using Si-32. The half-life of Si-32 is approximately 500 yr and has not as yet been precisely determined. In principle, this nuclide provides an entry to chronologies of silicious marine deposits in the interval of a few hundred to several thousand years.

Kharkar et al. (1969) analyzed three Antarctic cores for Si-32 and uranium series nuclides to obtain comparative sedimentation rates. The Si-32 rates over the last 2000 yr were approximately 500 mm/10^3 yr, considerably greater than the values of about 5 mm/10^3 yr obtained using the excess Th-230 technique over the last few hundred thousand years. Rates based on magnetic reversal stratigraphy (Opdyke et al., 1966; Watkins and Goodell, 1967) have also indicated that, over a long time scale, the rate of accumulation of diatomaceous sediments in the Antarctic region is of the order of mm/10^3 yr.

Kharkar and his co-workers conclude that, if the Si-32 values are to be accepted, either the rates of accumulation during the past few thousand years are abnormally high or that as time passes the chances of loss of material by winnowing, slumping, or resolution has eliminated about 97% of the sediment from the site of its initial deposition. Watkins and Goodell (1967) showed that in many of the Antarctic cores the rates of accumulation determined by means of magnetic stratigraphy decreased with increasing penetration into the past, which would be consistent with increased chances of loss by slumping and resolution.

Still, the future applications of the technique will await a more conclusive explanation of the lack of concordance found by Kharkar et al. (1969) between Si-32 geochronologies and those based on magnetic reversals and excess Th-230.

6. Geochronologies of Centuries and Less

Man's involvement in the major sedimentary cycle has been discernible since the beginning of the industrial revolution, about 200 yr ago. His influence on the composition of waters, airs, sediments, and organisms has become more intense during the last decades. Records of his industrial, agricultural, and social activities may be found in marine, lacustrine, and glacial deposits. His generation of materials into the marine environment is continually sought in the sediments, especially those near the coasts, and dating techniques for such deposits are especially valuable. For deposits accumulating at rates of the order of millimeters per year, the Pb-210 method has been quite rewarding. Several techniques for time periods of the order of a decade or so show promise, although studies of them have been rather limited. Included in this category are Th-228/Th-232, Ra-228/Ra-226, and fission product geochronologies.

A. Pb-210

Pb-210, a member of the U-238 natural radioactive series with a half-life of 22.3 yr, is a most useful time clock for geological processes with time periods of the order of a century. A series of favorable nuclear and chemical properties of itself and of its fellow members in the U-238 series combine to allow Pb-210 to become the parent isotope in nuclear decay schemes of the major sedimentary cycle.

Pb-210 is involved in sedimentary processes through the following series of events. The noble gas nuclide Rn-222, a precursor of Pb-210 in the U-238 series, diffuses out of the earth's crust after formation from its parent Ra-226. The Rn-222 (half-life of 3.8 days) decays in the atmosphere, where, followed by a series of short-lived intermediate nuclides, Pb-210 is formed. The Pb-210 is removed from the atmosphere with precipitation.

The initial geochronological work with Pb-210 was on permanent snow fields (Goldberg, 1963; Crozaz et al., 1964; Windom, 1969). Rates of sedimentation in lakes have recently been successfully sought (Krishnaswamy et al., 1971; Koide, Bruland, and Goldberg, 1973) with the assumption that the rate of deposition of unsupported Pb-210 was uniform with time for a given lake.

In the marine environment there is an additional significant source of Pb-210 from the decay of Ra-226 in the overlying water column. The Pb-210 formed in this manner, together with that introduced by rainfall and terrestrial runoff, is scavenged by biogenous and/or detrital materials and exists as an unsupported excess in the rapidly accumulating near-shore sediments. Koide et al. (1971) estimated that the residence time of the Pb-210 in the 500 m water column of the Santa Barbara basin is about 1 yr, while other estimates of Pb in the surface waters (upper 100 m) relative to deep waters range from 2 to 7 yr (Rama et al., 1961; Tatsumoto and Patterson, 1963).

Varved deposits from the Santa Barbara Basin, where annual layers are readily separable, provided Koide, Soutar, and Goldberg (1971) with a baseline to ascertain the reliability of the method in the marine environment. The agreement the Pb-210 data and the stratigraphic ages (Fig. 8) indicates a uniformity in the accommodation of Pb-210 in the sedimentary components per unit time, a relatively constant flux of Pb-210, and a residence time of Pb-210 in the waters overlying the sediment that is short with respect to its half-life.

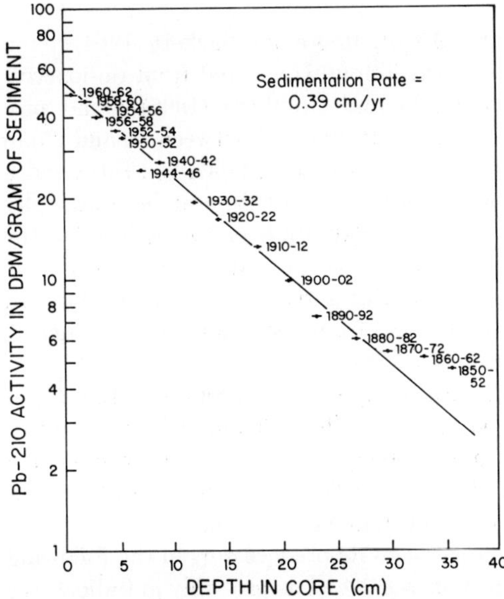

Fig. 8. Pb-210 activity as a function of depth in Santa Barbara basin sediments. The dates have been assigned on the basis of varves. The curve is drawn with the half-life of Pb-210. Koide et al. (1972).

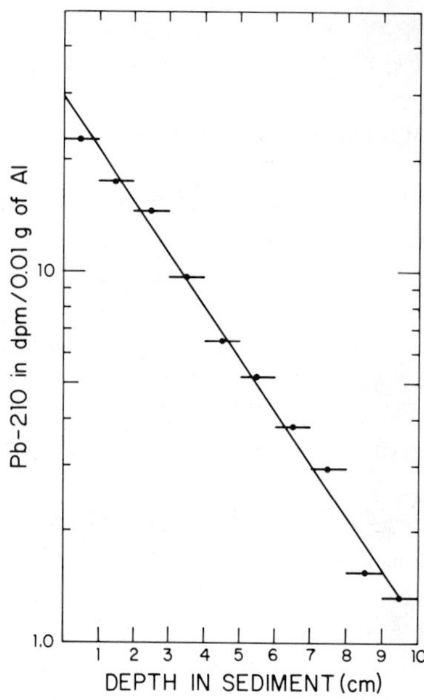

Fig. 9. Pb-210 activity (normalized to aluminum content of the sediment) as a function of depth in San Pedro Basin deposits. The sedimentation rate is 1 mm/yr. The aluminum normalization was made to take into account the varying water contents of the strata.

The applicability of the PB-210 technique to unvarved coastal sediments, depositing at rates of the order of fractions of a millimeter per year or greater has been successfully investigated by Koide, Bruland, and Goldberg (1973) and a typical curve of Pb-210 levels versus depth is given in Fig. 9.

B. *Th-228/Th-232 Geochronologies*

There is an excess of Th-228 over and above that supported by the parent Th-232 or Ra-228 in coastal marine sediments. This excess Th-228 ($t_{1/2}$, 1.91 yr) may be used both for dating purposes over time periods of the order of a decade and as permissive evidence that the uppermost levels of the deposit were obtained during the coring operation.

In surface and deep waters of the Atlantic Ocean, Moore and Sackett (1964) found a 15-fold excess of unsupported Th-228 over the amount expected from radioactive equilibrium with Th-232. Similarly, Somayajulu and Goldberg (1966) found pronounced disequilibria (the Th-228/Th-232 activity ratio varied between 10 and 25) in open ocean Pacific deep waters. On the other hand, the Th-228/Th-232 ratio had a value of 1.0 for a water sample taken from the Scripps Institution of Oceanography pier where the total thorium content was an order of magnitude or two higher that the values for the open ocean samples. Moore (1969) suggests that the most probable mechanism for explaining these high Th-228/Th-232 activity ratios is an upward diffusion of Ra-228 (the immediate parent of Th-228) from near-shore and continental shelf and rise sediments in contact with surface waters.

The Th-228 activities in leachates from surface layers of the Santa Barbara and Baja California sediments were found to be far above those required by radioactive equilibrium with Th-232 (Koide, Bruland, and Goldberg, 1973). In deeper strata, such as those deposited about a decade or so previously, the Th-228 activities can be significantly below those required by radioactive equilibrium with Th-232.

The total Th-228 in the sediment can be related to its predecessors in the following manner. One component exists in the detrital phases, which is probably in radioactive equilibrium with both Ra-228 and Th-232. Experimentally, Koide et al. (1973) assumed that this Th-228 would be retained in the HCl insoluble phase. A second component is the authigenic Th-228, measured in the HCl leachate. This can have three sources, each of which is independent of the other: (1) from seawater where it is derived from the excess Ra-228—the Th-228/Th-232 activity ratio appear to be of the order of 1.0 to 20; (2) from the authigenic Th-232 in the sediment, precipitated from seawater in the absence of its daughters Ra-228 and Th-228; and (3) from unsupported Ra-228 deposited in the sediments from seawater in the absence of its daughter Th-228. This model of the sources of Th-228 is described by the following three equations.

$$A_{\text{Th-228}_{\text{measured}}} = A_{\text{Th-226}_{\text{unsupported}}} + A_{\text{Th-228}_{\text{Th-232 growth}}} + A_{\text{Th-228}_{\text{Ra-228 growth}}} \quad (12)$$

or dividing by the activity of Th-232 found in the leachates:

$$\frac{A_{\text{Th-228}_{\text{measured}}}}{A_{\text{Th-232}}} = \frac{A_{\text{Th-228}_{\text{unsupported}}}}{A_{\text{Th-232}}} + \frac{A_{\text{Th-228}_{\text{Th-232 growth}}}}{A_{\text{Th-232}}} + \frac{A_{\text{Th-228}_{\text{Ra-228 growth}}}}{A_{\text{Th-232}}} \quad (13)$$

Utilizing the Bateman equations for the growth of Th-228 from its parents Ra-228 and Th-232 one obtains:

$$\frac{A_{\text{Th-228}_{\text{measured}}}}{A_{\text{Th-232}}} = \frac{A_{\text{Th-228}_{\text{unsupported}}}}{A_{\text{Th-232}}} + \left[1 + \frac{\lambda_{\text{Ra-228}} \exp(-\lambda_{\text{Th-228}} t) - \lambda_{\text{Th-228}} \exp(-\lambda_{\text{Ra-228}} t)}{\lambda_{\text{Th-228}} - \lambda_{\text{Ra-228}}}\right] + R \cdot \frac{\lambda_{\text{Th-228}}[\exp(-\lambda_{\text{Ra-228}} t) - \exp(-\lambda_{\text{Th-228}} t)]}{\lambda_{\text{Th-228}} - \lambda_{\text{Ra-228}}} \quad (14)$$

where the lambdas are the decay constants of the subscripted isotopes and R is the activity ratio $(A^0_{\text{Ra-228}}/A_{\text{Th-232}})$ with $A^0_{\text{Ra-228}}$ representing the activity of radium-228 at the time of sediment deposition. The data obtained by Koide et al. (1973) for Santa Barbara Basin deposits are presented in Table X and Fig. 10.

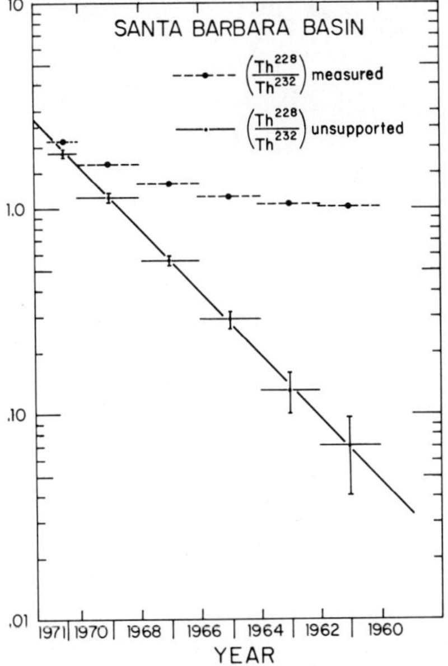

Fig. 10. Th-228/Th-232 activity ratios for leached materials from the Santa Barbara Basin sediments. A value of $R = 0.9$ was used in the calculation. Koide et al. (1972).

Table X

Thorium Isotopes in Santa Barbara Basin Sediments (Koide et al., 1973)

Depth in Sediment (cm)	Deposition Period (Yr)[a]	t (Yr)	$\frac{A_{Th-230}}{A_{Th-232}}$	Thorium (ppm)	$\frac{A_{Th-228}}{A_{Th-232}}$ Unsupported	$\frac{A_{Th-228}}{A_{Th-232}}$ Th–232 Growth	$\frac{A_{Th-228}}{A_{Th-232}}$ Ra–228 Growth $R = 0.9$
0–1.5	1970–1971	1.0	1.10	7.4	2.19	0.02	0.26
0–1.6	1970–1971	1.0	1.11	7.8	1.56	0.02	0.26
1.6–3.5	1968–1970	2.5	1.10	9.1	1.12	0.08	0.47
3.5–5.2	1966–1968	4.5	1.20	7.2	0.56	0.20	0.55
5.2–6.6	1964–1966	6.5	1.15	6.8	0.29	0.32	0.52
6.6–7.7	1962–1964	8.5	1.08	7.8	0.13	0.43	0.47
7.7–8.6	1960–1962	10.5	1.24	8.0	0.07	0.53	0.41
10.4–11.2	1954–1956	16.5	1.15	7.9	—	0.75	0.22

[a] From varves and from Pb–210 geochronology.

Implicit in this model is the assumption that there is no significant diffusion of radium over the time periods involved or disturbances in the deposits from organisms or near-bottom currents. Measurements of the Ra-228 contents are necessary to confirm the model. Most probably Th-228/Th-232 activity ratios can give reliable rates of accumulation for undisturbed coastal marine sediments for periods up to a decade, even in the absence of Ra-228 values.

A combination of Th-228/Th-232 rates with Pb-210 accumulation rates will provide, where concordant results are found, detailed geochronologies for periods up to a century.

C. Ra-228/Ra-226

Coral growth rates have been assigned by Moore and Krishnaswami (1972) on the basis of the decay of unsupported Ra-228 and Pb-210, where the nuclides were directly taken up from seawater. The Ra-228 results follow a predicted model and appear to be applicable to measurements of the last 30 yr of growth.

Moore (1969) found that the youngest part of a coral skeleton contained excess Th-228 over that required for equilibrium with Th-232. He attributed this disequilibrium to an incorporation in the coral of Ra-228, its immediate parent. Older sections of the coral did not show any excess Th-228. If the corals are assumed to initially incorporate a constant ratio of Ra-228 to Ra-226 from seawater, the 6.7 yr half-life can be used to obtain growth rates (Moore and Krishnaswami, 1972). The 1600-yr half-life of Ra-226 indicates that no measurable decay of this nuclide will occur during the dating interval.

Moore and Krishnaswami also examined the Pb-210/Ra-226 ratios, but found that the Pb-210 does not obey an ideal curve in the corals examined. Future work should include comparisons of the Ra-228/Ra-226 method with that of radioactivity bands and annual density bands in corals such as determined by Knutson, Buddemeier, and Smith (1972), discussed in the next section.

D. Artificial Radioisotopes

The fallout of fission products introduced to the atmosphere during nuclear device detonation can form the basis for measuring sedimentary accumulation rates. The fallout went through a maximum around 1963. Assuming a short residence time in the waters overlying sediments for a given nuclide this 1963 maximum provides a reference level to which a date can be assigned.

The initial work was on glacial Antarctic snow (Picciotto and Wilgain, 1963). In the marine environment Schreiber and co-workers (1966, 1968, 1970) have detected sediment layers containing fallout nuclides (Sr-90, Cs-137, Ce-144, Pm-147, and Eu-155) in parts of the Northern Adriatic and Ligurian Seas deposited during 1958 to 1969. These areas occur on a shallow continental shelf near major rivers, where sediment is accumulating relatively rapidly. In such environments with low wave and current action and with high sediment fluxes, distinct sediment layers may be deposited, covered, and preserved before they can be extensively burrowed by benthic organisms. Such seems to be the case in some of the sediment cores analyzed by Schreiber et al. (1968).

Figure 11 depicts the gross beta activity in a core collected on the Po delta in the Adriatic Sea compared to that of atmospheric fallout registered in Italy as a function of time. The core maintains a record of radioactive fallout in its strata in such a way that a comparison of the activity peaks with those from land fallout allows the assignment of ages to various levels. On such a basis, a sedimentation rate of 2 cm/yr is obtained (Fig. 11). The length of the core did not allow the investigators to observe an increase of activity corresponding to the 1959 fallout peak.

Another means of determining sedimentation rates utilizing Ce-144 was proposed by Schreiber (1966, 1968). This fission product has a half life of 285 days and reaches a

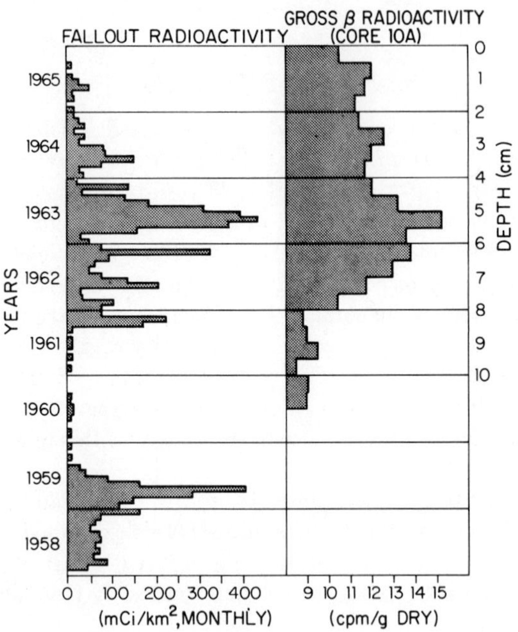

Fig. 11. A comparison of atmospheric fallout at Ispra, Euratom Center, Italy with the gross beta activity in an Adriatic Sea sediment collected near the Po River mouth in 1966. Schreiber et al. (1968). Sediment accumulation rate is about 2 cm/yr.

level no longer measurable after four half-lives or 3 yr. The decay of Ce-144 to this undetectable level was generally found a depth of 3 to 4 cm below the interface. Thus, it may be argued that the rate of deposition of such sediments corresponds to approximately 1 cm/yr (assuming no physical or biological mixing).

The utilization of Sr-90 and Cs-137 for time marker horizons in the sedimentary column is severely hampered by the diffusion characteristics of the ionic forms of these nuclides. The diffusion coefficients of Sr-90 and Cs-137 in sediments are about 10^{-8} to 10^{-7} cm^2/sec and 10^{-9} to 10^{-8} cm^2/sec, respectfully, compared to values for the rare earth metals of 10^{-11} to 10^{-10} cm^2/sec (Duursma and Gross, 1971). Thus, although the rate earth radionuclides, Ce-144, Pm-147, and Eu-155 would have negligible diffusion in these rapidly accumulating sediments; the concentration of Sr-90 and Cs-137 could be significantly altered by diffusional fluxes even in areas where the deposition rate is as high as centimeters per year.

Recently strontium-90 has been used as a coral-growth chronometer (Knutson, Buddemeier, and Smith, 1972). Radioactivity bands in the coral structure, caused by Sr-90, correspond to a specific series of nuclear tests (1948 to 1958). By correlating the

Table XI

Method	Primary Radio-nuclide	Half-Life	Source	Range of Applicability (Years)	Material or Process Dated	References Initial Work and Intercomparison with Other Methods
K-Ar	K-40	1.3×10^9	Primordial	$10^5 - 10^{10}$	Ash layers to obtain sedimentation rates	Dymond (1966); Dymond (1969)
					Nucleus (basaltic) material to obtain growth rate of Mn nodules	Barnes and Dymond (1967)
Fission-track	U-238	10^{16}	Primordial	$10^5 - 10^{10}$	Ash layers and microtektites to obtain sedimentation rates	Macdougall (1971); Gentner et al. (1970)
Be-10	Be-10	2.5×10^6	Cosmic-ray interaction	$0.5 \times 10^6 - 10^7$	Pelagic sediments (red clay)	Peters (1955); Amin et al. (1966); Amin (1970)
					Manganese nodules	Somayajulu (1967); Bhat et al. (1973)
U-He	U-238	4.5×10^9	Primordial	No limit	Corals and oolites	Fanale and Schaeffer (1965)
U-234/U-238	U-234	2.48×10^5	U-238 decay	$5 \times 10^4 - 10^6$	Corals and oolites	Thurber (1962); Thurber et al. (1965); Veeh (1966)
					Phosphorites	Kolodny and Kaplan (1970)
					Manganese nodules	Barnes and Dymond (1967); Ku and Broecker (1967)
					Pelagic sediments	Ku (1965)
Th-230	Th-230	7.52×10^4	U-234 decay	$2 \times 10^4 - 3 \times 10^5$	Pelagic sediments	Volchok and Kulp (1952); Ku, Broecker and Opdike (1968); Ku et al. (1972)
					Manganese nodules	Ku and Broecker (1967, 1969); Barnes and Dymond (1967)

(continued)

TABLE XI (*continued*)

Method	Primary Radio-nuclide	Half-Life	Source	Range of Applicability (Years)	Material or Process Dated	References Initial Work and Intercomparison with Other Methods
Th-230/Th-232	Th-230	7.52×10^4	U-234 decay	$2 \times 10^4 - 3 \times 10^5$	Pelagic sediments	Picciotto and Wilgan (1954); Goldberg and Koide (1958, 1962); Goldberg (1968); Amin (1970)
					Manganese nodules	Barnes and Dymond (1967); Bhat et al. (1973)
Pa-231	Pa-231	3.43×10^4	U-235 decay	$10^4 - 1.4 \times 10^5$	Pelagic sediments	Sackett (1960, 1965); Sarma (1964); Ku and Broecker (1967); Ku et al. (1972)
					Manganese nodules	Ku and Broecker (1969)
Pa-231/Th-230	Pa-231 Th-230	5.8×10^4 ratio	U-235, U-234 decay	$10^4 - 1.4 \times 10^5$	Pelagic sediments	Sackett (1960); Rosholt et al. (1961)
					Manganese nodules	Ku and Broecker (1969)
Th-230/U-234	Th-230	7.52×10^4	U-234 decay	$0 - 2 \times 10^5$	Corals and oolites	Barnes et al. (1956); Thurber et al. (1965) Blanchard et al. (1967); Kaufman et al. (1971)
Pa-231/U-235	Pa-231	3.43×10^4	U-235 decay	$0 - 10^5$	Corals and oolites	Rosholt and Antal (1962); Ku (1968)
C-14/C-12	C-14	5.57×10^3	Cosmic-ray interaction, bombs	$10^3 - 4 \times 10^4$	Calcareous pelagic sediments or near shore sediments with substantial organics or carbonate	Arrhenius et al. (1951); Broecker and Kulp (1956); Emery (1960); Emery and Bray (1962)
Si-32	Si-32	500	Cosmic-ray interaction	200–2000	Silicious sediments depositing at relatively high rates	Kharkar et al. (1963); Kharkar, Turekian and Scott (1969)
Pb-210	Pb-210	22.3	Rn-222 Ra-226 decay	10–100	Rapidly accumulating near shore sediments	Koide, Soutar, and Goldberg (1971); Koide, Bruland, and Goldberg (1973)
Ra-228/Ra-226	Ra-228	6.7	Th-232 decay	5–30	Rates of coral growth	Moore and Krishnaswamy (1973)
Th-228/Th-232	Th-228	1.91	Ra-228 decay	1–10	Rapidly accumulating near shore sediments	Koide, Bruland, and Goldberg (1973)
Artificial radionuclides	Variety		Nuclear tests, bombs, reactors	20	Rapidly accumulating near shore sediments, rate of coral growh	Schrieber et al. (1968); Knutson et al. (1972)

outer most intense band found in the corals with the large 1958 test, an average growth rate over the last decade or so can be obtained. There was good agreement between ages based on radioactivity inclusions and those determined by variations in the density of bands.

7. A Final Overview

The available dating techniques for marine sediments are summarized in Table XI, a nonexhaustive but critical compilation of recent investigations. Included are ranges of applicability and materials or geological processes that have had ages assigned on the basis of a given technique.

References

Amin, B. S., D. P. Kharkar, and D. Lal, 1966. Cosmogenic Be^{10} and Al^{26} in marine sediments. *Deep-Sea Res.*, **13**, 805.

Amin, B. S., 1970. Dating of ocean sediments by radioactive methods. M.Sc. thesis, Tata Institute of Fundamental Research, University of Bombay.

Arrhenius, G., G. Kjellburg, and W. F. Libby, 1951. Age determination of Pacific chalk ooze by radiocarbon and titanium content. *Tellus*, **3**, 222.

Barnes, J. W., E. J. Lang, and H. A. Potratz, 1956. Ratio of ionium to uranium in coral limestone. *Science*, **124**, 175–176.

Barnes, S. S. and J. R. Dymond, 1967. Rates of accumulation of ferromanganese nodules. *Nature*, **213**, 1218–1219.

Bender, M. L., T. L. Ku, and W. S. Broecker, 1970. Accumulation rates of manganese in pelagic sediments and nodules. *Earth and Planet. Sci. Letters*, **8**, 143–148.

Bernat, M., R. H. Bieri, M. Koide, J. J. Griffin, and E. D. Goldberg, 1970. Uranium, thorium, potassium and argon in marine phillipsites. *Geochim. Cosmochim. Acta*, **34**, 1053–1071.

Bhat, S. G., S. Krishnaswamy, D. Lal, Rama and B. L. K. Somayajulu, 1973. Radioactive and trace elemental studies of ferromanganese nodules. *Proc. Symposium on Hydrogeochemistry and Biogeochemistry* (*Tokyo 1970*), **1**, 443–462.

Blanchard, R. L., 1965. U-234/U-238 ratios in coastal marine waters and calcium carbonates. *J. Geophys. Res.*, **70**, 4055–4061.

Blanchard, R. L., M. H. Cheng, and H. A. Potratz, 1967. Uranium and thorium series disequilibria in recent and fossil marine molluscan shells. *J. Geophys. Res.*, **72**, 4745–4757.

Broecker, W. S. and J. L. Kulp, 1956. The radiocarbon method of age determination. *Amer. Antiq.*, **22**, 1–11.

Broecker, W. S., 1963. A preliminary evaluation of uranium series inequilibrium as a tool for absolute age measurement on marine carbonates. *J. Geophys. Res.*, **68**, 2817–2834.

Broecker, W. S. and D. L. Thurber, 1965. Uranium series dating of corals and oolites from Bahaman and Florida Key limestones. *Science*, **149**, 58–60.

Broecker, W. S. and J. van Donk, 1970. Insolation changes, ice volumes, and the O^{18} record in deep-sea cores. *Rev. Geophys. Space Phys.*, **8**, 169–198.

Broecker, W. S., K. K. Turekian, and B. C. Heezen, 1958. The relation of deep-sea sedimentation rates to variations in climate. *Am. Jour. Sci.*, **256**, 503.

Cherdyntsev, V. V. (with P. I. Chalov, M. E. Khitrik et al.), 1955. Ob izotopnom sostave radio elementov—V privodnykh obyektakh V sviazi S voprosami geokhronologii. (On isotopic composition of radioelements in natural objects, and problems of geochronology.) *Trudy III Sessii Komissi Opred. Absol. Yozrastu*, 175–233, Izd. Akad. Nauk SSSR, Moscow.

Cherdyntsev, V. V., D. P. Orlov, E. A. Isabaev, and V. I. Ivanov, 1961. Isotopic composition of uranium in minerals. *Geochemistry*, 927–936.

Cox, A., R. R. Doell, and G. B. Dalrymple, 1964. Reversals of the earth's magnetic field. *Science*, **144**, 1537.

Crozaz, G., E. Picciotto, and W. DeBrueck, 1964. Antarctic snow chronology with Pb-210. *J. Geophys. Res.*, **69**, 2597–2604.

Dasch, E. J., 1969. Strontium isotopes in weathering profiles, deep-sea sediments, and sedimentary rocks. *Geochim. Cosmochim. Acta*, **33**, 1521–1552.

Dooley, J. R., Jr., H. C. Granger, and J. N. Rosholt, 1966. Uranium-234 fractionation in the sandstone-type uranium deposits of the Ambrosia Lake district, New Mexico. *Econ. Geology*, **61**, 1362–1382.

Duursma, E. K. and M. G. Gross, 1971. Marine sediments and radioactivity. In *Radioactivity in the Marine Environment*. National Academy of Sciences.

Dymond, J. R., 1966. Potassium argon geochronology of deep-sea sediments. *Science*, **152**, 1239.

Dymond, J., 1969. Age determinations of deep-sea sediments: A comparison of three methods. *Earth and Planet. Sci. Letters*, **6**, 9–14.

Dymond, J., 1970. Excess argon in submarine basalt pillows. *Geol. Soc. Amer. Bull.*, **81**, 1229–1232.

Emery, K. O. and R. S. Dietz, 1941. Gravity coring instruments and mechanics of sediment coring. *Bull. Geol. Soc. Amer.*, **52**, 1685.

Emery, K. O., 1960. The sea off Southern California. Wiley, New York, 366 pp.

Emery, K. O. and E. E. Bray, 1962. Radiocarbon dating of California basin sediments. *Am. Assoc. Petroleum Geologists Bull.*, **46**, 1839–1856.

Ericson, D. B. and Goesta Wollin, 1956. Correlation of six cores from the equatorial Atlantic and Caribbean. *Deep-Sea Res.*, **3**, 104–125.

Fanale, F. P. and O. A. Schaeffer, 1965. The helium-uranium method for dating marine carbonates. *Science*, **149**, 312–317.

Funkhouser, J., D. E. Fisher, and E. Bonatti, 1968. Excess argon in deep-sea rocks. *Earth and Planet. Sci. Letters*, **5**, 95–100.

Gentner, W., B. P. Glass, D. Storzer, and G. A. Wagner, 1970. Fission track ages and ages of deposition of deep sea microtektites. *Science*, **168**, 359–361.

Goldberg, E. D., 1968. Ionium/thorium geochronologies. *Earth and Planet. Sci. Letters*, **4**, 17–21.

Goldberg, E. D., 1963. Geochronology with lead-210, Radioactive Dating, IAEA, Vienna.

Goldberg, E. D. and M. Koide, 1962. Geochronological studies of deep-sea sediments by the Io/Th method. *Geochim. Cosmochim. Acta*, **26**, 417–450.

Goldberg, E. D. and M. Koide, 1958. Ionium/thorium chronology in deep-sea sediments of the Pacific. *Science*, **128**, 1003.

Goldberg, E. D., M. Koide, J. J. Griffin, and M. N. A. Peterson, 1964. A geochronological and sedimentary profile across the North Atlantic Ocean. In *Isotopic and Cosmic Chemistry*. North-Holland Pub. Co., Amsterdam, 553 pp.

Goldberg, E. D. and J. J. Griffin, 1964. Sedimentation rates and mineralogy in the South Atlantic. *J. Geophys. Res.*, **69**, 4293–4309.

Harrison, C. G. A. and B. L. K. Somayajulu, 1966. Behavior of the earth's magnetic field during a reversal. *Nature*, **212**, 1193–1195.

Holmes, C. W., 1965. Rates of sedimentation in the Drake Passage. Ph.D. thesis, Florida State University, Tallahassee.

Horn, D. R., M. N. Delach, and B. M. Horn, 1969. Distribution of volcanic ash layers and turbidites in the North Pacific. *Geol. Soc. America Bull.*, **80**, 1715–1724.

Hurley, P. M., B. C. Heezen, W. H. Pinson, and H. W. Fairbairn, 1963. K-Ar age values in pelagic sediments of the North Atlantic. *Geochim. Cosmochim. Acta*, **27**, 393–399.

Joly, J. J., 1908. On the radium content of deep-sea sediments. *Phil. Mag.*, **16**, 190.

Kaufman, A., W. S. Broecker, T. L. Ku, and D. L. Thurber, 1971. The status of U-series methods of mollusk dating. *Geochim Cosmochim. Acta*, **35**, 1155–1183.

Kharkar, D. P., D. Lal, and B. L. K. Somayajulu, 1963. Investigations in Marine environments using radioisotopes produced by cosmic rays. In *Radioactive Dating*. IAEA, Vienna, 440 pp.

Kharkar, D. P., K. K. Turekian, and M. R. Scott, 1969. Comparison of sedimentation rates obtained by Si-32 and uranium decay series determinations in some siliceous Antarctic cores. *Earth and Planet. Sci. Letters*, **6**, 61–68.

Knutson, D. W., R. W. Buddemeier, and S. V. Smith, 1972. Coral chronometers: seasonal growth bands in reef corals. *Science*, **177**, 270–272.

Koide, M. and E. D. Goldberg, 1965. Uranium-234/uranium-238 ratios in sea water. In *Progress in Oceanography*. Vol. 3. M. Sears, ed. Pergamon Press, New York, pp. 173–177.

Koide, M., A. Soutar, and E. D. Goldberg, 1971. Marine geochronology with Pb-210. *Earth and Planet. Sci. Letters*, **14**, 442–446.

Koide, M., K. W. Bruland, and E. D. Goldberg, 1973. Th-228/Th-232 and Pb-210 geochronologies in marine and lake sediments. *Geochim. Cosmochim. Acta*, **37**, 1171–1187.

Kolodny, Y. and I. R. Kaplan, 1970. Uranium isotopes in sea-floor phosphorites. *Geochim. Cosmochim. Acta*, **34**, 3–24.

Krylov, A. Y., A. P. Lisitzin and Y. I. Silin, 1961. The significance of Ar-K ratios in oceanic muds. *Izvestia Akad. Nauk SSSR*, Ser. Geol., No. 3.

Krylov, A. Ya and Yu-I. Silin, 1963. Comparison of absolute ages of rocks, micas and feldspars carried out by the argon method. Akad. Nauk USSR Kom. Opredeleniyu Absolyut. Vozrasta Geol. Formatisy Trudy, 11 Sess., 194.

Krishnaswamy, S., D. Lal, J. M. Martin, and M. Meybeck, 1971. Geochronology of lake sediments. *Earth and Planet. Sci. Letters*, **11**, 407–414.

Ku, T. L., 1965. An evaluation of the U-234/U-238 method as a tool for dating pelagic sediments. *J. Geophys. Res.*, **70**, 3457–3474.

Ku, T. L., 1965b. Dating of deep-sea sediments by the Th-230 and Pa-231 methods: an evaluation (Abstract). *Trans. Amer. Geophys. Union*, **46**, 168.

Ku, T. L., 1968. Protactinium 231 method of dating coral from Barbados Island. *J. Geophys. Res.*, **73**, 2271–2276.

Ku, T. L. and W. S. Broecker, 1966. Atlantic deep-sea stratigraphy: extension of absolute chronology to 320,000 yrs. *Science*, **151**, 448–450.

Ku, T. L. and W. S. Broecker, 1967. Rates of sedimentation in the Arctic Ocean. In *Progress in Oceanography*. Vol. 4. Pergamon, Oxford, pp. 95–104.

Ku, T. L. and W. S. Broecker, 1969. Radiochemical studies of manganese nodules of deep sea origin. *Deep-Sea Res.*, **16**, 625–637.

Ku, T., W. S. Broecker, and N. Opdyke, 1968. Comparison on sedimentation rates measured by paleomagnetic and the ionium methods of age determination. *Earth and Planet. Sci. Letters*, **4**, 1–16.

Ku, T., J. L. Bischoff, and Anne Boersma, 1972. Age studies on Mid Atlantic ridge sediments near 42°N and 20°N. *Deep-Sea Res.*, **19**, 233–248.

Lal, D., E. D. Goldberg, and M. Koide, 1960. Cosmic-ray produced Si-32 in nature. *Science*, **131**, 332–7.

Lal, D. and H. E. Suess, 1968. The radioactivity of the atmosphere and hydrosphere. *Annual Review of Nuclear Science*, **18**, 407–434.

Macdougall, D., 1971. Fission track dating of volcanic glass shards in marine sediments. *Earth and Planet Sci. Letters*, **10**, 403–406.

Miyake, Y., Y. Sugimura, and T. Uchida, 1966. Ratio U-234/U-238 and the uranium concentration in seawater in the western North Pacific. *J. Geophys. Res.*, **71**, 3083–3087.

Moore, W. S. and W. M. Sackett, 1964. Uranium and thorium series inequilibrium in sea water. *J. Geophys. Res.*, **69**, 5401–5405.

Moore, W. S., 1969. Measurement of Ra-228 and Th-228 in sea water. *J. Geophys. Res.*, **74**, 694–704.

Moore, W. S. and S. Krishnaswamy, 1972. Coral growth rates using Ra-228 and Pb-210. *Earth and Planet. Sci. Letters*, **15**, 187–190.

Noble, C. S. and J. J. Naughton, 1968. Deep-ocean basalts: inert gas content and uncertainties in age dating. *Science*, **162**, 265–267.

Olsen, E. A. and W. S. Broecker, 1959. Lamont natural radiocarbon measurements V. *Radiocarbon*, **1**, 1–29.

Olson, E. A. and W. S. Broecker, 1961. Lamont natural radiocarbon measurements VII. *Radiocarbon*, **3**, 141–175.

Opdyke, N. D., B. Glass, J. D. Hays, and J. Foster, 1966. A paleomagnetic study of Antarctic deep sea cores. *Science*, **154**, 349.

Osmond, J. K., J. R. Carpenter, and H. L. Windom, 1965. Th^{230}/U^{234} age of the Pleistocene corals and oolites of Florida. *J. Geophys. Res.*, **70**, 1843–1847.

Peters, B., 1955. Radioactive beryllium in the atmosphere and on the earth. *Proc. Ind. Acad. Sci.*, **41**, 67.

Pettersson, H., 1937. The proportion of thorium to uranium in rocks and in the sea. Anz. Akad. Wiss. Wien. Matl.-Nature K. L., 127.

Picciotto, E. and S. Wilgain, 1954. Thorium determination in deep-sea sediments. *Nature*, **173**, 632.

Picciotto, E. and S. Wilgain, 1963. Fission products in Antarctic snow, a reference level for measuring accumulation. *Jour. Geophys. Res.*, **68**, 5965–5972.

Piggot, C. S. and W. D. Urry, 1941. Radioactivity of ocean sediments. *Amer. J. Sci.*, **239**, 81–91.

Piggot, C. S. and W. D. Urry, 1942. The radium content of sediments of the Cayman trough. *Am. J. Sci.*, **240**, 1.

Rama, M. Koide and E. D. Goldberg, 1961. Lead-210 in natural waters. *Science*, **134**, 98–99

Richards, A. F., 1961. Investigations of deep-sea sediment cores, I. shear strength, bearing capacity and consolidation. Tech. Rep. Hydrogr. Off. Wash. 63, 70 pp.

Rosholt, J. N., Cesare Emiliani, Johannes Geiss, F. F. Koczy, and P. J. Wangersky, 1961. Absolute dating of deep-sea cores by the Pa-231/Th-230 method. *J. Geol.*, **69**, 162–185.

Rosholt, J. N., Cesare Emiliani, Johannes Geiss, F. F. Koczy, and P. J. Wangersky, 1962. Pa-231/Th-230 dating and O^{18}/O^{16} temperature analysis of core A 254-BR-C. *J. Geophys. Res.*, **67**, 2907–2911.

Rosholt, J. N. and P. S. Antal, 1962. Evaluation of the Pa-231/U-th-230/U method for dating Pleistocene carbonate rocks. U.S. Geol. Surv. Prof. Paper 450-E, article 209, E108.

Rosholt, J. N., W. R. Shields, and E. L. Garner, 1963. Isotopic fractionation of uranium in sandstone. *Science*, **139**, 224–226.

Rosholt, J. N., B. R. Doe, and Mitsunobu Tatsumoto, 1966. Evolution of the isotopic composition of uranium and thorium in soil profiles. *Geol. Soc. America Bull.*, **77**, 987–1003.

Rosholt, J. N., 1967. Open system model for uranium series dating of Pleistocene samples. In *Radioactive Dating and Methods of Low-Level Counting*. Symposium, Monaco, Proc. Vienna, IAEA, 744 pp. Pp. 299–311.

Ross, D. A. and W. R. Reidel, 1967. Comparison of upper parts of some piston cores with simultaneously collected open-barrel cores. *Deep-Sea Res.*, **14**, 285–294.

Rubin, Meyer and H. E. Suess, 1955. United States Geological Survey natural radiocarbon measurements II. *Science*, **121**, 481–488.

Sackett, W. M., 1958. Ionium-Uranium ratios in marine deposited calcium carbonates and related materials. Ph.D. dissertation, Washington University, St. Louis, Mo., 106 pp.

Sackett, W. M., 1960. Protactinium-231 content of ocean water and sediments. *Science*, **132**, 1761–1762.

Sackett, W. M., 1964. Measured deposition rates of marine sediments and implications for accumulation rates of extraterrestrial dust. *Annals of the New York Academy of Sciences*, **119**, 339–346.

Sackett, W. M., 1965. Deposition rates by the protactinium method. Third Annual Symposium on Marine Geochem., University of Rhode Island Occasional Publication No. 3, 29.

Sackett, W. M., 1966. Manganese nodules: thorium-230: protactinium-231 ratios. *Science*, **154**. 646–647.

Sakanoue, M., K. Konishi, and K. Komura, 1967. Stepwise determinations of thorium, protactinium, and uranium isotopes and their application for geochronological studies. Symposium on radioactive dating and method of low-level counting. SM-87/28, IAEA, Monaco.

Sarma, T. P., 1964. Dating of marine sediments by ionium and protoactinium methods. Ph.D. Thesis. Carnegie Institute of Technology, Pittsburgh.

Schreiber, B., 1966. Radionuclides in marine plankton and in coastal sediments. In *Radioecological Concentration Process*. B. Aberg and F. P. Ungate, eds. Pergamon Press, pp. 753–770.

Schreiber, B., 1968. Essay of a method of absolute dating of the coastal marine sediments by means of the vertical distribution of the fallout radionuclides. Estratto dal Fasc. 6, Serie VIII, Vol. XLV, 515–521.

Schreiber, B., I. Tassi Pelati, M. G. Mezzadri, and G. Motta, 1968. Gross beta radioactivity in sediments of the North Adriatic Sea: a possibility of evaluating the sedimentation rate. *Arch. Oceanogr. Limnol.*, **16** (1), 45–62.

Schreiber, B., E. Cerrai, M. G. Mezzadri, and C. Triulzi, 1970. Some radioactivity measurements of sediment samples collected in the North Adriatic Sea. *Energia Nucleare*, **17**, 176–181.

Somayajulu, B. L. K., 1967. Be-10 in a manganese nodule. *Science* **156**, 1219–1229.

Somayajulu, B. L. K. and E. D. Goldberg, 1966. Thorium and uranium isotopes in sea water and sediments. *Earth and Planet. Sci. Letters*, **1**, 102–106.

Starik, I. E., F. E. Starik, and B. A. Mikhailov, 1958. Shifts of isotopic ratios in natural materials. *Geokhimiya*, No. 5, 462.

Suess, H., 1954. U.S. Geological Survey radiocarbon dates I. *Science*, **120**, 467–473.

Szabo, B. J. and J. N. Rosholt, 1969. Uranium-series dating of Pleistocene molluscan shells from Southern California—an open system model. *J. Geophys. Res.*, **74** (12), 3253–3260.

Szabo, B. J. and J. G. Vedder, 1971. Uranium-series dating of some Pleistocene marine deposits in Southern California. *Earth and Planet. Sci. Letters*, **11**, 283–290.

Tatsumoto, M. and E. D. Goldberg, 1959. Some aspects of the marine geochemistry of uranium. *Geochim. Cosmochim. Acta*, **17**, 201–208.

Tatsumoto, M. and C. C. Patterson, 1963. The concentration of common lead in sea water. In *Earth Science and Meteoritics*. J. Geiss and E. D. Goldberg, eds. North Science Publishing Co., Amsterdam, pp. 74–89.

Thurber, D. L., 1962. Anomalous U^{234}/U^{238} in nature. *J. Geophys. Res.*, **67**, 4518–4520.

Thurber, D. L., 1963. Natural variations in the ratio of U-234 to U-238. In *Symposium on Radioactive Dating*. Athens, 1962. Proc. Ser., Vienna, IAEA Pub. 68, 113–120.

Thurber, D. L., W. S. Broecker, R. L. Blanchard, and H. A. Potratz, 1965. Uranium series ages of Pacific atoll coral. *Science*, **149**, 55–58.

Turekian, K. K. and M. Stuiver, 1964. Clay and carbonate accumulation rates in three South Atlantic deep-sea cores. *Science*, **146**, 55–56.

Turekian, K. K., D. P. Kharkar, J. Funkhouser and O. A. Schaeffer, 1970. An evaluation of the uranium-helium method of dating fossil bones. *Earth and Planet. Sci. Letters*, **7**, 420–424.

Turekian, K. K. and L. H. Chan, 1971. The marine geochemistry of the uranium isotopes, Th-230 and Pa-231. In *Activation Analysis in Geochemistry and Cosmochemistry*. A. O. Brunfelt and E. Steinnes, eds. Universitets forlaget.

Umemoto, Shunji, 1965. U-234/U-238 in sea water from the Kuroshio region. *J. Geophys. Res.*, **70**, 5326–5327.

Van Andel, Tjeerd H., 1964. Recent marine sediments of Gulf of California, In *Marine Geology of the Gulf of California*. T. H. Van Andel and G. G. Shor, eds. Memoir 3, AAPG.

Veeh, H. H., 1966. Th-230/U-238 and U-234/U-238 ages of Pleistocene high sea level stand. *J. Geophys. Res.*, **71**, 3379–3386.

Veeh, H. H., 1967. Deposition of uranium from the ocean. *Earth and Planet. Sci. Letters*, **3**, 145–150.

Veeh, H. H., 1968. U-234/U-238 in the East Pacific sector of the Antarctic Ocean and in the Red Sea. *Geochim. Cosmochim. Acta*, **32**, 117–119.

Volchok, H. L. and J. L. Kulp, 1952. Age determination of deep sea cores by the ionium method. *Geol. Soc. Amer. Bull.*, **63**, 1386–1387.

Watkins, N. D. and H. G. Goodell, 1967. Confirmation of the reality of the Gilsa geomagnetic polarity event. *Earth and Planet. Sci. Letters*, **2**, 123.

Windom, H. L., 1969. Atmospheric dust records in permanent snowfields, implications to marine sedimentation. *Geol. Soc. Amer. Bull.*, **80**, 761–782.

15. AUTHIGENIC MINERALS IN DEEP-SEA SEDIMENTS

D. S. Cronan

1. Introduction

Authigenic minerals in deep-sea sediments have been of interest to oceanographers and marine geologists ever since they were first found to be abundant in certain parts of the oceans during the last three decades of the nineteenth century. It was realized by the early workers that these minerals could be used to elucidate chemical processes operating on the ocean floor, and this remains one of the principal reasons for their continuing investigation. Because they are formed *in situ* in the sediments, they can provide a record of physicochemical and biological reactions operating and having operated at their site of deposition during the period of their formation. For example, study of the layer-by-layer composition of manganese nodules might provide information on changes in the chemistry of the environment of deposition with time (Aumento et al., 1968; Scott et al., 1972). Similarly, study of radioactive nuclides in marine barite and phillipsite can provide information on the processes by which such elements are removed from seawater (Bernat and Goldberg, 1969; Bernat et al., 1970; Church and Bernat, 1972). Furthermore, once the relationship between the nature of present day authigenic minerals and that of their environment of deposition has been reasonably well established, study of ancient authigenic minerals can, by analogy, lead to a reconstruction of their environments of deposition. Examples of this application include studies of fossil manganese nodules from Timor and Sicily (Audley-Charles, 1965; Jenkyns, 1970), and the iron oxide deposits that underlie normal pelagic sediments in many young oceanic areas (Bostrom et al., 1972). There are a large variety of authigenic minerals in deep-sea sediments, most of them fairly rare. Four groups are relatively abundant, however, and have been the subject of increasing attention in recent years. These are barite, zeolites, iron oxides, and manganese nodules, and form the subject of this chapter.

2. Marine Barite

Barite ($BaSO_4$) is the most common mineral of barium and is widespread in deep-sea sediments. On land, its principal occurrences are as a gangue mineral in hydrothermal veins, and as veins, cavity fillings, and concretions in sedimentary rocks (Deer, et al., 1963). In the oceans, however, these associations, while extant, are less important than the association with biogenous remains of various types. Marine barite was first described by Murray and Renard (1891). More recently it has been reported from various oceans in the form of fecal pellets (Goldberg and Arrhenius, 1958), nodules (Vinogradov, 1953; Revelle and Emery, 1951) and euhedral crystals up to $30 \times 50\ \mu$ in size (Arrhenius, 1963). However according to Church (1970), it generally occurs as microcrystalline phases in deep-sea sediments (Fig. 1) and, while averaging about 1%, may be present in concentrations of as much as 10% by weight in the calcium carbonate-free fraction of some Pacific sediments (Arrhenius and Bonatti, 1965).

Compositionally, marine barite has a high degree of purity, but can contain foreign atoms by heterogenous occlusion or solid solution. Up to 3% Sr has been reported in solid solution by Church (1970). Barites from continental, continental borderland, and deep-sea environments show no consistent differences in their Sr contents, nor does Sr vary with crystal size or depth of burial. Calcium and potassium commonly

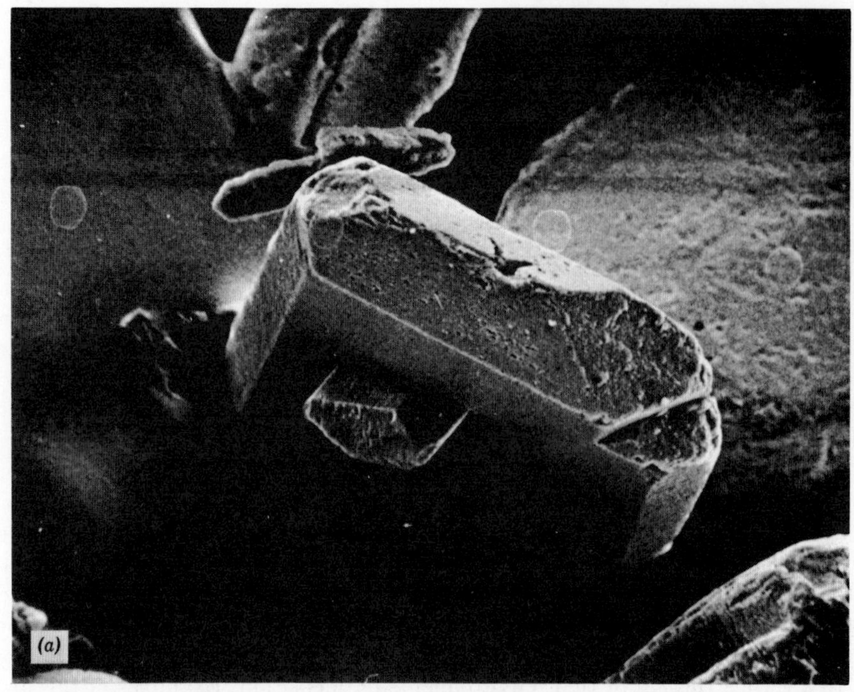
(a)

(b)

Fig. 1. Four photographs showing crystals of marine barite: (*a*) Barite twin × 2000. (*b*) Barite euhedra × 3000. (*c*) Barite microcrystals × 3000. (*d*) Barite euhedra and common microcrystals × 600. Photomicrographs were taken on samples prepared by T. Church and M. Bernat with a CAMECA, Inc., scanning electron microscope under support of the Centre National de la Recherche Scientifique, France.

have concentrations between 0.01 and 0.1% in barites of both marine and continental origin (Church, 1970), but higher values occur. A portion of these elements may be related to the presence of small amounts of feldspar as impurities in the separates used for analysis. Neither K nor Ca show any relationship to crystal size in barite, nor to the abundance of Sr. Calcium shows no preference for marine or continental barites, but K is slightly enriched in deep-sea barites relative to its content in continental and borderland varieties, and may serve to distinguish the two. Deep-sea barites can, however, be better distinguished from continental and continental borderland varieties on the basis of their Th and U contents, and the Th/U ratio (Goldberg et al., 1969). Marine barites were found to have Th and U concentrations of approximately 35 and 2.5 ppm, respectively, whereas the continental varieties had values of Th less than 1 ppm, with U beneath detection. Other minor elements such as Fe, Cr, Zn, Cu, Ni, Pb, Mn, Co, and Zr are generally present in marine barite in concentrations of between about 10 and 350 ppm (Church, 1970), but Arrhenius (1963) has reported Cr and B values of 1000 and 1400 ppm, respectively, in some marine celestobarite crystals.

The distribution of barite in deep-sea sediments has been discussed by a number of authors. Turekian and Imbrie (1966) found Ba concentrations higher than the Atlantic average in sediments associated with the Mid-Atlantic Ridge, and Arrhenius and Bonatti (1965) found maximum concentrations of 7 to 9% barite on a carbonate-free basis over parts of the East Pacific Rise (Fig. 2). The latter area was surrounded by a zone of intermediate barite concentrations, which also extended westward into the equatorial zone of high carbonate productivity. More recently, Church (1970) has examined fresh data on the distribution of barite in the southeastern Pacific and found it to be more irregular than had been reported previously, with highest concentrations occurring in the equatorial and southeastern sections of the basin (Fig. 3). Notable absences of barite occur on parts of the crest of the East Pacific Rise. In general, it was found to be associated with sediments containing an abundance of biological remains such as carbonate and silica tests, or an abundance of ferromanganese or iron oxide phases. In three east-west traverses across the East Pacific Rise, the occurrence of barite correlates directly with calcium carbonate. It was also found to be inversely correlated with phillipsite, possibly because phillipsite-harmotome could compete with barite for Ba ions and thus limit the growth of the barite crystals (Church, 1970).

Recent studies on deeply buried sediments obtained during the JOIDES Deep Sea Drilling Project have shown that barite is probably at least as abundant beneath the sediment surface as on it, and according to Church (personal communication) is indistinguishable in size, REE chemistry, and other properties from modern varieties. Barite-bearing sediments were found in the Atlantic off Brazil during Leg IV of the project, the mineral occurring principally in the 2 to 10 μ fraction of the sediments. However, the highest concentrations to date have been recorded in the Pacific Ocean. In the vicinity of the Mendocino Fracture Zone, for example, barite comprises as much as 6% of the sediment. In two widely separated cores from this area, barite is associated with sediments containing an abundant reworked fauna, indicating that the mineral could have been introduced by slumping from nearby shallower areas (Rex and Murray, 1970). Much of the barite in Deep Sea Drilling Cores from the western Pacific seems to be concentrated in sediments of Miocene age, although it has also been found in both younger and older deposits. It occurs in Upper and Middle Miocene chalk oozes, for example, in both DSDP 55 and 56 cored in the vicinity of the Caroline Ridge. In DSDP 64 it occurs in predominantly calcareous sediments of Miocene to Eocene age, and in DSDP 66 in Middle Miocene radiolarian oozes (Cook

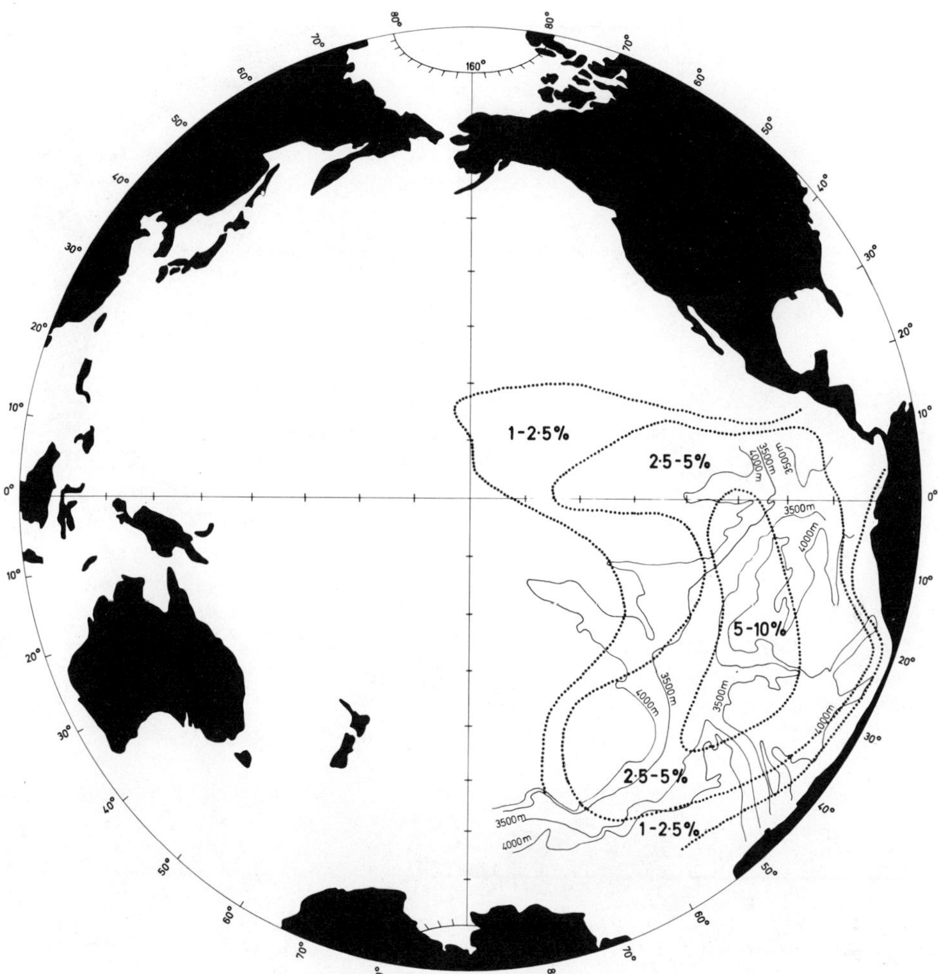

Fig. 2. Barite concentrations in Pacific pelagic sediments. After Arrhenius and Bonatti (1965).

et al., 1971). It is also abundant in the central and southern Pacific. In DSDP 69 it occurs in the finer than 2-μ fraction of Miocene sediments, but in the coarser than 2-μ fraction of the underlying Oligocene calcareous deposits. It increases in concentration with depth in the latter, and is also abundant in bulk samples of the Eocene radiolarian oozes making up the base of the section at this site. It is principally associated with radiolarian oozes of Middle Miocene to Pliocene age in DSDP 70, 73, and 74, and with radiolarian oozes of Eocene age in DSDP 70 and 74 (Cook and Zemmels, 1971). These horizons also contain variable amounts of ferromanganese oxides, together with phillipsite associated with the barite in several instances. These associations are generally similar to those found by Church (1970) in surface sediments, namely the occurrence of barite in sediments containing an abundance of calcareous or siliceous tests, or ferromanganese oxide deposits. However, the barite-phillipsite association is at variance with the behavior of these minerals in surface sediments. Cook and Zemmels (1971) also noted that the cores containing the most barite were those that were closest to the equator, confirming the findings of Arrhenius and

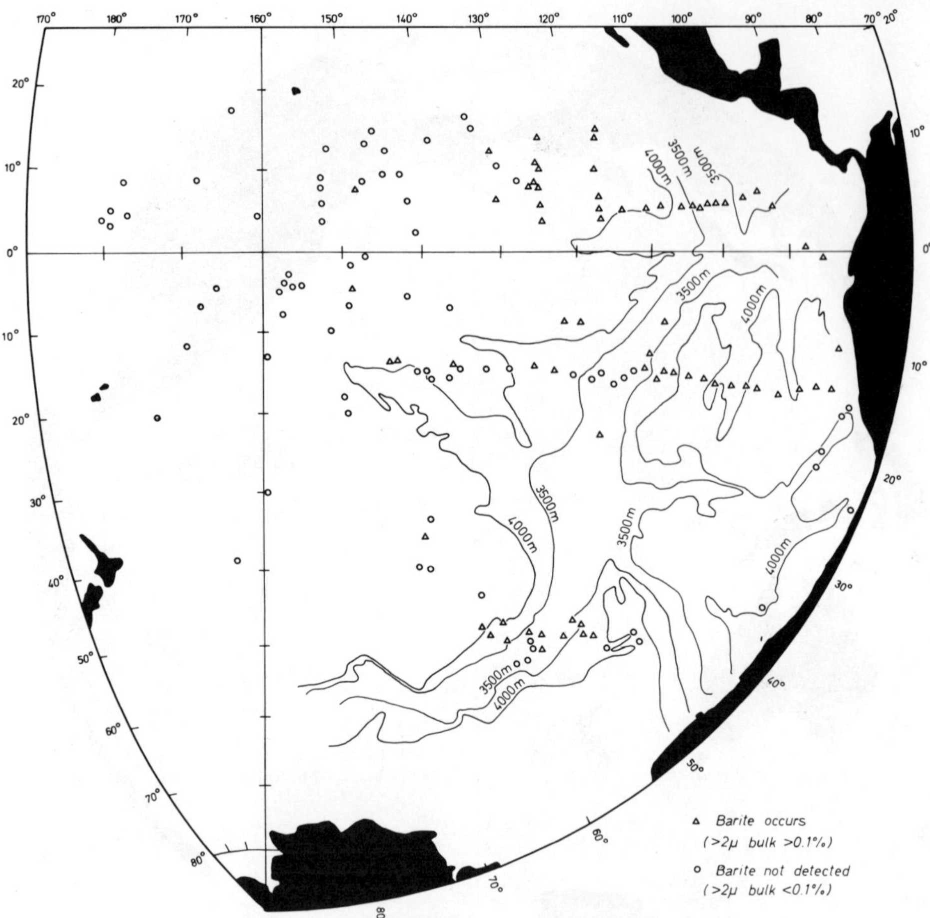

Fig. 3. Barite distribution in the southeastern Pacific. After Church (1970).

Bonatti (1965) in the eastern Pacific. The occurrence of barite at considerable depths within the sediment column in the deep oceans demonstrates that it is not a diagenetically unstable phase in deep-sea sediments. Indeed, evidence to be reviewed subsequently indicates that it may form within the sediment after burial.

There are basically two schools of thought with regard to the origin of marine barite. The first is that the barium they contain is supplied by submarine volcanic activity; the second is that the element is concentrated by marine biological processes and is released to form barium sulphate during the breakdown of organic phases in marine sediments.

A hydrothermal origin for barite in nodules occurring off the coast of California was suggested by Revelle and Emery (1951), who proposed that sulfate-rich interstitial waters reacted with ascending Ba- and Sr-rich magmatic solutions, the nodules being located near a fault through which the hydrothermal solutions could have moved. More recent work on California borderland barites has, however, indicated that they are nonmarine in origin, as they have values of Th, U, and a Th/U ratio similar to continental barites (Goldberg et al., 1969). Geochemical evidence indicated that these barites had not been formed *in situ*. They may have had a hydrothermal or restricted lagoonal origin, and the crystals may have been weathered out of host rocks outcropping along the coast.

Arrhenius and Bonatti (1965) sought to explain the high concentrations of barite over the East Pacific Rise (Fig. 2) in terms of submarine hydrothermal activity. They considered much of the barium in seawater in this area to be derived from hydration and cation exchange with lavas, or hydrothermal transport from magmatic reservoirs. Recent work on Mid-Atlantic Ridge basalts has shown that they may lose certain elements to seawater on cooling (Corliss, 1970), although Ba was not one of the elements studied. Much of any barium entering seawater from volcanic sources was thought to react with dissolved sulfate and crystallize fairly rapidly as barite. However, in order to explain the intermediate barite concentrations under the equatorial zone of high productivity, it was assumed that deep waters containing residual barium were moving north and northwest away from the East Pacific Rise. Near the equator, this barium would be extracted from seawater by organisms in the zone of high productivity, and accumulate in the organic-rich sediments typical of this area. According to Goldberg and Arrhenius (1958), barite granules possibly formed in the protoplasts of marine organisms occur in relatively high concentrations in equatorial sediments.

An alternative model to account for the origin of marine barite is based on organisms as a source for the barium (Church, 1970). Evidence in support of a barium-calcium carbonate association is strong. Revelle (1944) noted a covariance of Ba with carbonate oozes in the equatorial Pacific, and Goldberg and Arrhenius (1958) found a considerable increase in the BaO/TiO_2 ratio of sediments as the equatorial zone of high productivity was approached. The rate of accumulation of TiO_2 was considered to be relatively constant, providing a good reference against which fluctuating rates of accumulation of other constituents could be measured. Data on the enrichment of Ba in the soft parts of organisms are abundant (Arrhenius, 1963; Goldberg, 1965; Thompson and Bowen, 1969). Church (1970) proposed that Ba is extracted from seawater by marine organisms and is released at depth through oxidation of their remains as they fall to the sea floor. Such oxidation was considered to take place within the water column and in the surface sediments, enriching barium in both the bottom and interstitial waters. Barite would then be precipitated in the sediments on barium saturation. Church (1970) considered that high concentrations of barite in deep-sea sediments are related not only to areas of high biological productivity, but also to other areas that accumulate biological remains, such as the major ocean ridge systems. Balance calculations have indicated that biological sources are generally adequate to account for the observed barite levels in such areas, although they may be locally augmented by hydrothermal activity. Most marine barites, however, would appear to be nonvolcanic in origin.

Further data on the origin of marine barites have been provided by investigation of their radioactive element content (Church and Bernat, 1972). Thorium, for example, is generally concentrated in barites from equatorial Pacific oozes relative to its concentration in the associated bulk sediments. However, with burial there is an increase in the absolute amount of the barite, but a decrease in its thorium content. This indicates that barite may be growing diagenetically within the sediment, and that the supply of Th is limited during growth. Further evidence for the growth of barite within the sediments is provided by calculations of barium sulfate saturation in seawater and interstitial waters (Church and Wolgemuth, 1972), and by differences in the $^{230}Th/^{232}Th$ ratio between marine barites and associated bulk sediments. The latter result from barite being precipitated from deep-sea or interstitial waters that have an isotope ratio different from that of surface waters where Th nuclides in the bulk of the biogenous sediments associated with the barite would originate. Such a difference in isotope ratios was predicted by Goldberg et al. (1964).

Some barites contain lower than average Th concentrations—less, in fact, than are found in their associated sediments (Church and Bernat, 1972). These barites are associated with ferromanganese oxide minerals, the nuclei of which are usually volcanic, and in one instance with minerals of possible hydrothermal origin. They bear a close resemblance to continental and continental borderland barites that, having formed from solutions different in composition from seawater (Goldberg et al., 1969), contain less Th than do the deep-sea varieties. Such barites may not be true marine barites at all in that the bulk of their barium was not derived from normal solution in seawater. Other crystals of barite have been found associated with areas of low sedimentation rates, or on disconformities. These may form as a result of the decomposition of the organic matrix binding microcrystalline barite grains together, and subsequent growth around barite nuclei (Goldberg and Arrhenius, 1958).

3. Zeolites

Zeolites are a common constituent of slowly accumulating deep-sea sediments deposited, for the most part, in areas far from land. They reach their greatest abundance in some of the buff to dark chocolate brown clays that characterize much of the Pacific floor beneath the carbonate compensation depth, but also occur in other areas, particularly where the influence of submarine volcanism is important. Reports of zeolites are less common in the Atlantic and Indian Oceans than in the Pacific, particularly in the Atlantic (Turekian, 1965). Of the various zeolites that have been described in recent sediments (Hay, 1966), two are of considerable importance in deep-sea deposits and will be dealt with here. They are the phillipsite-harmotome series and clinoptilolite (Figs. 4 and 6).

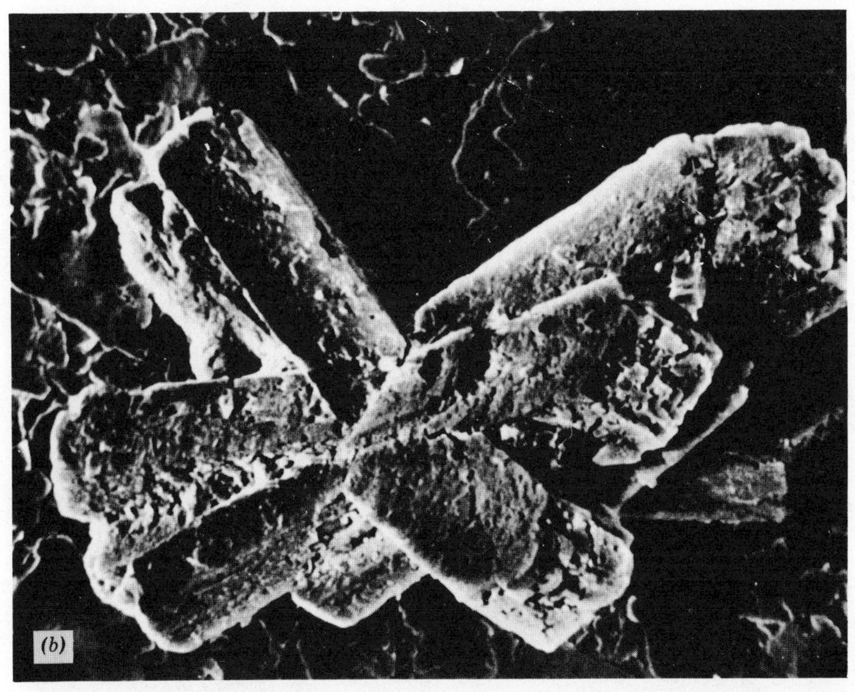
(b)

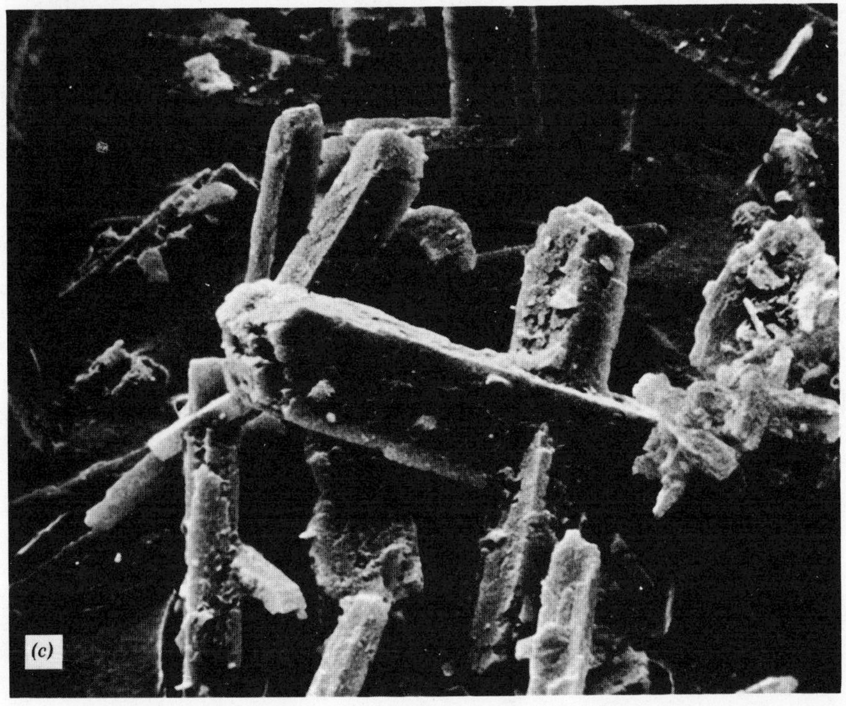
(c)

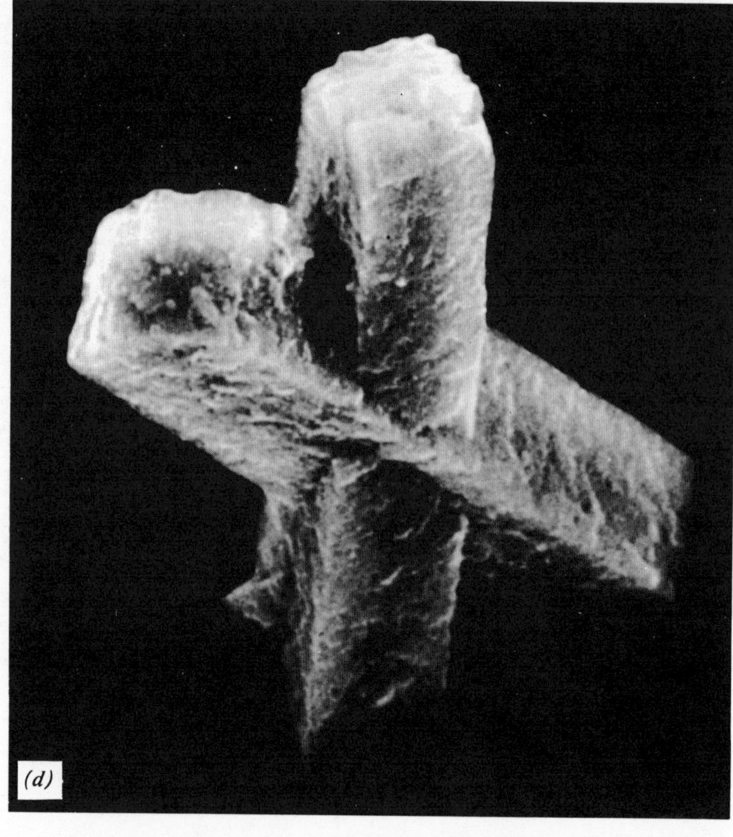

Fig. 4. Four photographs showing crystals of marine phillipsite. (*a*) Composite of Phillipsite crystals × 600. (*b*) Phillipsite multitwin × 4000. (*c*) Phillipsite twins × 2400. (*d*) Phillipsite twin × 5000. Photomicrographs (*a*) to (*c*) were taken on samples prepared by T. Church and M. Bernat with a CAMECA, Inc., scanning electron microscope under support of the Centre National de la Recherche Scientifique, France. Photomicrograph (*d*) was kindly supplied by W. S. Ferguson of Colorado State University.

A. Phillipsite

Phillipsite ($KCa[Al_3Si_5O_{16}] \cdot 6\,H_2O$; Strunz, 1970) is quantitatively the most important zeolite in deep-sea sediments, and was first described in these deposits by Murray and Renard (1891). More recently, Sheppard et al. (1970) have described phillipsites from the Pacific and Indian Oceans that occur as elongated prismatic crystals, chiefly subhedral to euhedral (Fig. 4). Individual crystals range from less than 8 to 250 μ in length, but most are 10 to 120 μ long. A complex sector twinning is common, the cruciform twinning described by Murray and Renard (1891) being relatively rare. The samples are colorless to yellowish brown, the latter being related to the presence of inclusions of iron oxide. Some marine phillipsites can grow to considerable size. Those used for structural investigations by Steinfink (1962), for example, were complexly twinned specimens approximately 5 mm long and 2 to 3 mm in cross section.

Steinfink (1962) determined the crystal structure of marine phillipsite from the 0*kl*, *h*0*l*, and *hk*0 electron density projections. The unit cell is pseudoorthorhombic, *B*2*mb*, $a = 9.96$, $b = 14.25$, $c = 14.25$, and the silicate framework consists of a fundamental unit of two (Si, Al)O_4 tetrahedra linked head to head through an apical oxygen atom. Channels exist parallel to both *a* and *b*, cavities occurring where the two sets intersect. These cavities accommodate the water units and large cations that are present in the zeolite structure. The former move through the channels so that water can be removed and resorbed without disrupting the linkages of the aluminosilicate framework, while the distribution of the latter among sites in the structure is such that they can be easily exchanged for other cations (Deer et al., 1963). Zeolites of the phillipsite structural group can be readily synthesized at low temperatures (Hay, 1966). Arrhenius (1963) has indicated that phillipsite and harmotome are stable from a lower pH limit between 7 and 8 to an upper limit between 9 and 10 in a potassium-hydrogen cation system. Above this limit feldspar was thought to be the stable phase at low temperatures. The mean index of refraction in deep-sea phillipsites ranges from 1.477 to 1.486 and the birefringence is low, about 0.002 (Sheppard et al., 1970). The former varies inversely with the SiO_2 content of sedimentary phillipsites in general (Hay, 1964), but Sheppard et al. (1970) noted no such correlation in deep-sea phillipsites. However, they did note that increase in the refractive index can be correlated both with increase in the Ba content and decrease in the Na_2O content of the samples they examined.

The original chemical analyses of marine phillipsite given in Murray and Renard (1891) showed them to be alkalic and relatively siliceous in comparison with phillipsites from basic igneous rocks. These conclusions have been substantiated by later workers (Goldberg, 1961; Rex, 1967; Sheppard et al., 1970). Based on the analyses of 12 samples (Table I), Sheppard et al. (1970) have shown that deep-sea phillipsites are intermediate in composition relative to those from basic igneous rocks and silicic tuffs, having a Si/Al ratio of about 2.3 to 2.8 and being rich in alkalis with K in excess of Na. Si, Al, K, and H_2O showed little overall variation in these samples, whereas Na, Ba, and especially Mg and Ca varied greatly (Table I). Minor element determinations in marine phillipsites are rare. Goldberg (1961) has reported 0.02% Ti and 0.09% P in one Pacific sample, Bernat and Goldberg (1969) found Th concentrations from 2.95 to 13.2 ppm in a series taken down the length of one Pacific core, and Bernat et al.

TABLE I

Average Composition of Marine Phillipsites (in Weight Percent)

	Maximum[a]	Minimum[a]	Average[a]	Goldberg[b]	Rex[c]
SiO_2	55.92	52.05	54.06	53.47	53.20
Al_2O_3	18.50	16.95	17.71	16.62	16.80
MgO	1.28	0.02	0.49	0.06	0.30
CaO	5.41	0.02	1.29	0.29	0.30
BaO	0.73	0.07	0.24		
Na_2O	5.60	1.11	3.82	7.41	7.40
K_2O	7.54	4.79	6.77	6.14	6.0
H_2O	17.55	14.19	15.58		15.70

[a] Data of Sheppard et al. (1970).
[b] Data of Goldberg (1961).
[c] Data of Rex (1967).

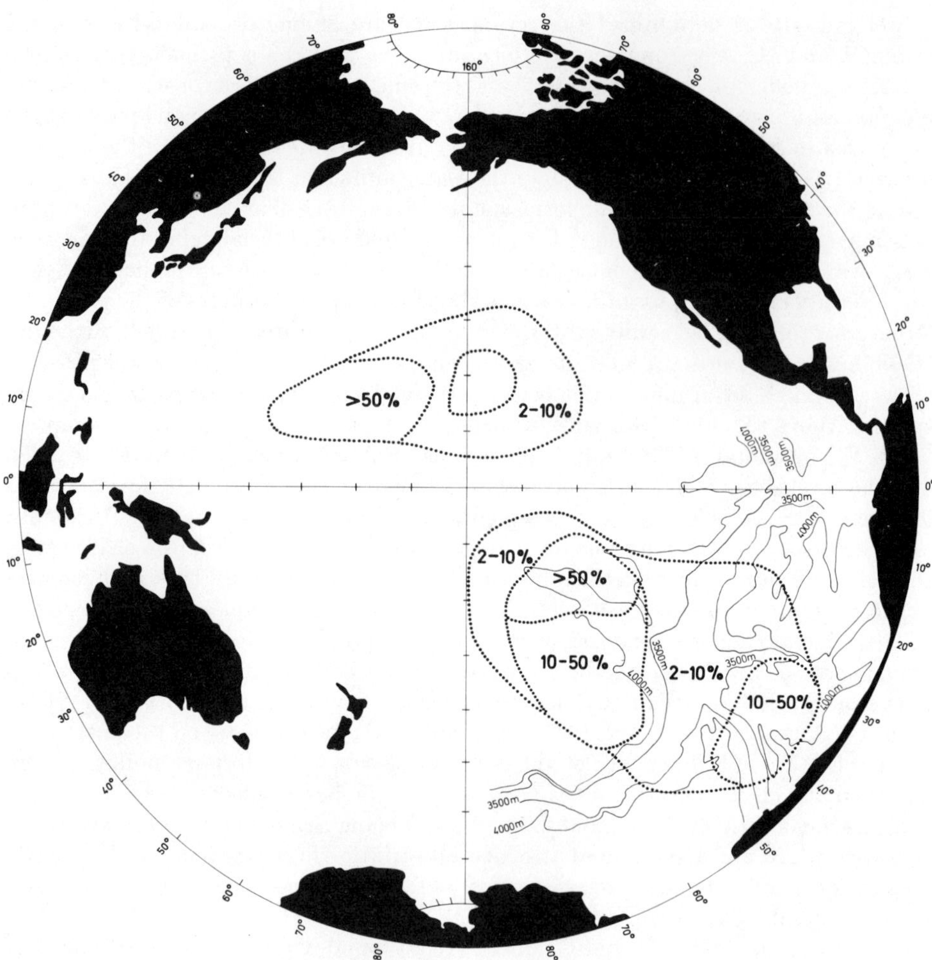

Fig. 5. Phillipsite concentrations in Pacific pelagic sediments. After Bonatti (1963).

(1970) have reported Th values ranging from 0.6 to 8.3 ppm and U values from 0.25 to 0.69 ppm in phillipsite samples from Pacific cores. According to Sheppard et al. (1970), variations in the chemical composition of deep-sea phillipsites appear to have no perceptible effect on their cell parameters.

The distribution of zeolites in surface Pacific sediments has been examined by Goldberg (1961) and Bonatti (1963). Phillipsite often comprises more than 50% of the sediment on a carbonate-free basis in regions of slow sedimentation far from land (Fig. 5). There are lower concentrations in the surrounding areas, and very low concentrations in the equatorial zone. However, phillipsite distribution also varies quite considerably on a local scale, even within regions where it is abundant. The boundaries between areas of high and low concentrations are often quite sharp, and bear no apparent relationship to sedimentation rates. Associated with Pacific phillipsites are iron and manganese oxides, together with clay minerals of the smectite group and ubiquitous small grains of palagonite and other volcanic debris (Bonatti, 1963; Rex, 1958). Murray and Renard (1891) noted that phillipsite occurred most abundantly in red clays, more rarely in siliceous oozes, and more rarely still in calcareous deposits.

However, Goldberg (1961) has shown that these associations are not always valid as he reported high phillipsite concentrations in calcareous sediments from the southeastern Pacific and a general lack of association of the mineral with siliceous organic remains. High concentrations of phillipsite in South Pacific sediments were also reported by Skornyakova and Petelin (1967), and were everywhere associated with slowly accumulating sediments containing palagonite and palagonite tuffs. Phillipsite is not restricted, however, to sediments containing low proportions of terrigenous material or with low overall sedimentation rates. Bonatti (1963) has noted its occurrence in areas such as the Gulf of Alaska where terrigenous sedimentation rates are high. However, in these instances the mineral is generally associated with material of volcanic origin. Phillipsite in the Indian Ocean is abundant in sediments of Miocene to Pleistocene age, being more common in the central part of the ocean, especially around the Mid-Indian Ridge, than in the peripheral regions (Venkatarathnam and Biscaye, 1971). As in the Pacific, it is associated with sediments containing a high proportion of volcanic material, particularly smectite.

Phillipsite has also been found to have a widespread stratigraphic and geographic distribution in cores obtained during the Deep Sea Drilling Project. As in the case of barite, it is more common in Pacific cores than in those from the Atlantic, but in both oceans its associations are similar to those occurring in surface sediments. Rex (1967) has reported phillipsite of pre-Eocene age in cavities in tuff breccia on Sylvania Guyot in the Marshall Islands. The mineral appears to have been in contact with seawater for 60 million years or more, and has undergone a slight resolution.

The origin of marine phillipsite has been the subject of considerable attention (Murray and Renard, 1891; Goldberg, 1961; Arrhenius, 1963; Bonatti, 1963; Sheppard et al., 1970; Bernat et al., 1970). Based largely on its volcanic associations, Murray and Renard (1891) were the first to suggest that it was formed from the breakdown of volcanic debris on the ocean floor; this view has met with the support of most subsequent workers. Bonatti (1963) considered that the association of zeolite crystals with palagonite grains in Pacific sediments was such to suggest that the former resulted from submarine alteration of the latter. Observed changes in palagonite included all stages from the formation of small zeolite crystals on the palagonite grains to the development of well-formed crystals at the expense of the palagonite. Contact with seawater or interstitial waters appeared to be a prerequisite for phillipsite formation.

An alternative view of phillipsite formation has been proposed by Arrhenius (1963). He noted that the amount of Al passing through the oceans in a dissolved state is of the same order of magnitude as the rate of accumulation of zeolites, and that synthesis experiments had indicated that precipitation of such Al could lead to zeolite formation. The observed growth of zeolites within the dissolving skeletons of siliceous organisms in sediments free of volcanic debris was considered evidence for the derivation of the zeolite constituents from biotic sources and dissolved species in seawater.

Bernat and Goldberg (1969) have found that the ^{232}Th content of phillipsite decreases with increasing depth in sediments, indicating that the mineral, like barite, may continue to grow within the sediment column after burial. This decrease is thought to result from the removal of the bulk of the nuclide from interstitial solutions during the early stages of phillipsite formation. Subsequent growth results in a decrease in the ^{232}Th content of the entire mineral. Further support for this hypothesis is provided by uranium, which, like thorium, decreases in phillipsite with increasing depth of burial in conjunction with an increase in phillipsite abundance (Bernat et al., 1970). The continuing formation of phillipsite within the sediment column after burial indicates that low sedimentation rates leading to prolonged contact of zeolite-forming materials with seawater is not a prerequisite for phillipsite formation. The low concentration of phillipsites in volcanically active areas where sediment accumulation is rapid, such as the East Pacific Rise (Bonatti, 1963), is perhaps more likely to be due to their dilution by biogeneous materials than to their lack of growth as a result of their rapid removal from the sediment-water interface. Bernat et al. (1970) also investigated K-Ar ages in marine phillipsites and found that surface samples had "apparent ages" of around 3 million years. In order to account for this, they proposed that phillipsites nucleate around argon-bearing relic materials, most probably volcanic debris. With continuing phillipsite growth within the sediment, potassium then accumulates in the absence of argon leading to an initial decrease in the apparent K-Ar age with depth. Finally, with further burial and growth, the addition of argon by ^{40}K decay overcompensates for the dilution of the inherited argon by new crystal growth and the $^{40}Ar/^{40}K$ ratio of the mineral increases.

Although the association of phillipsite with the products of submarine volcanism is clear in most instances, the actual mechanism by which the mineral is formed is not. Nevertheless, the composition of the parent material does appear to influence zeolite composition. Sheppard et al. (1970) have attributed the high Si/Al ratios in lacustrine phillipsites relative to that of those formed in the oceans to the derivation of the former from silicic glass: most deep-sea phillipsites have a basaltic precursor. Similarly, differences in the Na/K ratio between marine and lacustrine phillipsites may be related to the composition of the waters in which they are formed. Further studies on deep-sea phillipsites from different oceanic environments may result in the discovery of compositional variations that can be related to variations in the marine environment of deposition.

Harmotome is a barium-rich phillipsite that has been reported several times in deep-sea sediments. According to Strunz (1970), the ideal composition is $Ba[Al_2Si_6O_{16}]\cdot 6\ H_2O$. It is monoclinic: $a = 9.82$, $b = 14.13$, and $c = 8.68$. As in phillipsite, potassium is the dominant alkali cation, but sodium is also present. According to Arrhenius and Bonatti (1965), harmotome can occur as microcrystals dispersed through aggregates of the hydration products of volcanic glass, and represents an early stage of reaction between the glass and seawater. Morgenstein (1967) has reported the occurrence of harmotome as a cementing material in tuffaceous deposits near the Society Islands, and considers it to be an alteration product of palagonite. Goodell et al. (1970) and Sheppard et al. (1970) found low or negligible Ba concentrations in phillipsites from widespread localities in the deep ocean, indicating that harmotome may be a relatively uncommon mineral in deep-sea sediments.

B. *Clinoptilolite*

Clinoptilolite (Fig. 6) has been found to occur in a variety of deep-sea environments. According to Mumpton (1960), it is a high silica member of the heulandite structural group. The latter is monoclinic (pseudoorthorhombic): $a = 17.71$, $b = 17.84$, and $c = 7.46$. The composition of clinoptilolite can be derived from the formula of heulandite ($Ca[Al_2Si_7O_{18}]\cdot 6\ H_2O$) by the coupled substitution of NaSi for CaAl (Strunz, 1970). Clinoptilolite can be differentiated from heulandite both on the basis of this substitution and a greater water content. There are also differences in the ion exchange cations between the two; clinoptilolite, for example, like phillipsite, contains a major proportion of potassium. Although clinoptilolite and heulandite are isomorphous,

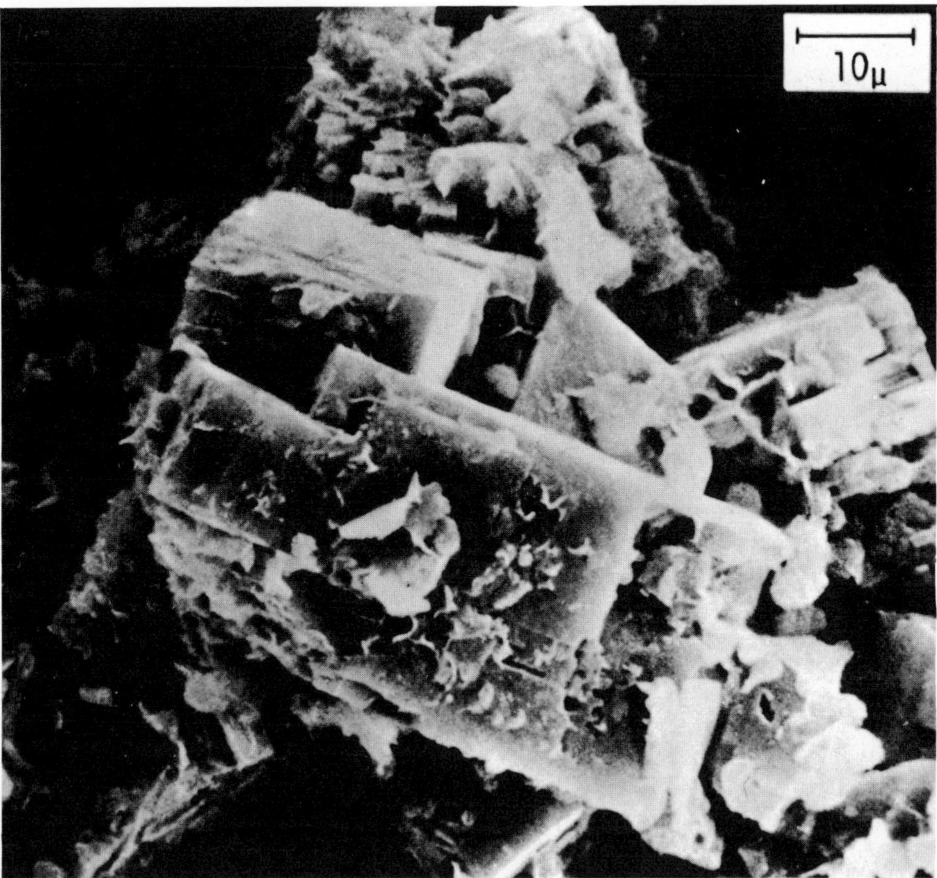

Fig. 6. Crystals of marine clinoptilolite. From Lancelot et al. (1972). × 1600.

there is little evidence to suggest that they form a solid solution series (Mumpton, 1960).

Clinoptilolite occurs in all three major oceans. It seems to be the most common zeolite in Atlantic sediments (Biscaye, 1964; Turekian, 1965) and is locally abundant in DSDP cores (Zemmels et al., 1972). It is also common in cores from the equatorial Pacific where it is usually associated with abundant volcanic debris in various stages of alteration (Cook and Zemmels, 1971, 1972). Volcanic associations are less evident in western Atlantic cores, but in one instance it comprises 70% of a silt band in Cretaceous sediments. In this and other cases where it is present in thin layers, it may be replacing volcanic ash bands. In other instances the clinoptilolite is associated with chert, as was found by Hathaway and Sachs (1965) in Mid-Atlantic Ridge sediments, and with palygorskite, as reported by Bonatti and Joensuu (1968) in deposits from the Barracuda Escarpment off the West Indies. In addition, it has been found to be locally abundant in DSDP cores from the eastern Atlantic, where it is commonly associated with radiolarian-rich sediments and often forms radiolarian casts (Berger and von Rad, 1972). Both phillipsite and clinoptilolite occur together in one core from the equatorial Pacific near the Tuamotu Archipelago (Cook and Zemmels, 1972). The phillipsite dominates the clinoptilolite, probably as a result of the basaltic nature of the associated volcanic debris. However, rhyolitic glass is abundant in sediments from nearer the coast of Central America, and here clinoptilolite is the only zeolite present. Clinoptilolite has also been found to occur in sediments of Cretaceous to Eocene age in the southwestern and southeastern Indian Ocean, often in association with chert and opal, and with smectite of probable volcanic origin (Venkatarathnam and Biscaye, 1971). These authors note that clinoptilolite is found in sediments older than those containing phillipsite, and suggest that more time is needed for its formation. This may be true, as the Atlantic clinoptilolites examined by Berger and von Rad (1972) were also primarily present in sediments of Cretaceous and Eocene age. Younger occurrences were thought to result largely from reworking. However, the dominance of phillipsite in the younger sediments of the central Indian Ocean could also be a reflection of the abundance of basaltic debris in these deposits, due to the proximity of the volcanically active Carlsberg and Mid-Indian Ridges.

It is generally considered that clinoptilolite forms as a result of the alteration of rhyolite or SiO_2-rich volcanic glass (Hathaway and Sachs, 1965; Hay, 1966, and references therein). However, Goodell (1965) was of the opinion that clinoptilolite in Southern Ocean sediments derived its silica from soluble opaline diatom and radiolarian frustules. Furthermore, Berger and von Rad (1972) concluded that the dissolution of siliceous microfossils was contributing silica to the formation of the clinoptilolites they examined. Evidently therefore, clinoptilolite can derive its silica from both volcanic and nonvolcanic sources.

Composite clinoptilolite-opal pseudomorphs of glass shards in some tuffs indicate that the clinoptilolite has precipitated on dissolution of the glass (Hay, 1963). Such alteration might help to explain the association and relative abundances of clinoptilolite and phillipsite in the oceans. Silicic volcanic glass is much less abundant in deep-sea sediments than basaltic glass, perhaps accounting for the generally smaller amounts of clinoptilolite than of phillipsite on much of the ocean floor.

4. Iron Oxides

Iron oxides have for long been known to be an important constituent of slowly accumulating deep-sea sediments (Goldberg and Arrhenius, 1958). They occur for the most part as amorphous or poorly crystalline reddish brown coatings on clay and other minerals and as minute globules scattered throughout the sediments. Occasionally, the mineral goethite (FeOOH) is present. According to Goldberg (1963, 1965), iron is principally present in seawater in the +3 valency state and occurs mostly in the form of colloidal $Fe(OH)_3$. The slow settling of this phase can probably account for the bulk of the free iron oxides in normal pelagic sediments.

Iron oxides are an important constituent of manganese nodules. Buser and Grütter (1956) considered that goethite and colloidal FeOOH were important components of the nodules they examined, and Andrushchenko and Skornyakova (1969) have reported hydrogoethite occurring in the form of collomorphic structures and laminae intergrown with the manganese oxides. Using Mössbauer spectroscopy, Johnson and Glasby (1969) have confirmed that Fe^{3+} compounds are the principal iron phases in manganese nodules, and have suggested that they are largely present in the form of goethite and lepidocrocite.

Iron oxides have been found in recent years to be important constituents of sediments on the crests and flanks of actively spreading midocean ridges. Such sediments were first reported by El Wakeel and Riley (1961) from near the crest of the East Pacific Rise, and consisted of brown calcareous ooze containing 13.8% Fe_2O_3 and

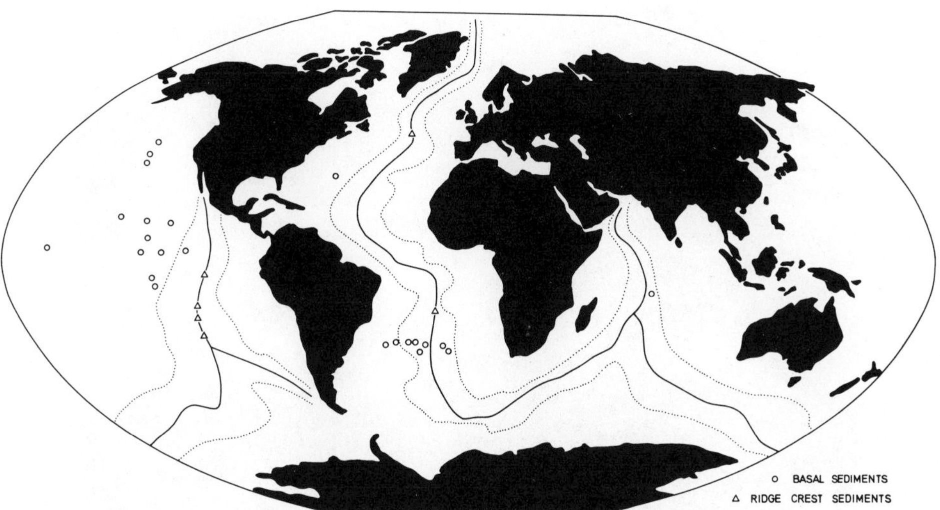

Fig. 7. Locations of iron oxide-rich sediments on the world midocean ridge system.

70.6% calcium carbonate. Bostrom and Peterson (1966) were the first to describe iron-rich deposits associated with active ridges in any detail. They analyzed sediments from two traverses across the East Pacific Rise and found them to be enriched in Fe, Mn, Cu, Cr, Ni, and Pb in areas of high heat flow near the rise crest. More recently, iron-rich sediments have been found on other parts of the world midocean ridge system (Fig. 7), and appear to be a common feature associated with the generation of new ocean floor.

The iron oxide constituents of these sediments are generally present in the form of spherical to subspherical grains and globules (Fig. 8) ranging in diameter from less than a micron to a few tens of microns (von der Borch and Rex, 1970; Cronan, 1973a). They vary from opaque to translucent, and are generally yellow to dark reddish-brown in color. Rarely do the iron oxides occur in an undiluted state. They can be associated with dark brown to black manganese micronodules, and with fragments of volcanic glass and zeolites (Cronan, in preparation). Often they are also admixed with varying quantities of calcareous and siliceous oozes, but characteristically the content of detrital materials is low. In their general appearance, they are similar to the amorphous goethite facies of the Red Sea metalliferous sediments described by Bischoff (1969). However, recent investigations by Dymond et al. (1973) have shown that the sediments are not actually amorphous at all. In addition to the constituents listed previously, coarse fractions include smectite aggregates and phosphatic fish debris, whereas the acid soluble components of the deposits are dominated by goethite which can be associated with variable concentrations of Fe-montmorillonite, psilomelane, todorokite, birnessite, and phosphorite. Acid insoluble residues have a similar mineralogical composition to normal pelagic sediments of equivalent age.

Further occurrences of iron oxide-rich sediments on the crest of the East Pacific Rise have been described by Bostrom and Peterson (1969), Bender et al. (1971), and Dasch et al. (1971). Occurrences on or near the Mid-Atlantic Ridge have been recorded by Bostrom (1970a), Horowitz (1970), and Cronan (1972b), and in the Indian Ocean by Bostrom and Fisher (1971). Iron oxide-rich sediments immediately overlying volcanic basement in DSDP cores have been reported in the Pacific by von der Borch and

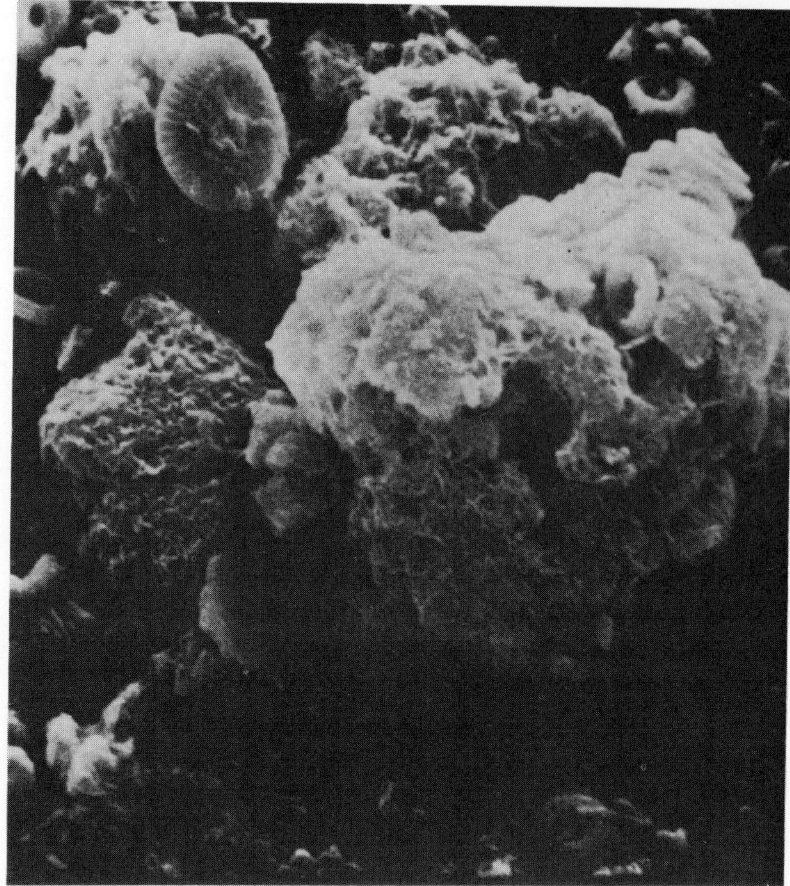

Fig. 8. Amorphous iron oxides in pelagic sediments. From von der Borch et al. (1971). × 8000.

Rex (1970), von der Borch et al. (1971), Cook (1971), Cronan et al. (1972), and Cronan (1973a); from the Atlantic by Peterson et al. (1970) and Bostrom et al. (1972), and from the Indian Ocean by Cronan (in preparation). It is evident, therefore, that these deposits have a widespread distribution in the oceans and can probably be considered to be the characteristic basal lithotype in young oceanic areas. They are not, however, found throughout the ocean basins. Basal sediments on the inactive Rio Grande Ridge in the Atlantic, for example, show no iron enrichment (Bostrom et al., 1972), nor do basal sediments over much of the western Pacific (Fischer et al., 1971; Winterer et al., 1971). Only one of the DSDP cores from the first cruises of *Glomar Challenger* to the western Pacific (Site 66, 2°23.63′N, 166°07.28′W) contained near-basal sediments rich in iron oxides (Heath and Moberly, 1971). The apparent scarcity of such deposits in this part of the ocean might result from a number of factors. Basalt basement was encountered in less than half the holes drilled during DSDP Legs 6 and 7, so it is possible that iron-rich basal sediments are present in the western Pacific but were not recovered. However, sufficient cores did penetrate to the basement to indicate that if such is the case, the sediments do not have a widespread distribution. For example, if present, the iron oxides might have been concentrated into depressions in the basement floor under the influence of gravity slumping, and have a distribution so patchy that the limited coring in the area failed to locate them. Alternatively, over much of the western Pacific the basal sediments appear to be older than the iron-rich sediments on the flanks of the East Pacific Rise (Fischer et al., 1971; Winterer et al., 1971). Diagenetic removal of the oxides with increasing age is therefore a possibility, although not a very likely one because the only iron oxide-rich sediments recovered in the western Pacific (Heath and Moberly, 1971) were among the oldest deposits encountered in this area. Also, there is no evidence of diagenetic alteration of basal iron-rich sediments in those areas where they do occur (von der Borch et al., Bostrom et al., 1972; Cronan et al., 1972). The further drilling done in the western Pacific during DSDP Leg 20 and to be done in the future, may help to solve some of these problems.

Iron-rich sediments from the crest and flanks of the East Pacific Rise are compositionally very similar (Table II). They are enriched in Mn, Ni, Cu, and Pb as well as Fe, relative to normal pelagic clays, but not in Co (Table II). They are characteristically low in Al, Si, and Ti (Bostrom et al., 1969). Sediments from the crest of the Mid-Atlantic Ridge near 45°N also contain high concentrations of Fe on a carbonate-free basis. Other elements that are enriched over their normal oceanic abundancies in such sediments include B, As, Cd, V, Hg, U, Tl, Zn, and Ag (Bostrom and Peterson, 1969; Bostrom and Fisher, 1969; Fisher and Bostrom, 1969; Horowitz, 1970; Cronan, 1972b). However, although ridge crest and basal iron oxide-rich sediments form a distinctive group of marine deposits, their composition is by no means uniform. For example, the iron and manganese contents of Mid-Atlantic Ridge sediments near 45°N are lower than in similar deposits from the East Pacific Rise, whereas their contents of As and Hg are somewhat higher (Cronan, 1972b). Furthermore, Horowitz (1970) has found that the concentrations of Pb, Ag, Tl, and Zn all vary between the East Pacific Rise, the Mid-Atlantic Ridge, and the Mid-Indian Ridge (Table III), most being highest in the Pacific and lowest in the Atlantic.

The origin of iron oxide-rich ridge crest and near-basal sediments has been the subject of considerable speculation. Most of this discussion has centered on those from ridge crests, as the basal varieties are of more recent discovery. However, the latter have been shown to be the ancient analogues of the former that have moved to their present positions as a result of sea floor spreading (Peterson et al., 1970; von der Borch and Rex, 1970; Cook, 1971; Cronan et al., 1972, Bostrom et al., 1972). Any discussion on the origin of ridge crest sediments is therefore equally applicable to these basal counterparts.

Bostrom and Peterson (1966) considered the ferruginous sediments at the crest of

TABLE II

Composition of Iron Oxide-Rich Sediments from the East Pacific Rise

	Fe (%)	Mn (%)	Ni (ppm)	Co (ppm)	Cu (ppm)	Pb (ppm)	Zn (ppm)
(1)	18.00	6.00	430	105	730	152*	380
(2)	17.50	4.50	535	83	917	145	358
(3)	5.06	0.48	211	101	323	68	

Key. (1) Average of carbonate-free surface sediments from the crest of the East Pacific Rise (Bostrom and Peterson, 1969; Horowitz, 1970*). (2) Average of carbonate-free basal sediments from the western flank of the East Pacific Rise (Cronan et al., 1972). (3) Average of surface Pacific pelagic clays (Cronan, 1969).

TABLE III

Average Concentrations of Al, Pb, Ag, Tl, Zn, As, Fe, and Mn in Selected Sediments from the Pacific, Indian, and Atlantic Oceans[a]

	Al (%)	Pb (ppm)	Ag (ppm)	Tl (ppm)	Zn (ppm)	As (ppm)	Fe (%)	Mn (%)
East Pacific	0.64	123	3.74	10.4	204	145	18.0	6.0
Indian		69	0.75	1.88	125			
North Atlantic	5.79	47	0.09	2.39	74.6	174	7.96	0.41

[a] Data from Horowitz (1970), Bostrom and Peterson (1969), and Cronan (1972b).

the East Pacific Rise to be hydrothermal in origin, and to have precipitated from mantle-derived magmatic solutions. More recently, Corliss (1970) proposed that the metal-bearing solutions could be produced by the leaching of newly extruded basalt. He found that the interiors of basalt flows from the Mid-Atlantic Ridge were depleted in several elements, including Fe and Mn, relative to the flow margins, and considered the differences to result from the loss of these elements from the interiors of the flows. Such elements were thought to be concentrated in residual solutions during crystallization so that they occupied accessible sites in the rock and could be dissolved by seawater entering along fractures formed during cooling. However, various alternative mechanisms not involving volcanic action could also possibly account for the origin of at least some of the components of the sediments. For example, a portion of the manganese and associated elements may simply be scavenged from seawater, the reaction possibly being catalyzed by the iron oxides. Alternatively, the deposits may have biological affinities; von der Borch et al. (1971) found structures of possible bacterial origin in some basal iron-rich sediments from the central Pacific. Alternatively again, the iron they contain might be derived from the submarine weathering of basalts (Bertine, 1972), or to deposition under reducing conditions (Turekian and Bertine, 1971). However, none of the hypotheses can unequivocally explain all the features of the sediments. They characteristically accumulate in oxidizing environments, and whereas Fe-rich reducing sediments can scavenge minor elements from seawater (Turekian and Bertine, 1971), the element enrichments described here are unlikely to originate in this way. Bostrom et al. (1972) considered from Al/Ti and Fe/Ti ratios in South Atlantic sediments that the weathering of basaltic material is an unlikely source of iron and manganese at the Mid-Atlantic Ridge crest, although Bertine (1972) considered it to be an important source of iron in Lau Basin deposits. Bostrom (1970b), Bender et al. (1971), and Dasch et al. (1971) have demonstrated that manganese accumulates faster in the iron-rich sediments on the East Pacific Rise than in normal pelagic sediments, possibly indicating its derivation from a local source. Furthermore, the isotopic composition of lead in the sediments indicates a source for this element other than normal seawater. Submarine volcanic activity could provide this source (Bender et al., 1971), and can explain many features of the deposits such as their association with volcanic materials like basaltic glass, their unusually high concentrations of many metals normally low in pelagic clays, and their restriction to past and present centers of sea floor spreading. However, volcanic contributions to the sediments could be supplemented by precipitation of elements from seawater, and thus there may be no single origin for all the components present.

Acceptance of at least a partial volcanic contribution to ridge crest sediments can lead to some interesting speculations concerning the nature of past and present volcanism on the world midocean ridge system. Apparent variations in the composition of sediments from different areas on present-day ridges could result from a number of factors. Varying rates of terrigenous sedimentation causing the dilution of the authigenic constituents of the sediments might lead to different concentrations of these phases in different parts of the oceans. For example, the low Fe and high Al contents of ferruginous sediments on the Mid-Atlantic Ridge near 45°N compared with those from the East Pacific Rise (Table III) might be due to the higher detrital sediment input in the Atlantic than in the Pacific (Cronan, 1972b). However, simple dilution of authigenic phases would affect all the elements they contain in a similar manner. It is not possible on this basis to explain the lack of low Hg and As concentrations in Mid-Atlantic Ridge sediments compared with those from the East Pacific Rise, indicating that dilution alone is not sufficient to explain interocean variations in the composition of these sediments. Horowitz (1970) has attempted to correlate interocean differences in the Pb, Ag, Tl, and Zn contents of ridge crest sediments with variations in the activity of the ridges themselves. The East Pacific Rise, where the highest concentrations of these metals occur, was considered to be the most active ridge, and the Mid-Atlantic Ridge the least active. A second alternative is that the variations represent actual differences in the composition of the ridge basalts along the world midocean ridge system. However, insufficient data are available on the minor element content of ocean ridge basalts for this possibility to be fully evaluated at the present time. In any event, when considering interocean differences in the composition of ridge crest sediments, it is of importance to note that such sediments can vary quite considerably in composition within relatively small areas (Cronan, 1972b). This may be a result of local variations in the composition of metal-bearing fluids, or the selective precipitation from seawater of the elements concerned. Apparent regional variations in the composition of these sediments might therefore, in part, reflect such local variations in conjunction with the limited sediment sampling conducted to date on active ridge crests.

From a study of DSDP cores collected in the South Atlantic, Boström et al. (1972) have concluded that the volcanic processes contributing to sedimentation at the crest of the Mid-Atlantic Ridge have been approximately constant in intensity since Eocene times. Available data also permit a preliminary evaluation of the importance of these processes during the Tertiary Epoch on the East Pacific Rise. The striking similarity of the average composition of the basal sediments collected during DSDP Leg 16 from the west flank of the Rise to that of the sediments on the crest (Table II) suggeststhat, on average, the volcanic processes that have contributed to sedimentation in this area have been similar since Eocene times to those prevailing at the present day. However, there may have been variations in the intensity of the volcanism at different periods in the past. On a carbonate and biogenous silica-free basis, Fe and Mn are highest on the west flank of the East Pacific Rise in Middle Eocene sediments (Cronan et al., 1972) and lowest in those of early Oligocene age. The data of Boström et al. (1972) indicate that some of the more anomalous sediments in terms of Fe, Mn, and Al on the flanks of the Mid-Atlantic Ridge in the South Atlantic are also of Middle Eocene age. Such observations could suggest that periodic fluctuations in the intensity of midocean ridge crest volcanism are reflected in the composition of the ridge crest sediments. If this is the case, more detailed study of metalliferous sediments on the flanks of actively spreading ridges might provide information on the development of the ridges themselves.

5. Manganese Nodules

Although manganese nodules and other ferromanganese oxide deposits have been known since the Challenger Expedition (1873 to 1876) to be abundant in the oceans, recent evaluation of their possible economic importance, among other things, has prompted intensive studies on them in the past few years. Their largest concentrations occur in the Pacific Ocean, with lesser amounts in the Indian and Atlantic Oceans, respectively (Menard and Shipek, 1958; Bezrukov, 1962, 1963; Skornyakova and Andrushchenko, 1970; Ewing et al., 1971; Horn et al., 1972a). Nodules cover 75% or more of the sea floor in parts of the northern tropical and southern Pacific, although locally their distribution can be very patchy (Bonatti and Nayudu, 1965). In addition to nodules, ferromanganese oxide coatings and encrustations are common on exposed rock surfaces, and are often chemically and mineralogically similar to the nodules with which they are sometimes associated. For this reason, nodules and encrustations can commonly be considered together for many purposes when discussing ferromanganese oxide deposition.

Structurally, manganese nodules often consist of segregations of ferromanganese oxides in a fine-grained silicate and iron oxide-rich ground-mass (Fig. 9), or as layers of colloform oxides developed concentrically around a nucleus (Fig. 10). However, other structures such as lamellae and dendrites of manganese and iron oxides are also common (Andrushchenko and Skornyakova, 1969). All gradations from simple colloform banding to radially elongated segregation structures can sometimes be observed along radial traverses within single nodules (Cronan and Tooms, 1968), suggesting that the segregations may have developed from the colloform layers on ageing. In other instances, however, columnar segregation structures extend right to the nodule surface (Fewkes, 1972), indicating that here the segregation of manganese and iron

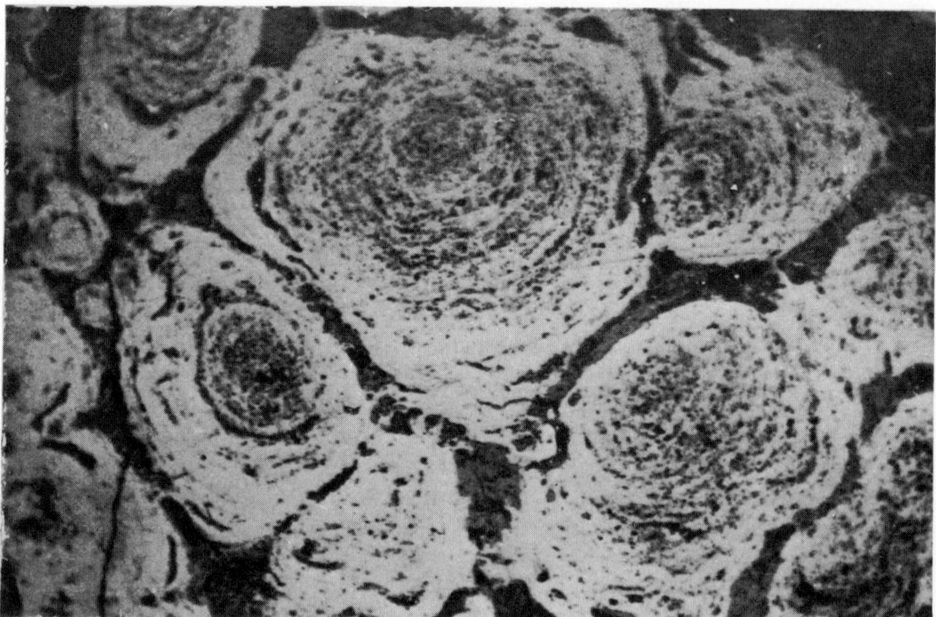

Fig. 9. Segregation structures in manganese nodules from the Carlsberg Ridge. × 160.

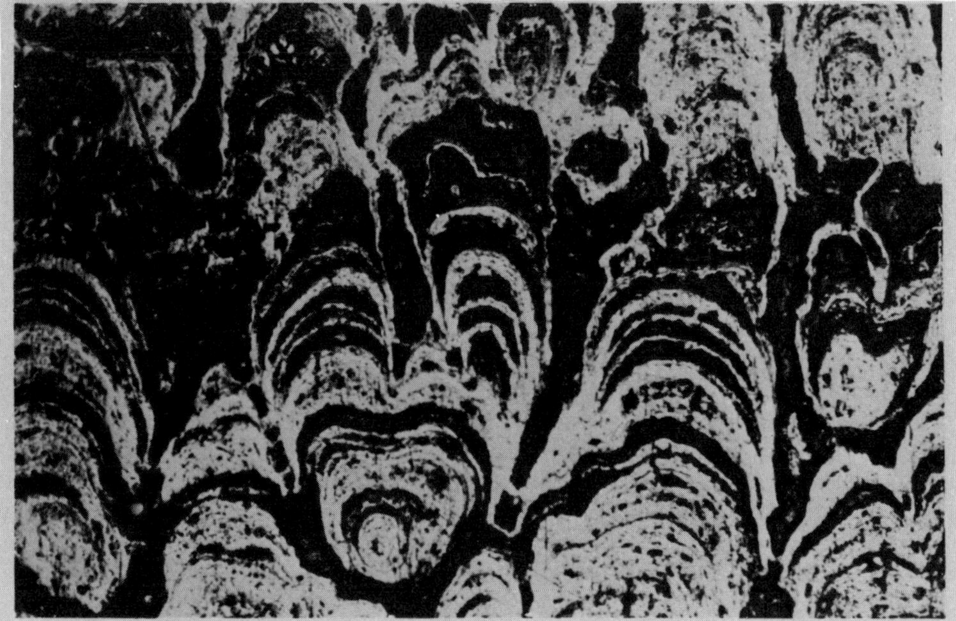

Fig. 10. Radially elongated segregation structures and colloform bonding in manganese nodules from the Carlsberg Ridge × 160.

oxides from the groundmass material is probably a primary depositional feature. On occasion, there are distinct chemical differences between the ferromanganese oxide segregations and the interstitial groundmass. In Carlsberg Ridge nodules, for example, the former contained the bulk of the Mn, together with large portions of the Ni, Cu, K, Ca, and Co, whereas the latter contained the bulk of the Fe, Si, and Al (Cronan and Tooms, 1968) (Fig. 11). However, such associations are not always present. Brooke (1968) found segregations of Fe oxides in nodules where manganese was fairly evenly distributed, and Glasby (1970) noted a complete lack of segregations in some shallow water, near-shore nodules, which he attributed to their rapid rate of growth. Element distribution patterns and interelement relationships within nodules can therefore be quite variable, and probably depend both on the environment of deposition of the concretions and the nature of the mineral phases that they contain.

Elucidation of the mineralogy of manganese nodules has posed some difficulties, largely owing to the poor crystallinity of their constituents and the common intergrowth of several very fine-grained, almost inseparable manganese minerals. However, most available data indicate the presence of at least two principal phases variously called 10 Å manganite or todorokite, and 7 Å manganite, δMnO_2 or birnessite (Buser and Grütter, 1956; Manheim, 1965; Cronan, 1967; Cronan and Tooms, 1969; Glasby, 1972). In this work the terminology of Cronan and Tooms (1969) is used. The main differences between the two minerals are in their degree of oxidation and hydration. Todorokite has a lower O:Mn ratio than birnessite, and is prone to form in less-oxidizing environments than the latter (Cronan and Tooms, 1969; Glasby, 1972). More recently, Giovanoli et al. (1971) and Giovanoli (written communication, 1972) have suggested from synthesis experiments that the previous terminology be modified and the two principal phases in nodules be called buserite and birnessite,

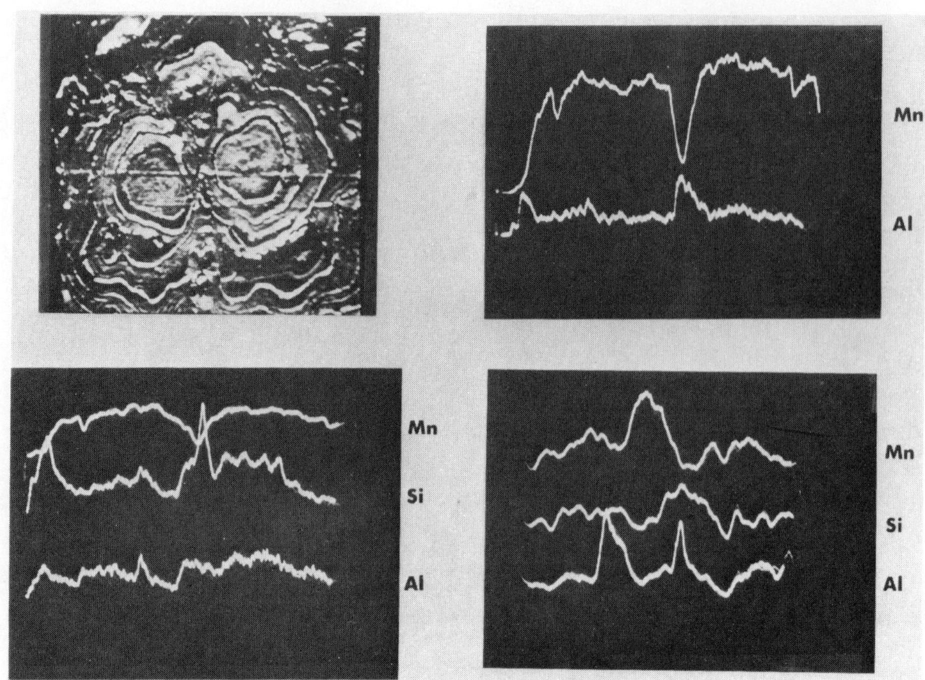

Fig. 11. Line scanning electron microprobe photographs showing the distribution of Mn, Si, and Al in part of a manganese nodule from the Carlsberg Ridge. Photographs courtesy of R. I. Lawson.

these being thought to be the equivalent of Buser and Grütter's (1956) 10 Å manganite and 7 Å manganite or δMnO_2, respectively. Giovanoli (written communication, 1972) has also suggested that todorokite might not be a pure mineral species at all, but a mixture of buserite and manganite ($\gamma MnOOH$) that can be produced synthetically by dehydrating buserite under reducing conditions. He has obtained electron micrographs of minerals identified as todorokite on the basis of their X-ray patterns, which he interprets as showing the remains of unaltered buserite coexisting with needles of manganite (Fig. 12). The characteristic 9.7 Å spacing was thought to be produced by the buserite. The existence of todorokite as a mixture of manganese oxides of different oxidation grades would not be at variance with its lower O:Mn ratio than that of birnessite, nor its general occurrence in environments of lower redox potential than the latter. The Eh of the environment of deposition is probably the major factor in determining the mineralogy of submarine ferromanganese oxide deposits.

The mineralogy of deep-sea nodules appears to exert an important control on their chemical composition (Burns and Fuerstenau, 1966; Barnes, 1967; Cronan and Tooms, 1969; Okada and Shima, 1970), but such a control is not so evident in their near-shore, shallow water counterparts. For example, todorokite-rich nodules from the deep oceans are enriched in Ni and Cu relative to those containing birnessite, but todorokite-rich near-shore and continental margin varieties show no such enrichments (Cronan and Tooms, 1969; Glasby, 1970). Deep-sea nodules generally accumulate slowly (Bender et al., 1966; Barnes and Dymond, 1967; Ku and Broecker, 1969), leading to a prolonged contact between ferromanganese oxides and seawater with

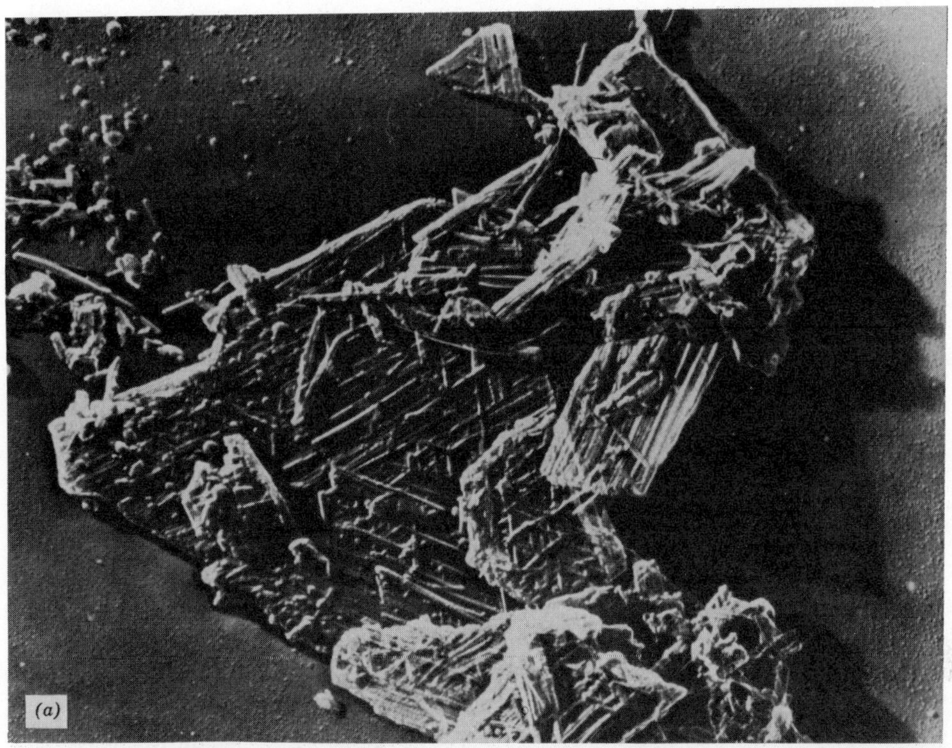

Fig. 12. Crystals of manganese oxides. Photographs courtesy of R. Giovanoli (*a*) × 20,000, (*b*) × 36,000.

concomitant increased scavenging of minor elements. Nickel and copper may both be able to substitute for divalent manganese in the todorokite structure (Buser and Grütter, 1956; Cronan and Tooms, 1969; McKenzie, 1971), thus accounting for their enrichment in todorokite-rich deep-sea nodules. Their lack of enrichment in the near-shore varieties could result from the much more rapid growth of the latter (Ku and Glasby, 1972), resulting in the removal of the ferromanganese oxides from reaction surfaces before appreciable scavenging has been able to take place. Near-shore nodules are often formed as a result of the diagenetic remobilization of manganese in buried sediments and its reprecipitation at or near the sediment-water interface (Lynn and Bonatti, 1965; Cronan, 1967; Price and Calvert, 1970). During this process the manganese could become separated from elements such as Ni and Cu, thus further contributing to their low concentrations in continental margin nodules.

The enrichment of Co and Pb in birnessite-rich deep-sea nodules is another possible example of the influence of mineralogical control on nodule composition. This may result from Co^{3+} and Pb^{4+} replacing Mn^{4+} (Goldberg, 1961a; Sillén, 1961), or the substitution of these elements for Fe^{3+} in FeOOH. However, as each of these elements is normally present in seawater in the divalent state (Goldberg, 1963), their oxidation is probably necessary before enrichment in birnessite-rich nodules can occur. This oxidation would be favored by the highly oxidizing conditions under which birnessite forms.

Variations in the mineralogy of nodules, in the source of the elements they contain, and in the nature of their environment of deposition all lead to regional variations in nodule composition throughout the World Ocean (Table IV) (Cronan, 1972c). In the Pacific, for example, there are high manganese values and Mn/Fe ratios in American continental borderland nodules ($>25\%$ Mn) (Mero, 1965; Cronan and Tooms, 1969), most probably as a result of the upward diffusion of reduced manganese due to low redox potentials caused by rapid sedimentation rates (Lynn and Bonatti, 1965; Price and Calvert, 1970). The Mn/Fe ratio then decreases in a general manner toward the western Pacific. However, high manganese concentrations in nodules from the north-eastern tropical pelagic Pacific ($>20\%$ Mn) (Mero, 1965; Cronan and Tooms, 1969) are unlikely to result from the diagenetic remobilization of manganese except possibly under the equatorial zone of high productivity, as this is largely an area of relatively slow sedimentation of red clay and siliceous ooze and is underlain by sediments rich in iron and manganese oxides near the basement (Hays et al., 1969; Horn et al., 1972c; Cronan et al., 1972). The high Mn/Fe ratios in this area (Price and Calvert, 1970; Cronan 1973b) may simply reflect the slow precipitation of manganese in an environment where there are few, if any, local diluent sources of iron. The data of Cronan and Tooms (1969) show that Mn is somewhat enriched in nodules associated with pelagic clays relative to its content in those associated with calcareous sediments, suggesting that manganese enrichment in deep-sea nodules, other than continental borderland varieties and possibly those in the equatorial zone, is favored by minimal sedimentation in areas beneath the carbonate compensation depth. In contrast, relatively low Mn/Fe ratios in ferromanganese oxides from elevated volcanic areas (Cronan, 1972c) and parts of the southern and western Pacific could perhaps result from their proximity to local sources of iron and, in the case of encrustations, from the lack of underlying manganese-bearing interstitial waters. Corliss (1970) has shown that iron is leached from submarine basalts on cooling, and Scott et al. (1972) have found that the lower layers of encrustations associated with volcanic activity have lower Mn/Fe ratios than do the upper layers, which were probably deposited by normal precipitation from seawater after volcanism had ceased.

TABLE IV

Average Abundances of Mn, Fe, Ni, Co, and Cu in Ferromanganese Oxide Concretions from the Atlantic, Pacific, and Indian Oceans, in Weight Percent (Cronan, 1972a)

	Atlantic			Pacific			Indian		
	Average	Maximum	Minimum	Average	Maximum	Minimum	Average	Maximum	Minimum
Mn	16.18	37.69	1.32	19.75	34.60	9.87	18.03	29.16	11.67
Fe	21.2	41.79	4.76	14.29	32.73	6.47	16.25	26.46	6.71
Ni	0.297	1.41	0.019	0.722	2.37	0.161	0.510	2.01	0.167
Co	0.309	1.01	0.017	0.381	2.58	0.052	0.279	1.04	0.068
Cu	0.109	0.884	0.022	0.366	1.97	0.034	0.223	1.38	0.029

Regional variations in the minor element content of deep-sea manganese nodules can be related, in part, to regional variations in nodule mineralogy. Todorokite-bearing nodules enriched in Ni and Cu have been found to be most abundant in the deep-water pelagic areas of the eastern Pacific. By contrast, those containing birnessite as their principal mineral phase and that are often enriched in Co and Pb are more widespread, and reach their greatest abundance in the elevated volcanic areas of the western Pacific and western Indian Oceans, such as the Mid-Pacific Mountains and the Carlsberg Ridge (Cronan and Tooms, 1969; Glasby, 1972). The causes of these regional mineralogical variations can most probably be related to regional variations in the redox potentials of the environments in which the minerals form. Birnessite is the more highly oxidized of the two, and elevated volcanic areas are among the most highly oxidizing environments in the oceans. Proximity of nodules to local volcanic sources of minor elements might also help to determine their regional compositional variations. Mercury, for example, has been found to be enriched in some nodules from volcanic areas (Harriss, 1968).

The influence of sea floor spreading on the regional geochemistry of manganese nodules has received little attention. Nodules forming at or near the crests of active mid ocean ridges should be transported progressively further away from the spreading centers with time into deeper water, and subsequently to subduction zones. Under these circumstances, ridge crest concretions which may have received a substantial portion of their constituents from volcanic sources might be expected to attract an increasing proportion of elements from normal seawater, and to change their composition accordingly. In particular, their Mn/Fe ratio should alter away from the ridge crest to approach values common in abyssal areas. Direct evidence in confirmation of this possibility is lacking, but comparison of nodules from the crest and flanks of the Mid-Atlantic Ridge lends it some support. Nodules from the ridge crest between 40° and 50°N have an average Mn/Fe ratio near 0.6, whereas those on its eastern flank have an average ratio of about 1.0 (Cronan, unpublished data). This might be explained on the basis of the concretions receiving decreasing amounts of Fe from volcanic sources, and increasing amounts of Mn from seawater as they move away from the ridge crest. Furthermore, owing to its diagenetic instability, Mn^{4+} in nodules may not be able to survive deep burial during subduction at leading plate margins, and thus may return to the sediment surface as Mn^{2+}. On this basis, diagenetic Mn rich nodules might be expected to occur in the vicinity of subduction zones, while much of any remobilized manganese could be recycled through seawater, thus helping to account for the abundant manganese on the ocean floor at the present time.

Superimposed on regional variations are local fluctuations in nodule composition and mineralogy, as well as the variations within individual nodules mentioned previously. The factors causing these are probably similar to those determining the regional variations, but are operating on a local scale or have operated in the past. On the Carlsberg Ridge, for example, Cronan and Tooms (1967b) suggested that fivefold differences in Ni, Cu, and Co between sites only 10 to 15 mi apart might be caused by local changes in the redox potential of the environment of deposition leading to the formation of todorokite at one station and birnessite at the other. Glasby (1972) has examined the mineralogy of additional concretions from the Carlsberg Ridge and has also found both mineralogical varieties of nodules at adjacent stations. Local compositional variations in nodules are not, however, restricted to areas of elevated and dissected topography, although it is in such areas that they have been found to be most prominent to date (Cronan, 1973c). For example, variations in the Mn/Fe ratio of nodules from stations 3 mi apart on an abyssal hill in the Pacific, although relatively small, were attributed by Hubred (1970) to the selective precipitation of volcanically derived Mn and Fe in the manner outlined by Bonatti and Nayudu (1965).

In addition to occurring at the sediment-water interface, manganese nodules are also fairly abundant within the sediment column (Menard, 1964; Cronan and Tooms, 1967a, Horn et al., 1972b). For the most part, nodules in the upper few meters of sediment are compositionally similar to their surface counterparts (Cronan and Tooms, 1969; Goodell et al., 1970). However, analyses of more deeply buried samples in DSDP cores show greater variations. For example, two buried nodules in DSDP 162 from the eastern Pacific are chemically quite distinct from those higher in the core (Cronan, 1973b). The deepest of these, at 131 m, was considered to be *in situ*, and may have formed at the expense of Fe and Mn previously disseminated throughout the surrounding sediments. Manganese micronodules are also common in buried sediments as well as at the surface. They occur in similar environments to those in which the larger nodules accumulate, and probably form by similar processes. They can range in size up to almost 1 mm in diameter, and are generally near spherical in shape. In some instances they are concentrated into discrete horizons, often where sedimentation rates are lowest (Riedel and Funnell, 1964; Watkins, personal communication, 1972). Chester and Hughes (1969) have analyzed the different fractions of a North Pacific clay core and found that approximately 85% of the manganese is present in the micronodule fraction. Associated with this fraction is a major portion of the cobalt in the sediments and smaller portions of the Ni and Cu. Elderfield (1972) has suggested that micronodules exhibit regional variations in composition just as their associated larger nodules do.

The origin of manganese nodules has been the subject of much speculation for a considerable period of time. Much of the controversy has centered on whether the metals they contain are derived from the continents or from local volcanic sources. However, it has been apparent for some time that manganese in interstitial waters or at the sediment-water interface derived from any source, be it continental, volcanic, hydrothermal, or diagenetic, is a potential constituent of nodules (Cronan, 1967), and thus further discussion on its ultimate origin is beyond the scope of this chapter.

According to Stumm and Morgan (1970), the oxidation of divalent manganese in natural environments is catalyzed by a reaction surface. Such a surface permits the precipitation of MnO_2, which adsorbs additional Mn^{2+} and Fe^{2+}, each in turn becoming oxidized and adsorbing more manganese and iron. In this way, manganese and iron oxides can continue to accrete, providing that there is an uninterrupted supply of the elements to the reaction surface. The need for a surface to catalyze manganese oxidation and precipitation in nodules was proposed by Goldberg and Arrhenius (1958). These authors suggested that ferric oxide could provide such a surface on which manganese oxidation would take place according to the reaction:

$$2\,OH^- + Mn^{2+} + \tfrac{1}{2}\,O_2 = MnO_2 + H_2O$$

Evidence in support of this hypothesis has been provided by Burns and Brown (1972), who found from electron probe studies that a thin layer of iron oxides coat the nuclei of the nodules they examined, underlying the manganese phases. Nodule nuclei of volcanic origin often contain less iron than the rocks of which they are the alteration products (Bonatti and Joensuu, 1966; Varentsov, 1971), and the initial coatings around these nuclei could therefore represent some of the iron leached from the original volcanics during submarine weathering processes. For example, Morgenstein and Felsher (1971) have suggested that the alteration of palagonite could provide a requisite source of iron to catalyze manganese oxidation and precipitation on volcanic rocks in which palagonite occurs. Such observations might account for the majority of nodules accreting around altered volcanic nuclei. However, similar processes cannot account for the accretion of nodules around nonvolcanic nuclei such as shark teeth, phosphorites, and corals, indicating alternate sources of iron or that other surfaces or catalytic mechanisms can also promote the accumulation of ferromanganese oxides.

Acknowledgments

I wish to thank Edward Hearn for drawing the diagrams, and Sue Groulx and Sue Meunier for typing the manuscript. Thanks also to Drs. Thomas Church, Donald Hogarth, and Brian Rust for critical review. Dr. Church also kindly supplied the photomicrographs of barite and phillipsite.

References

Andrushchenko, P. F. and N. S. Skornyakova, 1969. The textures and mineral composition of iron-manganese concretions from the southern part of the Pacific Ocean. *Oceanology*, **9**, 229–242.

Arrhenius, G., 1963. Pelagic Sediments. In *The Sea*. M. N. Hill, ed. Vol. 3. Wiley-Interscience, New York, pp. 655–727.

Arrhenius, G. and E. Bonatti, 1965. Neptunism and vulcanism in the ocean. In *Progress in Oceanography*. M. Sears, ed. Vol. 3. Pergamon, London, pp. 7–22.

Audley-Charles, M., 1965. A geochemical study of Cretaceous ferromanganiferous sedimentary rocks from Timor. *Geochim. Cosmochim. Acta*, **29**, 1153–1173.

Aumento, F., D. E. Lawrence, and A. G. Plant, 1968. The ferromanganese pavement on San Pablo Seamount. Geol. Surv. Can. Pap. 68–32, 1–30.

Barnes, S. S., 1967. Minor element composition of ferromanganese nodules. *Science*, **157**, 63–65.

Barnes, S. S. and J. Dymond, 1967. Rates of accumulation of ferromanganese nodules. *Nature*, Lond., **213**, 1218–1219.

Bender, M. L., T-H. Ku, and W. S. Broecker, 1966. Manganese nodules their evolution. *Science*. **151**, 325–328.

Bender, M. L., W. Broecker, V. Gornitz, U. Middel, R. Kay, S. S. Sun, and P. Biscaye, 1971. Geochemistry of three cores from the East Pacific Rise. *Earth and Planet. Sci. Letters*, **12**, 425–433.

Berger, W. H. and U. von Rad, 1972. Cretaceous and cenozoic sediments from the Atlantic Ocean. In *Initial Reports of the Deep Sea Drilling Project*, Vol. XIV. D. E. Hayes, et al., eds. U.S. Government Printing Office, Washington, D.C., pp. 787–954.

Bernat, M. and E. D. Goldberg, 1969. Thorium isotopes in the marine environment. *Earth and Planet. Sci. Letters*, **5**, 308–312.

Bernat, M., R. H. Bieri, M. Koide, J. Griffin, and E. D. Goldberg, 1970. Uranium, potassium and argon in marine phillipsites. *Geochim. Cosmochim. Acta*, **34**, 1053–1071.

Bertine, K. K., 1972. Submarine weathering of tholeitic basalts and the origin of metalliferous sediments. Manuscript submitted to *Science*.

Bezrukov, P. L., 1962. Distribution of ferromanganese concretions on the floor of the Indian Ocean. *Okeanologiya*, **2**, 1014–1019 (in Russian).

Bezrukov, P. L., 1963. Studies of the Indian Ocean during the 35th cruise of R. V. Vityaz. *Okeanologiya*, **3**, 540–549 (in Russian).

Biscaye, P., 1964. Mineralogy and sedimentation of the deep-sea sediment fine fraction in the Atlantic and adjacent seas and oceans. Ph.D. thesis, Yale University.

Bischoff, J. L. 1969. Red Sea geothermal brine deposits: their mineralogy, chemistry and genesis. In *Hot Brines and Recent Heavy Metal Deposits in the Red Sea*, E. T. Degens and D. Ross, eds. Springer-Verlag, New York, 368 pp.

Bonatti, E., 1963 Zeolites in Pacific pelagic sediments. *N.Y. Acad. Sci. Trans. II*, **25**, 938–948.

Bonatti, E. and O. Joensuu, 1966. Deep sea iron deposits from the South Pacific. *Science*, **154**, 643–645.

Bonatti, E. and O. Joensuu, 1968. Palygorskite from Atlantic deep-sea sediments. *American Mineral.*, **53**, 975–983.

Bonatti, E. and Y. R. Nayudu, 1965. The origin of manganese nodules on the ocean floor. *Am. J. Sci.*, **263**, 17–39.

Bostrom, K., 1970a. Geochemical evidence for ocean floor spreading in the South Atlantic Ocean. *Nature*, Lond., **227**, 1041.

Bostrom, K., 1970b. Submarine volcanism as a source of iron. *Earth Planet. Sci. Letters*, **9**, 348–354.

Bostrom, K. and D. E. Fisher, 1969. Distribution of mercury in East Pacific sediments. *Geochim. Cosmochim. Acta*, **33**, 743–745.

Bostrom, K. and D. E. Fisher, 1971. Volcanogenic U, V and Fe in Indian Ocean sediments. *Trans. Am. Geophys. Union*, **52**, 245.

Bostrom, K. and M. N. A. Peterson, 1966. Precipitates from hydrothermal exhalations on the East Pacific Rise. *Econ. Geol.*, **61**, 1258–1265.

Bostrom, K. and M. N. A. Peterson, 1969. The origin of aluminium poor ferromanganoan sediments in areas of high heat flow on the East Pacific Rise. *Mar. Geol.*, **7**, 427–447.

Bostrom, K., M. N. A. Peterson, O. Joensuu, and D. E. Fisher, 1969. Aluminium-poor ferromanganoan sediments on active oceanic ridges. *J. Geophys. Res.*, **74**, 3261–3270.

Bostrom, K. and S. Valdes, 1969. Arsenic in ocean floors. *Lithos.*, **2**, 351–360.

Bostrom, K., O. Joensuu, S. Valdes, and M. Riera, 1972. Geochemical history of S. Atlantic Ocean sediments since late Cretaceous. *Mar. Geol.*, **12**, 85.

Brooke, J. N., 1968. The texture and hydrometallurgical processing of manganese nodules. Ph.D. thesis, University of London.

Burns, R. G. and B. Brown, 1972. Nucleation and mineralogical controls on the composition of manganese nodules. In *Ferromanganese Deposits on the Ocean Floor*, D. R. Horn, ed. Lamont-Doherty Geol. Obs., 51–61.

Burns, R. G. and D. W. Fuerstenau, 1966. Electron-probe determinations of inter-element relationships in manganese nodules. *American Mineral*, **51**, 895–902.

Buser, W. and A. Grütter, 1956. Uber die natur der maganknollen. *Schweiz. Mineral. Petrog. Mitt.*, **36**, 49–62.

Chester, R. and M. J. Hughes, 1969. The trace element geochemistry of a North Pacific pelagic clay core. *Deep-Sea Res.*, **16**, 639–654.

Church, T. M., 1970. Marine barite. Ph.D. thesis, University of California, San Diego.

Church, T. M. and M. Bernat. 1972. Thorium and Uranium in marine barite. *Earth Planet. Sci. Letters*, **14**, 139–144.

Church, T. M. and K. Wolgemuth, 1972. Marine barite saturation. *Earth Planet. Sci. Letters*, **15**, 35–44.

Cook, H. E., 1971. Iron and manganese rich sediments overlying oceanic basalt basement, equatorial Pacific, Leg 9, Deep Sea Drilling Project. Geol. Soc. Amer. (Abs with programs). **3** (7), 530–531.

Cook, H. E. and I. Zemmels, 1971. X-ray mineralogy studies, Leg. 8. In *Initial Reports of the Deep Sea Drilling Project.* Vol. VIII. J. I. Tracey, Jr., et al., eds. U.S. Government Printing Office, Washington, D.C., pp. 901–950.

Cook, H. E. and I. Zemmels, 1972. X-ray mineralogy studies, Leg. 9. Deep Sea Drilling Project. In *Initial Reports of the Deep Sea Drilling Project.* Vol. IX. J. D. Hayes, et al., eds. U.S. Government Printing Office, Washington, D.C., pp. 707–777.

Cook, H. E., R. W. Rex, W. A. Eklund, and B. Murray, 1971. X-ray minerology studies, Leg. 7. In *Initial Reports of the Deep Sea Drilling Project.* Vol. VII. E. L. Winterer, et al., eds. U.S. Government Printing Office, Washington, D.C., pp. 913–963.

Corliss, J. B., 1970. Mid-Ocean Ridge basalts. Ph.D. thesis, University of California, San Diego.

Cronan, D. S., 1967. The geochemistry of some manganese nodules and associated pelagic deposits. Ph.D. thesis, University of London.

Cronan, D. S., 1969. Average abundances of Mn, Fe, Ni, Co, Cu, Pb, Mo, V, Cr, Ti, and P in Pacific pelagic clays. *Geochim. Cosmochim. Acta*, **33**, 1562–1565.

Cronan, D. S., 1972a. Composition of Atlantic manganese nodules. *Nature*, Lond., **235**, 171–172.

Cronan, D. S., 1972b. The Mid-Atlantic Ridge near 45°N, XVII: Al, As, Hg, and Mn in ferruginous sediments from the median valley. *Can. J. Earth Sci.*, **9**, 319–323.

Cronan, D. S., 1972c. Regional geochemistry of ferromanganese nodules in the World Ocean. In *Ferromanganese Deposits on the Ocean Floor*, D. R. Horn, ed. Lamont-Doherty Geol. Obs., 19–30.

Cronan, D. S., 1973a. Basal ferruginous sediments cored during Leg 16, Deep Sea Drilling Project In *Initial Reports of the Deep Sea Drilling Project*. Vol. XVI. Tj. H. van Andel, et al., eds. U.S. Government Printing Office, Washington, D.C. In press.

Cronan, D. S., 1973b. Manganese nodules in sediments cored during Leg 16, Deep Sea Drilling Project. In *Initial Reports of the Deep Sea Drilling Project*. Vol. XVI. Tj. H. van Andel, et al., eds. U.S. Government Printing Office, Washington, D.C. In press.

Cronan, D. S., 1973c. Manganese nodules and other ferromanganese oxide deposits. In *Chemical Oceanography*. Vol. 3. J. P. Riley and R. Chester, eds. Academic Press, London. In press.

Cronan, D. S., in preparation. Geochemistry of basal metalliferous sediments cored during Leg. 24, Deep Sea Drilling Project. In *Initial Reports of the Deep Sea Drilling Project*. Vol. XXIV. R. L. Fisher, et al., eds. U.S. Government Printing Office, Washington, D.C.

Cronan, D. S. and J. S. Tooms, 1967a. Subsurface concentrations of manganese nodules in Pacific sediments. *Deep-Sea Res.*, **14**, 117–119.

Cronan, D. S. and J. S. Tooms, 1967b. Geochemistry of manganese nodules from the N.W. Indian Ocean. *Deep-Sea Res.*, **14**, 239–249.

Cronan, D. S. and J. S. Tooms, 1968. A microscopic and electron probe investigation of manganese nodules from the Northwest Indian Ocean. *Deep-Sea Res.*, **15**, 215–223.

Cronan, D. S. and J. S. Tooms, 1969. The geochemistry of manganese nodules and associated pelagic deposits from the Pacific and Indian Oceans. *Deep-Sea Res.*, **16**, 335–359.

Cronan, D. S., Tj. H. van Andel, G. R. Heath, M. G. Dinkleman, R. H. Bennett, D. Bukry, S. Charleston, A. Kanaps, K. S. Rodolfo, and R. S. Yeats, 1972. Iron-rich basal sediments from the eastern equatorial Pacific: Leg. 16, Deep Sea Drilling Project. *Science*, **175**, 61–63.

Dasch, E. J., J. R. Dymond, and G. R. Heath, 1971. Isotopic analysis of metalliferous sediment from the East Pacific Rise. *Earth Planet. Sci. Letters*, **13**, 175–180.

Deer, W. A., R. A. Howie, and J. Zussman, 1963. *Rock-Forming Minerals*. Vol. 4. Framework Silicates. Longmans, London, 435 pp.

Dymond, J., J. B. Corliss, G. Ross Heath, Cyrus W. Field, E. Julius Dasch, and H. Herbert Veeh, 1973. Origin of metalliferous sediments from the Pacific Ocean. *Bull. Geol. Soc. Amer.* In press.

Elderfield, H, 1972. Compositional variations in the manganese oxide component of marine sediments. *Nature*, Lond., **237**, 110–112.

El Wakeel, S. K. and J. P. Riley, 1961. Chemical and mineralogical studies of deep-sea sediments. *Geochim. Cosmochim. Acta*, **25**, 110–146.

Ewing, M., D. Horn, L. Sullivan, T. Aitken, and E. Thorndike, 1971. Photographing manganese nodules on the ocean floor. Oceanology International. December 1971.

Fewkes, R. H., 1972. Conglomerate manganese nodules from the Drake Passage. In letters of the commission on manganese (IAGOD), *Acta. Miner. Petrograph. Szeged*, **xx/2**, 383–391.

Fischer, A. G., et al. 1971. *Initial Reports of the Deep Sea Drilling Project*. Vol. 6. U.S. Government Printing Office, Washington, D.C., 1329 pp.

Fisher, D. E. and K. Bostrom, 1969. Uranium rich sediments on the East Pacific Rise. *Nature*, Lond., **224**, 64–65.

Giovanoli, R., W. Feitknecht, and F. Fischer, 1971. Buserite, birnessite and the reduction of birnessite. Unpublished manuscript.

Glasby, G. P., 1970. The geochemistry of manganese nodules and associated pelagic sediments from the Indian Ocean. Ph.D. thesis, University of London.

Glasby, G. P., 1972. The mineralogy of manganese nodules from a range of marine environments. *Mar. Geol.*, **13**, 57–72.

Goldberg, E. D., 1961. Chemical and mineralogical aspects of deep-sea sediments. In *Physics and Chemistry of the Earth*. Vol. **4**, pp. 281–302.

Goldberg, E. D., 1961a. Chemistry in the oceans. In *Oceanography*. M. Sears, ed. Amer. Assoc. Adv. Sci., Washington, pp. 583–597.

Goldberg, E. D., 1963. The oceans as a chemical system. In *The Sea*. M. N. Hill, ed., Vol. 2. Wiley-Interscience, New York, pp. 3–25.

Goldberg, E. D., 1965. Minor elements in sea water. In *Chemical Oceanography*. Vol. 1. J. P. Riley and G. Skirrow, eds. Academic Press, London, pp. 163–196.

Goldberg, E. D. and G. Arrhenius. 1958. Chemistry of Pacific pelagic sediments. *Geochim. Cosmochim. Acta*, **13**, 153–212.

Goldberg, E. D., M. Koide, M., J. Griffin, and M. N. A. Peterson, 1964. A geochronological and sedimentary profile across the North Atlantic Ocean. In *Isotopic and Cosmic Chemistry.* North Holland, Amsterdam, pp. 211–232.

Goldberg, E. D., B. L. K. Somayajulu, J. Galloway, I. R. Kaplan, and G. Faure, 1969. Differences between barites of marine and continental origins. *Geochim. Cosmochim. Acta*, **33**, 287–289.

Goodell, H. G., 1965. The marine geology of the Southern Ocean. Contrib. 11, Sedimentology Res. Lab., Florida State University, 196 pp.

Goodell, H. G., M. A. Meylan, and B. Grant. 1970. Ferromanganese deposits of the South Pacific Ocean, Drake Passage and Scotia Sea. In *Antarctic Oceanology.* Vol. 1. J. L. Reid, ed. American Geophysical Union, Washington, pp. 27–92.

Harriss, R. C., 1968. Mercury content of deep-sea manganese nodules. *Nature*, Lond., **219**, 54–55.

Hathaway, J. C. and P. L. Sachs, 1965. Sepiolite and clinoptilolite from the Mid-Atlantic Ridge. *American Mineral.*, **50**, 852–867.

Hay, R. L., 1963. Stratigraphy and zeolite diagenesis of the John Day Formation of Oregon. *Univ. Calif. Pub. in Geol. Sci.*, **42**, 199–262.

Hay, R. L., 1964. Phillipsite in saline lakes and soils. *American Mineral.*, **49**, 1366–1387.

Hay, R. L., 1966. Zeolites and zeolitic reactions in sedimentary rocks. Geol. Soc. Amer. Spec. Paper 85. New York, 130 pp.

Hays, J. D., T. Saito, N. D. Opdyke, and L. H. Burckle, 1969. Pliocene-Pleistocene sediments of the Equatorial Pacific, their paleomagnetic, biostratigraphic and climatic record. *Geol. Soc. Amer. Bull.*, **80**, 1481–1514.

Heath, G. R. and R. Moberly, 1971. Noncalcareous pelagic sediments from the western Pacific, Leg 7, Deep Sea Drilling Project. In *Initial Reports of the Deep Sea Drilling Project.* Vol. VII. E. L. Winterer, et al., eds. U.S. Government Printing Office, Washington, D.C. pp. 987–990.

Horn, D. R., M. Ewing, Horn, B. M., and M. N. Delach, 1972a. Worldwide distribution of manganese nodules. *Ocean Industry*, January 1972.

Horn, D. R., M. Ewing, B. M. Horn, and M. N. Delach, 1972b. Distribution of ferromanganese nodules in the World Ocean. In *Ferromanganese Deposits on the Ocean Floor*, Lamont-Doherty. Geol. Obs., 9–17.

Horn, D. R., B. M. Horn, and M. N. Delach, 1972c. Ferromanganese deposits of the North Pacific, Lamont-Doherty Geol. Obs. Tech. Rept. No. 1, NSF/IDOE GX 33616, 78p.

Horowitz, A., 1970. The distribution of Pb, Ag, Sn, Tl, and Zn in sediments on active oceanic ridges. *Mar. Geol.*, **9**, 241–259.

Hubred, G., 1970. Relationship of morphology and tansition metal content of manganese nodules to an abyssal hill. University of Hawaii. Institute of Geophysics, Rep. No. H1G-70-18. 38 pp.

Jenkyns, H. C., 1970. Fossil manganese nodules from the West Sicilian Jurassic. *Eclog. Geol. Helv.*, **63**, 741–774.

Johnson, C. E. and G. P. Glasby, 1969. Mossbauer effect determination of particle size in microcrystalline iron–manganese nodules. *Nature*, Lond., **222**, 376–377.

Ku, T-L. and W. S. Broecker, 1969. Radiochemical studies on manganese nodules of deep-sea origin. *Deep-Sea Res.*, **16**, 625–637.

Ku, T-L. and G. P. Glasby, 1972. Radiometric evidence of rapid growth rates of shallow water continental margin manganese nodules. *Geochim Cosmochim. Acta.* In press.

Lancelot, Y., J. C. Hathaway, and C. D. Hollister, 1972. Lithology of sediments from the western North Atlantic, Leg 11. Deep Sea Drilling Project. In *Initial Reports of the Deep Sea Drilling Project.* Vol. XI. C. D. Hollister, et al., eds. U.S. Government Printing Office, Washington, D.C. pp. 901–949.

Lynn, D. C. and E. Bonatti, 1965. Mobility of manganese in diagenesis of deep-sea sediments. *Mar. Geol.*, **3**, 457–474.

Manheim, F. T., 1965. Manganese–iron accumulation in the shallow marine environment; in Symposium on marine geochemistry. *Occ. Publs. Univ. Rhode Island*, **3**, 217–76.

McKenzie, R. M., 1971. The synthesis of birnessite, cryptomelane, and some other oxides and hydroxides of manganese. *Mineral Mag.*, **28**, 493–502.

Menard, H. W., 1964. *The Marine Geology of the Pacific*, McGraw-Hill, 271 pp.

Menard, H. W. and C. Shipek, 1958. Surface concentrations of manganese nodules. *Nature*, Lond., **182**, 1156–1158.

Mero, J. L., 1965. *The Mineral Resources of the Sea*. Elsevier, Amsterdam, 312 pp.

Morgenstein, M., 1967. Authigenic cementation of scoriaceous deep-sea sediments west of the Society Ridge, South Pacific. *Sedimentology*, **9**, 105–118.

Morgenstein, M. and M. Felsher, 1971. The origin of manganese nodules: a combined theory with special reference to palagonitization. *Pacific Science*, **25**, 301–307.

Mumpton, F. A., 1960. Clinoptilolite redefined. *American Mineral.*, **45**, 351–369.

Murray, J. and A. F. Renard, 1891. Deep sea deposits. Rep. Scient. Results Explor. Voyage HMS *Challenger*, 1873–1876. H.M.S.O., 525 pp.

Okada, A. and M. Shima, 1970. Study on the manganese nodule. *J. Oceanog. Soc. Japan*, **26**, 151–158.

Opdyke, N. D. and J. H. Foster, 1970. Palaeomagnetism of cores from the North Pacific. Geol. Soc. Amer. Mem. 126, 83–119.

Peterson, M. N. A. et al., 1970. *Initial Reports of the Deep Sea Drilling Project*. Vol. II. U.S. Government Printing Office, Washington, D.C., 501 pp.

Price, N. B. and S. Calvert, 1970. Compositional variation in Pacific Ocean ferromanganese nodules and its relationship to sediment accumulation rates. *Mar. Geol.*, **9**, 145–171.

Revelle, R., 1944. Marine bottoms samples collected in the Pacific by the *Carnegie* on its seventh cruise. *Carnegie Inst. Wash. Publ.*, **556**, 1–180.

Revelle, R. and K. O. Emery, 1951. Barite concretions from the ocean floor. *Bull. Geol. Soc. Amer.*, **62**, 707–723.

Rex, R. W., 1958. Quartz in sediments of the central and north Pacific. Ph.D. thesis, University of California Scripps Institute of Oceanography.

Rex, R. W., 1967. Authigenic silicates formed from basaltic glass by more than 60 million years contact with seawater, Sylvania Guyot, Marshall Islands. *Clays & Clay Mins.*, **27**, 195–203.

Rex, R. W. and B. Murray, 1970. X-ray mineralogy studies. In *Initial Reports of the Deep Sea Drilling Project*. Vol. 5. D. A. McManus, et al., eds. U.S. Government Printing Office, Washington, D.C., pp. 441–484.

Rex, R. W., W. A. Eklund, and I. M. Jamieson, 1971. X-ray mineralogy studies, Leg. 6. In *Initial Reports of the Deep Sea Drilling Project*. Vol. VI. A. G. Fischer, et al., eds. U.S. Government Printing Office, Washington, D.C., pp. 753–810.

Riedel, W. R. and B. M. Funnell, 1964. Tertiary sediment cores and microfossils from the Pacific Ocean floor. *Quart. Jour. Geol. Soc. Lond.*, **120**, 305–368.

Scott, R. B., P. A. Rona, L. W. Butler, A. S. Nawalk, and M. R. Scott, 1972. Manganese crusts in the Atlantis fracture zone. *Nature*, Lond., **239**, 77–79.

Sheppard, R. A., A. J. Gude, and J. J. Griffin, 1970. Chemical composition and physical properties of phillipsite from the Pacific and Indian Oceans. *American Mineral.*, **55**, 2053–2062.

Sillén, L. G., 1961. The physical chemistry of seawater. In *Oceanography*. M. Sears, ed. American Assoc. Adv. Sci., Washington, pp. 549–582.

Skornyakova, N. S. and P. F. Andrushchenko, 1970. Ferromanganese nodules in the Pacific. In *The Pacific Ocean*. Vol. 6. *Sedimentation in the Pacific Ocean*. P. L. Bezrukov, ed. Nauka, Moscow, pp. 202–268.

Skornyakova, N. S. and V. P. Petelin, 1967. Sediments in the central part of the South Pacific. *Oceanology*, **6**, 779–792.

Steinfink, H., 1962. The crystal structure of the zeolite, phillipsite. *Acta Cryst.*, **15**, 644–651.

Strunz, H., 1970. *Mineralogische Tabellen*. Akademische Verlagsgesellschaft. Leipzig.

Stumn, W. and J. J. Morgan, 1970. *Aquatic Chemistry*. Wiley-Interscience, New York, 583 pp.

Thompson, G. and V. T. Bowen, 1969. Analyses of coccolith ooze from the deep tropical Atlantic. *J. Mar. Res.*, **27**, 32–38.

Turekian, K. K., 1965. Some aspects of the geochemistry of marine sediments. In *Chemical Oceanography*. Vol. 2. J. P. Riley and G. Skirrow, eds. Academic Press, London, pp. 81–126.

Turekian, K. K. and K. Bertine, 1971. Deposition of Mo and U along the major ocean ridge systems. *Nature*, Lond., **229**, 250–251.

Turekian, K. K. and J. Imbrie, 1966. The distribution of trace elements in deep-sea sediments of the Atlantic Ocean. *Earth and Planet. Sci. Letters*, **1**, 161–168.

Varentsov, I. M., 1971. On the leaching of manganese in the course of interaction of basic volcanic materials with seawater. Soc. Mining Geol. Japan, Spec. Issue 3, 466–473.

Venkatarathnam, K. and P. E. Biscaye, 1971. Zeolites from the sediments in the Indian Ocean. Geol. Soc. Amer. (Abs. with Programs), 738–739.

Vinogradov, A. P., 1953. The elementary chemical composition of marine organisms. Sears Found. *Marine Res.*, **2**, 647 p.

von der Borch, C. C. and R. W. Rex, 1970. Amorphous iron oxide precipitates in sediments cored during Leg 5, Deep Sea Drilling Project. In *Initial Reports of the Deep Sea Drilling Project.* Vol. V. D. A. McManus, et al., eds. U.S. Government Printing Office, Washington, D.C., pp. 541–544.

von der Borch, C. C., W. D. Nesteroff, and J. S. Galehouse, 1971. Iron rich sediments cored during Leg 8 of the Deep Sea Drilling Project. In *Initial Reports of the Deep Sea Drilling Project.* Vol. VIII. J. I. Tracey, Jr. et al., eds. U.S. Government Printing Office, Washington, D.C., pp. 829–836.

Winterer, E. L., et al., 1971. *Initial Reports of the Deep Sea Drilling Project.* Vol. VIII. U. S. Government Printing Office, Washington, D.C., 1757 pp.

Zemmels, I., H. E. Cook, and J. C. Hathaway, 1972. X-ray minerology studies, Leg XI. In *Initial Reports of the Deep Sea Drilling Project.* Vol. XI. C. D. Hollister et al., eds. U.S. Government Printing Office, Washington, D.C., pp. 729–790.

16. COMPOSITION AND ORIGIN OF INTERSTITIAL WATERS OF MARINE SEDIMENTS*, BASED ON DEEP SEA DRILL CORES

F. T. MANHEIM AND F. L. SAYLES

Abstract

The composition of interstitial waters associated with marine sediments is influenced by the hydrochemical history of the given area, sediment-water interactions (diagenesis), pore fluid convection, and diffusive movement of dissolved ions.

The diffusion of ions occurs readily through most oceanic sediments. For example, buried evaporite deposits have until now been invariably accompanied by concentration gradients of chloride (up to NaCl saturation) and other soluble constituents in the overlying sediments; salt bodies more than 3 km below penetrated strata have been detected in this fashion. By the same token, valid reconstruction of paleosalinities of seas must compensate for diffusion, which alters the composition of trapped pore fluids.

In most open ocean areas, interstitial chloride and sodium concentrations remain similar to concentrations in mean ocean water throughout the sedimentary section. Interstitial potassium decreases markedly in rapidly deposited terrigenous sediments. Magnesium is also depleted in many pore fluids due to uptake in both clays and carbonates, while sulfate is depleted through bacterial processes, especially in organic-rich sections. Sodium is also taken up by silicates. Calcium may be enriched up to tenfold, the more extreme examples evidently drawing on silicate sources. Strontium may be enriched more than tenfold in biogenic oozes showing extensive recrystallization of calcite. Silica is only slightly enriched in clayey terrigenous sediments and deep-sea red clays, but may increase markedly in biogenic (especially siliceous) oozes. Many of the changes may be linked to a model involving carbonate equilibria, sulfate reduction, and uptake of cations in siliceous minerals.

In nearshore areas and semi-isolated water bodies, interstitial waters may be highly variable in composition. Pore fluids ranging from nearly fresh water (the Black and Baltic Seas, and the Atlantic Ocean off Florida) to brine saturated with NaCl (Gulf of Mexico and Red Sea) have been found. Submarine discharge of fresh water from land has been shown to affect sediments as far as 120 km from the coast.

The following diagenetic processes have been identified: (1) dolomitization and recrystallization of calcium carbonate; (2) devitrification of silicates; (3) uptake of cations, especially magnesium and potassium, but also sodium, calcium, and lithium in the form of authigenic silicate formation; (4) replacement of iron in clays by magnesium as a result of sulfate reduction; and (5) ion exchange reactions sensitive to temperature. In terms of relative temperature influence, the interstitial ions follow the order: B, Si, K, Na, Li (decreasing enrichment with increasing temperature), Mg, Sr, Ca (depletion). Anions are not significantly affected.

1. Introduction

The study of pore fluids in marine sediments begins, as do many other aspects of oceanography, with members of the H.M.S. *Challenger* cruise of 1872–1876 and their collaborators. Hanging up a large canvas bag full of "blue terrigenous mud" from off the Scottish coast, Murray and Irvine (1895) caught the drippings, analyzed these

* Woods Hole Oceanographic Institution Contribution Number 2996; Publication authorized by the Director, U.S. Geological Survey.

fluids, and compared them to the overlying seawater. While this sampling method was crude, it served to show that the pore fluid differed little from seawater in sodium, potassium, magnesium, chloride, and bromide concentration. However, the fluids were sharply depleted in sulfate and strongly enriched in bicarbonate and ammonia. Murray and Irvine correctly concluded that the increase in bicarbonate was not due to breakdown of calcium carbonate from shells, but instead resulted from the reduction of sulfate and simultaneous oxidation of organic matter. They also surmised that dissolution of solid phases of the sediments could contribute significantly to ocean chemistry. These observations remained unsurpassed for more than 50 yr. Further progress on the study of pore waters did not occur until the end of World War II when Russian investigators led by S. V. Bruevich (1966, and references cited therein) initiated new studies. These investigators were followed by the research of Kullenberg (1952) in Sweden, Emery and Rittenberg (1952) in the United States, and others. Studies of pore fluids were greatly facilitated by the development of new apparatus such as the Kullenberg piston corer, and the effective extraction devices of Kriukov (1947). Interstitial water surveys were extended to many of the major seas and oceans, including the Azov, Baltic, Barents, Black, Bering, Caspian, Kara, and Mediterranean Seas; the Gulf of Mexico; and the Arctic, Atlantic, and Pacific Oceans (see review in Manheim, 1973).

A great advance in knowledge of porefluid chemistry followed the development of sea floor drilling and coring techniques for scientific purposes. Whereas analyses of pore fluids from the experimental Mohole, drilled off Mexico near Guadalupe Island, showed few significant changes with depth (Rittenberg, et al., 1963; Siever, et al., 1965), an experimental 1100m drill hole in shallow Caspian waters (Pushkina, 1965) found sharply contrasting conditions. Total interstitial salt increased from about 13 g/liter in surface sediments to about 140 g/liter at about 650 m, and thereafter declined to 58 g/liter in silty clays of Pliocene age.

A different aspect of the problem of interstitial waters of marine sediments was revealed as a result of porewater studies on the JOIDES (Joint Oceanographic Institutes' Deep Earth Sampling Program) scientific drilling expedition off Florida in 1965. Interstitial fluids taken from these cores included fresh waters having only 60 ppm Cl at a distance up to 120 km from shore (Manheim, 1967) (Figs. 1 and 2). Contamination was not a factor because the holes were drilled with seawater containing 19,000 ppm Cl (19.0‰). The fresh waters were concluded to be the result of sub-seabottom artesian flow from land aquifers in permeable Eocene and Cretaceous limestone strata, sealed by poorly permeable Miocene marls (Hawthorne formation). These results also showed conclusively that interstitial fluids could be obtained from wire line cores with virtually no contamination by drilling fluid, if suitable precautions were observed.

With the start of the Deep Sea Drilling Project (DSDP) in 1968, provisions were made for the routine shipboard collection and preservation of pore fluids. Most of the chemical analyses of these samples were carried out in shore laboratories following completion of each leg of the expedition. The program of quantitative analysis of the major inorganic constituents was chiefly assigned to our Woods Hole based group, while trace constituents and gases formed the center of activity for a University of California, Los Angeles team. As interest developed in the results, other specialists joined the program, culminating in the "Geochemical Leg" in the Caribbean Sea. These special geochemical studies involved experiments and analytical measurement on shipboard, coupled with intensive study of chemical and isotopic parameters of the sediments and pore fluids in the shore laboratories (see Vol. 15, *Initial Reports of the Deep Sea Drilling Project*). Sampling and archiving of more limited amounts of pore

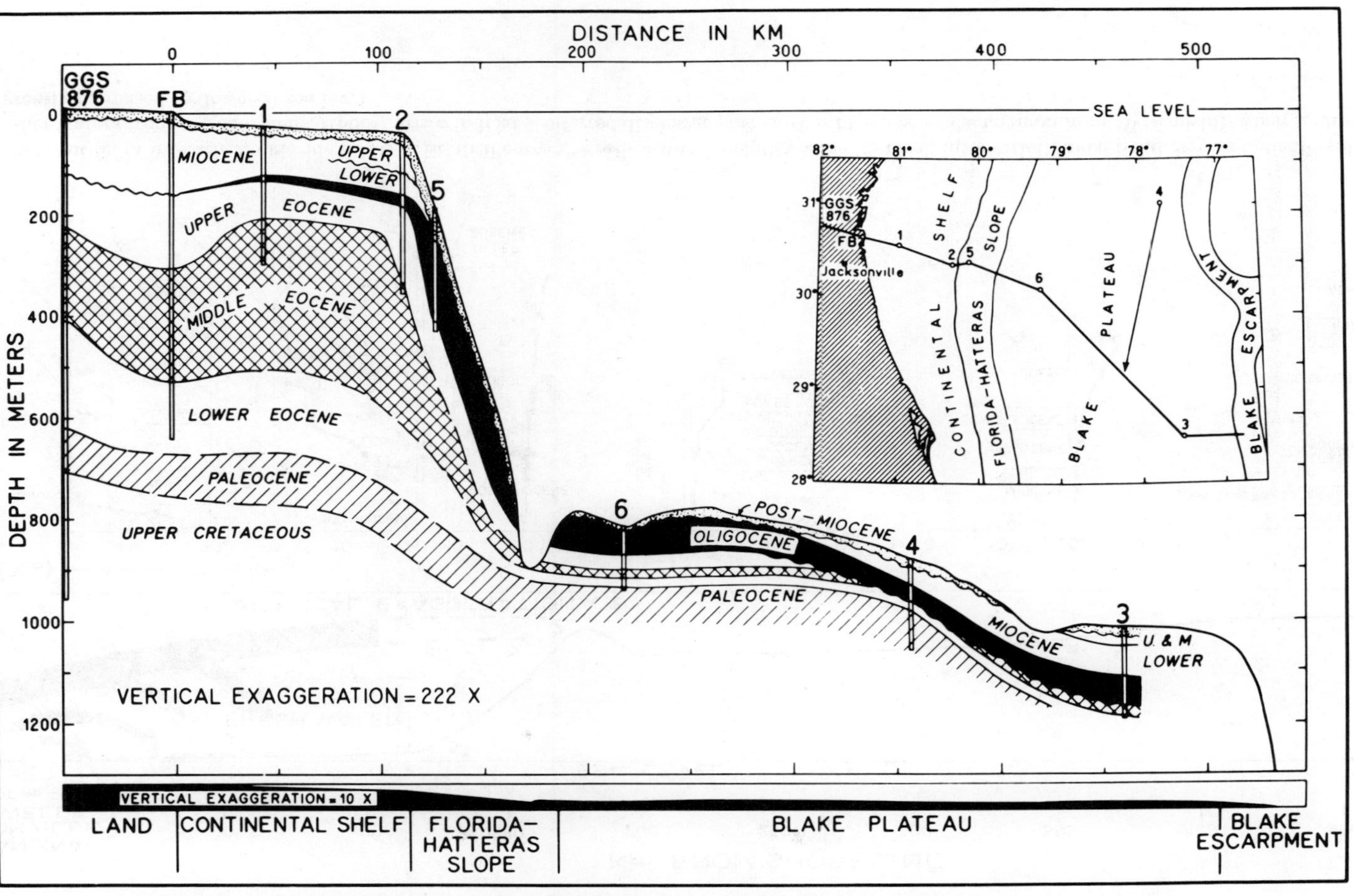

Fig. 1. Location and stratigraphy of JOIDES drill sites off Jacksonville, Florida. JOIDES (1963).

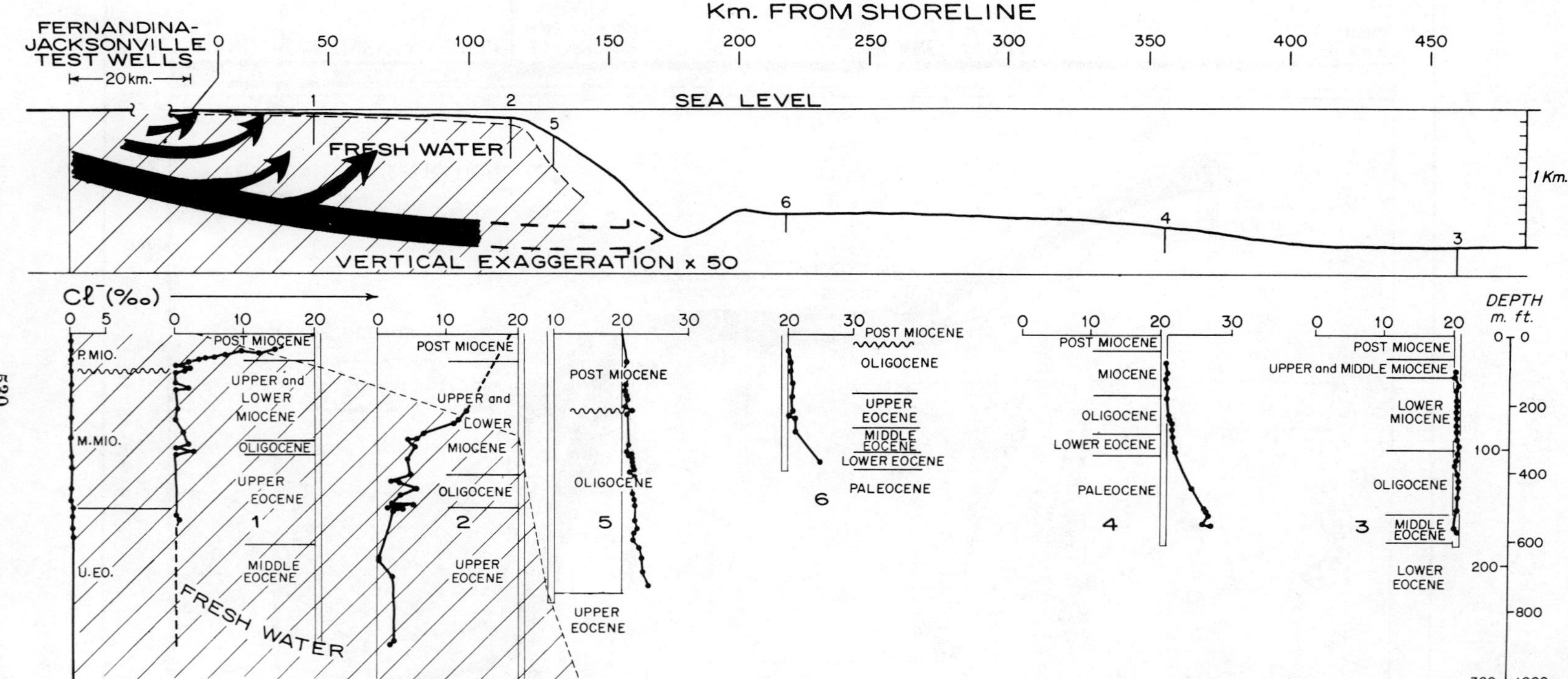

Fig. 2. Distribution of interstitial chloride in JOIDES drill cores. "Fresh water" includes some brackish interstitial fluids. Solid arrows indicate subsurface flow of fresher waters from the continent. Hollow arrow indicates inferred discharge path during Pleistocene glacial maximum (Wisconsin), when hydraulic gradient was greatly increased by lowered sea level.

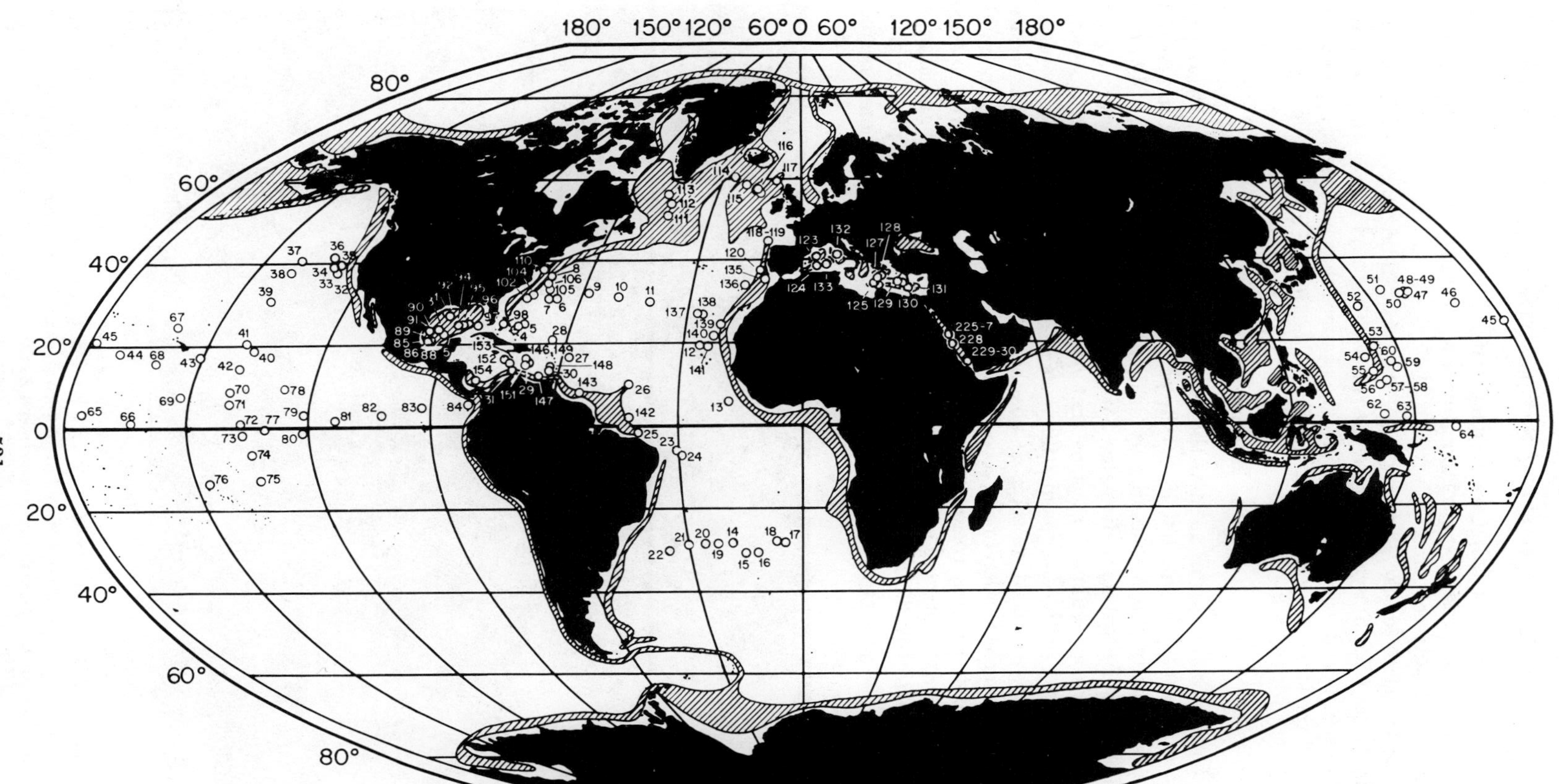

Fig. 3. Distribution of DSDP drill sites for interstitial fluids. Shaded areas represent areas of rapid (geosynclinal) deposition of sediments; greater than > 3 cm/1000 yr.

fluid will continue on the 3-yr DSDP extension through 1975, but routine and comprehensive analysis in the present shore laboratories will cease with the completion of work on samples already collected.

It is now appropriate to take an overview of the pore-fluid data gained from more than 160 drill sites (Fig. 3) available to us at this writing, and assess what we have learned about recent and fossil ocean waters, the changes that have occurred in them with time, and the story they tell about reactions affecting their enclosing rocks.

2. Methods

Pore-fluid analyses are only as valid as the samples of fluid on which they are performed. Experience has shown that if certain precautions are observed interstitial water samples virtually uncontaminated by drilling fluid can be routinely obtained from wire line cores of 4 to 6 cm in diameter. Samples were taken soon after cores were recovered on deck from sediment sections that had not been subjected to serious disturbance in drilling (with consequent admixture of drilling fluid). Interior portions of the cores were sequestered as soon as possible after recovery. This procedure eliminates the outermost portion of the cores, which are in contact with the liner and are often contaminated during coring operations. The pore fluids were extracted on board ship in hydraulic squeezers modified from Manheim (1966) (Fig. 4) and filtered through special micropore filter units into polyethylene/polypropylene pipe or glass ampules for later analysis. A few drops were placed in a temperature compensated

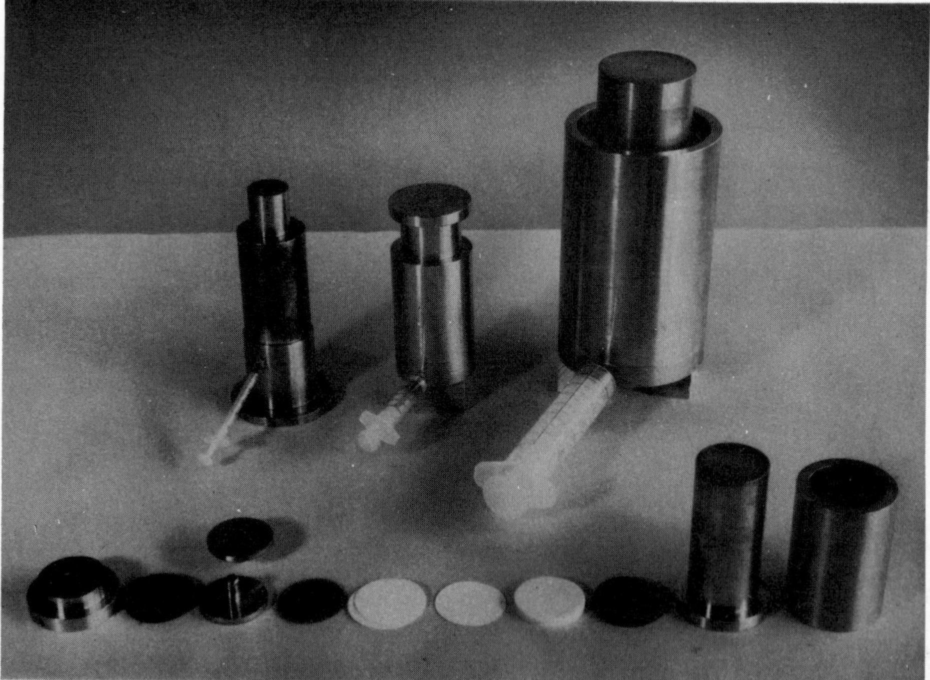

Fig. 4. Stainless steel squeezers, modified from Manheim (1966). The two right-hand models are standard on *Glomar Challenger* and the center model is shown in exploded view at the bottom: base ring gasket, filter retainer plate (top and bottom view), screen with silicone rubber (bathtub caulk) edging, filter papers, sediment (not shown), filter paper, teflon disk, rubber disk, piston, cylinder. Cylinder inner diameter is 4.25 cm.

hand refractometer for determination of salinity (total salt content). The accuracy of the measurement is approximately 0.2‰. At other times, pH, alkalinity, and other parameters were also measured on board ship. For larger samples of unconsolidated sediment, a teflon-lined squeezer operated by gas pressure (Presley, et al., 1967) was also available on board ship to obtain pore fluids for trace element determination.

The analytical methods used for the major and some minor constituents are briefly as follows:

1. *Subdivision of sample aliquots* is by weight on a semimicro balance. (Accuracy 0.1 mg): Total fluid volume 1 to 5 ml.

2. *Chloride* is determined on 0.2-g aliquots. Samples are microtitrated with silver nitrate delivered from a weight burette, using potassium dichromate as an indicator. Estimated standard deviation is 0.1‰ Cl or less. Titer of the $AgNO_3$ solution is obtained using Copenhagen seawater as a standard.

3. *Sulfate* is determined on 0.5 to 1.0-g aliquots by a modification of the microgravimetric method of Shishkina (1954). Barium sulfate is precipitated from hot acid solution, filtered through micropore filters, charred, ashed, and weighed in platinum foil crucibles on a microbalance. The gravimetric factor is determined with Copenhagen seawater. Standard deviation is 2%.

4. *Total alkalinity* is determined on 0.5-g aliquots, which are treated with an excess of standard HCl and backtitrated with dilute NaOH solution.

5. *Major cations* (*Na, K, Ca, Mg*) are determined on a 0.5-g aliquot by atomic absorption, using Copenhagen seawater dilutions (by weight) as standards, and the values of major constituents given for mean seawater by Culkin (1965). Standard of deviation is normally 1 to 3%. Sodium values by atomic absorption are insufficiently accurate to reveal natural variations in most cases. A better, although often still inadequate value, is obtained by summing remaining cations and obtaining sodium by difference from the anion sum, which can be determined quite accurately.

6. *Silica* is determined on 0.2-g aliquots by a standard molybdenum blue colorimetric method (Mullin and Riley, 1955). Also see below.

7. *Minor constituents* (Sr, Ba, Li, Mn, B, Si) are determined on 0.2-g aliquots by spark source emission spectrometry, using a high-voltage spark and "vacuum cup" capillary electrodes. Standard deviation is 4 to 20% or poorer, depending on element and concentration level. We also have drawn on trace analyses (Br, Li, NH_4, B, Mn, Zn, and other metals) performed by atomic absorption, colorimetry, and combined chemical pre-enrichment—atomic absorption (Presley and Kaplan, 1971a; Brooks et al., 1967).

For reasons of conserving valuable and relatively small diameter cores, methods utilizing small quantities of sediment have been stressed in the drill core sampling. Moreover, some consolidated or low-porosity sediments yielded only a few milliliters of fluid. The small sample size limits the reproducibility and accuracy of the data. Whereas this accuracy would be inadequate for open ocean work, most components other than sodium and chloride showed natural variations in interstitial fluids greater than the limits set by analytical and manipulative errors.

Systematic influences on composition due to sampling, storing, and manipulation proved to be more significant than analytical scatter. Influence of pressure (up to 19,000 psi or 1300 atm) has been shown by repeated experiments with squeezers of the present type to yield insignificant systematic error for interstitial fluids having the ionic strength of seawater (Manheim, 1966; Shishkina, 1968; Sayles, 1970; and references cited in these papers). However, Mangelsdorf et al. (1969) showed that the change in temperature from ambient sea floor values of about 1°C to those typical of shipboard laboratories where the sediment extractions were performed caused significant shifts in concentration of interstitial cations. The occurrence of these effects in sediments were later confirmed by Bischoff et al. (1971). The independent observations of

TABLE I

Mean Value of Temperature Effects. Positive Denotes Enrichment on Warming; Negative, the Reverse (Sayles et al., 1973b)

Element	Site 147 Clays and Marls % Change	Site 147 Clays and Marls Δ meq	Site 148 Clays and Marls % Change	Site 148 Clays and Marls Δ meq	Site 149 Calcareous (cores 2-8-17-29) % Change	Site 149 Calcareous (cores 2-8-17-29) Δ meq	Site 149 Siliceous Biogenic (cores 30-42) % Change	Site 149 Siliceous Biogenic (cores 30-42) Δ meq
K	+18	+1.4	+24	+1.8	+16	+1.2	+12	+0.6
Na	+0.9	+4.4	+1.3	+5.9	+1.0	+4.3	+0.5	+1.0
Ca	—	−0.4	−6.5	−1.1	−3.1	−1.3	−1.0	−1.1
Mg	−7.3	−5.1	−7.3	−6.2	−3.1	−2.6	−1.4	−0.7
	Net Δ meq = +0.3		Net Δ meq = +0.4		Net Δ meq = +1.6		Net Δ meq = −0.2	

Kazintsev (1968) and Krasintseva and Korunova (1968) agree qualitatively with the above findings. Even larger changes were observed for silica by Fanning and Pilson (1971). Cation anomalies appear to be largely but perhaps not entirely caused by changes in relative cation exchange capacity of sediments with temperature. The effects were reevaluated during the special geochemical studies conducted on Leg 15 of the DSDP by equilibrating and squeezing many sediments on shipboard at both low (4°C) and room (22°C) temperature (Sayles et al., 1973b). The analytical results are summarized in Tables I and II. The greatest shifts in interstitial concentration due to temperature were found in clays, as one might expect in view of their large exchange capacity. Absolute changes in warming followed the magnitudes: Mg $\geqslant$ Na $>$ K $>$ Ca $>$ Si $>$ Sr $>$ B $>$ Li, with monovalent cations showing enrichment and divalent cations showing depletion. Lithium showed no significant change with temperature. In terms of percent of interstitial water concentration (Table II), boron showed the most extreme changes, with as much as 60% increase, followed by silica and potassium enrichment with averages per site of up to 41 and 24%, respectively. No significant anomalies for the anions, chloride and sulfate, could be detected. Although clays account for a large part of observed anomalies, significant changes, particularly for potassium, remained for sediments of Site 149, which had very low clay concentration. The temperature-reactive sites in these biogenic oozes remain obscure. Equally puzzling is the absence of temperature anomalies in siliceous biogenic oozes. One would have expected that the increases in solubility of amorphous biogenic silica might have accounted for part of the observed silica increase on warming.

Although temperature-related factors significantly affect potassium, magnesium, and boron in most samples, they may perhaps be compensated for in the future when

TABLE II

Summary of Mean Changes in Interstitial Concentrations as a Result of Altered Temperature of Squeezing, DSDP Leg 15 (Sayles et al., 1973b). Changes Refer to Percentage Difference Between Extractions at 22 and 4°C, with respect to values for extractions at 4°C

Component	Site 147	Site 148	Site 149 (Carbonate)	Site 149 (Siliceous)
B	+30	+61	+7 (total site)	
Si (Col)	+26	+41	+27	0
K	+18	+24	+16	+12
Na	+0.9	+1.3	+1.0	+1.0
Li	−3(?)	0.0	0.0 (total site)	
Ca	Variable	−6.5	−3.1	−1.1
Mg	−7.3	−7.3	−3.1	−1.4
Sr	−19	−7	0.0 (total site)	
Cl	<0.5	<0.5	<0.5	<0.5
SO_4	<0.5	<0.5	<0.5	<0.5

better knowledge of thermal gradients in the deep sediments becomes available. However, in many sites the interstitial ionic variations far exceed the limits of the thermal effect, and therefore our conclusions about processes will not be affected.

Another source of error in interstitial water analysis is the precipitation of calcium carbonate on storage of pore fluids containing high alkalinity (usually from rapidly deposited sediments containing appreciable organic matter) (Berner et al., 1970; Gieskes, 1973). Alkalinity and calcium may be erroneously low in analyses of fluids from such sediments. The effect can be removed by adding measured amounts of acid to the storage vessel, but this was not done prior to Leg 15.

3. Sediment-Interstitial Water Provinces

A. Deep-Sea Pelagic Clay

In a series of studies on piston cores from the Pacific Ocean and adjoining seas from 1957 on, Shishkina (1966, 1972) found that major inorganic constituents in interstitial waters of "red clay" sediments differed little from mean seawater composition, with the exception of potassium (more than 10% enrichment) and magnesium (2 to 5% depletion). We now know that these deviations are almost wholly attributable to the temperature of extraction effect discussed earlier. Shishkina's results from the Pacific, as well as other areas, are noteworthy for their accuracy. Her sodium values, determined gravimetrically by the zinc-uranyl acetate method, were sufficiently precise so that she was able to obtain agreement within 1 mg-eq/kg between total anions and cations, each on the order of 600 mg-eq/kg. Typical results are given in Table III, comparing waters from clayey (terrigenous) mud from a site east of Shikoku Island, Japan, red clay from east of the Philippines, and a carbonate mud from north of New Guinea.

Similar results have been obtained from piston cores in the Atlantic Ocean (Shishkina and Bykova, 1964; Siever et al., 1965; Bischoff and Ku, 1970), and in the Indian Ocean (Shishkina and Zheleznova, 1964).

TABLE III

Typical Analysis of Major Interstitial Water Components from Terrigenous Red Clay, and Carbonate-Rich Cores in the Pacific Ocean (Shishkina, 1966). All Values are in meq/kg. Alkalinity Refers to Total Alkalinity

	Composition										Ratios						
Depth from Top (cm)	Cl^-	Br^-	SO_4^{-2}	Alk	Total Anions	Na^+	K^+	NH_4^+	Ca^{2+}	Mg^{2+}	Total Cations	Cl/Br	SO_4/Cl	Na/Cl	K/Cl	Ca/Cl	Mg/Cl
Normal Seawater																	
	545.8	0.83	56.2	2.3	605.1	468.0	9.9	—	20.6	106.6	605.1	293	0.139	0.556	0.020	0.022	0.067
Reducing Gray Clay, Sta. 3163 (East of Shikoku Island, Japan)																	
50–65	546	0.8	56.7	2.9	606	471	12.1	0.1	19.3	102	605	297	0.140	0.561	0.025	0.021	0.064
224–250	545	0.8	55.3	3.9	605	471	12.4	0.1	19.3	102	605	—	0.137	0.561	0.025	0.019	0.064
532–550	555	0.8	55.1	5.0	616	482	12.9	—	19.6	102	617	298	0.135	0.564	0.026	0.022	0.063
800–830	550	0.8	55.7	5.3	612	474	12.0	0.2	19.5	107	613	297	0.137	0.560	0.024	0.021	0.067
1135–1150	554	0.9	53.3	5.4	614	482	12.2	0.2	19.6	101	615	288	0.130	0.565	0.024	0.021	0.063
"Red Clay," Sta. 4011 (East of Philippine Islands)																	
0–22	550	0.83	54.1	0.7	606	470	11.7	0.10	19.5	103	604	293	0.133	0.555	0.023	0.020	0.064
113–140	549	0.8	56.6	1.2	608	476	13.3	0.10	18.2	99	607	288	0.140	0.563	0.027	0.019	0.062
228–252	552	0.9	55.7	1.0	610	475	12.7	0.10	19.5	101	608	285	0.137	0.562	0.025	0.020	0.063
315–340	549	0.83	56.5	1.4	608	477	12.5	0.10	18.5	99	607	293	0.139	0.564	0.025	0.019	0.062
Carbonate Mud, Sta. 3918 (North of New Guinea)																	
3–24	547	0.82	57.0	1.5	606	474	10.1	0.13	22.9	100	607	295	0.141	0.562	0.020	0.024	0.063
77–98	551	0.8	57.4	1.4	611	—	—	—	—	—	—	295	0.141	—	—	—	—
164–180	547	0.8	57.8	0.9	607	477	12.3	0.15	16.9	100	606	292	0.143	—	—	—	—
215–233	547	0.83	61.5	1.3	611	479	15.1	0.16	16.3	100	610	292	0.152	0.568	0.030	0.017	0.063

The analytical results of the DSDP studies extend our knowledge of this tendency toward compositional constancy throughout the entire length of sedimentary sections to basalt "basement." Typical analytical results are given from the east and central Pacific Ocean (Tables IV and V).

One should note here that sections sampled in those DSDP drillings to date have been deliberately biased, in the case of deep ocean sites, to favor sites with thinned sediment sections so that maximum age, and, if possible, basement, could be penetrated by the drill. As will be shown later, sites having greater sediment accumulation rates tend to also have greater interstitial water anomalies.

In Tables IV and V one may note that potassium values tend to decrease with depth to approach seawater values. This may in some cases be related to increases of the *in situ* temperature and consequent reduction of the temperature of squeezing effect; that is, no real anomaly may be involved, but rather, a sampling artifact. On the other hand, the frequent slight to moderate depletions in sulfate appear to be real. In view of the tendency for molecular diffusion of seawater sulfate to reduce or smooth out the anomalies, we may assume that although the sediments are poor in inorganic matter some bacterial sulfate reduction must still be taking place at depth in the sediment column. This sulfate reduction must be supported by further oxidation of organic matter.

An exception to the rule of relative uniformity in composition occurred in Site 53, in a sediment fan on the west side of Iwo Jima in the Philippine Sea. Here an extraordinary increase in calcium concentration to 3‰ and almost total depletion in magnesium occurred in a section of alternating ash and lithified, recrystallized chalk ooze (Table VI). The latter was regarded by shipboard observers as "baked" and apparently subjected to hydrothermal action. The very low alkalinity as well as total CO_2 content (Presley and Kaplan, 1971a) in the pore fluids indicate that the source of the calcium cannot be simple dissolution of carbonate. Instead, carbonate ion diffusing downward in response to the concentration gradient should react with the excess calcium to form additional calcite and ultimately cement the section tightly. The fact that this has not yet occurred indicates that the reactions causing the excess supply of calcium are probably still active. They may involve submarine weathering or breakdown of silicates, but the data of Hart (1970) suggest that Mg, as well as Ca, is released during the submarine weathering of basalt. No significant increase in chloride or boron content attributable to input of volatile constituents of external origin was detected.

With the occasional exception of manganese, trace elements are generally only slightly enriched, if at all, in the pore fluids of oxidizing red clays and similar sediments (Table VII). Interstitial silica is enriched in radiolarian oozes, or sediments containing appreciable undevitrified volcanic ash. The role of such materials in supplying soluble silica to the sediments is clear. From four sites of Leg 6, large volume squeezings (Presley and Kaplan, 1971a) yielded the following mean elemental concentrations: Fe 19; Co 2; Ni 11; Cu 21 ug/kg.

These sections contain large reservoirs of oxidized sediment phases, often to the maximum depth drilled or to basaltic basement. In Site 42, for example, manganese micronodules, described from red clays of the *Challenger* Expedition (Murray and Renard, 1891; Riley and Sinhaseni, 1958), are likewise omnipresent in deeper red clays. Average manganese content of the dry sediment from Sites 45 to 59 ranges from 5,000 to 11,000 (Pimm et al., 1971).

In spite of the above evidence of oxidizing conditions, the observed bacterial sulfate depletions at intervals in the sediments lead one to conclude that sulfate reduction has been acting and probably continues to operate, although at very low levels, within the

TABLE IV

Major Constituents of Interstitial Waters from Red Clays, East Pacific Ocean (from Manheim et al., 1970). All values in g/kg unless otherwise noted. Comments and explanation below apply to all other tables citing major interstitial constituents from DSDP drill cores.

Sodium value shown is normally determined by difference between anions and cations, excluding sodium. Values for cations and anions in parentheses indicate uncertain value. Values for total cations incorporate the directly determined sodium. Where total cations or anions are in parentheses the values are taken to equal the sum of the oppositely charged species. HCO_3 is calculated from alkalinity, assuming this is entirely due to bicarbonate ion. Sum incorporates calculated Na values and excludes NH_4^+ and other trace constituents. These usually contribute less than 0.1‰ to the sum. pH and water content are taken from shipboard summaries and may refer to samples from approximately the same horizon as sediments from which interstitial water has been extracted. In a few cases a salinity determined by index of refraction is given to the right of "sum."

Depth below Sea Bed (cm)	Age	Description	Na	K	Ca	Mg	Total Cations (meq/kg)	Cl	SO_4	Alk (meq/kg)	HCO_3	Total Anions (meq/kg)	Sum	H_2O (%)
Hole 37 (40°58.7′N, 140°43.1′W, water depth 4682 m), Abyssal hills north of Mendocino fracture zone, northeast Pacific														
2	Pleistocene?	Light brown red clay soft	10.8	0.44	0.42	1.24	(603)	19.3	2.65	4.3	0.27	603	35.1	60.8
15	Lower Pliocene?	Zeolitic red clay	10.8	0.45	0.41	1.24	(604)	19.4	2.58	3.0	0.19	604	35.1	—
Hole 38 (38°42′N, 140°21.3′W, water depth 5137 m), Abyssal hills north of Mendocino fracture zone, northeast Pacific														
8	?	Yellow-brown zeolitic red clay	10.9	0.43	0.41	1.20	(604)	19.2	2.80	3.0	0.19	604	35.2	—
24	?	Yellow-brown zeolitic red clay	11.0	0.45	0.41	1.22	(612)	19.6	2.84	3.8	0.23	612	35.6	63.6
45	Lower Eocene	Nannofossil-foraminiferal ooze, ferrug.	11.1	0.43	0.37	1.18	(609)	19.7	2.44	3.0	0.18	609	35.4	53.4

Hole 39 (32°48.3′N, 139°34.3′W, water depth 4929 m), Abyssal hills north of Murray fracture zone, northeast Pacific													
4	?	Zeolitic red clay	10.9	0.45	0.38	1.23	606	19.4	2.74	2.8	0.18	608	35.3	—
Hole 40 (19°47.6′N, 139°54.1′W, water depth 5183 m)													
4	?	Zeolitic red clay with small Mn nodules	10.9	0.46	0.36	1.19	(602)	19.3	2.61	2.7	0.17	602	35.0	62.3
70	Middle Eocene	Brown radiolarian ooze, deformed	10.8	0.42	0.39	1.27	604	19.6	2.41	2.8	0.17	602	35.1	77.5
125	Lower Eocene	Brown radiolarian ooze, deformed	11.0	0.41	0.37	1.28	611	19.6	2.70	2.6	0.16	613	35.6	81.2
Hole 41 (19°51.2′N, 140°02.9′W, water depth 5339 m), Abyssal hill north of Clarion fracture zone, north-central Pacific													
4	?	Zeolitic red clay	10.9	0.46	0.37	1.22	(603)	19.4	2.62	2.5	0.16	603	35.0	—
Hole 43 (17°06.6′N, 151°22.5′W, water depth 5405 m), Abyssal hill southeast of Hawaiian Island, central Pacific													
5	?	Yellow-brown silty clay	10.8	0.44	0.34	1.20	601	19.1	2.73	2.8	0.18	599	34.8	64.1
		Seawater	10.8	0.39	0.41	1.29	608	19.4	2.71	(2.5)	(0.14)	607	35.0	—

TABLE V

Major Constituents of Red Clays from the Central Western Pacific Ocean (Manheim and Sayles, 1971). Values reported in g/kg fluid unless otherwise stated. Explanations as in Table IV

Depth (m)	Age	Description	Na^+	K^+	Ca^{2+}	Mg^{2+}	Total Cations (meq/kg)	Cl^-	SO_4^{2-}	Alk (meq/kg)	HCO_3^-	Total Anions (meq/kg)	Sum	H_2O (%)	pH
Hole 45 (24°15.9′N, 178°30.5′W, water depth 5508 m, southwest of Midway Island)															
2	?	Brown zeolitic clay	10.5	0.46	0.37	1.32	(596)	19.5	2.27	2.4	0.15	596	34.5	59	—
Hole 49 (32°24.1′N, 156°35.0′E, water depth 4282 m, west flank Shatsky Rise; sediment subcrop)															
3	Pleistocene	Brown mud with volcanic glass	10.7	0.44	0.41	1.32	(602)	19.3	2.76	1.6	0.10	602	35.1	56	7.6
Hole 49 (32°24.1′N, 156°35.0′E, water depth 4282 m, west flank Shatsky Rise; sediment subcrop)															
6	Upper Jurassic Lower Creta-ceous	Brown sandy zeolitic mud	10.6	0.46	0.44	1.28	(601)	19.4	2.62	—	—	601	34.8	60	7.5
Hole 50 (32°24.2′N, 156°36.0′E, water depth 4487 m, west flank Shatsky Rise; basement subcrop)															
7	Pleistocene	Brown clay with nano-plankton	10.6	(0.45)	0.36	1.33	(601)	19.4	2.63	1.7	0.10	601	34.8	50	7.6
30	?	Brown zeolitic clay	10.8	0.46	0.31	1.32	(608)	19.5	2.78	—	—	608	35.2	60	7.5

		Hole 51.0 (33°28.5′N, 153°24.3′E, water depth 5981 m, west flank Shatsky Rise; sediment pond)													
119	Miocene	Brown zeolitic clay with clay breccia (deformed)	10.6	0.40	0.46	1.27	(598)	19.4	2.43	1.8	0.11	598	34.7	57	7.5
		Hole 51.1 (33°28.5′N, 153°24.3′E, water depth 5981 m, west flank Shatsky Rise; sediment pond)													
25	Pleistocene	Gray-brown sandy volcanic mud	10.9	0.46	0.41	1.24	(610)	19.6	2.68	2.4	0.15	610	35.5	58	8.1
		Hole 52 (27°46.3′N, 147°07.8′E, water depth 5744 m, Abyssal swale east of Bonin Trench)													
6	?	Brown glassy clay	10.8	0.45	0.38	1.23	(603)	19.4	2.72	1.4	0.08	603	35.0	54	7.3
20	?	Brown clay	10.8	0.44	0.40	1.37	(611)	19.7	2.73	1.6	0.10	611	35.6	58	7.3
41	?	Brown ashy clay	10.7	0.42	0.40	1.32	(606)	19.5	2.64	3.2	0.20	606	35.2	64	7.4

TABLE VI

Major Constituents of Sediments in "Baked" Section from Sediment Fan West of Iwo Jima, Philippine Sea. Data and notes follow scheme of Table IV. Data from Sayles and Manheim, 1971

Depth (m)	Age	Description	Na	K	Ca	Mg	Total Cations (meq/kg)	Cl	SO_4	Alk (meq/kg)	HCO_3	Total Anions (meq/kg)	Sum	H_2O (%)	pH
Hole 53.0 (18°02.0′N, 141°11.5′E, water depth 4629 m. Sediment fan on west side of Iwo Jima in Philippine Sea)															
5	?	Dark brown zeolitic clay	10.4	0.45	1.09	0.90	(591)	19.4	2.05	2.2	0.13	591	34.5	65	7.4
18	Upper Miocene	Brown radiolarian silt with volcanic glass	10.9	0.35	1.87	0.44	(611)	19.8	2.50	0.7	0.04	611	35.9	50	7.2
28	Upper Miocene	Dark sandy volcanic ash	10.7	0.41	1.90	0.44	(605)	19.8	2.27	0.6	0.04	605	35.6	48	7.3
63	Middle-Upper Miocene	Gray silty volcanic ash	10.8	0.34	1.71	0.48	(607)	19.8	2.35	0.2	0.01	607	35.6	43	7.2
90	Middle Miocene	Gray sandy volcanic ash	(11.3)	0.28	1.52	0.48	(612	19.8	2.56	1.3	0.08	612	36.0	52	8.7
138	Lower Middle Miocene	Dark silty volcanic ash	10.6	0.28	2.02	0.30	(595)	19.6	2.08	0.8	0.05	595	34.9	41	8.5
195	Lower Oligocene-Lower Miocene	Interbedded ash and chalk ooze, lithified	9.6	0.08	3.03	0.17	(587)	19.6	1.65	0.5	0.03	587	34.2	30	7.8

TABLE VII

Trace constituents from DSDP Legs 5 and 6. Br, B, Mn, Zn, and Li (chiefly) from Presley et al. (1970) and Presley and Kaplan (1971a); Br, Sr, Ba, and Si from Manheim et al. (1970) and Manheim and Sayles (1971). Sample designation follows the scheme site- barrel- section-. Values in mg/kg

Sample	Depth (m)	Mn	Br	B	Sr	Ba	Li	Si	Zn	Notes
37-1-2	2	—	—	5	6.4	0.15	0.20	< 12	—	Red clay
37-3-1	15	—	67	6	6.4	0.16	0.22	9.4	—	Zeolitic red clay
38-2-4	8	—	65	6	6.2	0.20	0.20	5.2	—	Yellow-brown zeolitic clay
38-4-2	24	—	—	6	6.9	0.11	0.27	—	—	Zeolitic red clay
38-6-4	45	—	—	7	6.6	0.15	0.24	4.8	—	Brown foram-nanno ooze
39-1-3	4	—	67	7	8.1	< 0.1	0.22	5.1	—	Zeolitic red clay
40-1-3	4	0.1	67	6	7.5	< 0.1	0.17	13.0	0.7	Zeolitic red clay
40-8-3	70	0.1	68	4.9	7.5	< 0.1	0.17	29	0.62	Radiolarian ooze
40-14-3	125	0.1	68	4.9	6.9	< 0.1	0.16	26	0.38	Radiolarian ooze
40-16-3	142	0.1	67	4.7	6.6	0.12	0.17	28	0.44	Radiolarian ooze
42-1-3	4	—	67	5	7.0	< 0.1	0.21	22.0	—	Yellow-brown radiolarian ooze
43-2-2	5	—	67	5	7.0	< 0.1	0.19	11.0	—	Yellow-brown silty clay
45-1-1	2	0.1	62	7.0	8.0	< 0.1	0.20	6.0	0.54	Brown clay
49-1-2	3	< 0.05	—	3.6	9.0	< 0.1	0.19	9.3	0.54	Brown mud
49-1-3	6	0.10	71	4.9	7.9	< 0.1	0.20	9	0.44	Brown mud and Mn nod.
50-1-4	7	0.21	—	3.2	8.0	0.1	0.17	13.8	0.85	Nannoplankton clay (yellow)
50-3-5	30	< 0.05	69	5.0	9.0	< 0.1	0.20	—	0.56	Yellow zeolitic clay
51.0-1-4	119	0.22	—	6.8	7.0	< 0.1	0.23	5.5	1.1	Zeolitic clay
51.1-1-5	25	9.4	75	2.2	9.9	< 0.1	0.18	13.0	0.32	Gray volcanic mud
52-1-4	6	0.22	—	3.2	11.0	0.30	0.21	22.0	0.84	Brown ashy clay
52-3-2	20	4.1	62	3.4	9.0	0.20	0.18	15.4	0.68	Red-brown clay
52-5-3	41	0.37	75	6.1	8.0	< 0.1	0.30	5.2	0.49	Gray-brown clay
53.1-1-4	5	0.01	—	6.7	10.0	0.10	0.21	5.9	0.58	Dark brown zeolitic clay
53.2-1-4	18	2.8	70	4.8	10.3	—	0.27	16.6	0.56	Brown radiolarian silt and ash
53.1-2-5	28	4.2	—	4.3	14.0	0.20	0.22	20.5	0.60	Dark sandy ash
53.1-3-4	63	2.1	75	4.9	15.0	0.21	0.19	16.8	0.59	Gray silty ash
53.0-1-2	90	—	—	—	14.0	0.20	—	15.4	—	Gray silty ash
53-3-1	138	0.32	—	1.4	14.0	0.15	0.22	13	0.32	Dark silty ash
53-6-2	195	0.18	69	5.5	11.0	0.2	0.36	4	0.58	Lithified ash-chalk
Seawater	sea water	0.002	65	4.6	8.0	≤ 0.06	0.18	3	0.010	Acc. Goldberg, 1965

sediment column. Free oxygen should therefore be absent in sediments below a few meters depth. Manipulation of the sediment on board ship and consequent unavoidable admission of atmospheric oxygen may influence iron values, but apparently has little effect on manganese. These conclusions are supported by data on experimental storage and exposure of sediment cores and extracted fluids (J. L. Bischoff, oral communication).

According to Bender (1971), interstitial manganese concentrations less than

10 mg/kg cannot have any significant effect in recycling manganese to the sediment surface where the manganese-rich (e.g., "red clay") layers are more than 1 m thick. Since for the areas under consideration interstitial manganese is normally much less than 10 mg/kg and the manganese oxide-enriched zone is much thicker, we may relegate recycling of manganese—and even more so, iron—to a very minor role. Short-range remobilization is not excluded, however.

B. Biogenic Oozes

Biogenic deposits fall into two general categories. Slowly deposited pelagic oozes that usually retain a high water content, show relatively little evidence of diagenesis and alteration, and exhibit little change in pore fluid composition comprise the first group. The second type includes more rapidly deposited sediments that often show loss of sulfate, increases of silica, and changes in those constituents involved in carbonate equilibria.

Table VIII gives examples of biogenic oozes whose pore fluids show only relatively minor changes with depth. At Site 77, water content also remains high down to 167 m depth. Below that depth, water content drops to about 30% and remains at that level to 481 m, the bottom of the hole. Site 77 may be considered a transitional sediment type having a more rapid sedimentation rate than Sites 11, 19, and 98. Diagenesis is indicated by strontium increases up to 37 ppm in Site 77, as well as silica concentrations exceeding 30 ppm. Studies of the concentration of silica in pore fluids extracted at various temperatures (Sayles et al., 1973b) suggest that at bottom temperatures of about 1°C, pore fluids that are in equilibrium with sediments containing abundant biogenic silica may have about 27 ppm Si.

A sequence of cores (Sites 69–75 (Fig. 5)) across the equatorial productivity belt in the East Pacific provides a striking illustration of the influence of accumulation rate on both the degree of diagenesis of biogenic oozes, and associated interstitial water compositional changes. Sites 69, 72, 74, and 75 have lithologic composition rather similar to Sites 70 and 71. Yet, only the latter sites show marked evidence of recrystallization accompanied by decreases in magnesium and increases in calcium (Fig. 6). Strontium in particular increases almost log-linearly with accumulation rate (Fig. 7). Table IX gives the major element data for Sites 70 and 71, whereas Table X shows changes in cations, expressed as differences from mean seawater (in milliequivalents per kilogram). Table XI gives Sr, Ba, Li, and Si on the samples. Presley and Kaplan (1972—Leg 9) found between 5 and 6 mg/kg B, normal seawater levels for Br; Mn concentrations varying irregularly between <0.05 and 3 mg/kg, and on the large composite pore fluids 4–220, 2.0–4.0, 4.0–24, 3–79 for Fe, Co, Ni, and Cu, respectively in μg/kg. In addition, PO_4 concentrations ranging up to several mg/kg were observed.

The data in Table IX and in Figs. 5 to 7 show clearly that calcium is accumulating in pore fluids in increasing quantities with depth, while magnesium is decreasing. This suggests loss of calcium from calcium carbonate, while perhaps other, more magnesium-bearing carbonate phases (e.g., dolomite), are being precipitated. Carbonate overgrowths on discoasters and coccoliths were singled out for comment in the Leg 8 *Initial Reports*. Similar patterns of strontium anomalies and extensive evidence of recrystallization and corrosion were obtained in Leg 7 (Sayles and Manheim, 1971). However, the nature of the phases being corroded and precipitated and in particular, the source of the strontium need clarification.

The excess of interstitial Sr over seawater values exceeds 100 mg/kg in Site 71. The

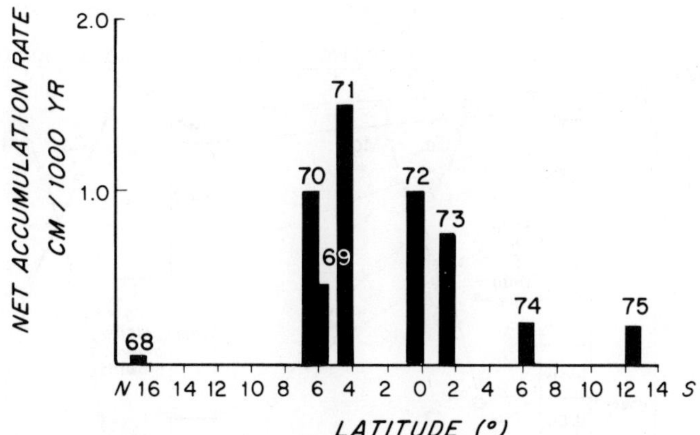

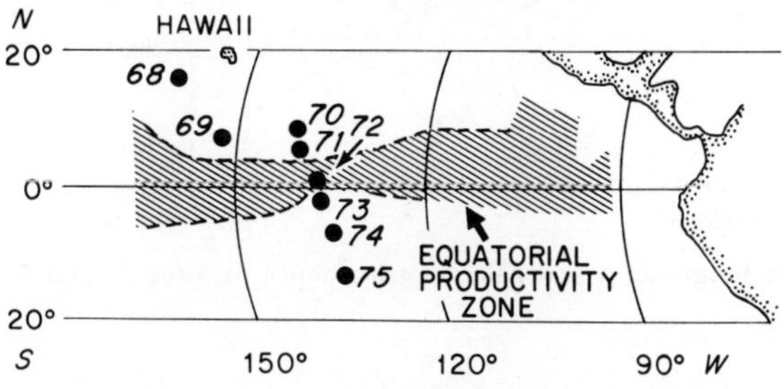

Fig. 5. Location and accumulation rate of sediments from DSDP drill sites across east Pacific equatorial zone. From Manheim et al. (1971).

corresponding ratios of excess Ca to excess Sr are less than 10/1, compared with Ca:Sr ratios in coccolith and foraminiferal oozes of more than 250:1. This means that mere dissolution of the coccolith oozes in Leg 8 cannot supply enough Sr, unless far greater calcium concentrations than correspond to interstitial calcium are solubilized. The highest strontium content known in organisms is about 1.0% in nonmolluscan aragonite (Milliman, 1973). Acantharian radiolaria are known to contain celestite ($SrSO_4$) (Hollande and Cachon-Enjumet, 1963), but dissolve rapidly on death and are not reported as being preserved in sediments (Kling, 1970). Very little is known about the composition of nonacantharian radiolaria, except that they have siliceous skeletons and hence are unlikely to contain large strontium concentrations. Finally, nondispersive microprobe analysis of typical coccolith tests from Site 71 revealed particles having unusual strontium concentrations.

In the absence of special organisms or phases containing unusual strontium concentrations, the present degree of enrichment can only be explained by the recrystallization of calcite or some other mineral containing less strontium. An examination of Mg and Sr content of organisms prominent in the biogenic oozes reveals concentrations of about 0.15% Sr and 0.11 to 0.16% Mg (Table XII). In contrast, a pure coccolith-foram ooze at depth at Site 3 of the 1965 JOIDES drillings off Jacksonville, Florida showed 0.094 and 0.28% Sr and Mg, respectively, calculated on the HCl-leachable fraction. Based on optical petrographic estimates of the relative amounts of recrystallized material at Site 3, as well as calculations and experiments of Katz et al.

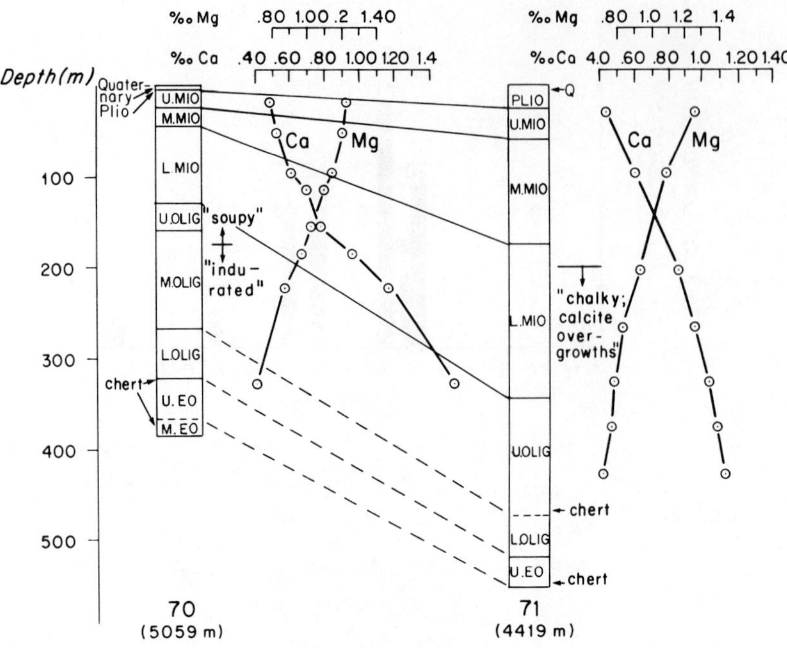

Fig. 6. Distribution of magnesium and calcium with depth in Sites 70 and 71. From Manheim et al. (1971).

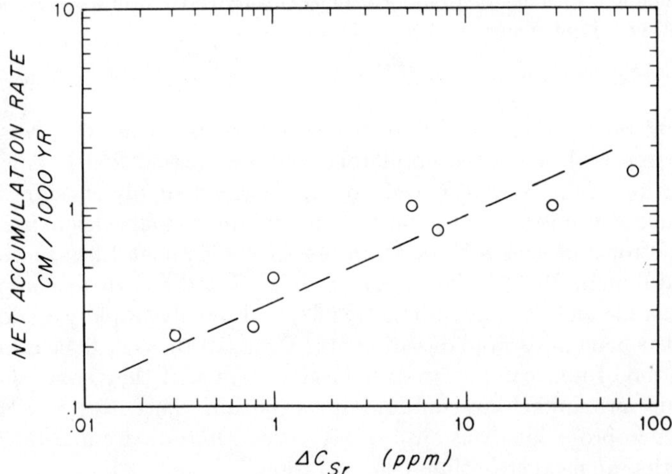

Fig. 7. Plot of strontium anomalies against accumulation rate for Sites 69 to 75, across Pacific equatorial productivity zone. ΔC is obtained by subtracting the value for strontium in mean ocean water (about 8 ppm) from the mean concentration of strontium in the pore fluids of each site. From Manheim et al. (1971).

Table VIII

Interstitial Water Analyses from Biogenic Deposits Showing Little Diagenetic Change; values in g/kg except where noted. Explanations follow those cited for Table IV. Data from Chan and Manheim (1970) (Hole 11); Manheim et al. (1970) (Hole 19); Sayles et al. (1971) (Hole 77); and Sayles et al. (1971) (Hole 98). Duplicate values in parentheses refer to duplicate samples analyzed. "Salinity" refers to total salt determination by index of refraction.

Depth Below Sea Bed (m)	Age	Description	Na	K	Ca	Mg	Total Cations (meq/kg)	Cl	SO_4	Alk	HCO_3	Total Anions (meq/kg)	Sum	Salinity	Water Content	pH
Hole 19 (28°32.1′S, 23°40.6′W, water depth 4677 m), South Atlantic Ocean																
7	Miocene(?)	Dark red-brown zeolitic clay	10.8	0.49	0.38	1.23	602	19.3	2.68	5.8	0.35	606	35.2	—	—	—
110	Middle Eocene	Light yellow-brown nanno-fossil chalk ooze	11.0	0.44	0.38	1.23	610	19.6	2.53	4.0	0.24	609	35.4	—	—	—
136	Middle Eocene	Yellow-brown nannofossil chalk ooze	10.8	0.45	0.38	1.23	605	19.2	2.21	15	0.9	(605)	35.2	—	—	—
Hole 11 (29°56.6′N, 44°44.8′W, water depth 3556 m), North Atlantic Ocean																
19	Quaternary	Pale brown foraminiferal-nannofossil ooze	10.9	0.41	0.39	1.29	608	19.7	2.25	2.04	2.04	600	34.9	—	—	—
266	Middle Miocene	Nannofossil-foraminifera ooze	10.8	0.41	0.41	1.29	608	19.6	2.31	2.53	0.14	607	35.2	—	—	—

(continued)

Table VIII (*continued*)

Depth Below Sea Bed (m)	Age	Description	Na	K	Ca	Mg	Total Cations (meq/kg)	Cl	SO_4	Alk	HCO_3	Total Anions (meq/kg)	Sum	Salinity	Water Content	pH
Hole 98 (25°23.0′N, 77°18.7′W, water depth 2750 m), Northeast Providence Channel, North Atlantic Ocean																
Surface	Ocean Water		11.1	0.41 (0.41)	0.44 (0.43)	1.35 (1.35)	630 (621)	20.07	2.83	—	—	624	36.3	36.0	—	—
8	Lower Pliocene	Cream white foraminiferal-nannofossil ooze	10.8	0.43	0.43	1.28	608	19.51	2.59	3.9	0.24	607	35.3	35.1	30	7.5
24	Upper Miocene	Light gray foraminiferal-nannofossil ooze	10.8	0.48	0.46	1.23	614	19.71	2.40	—	—	605	35.3	36.1	37	7.3
63	Middle Miocene	Light greenish-gray foraminiferal-nannofossil ooze; mottled	11.0	0.47	0.49	1.20	613	19.69	2.57	4.1	0.25	612	35.7	35.5	30	7.5
94	Upper Oligocene	Light grayish-green to light olive gray foraminiferal-nannofossil ooze	11.0	0.48	0.49	1.25	622	19.87	2.63	3.9	0.24	618	36.1	36.2	34	7.4
138	Middle Eocene	Light greenish-white foraminiferal-nannofossil ooze	11.0	0.45	0.48	1.16	601	19.64	2.59	2.4	0.15	610	35.3	35.5	28	7.3

172	Middle to Lower Eocene	Pinkish white foraminiferal-nannofossil ooze	10.8	0.48	0.47	1.26	613	19.66	2.57	2.5	0.15	610	35.5	35.2	30	7.3
233	Upper to Middle Paleocene	Yellowish white foraminiferal-nannofossil ooze	10.8	0.51	0.45	1.31	613	19.80	2.67	—	—	613	35.5	35.8	25	7.1
		Hole 77B (00°28.9′N, 133°13.7′W, water depth 4291 m), East Pacific Ocean														
14	Pleistocene	Varicolored interlaminated beds of foraminiferal-radiolarian-nannofossil ooze	10.7	0.43	0.42	1.25	596	19.41	2.60 (260)	3.5	0.21	604	34.9	35.3	47	7.6
78	Pliocene	Varicolored interlaminated beds of foraminiferal-radiolarian-nannofossil ooze	10.8	0.42	0.43	1.18	603	19.36	2.50	4.8 (4.0)	0.29 (0.25)	601	35.1	35.0	69	7.5
167	Upper Miocene	Varicolored interlaminated beds of foraminiferal-radiolarian-nannofossil ooze	10.6	0.47	0.45	1.14	589	19.38	2.35 (2.38)	5.3 (4.5)	0.33 (0.28)	590	34.7	35.0	55	7.6

TABLE IX

Major interstitial constituents from Sites 70 and 71 (see location map, Fig. 5). Values in g/kg unless otherwise indicated. See Table IV for general explanatory notes. Duplicate values in parentheses refer to duplicate samples analyzed. Second decimals have been listed in this table because unusually good reproducibility of results for this leg appeared to warrant retention. Note that total cations are calculated with original atomic absorption analysis for Na, not difference values (superior) shown.

Depth (m)	Age	Description	Na	K	Ca	Mg	Total Cations (meq/kg)	Cl	SO_4	(meq/kg)	HCO_3	Total Anions (meq/kg)	Sum	H_2O (%)	pH
Site 70 (6°20.1′N, 140°21.7′W, water depth 5059 m, continuation of north to south profile started on Leg 5)															
17	Middle Miocene	Dark grayish brown radiolarian ooze	10.9	0.44 (0.44)	0.46 (0.45)	1.23 (1.21)	602	19.52	2.57	3.6 (3.5)	0.22 (0.21)	608	35.3	32	7.5
55	Lower Miocene	Light brownish gray nannofossil-radiolarian ooze	10.8	0.43 (0.41)	0.53 (0.52)	1.20 (1.18)	607	19.51	2.51	3.0 (3.2)	0.18 (0.20)	606	35.2	32	7.5
98	Lower Miocene	White nannofossil chalk ooze	10.8	0.37 (0.37)	0.60 (0.60)	1.14 (1.15)	601	19.52	2.34	3.6	0.22	603	35.0	31	7.4
115	Lower Miocene	Yellowish-gray nanno-fossil-radiolarian ooze	10.8	0.37	0.69	1.09	607	19.53	2.37	1.7	0.10	602	35.0	39	7.4
157	Upper Oligocene	Light greenish-gray nannofossil-radiolarian ooze	10.7	0.35	0.77	1.04	603	19.45	2.31	2.5	0.15	599	34.8	61	7.3
189	Middle Oligocene	Light greenish-gray to pale blue nannofossil-radiolarian chalk	10.7	0.30 (0.32)	0.96 (0.98)	0.98 (0.96)	606	19.58	2.33	1.5 (2.1)	0.09 (0.13)	602	35.0	34	7.8
221	Middle Oligocene	Bluish white nannofossil chalk	10.7	0.26 (0.27)	1.17 (1.16)	0.86 (0.84)	593	19.57	2.21	2.2 (2.1)	0.13 (0.13)	600	34.9	32	7.7
329	Upper Eocene	Very pale brown semi-indurated radiolarian ooze	10.5	0.19	1.55	0.71	584	19.43	2.30	1.9	0.12	598	34.5	55	7.6

Site 71 (4°28.3′N, 140°18.9′W, water depth 4419 m)															
30	Upper Miocene	White and light brownish-gray nannofossil-radiolarian ooze	10.9	0.41 (0.43)	0.43 (0.42)	1.25 (1.24)	606	19.59	2.62	2.3 (2.4)	0.14 (0.15)	609	35.3	52	—
101	Middle Miocene	Very light gray nannofossil-radiolarian ooze	10.8	0.42	0.60	1.09	605	19.63	2.23	2.6	0.16	603	35.0	34	—
203	Lower Miocene	Light gray to grayish-green nannofossil-radiolarian ooze	10.9	0.35	0.86	0.93	591	19.63	2.29	3.3	0.20	605	35.0	36	—
265	Lower Miocene	Bluish-white foraminiferal-nannofossil ooze	10.9	0.35	0.96	0.85	606	19.65	1.93	2.4	0.15	603	35.1	32	—
232	Lower Miocene	Bluish-white foraminiferal-nannofossil-radiolarian chalk	10.9	0.35 (0.33)	1.03 (1.00)	0.77 (0.78)	596	19.66	2.08	2.1 (1.5)	0.13 (0.09)	600	34.9	28	—
375	Upper Oligocene	Bluish-white nannofossil chalk	10.9	0.32	1.09	0.75	622	19.70	2.10	2.3	0.14	602	35.0	28	—
430	Upper Oligocene	Bluish-white to light gray nannofossil chalk	10.9	0.34	1.14	0.71	603	19.70	2.06	1.9	0.12	600	35.0	28	—

Table X

Changes in Composition of Pore Fluids in Sites 70 and 71, Expressed as Differences from Mean Sea Water (mg-eq/kg)

Site	Depth (m)	K	Ca	Mg	Sr
70	17	+1.3	+2.3	−4.1	
	55	+1.0	+5.8	−7.3	+(0.07)
	98	−0.4	+9.3	−10.5	+0.01
	155	−0.4	+13.7	−15.5	+0.08
	157	−1.0	+17.7	−19.5	+0.07
	189	−2.0	+27.6	−25.3	+0.10
	221	−3.2	+37.1	−35.1	+0.13
	329	−5.0	+56.4	−46.7	+0.12
71	30	+0.8	+0.8	−1.5	+0.18
	101	+0.8	+9.2	−15.6	+0.49
	203	−1.0	+21.9	−28.6	+1.00
	265	−1.0	+27.1	−35.1	+0.89
	323	−1.2	+29.5	−40.9	+0.94
	375	−1.6	+33.5	−43.5	+1.27
	430	−1.2	+36.0	−46.7	+0.96

Table XI

Minor constituents from Sites 70 and 71, representing strong diagenesis of biogenic sediments. Values in ppm. From Manheim et al., 1971. Values in parentheses are duplicates. In addition, trace determinations by Presley and Kaplan (1971b) showed rather variable manganese below 1 ppm, and boron values between 5 and 6 ppm. Phosphate values, previously seen to vary from 0.2 to 2 ppm in Leg 9 (southeast Pacific), reached as high as 25 ppm (?) in siliceous oozes of Site 73

Depth (m)	Sr	Ba	Si(col.)	Li
Site 70 (6°20.1′N, 140°21.7′W, water depth 5059 m, Continuation of North to South Profile Started on Leg 5)				
17	7.9	<0.1(<0.1)	11(12)	0.16(0.18)
55	13.7	<0.1(<0.1)	21(26)	0.25(0.21)
98	9.1	0.1(<0.1)	24(25)	0.12(0.13)
115	14.6	<0.1	19	0.19
157	13.8	<0.1	18	0.16
189	16.7(18.0)	0.1(<0.1)	26(26)	0.16(0.17)
221	18.2(20)	<0.1(<0.1)	30(16)	0.17(0.17)
329	18.6	<0.1	38	0.22
Site 71 (4°28.3′N, 140°189.9′W, water depth 4419 m)				
30	22(25)	<0.1(0.12)	11(12)	0.23(0.24)
101	51	0.17	24	0.13
203	95	<0.1	30	0.11
265	98	0.1	—	0.06
323	96(84)	0.1(<0.1)	42(26)	0.10
375	119	0.11	24	0.07
430	92	0.13	24	0.08

(1972), we arrive at an estimate of about 500 ppm for the strontium content of recrystallized carbonate.

The magnesium is a more complex question that will be discussed later. From the above data we conclude that increases in interstitial strontium are a sensitive indicator of the degree of sediment recrystallization. Quantitatively the increase is, however, partly governed by the rate of deposition, and the loss of anamalous enrichments by diffusion.

Carbon isotope studies on the pore fluids (Presley and Kaplan, 1971) show irregular variations of δC^{13}, which are generally lighter than the carbonate carbon stable isotope values observed for Atlantic ocean waters (Deuser and Hunt, 1969). They attributed this difference to a small but measurable contribution of carbon dioxide from oxidizing

TABLE XII

Strontium and Magnesium in Carbonate Organisms Prominent in Oozes and Selected Sediments. Values in % Dry Weight (Manheim et al., 1971)

Description	Sr	Mg	Source
Coccolith ooze, gravity core from tropical Atlantic, 2 m length	0.150	0.11	Thompson and Bowen (1969)
Mean of three analyses (7,97,169 cm)			
Foraminiferal carbonate from Caribbean Sea (piston core)	0.160	0.15	Wangersky and Joensuu (1964)
Mean of 35 analyses			
Foraminiferal carbonate, Atlantic Ocean, 2 cores	0.160	0.13	Wangersky and Joensuu (1964)
More than 50 analyses			
Planktonic foraminifera, tops of Atlantic cores (*Globigerinoides rubra*, *Globigerina inflata*, and *Globorotalia truncatulinoides*)	0.150	0.16	Krinsley (1960)
Mean of analyses from Caribbean, Azores, Bermuda, Cape Verde, and Canary Islands			

organic matter at depth. Lawrence (1973) found more marked variations in oxygen isotopic ratios in pore fluids from Site 149 (biogenic) in the Caribbean Sea. A δO^{18} minimum of -2.7% was reached in the lower portion of the hole at 285 m. Lawrence has suggested that this low ratio reflects a strong influence of diagenetic reaction, both of $CaCO_3$ recrystallization and reactions involving biogenic silica. Sources of low O^{18} water from depths below the bottom of the hole could not be ruled out.

C. Terrigenous Muds

The largest diagenetic effects in oceanic sediments are found in clayey, relatively organic-rich, and rapidly deposited sediments within influence of the continents. Such areas are indicated in Fig. 1 as the "geosynclinal" zones of rapid deposition. The reduction of sulfate, oxidation of organic matter, and synthesis of methane are accompanied by loss of interstitial potassium, magnesium, calcium, and sodium, with

Table XIII

Major Constituents in Interstitial Waters of Terrigenous Muds. Concentrations in g/kg unless otherwise indicated. Other explanatory notes as in Table IV. From Sayles et al. (1970) (Site 26). Manheim et al. (1970) (Site 35), and Manheim et al. (1972) (Site 113)

Depth (m)	Age	Description	Na	K	Ca	Mg	Total Cations (meq/kg)	Cl	SO_4	Alk (meq/kg)	HCO_3	Total Anions (meq/kg)	Sum	H_2O	pH
Hole 26 (10°53.6′N, 44°02.6′W, water depth 5160 m, Vema fracture zone), Equatorial Atlantic Ocean															
103	Pleistocene	Clay, dark olive, silty	10.2	0.30	0.23	1.04	548	19.3	1.24	10.5	0.64	566	32.9	31.6	—
230	Pleistocene	Clay, olive-gray, silty	10.3	0.24	0.24	0.81	534	19.1	0.06	4.71	0.29	545	31.1	26.1	—
482	Pleistocene	Clay, olive, gray, calcareous	10.9	0.16	0.47	0.71	559	19.2	0.49	3.13	0.19	555	32.1	22.3	—
Hole 35 (40°40.4′N, 127°28.5′W, water depth 3373 m), West Escanaba Trough (alternating terrigenous and pelagic muds), Pacific Ocean off Oregon															
41	Pleistocene	Dark, green-gray silty clay	11.1	0.48	0.32	1.23	612	19.2	1.64	17.6	1.08	594	35.1	37.1	—
160	Pleistocene	Dark zeolitic clay, banded	10.9	0.48	0.31	0.95	580	19.7	0.34	7.1	1.04	580	33.7	32.8	—
237	Pleistocene	Olive silty clay mud	11.0	0.20	0.73	0.60	568	19.9	0.21	4.7	0.28	571	33.0	26.2	—
287	Pleistocene	Calcareous zeolitic clay	11.4	0.15	0.81	0.46	578	19.9	0.20	2.9	0.17	571	33.2	25.4	—
Site 113 (56°47.4′N, 48°19.9′W, water depth 3629 m, Mid-Labrador Sea Ridge), North Atlantic Ocean															
Surface Ocean Water			10.7	0.38	0.41	1.22	583	19.1	2.68	3.4	0.21	597	34.7	—	—
55	Pleistocene	Gray silty clay; disturbed by coring	10.5	0.40	0.59	1.16	597	19.3	2.26	2.6	0.16	594	34.4	45	7.5
102	Pleistocene	Gray silty clay; disturbed by coring	10.8	0.33	0.86	0.85	592	19.5	1.97	1.2	0.08	592	34.3	33	7.5
206	Pleistocene(?)	Gray silty clay; extensive distortion and flowage resulting from coring	10.6	0.28	1.12	0.72	588	19.6	1.48	2.0	0.12	585	33.9	34	8.2
550	Pliocene	Gray clay and radiolarian ooze; clasts in a matrix of silty quartz sand	10.0	0.26	2.56	0.25	590	19.6	1.65	1.0	0.06	588	34.2	—	7.2

concomitant uptake of those ions in silicate and carbonate minerals Table XIII. If carbonate detritus is present, its breakdown and possible recrystallization can cause increases in interstitial calcium and strontium. Ammonia is liberated by the breakdown of organic matter. In the absence of sulfate, barium is often enriched to the 1 ppm level. Manganese concentrations on the order of 1 ppm are typical. Some trace elements such as lithium and strontium also appear to be taken up along with the major cations in the layer silicate lattices. However, depletions of interstitial trace elements may not be observed when other reactions, such as dissolution of carbonate, supply compensating amounts of pore fluid constituents (Table XIV).

Mechanisms governing the concentration changes in interstitial components are discussed in the section titled "Diagenesis," however, one can add that rapidity of deposition aids in retention of anomalies in the pore fluids. Under conditions of slow deposition, which characterize much of the sea floor, diffusion is able to keep pace with reactions occurring between pore fluid and solids so most anomalies are reduced to low levels. In rapidly deposited Pleistocene sediments found at depth at some sites, reactive ion anomalies are accompanied by minor changes in chloride. Chloride does not react significantly with mineral phases in most nonevaporitic sediments. Some of the normal small variations in chloride that are observed are due to manipulative artifacts and other noise. However, increases in chloride such as are noted in Sites 35 and 113 (Table XIII) appear to be real, and may be associated with minor changes in ocean salinity during Pleistocene time. Decreases (Site 153, Leg 15) (Presley et al., 1973) in chloride may be associated with migration of fresher water from the continent.

TABLE XIV

Minor constituents in interstitial waters of terrigenous muds. Concentrations in mg/kg. From authors cited in Table XIII and Presley et al. (1970)

Depth (m)	Sr	Ba	Li	Si	Mn	Zn	Br	B
				Site 26 (Vema Trench, off Brazil)				
103	6.6	1.4	0.05	7.3	0.20	0.22	66	4.7
230	7.0	1.7	0.05	7.9	0.10	0.21	71	3.7
482	10.7	1.6	0.14	7.2	0.10	0.21	69	1.7
				Site 35 (Escanaba Trough, off Oregon)				
41	6.9	0.09	0.07	21	—	—	—	—
160	9.2	4.6	0.13	12	—	—	—	—
237	13.0	5.4	0.72	5.9	—	—	—	—
287	17.0	6.2	0.44	3.4	—	—	—	—
330	14.0	6.2	0.71	5.5	—	—	—	—
				Site 113 (Mid-Labrador Sea Ridge)				
Surface sea	8.2	0.3	—	0.1	—	—	—	—
35	9.1	0.3	—	13.8	—	—	—	—
102	9.0	0.3	—	6.6	—	—	—	—
206	8.4	0.3	—	15.4	—	—	—	—
550	8.3	0.3	—	4.6	—	—	—	—

D. Influence of Buried Evaporites and Molecular Diffusion of Salt

Halite or other readily soluble evaporitic rocks at depth in sediment strata produce a characteristic interstitial concentration gradient outward and upward from the source of the soluble components. Such interstitial gradients in salinity, chloride, and other individual components were first demonstrated by Manheim and Bischoff (1969) in young Tertiary sediments overlying diapiric features (rock salt) on the northern slope of the Gulf of Mexico (Fig. 8). Subsequently, similar features were also observed in nondiapiric areas in the deep Gulf of Mexico (Manheim and Sayles, 1970; Manheim et al., 1973), the Mediterranean (Sayles et al., 1973), off West Africa and Brazil (Waterman et al., 1972), and in the Red Sea (Manheim et al., 1973). The hot brines of the Red Sea (Brewer and Spencer, 1969; Brooks et al., 1969; Hendricks et al., 1969) represent one of the most extraordinary examples of the influence of evaporites on pore fluids. Discharge of saturated NaCl brine from the Rift Valley of the Red Sea has led to the precipitation of metalliferous sediments of considerable economic and scientific value.

Where the intrusion of salt into overlying sediment is young, as in salt domes on the northern Gulf of Mexico slope, or where slumping has suddenly exposed salt to new strata, diffusion may not have reached a steady-state condition, and the curve of increased chloride with depth is concave to higher values (Fig. 8). Where a steady-state has been reached, the depth-chloride profile will approximate a straight line,

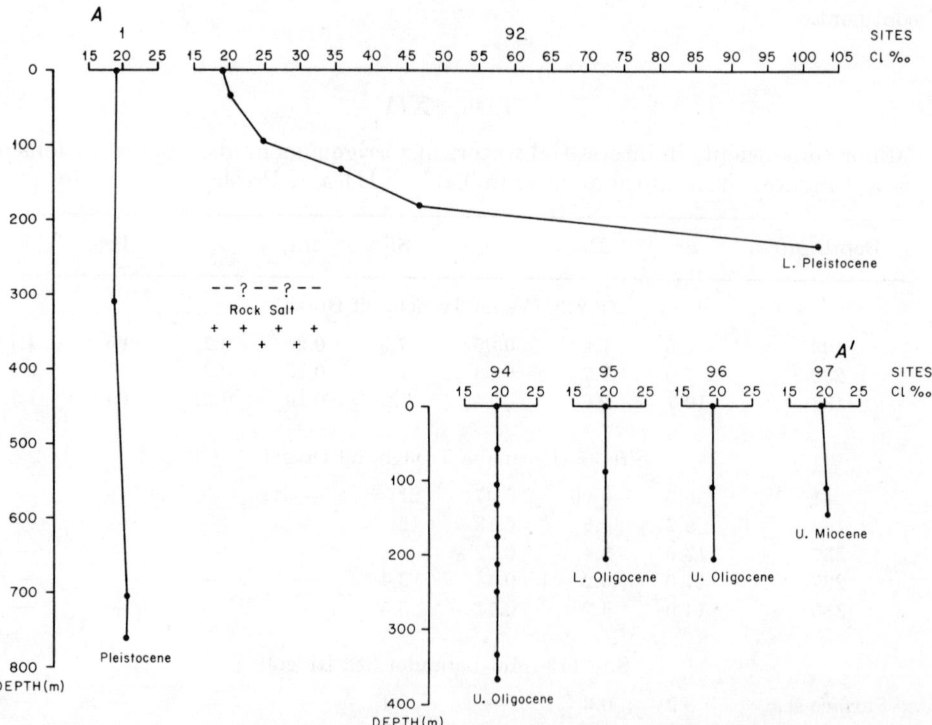

Fig. 8. Distribution of chloride with depth in drill holes in the Gulf of Mexico, DSDP Legs 1 and 10. Manheim et al. (1972). Sites 1 and 92 are on the Sigsbee Scarp, off the Louisiana continental slope (water depth, 2600 m). The remaining sites are on a traverse on the south-central Gulf of Mexico, toward Cuba.

neglecting changes in diffusion constant with depth and influence of continuing sedimentation. The steepness of the gradient depends on the depth to the salt deposit the coefficient of diffusion in the sediment (which is enhanced by increasing temperature), and by the time elapsed if there has not been sufficient time to approach a steady state.

For steady-state conditions the vertical flux of diffusing ions and distribution of concentration with depth is described by the simple relationship:

$$F = -k\frac{dc}{dx} = -\frac{c - c_0}{x - x_0}; \qquad \frac{dc}{dt} = \frac{d^2c}{dx^2} = 0$$

where c = concentration in g/cm^3
k = diffusion coefficient in cm^2/sec
t = seconds
x = distance above salt plug to sediment-water interface

For a salt dome at 130 m depth on the northern slope of the Gulf of Mexico a reasonably straight line chlorinity gradient was obtained, giving a flux of 5×10^{-11} g Cl/sec (Manheim and Bischoff, 1969). Given porosity of 0.47 and a diffusion coefficient of 4×10^{-6} cm^2/sec in the sedimentary section, the time required for complete exchange (renewal) of salt in the column was calculated to be only 370,000 yr. At greater depths, the lower gradient, and decreased permeability and diffusive permeability of the sediments require much longer geologic time for establishment of a steady-state gradient.

In the deep Gulf of Mexico a chlorinity distribution approaching a steady-state type has apparently been established in a sediment layer more than 4 km thick. Here, however, the age of the salt is presumed to be Jurassic (correlative with the widespread Louann salt sequence), which allows 150 million years for the establishment of steady-state conditions (Manheim and Sayles, 1970). The simple, nonsteady-state model is given by the following equation for vertical diffusion distribution between two semi-infinite (horizontal) reservoirs having different concentrations of dissolved species (Duursma, 1966):

$$\frac{dc}{dt} = \frac{k\delta^2 C}{\delta t^2}; \qquad \frac{c - c_0}{c_s - c_0} = \tfrac{1}{2}\,\mathrm{erfc}\, 2\frac{x}{\sqrt{kt}}$$

where the error functions, erfc and erf, can be obtained from standard curves or tables (Carslaw and Jaeger, 1959), c is concentration at distance x from the salt body, t is time, and k is the diffusion coefficient for chloride. Such a model would apply to a salt body intruded into a sediment layer at time t_0. At the salt-sediment interface the interstitial chloride concentration (c_s) would be saturated with respect to halite (about 160 g/kg Cl). At the sediment-seawater interface, c_0 would be 19 g/kg Cl, corresponding to normal marine chlorinity. Depending on which parameters are known, the equation can be solved for any of the component variables or constants.

While continuing sedimentation complicates the calculations, Lerman and Weiler (1970) use equations developed for heat flow calculations (Carslaw and Jaeger, 1959) to show that normal marine sedimentation rates are too slow to have much influence on the equation cited above. However, in rapidly accreting geosynclinal basins, sedimentation rate can be significant. Using the appropriate equations and the distribution of chloride in piston cores, Manheim and Chan (1973) calculate that the original chlorinity of the Black Sea during its isolation from the Mediterranean Sea in the Wisconsin glacial epoch was about 3.5 g/kg, contrasted to about 12 g/kg at present.

More complicated boundary conditions involving consolidation, advection, chemical reactions, or changing diffusion constants involve a marked increase in mathematical complexity. Such conditions are discussed in Anikouchine (1967), Berner (1971), Manheim (1970), Michard (1971), Smirnov (1972), and references cited in these papers.

4. Diagenesis

The diagenetic alteration of sediments and sedimentary rocks has received considerable study (see Dunoyer de Segonzac, 1970, for a review). Numerous studies have concentrated on changes in the solids of the sediments. Such studies, particularly mineralogical, have often detected relatively little alteration of the assumed original sediment from near surface to some hundreds of meters burial; yet, petrographic observations made during the Deep Sea Drilling Project do provide evidence of reactivity: widespread cherts in older Tertiary sediments, zeolites in pelagic clays, montmorillonite presumably formed from volcanic ash, lithified carbonates, and a variety of minerals such as dolomite, siderite, rhodochrosite, barite, pyrite, cristobalite, sepiolite, and palygorskite. Interstitial waters are particularly valuable tools in detecting the presence and nature of incipient chemical and mineralogical changes in solids, for very minor changes in the solid phases can have pronounced effects on associated pore fluids. For example, a change in Mg content of bulk solids from 2.00% to 1.99% will cause a 10% increase in interstitial Mg^{2+} ion in a sediment with 50% water content.

Interpretation of compositional changes and identification of the reactions is complicated by the fact that several reactions may proceed at the same time. The composition of the pore fluid records only the net reactions. However, the great variety of marine sediment types and environments now investigated through pore-fluid studies has yielded several "end member" reactions, which together with petrographic and other evidence can be used to delineate some of the major diagenetic processes. We first discuss some of the simpler reactions before treating more complex or mixed ones. We also wish to emphasize that it is still impossible to explain all observed variations. We have therefore restricted ourselves to a consideration of relationships that recur frequently, and we have concentrated on oceanic sediments recovered in the DSDP instead of on sediments from more complex and highly variable nearshore environments.

Pelagic biogenic sediments are among the least complex deposits, and form a convenient starting point. To a first approximation, gains in interstitial Ca^{2+} in many of these deposits are balanced mole for mole by Mg^{2+} losses. Relatively small depletions of SO_4^{2-} occur (<5 mM/kg) and little or no significant change in HCO_3^-, Na^+, and K^+ are observed. The relationship between Ca^{2+} and Mg^{2+} for several DSDP sites is summarized in Fig. 9. The scatter of the data is greater than analytical error and arises from the assumption that Ca^{2+} and Mg^{2+} are completely independent of HCO_3^- and SO_4^{2-} changes. Nevertheless, the scatter is second order, and does not obscure the 1:1 correspondence between Ca^{2+} gains and Mg^{2+} losses.

The exchange of Mg for Ca appears to reflect carbonate reactions. As noted in preceding sections, calcareous sediments undergoing recrystallization almost always show large Sr^{2+} enrichment in their interstitial waters, attributable to lower Sr^{2+} in the recrystallized calcite. However, Mg^{2+} is a more difficult problem. Two possibilities for the exchange of Ca^{2+} and Mg^{2+} appear. Berner (1971) has calculated the equilibrium concentration of $MgCO_3$ in calcite exposed to seawater at 25°C as 3.5 mol%. This corresponds to 0.8% Mg by weight. Data on the Mg content of planktonic biogenic

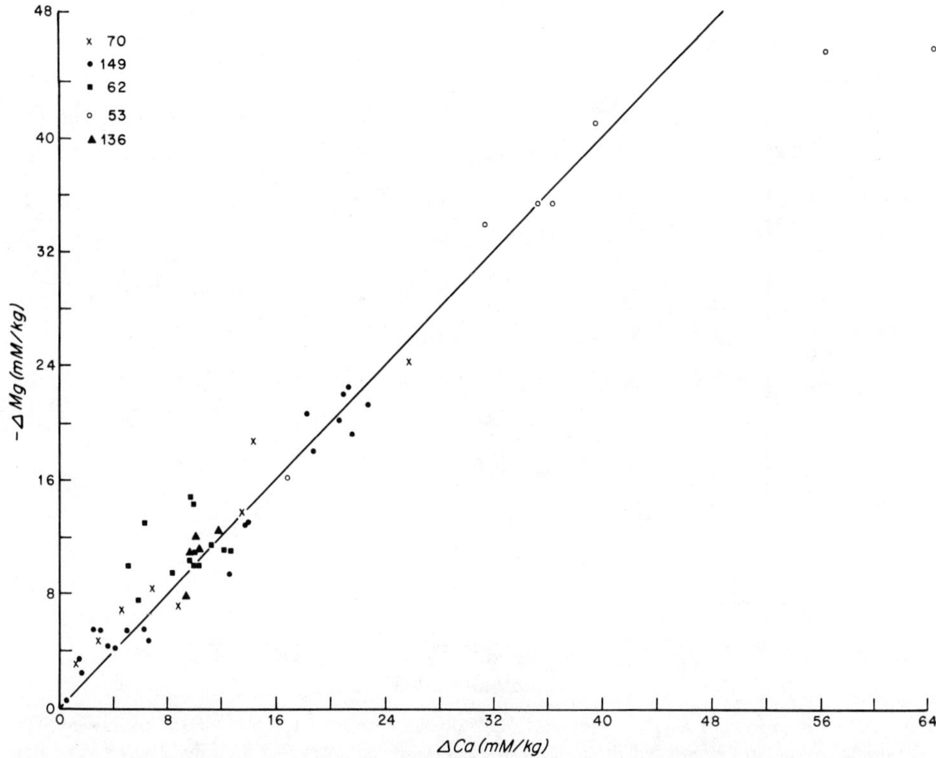

Fig. 9. The relationship between Mg^{2+} loss and Ca^{2+} loss. The original data are presented in the *Initial Reports of the Deep Sea Drilling Project*. The line drawn is that expected for a 1:1 correspondence between Ca^{2+} gain and Mg^{2+} loss. The Δ convention used is $\Delta =$ (porewater concentration—standard seawater concentration). The numbers given are the DSDP site numbers.

carbonate demonstrate that it contains only 0.1 to 0.2% Mg, as a rule (Table XII). Thus, if Berner's estimate is correct, recrystallization of tests to an equilibrium calcite having higher Mg content is thermodynamically possible. However, Thompson et al. (1968) report analyses of several lithified carbonates from the deep sea, in which the Mg content seems to be essentially independent of the ratio of authigenic to skeletal carbonate, and may be 0.16 or even less. Milliman (1966) also described the recrystallization of high magnesian calcite to calcite with less than 0.5% Mg. We know of no studies of deep-sea carbonates that have demonstrated alteration of typically low magnesian calcite of pelagic skeletal origin to slightly Mg-richer calcite. Studies of the composition of bulk sediments (Wiseman, 1961) cannot be used as evidence either way, as distinction of the composition of discrete phases must be made.

The second, and our preferred alternative, is the exchange of Mg^{2+} for Ca^{2+} in the formation of dolomite. Lithified dolostone has been observed on the ocean floor (e.g., Thompson et al., 1968), but more important, dolomite has been observed to be a very common mineral in drill cores of carbonate-containing sediments from the deep sea (Beall and Fisher, 1969; Rex and Murray, 1970a, 1970b, and many other reports from the DSDP). Dolomite ranges in form from isolated rhombs to lithified layers. The dolomitization of $CaCO_3$ may be represented by:

$$2CaCO_3 + Mg^{2+} \rightleftharpoons CaMg(CO_3)_2 + Ca^{2+} \quad (1)$$

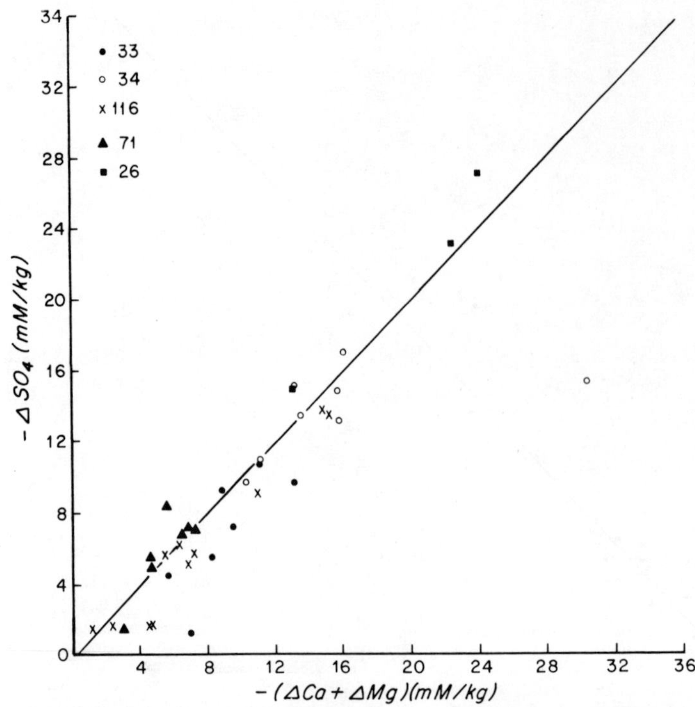

Fig. 10. Comparison of SO_4^{2-} losses and Mg^{2+} losses corrected for Mg^{2+}-Ca^{2+} exchange. The original data are presented in the *Initial Reports of the Deep Sea Drilling Project*. The line shown is that expected for a 1:1 correspondence for SO_4^{2-} and "excess" Mg^{2+} loss. The Δ convention used is Δ = (porewater concentration—standard seawater concentration). The numbers given are the DSDP site numbers.

One may note that without a source of Mg^{2+} other than the pore fluids associated with sediments, dolomitization must be limited to several tenths of a percent of the sediment. Mg^{2+} will also be supplied by diffusion from seawater through the sediment column, but in deeply buried sediments as those studied, this addition can only raise the upper limit of dolomite to a few percent. Where more than a few percent dolomite is identified and no solid source of Mg can be found, the dolomite must be detrital or must have formed at or near the sediment-water interface.

In biogenic sediments deposited at rates higher than a few centimeters per 1000 yr, and in terrigenous sediments, Mg^{2+} losses are higher than the small Ca gains that generally characterize these sediments. Typically, SO_4^{-2} is also depleted with depth. The loss of SO_4^{2-} roughly balances the loss of Mg^{2+} in excess of Ca^{2+} gains. These relationships are illustrated in Fig. 10 for several DSDP sites. Assuming that dolomitization occurs, SO_4 losses have been plotted against excess Mg^{2+} loss (loss of Mg^{2+} greater than Ca^{2+} gains according to equation 1). Although there is considerable scatter, a 1:1 correspondence can again be delineated. Deviations result mainly from ignoring the small alkalinity increases that are found in the sediments.

Losses of SO_4^{2-} from pore fluids of pelagic sediments have been well documented in many previous studies of piston cores (e.g., Shishkina, 1966, 1972; Presley et al., 1970; Bischoff and Ku, 1971, and references cited therein). Depletion results from utilization of SO_4^{2-} by bacteria to oxidize organic carbon in the absence of oxygen.

For our purposes it is sufficient to depict a general reaction between SO_4^{2-} and organic carbon such as

$$2CH_2O + SO_4^{2-} \rightarrow H_2S + 2HCO_3^- \quad (2)$$

The compound CH_2O symbolizes organic matter, and the chief result of the reaction is the production of 2 meq of alkalinity in the course of reduction of 1 mole of SO_4^{2-}.

Enrichment of HCO_3^- in the pore fluids of sites plotted in Fig. 10 is not sufficient to balance SO_4^{2-} losses according to equation 2. At these sites alkalinities usually rise by only 2 to 4 meq/kg, whereas SO_4 depletion ranges to 56 meq/kg, often being in excess of 24 meq/kg. To explain the discrepancy requires a reaction or reactions that remove alkalinity produced during SO_4^{2-} reduction, and also remove Mg^{2+}. Magnesite forms chiefly in hypersaline environments at low temperature and is unknown in open ocean sediments. The same is true of nesquehonite ($MgCO_3 \cdot 3H_2O$) and hydromagnesite ($Mg_5(CO_3)_4(OH)_2 \cdot 4H_2O$). However, a variant of the dolomitization reaction 1, in which alkalinity is consumed, is given in equation 3.

$$CaCO_3 + Mg^2 + 2HCO_3 \rightleftharpoons CaMg(CO_3)_2 + CO_2 + H_2O \quad (3)$$

Alternate silicate reactions, termed reverse weathering, have been suggested by MacKenzie and Garrels (1966) (equations 4 and 5):

$$\underset{\text{(kaolinite)}}{Al_2Si_2O_5(OH)_4} + 5Mg^{2+} + 10HCO_3^- + SiO_2 \rightleftharpoons \underset{\text{(chlorite)}}{Mg_5Al_2Si_3O_{10}(OH)_8} + 10\,CO_2 + 3\,H_2O \quad (4)$$

$$2\,Mg^{2+} + 3\,SiO_2 + 4\,HCO_3^- + (n-2)\,H_2O \rightleftharpoons \underset{\text{(sepiolite)}}{Mg_2\,Si_3O_8 \cdot nH_2O} + 4\,CO_2 \quad (5)$$

Equilibrium data at 25°C (Wollast et al., 1968) suggest that pore fluids of these sediments with a pH > 7.8 are close to saturation or even supersaturation with respect to sepiolite, where Si exceeds 30 ppm. Thus equation 5 is a distinct possibility. One should note that equations 3 to 5 all lead to an increase in CO_2 (aq), which may diffuse out of the sediment or should be detected in the porewaters. Unfortunately, there are few reliable test cases in which sufficient data on CO_2 are available and where additional reactions that could produce or remove CO_2 are absent. All three reactions (3 to 5) may be accommodated within the framework of observed pore-fluid changes. Uptake of silicate (reactions 4 and 5) can also be achieved by reactions discussed later.

The greatest and most complex changes occur in pore fluids of rapidly accreting deposits on the continental margin (slopes). The increased number of constituents showing change creates many possible reactions. Furthermore, concentration gradients are larger than in previously discussed cases, leading to diffusional gains and losses that may exceed quantities originally contained in the pore fluids. Moreover, diffusion proceeds at different rates for different ions. Reaction 2 remains valid for depletion of SO_4^{2-}. When all SO_4^{2-} is gone, organic-rich environments such as Saanich Inlet, British Columbia (Nissenbaum, 1972) may produce abundant CH_4, partly through fermentation of organic acids, but probably chiefly through synthesis from H_2 and CO_2 by methane-producing bacteria (as in the stomachs of cows and other ruminants and in formation of marsh gas) (Wolfe, 1971). Excess quantities of gas have caused several DSDP sites to be abandoned before reaching their target depths (e.g., sites in the Gulf of Mexico, Cariaco Trench, and Red Sea).

The consistent occurrence of Ca^{2+} depletions with large HCO_3^- enrichment may be explained by $CaCO_3$ precipitation. Removal of Ca^{2+} is superimposed on the basic trend toward Ca^{2+} enrichment and Mg^{2+} depletion, mentioned previously. Where sufficiently deep samples are available (e.g., Sayles et al., 1972b, 1973b) Ca^{2+} can be seen to increase gradually from a minimum in the first 100 m to concentrations equal to or greater than that of seawater. Corresponding depletions in HCO_3^- occur in keeping with an activity product of ($CaCO_3$) close to calcite saturation (Hammond, 1973).

In terrigenous clays depletion of all cations occurs, including Na^+ and K^+. Removal of Na^+ and K^+ are not attributable to cation exchange reactions (Manheim and Chan, 1973). Instead, the fact that depletions in Na^+ and K^+ are accompanied by loss of alkalinity, and usually relatively low silica values, even where amorphous silica is present in solid form, indicate that these cations are probably lost through reactions of the "reverse weathering" type (MacKenzie and Garrels, 1968) (equations 4 and 5). Analogous reactions for Na^+ and K^+ would lead to formation of illitic and Na-montmorillonite clays.

Still another reaction leading to the loss of Mg^{2+} in reducing sediments has been proposed by Drever (1971). Where H_2S is produced abundantly through reduction of sulfate, it may not only combine with iron oxides, but also with Fe^{3+} ion from the lattices of clay minerals such as chlorite and montmorillonite. The formation of solid iron sulfide leaves a charge deficit that is filled by Mg^{2+}. The reaction may be represented schematically by conversion of a nontronite (Fe^{3+} montmorillonite) to a saponite (Mg montmorillonite):

$$\text{nontronite} + 6\,Mg^{2+} + 8\,SO_4^{2-} + 15\,C + 2\,H_2O \rightleftharpoons \text{saponite} + 4\,FeS_2 + 11\,CO_2 + 4\,HCO_3^- \quad (6)$$

Although some empirical evidence linking stagnant sediments with iron-poor chlorites lends support to the existence of Drever's reaction, a similar net pore fluid reaction could be achieved through combination of equations 2 and 4. Existing information is insufficient to decide which system is more significant.

At some DSDP sites Mg^{2+} depletions appear to be proportional to Na depletions. Although the depletions are small enough to be partly obscured by scatter in the Na data, we may approach the relationship indirectly through an alkalinity balance. Electrical neutrality requires that the net change in cations balance net change in anions. Therefore,

$$\Delta\text{Alk} = -\,\Delta SO_4^{2} + \Delta Na^+ + \Delta K^+ + \Delta Ca^{2+} + \Delta Mg^{2+} + NH_4^+ \quad (7)$$

where Δ ion represents the gain or loss of the ion with respect to seawater. Rearranging equation 7,

$$\Delta Mg = \Delta\text{Alk} + \Delta SO_4^{2+} - \Delta Na^+ - \Delta K^+ - \Delta Ca^{2+} - NH_4^+ \quad (8)$$

If the ΔNa^+ term is omitted from equation 8, the deviation of a plot of the left side of equation 8 against the right side should be due to ΔNa^+.

Figure 11 presents such plots for two anoxic DSDP sites (147 and 148) and one having oxidizing conditions (149). Below 27 m the data for Site 147 show little coherency (perhaps partly because vigorous discharge of methane gas from cores on deck may have distorted carbonate equilibria in the pore fluids). However, points above 27 m and the remainder of the data plotted demonstrate a consistent relationship between ΔNa^+ and ΔMg^{2+}; that is, a linear least squares analysis of the combined data yield coefficients for ΔMg of 1.32 and 1.25 for Sites 147, 148 and 149, respectively.

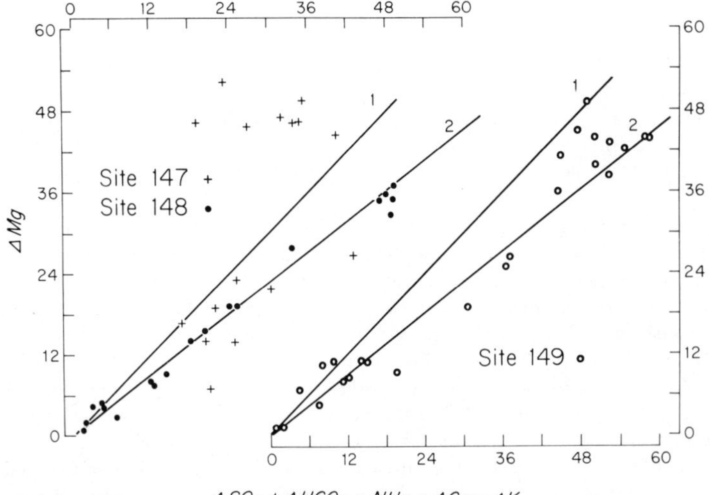

Fig. 11. Data from three sites plotted according to equation 8, with ΔNa omitted from the right side of the equation (abscissa as plotted). The original data are presented in the *Initial Reports of the Deep Sea Drilling Project*. Vol. 15. Sayles et al. (1973). The Δ convention used is Δ = (porewater concentration − mean seawater concentration). Line 1 indicates the relationship if no Na uptake occurs. Line 2 depicts a ΔMg/ΔNa ratio of 1.3.

Were uptake of Na^+ independent of Mg^{2+} one should expect scatter below a 1:1 slope and a nonzero intercept. Thus, Mg appears to be accompanied by Na depletion in the ratio 1.3:1.

Several previous studies of near-surface sediments have used alkalinity balance without considering Na^+, K^+, and Mg^{2+}. Berner et al. (1970) found that balance could be achieved (equation 6) by considering only ΔSO_4^{2-}, ΔAlk, and NH_4^+. Sholkovitz (1972) found a balance with ΔSO_4^{2-}, ΔAlk, NH_4^+, and ΔCa^{2+}. We have shown here that all of the cations must be considered in such alkalinity balances, at least for deeply buried reducing sediments, and the depletion in Na^+ and K^+ appears to require silicate reactions.

Synthesis of a considerable volume of data has resulted in the emergence of some reasonably consistent patterns of reactions that can be used to explain many observed pore-fluid compositions. Nevertheless, we do not wish to imply that the cited reactions give the complete story. Some exceptions to the patterns may come from analytical or manipulative error, particularly in changes that come about as a result of moving the sediment-water system from a high-pressure atmosphere to the surface of the sea. Data from Site 53 have been cited to show very large calcium enrichment in excess of Mg depletion and insignificant bicarbonate, implying a silicate or other source of soluble calcium (Table VI). Takahashi, as reported in Hammond (1973), demonstrated that at DSDP Site 148 CO_2 and alkalinity decrease together at a 1:1 ratio. This defies the expectation that CO_2 should increase at the expense of alkalinity.

Acknowledgments

We would like to express our appreciation to P. C. Mangelsdorf, Jr. and L. S. Waterman for helpful criticism of the manuscript. Support for the studies of the interstitial waters of the Deep Sea Drilling Project has been provided by the National Science Foundation, Grant GA 14523.

References

Anikouchine, W. A., 1967. Dissolved chemical substances in compacting marine sediments. *J. Geophys. Res.*, **72**, 505.

Beall, A. O. and A. G. Fischer, 1969. Sedimentology. In *Initial Reports of the Deep Sea Drilling Project*. Vol. 1, pp. 521–594.

Bender, M. L., 1971. Does upward diffusion supply the excess manganese in pelagic sediments. *J. Geophys. Research*, **70**, 4214–4215.

Berner, R. A., 1971. *Principles of Chemical Sedimentology*. McGraw-Hill, New York, 240 pp.

Berner, R. A., M. R. Scott, and Catherine Thomlinson, 1970. Carbonate alkalinity in the pore waters of anoxic marine sediments. *Limnol. Oceanog.*, **15**, 544–549.

Bischoff, J. L. and T. L. Ku, 1970. Pore fluids of recent marine sediments: 1. Oxidizing sediments of 20°N, continental rise to mid-Atlantic ridge. *J. Sediment. Petrol.*, **40**, 960–972.

Bischoff, J. L. and T. L. Ku, 1971. Pore fluids of modern marine sediments: II. Anoxic sediments of 35° to 45°N, Gibraltar to mid-Atlantic ridge. *J. Sediment. Petrol.*, **41**, 1008–1017.

Bischoff, J. L., R. E. Greer, and R. O. Luistro, 1970. Composition of interstitial waters of marine sediments: temperature of squeezing effect. *Science*, **167**, 1245–1246.

Brewer, P. G. and D. W. Spencer, 1969. A note on the chemical composition of the Red Sea brines. In *Hot Brines and Recent Heavy Metal Deposits in the Red Sea*. E. T. Degens and D. A. Ross, eds. pp. 174–179.

Brooks, R. R., I. R. Kaplan, and M. N. A. Peterson, 1969. Trace element composition of Red Sea brine and interstitial water. In *Hot Brines and Recent Heavy Metal Deposits in the Red Sea*. pp. 180–203.

Brooks, R. R., B. J. Presley, and I. R. Kaplan, 1967. The APDC-MIBK extraction system for the determination of trace elements in saline waters by atomic absorption spectrophotometry. *Talanta*, **14**, 809–816.

Bruevich, S. V., ed., 1966. Khimiya gruntovykh rastvorov Tikhogo okeana (Chemistry of interstitial waters in sediments of the Pacific Ocean). In *Khimiya Tikhogo Okeana*. Vol. 2. Izdatel'stvo Akad. Nauk, Moscow. pp. 263–358.

Carslaw, H. S. and J. C. Jaeger, 1959. *Conduction of Heat in Solids*. Oxford University Press, London.

Chan, K. M. and F. T. Manheim, 1970. Interstitial water studies on small core samples: Deep Sea Drilling Project, Leg 2. In *Initial Reports of the Deep Sea Drilling Project*. Vol. 2. M. N. A. Peterson et al., eds. Washington, D.C., U.S. Government Printing Office, pp. 367–371.

Christ, C. L. and P. B. Hostetler, 1970. Studies in the system $MgO–SiO_2–CO_2–H_2O$ (11): The activity product constant of magnesite. *Amer. J. Sci.*, **268**, 439–453.

Cronan, D. S., T. H. van Andel, G. R. Heath, M. G. Dinkelman, R. H. Bennett, D. Bukry, S. Charleston, A. Kaneps, K. S. Rodolfo, and R. S. Yeats, 1972. Iron-rich basal sediments from the eastern equatorial Pacific: Leg 16, Deep Sea Drilling Project. *Science*, **175**, 61–63.

Culkin, F., 1965. The major constituents of sea water. In *Chemical Oceanography*. Vol. 1. J. P. Riley and G. Skirrow, eds. Academic Press, London, pp. 121–161.

Deuser, W. G. and J. M. Hunt, 1969. Stable isotope ratios of dissolved inorganic carbon in the Atlantic. *Deep-Sea Res.*, **16**, 221–225.

Dunoyer de Segonzac, G., 1970. The transformation of clay minerals during diagenesis and low-grade metamorphism: A review. *Sedimentology*, **15**, 281–346.

Duursma, E. K., 1966. The mobility of compounds in sediments in relation to exchange between bottom and supernatant water. Koninkl. Nederl. Akad. van Wetensch., Proceedings Symposium I.B.P., Amsterdam, pp. 288–296.

Emery, K. O. and S. C. Rittenberg, 1952. California basin sediments in relation to origin of oil. *Bull. Amer. Assoc. Petroleum Geologists*, **36**, 735–806.

Fanning, K. A. and M. E. Q. Pilson, 1971. Interstitial silica and pH in marine sediment: some effects of sampling procedures. *Science*, **173**, 1228–1231.

Gieskes, J. M. T. M., 1973. Interstitial Water Studies, Leg 15. In *Initial Reports of the Deep Sea Drilling Project*. Vol. 15. In press.

Goldberg, E. D., 1965. Minor elements in sea water. In *Chemical Oceanography*. Vol. 1. J. P. Riley and G. Skirrow, eds. Academic Press, London, pp. 163–194.

Hammond, D. E., 1973. Interstitial water studies, Leg 15. A comparison of the major elements and carbonate chemistry data from sites 147, 148, and 149. In *Initial Reports of the Deep Sea Drilling Project*. Vol. 15. In press.

Hart, R., 1970. Chemical exchange between sea water and deep ocean basalts. *Earth and Planet. Sci. Letters*, **9**, 269–279.

Hendricks, R. L., F. B. Reisbick, E. J. Mahaffey, D. B. Roberts, and M. N. A. Peterson, 1969. Chemical composition of sediments and interstitial brines from the Atlantis II, Discovery and Chain Deeps. In *Hot Brines and Recent Heavy Metal Deposits in the Red Sea*. Springer Verlag, New York, E. T. Degens and D. A. Ross, eds. pp. 407–440.

Hollande, A. and M. Cachon-Enjumet, 1963. Sur la constitution chimique des spicules d'Acanthaires. *Bull. de l'Inst. Ocean. Monaco*, **60**, 1263.

JOIDES (Joint Oceanographic Institutions' Deep Earth Sampling Program, 1965). Ocean drilling on the continental margin. *Science*, **150**, 709–716.

Katz, A., E. Sass, A. Starinsky, and H. R. Holland, 1972. Strontium behavior in the aragonite-calcite transformation. An experimental study at 40–98°C. *Geochim. Cosmochim. Acta*, **36**, 481–496.

Kazintsev, E. A., 1968. Porovye rastvory maikopskoi tolshchi Vostochnogo Predkavkaz'ya i metodika otzhima porovykh vod pri vysokikh temperaturakh. (Interstitial waters of Maikop sediments of the eastern Caucasus region and methods of extracting pore fluids at high temperatures). In *Porovye rastvory i metody ikh izucheniya*. G. V. Bogomolov, ed. Izdatel'stvo Nauka i tekhnika, Minsk, pp. 178–190.

Kling, S. I., 1970. Oral communication, Cities Services Oil Co., Tulsa, Okla.

Krasintseva, V. V. and V. V. Korunova, 1968. Vliyanie davleniya i temperatury na sostav vydelyayushchegosya rastvora pri otzhimanii ila. (Influence of pressure and temperature on the composition of fluids extracted from muds). In *Porovye rastvory i metody ikh izucheniya*. G. V. Bogomolov, ed. Izdatel'stvo Nauka i tekhnia, Minsk, pp. 191–204.

Kriukov, P. A., 1947. Metody vydeleniya pochvennyky rastvorov. (Methods of separating soil interstitial solutions). In *Sovremennye metody issledovaniya fiziko-khimicheskikh svoistv pochv*. Vol. 2, No. 2. Moskow. Original unavailable for examination. See extensive summary of this and subsequent work by author in Kriukov, 1971.

Kriukov, P. A., 1971. *Gornye pochvennye i ilovye rastvory*. (*Interstitial waters of soils and sedimentary rocks*). Izdatel'stvo Nauka, Moskow, 219 pp.

Kullenberg, B., 1952. On the salinity of the water contained in marine sediments. Meddelanden fran Oceanografisk Institut Göteborg, No. 21, 38 pp.

Lawrence, J. R., 1973. Stable oxygen and carbon isotope variations in the pore waters, carbonates and silicates from the Venezuela Basin and the Aves Rise—sites 149 and 148. In *Initial Reports of the Deep Sea Drilling Project*. Vol. 15. In press.

Lerman, A. and R. R. Weiler, 1970. Diffusion and accumulation of chloride and sodium in Lake Ontario sediment. *Earth and Planet. Sci. Letters*, **10**, 150–156.

MacKenzie, F. T. and R. M. Garrels, 1966. Chemical mass balance between rivers and oceans. *Amer. J. Sci.*, **264**, 507–525.

Mangelsdorf, P. C., T. R. S. Wilson, and E. Daniel, 1969. Potassium enrichments in interstitial waters of recent marine sediments. *Science*, **165**, 171–174.

Manheim, F. T., 1966. A hydraulic squeezer for obtaining interstitial water from consolidated and unconsolidated sediments. U.S. Geol. Survey Prof. Paper 550-C, pp. 256–261.

Manheim, F. T., 1967. Evidence for submarine discharge of water on the Atlantic continental slope of the southern United States, and suggestions for further search. *Trans. New York Acad. Sciences*, Ser. II. Vol. 29, No. 7. pp. 839–853.

Manheim, F. T., 1970. The diffusion of ions in unconsolidated sediments. *Earth and Planet. Sci. Letters*, **9**, 307–309.

Manheim, F. T., 1973. Interstitial waters of marine sediments. In *Treatise on Chemical Oceanography*. Vol. III. J. P. Riley and R. Chester, eds. In preparation. V. III.

Manheim, F. T. and J. L. Bischoff, 1969. Geochemistry of pore waters from Shell Oil Company drill holes on the continental slope of the northern Gulf of Mexico. *Chemical Geology*, **4**, 63–82.

Manheim, F. T. and K. M. Chan, 1973. Interstitial waters of Black Sea sediments: new data and review. In *The Black Sea; its Chemistry, Biology and Geology*. E. T. Degens and D. A. Ross, eds. AAPG Memoir. In press.

Manheim, F. T. and F. L. Sayles, 1970. Brines and interstitial brackish water in drill cores from the deep Gulf of Mexico. *Science*, **170**, 57–61.

Manheim, F. T. and F. L. Sayles, 1971. Interstitial water studies on small core samples: Deep Sea Drilling Project, Leg 6. In *Initial Report of the Deep Sea Drilling Project.* Vol. 6. pp. 811–821.

Manheim, F. T., K. M. Chan, and F. L. Sayles, 1970. Interstitial water studies on small core samples: Deep Sea Drilling Project, Leg 5. In *Initial Reports of the Deep Sea Drilling Project.* Vol. 5. D. A. McManus et al., eds. Washington, D.C., U.S. Government Printing Office, pp. 501–511.

Manheim, F. T., F. L. Sayles, and L. S. Waterman, 1971. Interstitial water studies on small core samples: Deep Sea Drilling Project, Leg 8. In *Initial Reports of the Deep Sea Drilling Project,* J. I. Tracey, Jr. et al., eds. U.S. Government Printing Office, Washington, D.C., pp. 857–872.

Manheim, F. T., F. L. Sayles, and L. S. Waterman, 1973a. Interstitial water studies on small core samples, Leg 10. In *Initial Reports of the Deep Sea Drilling Project.* Vol. 10. J. L. Worzel, ed. U.S. Government Printing Office, Washington, D.C. In press.

Manheim, F. T., F. L. Sayles, and L. S. Waterman, 1973b. Interstitial water studies on small core samples, Leg 23. In *Initial Reports of the Deep Sea Drilling Project.* R. B. Whitmarsh et al., eds. U.S. Government Printing Office, Washington, D.C. In preparation.

Manheim, F. T., K. M. Chan, D. Kerr, and W. Sunda, 1970. Interstitial water studies on small core samples: Deep Sea Drilling Project, Leg 3. In *Initial Reports of the Deep Sea Drilling Project.* Vol. 3. A. E. Maxwell et al., eds. U.S. Government Printing Office, Washington, D.C., pp. 663–666.

Michard, G., 1971. Theoretical model for manganese distribution in calcareous sediment cores. *J. of Geophys. Res.*, **76**, 2179–2186.

Milliman, J. D., 1966. Submarine lithification of carbonate sediments. *Science*, **153**, 994–997.

Milliman, J. D., 1973. *Marine Carbonates.* Springer Verlag, New York–Heidelberg. In press.

Mullin, J. B. and J. P. Riley, 1955. The determination of silicon in sea water. *Anal. Chim. Acta*, **12**, 162–176.

Murray, J. and R. Irvine, 1895. On the chemical changes which take place in the composition of the sea water associated with blue muds on the floor of the ocean. *Trans. Royal Soc. Edinburgh.* Vol. 37. pp. 481–507.

Murray, J. and A. F. Renard, 1891. Report on deep sea deposits, based on specimens collected during the voyage of H.M.S. *Challenger*, 1872–1876. Reports on the scientific results of the voyage of H.M.S. *Challenger* during the years 1873–1876. *Deep Sea deposits.* 525 pp.

Nissenbaum, A., B. J. Presley, and I. R. Kaplan, 1972. Early diagenesis in reducing fjord, Saanich Inlet, British Columbia–I. Chemical and isotopic changes in major components of interstitial water. *Geochim. Cosmochim. Acta*, **36**, 1007–1027.

Pimm, A. C., R. E. Garrison, and R. E. Boyce, 1971. Sedimentology synthesis: Lithology, chemistry and physical properties of sediments in the northwestern Pacific Ocean. In *Initial Reports of the Deep Sea Drilling Project.* Vol. 6. A. G. Fischer et al., eds. U.S. Government Printing Office, Washington, D.C., pp. 1131–1252.

Presley, B. J. and I. R. Kaplan, 1971a. Interstitial water chemistry: Deep Sea Drilling Project, Leg 6. In *Initial Reports of the Deep Sea Drilling Project*, Vol. 6. A. G. Fischer et al., eds. U.S. Government Printing Office, Washington, D.C., pp. 823–828.

Presley, B. J. and I. R. Kaplan, 1971b. Interstitial water chemistry: Deep Sea Drilling Project, Leg 8. In *Initial Reports of the Deep Sea Drilling Project.* Vol. 8. J. I. Tracey et al., eds. U.S. Government Printing Office, Washington, D.C., pp. 853–836.

Presley, B. J. and I. R. Kaplan, 1972. Interstitial water chemistry: Deep Sea Drilling Project, Leg 7. In *Initial Reports of the Deep Sea Drilling Project.* Vol. 9. U.S. Government Printing Office, Washington, D.C., pp. 841–844.

Presley, B. J., R. R. Brooks, and H. M. Kappel, 1967. A simple squeezer for removal of interstitial water from ocean sediments. *J. Marine Res.*, **25**, 355–357.

Presley, B. J., M. B. Goldhaber, and R. I. Kaplan, 1970. Interstitial water chemistry: Deep Sea Drilling Project, Leg 5. In *Initial Reports of the Deep Sea Drilling Project.* Vol. 5. D. A. McManus et al., eds. U.S. Government Printing Office, Washington, D.C., pp. 513–522.

Presley, B. J., J. Culp, C. Petrowski, and I. R. Kaplan, 1973. Interstitial water chemistry: Deep Sea Drilling Project, Leg 15. In *Initial Reports of the Deep Sea Drilling Project.* Vol. 15. In Press.

Pushkina, Z. V., 1965. Porovye vody glinistykh porod i ikh izmeneniyu po razrezu. (Interstitial waters of clayey rocks and their change with depth). In *Postsedimentatsionnye izmeneniya chetvertichnykh i pliotsenovykh glinistykh otlozhenii Bakinskogo archipelago.* N. M. Strakhov, ed. Izdatel'stvo Nauka, Moscow, pp. 160–202.

Rex, R. W. and B. Murray, 1970a. X-ray mineralogy studies, Leg 4. In *Initial Reports of the Deep Sea Drilling Project.* Vol. 4. U.S. Government Printing Office, Washington, D.C., pp. 325–370.

Rex, R. W. and B. Murray, 1970b. X-ray mineralogy studies. In *Initial Reports of the Deep Sea Drilling Project.* Vol. 5. U.S. Government Printing Office, Washington, D.C., pp. 441–483.

Riley, J. P. and P. Sinhaseni, 1968. Chemical composition of three manganese nodules from the Pacific Ocean. *J. Marine Res.*, **17**, 466–482.

Rittenberg, S. C., K. O. Emery, J. Hülsemann, E. T. Degens, R. C. Fay, J. H. Reuter, J. R. Grady, S. H. Richardson, and E. E. Bray, 1963. Biogeochemistry of sediments in Experimental Mohole. *J. Sediment. Petrol.*, **33**, 140–172.

Sayles, F. L., 1970. Preliminary geochemistry. In *Initial Reports of the Deep Sea Drilling Project.* Vol. 4. R. G. Bader et al., eds. U.S. Government Printing Office, Washington, D.C., pp. 645–655.

Sayles, F. L. and F. T. Manheim, 1971. Interstitial water studies on small core samples: Deep Sea Drilling Project, Leg 6. In *Initial Reports of the Deep Sea Drilling Project.* Vol. 6. A. G. Fischer et al., eds. U.S. Government Printing Office, Washington, D.C., pp. 811–821.

Sayles, F. L., F. T. Manheim, and K. M. Chan, 1970. Interstitial water studies on small core samples, Leg 4. In *Initial Reports of the Deep Sea Drilling Project.* Vol. 4. U.S. Government Printing Office, Washington, D.C., pp. 401–414.

Sayles, F. L., F. T. Manheim, and L. S. Waterman, 1971. Interstitial water studies on small core samples: Deep Sea Drilling Project, Leg 7. In *Initial Reports of the Deep Sea Drilling Project.* Vol. 7, Part 2. E. L. Winterer et al., eds. U.S. Government Printing Office, Washington, D.C., pp. 871–881.

Sayles, F. L., F. T. Manheim, and L. S. Waterman, 1972a. Interstitial water studies on small core samples, Leg 9. In *Initial Reports of the Deep Sea Drilling Project.* Vol. 9. J. D. Hayes et al., eds. U.S. Government Printing Office, Washington, D.C., pp. 845–855.

Sayles, F. L., F. T. Manheim, and L. S. Waterman, 1972b. Interstitial water studies on small core samples, Leg 11. In *Initial Reports of the Deep Sea Drilling Project.* Vol. 11. C. D. Hollister et al., eds. U.S. Government Printing Office, Washington, D.C., pp. 997–1008.

Sayles, F. L., F. T. Manheim, and L. S. Waterman, 1973a. Interstitial water studies on small core samples, Leg 13. In *Initial Reports of the Deep Sea Drilling Project.* Vol. 13. In press.

Sayles, F. L., F. T. Manheim, and L. S. Waterman, 1973b. Interstitial water studies on small core samples, Leg 15. In *Initial Reports of the Deep Sea Drilling Project.* Vol. 15. In press.

Shishkina, O. V., 1954. Metodika opredeleniya sul'fat iona v morskikh vode. (Method of determining sulfate ion in marine water). *Trudy Instituta Oceanologii, Akad. Nauk, SSSR,* Vol. 8. pp. 253–268.

Shishkina, O. V., 1966. Osnovnoi solevoi sostav. (General chemical composition). In *Khimiya Tikhogo okeana; Part 2, Khimiya gruntovykh rastvorov Tikhogo okeana* (*Chemistry of the Pacific Ocean, Pt. 2, Chemistry of interstitial waters in the Pacific Ocean*). Bruevich, ed. pp. 289–307; combined references, pp. 342–358.

Shishkina, O. V., 1968. Metody issledovaniya morskikh i okeanicheskikh ilovykh vod (Methods of studying marine and oceanic pore fluids). In *Porovye rastvory i metody ikh izucheniya.* G. V. Bogomolov, ed. Izdatel'stvo Nauka i tehhnika, Minsk, pp. 167–177.

Shishkina, O. V., 1972. *Geokhimiya morskikh i okeanicheskikh ilovykh vod* (*Geochemistry of marine and oceanic interstitial waters*). Izdatel'stvo Nauka, Moscow, 227 pp.

Shishkina, O. V. and Bykova, 1964. *Trudy Morskogo gidrofizicheskogo instituta,* Vol. 25, pp. 187–194.

Shishkina, O. V. and A. A. Zheleznova, 1964. *Trudy Inst. Okeanologii Akad. Nauk, SSSR,* Vol. 64, pp. 144–153.

Siever, R., K. C. Beck, and R. A. Berner, 1965. Composition of interstitial waters of modern sediments. *J. Geol.*, **73**, 39–73.

Smirnov, S. I., 1972. *Proiskhozhdenie solenosti podzemnykh vod sedimentatsionnykh basseinov* (*On the Origin of the Saline Ground Waters of Sedimentary Basins*). Nedra, Moscow, 216 pp.

Thompson, G., V. T. Bowen, W. G. Melson, and R. Cifelli, 1968. Lithified carbonates from the deep sea of the equatorial Atlantic. *J. Sediment. Petrol.*, **38**, 1305–1312.

Turekian, K. K., 1964. *New York Acad. Sci. Trans.*, Ser. 2, Vol. 26, pp. 312–320.

Waterman, L. S., F. L. Sayles, and F. T. Manheim, 1972. Interstitial water studies on small core samples, Leg 14. In *Initial Reports of the Deep Sea Drilling Project.* Vol. 14. D. E. Hayes et al., eds. U.S. Government Printing Office, Washington, D.C., pp. 753–762.

Wiseman, J. D. H., 1965. Calcium and magnesium carbonate in some Indian Ocean sediments. In *Progress in Oceanography.* Vol. 3. M. Sears, ed. pp. 373–383.

Wolfe, Ralph, 1971. Microbial formation of methane. In *Advances in Microbial Physiology.* Vol. 6. A. H. Rose and J. F. Wilkinson, eds. pp. 107–146.

Wollast, R., F. T. MacKenzie, and O. P. Bricker, 1968. Experimental precipitation and genesis of sepiolite at earth surface conditions. *Am. Mineral,* **53**, 1645.

17. THE SULFUR CYCLE*

M. B. Goldhaber and I. R. Kaplan

1. Introduction

The major ion chemistry of the ocean is controlled over long time intervals by reactions occurring between the aqueous phase and various solid phases of lithogenous and biogenous origin (Sillén, 1961; Garrels and Mackenzie, 1971; Broecker, 1971; Pytkowicz, 1967; Siever, 1968). These reactions may approach steady-state conditions (but not necessarily equilibrium), implying that reaction rates can determine the concentrations of dissolved species (Morgan, 1967). Microorganisms can be particularly instrumental in influencing the rates of many geochemically important reactions. For example, thermodynamic calculations indicate that the sulfate ion SO_4^{2-} should be reduced to sulfide by organic matter in the absence of oxygen (e.g., Bostrom, 1967; Thorstenson, 1970). However, this reaction is known not to take place at earth surface temperatures and pressures, except when biologically mediated. The microorganisms involved in the transformation of sulfur compounds for the purpose of energy utilization are among the most ubiquitous in the aqueous environment. Their metabolic activities have both short- and long-term geochemical consequences.

Biological sulfate reduction is an anoxic process. It can occur in a water column as a result of above-average oxygen consumption or poor circulation. High rates of oxygen removal are related to the content of dissolved and particulate organic matter and to hydrodynamic stability, which prevents the addition of oxygenated water by diffusion or advection (Richards, 1965; Wyrtki, 1962). A complete removal of dissolved oxygen is required to initiate the process of bacterial sulfate reduction. Two of the well-documented environments of this type are the Black Sea (Caspers, 1957) and the Cariaco Trench (Richards and Vaccaro, 1956), although numerous other localized estuaries, lagoons, and fjords undergo stagnation (Richards, 1965; Strøm, 1939). Other areas in the ocean (e.g., basins off southern California or the eastern tropical Pacific Ocean) also approach zero oxygen content, but no sulfate reduction is observed. If the atmospheric content of oxygen were slightly lower, such areas would presumably be sites of sulfate reduction. Water column sulfate reduction, while only locally important under present geochemical conditions, could have been of more widespread significance in the geologic past.

Beneath the water column, however, anoxic conditions are frequently established at, or just beneath, the water-sediment interface, again as a consequence of the accumulation of organic matter and restrictions imposed on the rate of addition of oxygen. Dissolved sulfate in the porewaters of such sediments may be removed by sulfate-reducing bacteria within a depth of less than 1 to 2 m. The resulting hydrogen sulfide released is toxic to all respiratory organisms and probably to many anaerobes as well. The species of bacteria involved in sulfate reduction will then assume a dominant role in degradation of organic matter within the sediment. The metabolic products of these bacteria (CO_2, H_2S, NH_3, PO_4) are chemically reactive and will therefore influence subsequent diagenetic processes. Metal sulfide precipitation, carbonate precipitation, pH modification, and control of methane generation are associated with the bacterial activity.

In addition to producing modifications in porewater and sediment chemistry, the

* Contribution No. 1086, Institute of Geophysics & Planetary Physics, University of California at Los Angeles.

transfer of sulfate from seawater to sediments during sulfate reduction, is an important mechanism that helps to maintain a relatively constant composition of the ocean through removal of sulfur added to the oceans by the long-term erosion cycles (Holser and Kaplan, 1966; Berner, 1971a; Garrels and Mackenzie, 1972). The quantitative evaluation of these cycles requires a prior knowledge of the amount of sulfur removed to sediments in any given time.

This chapter examines some geochemical aspects of the marine sedimentary sulfur cycle. Stress has been placed on examining the pathways followed by the various processes involved as a consequence of biological oxidation and reduction. The organisms involved in the sulfur cycle are described and their metabolic functions discussed. Questions are raised relative to the controlling mechanisms for pyrite formation and an analysis is given relating to the nature and extent of exchange of sulfur between porewater and overlying seawater. Consequences of sulfate reduction on the chemistry of interstitial water are examined and an attempt is made to relate sulfate reduction to some problems of organic degradation. Sulfur isotope data, S^{34}/S^{32} (or δS^{34}), are used to test some conclusions reached from analytical studies. In the light of the conclusions reached, an attempt is made to examine whether strataform ore deposits can form under normal marine conditions and whether such formations presently occur on the ocean floor. We believe considerable advances have been made in our understanding of the low-temperature geochemistry of sulfur, since an article with a similar title was published by Galliher (1933).

2. Biological Sulfur Metabolism

A. Assimilatory Processes

All plants, animals, and bacteria in the marine environment metabolize sulfur for the purpose of synthesizing proteins. The sulfur can either be adsorbed as dissolved sulfate or ingested directly as sulfate-containing organic molecules. The sulfur concentration of a variety of animals and algae is given in Tables IA and IB. Some algae are capable of binding sulfate directly to polysaccharides. For example, the red alga *Porphyra umbilicus* is believed to contain an enzyme (glycosulfatase) that will degrade polysaccharide sulfate porphyrin from seaweed to liberate a variety of D- and L-galactose sugars and sulfate (Rees, 1961). The algal polysaccharides fucoidin and chondroitin 4-sulfate, which are K or Ca salts of sulfuric acid esters of the polysaccharides, can also be degraded by sulfatase enzymes (Roy and Trudinger, 1970).

Although decomposition of the polysaccharide sulfate esters normally liberates sulfate, there is also evidence that reduced sulfur compounds can be liberated, notably methyl sulfides or mercaptans [CH_3SH or $(CH_3)_2S$]. In a comprehensive review by Challenger (1959), examples are given for mercaptan release by red algae of the genus *Polysiphonia* as well as by fungi and plants.

However, the process of universal importance is the reduction of sulfate by cells during assimilation of sulfur and subsequent protein synthesis through amino acid production. The general pathways followed are discussed by Nicholas (1967) and Trudinger (1969). Sulfate is activated by binding sites in cells and then reduced to sulfite and hydrogen sulfide by a series of energy-yielding transport mechanisms (see Fig. 1). The sulfide will then react with the amino acid serine to yield cysteine ($CH_2SHCHNH_2COOH$). Further transformations will yield methionine (CH_3SCH_2 CH_2CHNH_2COOH) or cystine [$(CH_2SCHNH_2COOH)_2$]. Thiosulfate and possibly elemental sulfur can also be incorporated in the pathway. Normally, all the sulfate

TABLE IA

Sulfur Contents of Some Marine Animals Given as Percent Dry Weight

Organism	Type	Total S	Combustible S	Ash S	Shell S
Haliotis cracherodii	Gastropod	2.80	0.85	0.42	0.046
Mytilus californicus	Pelecypod	1.35	0.80	0.16	0.047
Clam, brittle stars, crab, shrimp, proboscis worm	Small bottom-dwelling organisms	0.86	—[a]	—	—
Astropecten armatus	Asteroid	0.47	0.14	0.41	—
Chaetopterus variopedatus	Polychaete	0.94	—	—	0.29
Leioptilus guerneyi	Sea pen	0.65	0.39	0.23	—
Fish lavae	Surface plankton	0.93	—	—	—
Chlamys latiaurata	Pelecypod (pecten)	0.80	0.98	0.05	0.26
Arguroplecus affinis Diaphus theta	Deep-water fish	0.45	0.46	0.08	—
Sergestid shrimps	Deep water	0.71	—	—	—
Pasiphaea	Large shrimp	0.47	—	—	—
Myctophidae	Lantern fish	0.49	0.31	0.01	—
Decapod and mysid shrimps	Crustaceans	0.72	0.27	0.58	—
	Average total S	0.89			

[a] — refers to not determined.

TABLE IB

Sulfur Contents of Some Marine Algae Given as Percent Dry Weight

Organism	Class	Total S	Water soluble[a]	Acid soluble[a]	Combustible	Ash
Corallina vancouveriensis	*Rhodophyceae*	0.49	0.15	0.13	0.05	0.24
Gigartina canaliculata		2.43	1.06	0.42	—[b]	—
Gelidium crinale		0.60	—	—	—	—
Gigartina leptorhynchos		3.30	—	—	1.70	1.61
Chaetomorpha aerea	*Chlorophyceae*	1.08	0.16	0.47	—	—
Ulva californica		0.88	—	—	0.44	0.44
Macrocystis pyrifera	*Phaeophyceae*	0.75	0.26	0.35	0.05	—
Egregia laevigata		0.91	—	—	0.20	0.65
Phyllospadix sp	Flowering plant	0.74	0.32	0.16	—	—
Gonyaulax polyhedra	Dinoflagellate	0.30	—	—	—	—
	Average total S	1.15				

[a] Extracted with water and dilute hydrochloric acid prior to combustion.
[b] — refers to not determined.

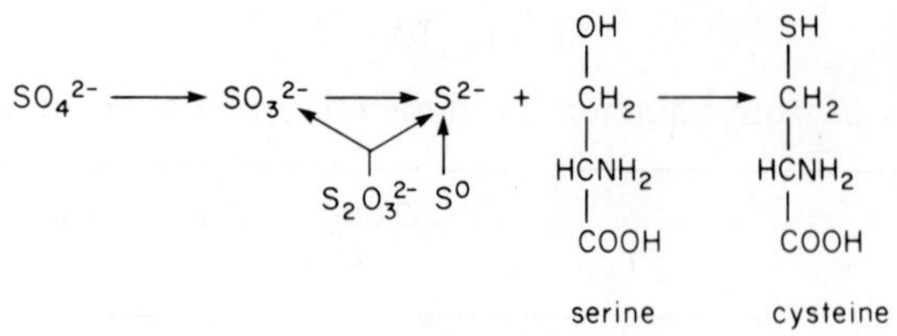

$$SO_4^{2-} \longrightarrow SO_3^{2-} \longrightarrow S^{2-} + \underset{\text{serine}}{HOCH_2CH(NH_2)COOH} \longrightarrow \underset{\text{cysteine}}{HSCH_2CH(NH_2)COOH}$$

($SO_3^{2-} \rightleftarrows S_2O_3^{2-} \rightarrow S^{2-}$; $S^0 \rightarrow S^{2-}$)

Fig. 1. Pathways for assimilation of sulfur into amino acids.

that enters the cell is metabolized to protein or other organic sulfur compounds. However, under some conditions of nutrient deficiency or under conditions where the organism is presented with SO_3^{2-} or S^0, hydrogen sulfide will be released, as, for example, by yeast (Wainwright, 1970).

B. Dissimilatory Sulfate Reduction

All sulfur compounds with an oxidation state above sulfide are capable of acting as electron acceptors in biological oxidation of organic matter. As sulfate is by far the most abundant dissolved sulfur compound in aqueous environments, the organisms are grouped together under the descriptive title of "sulfate reducers." The most important class of organisms capable of sulfate reduction is the *Schizomycetes* in the order *Eubacteriales* (bacteria). As a result of recent reclassification, two genera of bacteria are now recognized. *Desulfovibrio* is the genus represented by nonsporulating curved bacteria, commonly possessing a single polar flagellum. It is probable that most, if not all, marine sulfate-reducing bacteria belong to this genus. The other genus is *Desulfotomaculum*, which contains at least three known spore-forming species (Postgate, 1965). Species related to the thermophile *Desulfotomaculum nigrificans* (previously known as *Clostridium nigrificans*) may have been responsible for sulfate reduction in the lower water mass of the Dead Sea (Kaplan and Friedman, 1970).

Sulfate-reducing bacteria generally grow best at approximately neutral pH in the absence of oxygen. In nature they are found to occur over a large range of pH and salt concentrations, often in sediment underlying saline or gypsum deposits in evaporite beds, in deep-sea sediments, and in oil wells (ZoBell, 1958). The organisms can tolerate heavy metals, although Cu^{2+} has been reported to be toxic from 0.25 to 2.5 ppm in one study and from 20 to 50 ppm in another (Trudinger et al., 1972). The organisms are tolerant to dissolved sulfide in concentration up to 2% (Miller, 1950). Thus, sulfide, which is toxic to most other organisms, does not appear to influence the metabolic functions of sulfate-reducing bacteria. A variety of organic molecules are inhibitory to growth, and surprisingly among them are the low molecular-weight fatty acids such as butyric, propionic, and acetic acids (Ghose and Wiken, 1955).

Sulfate-reducing bacteria are thought to be largely heterotrophic, in that most of the carbon fixed is derived from organic matter. However, it has been shown that in the presence of a minimal supply of organic matter, up to 25% CO_2 can be fixed in the presence of molecular hydrogen or organic compounds, which act purely as hydrogen donors. Under controlled conditions, where organic impurities are eliminated from growth media, growth will not occur in the presence of CO_2 as the only carbon source (Mechalas and Rittenberg, 1960; Postgate, 1960).

Sulfate-reducing bacteria appear to require small concentrations of complex organic media to satisfy their growth requirements. There is some uncertainty whether specific organic carbon compounds are needed to satisfy nutritional requirements, or whether organic matter acts as a chelating agent for Fe^{2+}, preventing its precipitation as FeS in the presence of high concentrations of HS^- (Postgate, 1965).

The early claim by Sisler and ZoBell (1951) that certain sulfate-reducing bacteria can fix molecular nitrogen was confirmed more recently by LeGall and Senez (Senez, 1962). However, most strains of *Desulfovibrio* do not fix nitrogen, and those that do prefer to use ammonia. The efficiency of ammonia metabolism in terms of cell growth and energy production appears to be twice as great as metabolism during nitrogen fixation. As ammonia is present in relatively high concentrations in interstitial water where sulfate is reduced, it is doubtful whether nitrogen would be used under these circumstances.

Although sulfate-reducing bacteria need small quantities of specific complex organic compounds for growth (generally satisfied by yeast extract in culture media), these compounds are not used to generate energy. It is widely recognized that only certain organic substrates such as lactic and pyruvic acids, or their salts, are used for energy transfer. The stoichiometric relationship for sulfate reduction by lactic and pyruvic acids is shown in equations 1 and 2, where acetic acid is a product.

$$\underset{\text{lactic acid}}{2\,CH_3\cdot CHOH\cdot COOH} + SO_4^{2-} \rightarrow 2\,CH_3COOH + HS^- + H_2CO_3 + HCO_3^- \quad (1)$$

$$\underset{\text{pyruvic acid}}{4\,CH_3COCOOH} + SO_4^{2-} \rightarrow 3\,CH_3COOH + CH_3COO^- + 4\,CO_2 + HS^- \quad (2)$$

Succinate, fumarate, malate, and some other three- or four-carbon compounds have also been reported as supporting growth of sulfate-reducing bacteria, but only of some strains (Starkey, 1960). It is apparent that lactate and pyruvate are the two most readily metabolized compounds tested in artificial culture, and that acetate is the product and cannot be further metabolized.

Desulfovibrio desulfuricans has been shown to metabolize a variety of inorganic sulfur compounds with intermediate oxidation states including sulfite, thiosulfate, tetrathionate, dithionate, and pentathionate. It is probable that, with the exception of sulfite and elemental sulfur, the other compounds are not in the metabolic pathway for sulfate reduction (Roy and Trudinger, 1970). For example, although the suggested overall reactions for reduction of thiosulfate and tetrathionate by cell suspensions using molecular hydrogen are (3) and (4), sulfite has been detected in media containing thiosulfate as the starting sulfur salt (Roy and Trudinger, 1970).

$$S_2O_3^{2-} + 4\,H_2 \rightarrow 2\,HS^- + 3\,H_2O \quad (3)$$

$$S_4O_6^{2-} + 9\,H_2 \rightarrow 2\,HS^- + 2\,H_2S + 6\,H_2O \quad (4)$$

It is therefore probable that the initial activation process is followed by disproportionation of thiosulfate and polythionates to sulfite and elemental sulfur, which are then metabolized directly.

A great deal has been learned about the activation process and enzymes involved in the metabolism of sulfate. A schematic representation of the pathway of dissimilatory sulfate reduction in *Desulfovibrio* is shown in Fig. 2. A total of eight electrons are involved in the reduction process. Sulfite is the only intermediate so far isolated. The rate-limiting step appears to be the initial reduction of sulfate to sulfite. Little is known about the enzymes responsible for reduction of sulfite to hydrogen sulfide.

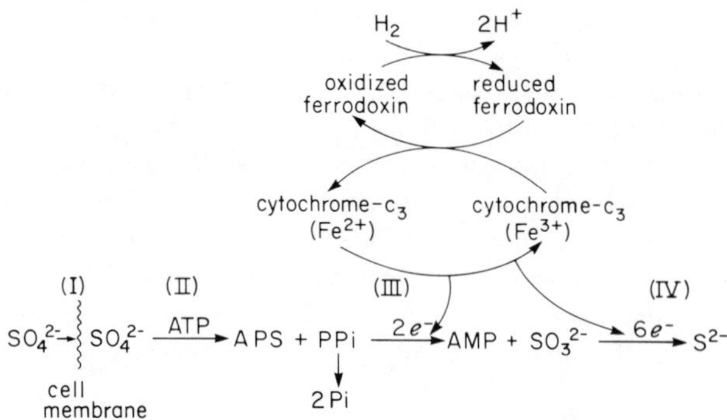

Fig. 2. Pathway for the dissimilatory reduction of sulfate to sulfide. The rate limiting steps involve the electron transfer system and steps I to IV, which may produce isotopic fractionation. ATP = adenosine-5′-triphosphate; AMP = adenosine-5′-phosphate; PP_i = pyrophosphate; APS = adenylsulfate.

C. *Microbiological Oxidation of Inorganic Sulfur Compounds*

In the marine environment, biological oxidation of reduced sulfur compounds is probably restricted to the chemosynthetic and photosynthetic bacteria. Little is known about the role or significance of other organisms. Table II summarizes the principal families of lithotrophic bacteria involved in sulfur oxidation. They are all primarily autotrophic, capable of fixing CO_2 for cell synthesis, and derive energy from the oxidation of reduced sulfur. The chemolithotrophs are aerobes, whereas the photolithotrophs are anaerobes.

Beggiatoa and thiothrix are commonly found associated with hot springs and also occur in fresh water and marine environments where sulfide is forming. They have been cultured in complex media where organic matter is present and hydrogen sulfide is formed. It had generally been assumed that these filamentous organisms derive energy primarily by hydrogen sulfide oxidation, but this assumption has been challenged (Burton and Morita, 1964). Bacteria belonging to the family *Thiobacteriaceae* are believed to be the most widespread and probably the most important organisms involved in the oxidation of reduced sulfur compounds to sulfate. The most studied species belong to the genus *Thiobacillus* and are usually referred to as thiobacilli. Table III lists several representative species of thiobacilli.

The ultimate product of oxidation of reduced sulfur by thiobacilli is sulfate, yet today, 70 yr after the first description of the genus (Nathansohn, 1902), the exact nature of the pathway for oxidation is still very much in dispute. The problem is twofold. First, because oxidations are aerobic, they may occur spontaneously without the direct involvement of the organisms. Second, many of the products formed are unstable and undergo reaction with the starting substrate. Hence, many intermediates are produced that may be incidental to the pathway.

During oxidation of sulfide by *T. thio-oxidans*, *T. thioparus*, and *T. concretivorous*, elemental sulfur and thiosulfate are common products, but polythionates have also been reported (Roy and Trudinger, 1970). As heat-treated cell extracts have been found to catalyze sulfide oxidation, it has been proposed that physiological oxidation may occur only after an initial abiological oxidation. Thus, the first product of sulfide oxidation will be elemental sulfur:

$$2\,H_2S + O_2 \rightarrow 2\,S^0 + 2\,H_2O \tag{5}$$

TABLE II

The Lithotrophic Sulfur Microorganisms[a]

Family	General Characteristics	Habitat	Genera
	CHEMOLITHOTROPHS		
Thiobacteriaceae	Colorless, coccoid, straight, or curved rod-shaped bacteria; polar flagellate when motile. Oxidize sulfur compounds and usually deposit sulfur granules within or without the cells	A wide variety of fresh-water and marine environments containing H_2S. *Thiobacillus* found in soil, mine waste-waters, sewage, industrial effluents	*Thiobacterium* *Macromonas* *Thiovulum* *Thiospira* *Thiobacillus*
Beggiatoaceae	Colorless cells occurring in trichromes within which they are arranged in chains. The trichromes show a gliding motion when in contact with a substrate. When grown in the presence of hydrogen sulfide the trichromes contain sulfur globules	Fresh water and marine environments containing H_2S	*Beggiatoa* *Thiospirillopsis* *Thioplaca* *Thiothrix*
Achromataceae	Large spherical, ovoid, or short cylindrical cells containing sulfur granules and sometimes inclusions of calcium carbonate	Fresh water and brackish mud containing H_2S	*Achromatium*

(*continued*)

TABLE II (*continued*)

Family	General Characteristics	Habitat	Genera
	PHOTOLITHOTROPHS		
Thiorhodaceae	Unicellular organisms often developing as cell aggregates or families of variable size and shape. Single cells have the form of spheres, ovoids, short rods, vibrios, spirals, and sometimes chains; contain bacteriochlorophyll and carotenoids; strictly photosynthetic; anaerobic or microaerophilic. Colors range from bluish violet through purple to deep red. Sulfur accumulates within the cells	Most commonly found in mud and stagnant waters containing H_2S, and exposed to light. Many organisms found in sulfur springs	*Thiosarcina* *Thiopedia* *Thiocapsa* *Thiodictyon* *Thiothece* *Thiocystis* *Lamprocystis* *Amoebobacter* *Thiopolycoccus* *Thiospirillum* *Rhabdomonas* *Rhodothece* *Chromatium*
Chlorobacteriaceae	Small bacteria of varying morphology. Color green due to presence of chlorophyllous pigments. Frequently deposit elemental sulfur outside the cells. Strictly photosynthetic, anaerobic	Marine and fresh-water muds containing H_2S and exposed to light; sulfur springs	*Chlorobium* *Pelodictyon* *Clathrochloris* *Chlorobacterium*

[a] From Roy and Trudinger (1970).

TABLE III

The Thiobacilli. Members of this genus are Gram-negative, non-sporulating rods measuring 0.5 by 1–3 μ. Motile forms are polarly flagellated. All but one are capable of strictly autotrophic growth and most oxidize sulfide, elemental sulfur and thiosulfate to sulfate[a]

Organism	Habitat	General Characteristics
T. thioparus	Canal water, mud, soil	Growth pH range 7.8–4.5 with an optimum near neutrality; generally aerobic and motile. Some strains grow anaerobically in the presence of nitrate
T. neapolitanus (*Thiobacillus X*)	Seawater, corroding concrete structures	Strict aerobe with properties very similar to those of *T. thioparus*
T. dentrificans	Canal and river water, salt water, peat composts, mud	Optimum growth pH near neutrality; oxidizes sulfur compounds anaerobically in the presence of nitrate; denitrifying ability lost on culturing in air; motile
T. thio-oxidans	Soil	Optimum growth pH around 2; withstands 5% H_2SO_4; strict aerobe; motile
T. concretivorus	Corroding concrete structures	Very similar to *T. thio-oxidans*
T. ferro-oxidans	Acid mine and soil waters containing hydrogen sulfide	Strict aerobe; optimum pH growth range 2.5–5.8; also utilizes oxidation of ferrous iron as a source of energy; motile
T. novellus	Soils	Facultative autotroph; nonmotile; optimum growth pH near neutrality
T. intermedius	Fresh-water mud	Facultative autotroph; growth pH range 2.0–7.0; motile; autotrophic growth stimulated in the presence of organic matter
T. thiocyanoxidans	Gas works liquor; sewage effluent	Very similar to *T. thioparus*; thiocyanate oxidation serves as an energy source; oxidizes formate
T. perometabolis	Soil	Motile; no growth in mineral salts without yeast extract or casein hydrolysate: reduced sulfur compounds nevertheless are oxidized to sulfate and the oxidation stimulates growth

[a] From Roy and Trudinger (1970).

Oxidation of elemental sulfur will lead to formation of thiosulfate, polythionates, sulfite, and sulfate. It had been thought that thiosulfate forms directly as the first product (see equation 6):

$$2\,S^0 + O_2 + H_2O \rightarrow S_2O_3^{2-} + 2\,H^+ \qquad (6)$$

More recently it has been suggested that the first product of biological sulfur oxidation is sulfite, which reacts abiologically with the original sulfur to produce thiosulfate (equations 7 and 8):

$$S^0 + O_2 + H_2O \rightarrow SO_3^{2-} + 2\,H^+ \qquad (7)$$

$$SO_3^{2-} + S^0 \rightarrow S_2O_3^{2-} \qquad (8)$$

The mechanism for activating elemental sulfur is still a puzzle, as it is hydrophobic and has an extremely low solubility in aqueous solutions. The many possible mechanisms suggested by numerous investigators can be summarized into two alternative processes.

1. Sulfur may be solubilized by some complex component externally excreted by the bacterium.

2. Activation of sulfur may occur prior to diffusion across the cell membrane, by reaction with an enzyme or cofactor at the cell boundary.

There is considerable evidence that elemental sulfur is acted on by reduced glutathione (GSH) to form a disulfide linkage GSSG or GSSH prior to intracellular transfer and metabolism.

Oxidation of thiosulfate is a common characteristic of the thiobacilli. Besides sulfate, tetrathionate is a common product, and the first polythionate detected during thiosulfate oxidation. Nathansohn (1902) originally suggested the oxidation followed equation 9:

$$2\,S_2O_3^{2-} + H_2O + \tfrac{1}{2}\,O_2 \rightarrow S_4O_6^{2-} + 2\,OH^- \qquad (9)$$

Small amounts of trithionate and pentathionate are also formed during the oxidation. This may arise from disproportionation of tetrathionate (equations 10 and 11):

$$S_4O_6^{2-} + S_2O_3^{2-} \rightleftharpoons S_5O_6^{2-} + SO_3^{2-} \qquad (10)$$

$$S_4O_6^{2-} + SO_3^{2-} \rightleftharpoons S_3O_6^{2-} + S_2O_3^{2-} \qquad (11)$$

Little is known about the metabolism of polythionates to sulfate. Numerous reactions occur between intermediate products and the substrate depending on growth conditions, including concentration of starting material, pH, and oxygen partial pressure. Elemental sulfur is often a product of thiosulfate and polythionate oxidation.

It should be apparent from the brief description above that the exact pathways for chemolithotrophic oxidation of sulfur compounds are still unknown. A summary of the proposed steps is given in Fig. 3.

Photosynthetic oxidation of sulfide occurs in the photic zone of lake and lagoon waters, as well as in reducing sediment. The organisms largely responsible for this oxidation belong to the genera *Chromatium* and *Chlorobium*, often referred to as the purple and green sulfur bacteria because of their visible photosynthetic pigments. They are strict anaerobes and can tolerate a wide range of salinity. The purple bacterium *Chromatium* may often be seen underlying a salt crust, above a black reducing sediment.

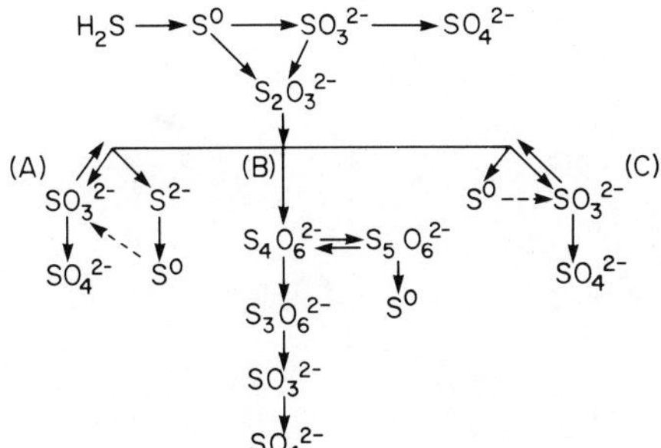

Fig. 3. Pathways in oxidation of reduced sulfur compounds to sulfate by thiobacilli.

The organisms are known to oxidize sulfide, elemental sulfur, and thiosulfate. This is accomplished through the photolytic transfer of electrons from sulfur to carbon dioxide according to the generalized theory of photosynthesis first suggested by van Niel (1931, 1941), as shown in equation 12:

$$CO_2 + 2\,H_2A \xrightarrow{\text{light}} \underset{\substack{\text{cell}\\\text{material}}}{[CH_2O]} + 2\,A + 2\,H_2O \qquad (12)$$

When H_2A is H_2S, elemental sulfur is an initial product. In *Chromatium* this generally accumulates within cells, whereas in the green bacteria it precipitates extracellularly. Sulfur also forms during oxidation of thiosulfate, probably by splitting the sulfane sulfur from the sulfonate group.

Oxidation of reduced sulfur can also be accomplished by heterotrophic microorganisms. The physiological significance of this process is not understood, but it is thought to be only of incidental importance to their metabolic function and energy-yielding process. However, a recently published study by Tuttle and Jannasch (1972), who investigated 136 isolates from a variety of marine environments, suggests that heterotrophic oxidation may be more prevalent than previously considered. Furthermore, it is possible that marine thiobacilli are capable of tolerating higher concentrations of organic matter than the chemoautotrophic bacteria described in Table III.

For detailed accounts of the physiology and metabolic function of sulfur-oxidizing organisms, readers may study Sokolova and Karavaiko (1964), Trudinger (1969), and Roy and Trudinger (1970).

D. *Ecology of the "Sulfuretum"*

The community of organisms involved in metabolism of sulfur compounds was first termed sulfuretum by Baas-Becking (1925). The biological sulfur cycle is portrayed in Fig. 4. The steps involved in sulfur assimilation and dissimilatory processes involving oxidation or reduction of sulfur for the purpose of energy production have all been discussed above. No mention has yet been made of the significance of HS^- production from protein during proteolysis. In most marine or brackish water environments, this source of sulfide is quantitatively not too important. In a sediment where 1% organic carbon (per dry weight sediment) is biologically degraded, and the organic matter has a C/S ratio ≈ 16 (Nissenbaum and Kaplan, 1972), 0.06% sulfur would be released in the sediment. In an isotopic study conducted by Kaplan et al. (1963), it was demonstrated that HS^- produced by sulfhydrase enzymes from organic matter must be small compared to that formed by sulfate reduction. This may not be the case in organic-rich, fresh-water environments where dissolved sulfate is low.

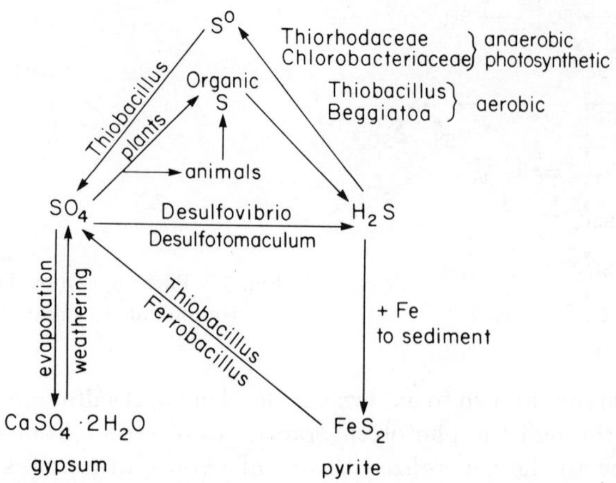

Fig. 4. The sulfuretum, showing known genera of microorganisms involved in the transformation of sulfur compounds.

It was indicated above that lactic acid is rapidly metabolized by sulfate-reducing bacteria as a hydrogen source. Although lactic acid is a common component of cells, it is probable that it would be rapidly destroyed in early diagenesis. Sulfate reduction would therefore quickly terminate if the short-chain carboxylic acids could not be generated *in situ*. This can be readily accomplished by a number of heterotrophic bacteria. For example, it is well known that polysaccharides (e.g., cellulose) can be hydrolyzed to their component monosaccharides, which are then degraded further during anaerobic fermentation to produce a variety of two-, three-, and four-carbon compounds (see Lamanna and Mallette, 1953; Stanier et al., 1971). The well-known production of lactic acid from silage or vegetable matter (e.g., cabbage) by the lactic acid bacteria is a homofermentative process involving breakdown of sugars (13):

$$\underset{\text{fructose}}{CH_2OH\text{–}CO\text{–}CHOH\text{–}CHOH\text{–}CHOH\text{–}CH_2OH} \rightarrow 2\ \underset{\text{lactic acid}}{CH_3\text{–}CHOH\text{–}COOH} \quad (13)$$

An alternative path is the production of alcohol during fermentation, common for yeast but not for bacteria (14), and therefore, probably not important in sediment diagenesis.

$$\text{Fructose} \rightarrow 2\ CH_3CH_2OH + 2\ CO_2 \quad (14)$$

A number of organisms (e.g., *Escherichia*) are known to carry out a mixed acid fermentation, producing ethanol, lactic acid, acetic acid, H_2 and CO_2. Several organisms, in particular the spore-forming genus *Clostridium*, are capable of degrading proteins to their component amino acids which are further decomposed to acids. For example, equation 15 shows the degradation of alanine to acetic acid through pyruvic acid:

$$CH_3\text{–}CHNH_2\text{–}COOH \rightarrow CH_3\text{–}CO\text{–}COOH + NH_3 \rightarrow CH_3COOH + CO_2 \quad (15)$$

It is obvious from the above that lactic acid should be one of the important products of anaerobic fermentations. Following sulfate reduction, acetate will probably become the dominant small molecule. Few measurements have been made on the short-chain carbon compounds in sediment, but one such study by Hoering (1967) shows acetic acid to be the most abundant acid by about an order of magnitude over the C_3 acid (Table IV).

TABLE IV

Low Molecular Weight Acids Isolated by Steam Distillation from Recent Sediments in Southern California Continental Shelf Basins (From Hoering, 1967)[a]

Acid	San Nicholas Basin	San Pedro Basin	Tanner Basin
Acetic	1810	1350	459
Propanoic	97	179	37
Isobutanoic	13	36	13
n-Butanoic	4	40	11
Isopentanoic	8	46	16
n-Pentanoic	—	24	1
Isohexanoic	—	—	—
n-Hexanoic	32	63	24
n-Heptanoic	41	113	13
n-Octanoic	10	25	12
n-Nonanoic	—	6	1
Total	2015	1882	587

[a] Units are in parts per million of the organic matter in the sediment (in all three basins, organic matter was 7% of dry weight sediment).

Acetate is readily oxidized by many aerobic respiratory organisms, but under natural anaerobic conditions in marine sediments, methane bacteria are probably the only important group that will degrade acetate. Acetate can probably be broken down directly to methane according to (16), although the mechanism is not understood.

$$CH_3COOH \rightarrow CH_4 + CO_2 \tag{16}$$

Recently, it has become apparent that organisms previously thought capable of the direct fermentation of organic substrates to methane (such as *Methanobacillus omelianskii*) may be symbiotic communities of two or more organisms. The first step in degradation of simple carbon compounds such as ethanol is the formation of hydrogen and acetic acid (equation 17). The true methanogenic organisms then reduce carbon dioxide produced by reactions (1), (14), and other fermentative reactions to methane (equation 18) with the hydrogen (Toerien and Hattingh, 1969).

$$2\,CH_3CH_2OH + 2\,H_2O \rightarrow 2\,CH_3COOH + 4\,H_2 \tag{17}$$

$$CO_2 + 4\,H_2 \rightarrow CH_4 + 2\,H_2O \tag{18}$$

It appears that besides CO_2, only acetate, formate, and methanol can be used directly for methane production. Evidence for direct hydrogenation of CO_2 in marine sediments has recently been presented based on C^{13}/C^{12} measurements (Nissenbaum et al., 1972).

Surprisingly, methane formation does not seem to occur in marine sediment until sulfate reduction is complete. This may be due to two factors: (1) sulfate-reducing bacteria compete favorably for H_2 liberated during fermentation, or (2) H_2S is toxic for methane bacteria. The question is unresolved at present.

From published literature and studies undertaken in our laboratory, it is apparent that the succession of major recognizable microbiological processes from the sediment-water interface to depth is: respiration using oxygen → respiration using nitrate → respiration using sulfate → respiration using bicarbonate. Accompanying the last two steps is bacterial fermentation, where complex structural organic matter is degraded to simple organic acids and possibly alcohols. These reactions follow the energy release as calculated from simple free energy equations using data from standard references and assuming a constant consumption of organic matter that can be equated with H_2 for the purpose of simplicity (see Table V).

TABLE V

Free Energy ($\Delta F°$) of Reaction Between Hydrogen (Equal to Constant Organic Source) and Different Oxidizing Agents

Reaction	$\Delta F°$ kcal/mol
$3\,O_2 + 6\,H_2 \rightarrow 6\,H_2O$	−340.2
$2\,NO_3{}^-{}_{(aq)} + 6\,H_2 \rightarrow 6\,H_2O + N_2$	−287.4
$1\frac{1}{2}\,SO_4{}^{2-}{}_{(aq)} + 6\,H_2 \rightarrow 4\frac{1}{2}\,H_2O + 1\frac{1}{2}\,HS^-{}_{(aq)} + 1\frac{1}{2}\,OH^-$	−42.1
$1\frac{1}{2}\,HCO_3{}^-{}_{(aq)} + 6\,H_2 \rightarrow 3\,H_2O + 1\frac{1}{2}\,CH_4 + 1\frac{1}{2}\,OH^-$	−34.0

E. Kinetics of Sulfate Reduction

Although the reduction of sulfate by molecular hydrogen (and other reducing agents, such as organic matter) is thermodynamically favorable at temperatures of the ocean (Table V), chemical reduction using hydrocarbons has only been performed at temperatures above 250°C (Toland, 1960). Recent results (J. W. Smith, personal communication) indicate that the inorganic reduction of sulfate to sulfide may be catalyzed by the presence of elemental sulfur, sulfide, or organic sulfur and may proceed through prior S–S bond formation, but the kinetics of the reduction have not been studied.

The kinetics of bacterial sulfate reduction have been investigated by several workers. Postgate (1951) undertook comprehensive studies on pure cultures of the sulfate-reducing bacterium *D. desulfuricans*, and found that during growth of this organism under optimum nutrient conditions, cell production was directly dependent on sulfate concentration to 10 mM. Above this concentration (to ~100 mM) the growth rate appeared to be independent of the amount of sulfate. Jones and Starkey (1957) provide data for mass culture of *D. desulfuricans* using gypsum as the sulfate source (solubility = 2.41 g/liter or 13.4 mM). By recalculating their data, for values between 6.3 and 58% total sulfate reduced, it is apparent that they are consistent with a first-order reaction, indicating a dependence of reduction rate on the concentration.

In resting cell experiments (where there is no protein synthesis and hence, no growth) Postgate (1951), Harrison and Thode (1958), and Kaplan (1962) found the rate of reduction to be essentially independent of sulfate concentrations at or near 10 mM. Postgate (1951) found that the rate of hydrogen uptake was relatively independent of the sulfate content in the range 1 to 100 mM.

Nakai and Jensen (1964) carried out bacterial sulfate reduction experiments with seawater and reducing sediment, monitoring the quantity of sulfate reduced and sulfide produced (Fig. 5) over a period of 65 days. If bacterial sulfate reduction follows

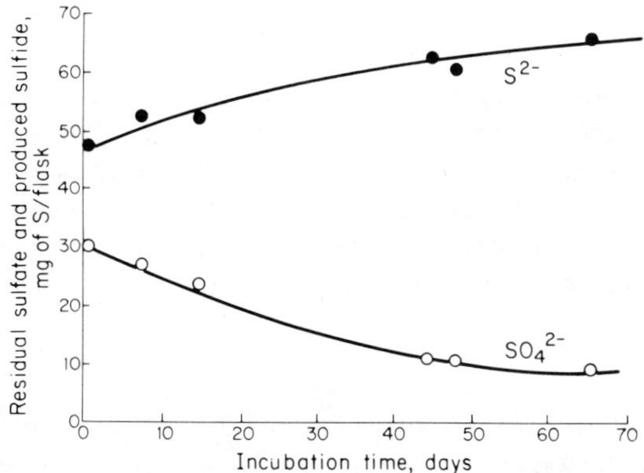

Fig. 5. Rates of bacterial reduction of sulfate to sulfide under laboratory conditions. After Nakai and Jensen (1964).

first-order reaction kinetics, equation 19 predicts the decrease of sulfate as a function of time:

$$\ln \frac{[SO_4^{2-}]_0}{[SO_4^{2-}]t} = K_1 t \tag{19}$$

where $[SO_4^{2-}]_0$ = initial concentration of sulfate
$[SO_4^{2-}]t$ = concentration of sulfate at time t
K_1 = first-order rate constant

Under the experimental conditions pertaining, the calculated rate constant, K_1, fell in the range 1.91 to 2.40 × 10^{-2}/day. As shown in Table VI, apart from two values, the calculated K is fairly constant. This was taken by Nakai and Jensen (1964) to be evidence for a first-order reaction. It has been pointed out by Sakai (1972; personal communication) that the reaction might also be considered as zero order, governed by equation 20:

$$[SO_4^{2-}]_0 - [SO_4^{2-}]t = K_0 t \tag{20}$$

for which rate constants are also given in Table VI. Under this interpretation, K_0 becomes nonlinear at lower concentrations of $[SO_4^{2-}]$, representing a change from zero-order to first-order kinetics, dependent on sulfate concentration.

In laboratory experiments with anaerobic marine muds, Benninger and Berner

TABLE VI

Calculation of Rate Constant K from Experimental Data of Nakai and Jensen (1964)

	t(days)	7	14	44	47	65
Nakai and Jensen (1964)	K_1 at 32°C (10^{-2}/day)	1.909	1.929	2.395	2.262	1.907
Sakai (1972)	K_0 at 32°C (mgS/day)	0.54	0.51	0.45	0.42	0.33

(personal communication) have shown that the rate of sulfate reduction is apparently independent of sulfate concentration down to <2 mM SO_4^{2-}.

In a recent theoretical evaluation of the kinetics of sulfate reduction, Rees (1973) states that the process of bacterial sulfate reduction is only first order at sulfate concentrations that are insufficient to saturate enzyme activation sites. At higher concentrations (in the range of seawater, 28 mM) a zero-order reaction rate governs with respect to sulfate (but may be first order with respect to nutrients or hydrogen donors). He envisages the reaction series to be depicted by the generalized equation 21:

$$A \underset{K_{ba}}{\overset{N_{ab}}{\rightleftharpoons}} B \xrightarrow{K_{bc}} C \tag{21}$$

A is the starting sulfate, B is an intermediate (or could be several intermediates in a pathway), and C is the final product, H_2S. Under conditions where sulfate is saturated, the rate represented by N_{ab} is zero order.

The flows from B are first order and have rate constants K_{ba} and K_{bc}. If the initial concentration of B is zero, then the concentration of an intermediate product (or activated complex) can be represented by equation 22:

$$B = \frac{N_{ab}}{K_{ba} + K_{bc}} [1 - e^{-(K_{ba}+K_{bc})t}] \tag{22}$$

Under steady-state conditions (i.e., for large t), the concentration of the intermediate products, B, reaches the value $N_{ab}/(K_{ba} + K_{bc})$. The starting sulfate decreases with time and the hydrogen sulfide product increases. At some point of sulfate depletion, Rees envisages the first reaction step, N_{ab}, to decrease so that $K_{bc} \gg K_{ba}$. Under these conditions, the entire sequence is controlled by first-order kinetics with respect to sulfate.

It is therefore probable that in natural environments, the reaction kinetics of sulfate reduction depend on the interplay between (at least) three factors: sulfate concentration, availability of organic matter, and other nutrients, and the size and density of the bacterial population. If organic matter and nutrients are abundant, the bacterial population can expand to the point where sulfate activation sites are not saturated. Under these conditions, the rate of sulfate reduction is limited by the concentration of sulfate. If the population of sulfate-reducing bacteria is limited by organic matter and nutrients, sulfate reduction will be independent of sulfate concentration. In the latter case, as sulfate is utilized, the rate-controlling step will become dependent on either or both nutrient and sulfate concentrations.

F. Kinetic Isotope Effect: Inorganic

The kinetic isotope effect during inorganic reduction of sulfate to sulfide was studied by Harrison and Thode (1957). Assuming the reaction to be irreversible, the rate of reduction of sulfur isotopes, S^{32} and S^{34}, may be represented by equations 23 and 24:

$$S^{32}O_4^{2-} \xrightarrow{k_1} H_2S^{32} \tag{23}$$

$$S^{34}O_4^{2-} \xrightarrow{k_2} H_2S^{34} \tag{24}$$

Because the energy necessary to break a sulfur-oxygen bond in a molecule containing S^{32} is smaller than that in a chemically identical molecule containing S^{34}, reactions involving isotopically light sulfur will proceed at a faster rate than for the heavy isotope. Bigeleisen (1949) developed a theoretical basis for predicting kinetic isotope effects. The ratio of rate constants k_1/k_2 can be estimated from a knowledge of statistical mechanical parameters (mainly vibration frequencies) of the reactants and the activated complex. Using an approximation of Bigeleisen's method, Harrison and Thode (1957) calculated k_1/k_2 for two limiting choices of the nature of the activated complex, representing zero bond breakage or complete bond breakage of the S–O bond. If the activated complex is considered to be similar to the initial sulfate (zero bond breakage), a ratio k_1/k_2 of 1.010 is predicted; that is, S^{32} should react 1% faster than S^{34}. The alternative choice for the activated complex was sulfite ion, SO_3^{2-}, (representing complete S–O bond breaking). The rate ratio k_1/k_2 for this case was calculated to be 1.035. The experimental kinetic isotope effect determined by reduction of sulfate with hydroiodic acid according to equation 25 was found to be 1.022.

$$SO_4^{2-} + 8\,I^- + 10\,H^+ \rightarrow H_2S + 4\,H_2O + 4\,I_2 \tag{25}$$

This result (halfway between the two limiting cases), was interpreted to mean that the rate-limiting step is the initial S–O bond breakage.

G. Kinetic Isotope Effect: Biological

It is now well established that biological systems are capable of selectively metabolizing the stable isotopes of sulfur (Thode et al., 1951; Jones and Starkey, 1957; Harrison and Thode, 1958; Kaplan and Rittenberg, 1964). The process can be divided into assimilatory or dissimilatory, and reductive or oxidative functions. The maximum fractionation for various metabolic processes measured by Kaplan and Rittenberg (1962) can be seen in Table VII. The data in this table can be compared with the pathways shown in Fig. 6.

During assimilation of sulfate by laboratory-grown microorganisms, as well as by naturally occurring plants and animals, the measured fractionation is in the range of −2 to −3‰. This is in marked contrast to assimilated carbon (Park and Epstein, 1960), but resembles the small effect measured during nitrogen fixation (Delwiche and Steyn, 1970). It is probable that in the carbon system, stepwise enrichment occurs among various carbon compounds, as well as exchange between internal and external environment. In the case of sulfur and nitrogen, fractionation only occurs in the initial activation step. Once sulfate or nitrogen has been transferred into the cell, it is completely reduced to the protein.

Hydrogen sulfide can be liberated by hydrolysis of cysteine and other sulfur-containing amino acids by proteolytic bacteria. A small isotope effect of ~5‰ enrichment in S^{32} of the H_2S relative to the organic acid was detected by this process.

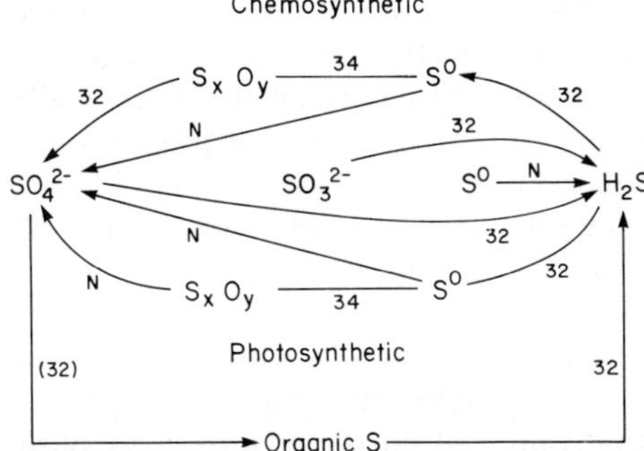

Fig. 6. Fractionation patterns of S^{32} and S^{34} by biological processes in the sulfur cycle. The isotope enrichment is indicated in the final and intermediate products. No fractionation is designated by *N*.

TABLE VII

Maximum Fractionations Measured in the Metabolites Formed by Microorganisms of the Sulfur Cycle Under Controlled Conditions. All Enrichments Are Given Relative to the S^{34}/S^{32} of the Starting Compound

Primary Process	Organism	Starting Substance	End Product	$\Delta\delta S^{34}$ [a] ‰
Sulfate reduction	*D. desulfuricans*	SO_4^{2-}	H_2S	−46.0
Sulfite reduction	*D. desulfuricans*	SO_3^{2-}	H_2S	−14.3
Sulfite reduction	*S. cerevisiae*	SO_3^{2-}	H_2S	−41.0
Sulfate assimilation	*E. coli*	SO_4^{2-}	Organic S	−2.8
	S. cerevisiae			
Cysteine hydrolysis	*P. vulgaris*	Cysteine	H_2S	−5.1
Chemosynthetic oxidation	*T. concretivorus*	H_2S	S^0	−2.5
		H_2S	SO_4	−18.0
		H_2S	S_xO_y	+19.0
Photosynthetic oxidation	*Chromatium*	H_2S	S^0	−10.0
		H_2S	SO_4	0
		H_2S	S_xO_y	+11.2

[a] $$\delta S^{34}‰ = \frac{S^{34}/S^{32}\ \text{sample} - S^{34}/S^{32}\ \text{standard}}{S^{34}/S^{32}\ \text{standard}} \times 1000$$

Reduction of elemental sulfur to H_2S by yeast, oxidation of elemental sulfur by thiobacilli, and chromatium and oxidation of metal sulfides (Nakai, 1963) by thiobacilli does not give rise to any appreciable fractionation in the sulfate product. This was interpreted by Kaplan and Rittenberg (1962) to indicate that sulfur moves across the cell membrane without first being reduced by extracellular enzyme systems. Once activated, it does not reequilibrate with the original substrate.

Oxidation of hydrogen sulfide by thiobacilli produces a slight S^{32} enrichment in the S^0 and a marked enrichment (18‰) in the sulfate. Photosynthetic oxidation of H_2S by the purple sulfur bacteria produced a significant S^{32} enrichment in S^0 (10‰) but no enrichment in the product sulfate. This may signify the difference in the initial activation step of sulfide. In both cases, the polysulfide was markedly enriched in the heavy isotope, indicating that possible exchange reactions may have occurred (see above for discussion on metabolic pathways).

The greatest isotope effects were measured during dissimilatory sulfate reduction by sulfate-reducing bacteria and sulfite reduction by baker's yeast. Sulfide produced from sulfate was consistently more enriched in the light isotope than sulfide produced from sulfite by growing or resting cells of *Desulfovibrio*. Harrison and Thode (1958) and Kaplan and Rittenberg (1964) found that the fractionation factor was generally inversely proportional to the rate of reduction, but the hydrogen source was an important moderating factor. The greatest enrichment in S^{32} (46‰) was obtained using ethanol as the electron source. When molecular hydrogen was used (see Fig. 7), isotopic enrichment was low (α = 1.003 to 1.016) and directly proportional to the rate of reduction.

Kemp and Thode (1968) found that under their experimental conditions, the maximum fractionation during reduction of sulfate with molecular hydrogen is approximately equal to the asymptotic value of that obtained during lactate metabolism

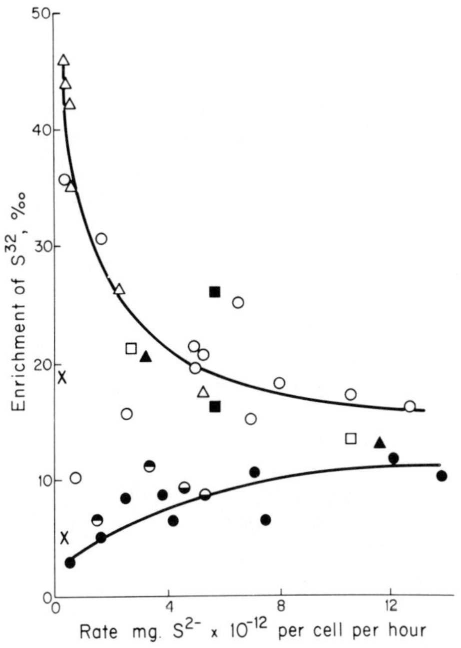

Fig. 7. Enrichment of S^{32} in hydrogen sulfide as a function of rate of sulfate reduction by *Desulfovibrio desulfuricans*. Temperature 10 to 45°C, 0.06M—SO_4^{2-}; and lactate O ethanol △; or hydrogen ●. Exceptions are: *X*, lactate at 0°C; ▲, lactate + 0.01M SO_4^{2-}; □, lactate + 0.02M SO_4^{2-}; ■, lactate + 0.12M SO_4^{2-} ○, hydrogen + 0.02M SO_4^{2-}; ○, hydrogen + 0.18M SO_4^{2-}. After Kaplan and Rittenberg (1964).

(Fig. 7). Furthermore, Harrison and Thode (1958) found that at very low concentrations of sulfate ($\sim 10^{-4}$ M), no significant fractionation occurs during reduction. Kaplan and Rittenberg (1964) noted anomalously small fractionations at very low temperatures ($\sim$0°C).

Summing the experimental evidence presented above for sulfate reduction, and combining the interpretations offered by Harrison and Thode (1957, 1958), Kaplan and Rittenberg (1964), Kemp and Thode (1968), and Rees (1973), the following explanation emerges. At least five rate-limiting steps may be operative (Fig. 2). Fractionation can occur at any step between I and IV.

Diffusion of sulfate (step I) and its activation (step II) appear to produce a small fractionation (± 3‰). During growth, all the sulfate that enters the cell is metabolized without release of sulfur. Hence, steps I and II are rate limiting. This probably also occurs at very low temperatures of metabolism, indicating that rate control of reduction resides in the cell membrane.

As the temperature is raised, the rate-limiting step moves to the electron transfer process. In this event, it is assumed that activated sulfur species are able to exchange with the external medium. This is the only manner in which an isotope fractionation can occur, unless the organism concentrates a large internal reservoir of S^{34}-enriched sulfate, for which there is presently no evidence. Rees (1973) believes that the two steps where fractionation can occur are reduction of APS $\rightarrow SO_3$ (step III) and reduction of $SO_3 \rightarrow H_2S$ (step IV). In each case, a maximum effect of 1.025 is suggested. Hence, where the rate-limiting step is electron transfer, as was the case for metabolism with ethanol, a maximum fractionation $\sim$50‰ may be expected.

In intermediate cases, when both the nutrients and sulfate are optimum, the rate-limiting step should be controlled by step III, APS $\rightarrow SO_3$, and the isotope effect should be 1.025. During very fast reduction, step I may become partially rate limiting and may alternate with step III. The resulting isotope effect would then be an average of the processes controlled by these two steps and should be in the range 1.000 to 1.025.

Although the explanations are appealing, the fractionation mechanism is presently not understood, and in fact, the interpretation may be wrong. Kaplan and Rittenberg (1964) and Kaplan et al. (unpublished) have shown that dissimilatory reduction of sulfite by yeast leads to enrichment of S^{32} in H_2S of 40 to 45‰. According to the kinetic interpretation above, one-step reduction of $SO_3 \rightarrow H_2S$ should lead to a maximum fractionation of only 25‰.

In nature, large fractionation factors in the range 1.06 to 1.07 have been measured, and numerous measurements fall in the range 1.05 (Kaplan et al., 1963; Vinogradov et al., 1962). These higher fractionations usually take place in an "open system," where the sulfate concentration is not limiting and the rate of sulfate reduction is relatively high. This problem is considered in greater detail below.

H. Microbiologically Produced Deposits

The sulfur cycle on a microscale is very common and exists worldwide, especially along fault lines where H_2S-rich waters emerge. In special areas, sulfur deposition occurs on a noticeable scale and may become sufficiently important to produce elemental sulfur in quantities suitable for harvesting. The deposit described in greatest detail is in the Libyan Desert (Butlin and Postgate, 1954). Warm ($\sim$30°C) and sulfide-enriched spring water, which also contains high concentrations of dissolved salts ($NaCl \sim 19.3$‰ and $CaSO_4 \sim 2.6$‰) issues into depressions and forms lakes. Within these sulfate-rich waters, sulfate reduction produces H_2S in the lower water mass (which contains 108 mg H_2S/liter). The sulfide that diffuses up is then oxidized by thiobacilli and photosynthetic sulfur bacteria to elemental sulfur in the surface water. Lake Ain-ez-Zauia, described in some detail by Butlin and Postgate (1954), is about 8 km^2 and in 1950, produced 200 tons of elemental sulfur. Similar evaporite environments in the USSR, especially those in Lake Sernoye, have been described by Kuznetsov et al. (1963).

Of particular interest is the Kona sulfur deposit on the coast near Masulipatam, Madras, India, which consists of lenticular lenses of sulfur-rich clays (with 27 to 35% S^0) at depths of from 15 to 30 cm below the surface. The deposits are underlain by H_2S-saturated clays and overlain by yellow and red ferric oxide-rich clay. Iya and Sreenivasaya (1944) and Subba Rao et al. (1947) have described the deposits as the result of annual flooding of low-lying coastal areas along the Bay of Bengal. Sulfate reduction occurs in the organic-rich and seawater-saturated clays. Elemental sulfur is thought to form from oxidation of both H_2S and iron sulfide, which forms in the clay. Oxidation of the iron sulfide produces geothite and other iron oxides as well as sulfur. The sulfuretum was described by the afore-mentioned authors.

The enormous salt dome sulfur deposits of the Gulf of Mexico are also thought to have arisen from microbial cycling described above (Feely and Kulp, 1957). Of particular interest, and still unanswered, is whether many of the world's copper, zinc, and lead strataform sulfide deposits have originated by sulfate reduction in the marine environments (Stanton, 1972; Trudinger et al., 1972). This is discussed at the end of the chapter.

3. Diagenesis of Sulfur Within the Sediment Column

It should be clear from the foregoing discussion that microorganisms are unquestionably important in transformations among sulfur compounds in nature. Their metabolic function, in which carbon is fixed heterotrophically as organic matter, or else autotrophically as carbon dioxide derived from organic matter, is to derive energy through oxidation-reduction reactions. The result of such biological processes occurring in sediments is a modification of the geochemical properties by diagenetic reactions.

According to Pettijohn (1949), diagenesis primarily refers to reactions that take place within a sediment between one mineral and another or between minerals and the interstitial fluid. This definition emphasizes chemical changes as opposed to physical processes such as compaction, although this emphasis is not unreasonable for shallow depths of burial. During early diagenesis, the yield of new and altered minerals may be too low to be observed by such standard techniques as X-ray diffraction. This problem is especially acute when the reactions involve materials such as carbonates or silicates normally present in high concentrations as detrital phases. Unrecognizable changes in the solid phase may be accompanied by marked alteration in porewater chemistry, thus allowing inferences to be drawn about the nature of diagenetic reactions (Siever et al., 1965).

The diagenesis of sulfur presents a different picture. Authigenic pyrite that forms from bacterial sulfate reduction (Ostroumov, 1953; Kaplan et al., 1963; Berner, 1964a, 1970) produces measurable changes in the solid phase, as well as in the chemistry of the enclosing porewaters. Considering also the important changes in stable sulfur isotope distribution caused by bacterial sulfate reduction, the "pyritologist" has several profitable avenues of investigation.

A. Sulfide Mineral Phases

This section describes the most important mineral phases formed by reaction between bacterially produced sulfide and the enclosing sediment. A number of base and transition metal sulfides have exceedingly low solubility products and might be expected to form during early diagenesis. However, with the exception of iron, these metals are present in only trace amounts in normal marine sediments (Chester, 1965). Iron sulfides are therefore the only metal sulfides recognized in normal marine sediments.

Several iron sulfide phases have been formed synthetically in laboratory experiments at temperatures below 100°C. These are: (1) "amorphous" iron sulfide, $FeS_{0.9}$, (2) mackinawite, $FeS_{0.9}$, (3) cubic iron sulfide, FeS, (4) hexagonal pyrrhotite, $FeS_{1.1}$, (5) greigite, Fe_3S_4, (6) smythite, Fe_3S_4, (7) marcasite, orthorhombic FeS_2, and (8) pyrite, cubic FeS_2. Smythite and cubic FeS are thought not to form under sedimentary conditions (James, 1966) and will not be further discussed. Marcasite, which is stoichiometrically identical to pyrite, is present in some ancient sediments, but has not been identified in recent marine sediments. It is thought to require a low pH for formation. Of the remaining minerals, pyrrhotite and pyrite represent the only thermodynamically stable phases at the temperatures and pressures of early diagenesis. Amorphous iron sulfide, mackinawite, and greigite are metastable with respect to pyrite and/or stoichiometric pyrrhotite (Berner, 1967).

Despite its predicted stability, hexagonal pyrrhotite is very rare as an authigenic phase in sedimentary rocks (James, 1966), although it has been reported occurring in recent sediments from the Sea of Japan (Kobayashi and Nomura, 1972). In the sulfur-rich environment of marine sediments, pyrite is the normal end product of sulfate reduction. The kinetics of transformations involving various iron sulfides may be slow, however, allowing the persistence of metastable phases for considerable periods of time (see below). Operationally it is possible to discriminate between pyrite and other sedimentary iron sulfides, as pyrite is insoluble in hot hydrochloric acid while the remaining phases are soluble. On the basis of this criterion the metastable iron sulfides (plus hexagonal pyrrhotite) are often termed "acid-volatile" sulfides. It is generally difficult to further categorize acid-volatile sulfide in terms of the various iron sulfide phases present, as this material is finely divided and readily oxidizes in air, producing iron oxide plus elemental sulfur. Furthermore, the acid-volatile sulfide is normally present in relatively low concentrations (less than 1% by dry weight of sediment, as S). Both of these factors make X-ray analysis of acid-volatile sulfide difficult or impossible under normal circumstances. Emphasis has thus been placed here on discussion of laboratory synthesis of iron sulfides under conditions approximating those in sediments in an attempt to understand their role in sulfur diagenesis.

B. "Amorphous" Iron Sulfide

The initial product formed from reaction of ferrous iron with hydrogen sulfide at neutral pH is a black, inklike acid-soluble precipitate (equation 26):

$$Fe^{2+} + HS^{-} \rightarrow FeS_{amorph} + H^{+} \tag{26}$$

Berner (1964b) found this material to be amorphous. Chemical analysis gave a composition between $FeS_{0.9}$ and $FeS_{1.1}$. The more sulfur-rich composition may be in error due to adsorbed hydrogen sulfide (Berner, 1964b; Rickard, 1969). In later studies (Berner, 1967), the free energy of formation of the initial precipitate was determined by solubility measurements. The measured free energy was less negative than that of mackinawite by an amount larger than the uncertainty in the data, implying that the initial iron sulfide precipitate and mackinawite are distinct phases. Rickard (1969), however, found by using an improved X-ray diffraction technique that the initial precipitate always yielded one or more of the characteristic peaks of mackinawite. This was interpreted to mean that the initial iron sulfide precipitate is poorly crystallized mackinawite. Sweeney and Kaplan (1973a), using stable isotope techniques, determined that the composition of the initial precipitate is between $FeS_{0.87}$ and $FeS_{0.92}$. This compositional range is similar to that of mackinawite.

C. Mackinawite

The mineral mackinawite, named for the Mackinaw Mine in Snohomish County, Washington, is a sulfur-deficient tetragonal iron sulfide that can contain appreciable Ni and Co substituting in the crystal structure (Evans et al., 1964). Compositional determinations of mackinawite have been reported by several workers. Clark (1966) summarized some of the earlier results and suggested a composition in the range $MS_{0.93} - MS_{0.96}$, where $M = Fe^{2+} + Ni^{2+} + Co^{2+}$, with nickel ranging up to 10% by weight. Later results (Clark and Clark, 1968), based on electron microprobe analysis of Ni and Co-free mackinawite, gave ratios of $FeS_{0.9} - FeS_{0.946}$. Ward (1970) concludes that mackinawite is a pure phase in the Fe-S system and can be represented by a formula near $FeS_{0.94}$.

Crystalline mackinawite, with the characteristic X-ray diffraction pattern, may be formed by aging of the initial "amorphous" precipitate. The aging process requires less than 1 hr at 85 to 95°C for iron sulfide formed from ferrous sulfate and hydrogen sulfide at pH 3, and longer for material aged at lower temperatures (Berner, 1964b). Mackinawite has been synthesized directly in aqueous solution by the action of hydrogen sulfide on metallic iron over the pH range, 4 to 9 (Berner, 1962, 1964b, 1967; Takeno et al., 1970; Vaughn and Ridout, 1971). This reaction apparently produces a reasonably well-crystallized synthetic product (Vaughn and Ridout, 1971). The mackinawite synthesizing reaction most closely approximating the sedimentary environment is that of goethite (hydrous iron oxide, $FeO \cdot OH$) with H_2S (Berner, 1964b; Rickard, 1969). Berner found that in weakly acid solution (pH $\approx$ 4) mackinawite and pyrite were simultaneously produced (equation 27):

$$2\,FeO \cdot OH + 3\,H_2S_{aq} \rightarrow FeS_{mack} + FeS_{pyrite} + 4\,H_2O \tag{27}$$

In neutral to basic solution (where the bisulfide ion HS^- is the dominant aqueous sulfide species), the only iron sulfide phase to form was mackinawite (equation 28):

$$2\,FeO \cdot OH + 3\,HS^- \rightarrow 2\,FeS_{mack} + S^0 + 3\,OH^- + H_2O \tag{28}$$

The occurrence of mackinawite in association with various sulfide ore deposits has been summarized by Takeno and Clark (1967), and will not be further discussed here. The presence of tetragonal iron sulfide in sediments was first reported by Berner (1962) in samples from the Mystic River, Massachusetts. In a later paper, Berner (1964b) suggested that X-ray data published by Volkov (1961) for a sulfide concretion from the Black Sea was consistent with the presence of both mackinawite and greigite. It was argued in the same paper that much of the unstable black acid-volatile sulfide in sediments, termed hydrotroilite in the earlier literature, is probably poorly crystallized mackinawite.

D. Greigite

Greigite is a cubic iron sulfide with the composition Fe_3S_4 and the spinel structure (Skinner et al., 1964). It has been shown to be identical with the mineral melnikovite, which appears in earlier literature (e.g., Lepp, 1957). Both the natural and synthetic materials are sooty black powders with strong magnetic properties (Ward, 1970). Some controversy exists as to whether the iron in the structure exists partially or totally as ferrous iron. Berner (1967), assigned a composition $Fe_3{}^{2+}S^0S_3{}^{2-}$ to greigite. In agreement with this view, Rickard (1969) pointed out that under the conditions of synthesis, large amounts of ferric iron cannot form. This conclusion is supported by the mössbauer studies of Morice et al. (1969), who detected only the presence of ferrous iron. Vaughn and Ridout (1971), however, concluded from an investigation of mössbauer spectra that greigite is probably an inverse spinel with the composition $Fe_2{}^{3+}Fe^{2+}S_4{}^{2-}$.

Controversy also exists as to the necessity of oxygen for greigite formation. Berner (1964b) and Sweeney (1972) produced cubic iron sulfide by reaction of ferrous sulfate and hydrogen sulfide over the pH range 3 to 9, only in the presence of air. Uda (1965) synthesized greigite by heating precipitated FeS in a sealed glass tube at 190°C. In this procedure, air was excluded by means of a vacuum pump. Rickard (1969) found that heating mackinawite in an evacuated tube at temperatures as low as 70°C rapidly produces greigite. Nonetheless, it appears that the reaction to form greigite from mackinawite is an oxidation process, as the former contains oxidized sulfur (or iron). Therefore, if air is absent, some other oxidizing agent must be present. An obvious candidate is elemental sulfur, and in natural environments iron oxides may also be important.

Naturally occurring black magnetic iron sulfide was first reported in clays of Miocene age in Samara, Russia by Doss (1921, quoted by James, 1966). Since then, several other sedimentary occurrences have been reported. One well-documented locality of greigite occurrence is in lacustrine sediments of Tertiary age, in San Bernadino County, California (Skinner et al., 1964). It has been reported from unconsolidated sediments of Lake Superior (Dell, 1972). As mentioned above (Berner, 1964b) showed that the X-ray properties of an iron sulfide concretion from Black Sea bottom muds (Volkov, 1961) was a mixture of mackinawite and greigite. A more recent report of concretionary sulfides in Black Sea sediments also mentions the existence of a magnetic iron sulfide, presumably greigite (Volkov et al., 1971). Jedwab (1967) reported greigite both as concretions and as particles inside cavities of plant and animal microfossils in recent sediments.

E. Pyrite

Pyrite (FeS_2) belongs to the isometric crystal class. Sedimentary pyrite is a common authigenic mineral in recent marine and lacustrine environments, as well as in sedimentary rocks, particularly dark shales (Love and Amstutz, 1966). It typically occurs as microscopic single crystal grains 1 to 10 μ in size, as "framboidal spherules" up to 250 μ in diameter (Vallentyne, 1963; Love and Amstutz, 1966; Love, 1969; Sweeney, 1972) and as groups of framboidal spheres termed polyframboids (Love, 1971). The term "framboidal" (Rust, 1935) refers to a unique, raspberrylike microtexture (Fig. 8), which has been the object of numerous studies. The single crystals and framboids are present in the clay and silt-size sediment fraction, or as infillings of foram, diatom, and radiolarian tests.

Pyrite is a ferrous polysulfide (Morice et al., 1969). To maintain charge neutrality the sulfur atoms can be regarded as possessing a formal charge of -1 each, or alternatively, one atom divalent and the other zerovalent ($S^{2-}S^0$). This implies that pyrite cannot be formed from ferrous iron and hydrogen sulfide without production of zerovalent sulfur.[1] This requirement is reflected in the low-temperature laboratory syntheses of pyrite summarized in Table VIII, in which elemental sulfur from three

TABLE VIII

Summary of Laboratory Syntheses of Pyrite by Various Workers

Reactants	pH	Time (days)	Temperature (°C)	Products[a]	References
$Fe^{2+} + H_2S + S^0$	Alkaline	7	100	FeS_2	Allen et al. (1912); quoted by Berner (1970)
$FeS + S^0$	4.5	7	22	FeS[b], No FeS_2	Roberts et al. (1972)
$FeS + S^0 + O_2$	5.5	36	25	$FeS_2 + S^0$	Roberts et al. (1972)
$FeS + Na_2S_x$ sodium polysulfide	6.9–7.9	77	65	FeS, no FeS_2	Berner (1970)
$FeS + S^0 + Na_2S_x$	6.9–7.9	14	65	FeS_2	Berner (1970)
$FeS + Na_2S_x$	7	7	25	FeS_2 (S^0)	Rickard (1969)
$FeS + S^0$		7	60–85	FeS_2	Sweeney (1972)
$FeSO_4 + H_2S + O_2$	3	15 min	85–90	Fe_3S_4, FeS_2	Berner (1964b)
$FeSO_4 + H_2S + O_2$	3	2	60–65	FeS_2	Berner (1964b)
$FeSO_4 + H_2S + O_2$	3	25	40	FeS_2	Berner (1964b)
$FeO \cdot OH + H_2S$ goethite	4	14 hr	20–25	FeS_2, FeS	Berner (1964b)
$FeO \cdot OH + H_2S$	4.4–7.0	7	25	FeS_2 (FeS)	Rickard (1969)
$FeO \cdot OH + H_2S$	3.8–6.5	24 hr	25	FeS_2	Roberts et al. (1969)

[a] Minor products in parentheses
[b] FeS indicates acid-volatile sulfide.

[1] Berner (1970) has shown that pyrite formation proceeds by addition of sulfur rather than loss of iron. See also Sweeney and Kaplan (1973a).

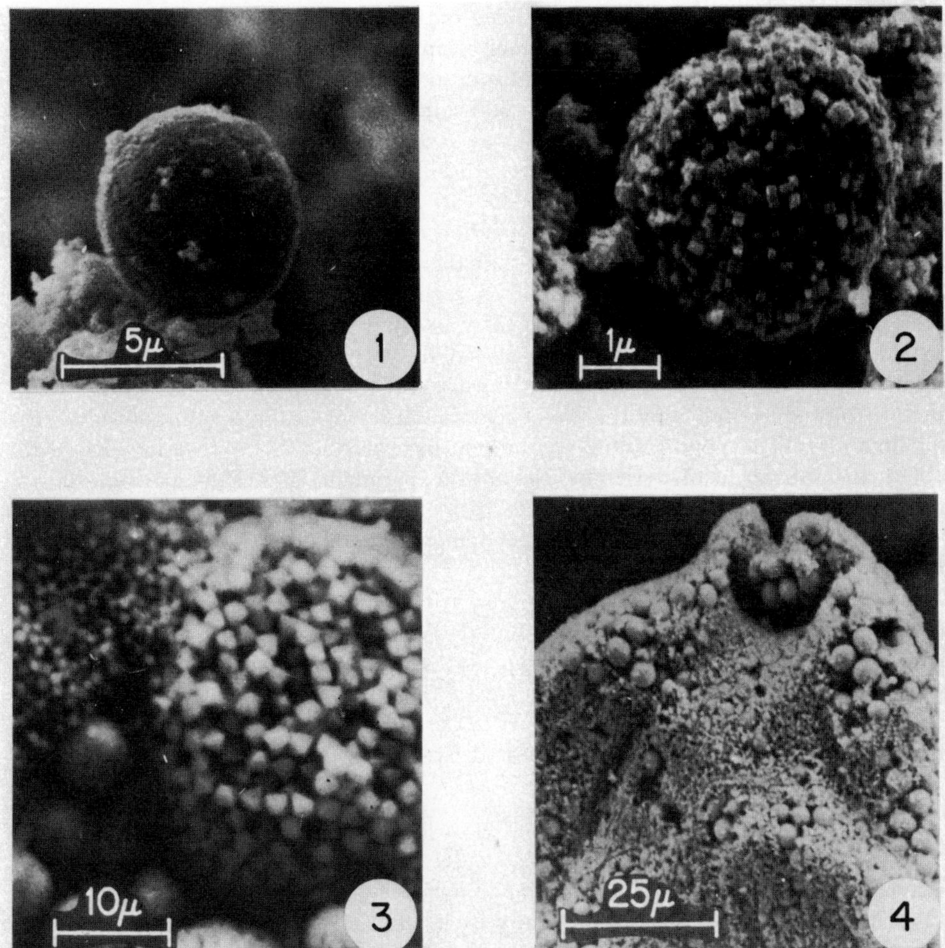

Fig. 8. Scanning electron micrographs of iron sulfides. (1) Spherical texture developed during laboratory synthesis of greigite under anhydrous conditions. (2) Framboid developed during laboratory synthesis of pyrite in aqueous solution. (3) San Diego Trough (0 to 20 cm). Framboids showing internal pyrite crystals. (4) Tanner Basin. Pyrite crystal—framboid aggregate. Disc-shaped tests of the same dimensions were also present in the sediment.

different sources has been employed: (1) oxidation of H_2S at acidic pH by oxygen, (2) oxidation of H_2S by goethite according to reaction 29, which also provides a source of ferrous iron:

$$2\,FeO\cdot OH + H_2S \rightarrow S^0 + 2\,Fe^{2+} + 4\,OH^- \tag{29}$$

and (3) direct addition of elemental sulfur as such, or in the form of a polysulfide solution.

Pyrite has been produced in the laboratory by three methods. A reaction verified by several workers is that of acid-volatile sulfide with excess solid elemental sulfur (Feld, 1911; Roberts et al., 1969; Berner, 1970; Sweeney and Kaplan, 1973a), according to equation 30;

$$FeS + S^0 \rightarrow FeS_2 \tag{30}$$

Berner (1970) observed pyrite crystallizing on the surface of elemental sulfur in his experiments and surmised that the nucleation properties of the surface of orthorhombic sulfur promotes pyrite crystallization from FeS. Observed rates of pyrite formation are slow, consistent with a solid-solid mechanism for the transformation. For example, at pH 4 and 25°C, Roberts et al. (1969) were unable to produce pyrite by this reaction in seven days. Berner synthesized pyrite by reaction 3 at 65°C in 14 days.

A modification of the above is the reaction of Fe^{2+} with H_2S in the presence of oxygen (Berner, 1964b). It is believed that this first involves oxidation of $H_2S \rightarrow S^0$ and subsequent reaction of S^0 with FeS by reaction 30.

A second approach to pyrite synthesis was undertaken by Rickard (1969), who reacted ferrous iron or acid-volatile iron sulfide with sodium polysulfide solutions, producing pyrite and elemental sulfur. Berner (1970) and Roberts et al. (1969) were unable to produce pyrite by the direct reaction of ferrous sulfate with polysulfide at alkaline pH. As elemental sulfur was present as a product of the reaction (Rickard, 1969), the formation of pyrite in Rickard's experiment is perhaps attributable to reaction of initially formed mackinawite with elemental sulfur (equation 30).

A third group of synthetic experiments demonstrates that pyrite may be formed by reaction of goethite (FeO·OH) with hydrogen sulfide (Berner, 1964b; Rickard, 1969; Roberts et al., 1969). At pH 6.5 or less, pyrite is invariably present as a product (Table VIII). Acid-volatile sulfide was reported as absent or minor in two of the three studies (see Table VIII). At pH values greater than 6.5, acid-volatile sulfide (specifically mackinawite) and elemental sulfur were the only products (equation 28).

The pyrite-forming reaction below pH 6.5 presumably proceeds first by an oxidation-reduction step (equation 29), followed by the precipitation of pyrite (equation 31):

$$Fe^{2+} + S^0 + H_2S \rightarrow FeS_2 + 2\,H^+ \tag{31}$$

In contrast to reaction 30, the production of pyrite is quite rapid through the sequence (29) and (31). Berner (1964b) obtained pyrite in 14 hr at pH 4 and room temperature. Roberts et al. (1969) obtained comparable results at pH 4 to 6. This implies that the pyrite-forming step (equation 31) does not proceed through an initial precipitation of FeS followed by reaction with solid elemental sulfur, as this was previously shown to be a relatively slow reaction (even at low pH). Noting this, Roberts et al. (1969) proposed that following the oxidation-reduction step, pyrite is precipitated homogeneously from solution through the action of a disulfane (equations 29, 32 and 33).

$$2\,FeO\cdot OH + H_2S \rightarrow 2\,Fe^{2+} + S^0 + 4\,OH^- \tag{29}$$

$$H_2S + S^0 \rightarrow H_2S_2 \tag{32}$$

$$Fe^{2+} + H_2S_2 \rightarrow FeS_2 + 2\,H^+ \tag{33}$$

Of the pyrite-forming reactions discussed above, equation 33 represents the only one proposed in which acid-volatile sulfide does not precede the formation of pyrite. It has previously been supposed that acid-volatile sulfides were prerequisite to pyrite formation (Feld, 1911; Harmsen et al., 1954; Kaplan et al., 1963; Berner, 1964c, 1970).

The pH dependence of the products of reaction between goethite and H_2S may reflect the relative solubility of mackinawite and pyrite. The solubility product of mackinawite (equation 34) was measured by Berner (1967) to be 2.8×10^{-18}:

$$[Fe^{2+}][S^{2-}] = Ksp_{mack} = 2.8 \times 10^{-18} \tag{34}$$

where brackets represent activities.

Assuming saturation with solid orthorhombic sulfur (whose activity is unity), the solubility product of pyrite may be written:

$$FeS_2 \rightleftharpoons S^{2-} + S^0 + Fe^{2+} \tag{35}$$

$$[1][Fe^{2+}][S^{2-}] = Ksp_{pyrite} \tag{36}$$

Using free energy data of Garrels and Christ (1965), the solubility product of pyrite is calculated to be 2.4×10^{-28}. Comparison of the two values indicates that pyrite in equilibrium with excess elemental sulfur has a solubility product 10 orders of magnitude less than that of mackinawite.

The activity of sulfide ion in equations 34 and 36 is dependent on (among other things) the total concentration of dissolved sulfide and pH. At pH greater than 6.5 and high total dissolved sulfide, the reaction between goethite and dissolved sulfide produces mackinawite and elemental sulfur. This is tentatively interpreted to indicate that at high pH, the solution is supersaturated with mackinawite, and it will precipitate preferentially (i.e., rapidly) despite the much larger supersaturation with respect to pyrite. This is apparently also the case in alkaline polysulfide solution (Roberts et al., 1969; Berner, 1970). Once formed, mackinawite transforms only slowly to pyrite through reaction 30. Such a situation is similar to the precipitation of aragonite under conditions in which calcite is the stable phase (Ernst, 1969). Under conditions of low pH, mackinawite may become undersaturated. Pyrite, by virtue of its much smaller solubility product would, at this point, still be highly supersaturated and could precipitate without competition from mackinawite, as proposed by Roberts et al. (1969). It is implicitly assumed that the rate at which ferrous iron is released by reaction 29 is independent of pH.

F. Framboid Formation

Two general hypotheses have been proposed for the formation of framboids. Schneiderhohn (1923), Love (1965), and others suggest that framboids are produced by replacement of aggregates of organic cells with pyrite. Rickard (1970) believes that an organic globule is replaced. In both these hypothesized mechanisms, the characteristic spheroidal texture of the framboid is a pseudomorph requiring biogenic involvement. Alternatively, Schouten (1946) suggested framboids are formed by multiple crystallization of pyrite from a "hydrous iron monosulfide precursor gel" of spherical form. This mechanism would allow framboid texture to develop in abiotic systems.

Abiotically formed pyrite crystal clusters have been observed in volcanic rock (Love and Amstutz, 1969). Comparison of the textures of volcanic and sedimentary pyrite crystal aggregates moved these authors to conclude that the two can be distinguished from one another. Volcanic pyrite is found as clusters of crystals of various sizes, in contrast to framboids of sedimentary pyrite, which are composed of uniform euhedral crystals. Rickard (1970) attributes nonsedimentary framboids to infilling of gas vacuoles. Recent laboratory syntheses of inorganically formed framboids (Berner, 1969a; Farrand, 1970; Sunagawa et al., 1971; Sweeney and Kaplan, 1973a) have eliminated the necessity of organic cells or globules to act as structures for framboid development.

A study of the pathway of framboid formation was recently undertaken in our laboratory (Sweeney and Kaplan, 1973a). Experiments were set up to identify microtextures produced during pyrite formation. Freshly precipitated iron sulfide was sulfurized by reaction 30. The iron sulfide phases resulting from this reaction were identified by X-ray diffraction, and the accompanying textures present were described by scanning electron microscopy. Three sets of conditions were studied: (1) under vacuum (anhydrous) at temperatures up to 172°C, (2) in aqueous solution at temperatures up to 85°C, and (3) filtered but undried, at temperatures up to 85°C. Under conditions 2 and 3, some experimental runs produced the framboid texture (Fig. 8). Spheres of greigite (containing no discernible microcrysts) were formed and identified under conditions 1 and 2 (Fig. 8). Experimental runs in which the initial iron sulfide precipitate underwent no phase change did not produce identifiable texture.

The mechanism for framboid formation deduced from these studies holds for both solution and anhydrous conditions. Spherical texture is developed when the initial iron sulfide precipitate is transformed to greigite. As the greigite converts to pyrite, the spherical texture is either retained or changed by internal nucleation of pyrite crystals to form framboids. Greigite spheres were produced under anhydrous, as well as hydrous, conditions. This showed that the spherical form is due to properties of the solid, and not to "gellike" properties of intermediate sulfides in solution. The pathway is summarized in Fig. 9. Framboidal texture is therefore presumptive evidence for precursor, metastable iron sulfide phases. It was pointed out previously that sedimentary pyrite also occurs as single crystals. The two morphologies may reflect two distinct pathways of pyrite formation. To the best of our knowledge, there is no quantitative data to determine the relative abundance of each form.

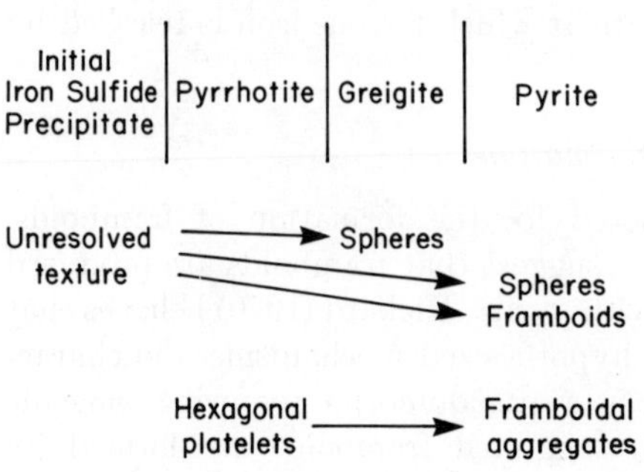

Fig. 9. Schematic representation of intermediate phases and morphologies involved in pyrite framboid formation. After Sweeney and Kaplan (1973a).

G. "Excess" Sulfur in Sediments

A remarkable feature of the biogeochemistry of marine sediments is the large amounts of reduced sulfur (dominantly pyrite, but also acid-volatile sulfide, elemental sulfur, and dissolved sulfide) that may be formed in the presence of abundant organic matter. Such reduced sulfur may be present in greater amounts than that originally enclosed with the sediment as sulfate in porewaters, plus that added as organically bound sulfur (Kaplan et al., 1963; Berner, 1964a; Hartmann and Nielsen, 1969). This is illustrated with data of Berner (1964a) from Gulf of California sediments (Table IX). The column headed "Pyrite plus Organic S" is a good estimate of total reduced sulfur, because other forms were shown to be much less abundant in these sediments. Expected total sulfur is the amount originally buried with the sediment as

TABLE IX

Excess Sulfur in Marine Sediments Over that Formed from Complete Reduction of Porewater Sulfate[a]

Core L-42 Depth (cm)	Pyrite Plus Organic S (%)	Expected Totals (%)	Excess S (%)
4–12	0.88	0.3	0.58
16–24	1.23	0.24	0.99
43–51	1.14	0.20	0.94
63–71	1.85	0.19	1.66

[a] After Berner (1964a).

seawater sulfate, corrected for the loss of water due to compaction. The difference between these two columns is shown in column 4, headed "Excess S." In the data shown, this excess may amount to well over 1% dry weight of the sediment. Organically bound sulfur, which is the other possible source, will amount to less than 10% of the total sulfur in the sediments (Kaplan et al., 1963; Hartman and Nielsen, 1969). Such data may be taken as *ad hoc* evidence for addition of sulfate sulfur to sediments during or after burial in amounts larger than that trapped in the interstitial fluids.

H. Distribution of Reduced S in Sediments

The presence of reduced sulfur compounds formed authigenically in sediments has typically been associated with a rather restricted range of sedimentary environments. Dunham (1961), for example, lists the following:

1. Ill-drained terrestrial swamps.
2. Eutrophic (high nutrient) lakes.
3. River estuaries, tidal lagoons, and tops of deltas.
4. Deep land-locked sea basins separated by sills from the open ocean (e.g., the Black Sea).
5. Basins (or trenches) in the sea bottom (e.g., Santa Barbara Basin off the coast of Southern California).

A feature that these environments have in common is an unusually rapid removal of dissolved oxygen, allowing initiation of sulfate reduction. The removal of oxygen is accomplished by aerobic respiration in the presence of abundant organic matter. Evidence is now accumulating, however, that reduced sulfur-bearing sediments are more widespread than was previously suspected. Table X lists a number of occurrences. Of particular interest are references to pyrite in marginal sea, continental shelf, slope, and rise environments. The sparse data of Table X, of course, are not intended to indicate that pyrite formation is a ubiquitous phenomenon in all such sediments. In cases where quantitative data are available, the amount of reduced sulfur present, while large compared to the amount of sulfur initially trapped with the sediments, is relatively low in an absolute sense (generally less than 1% sulfur by dry weight of sediment). As a result, wet chemical analysis is the preferred analytical technique for quantitative determination because of its sensitivity. Nonetheless, X-ray diffraction data for sediments recovered by the Deep Sea Drilling Project (JOIDES) have

TABLE X

Reported Occurrences of Pyrite from Gravity and Piston-Core Sampling

Location	% S	Environment	References
Southern California continental borderland	0.02–1.0	Basins in continental shelf	Kaplan et al. (1963) Sholkovitz (1972) Sweeney and Kaplan (1973b)
Gulf of California	0.5–2.0	Basins and shelves	Berner (1964a)
Northwestern Pacific Ocean	0–0.05 (FeS only)	Trench	Ostroumov and Shilov (1956)
Connecticut Coast	0.1–2.0	Shelf	Berner (1970)
Wadden Sea	Present	Land-locked sea	van Straaten (1954)
Sea of Japan	Present	Marginal sea	Kobayashi and Nomura (1972)
Sea of Okhotsk	Present	Marginal sea	Strakhov (1967)
Baltic Sea	0.1–2.0	Land-locked sea	Hartmann and Nielson (1969)
Black Sea	0.1–2.0	Land-locked sea	Ostroumov (1953) Vinogradov et al. (1962) Berner (1971b)
Eastern Pacific off South America	0.4	Continental rise	Bonatti et al. (1971)
West Coast of North Africa	0.1–0.9	Continental rise	Regnell (1961)

recorded the presence of pyrite. In particular, pyrite is found to be present in sites drilled in relative proximity to land. A selection of such occurrences is described in Table XI.

Acid-volatile sulfides (i.e., mackinawite and greigite) are present in greatest abundance relative to pyrite in rapidly deposited sediments. The black color of some lakes, tidal flats, and coastal muds is due to the ability of this material to act as a pigmenting agent (Van Straaten, 1954; Love, 1967; Doyle, 1968; Berner, 1970). In some cases, acid-volatile sulfide may exceed pyrite when both are expressed as percent sulfur. With increasing depth of burial, the acid-volatile sulfides generally decrease in abundance (Strakhov, 1967; Kaplan et al., 1963; Berner, 1970).

Acid-volatile sulfide abundance in surface sediments within a single depositional

TABLE XI

Selection of Pyrite Occurrences from JOIDES Deep Sea Drilling Project

Leg	Site	Location	References
I	1, 2, 3	Gulf of Mexico	Rex (1969)
	4, 5	East of Bahamas	
IV	24-A	Foot of continental rise in the Western Brazil Basin	Rex and Murray (1970a)
	27	Western part of the Atlantic Basin 250 mi east of the Lesser Antilles Inland Arc	
	30	Avis ridge in the eastern Caribbean	
V	34	Seaward margin of Delgada Fan off northwestern United States	Rex and Murray (1970b)
XI	99–106	Continental Rise off eastern United States	Zemmels et al. (1972)

basin may present a symmetrical appearance. For example, in the Sea of Okhotsk, high values were measured around the periphery, with decreasing amounts toward the center of the basin (Strakhov, 1967). A similar result has been found for the Black Sea (Strakhov, 1967). These distribution patterns may be directly correlated with sedimentation rates, which decrease with distance from land.

In more slowly depositing sediments, acid-volatile sulfides may be minor components, or even absent, despite an abundance of pyrite. This is illustrated in Table

TABLE XII

Relative Contents of Acid-Volatile Sulfur and Pyrite, Santa Catalina Basin

Depth (cm)	Sulfide S[a] (% dry weight)	Pyrite Sulfur
0–10	Trace	0.12
20–30	Trace	0.20
40–50	Trace	0.13
65–70	<0.001	0.07
120–125	Trace	0.15
214–225	0.002	0.16
320–330	0.001	0.33
360–370	0.002	0.21

[a] Acid-volatile + dissolved.

XII. Pyrite sulfur in Santa Catalina Basin sediments exceeds 0.3%, whereas sulfide sulfur (dissolved plus acid-volatile) is present in only trace amounts. Similar results have been reported by Emery and Rittenberg (1952) and Berner (1964a). Emery and Rittenberg (1952) attribute low "FeS" values to either of the following:

1. A sufficiently slow rate of deposition as compared to nearshore areas, such as tidal flats, enabling the transformation of "FeS" to go to completion at the upper surface of the sediment.

2. Extremely slow reactions between resistant iron compounds and H_2S, enabling direct formation of pyrite without an intermediate acid-volatile stage.

To these, Berner (1964a) had added a third possibility:

3. At the sediment-water interface, an abundant supply of both reactive sulfur and oxidizing agents enables complete transformation to pyrite by reactions similar to equation 30.

Elemental sulfur in sediments is of great interest, as it is postulated to play an important role in transformations among iron sulfide phases (equation 30). Unfortunately, the sampling techniques and analytical procedures used in its analysis may generate elemental sulfur in addition to the *in situ* amount, and therefore yield high results (Berner, 1964a). Even so, those studies that have determined "free sulfur" have found only low concentrations compared to other forms of sulfur (Kaplan et al., 1963; Berner, 1964a, 1970). This has been interpreted as indicating continual formation and removal of sulfur, by processes whose relative rates are such that elemental sulfur never builds up to high concentrations (Kaplan et al., 1963). If this is the case, elemental sulfur could become rate limiting in the acid-volatile sulfide to pyrite transformation (Berner, 1970).

I. Organic Carbon and Sulfur Distribution in Recent Marine Sediments

Because sulfate-reducing bacteria in anoxic sediments combust organic matter while producing sulfide (equation 1), it is not unreasonable to expect some quantitative relationship between reduced sulfur and organic carbon (which provides a crude measure of available organic matter). This question is discussed by Berner (1970) and Sweeney and Kaplan (1973b). Berner found a linear relationship between organic carbon and pyrite sulfur in the topmost portion (upper 3 cm) of Connecticut coastal sediments. It was concluded that organic carbon acts as an intensity factor, limiting the amount of pyrite that forms.

Sweeney and Kaplan (1973b) extended this discussion to include depths greater than the uppermost layers. Assuming that other terminal degradative organic carbon reactions below the sediment-water interface are insignificant during earliest diagenesis in marine sediments, then a time-dependent inverse correlation exists between the amount of sulfate reduced and the amount of organic carbon remaining in the sediment:

$$\text{C remaining} = \text{C deposited} - \text{C oxidized by sulfate reduction} \tag{37}$$

Using the relationship shown in (43), 2 mol of carbon are utilized for each mole of sulfate reduced, or in terms of weights involved, 1 g of carbon is oxidized for each $\frac{4}{3}$ g hydrogen sulfide sulfur produced.

The relationship between the organic carbon in the sediment and the sulfide produced may be quantitatively expressed in terms of the fraction of carbon utilized during sulfate reduction.

$$\begin{aligned} C_D &= C_M + C_O \\ C_O &= KC_D \\ C_O &= \tfrac{3}{4}S_R \\ C_M &= C_O\left(\frac{1}{K} - 1\right) \end{aligned}$$

where C_D = percent organic carbon deposited in sediment
C_O = percent organic carbon oxidized, and lost from sediment.
C_M = percent organic carbon measured in sediment
K = fraction of deposited carbon oxidized during sulfate reduction (assumed constant)
S_R = percent reduced sulfur in sediment

$$C_M = \frac{3S_R}{4}\left(\frac{1}{K} - 1\right) \tag{38}$$

Not all the H_2S formed may be trapped in the solid portion of the sediment; some sulfide may be reoxidized back to sulfate. If this happens, and assuming the amount reoxidized is a linear function of that reduced:

$$\begin{aligned} S_O &= XS_R \\ S_R &= S_M + S_O \\ S_M &= S_R - XS_R \\ S_M &= (1 - X)S_R \\ S_R &= \frac{S_M}{(1 - X)} \end{aligned}$$

TABLE XIII

Fraction of Organic Carbon Utilized During Sulfate Reduction, Calculated from Slope ($M = 0.36$) Fig. 10, Using Equation 41

Fraction of sulfide lost from sediment (X)	0	0.5	0.9
Fraction of organic carbon utilized for sulfate reduction (K)	0.21	0.35	0.73

where S_O = amount of sulfide reoxidized to sulfate, in terms of percent total sulfur in sediment

X = fraction of sulfide reoxidized and lost from sediment

S_M = amount of sulfide measured in the sediment, as percent of total sulfur

Then equation 38 becomes:

$$C_M = \frac{3S_M(1/K - 1)}{4(1 - X)} \tag{39}$$

The slope M (where $M = S_M/C_M$) depends on the two variables, X and K in equation 39. The fraction of organic carbon utilized during sulfate reduction K is shown in Table XIII for different possible values of X (fraction of sulfide oxidized to sulfate and lost from the sediment) calculated from equation 40:

$$K = \frac{3M}{4(1 - X) + 3M} \tag{40}$$

Data of organic carbon and sulfur in marine sediments from various sources are shown in Fig. 10. They include analyses in the sediment at various depths from the surface to 500 cm. It is assumed that the destruction of organic matter by metabolic

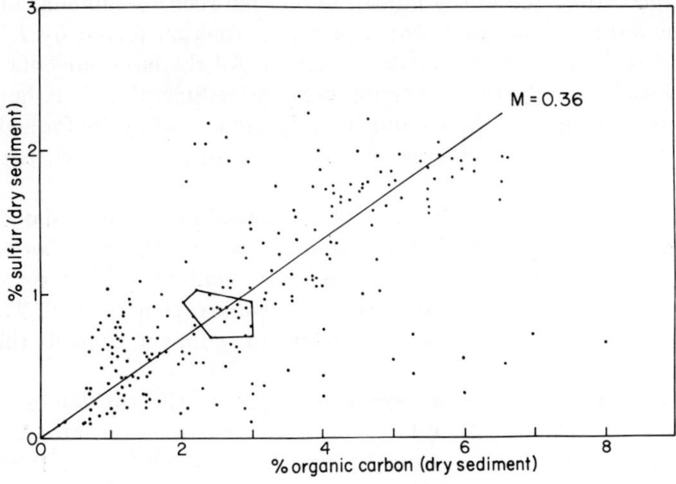

Fig. 10. Sulfur and organic carbon measurements from solid fraction of different depths in sediment from recent marine environments. Santa Catalina Basin, East Cortez Basin, and Santa Barbara Basin, from Sweeney and Kaplan (1973b). Additional data from Kaplan et al. (1963), Hartmann and Nielsen (1969), Palacas et al. (1968), and Borodovskiy (1965).

function is essentially complete in the thin sediment layer (approximately 0 to 10 cm below the surface) and that only a small reduction occurs by continuing sulfate reduction after burial. If this assumption were invalid, the relationship between C_M and S_M would be modified. For example, if a significant amount of organic matter were combusted at depth and the resulting sulfide immediately precipitated, a point on the S_M/C_M plot would tend toward lower C_M and higher S_M with respect to the value established at the sediment surface.

The results (Fig. 10) do indicate a correlation between measured organic carbon and pyrite values, as approximated by the slope ($M = 0.36$) drawn through data points. This was interpreted by Sweeney and Kaplan (1973b) as indicating the essential validity of equation 39. There is, however, a good deal of scatter in the data. This arises from several sources:

1. If organic carbon is inhomogeneously distributed with depth then C_M and S_M must be measured on the same sample instead of an adjacent sample for equation 39 to be valid. Some data included in Fig. 10 suffer from this defect.

2. For all points on Fig. 10 to fall on the same line, they would have an identical "K." This may not be reasonable to expect when comparing many environments. For this reason, data from individual environments show less scatter (for example, Berner, 1970).

3. Sulfate reduction does, in fact, continue at a reduced rate after burial as described in the porewater chemistry discussion below. This causes a deviation from the average slope.

4. The extent of sulfide oxidation, X, may differ from environment to environment or with depth in a single sediment column.

The extent of sulfide oxidation is unknown and cannot be determined from this data. If X is assumed to be relatively small, K can be calculated from equation 40 using the value for M (0.36) from Fig. 10. The derived value is ≈ 0.2, indicating that 20% of the deposited carbon is utilized by sulfate reduction, which agrees reasonably well with the value of 16% calculated by Kaplan et al. (1963) for the Santa Barbara Basin. In a qualitative sense, the linear relation between the amount of sulfur and carbon in the sediment suggests that a preferred fraction (given by K) of organic matter deposited is utilized for sulfate reduction. All the environments included in the data have sulfate reduction occurring near the sediment surface, but not in the overlying water column. For these sediments, the amount of pyrite formed appears to be dependent on the extent of organic carbon deposition as previously shown by Berner (1970).

Several cores included in Fig. 10 have a large spread in the vertical distribution of the amount of sulfur and carbon in the sediment. Data for the East Cortez Basin are shown in Fig. 11. The large fluctuations in pyrite content are not correlated with depth, but instead, are correlated directly with organic carbon content. This supports the conclusion that the organic carbon content of sediment controls the degree of reduction.

Evidence that sulfate reduction occurs primarily in the top few centimeters of sediment is given by Berner (1970) for Connecticut coastal sediments. A similar conclusion was reached by Hartmann and Nielsen (1969), based on data from Kiel Bay. The organic carbon/sulfur ratio calculated from their data is shown in Fig. 12. This ratio rapidly decreases in the surface 5 cm and then remains more or less constant with burial. Additional sulfate reduction is occurring at depths greater than 5 cm in

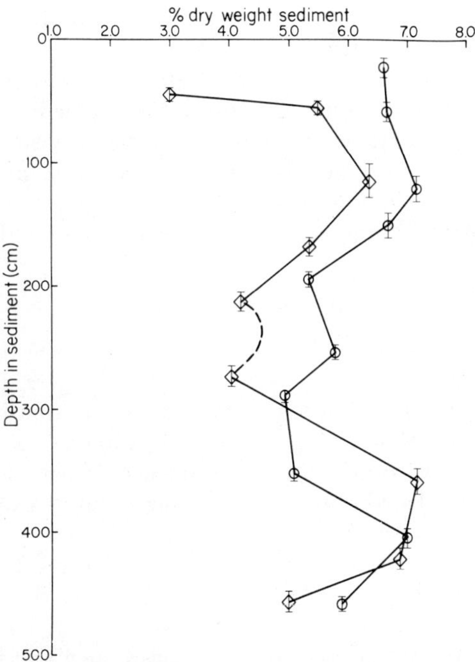

Fig. 11. Measurements of organic carbon and reduced sulfur with depth in sediment from East Cortez Basin. ◇, sulfur (% dry sediment × 10). ○, organic carbon (% dry sediment).

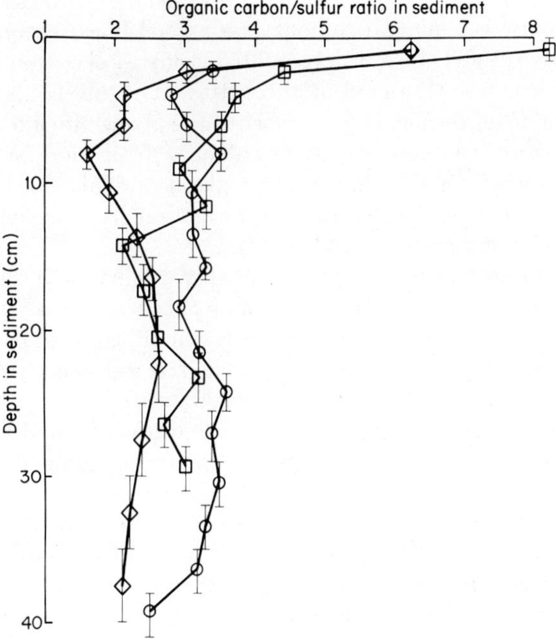

Fig. 12. Organic carbon:sulfur ratio for solid fraction of sediment from Kiel Bay. Hartmann and Nielsen (1969). Ratio becomes relatively constant below 5 cm depth, indicating that most sulfide forms through organic carbon oxidation above this depth. ◇, core 2091; □, core 2092; ○, core 2094.

these sediments as shown by a continuing decrease in porewater sulfate. This is apparently not sufficient to significantly modify the observed carbon/sulfur ratio.

It is concluded that addition of pyrite, formed from sulfate reduction after burial, may contribute measurable amounts of sulfur to the sediment. However, the fluctuations in the amount of organic matter deposited with time can produce large variations in the quantity of pyrite formed in the surface sediment. Variation in pyrite initially formed, due to nonuniform deposition of organic matter, is often large enough to mask the increase in pyrite content due to sulfate reduction after burial.

J. *Source of Iron*

In sedimentary environments where pyrite formation is extensive, a significant proportion of the available iron can be diagenetically transferred to the sulfide phase. In the Santa Barbara Basin where pyrite content equals approximately 1%, pyrite iron constitutes 0.5% (by weight of the sediment) (Kaplan et al., 1963), which would represent one-eighth of the total iron content of the sediment (Emery, 1960). It is of interest to consider the redistribution of iron during sulfur diagenesis and the possible role of iron as a limiting factor in pyrite formation.

Iron is initially incorporated into sediments in several forms. In nearshore sediment, it is included as detrital phases such as augite, hornblende, magnetite, goethite, and hematite (Chester, 1965). Carbonate shell material can contribute iron, which is presumably adsorbed on the surface as oxide coatings (Riley and Chester, 1971). Such coatings may average 0.1% by weight of foraminiferal shells (Turekian, 1965). Iron can also be added with organic matter. Kaplan et al. (1963) calculated that a sediment with 5% organic matter would initially contain 5×10^{-3} % organic iron.

A major source of iron in many sediments is associated with the clay fraction. Plots of total iron versus clay mineral content give a good linear correlation (Hirst, 1962; Moore, 1963; Love, 1967). In a widely quoted study of clay-iron association, Carroll (1958) listed three types: (1) an essential constituent of the clay lattice in phases such as nontronite, chlorite, vermiculite, chamosite, and glauconite, (2) a minor constituent of the crystal lattice, where it is in isomorphous substitution, and (3) an iron oxide coating on the surface of the clay mineral platelets. This third type is commonly produced during rock weathering and soil formation. It represents the bulk of iron transported by clay minerals (Carroll, 1958).

Iron contained in sedimentary pyrite probably originates to some extent from the entire range of source materials. However, some phases are more resistant than others. Regnell (1961) noted in pyrite-bearing cores taken off the west coast of North Africa that red grains consisting of admixtures of quartz and hematite seemed to be unaffected by the pyrite-forming process. Berner (1970) found that sand or silt-sized grains of magnetite, hematite, goethite, hornblende, augite, and biotite released iron much less readily in both HCl and H_2S than more fine-grained hematite, limonitic goethite, or chlorite.

There seems little doubt that fine-grained clays and other silicates can release structural iron. Curtis (1967) concluded from a detailed study of lithified marine sediments that iron is removed from both silicate and iron hydroxide phases during diagenesis in a proportion dependent on the activation energies of the two solubilizing mechanisms. Menon (1967) observed pyrite in a limestone from India, which was produced by alteration of detrital iron-bearing mica. Drever (1971a, 1971b) found that structural iron was replaced by magnesium in the clay fraction of sulfide-rich sediments from Bandaras Bay, Mexico. Iron produced in this way was thought to participate in pyrite formation (Drever, 1971a).

However, the most readily utilizable source of iron is adsorbed oxide coatings on clay minerals. This material is abundant, readily accessible, and tends to be unstable because of poor crystallinity and fine grain size (Langmuir and Whittemore, 1972). Several workers have shown that when iron oxide coatings are removed from clay surfaces, previously blocked ion exchange sites are exposed, hence increasing ion exchange capacity of the clay (Carroll, 1958; Carstea, 1968; Kozak and Huang, 1971; Singleton and Harward, 1971; Townsend and Reed, 1971). In discussing porewater chemistry of sediments from the Santa Barbara Basin, Sholkovitz (1972) concluded that uptake of magnesium on clay exchange sites made available by iron oxide removal (associated with pyrite formation) is the mechanism producing observed magnesium depletion in the interstitial water.

Accepting iron oxide coatings on grains as a major source of iron for pyrite formation leads to an additional requirement. A suitable reducing agent must be available to produce ferrous iron from the ferric iron of the oxide phase. Hydrogen sulfide, as well as numerous organic compounds that are (thermodynamically) suitable reductants for ferric iron (Stumm and Morgan, 1970) fulfill this requirement. There is some indication from laboratory studies, for example, that humic acids reduce ferric iron to ferrous (Szilagyi, 1971). Berner (1969b) found experimentally that certain amino acids can act as reducing agents for ferric iron.

The solution of oxide coatings prior to pyrite formation is consistent with the observation that sedimentary pyrite does not occur as coatings on mineral grains (Love, 1967; Sweeney, 1972), as does the iron oxide. Furthermore, Love (1967) noted

TABLE XIV

Degree of Pyritization of Connecticut Coastal Sediments (After Berner, 1970)

Depth (cm)	P^a
Core 1	
0–2	0.10
2–4	0.15
4–6	0.20
6–8	0.21
8–10	0.18
10–12	0.21
14–16	0.28
18–20	0.29
22–24	0.25
26–28	0.29
34–36	0.22
50–52	0.24
Core 2	
0–2	0.30
4–6	0.35
7–9	0.35
12–15	0.34
18–21	0.30
25–28	0.35

[a] See equation 41.

that the occurrence of pyrite within foraminiferal and diatom shells where the pores are distinctly smaller than the contained pyrite framboids implies that iron must have been available in solution. Additional evidence for removal of iron oxide coatings by reduction of this iron is given by Van Andel (1964) who determined the distribution in Gulf of California sediments of "red detrital material," much of which was presumably iron oxide-coated quartz grains. It was concluded that this red pigment is removed by reducing conditions prevalent in fine-grained deep-water sediments.

The role of iron as a possible limiting factor in determining the extent of pyrite formation was evaluated by Berner (1970) in sediment from Long Island Sound. He found there that abundant reactive iron was available and therefore was not limiting to pyrite formation. This is demonstrated in Table XIV, which contains results of a calculation for the degree of pyritization, P, defined by Berner as equation 41:

$$P = \frac{\%\ \text{Fe in pyrite}}{\%\ \text{Fe in pyrite} + \%\ \text{Fe soluble in HCl}} \tag{41}$$

The percent of Fe extractable by acid was estimated by boiling the sediment in 12 N HCl for 1 min. Since pyrite is not soluble in hot 12 N HCl, the acid-soluble fraction gives an estimate of the amount of iron available for further reaction with sulfide. Measured values of P are less than 0.4, indicating incomplete conversion to pyrite of HCl-soluble iron in the sediment.

4. Porewater Chemistry

A. Sulfate Reduction

Probably the first measurements on the chemistry of marine interstitial water were performed by Murray and Irvine (1895). After obtaining blue mud by use of a pail converted into a dredge, Murray and Irvine collected the associated "mud water" by placing the material in a large canvas bag hung from the rigging of their yacht. The water dripping from the bag was stored and chemically analyzed on shore. This analysis revealed that the waters ". . . contain less sulfuric acid than is found in normal seawater." Also noted was the fact that ". . . the alkalinity of the mud waters (evidently due to the presence of carbonates) was increased in a most striking manner when compared with the water overlying the mud, and depended directly upon the chemical changes that had taken place in the seawater salts in the water associated with the blue mud."

It was thus realized at an early date that sulfate removal and associated chemical changes involving the carbonate system are processes occurring in unconsolidated sediments. Subsequent studies have documented the progressive depletion of sulfate ion from porewaters of "reducing" sediments (e.g., Emery and Rittenberg, 1952; Ostroumov, 1953; Sugawara et al., 1953; Kaplan et al., 1963; Berner, 1964a).

Sulfate reduction is not a feature of all marine sediments. A principal controlling factor is the abundance and type of organic matter present (Shishkina, 1964; Strakhov, 1967; Berner, 1970, 1972). Evidence of this has been previously presented in the form of the organic carbon reduced sulfur correlation (Fig. 10) for surface sediment. Gradients in dissolved sulfate over considerable thicknesses of sediment point to continued bacterial reduction in addition to this near-surface activity (Berner, 1972).

Rapid porewater sulfate depletion is typically associated with high organic carbon content. Nissenbaum et al. (1972) found sulfate absent at depths less than 0.5 m in porewaters of cores taken in Saanich Inlet, British Columbia (Table XV) with organic

TABLE XV

Dissolved Sulfate and Organic Carbon Content of Sediments in Saanich Inlet[a]

Depth	SO_4 g/liter	Organic Carbon (%)
Core 1		
0–15	2.20	1.2
40–50	1.10	—
85–100	0.03	—
135–150	0.07	—
175–185	0.03	1.1
Core 2		
0–15	0.13	2.7
75–85	0.02	2.6
150–165	0.05	—
225–235	Trace	2.4
Core 3		
0–10	0.12	3.9
50–60	0.03	—
100–110	0.03	—
150–160	Trace	—
190–200	Trace	3.5
Core 4		
0–15	0.21	4.8
50–65	0.18	4.6
100–110	0.12	1.3
150–160	Trace	3.8
200–210	0.02	5.1
240–250	0.02	4.7

[a] After Nissenbaum et al. (1972).

carbon contents reaching 5%. The very low dissolved sulfate values at the "sediment-water interface" of some of the cores may be due, in part, to loss of the actual surface sediment during coring. Even assuming this to be so, the rapid sedimentation rate in this environment (4 m/1000 yr) (Nissenbaum et al., 1972), implies that sulfate is completely removed from porewaters in times measured in hundreds of years.

In more slowly accumulating sediments with lower organic carbon contents, sulfate reduction may take place over much longer time intervals. Figure 13 is a plot of dissolved sulfate in Site 34 (200 mi west of Cape Mendicino, California) from Leg 5 of the JOIDES Deep Sea Drilling Program. The sulfate data plotted is taken from Manheim et al. (1970) and Presley et al. (1970). It suggests sulfate reduction continues over periods of several million years and to depths of several hundred meters within the sediment column. Holes drilled further offshore (e.g., Site 36) show no sulfate depletion, a result typical of most pelagic sediments. Porewater sulfate gradients intermediate between Saanich Inlet and Site 34 are exhibited by many shelf and basin sediments (e.g., Emery and Rittenberg, 1952; Shishkina, 1958; Kaplan et al., 1963;

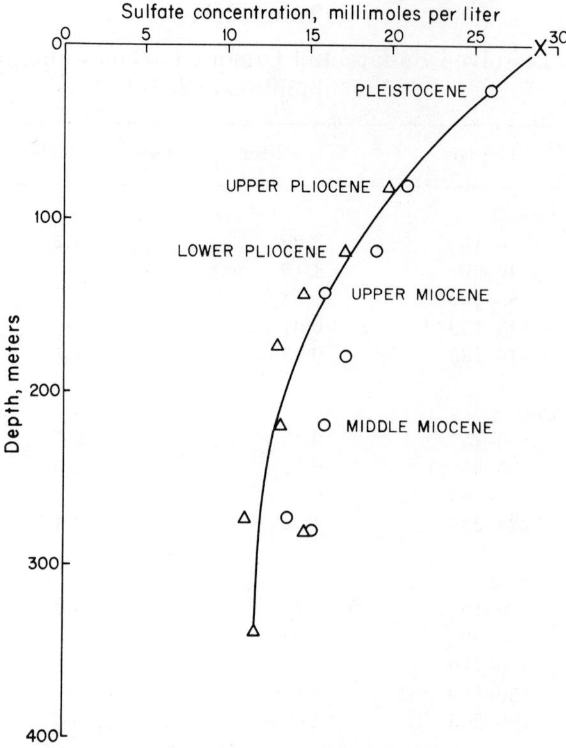

Fig. 13. Sulfate concentration in porewaters from JOIDES site 34. ○ Manheim et al. (1970). △ Presley et al. (1970).

Berner, 1964a; Presley and Kaplan, 1968; Bischoff and Ku, 1971; Rozanov et al., 1971). Shishkina (1958) measured porewater sulfate profiles in several cores from the Sea of Okhotsk (Fig. 14). These data give some indication of the variability possible in a single depositional basin. Organic carbon was also determined on the same cores. Values ranged from about 0.4 to 2% dry weight of sediment, with the higher carbon content corresponding in general to steeper sulfate gradients (see Strakhov, 1967).

The qualitative correlation between organic carbon content and porewater sulfate decrease does not always hold. Some data show sulfate ion remaining relatively constant at near-seawater values in sediments either measured or inferred to contain abundant organic carbon and reduced sulfur. Sholkovitz (1972) studied two cores from the basin floor and one core from the slope in adjacent areas of the Santa Barbara Basin. The sediments contained nearly equal amounts of organic carbon and sedimentary pyrite (Table XVI). Mineralogy and sedimentation rates were comparable, although dissolved oxygen in the overlying waters was higher in the case of the slope sediments. The basin sediments, however, were strongly depleted in porewater sulfate, whereas the slope sediments were not (Fig. 15). An abundance of reduced sulfur in the slope sediments (nearly 0.6% by dry weight S), together with the fact that pyrite is not expected to be a detrital phase (Kaplan et al., 1963) implies that considerable sulfate reduction occurred (but is not reflected in the dissolved sulfate). Similar sulfate- sulfide- organic carbon relationships have been observed in other areas of the Southern California borderland (Kaplan et al., 1963) and in the Gulf of California (Berner 1964a).

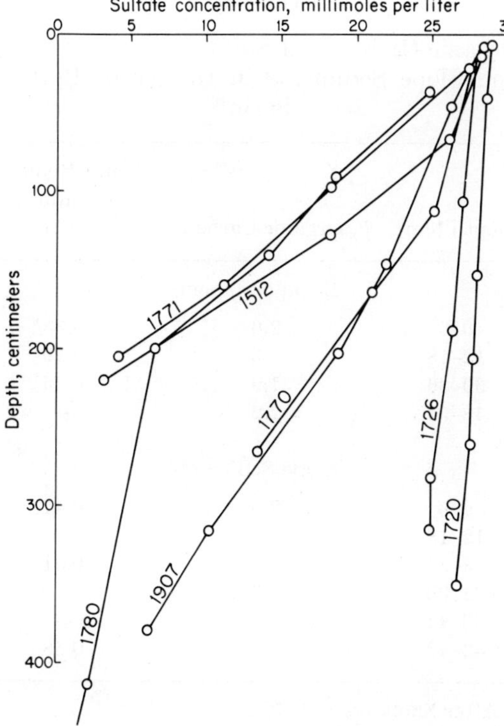

Fig. 14. Sulfate concentration in porewaters of sediments from the Sea of Okhotsk. Data from Shishkina (1958). Numbers designating individual cores are those of Shishkina.

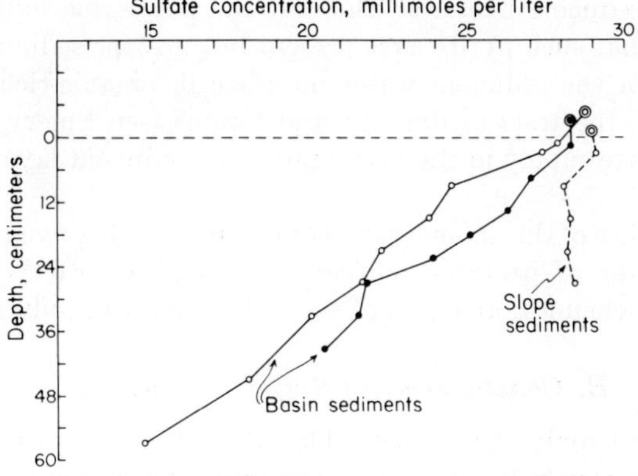

Fig. 15. Sulfate concentration in porewaters of sediments from the vicinity of the Santa Barbara Basin. Data from Sholkovitz (1972). Basin floor and slope sediments are separated by 15 km and have similar mineralogies. ⧫, box core. ϕ, gravity cores.

TABLE XVI

Organic Carbon and Sulfur Content of Basin and Slope Sediments in the Santa Barbara Basin[a]

Depth (cm)	% Organic Carbon	Total Reduced Sulfur (%)
	Basin Sediments	
0–6	2.6	0.35[b]
12–18	2.3	0.50
30–36	1.9	0.35
48–54	2.2	—
	Slope Sediments	
0–6	2.6	0.47
12–18	2.3	—
18–24	—	0.51
24–30	2.2	—
36–42	2.1	—
42–48	—	0.58

[a] After Sholkovitz (1972).
[b] Based on data of Sweeney (unpublished).

Two explanations have been offered for these pyrite-rich sediments with no diminution in porewater sulfate. Berner (1964a) believes that concentration gradients of sulfate (inferred from high pyrite content) may be eliminated by the processes of sedimentation and diffusion when the rate of sulfate reduction decreases, eventually resulting in uniform sulfate profiles at seawater values. Sholkovitz (1972) argues that in the case of the Santa Barbara sediments, higher dissolved oxygen content in the waters overlying the slope sediments as compared to the basin floor results in oxidative metabolism of a reactive portion of the organic matter which would be otherwise available to sulfate-reducing bacteria. This inhibits porewater sulfate reduction. It was further argued that such pyrite as is present in the slope sediments forms in the immediate vicinity of the sediment-water interface in organic-rich "microenvironments" for example, the tests of diatoms and forams (see Emery and Rittenberg, 1952). Dissolved sulfate supply in the very uppermost sediment layers is presumed to be unlimited.

Whatever is the cause of the anomaly, it is apparent that dissolved sulfate is not the most reliable indicator of bacterial sulfate reduction. A better estimate may be obtained from direct chemical analyses of solid phase reduced sulfur.

B. Consequences of Sulfate Reduction

Given an adequate supply of metabolizable substrate under anaerobic conditions, bacterial sulfate reduction will commence. The overall stoichiometry of this process may be schematically indicated by invoking the concept of "average composition" of marine organic matter (Fleming, 1940; Redfield et al., 1963). Richards (1965) has

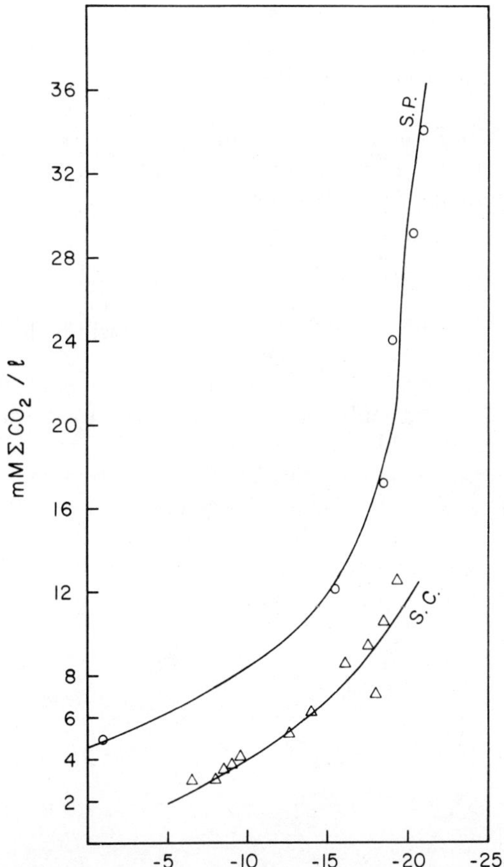

Fig. 16. Change in δC^{13} with respect to the total dissolved CO_2 species in the interstitial water of San Pedro (SP) and Santa Catalina (SC) Basins.

presented a generalized reaction describing combustion of organic carbon with sulfate (equation 42) using such an average composition:

$$\tfrac{1}{53}\,(CH_2O)_{106}(NH_3)_{16}H_3PO_4 + SO_4^{2-} \rightarrow 2\,HCO_3^- + H_2S + \tfrac{16}{53}\,NH_3 + \tfrac{1}{53}\,H_3PO_4 \quad (42)$$

This reaction indicates that several products are released during the oxidation of organic matter by sulfate. For this reason, the consequences of sulfate reduction within sediments reach beyond changes directly related to sulfur compounds. Metabolic products of sulfate-reducing bacteria, for example, are known to influence carbonate equilibria and the pH of porewaters.

Presley and Kaplan (1968) showed that dissolved carbon dioxide (mainly in the form of bicarbonate ion) increases with depth in biologically reactive sediments. This increase is directly related to a decrease in dissolved sulfate content. The source of the CO_2 is organic matter. This is demonstrated by Fig. 16, which shows the change in δC^{13} with increase in dissolved carbon dioxide in two cores taken from the Southern California borderland.[2] Carbon dioxide becomes progressively enriched in the light

[2] $\delta C^{13}\text{‰} = \dfrac{C^{13}/C^{12}\ \text{sample} - C^{13}/C^{12}\ \text{standard}}{C^{13}/C^{12}\ \text{standard}} \times 1000.$

isotope as its concentration increases, reaching a final value of δC^{13} near $-20‰$, approximately equal to the δC^{13} value of organic matter in marine sediments (Degens, 1965). For comparison, the solid carbonate in these sediments was found to be about 0‰.

If the reactive portion of organic matter in sediments can be considered to have the oxidation state of carbohydrate, bacterial reduction of sulfate will follow the stoichiometry of reaction 42. Omitting the nitrogen and phosphorus components, the reaction may be written:

$$2\,[CH_2O] + SO_4{}^{2-} \rightarrow 2\,HCO_3{}^{-} + H_2S \tag{43}$$

Electroneutrality requires a shifting of negative charge, as sulfate reduction progresses from a species not involved in equilibria with protons (i.e., sulfate ion)[3] to anions of weak acids, such as bicarbonate ion. This will increase titration alkalinity; defined as the amount of strong acid in equivalents necessary to titrate all of the anions of carbonic and weaker acids in 1 kg of water (Skirrow, 1965; Edmond, 1970). Reactions 42 or 43 will lead to an increase of 2 meq of alkalinity per kilogram of solution for each millimole of sulfate reduced. The alkalinity produced by sulfate reduction has been written in equation 43 as being held by the bicarbonate ion, although in the pH range 7 to 8 typical of porewaters part of the alkalinity will be held by the bisulfide ion, HS^-. Figure 17 (from Goldhaber and Kaplan, 1973) shows the relative propor-

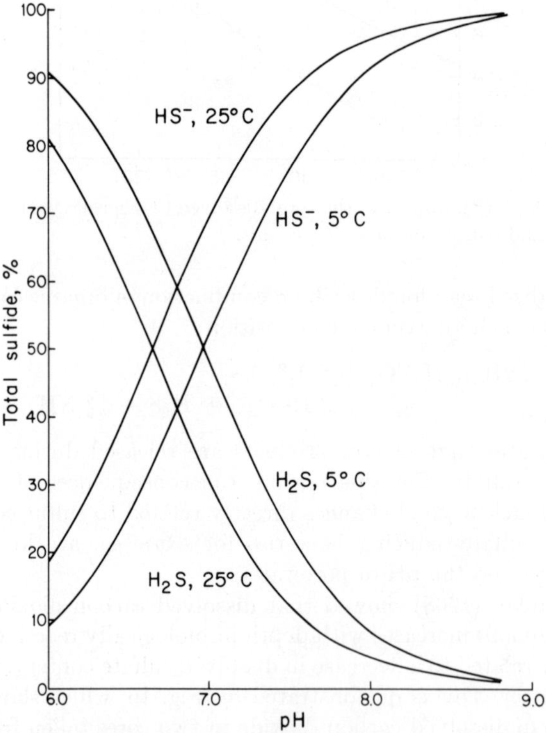

Fig. 17. Percentages of dissolved hydrogen sulfide (H_2S) and dissolved bisulfide ion (HS^-) in seawater of 18.8‰ Cl at two temperatures.

[3] The bisulfate ion, $HSO_4{}^-$, may be considered to be insignificant in the pH range of porewaters.

tions of bisulfide ion and hydrogen sulfide present in seawater of 18.8‰ chlorinity as a function of pH. Bisulfide ion represents 50 to 90% of the total sulfide between pH 7 to 8 at 5°C. Dissolved sulfide, however, is removed preferentially to the solid phase by reaction with iron. Berner et al. (1970) argued that removal of sulfide by reaction with iron oxide (or hydrous iron oxide) does not affect alkalinity.

$$6\,[CH_2O] + 3\,SO_4^{2-} \rightarrow 3\,HCO_3^- + 3\,H_2CO_3 + 3\,HS^- \quad (44)$$

$$H_2O + HS^- + 2\,FeO\cdot OH \rightarrow 2\,Fe^{2+} + S^0 + 5\,OH^- \quad (45)$$

$$2\,Fe^{2+} + S^0 + 2\,HS^- \rightarrow FeS + FeS_2 + 2\,H^+ \quad (46)$$

$$3\,H_2CO_3 + 3\,OH^- \rightarrow 3\,HCO_3^- + 3\,H_2O \quad (47)$$

$$2\,FeO\cdot OH + 6\,[CH_2O] + 3\,SO_4^{2-} \rightarrow 6\,HCO_3^- + FeS + FeS_2 + 4\,H_2O \quad (48)$$

Equation 48 yields the same result with respect to alkalinity as when iron sulfide precipitation was not explicitly included (equation 43). This is not a general result for all sources of iron, but arises because an intermediate step, the reduction of iron oxide, produces hydroxide ion (Bostrom, 1967), which offsets the alkalinity lost when the sulfide ion is precipitated.

Increase in alkalinity in a given porewater sample is not only a result of sulfate reduction, although this is the predominant alkalinity modifying process during early diagenesis. Berner et al. (1970) recognized three additional reactions affecting alkalinity and proposed a closed system model relating those reactions.

Calcium carbonate precipitation reduces alkalinity by removing carbonate ion (Skirrow, 1965). This process may be traced through the depletion of dissolved calcium with respect to its seawater concentration. For each millimole of calcium removed per liter, 2 meq of alkalinity are removed. Precipitation is induced by the buildup of bicarbonate (and carbonate) ions resulting from sulfate reduction (Berner, 1966; Presley and Kaplan, 1968). Although calcium depletions occur in porewaters, implying that some $CaCO_3$ has formed (Presley and Kaplan, 1968; Sholkovitz, 1972), carbonate precipitation during early diagenesis is apparently hindered to some extent by the presence of magnesium ion (e.g., Weyl, 1967) and the presence of protective organic coatings (Chave, 1965; Chave and Suess, 1967; Smith et al., 1968). This inhibition may lead to large supersaturations with respect to calcite (Presley and Kaplan, 1968; Berner, 1970).

Liberation of ammonia by hydrolysis of basic nitrogen compounds (equation 49) leads to an increase in alkalinity (reaction 50) of 1 meq for each millimole of ammonium ion formed:

$$CH_2NH_2COOH + 2\,(H) \rightarrow NH_3 + CH_4 + CO_2 \quad (49)$$

$$NH_3 + CO_2 + H_2O \rightarrow NH_4^+ + HCO_3^- \quad (50)$$

Finally, authigenic silicate formation, if occurring, may be linked to removal of alkalinity by the "reverse weathering" reaction (Garrels and Mackenzie, 1971; Berner, 1970). These reactions may be monitored through changes in potassium or magnesium (equation 51):

$$3\,Al_2Si_2O_5(OH)_4 + 2\,K^+ + 2\,HCO_3^- \rightarrow 2\,KAl_3Si_3O_{10}(OH)_2 + 2\,CO_2 + 5\,H_2O \quad (51)$$

Berner et al. (1970) obtained good agreement in the sediments studied between measured titration alkalinity and that predicted by sulfate reduction and ammonium ion formation (Fig. 18). Calcium, potassium, and magnesium concentration changes were minor, such that no rigorous test of their role in alkalinity modification was possible in the porewaters studied. Sholkovitz (1972) applied a similar alkalinity balance to porewaters in which both calcium and magnesium were depleted with respect to their seawater values. He found that sulfate reduction plus ammonia formation, together with calcium carbonate precipitation, explained the observed alkalinity. Magnesium was not associated with an alkalinity shift.

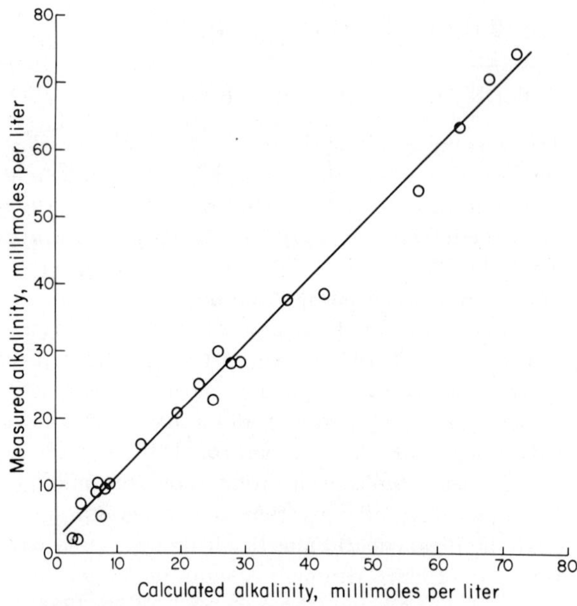

Fig. 18. Plot of titration alkalinity versus alkalinity predicted by taking into account sulfate reduction (equation 43) and ammonia generation (equation 50). After Berner et al. (1970).

C. *pH Buffering*

The majority of pH values measured in porewaters are in the narrow band of 6.9 to 8.2, despite the fact that the seawater initially buried is poorly buffered. It may be shown, however, that constraining the molar ratios of by-products of sulfate reduction in a manner consistent with the average composition of marine organic matter (equation 42) leads to pH values in the required range (Thorstenson, 1970; Nissenbaum et al., 1972; Ben-Yaakov, 1973).

If all sulfate is reduced from a given parcel of porewater, and the products remain in solution, the resulting total concentrations of CO_2, H_2S, and NH_4^+ will be 0.054, 0.027, and 0.008 M, respectively (equation 42). The pH of such a solution was calculated (with additional restriction of charge balance) to be 7.0 (Nissenbaum et al., 1972). Ben-Yaakov (1973) presented a more general discussion. Figure 19 (after Ben-Yaakov, 1973) shows the calculated changes in porewater pH for a progressive depletion of sulfate acting on the same composition of organic matter as in equation 42. The resulting pH is dependent on the amount of dissolved sulfide remaining in solution. Three curves are drawn for different quantities of sulfide remaining in solution.

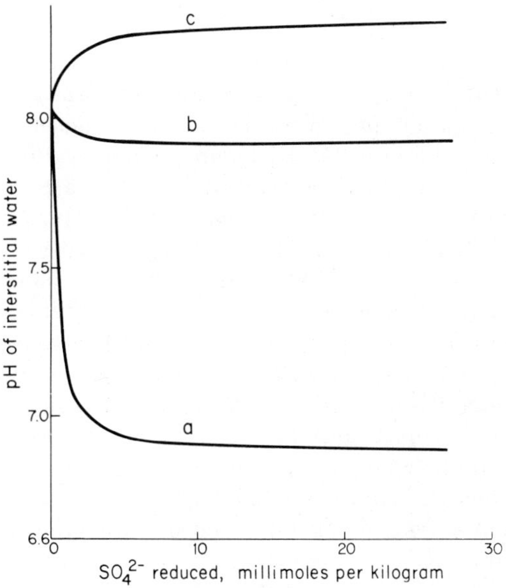

Fig. 19. Predicted pH of porewater of anoxic marine sediments as a function of the amount of sulfate reduced, for different sulfide concentrations: $\sum H_2S = -\Delta SO_4^{2-}$ (curve *a*), $\sum H_2S = -0.2\Delta SO_4^{2-}$ (curve *b*), $\sum H_2S = 0$ (curve *c*). After Ben-Yaakov (1973).

Curve *a* is calculated for the case where all the sulfide produced remains in solution and yields a final pH of 6.9. The result of partial sulfide removal (assumed to be by reaction with iron oxide) is to drive the pH higher (curve *b*). Eventually, if no sulfide remains (curve *c*), the maximum pH attained is 8.3. Curve *a* may be compared to the data of Thorstenson and Mackenzie (1971) (Table XVII), who experimentally decomposed algae in seawater and followed resulting chemical changes with time. The alkalinity has been recalculated as titration alkalinity minus ammonium ion concentration and is equal to twice sulfate reduced in millimoles per liter. It may be seen that the pH rapidly approaches a value near 6.9 as predicted.

Table XVII

Change in pH During Experimental Decomposition of Algae[a]

Time (days)	Alkalinity[b] (millimoles/liter)	pH
1	2.7	7.5
30	4.0	7.0
90	7.1	6.7
150	7.8	6.8

[a] After Thorstenson and Mackenzie (1971).
[b] Titration alkalinity minus ammonia concentration.

D. Dissolved Sulfide

As discussed previously, titration alkalinity provides a convenient measure of the extent of sulfate reduction. A 2 : 1 ratio is expected between titration alkalinity and aqueous sulfide concentration provided that ammonia generation and carbonate precipitation are accounted for separately. Figure 20, modified from Thorstenson and Mackenzie (1971), is a plot of total dissolved sulfide ($H_2S + HS^-$) versus "corrected" titration alkalinity (alkalinity minus ammonia concentration) for sediment from Devil's Hole, Bermuda. The data are averaged over several cores with the variability between samples shown as a circle. Indicated on the same figure is the theoretical relationship for closed-system sulfate reduction. The sediments are dominantly fine-grained carbonate, with no solid iron sulfide present (Thorstenson and Mackenzie, 1971), as the necessary iron is unavailable for reaction. Dissolved sulfide is not being extensively removed and it is not surprising that the 2 : 1 relationship is approached. Correction for calcium carbonate precipitation (if any) would improve the agreement between theoretical and observed values.

In more typical sediments containing abundant detrital iron, available data show dissolved sulfide present at significantly lower concentration than simple mass balance calculation would predict (Kaplan et al., 1963; Berner, 1964a; Hartmann and Nielsen, 1969; Rozanov et al., 1971; Nissenbaum et al., 1972). Figure 21 illustrates this with data obtained from Gulf of California sediments (Berner, 1964a). The maximum sulfide concentration attained (7.4 mM at 110 cm) is 33% of the closed-system amount of sulfate reduced. This latter quantity is the difference in concentration between seawater sulfate and the sulfate at 110 cm. Inspection of published data in the references previously cited indicates that 30% is near the maximum percentage of sulfide remaining in solution in nearshore sedimentary environments. Because of diffusive flow of sulfate into the sediment, it is likely that the actual amount of sulfate reduced is larger than the closed-system amount.

An interesting feature observed in many dissolved sulfide analyses is the presence

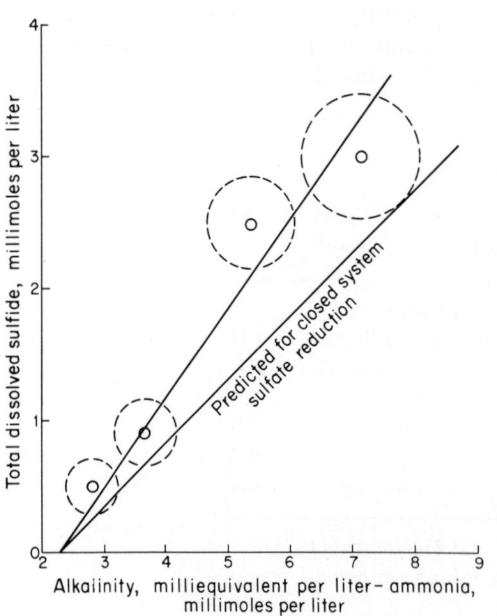

Fig. 20. Relationship between dissolved H_2S and titration alkalinity in pore-waters of sediments from Devil's Hole, Bermuda. Titration alkalinity has been corrected for ammonium ion formation. Data represents the average of several cores at depths of about 20, 40, 60, and 80 cm (left to right in the figure). Dashed circles represent variability between cores. The theoretical relationship is that given in equation 43. Modified from Thorstenson and Mackenzie (1971).

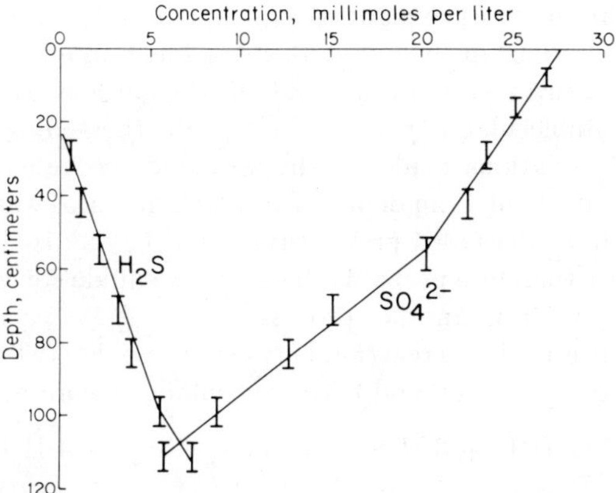

Fig. 21. Concentrations of sulfate and sulfide in porewaters of a core from the Gulf of California. After Berner (1964a).

in the surface layers of a zone in which dissolved sulfide is below limits of detection, despite indications of sulfate reduction such as depletion of porewater sulfate and the presence of pyrite sulfur. This is the case for the data plotted in Fig. 21, as well as the data of Rozanov et al. (1971), and is also true for the upper layers of the Santa Barbara Basin (Fig. 22). These data were obtained from porewater from a box core made available to us by Dr. Sholkovitz. Sulfate data from this core has previously been presented (Fig. 15). Dissolved sulfide measured by the sensitive colorimetric technique of Cline (1969) was less than the detection limit of 2×10^{-6} M in the upper 9 cm, although solid sulfides (acid-volatile and pyrite) were found to be abundant (Table XXIII). The fact that this zone is so thin (i.e., 9 cm) implies that it may not be observed by using sampling techniques, such as piston coring, which may lose

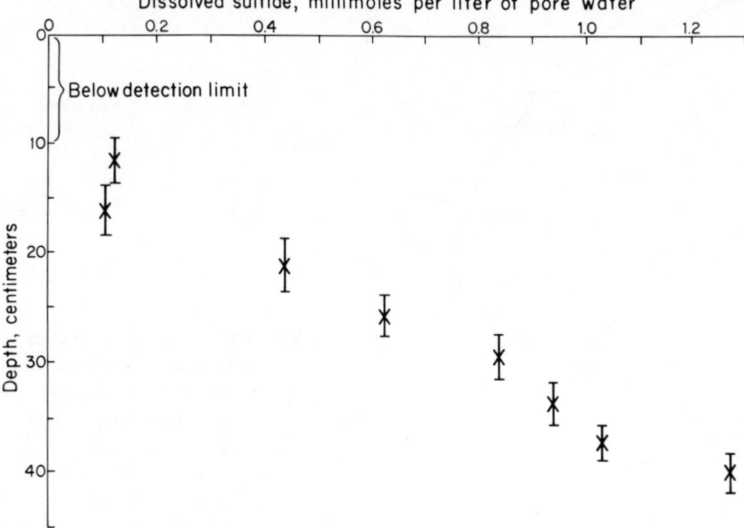

Fig. 22. Concentration of dissolved sulfide in porewater of a box core from the Santa Barbara Basin.

surface sediment. This perhaps explains why Kaplan et al. (1963) found dissolved sulfide present to the surface in the Santa Barbara Basin in an earlier study.

The absence of measurable dissolved sulfide in the surface layers may in part be due to oxidation by molecular oxygen diffusing into the sediment from overlying waters. However, observations made on the sediments revealed a color transition from orange to black at about 1 cm depth. This black material was shown to be acid-volatile sulfide, which, as discussed previously, would be oxidized in the presence of molecular oxygen. It is therefore probable that the low sulfide concentrations between 1 and 9 cm depth results from another process.

The most feasible alternative is reaction between iron oxide (which is the dominant source of iron in many sediments) and hydrogen sulfide, according to equation 52:

$$2\,FeO\cdot OH_s + 3\,H_2S_{aq} \rightleftharpoons 2\,FeS_S + S_S{}^0 + 4\,H_2O \tag{52}$$

Assuming excess of solid phases, the equilibrium constant describing this reaction is (53):

$$K = \frac{1}{[H_2S]^3} \tag{53}$$

If equilibrium is attained, the hydrogen sulfide concentration will be buffered between 10^{-6}–10^{-8} M by this reaction (Berner, 1969b). This range is associated with the range in free energy values, which may be assigned to the iron oxide phase. Berner suggests that iron oxide in the upper zone, which is free of dissolved sulfide, is "titrated" by addition of sulfide (equation 52), and the concentration of dissolved sulfide will not increase until "reactive" iron oxide is converted to iron sulfide.

The Santa Barbara Basin has a very low concentration of dissolved oxygen in the bottom waters as well as a high content of organic carbon in the sediments (Emery,

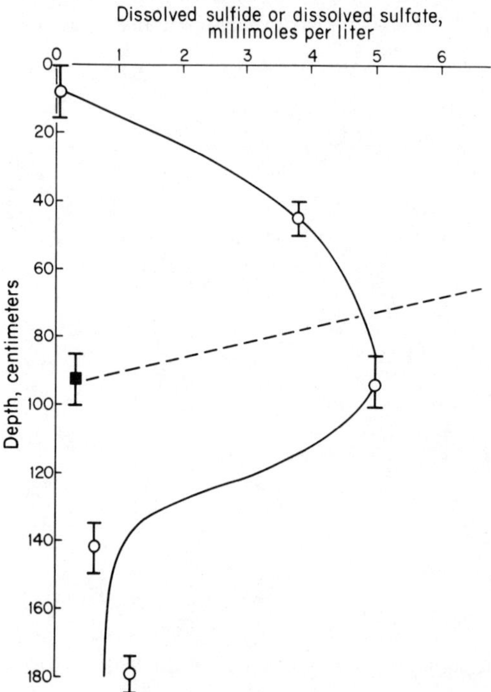

Fig. 23. Concentrations of sulfate and sulfide in porewaters of a core from Saanich Inlet, British Columbia. ■, sulfate. ○, sulfide. Dashed line represents extrapolated sulfate. Note that as the sulfate concentration approaches zero, at 90 cm depth, the sulfide concentration exhibits a maximum, and below this depth decreases. Data from Nissenbaum et al. (1972).

1960), both of which are conducive to the rapid onset of sulfate reduction. It would be expected that the rate of sulfide generation, and consequently, the rate of titration of iron oxide, is more rapid in these sediments than in many other environments. The existence of a dissolved sulfide-free upper layer in the Santa Barbara Basin may, therefore, argue for similar layers as a common feature of other biologically active shelf and basin sediments. This will not hold true, however, in fjords and some landlocked seas that contain dissolved sulfide in the water column.

Equation 53 only holds at equilibrium. If the reaction of iron oxides with sulfide is much more rapid than the rate of addition of sulfide, the expression will still be valid. As discussed previously, iron oxides exhibit a range of reactivities toward dissolved sulfide. The most reactive oxide presumably is removed rapidly to form iron sulfide, leaving progressively more refractory materials behind. Eventually, the sulfide addition rate may overtake the removal rate. This is the depth at which dissolved sulfide begins accumulating. Other sources of iron besides oxides are also present in the sediment and some sulfide removal may proceed by reaction with these materials.

Because iron is so abundant in most sediments, reaction of sulfide with the sediment could continue at all depths at which sulfide is present. Direct evidence supporting this is available from the data of Nissenbaum et al. (1972) from a fjord, Saanich Inlet, in British Columbia. At the depth where sulfate is no longer present in the porewaters (and therefore no more sulfide can be generated), the sulfide concentration exhibits a maximum, and below this depth decreases (Fig. 23). If sulfide was not reacting with the sediment, no change in sulfide concentration would be observed following the cessation of sulfate reduction. Sulfate reduction in this case is more rapid than sulfide removal over the interval in which sulfate is present. This is not a general relationship, however, as shown for data in Fig. 24, which we obtained during the Hypogene Expedition of Scripps Institution of Oceanography to the Gulf of California (1972). It depicts dissolved H_2S (measured colorimetrically) and dissolved sulfate from a core in the North Pescadero Basin. Dissolved sulfide attains a maximum of only 5×10^{-5} M at 0.5 m depth and is completely absent at 1 m, despite the fact that sulfate

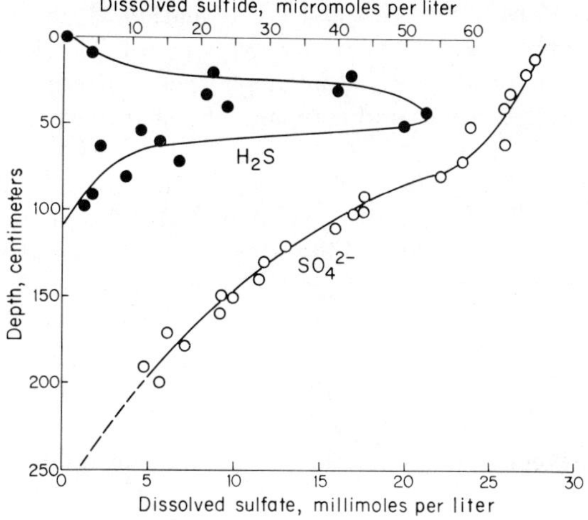

Fig. 24. Concentrations of sulfate and sulfide in porewaters of a core from the Gulf of California. Note that the maximum sulfide concentration attained is only 54 micromolar. Below 1 m, sulfide is not present, although sulfate reduction is continuing as evidenced by continuing sulfate depletion.

reduction is active over 2 m of sediment thickness. Scatter in the data may in part be due to difficulty in analyzing such low sulfide concentrations. Other cores from the Gulf of California (Goldhaber and Kaplan, unpublished results) show results similar to those of both Figs. 23 and 24. Maxima in dissolved sulfide have been reported for the Santa Barbara Basin (Kaplan et al., 1963) and the continental slope of the Northwest Pacific Ocean (Rozanov et al., 1971).

It is concluded that sulfide rapidly reacts by "titration" of iron oxide in the uppermost sediment layers, and that sulfide continues to react at a reduced rate at depth.

F. Open-System Model

The depletion of sulfate with depth in a sediment gives rise to a concentration gradient. As a result, sulfate will flow by diffusion producing a flux, which under steady-state conditions may be calculated using Fick's first law (equation 54):

$$J_D = -D_i \frac{\partial ci}{\partial X} \tag{54}$$

where J_D = the diffusive flux of the ith species in mol/cm²/sec.
Di = whole sediment diffusion coefficient for the ith species in $cm^2\ sec^{-1}$; assumed constant
ci = concentration of the ith species in porewaters in mol/cm^3
X = depth in sediments in cm (positive X directed down)

This equation holds for the isothermal diffusion of an uncharged species (or the diffusion of a constituent present in trace amounts). For an electrolyte such as seawater, the flux of a given ion will be modified by the existence of diffusion-induced electrical forces (Vinograd and McBain, 1941; Robinson and Stokes, 1970). The diffusion of salts from seawater into dilute solution, for example, has been shown to result in the generation of a potential gradient (Ben-Yaakov, 1972a). This modifies the fluxes of ions with respect to those predicted in the absence of the gradient by about −20% for chloride, +20% for divalent cations, and +10% for univalent cations. Kemper and Van Schaik (1966) found the effects due to such electrical forces to cause 25% deviations from Fick's first law (equation 54) for diffusion of NaCl and $CaCl_2$ through clay plugs. For calculations involving diffusion in sediments, however, other uncertainties may at present outweigh those introduced by neglecting the presence of electrical potential gradients, and the latter have been omitted in most diffusion calculations.

Several discussions of diffusion coefficients in sediments are available in the literature of geochemistry (Duursma, 1966; Manheim, 1970; Berner, 1971; Golubev and Garibyants, 1971), as well as the soil literature (e.g., Olsen and Kemper, 1968). The decrease in the magnitude of the diffusion coefficient due to purely physical properties of the sediment may be expressed (Berner, 1971b) by equation 55:

$$D_i = \frac{Do}{\theta^2} \tag{55}$$

The diffusion coefficient in free solution, Do, is modified by the tortuosity, θ, defined by equation 56:

$$\theta = \frac{dl}{dX} \tag{56}$$

where dl is the length of the actual sinous diffusion path over a distance, dX. Tortuosity increases with depth and thus, Di will decrease. For many ions, Do is about 10^{-5} cm^2/sec and therefore, $Di \leqslant 10^{-5}$.

Specific chemical reactions between diffusing ions and sediment particles further reduce diffusive fluxes. In clay-rich sediments, these reactions include ion exchange. This is expected to be a more important process for cations than anions, and more important for divalent than univalent cations.

Of particular interest in describing the process of sulfur diagenesis is the diffusion coefficient of the sulfate ion. At infinite dilution in water, the diffusion coefficient may be calculated from the limiting equivalent conductivity given by Robinson and Stokes (1970). This value is 1.1×10^{-5} cm^2/sec at 25°C and is reduced to 0.5×10^{-5} cm^2/sec at 0°C. Using a concentration cell to measure liquid junction potentials between seawater and modified seawater, Ben-Yaakov (1972b) determined that charged sulfate ion pairs (i.e., $NaSO_4^-$) have a very much lower mobility than free sulfate ions. Such ion pairs represent nearly 40% of the total dissolved sulfate, according to the Garrels and Thompson (1962) seawater model. The effective diffusion coefficient of sulfate in seawater will therefore be diminished as compared to pure water (Ben-Yaakov, 1972b). Only one experimental value has been reported for $D_{SO_4^{2-}}$ in porous media. Duursma (1966) measured 0.3×10^{-5} cm^2/sec for the diffusion coefficient of sulfate in clean fine sand at 20°C. Berner (1964d) estimated from modeling the dissolved sulfate profile in Santa Barbara Basin sediments that $D_{SO_4^{2-}}$ is 0.3×10^{-5} cm^2/sec.

Despite some uncertainty in picking a unique value for $D_{SO_4^{2-}}$, it is possible to compare the relative importance of diffusion in two sedimentary columns that differ in sedimentation rate and gradients in dissolved species. Consider a sediment column building up from a fixed basement. If the concentration profile of porewater sulfate is maintained as a steady-state feature, then sulfate will be continuously diffusing into the sediments (equation 54) at the same time it is biologically reduced. In addition, sulfate will be trapped by the accumulating sediment within the pore spaces. The ratio R of sulfate added by sedimentation, to the total sulfate transported across the (moving) sediment-water interface by diffusion plus sedimentation, is a measure of the relative importance of diffusion (equation 57):

$$R = \frac{W[SO_4^{2-}]_0}{-D\left(\frac{\partial[SO_4^{2-}]}{\partial X}\right)_{X=0} + W[SO_4^{2-}]_0} \tag{57}$$

where W is the sedimentation rate (cm/sec) and $[SO_4^{2-}]_0$ is the seawater sulfate concentration (mol/cm^3).

It can be seen that for a fixed sulfate gradient, R will approach unity as the sedimentation rate becomes very large. In this extreme, diffusion would be of relatively small importance in transporting sulfate across the sediment-water interface. On the other hand, as R decreases, diffusion becomes relatively more important. Equation 57 may be applied to a depth in the sediment column beneath the sediment-water interface (defined as $X = 0$). This may be appropriate in cases of highly porous (>90% porosity) upper sediment layers that more closely resemble seawater than underlying sediment in their properties.

Table XVIII contains results of calculations of the quantity R made for Site 34 of the Deep Sea Drilling Project (JOIDES) and the Santa Barbara Basin off the Southern California coast. For Site 34, an estimate was made of the sedimentation rate in the vicinity of the upper layers using the sedimentation rate over the interval 25 to 80 m

TABLE XVIII

Relative Importance of Diffusion in Transporting Sulfate Across the Sediment-Water Interface

10^6 D_{SO_4} (cm^2/sec)	Santa Barbara Basin R[a]	JOIDES Hole 34 R[a]
1	0.46	0.79
2	0.30	0.65
3	0.22	0.56
5	0.14	0.43

[a] See text for discussion.

(based on age measurements of McManus et al., 1970) and a porosity of 0.75 over this interval (McManus et al., 1970). The porosity of the surface sediments is assumed to be 0.85. The initial sedimentation rate, Wo, may be obtained by a modification of an equation given by Berner (1971b):

$$Wo = W_{25_m}\left(\frac{1}{1 - 0.85}\right) \Big/ \left(\frac{1}{1 - 0.75}\right) \tag{58}$$

For $W_{25} = 0.76 \times 10^{-10}$ cm/sec, Wo is 1.3×10^{-10} cm/sec. The initial sulfate gradient is obtained from fitting the sulfate data (Fig. 12) to an exponential function:

$$[SO_4^{2-}] = (28.2 \times 10^{-6}) \exp(-\lambda X) \tag{59}$$

with $\lambda = 3.4 \times 10^{-5}$/cm, the initial gradient obtained by differentiating equation 59 with respect to X and solving for $X = 0$, is 0.96×10^{-9} mol/cm^4.

The derived values for R for Santa Barbara Basin sediments (Table XIX) were calculated for 15 cm depth in the core using sedimentation rate data of Koide et al., 1972. Porewater sulfate data has been presented previously (Fig. 14), and a linear gradient was assumed.

Comparison of the calculated values of R for the same value of $D_{SO_4^{2-}}$ in Table XVIII show that diffusion is relatively more important in the Santa Barbara Basin than for Site 34, a result that would still hold if no correction were made for initial sedimentation rate in Hole 34. In the Santa Barbara Basin, the rate of sulfate reduction (and hence the sulfate gradient) has increased more rapidly than has sulfate addition by sedimentation, when both are compared to Site 34. Therefore, high sedimentation rate by itself does not imply that diffusion will be unimportant with respect to sedimentation in transporting sulfate across the sediment-water interface. High organic carbon contents are known to be associated with rapid sedimentation rates, which protect the organic compounds from extensive aerobic combustion at the sediment-water interface (Price and Calvert, 1970; Riley and Chester, 1971; Berner, 1972). As discussed previously, high carbon content may lead to more rapid disappearance of porewater sulfate.

G. Diffusion Reaction Models

The maintenance of a concentration gradient in the presence of gradient-lowering processes, such as diffusion and sedimentation, requires that sulfate be continuously removed. The relationship among addition and removal processes may be described for sulfate through the use of the continuity equation (Berner, 1964c, 1971b, 1972; Tzur, 1971). At steady state, this equation may be written:

$$pD\frac{\partial^2 S}{\partial X^2} - Wp_\infty \frac{\partial S}{\partial X} - R(X) = 0 \tag{60}$$

where p is the porosity (assumed constant) in the zone of sulfate reduction, D is the diffusion coefficient of sulfate (assumed independent of depth), S is the sulfate concentration in moles per cubic centimeter porewater, W is the sedimentation rate (deposition minus compaction) in centimeters per second at a depth where porosity has reached a constant value of p_∞, and R is the rate at which sulfate is removed. The nature of the solution to equation 60 will depend on the form chosen for the reaction term R. Berner has developed sulfate reduction models using both zero-order and first-order (with respect to sulfate) reaction terms. The model involving zero-order sulfate reduction is presented here, although at low sulfate concentrations, the rate may become first order (see Section 1). In the zero-order case (Berner, 1964d), R is assumed independent of sulfate concentration, but is proportional to concentration of metabolizable carbon C (moles per cubic centimeter porewater) (equation 61):

$$R = Lk^\circ \mathrm{C} \tag{61}$$

where L is a stoichiometric factor relating moles of carbon to moles of sulfur and k° is the rate constant. Metabolizable carbon, in turn, is assumed to be exponentially distributed with depth according to equation 62, where V is the attenuation factor (cm^{-1}):

$$L\mathrm{C} = \overline{\mathrm{C}o}e^{-VX} \tag{62}$$

$$R = k^\circ\overline{\mathrm{C}o}e^{-VX} \tag{63}$$

The quantity $\overline{\mathrm{C}o}$ includes the stoichiometric factor $L(=\frac{1}{2})$, relating moles of carbon utilized to moles of sulfate reduced (equation 43). The solution of equation 60 with the zero-order reaction term (equation 63) is given by Tzur (1971), for the boundary conditions that (1) concentration of sulfate (S) remain finite as $X \to \infty$ and (2) $\mathrm{S} = \mathrm{S}^\circ$ at $X = 0$.

$$\mathrm{S} = (\mathrm{S}o - \mathrm{S}f)e^{-VX} + \mathrm{S}f \tag{64}$$

where

$$\mathrm{S}o - \mathrm{S}f = \frac{k^\circ\overline{\mathrm{C}o}}{pDV^2 + Wp_\infty V} \tag{65}$$

So and Sf are the initial and final sulfate concentrations, respectively. Equations of this type were applied by Berner to the data of Kaplan et al. (1963) from the Santa Barbara Basin. The sulfate and organic carbon results are reproduced in Figs. 25 and 26, respectively. The curve drawn through the sulfate concentration profile (Fig. 25) has the same form as equation 64 with the parameters:

$$\mathrm{S}o = 27 \times 10^{-6}\ \mathrm{mol/cm^3}$$
$$\mathrm{S}f = 8 \times 10^{-6}\ \mathrm{mol/cm^3}$$
$$V = 0.015/\mathrm{cm}$$

A special case of equations 64 and 65 is when $V = k^\circ/W$. This occurs when sulfate

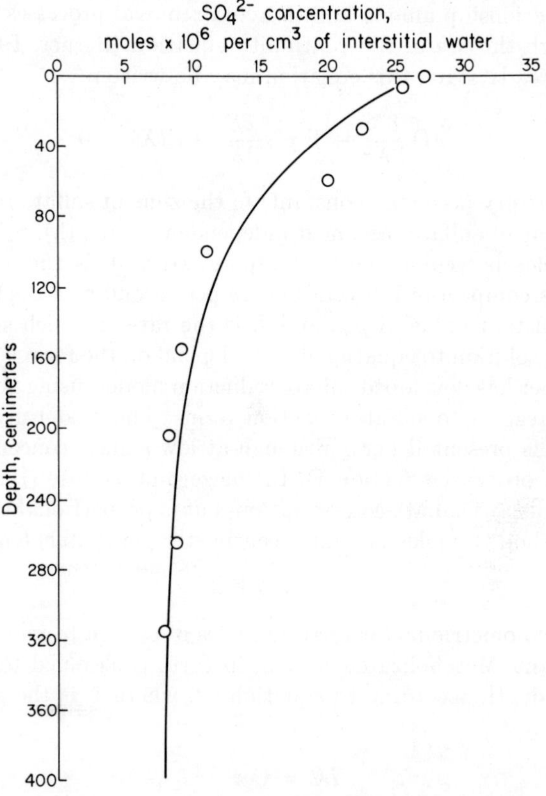

Fig. 25. Sulfate concentration in porewaters of sediments from the Santa Barbara Basin. Data from Kaplan et al. (1963). The curve drawn through the points is given by equation 64 with the parameters $So = 27 \times 10^{-6}$ mol/cm³, $Sf = 8 \times 10^{-6}$ mol/cm³, $V = 0.015$/cm. After Berner (1964d).

reduction is the only process destroying metabolizable organic matter. Making this assumption, equation 65 becomes:

$$\mathrm{S}o - \mathrm{S}f = \frac{\overline{\mathrm{C}o}\,W^2}{pDk^\circ + W^2 p_\infty} \tag{66}$$

or

$$D = \frac{\overline{\mathrm{C}o}\,W^2 - p_\infty W^2(\mathrm{S}o - \mathrm{S}f)}{(\mathrm{S}o - \mathrm{S}f)pk^\circ} \tag{67}$$

Using a measured value of $W = 5 \times 10^{-9}$ cm/sec, k° may be calculated to be 7.5×10^{-11}/sec, by applying the value of V obtained from fitting the sulfate profile. Substituting this value, 0.8 for p, 0.5 for p_∞, and the values of So and Sf in equation 67, one obtains:

$$D = \overline{\mathrm{C}o}2.3 \times 10^{-2} - 0.2 \times 10^{-6} \tag{68}$$

This equation emphasizes the dependence of the calculated diffusion coefficient on the parameter $\overline{\mathrm{C}o}$, which must be independently estimated. Berner (1964c) picked $\overline{\mathrm{C}o}$

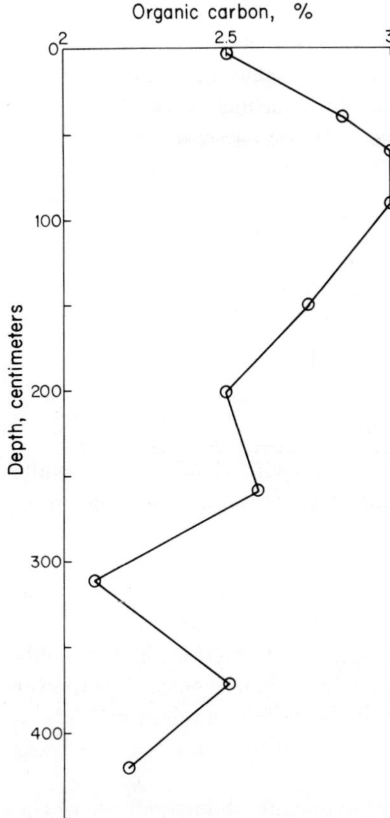

Fig. 26. Organic carbon in Santa Barbara Basin sediments. After Kaplan et al. (1963).

to be the difference between the values for the average total organic carbon concentration near the surface and at the 315 cm level (Fig. 26). This difference is about 1% carbon by dry weight sediment, or $\overline{Co}$ is 1.3×10^{-4} mol/cc of porewater (0.13 mol/liter) and D is calculated to be 3×10^{-6} cm^2/sec.

Setting $\overline{Co}$ equal to 0.13 mol/liter requires that at great depth in the core (i.e., large X), 0.13 mol of sulfate per liter of porewater would have been reduced. This follows from integration of the rate expression (equation 63), after substituting $k°/W$ for V (Berner, 1972). As the initial porewater sulfate concentration is about 0.03 mol/liter, more than four times the initial amount of sulfate must have diffused into the sediments by the time all metabolizable organic carbon has reacted. Because the H_2S so formed is in part free to diffuse toward the sediment-water interface (see below), an amount of pyrite sulfur corresponding to the amount of sulfate reduced may not be formed in the sediment (Berner, personal communication).

It has been stressed that this model is sensitive to the choice of $\overline{Co}$. Inspection of Fig. 26 indicates that the major depletion in organic carbon occurs below 1 m, whereas the major portion of sulfate reduction occurs above 1 m. This is inconsistent with the assumptions of the model, which predict the most rapid carbon decrease at the sediment surface and may indicate nonsteady-state diagenesis. Organic carbon distributions in the Santa Barbara Basin sediments, which do approximate the expected exponential decrease, have been presented previously (Table XVI). A similar carbon decrease is found in adjacent "basin" and "slope" sediments. As the slope sediments show no gradient in dissolved sulfate (Fig. 14), diffusion is unlikely in this case. The agreement between the two carbon distributions, if it is not fortuitous, may therefore in part indicate a change in depositional conditions with time and not continuing sulfate reduction. It may therefore be possible that the appropriate value of $\overline{Co}$ for use in equation 68 is less than 1% organic carbon and D is smaller than 3×10^{-6} cm^2/sec. Sulfur isotopic evidence is presented below, which suggests that this is the case.

Berner (1972) points out that the initial rate of sulfate reduction (at $X = 0$) calculated from his model is lower than the rate estimated for the same sediments by Kaplan et al. (1963) from the measured pyrite content and sedimentation rate. He explains this discrepancy as abundance of easily decomposable organic matter near the sediment-water interface that can be readily utilized by sulfate-reducing bacteria, thus enabling high metabolic rates and rapid pyrite formation.

H. Diffusion of Sulfide

Many sediments show an increase in dissolved sulfide with depth. As a result, sulfide should diffuse toward the sediment-water interface. This process, depending on its magnitude, might modify the distribution of solid iron sulfide (pyrite plus acid-volatile sulfide). If, at one extreme, sulfide diffusion does not occur (i.e., all the sulfide reacts at the level in the sediment at which it is produced), then neglecting expulsion of water during compaction, the depth distribution of pyrite will be the integrated rate of sulfate reduction to that depth. If, however, a significant fraction of the sulfide diffuses upward, the solid iron sulfide distribution would be biased toward shallower sediment depths than in the previous case. Finally, if the sulfide gradient extends to the sediment-water interface, sulfide could presumably diffuse into the overlying waters.

For the last two possibilities to be quantitatively significant, the magnitude of the flux of sulfide toward the sediment-water interface must be large. Given a steady-state sulfide profile, this flux could be calculated by applying Fick's first law (equation 54), plus a term due to advection (see Tzur, 1971). In view of uncertainties associated with picking a value for the diffusion coefficient, such a calculation would be highly speculative. One constraint that can be derived, however, is a relationship between the diffusion coefficients of the sulfate and bisulfide ions. Such a relationship would allow conclusions regarding the diffusion of sulfate in sediments to be generalized to include sulfide diffusion.

When sulfate ion flows into a sediment column, it carries with it negative charge. In order to maintain electrical neutrality, the flux of sulfate into the sediments must be balanced by either a flux of another anion directed in the opposite sense, or an accompanying cation flux into the sediment (Ben-Yaakov, 1972a). This requirement is expressed by equation 69:

$$\sum J_i Z_i = 0 \tag{69}$$

where J_i is the flux and Z_i the charge of the ith ion. This expression may be used in conjunction with equation 54 to relate the fluxes of individual ions. Advection is neglected in the calculation.

Porewater sulfide and sulfate data for the surface layers of Santa Barbara Basin sediments are shown in Figs. 22 and 15, respectively, while data for the other major and minor species in the same core are given by Sholkovitz (1972). The calculation is performed for a depth of ~20 cm in the sediment. Inspection of the analytical data allows equation 69 to be written specifically in terms of those ions exhibiting gradients in concentration (equation 70):

$$-2J_{SO_4^{2-}} + 2J_{Ca^{2+}} + J_{NH_4^+} - J_{HS^-} - J_{HCO_3^-} = 0 \qquad (70)$$

Other ions such as Cl^-, Mg^{2+}, and K^+ showed gradients smaller than the ionic species included in equation 70. Then, substituting equation 54 for the individual ions and inserting the appropriate gradients estimated from the data of Sholkovitz, as well as the sulfide results of Fig. 21, one obtains equation 71:

$$\begin{aligned}+2D_{SO_4^{2-}}(0.25 \times 10^{-6}) = 2D_{Ca^{2+}}(0.06 \times 10^{-6}) - D_{NH_4^+}(0.03 \times 10^{-6})\\ + D_{HS^-}(0.05 \times 10^{-6}) + D_{HCO_3^-}(0.25 \times 10^{-6}) \qquad (71)\end{aligned}$$

Because measured values of the pH of the porewaters in question is in the range 7.8 to 8.2, at *in situ* temperatures (Goldhaber, unpublished results) the dissolved sulfide can be considered to be present as bisulfide ion (see Fig. 17). Bicarbonate in equation 71 is approximated as titration alkalinity minus bisulfide concentration. It may reasonably be assumed for this estimate that the magnitude of the diffusion coefficients of HS^- and HCO_3^- are similar and may, as a first approximation, be set equal to each other. Making this substitution, equation 71 becomes:

$$\begin{aligned}2D_{SO_4^{2-}}(0.25 \times 10^{-6}) = D_{HS^-}(0.30 \times 10^{-6}) + 2D_{Ca^{2+}}(0.06 \times 10^{-6})\\ - D_{NH_4^+}(0.03 \times 10^{-6}) \qquad (72)\end{aligned}$$

The diffusion coefficients of cations in clay-rich sediments are probably much smaller than those of anions due to cation exchange phenomena. Furthermore, gradients in cationic species are small with respect to those of the anions, and cation fluxes are directed in an opposite sense so as to partially cancel each other. One assumption that may be made, therefore, is that the fluxes of cations may be neglected in equation 72, yielding:

$$\frac{D_{HS^-}}{D_{SO_4^{2-}}} \cong \frac{2(0.25 \times 10^{-6})}{0.30 \times 10^{-6}} = 1.7 \qquad (73)$$

Equation 72 may also be solved for specific choices of the cation terms. If, for example, $D_{NH_4^+} \cong D_{HS^-}$, and $D_{Ca^{2+}} \cong 0.5D_{HS^-}$, the calculated ratio becomes 1.5. Other reasonable choices of cation diffusion coefficients would not yield markedly different results.

For comparison, the ratio of diffusion coefficients of chloride-to-sulfate reported by Duursma (1966) in fine sand is 1.8, while the ratio of the self-diffusion coefficients at infinite dilution in 25°C water is 1.6 for HCO_3^- to SO_4^{2-} (calculated from data contained in Robinson and Stokes, 1970).

The relationship derived in equation 73 is equivalent to a relationship between the fluxes of the two ions. The ratio of the upward sulfide flux to the downward sulfate flux is given by equation 74:

$$\frac{J_{HS^-}}{J_{SO_4^{2-}}} = \frac{-D_{HS^-}\left(\frac{\partial HS^-}{\partial X}\right)_{X=20\text{ cm}}}{-D_{SO_4^{2-}}\left(\frac{\partial SO_4^{2-}}{\partial X}\right)_{X=20\text{ cm}}} \qquad (74)$$

or, substituting the appropriate gradients:

$$\frac{J_{HS^-}}{J_{SO_4^{2-}}} = \frac{-D_{HS^-}(0.05 \times 10^{-6})}{-D_{SO_4^{2-}}(0.25 \times 10^{-6})} \qquad (75)$$

Equation 73 gives the required ratio of diffusion coefficients which may be substituted into 75, yielding:

$$J_{HS^-} \approx 0.4 J_{SO_4{}^{2-}} \tag{76}$$

Equation 76 suggests that approximately 40% of the sulfate sulfur diffusing past a depth of 20 cm in the sediment is returned toward shallower depths as a sulfide flux. The remaining 60% represents a net addition of sulfur to deeper sediment layers. Reactions removing dissolved sulfide from the porewaters probably account for the fact that considerably less than 100% of the downward sulfate flux is returned. Such reactions have been discussed in previous pages.

Despite the fact that the calculation shows a considerable percentage upward sulfide flux passes the 20 cm level, this sulfide is not released into the overlying waters. It will be noted in Fig. 22 that the zone 0 to 9 cm does not contain measurable dissolved sulfide. The absence of dissolved sulfide has been attributed to rapid reaction between H_2S and iron oxide (equation 53). This uppermost zone therefore acts as a "lid," containing the upward diffusing sulfide to depths greater than 9 cm.

Of course, the absolute magnitude of the fluxes of sulfate and sulfide have not been specified in the above discussion, only the relation between them. If fluxes are small, the calculated relationship shown in equation 76 will still be valid, but the role of diffusion in adding sulfate to the sediments and redistributing sulfide will be minor.

Equation 75 is only strictly valid at depths for which the gradients are as shown.

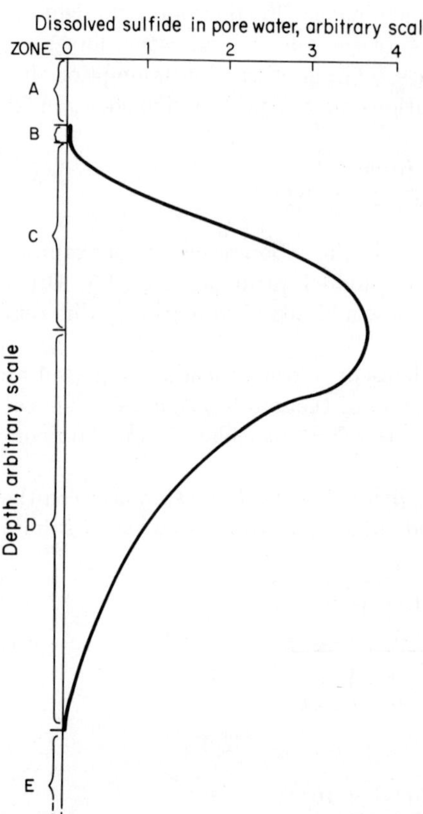

Fig. 27. Schematic representation of steady-state diffusion-reaction regimes of interstitial water sulfide in marine sediments. Zone A: Essentially no dissolved sulfide present; removal of dissolved sulfide by reaction with iron oxide more rapid than rate of sulfide addition. Zone B: Sulfide first appears; removal of upward diffusing sulfide from zone C. Zone C: Sulfide increases; that is, rate of addition of sulfide more rapid than rate of removal. Sulfide diffuses toward zone B. Zone D: Sulfide decreases; rate of removal of dissolved sulfide more rapid than addition. Sulfide diffuses toward zone E. Zone E: Diagenetic reactions involving (measurable) dissolved sulfide are complete. If sulfate reduction ceases above zone E, early sulfur diagenesis is complete.

It is worthwhile to point out that Kaplan et al. (1963) found a maximum in dissolved sulfide concentration similar to that shown in Figs. 23 and 24, at approximately 1 m depth in a piston core from the Santa Barbara Basin. Below 1 m, the sign of the sulfide term in equations 71 or 75 would therefore be reversed, because the sign of the sulfide gradient would change. In this case, sulfide diffuses into deeper sediment layers instead of toward the sediment-water interface.

The various diffusion reaction regimes discussed above which precede the completion of diagenetic reactions of dissolved H_2S are schematically summarized in Fig. 27.

5. Sulfur Isotope Geochemistry

From the description given in Section 2, it is apparent that the biological fractionation of stable isotopes can lead to products with a wide range of S^{34}/S^{32} ratios. The results of laboratory studies can be used to interpret the natural isotopic distribution by (1) using δS^{34} values as tracers, and (2) assuming the mechanisms of biological laboratory fractionation during metabolism applies with equal validity to natural systems.

Sulfur isotope studies on recent marine sediments have been undertaken by several workers (Thode et al., 1960; Vinogradov et al., 1962; Kaplan et al., 1963; Hartmann and Nielsen, 1969; Sweeney and Kaplan, 1973b), and the general features of S^{34}/S^{32} partitioning among various S-bearing phases are well-documented. For example, Table XIX contains data from Kiel Bay, Western Baltic Sea, recalculated from Hartmann and Nielsen (1969), which displays some of these features. Dissolved sulfate in the porewaters is progressively depleted as a function of depth in the sediment. Associated with this depletion is an increasing enrichment in the heavy isotope (δS^{34} becomes larger). Dissolved hydrogen sulfide in the surface porewater is isotopically enriched in the light isotope, S^{32}, by $\approx -40‰$ compared to dissolved seawater sulfate, and also becomes increasingly enriched in S^{34} with depth. Isotopic discrimination between SO_4 and H_2S is large ($\alpha > 1.03$) and is consistent with

TABLE XIX

Distribution and Isotopic Abundance of Sulfur in Sediments of the Western Baltic Sea[a]

Depth in Sediment (cm)	Dissolved SO_4^{2-}		Dissolved Sulfide		Water Insoluble S in Sediment		Organic Carbon (%)
	Millimole/ Liter	δS^{34} ‰	Millimole/ Liter	δS^{34} ‰	%S	δS^{34} ‰	
0–1.5	19.8	+20.0	0.002	—	0.38	−20.2	3.15
1.5–3	16.56	+28.0	0.09	—	0.65	−22.1	2.85
3–5	15.16	+29.3	0.30	−24.6	1.05	−23.4	3.90
5–7	13.16	+33.3	0.37	−21.9	1.09	−23.4	3.83
8–10	11.59	+39.7	0.35	−18.7	1.48	−23.3	4.35
10–13	9.88	+41.2	0.99	−16.3	1.05	−22.0	3.50
13–16	7.91	+47.6	1.47	−13.1	1.45	−27.6	2.98
16–19	7.41	+51.0	1.64	−9.2	1.45	−22.4	3.43
19–22	6.22	+51.0	1.28	−6.4	1.77	−20.2	4.56
22–25	6.31	+56.0	1.93	−3.9	1.28	−20.1	4.03
25–28	4.88	+56.5	2.32	−1.0	1.53	−19.4	4.11
28–31	3.72	+60.7	2.49	+2.0	1.38	−19.3	4.20

[a] After Hartmann and Nielsen (1969).

fractionation occurring during bacterial sulfate reduction. Total sulfur in the solid phases increases within the top 10 cm of depth, and below this the rate of increase is greatly diminished. Near the surface, δS^{34} of the water-insoluble sulfur (reduced total sulfur in the sediment) is very similar to that of dissolved sulfide. In contrast to dissolved sulfide, which systematically becomes isotopically heavier with depth, the solid phase sulfur displays only minor increase in δS^{34} with depth. This distribution was interpreted by Kaplan et al. (1963) and Hartmann and Nielsen (1969) to signify that the process of sulfate reduction mainly occurs near the sediment surface, and a relatively small proportion of pyrite forms in the zone of deeper burial, notwithstanding the fact that sulfate reduction continues in the interstitial waters.

In order for the observed net burial of isotopically light sulfur to take place, heavy sulfur must be leaving the system. If the majority of pyrite formation takes place very near the sediment surface, this loss could perhaps be explained by exchange between residual unreduced porewater sulfate and sulfate in the overlying waters. Such exchange must be more rapid than the rate at which sulfate is reduced, as the porewater sulfate at the top of the core is isotopically the same as seawater. In addition, the chemical properties of porewater in environments where pyrite sulfur is abundant in the shallowest samples (e.g., Sholkovitz, 1972) show no marked enrichment in products of organic matter decomposition by sulfate reduction. Dissolved bicarbonate, phosphate, and ammonia only increase to high concentrations in deeper layers. Therefore, the process or processes exchanging sulfate with the overlying water may also regenerate nutrients to the overlying water. It is not known to what sediment depth exchange can occur with overlying waters, although without the intervention of mixing due to the activity of burrowing macrofauna, exchange is not likely below a few centimeters deep. Results such as those summarized in Table XIX further indicate that only small quantities of sulfur arise from organic sulfur compounds, as δS^{34} in this sulfur should be very close to the δS^{34} in the seawater (see Table XX).

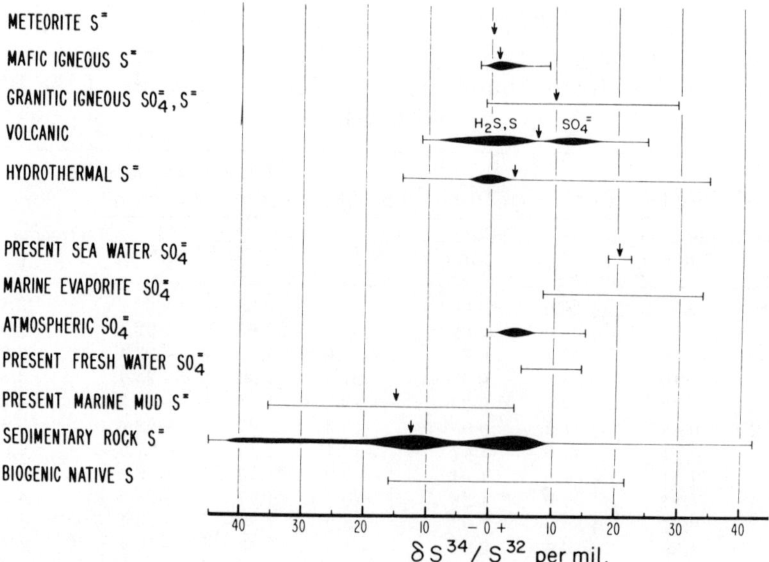

Fig. 28. Summary of ranges in δS^{34} for sulfur from various terrestrial materials. After Holser and Kaplan (1966).

Pyrite in lithified sediments is also usually isotopically enriched in S^{32}, and can be distinguished from volcanic or hydrothermal pyrite deposits on the basis of δS^{34} values (see Fig. 28). In coexisting metal sulfides of hydrothermal or igneous origin, the high temperature of formation often allows isotope exchange to occur between the different mineral species (e.g., Sakai, 1968). However, there is no evidence that isotopic exchange occurs in minerals formed within the depositional and early diagenetic environment.

Seawater contains sulfate sulfur with an isotopic ratio, $\delta S^{34} \approx +20‰$. Meteoritic, lunar, and igneous terrestrial sulfur appear to have S^{34}/S^{32} ratios very close to each other, and by convention, the δS^{34} of troilite (FeS) in meteorites has been given a value, 0‰. It therefore follows that seawater is enriched in heavy isotopes of S,

TABLE XX

Isotopic Fractionation of Sulfur During Its Incorporation Into the Cytoplasm and Exoskeletons of Marine Algae and Animals off Southern California Relative to δS^{34} of Seawater

Name of Organism	Total S $\Delta\ \delta S^{34}‰$	Combustible S $\Delta\ \delta S^{34}‰$	Ash S $\Delta\ S^{34}‰$	Shell S $\Delta\ \delta S^{34}‰$
Algae				
Gigartina canaliculata	−0.6			
Gigartina leptorhynchos	−0.1	−2.2	+3.4	
Ulva californica	−1.0			
Macrocystis pyrifera	−1.0			
Egregia laevigata	−0.9			
Gonyaulax polyhedra	−1.0			
Animals				
Haliotis cracherodii	+0.5	−1.1	+3.7	+3.1
Small benthic animals (clams, brittle stars, shrimps)	−3.5			
Chaetopterus variopedatus	−12.8[a]			Tubes: −7.3[a]
Chlamys latiaurata	−2.7			−0.2

[a] May indicate pyrite-containing sediments have not been removed.

compared to the primordial composition of the earth's sulfur. The only rational conclusion is that isotopically light sulfur is buried in the sediment (Thode and Monster, 1965; Holser and Kaplan, 1966; Nielsen, 1966). This could only occur if pyrite formation is associated with a large fractionation (e.g., $\alpha \approx 1.03$ to 1.04) relative to δS^{34} of seawater sulfate, leaving behind residual seawater sulfate enriched in S^{34}. As shown below, this can only take place in the upper layers of sediment.

A. Fractionation Factors During Sulfate Reduction in Sediment

Isotope fractionation factors during sulfate reduction can be estimated by measurement of δS^{34} and concentration of residual sulfate in interstitial water of marine sediment (Sweeney et al., 1973). This calculation is only applicable to systems that are closed with respect to addition or subtraction of sulfate other than biological sulfate reduction. The decrease in the quantity of sulfate in the reservoir can be related to the isotopic enrichment according to the Rayleigh distillation equation. The expression employed here assumes first-order kinetics, although the form of the equation would be the same for a zero-order reaction (Rees, 1973). Rearrangement of the general equation 77 (Nakai and Jensen, 1964) transfers the equation into a form that can graphically relate the concentration at time T to the isotopic ratio S^{32}/S^{34} (R), with respect to the isotopic fractionation factor (α) during reduction:

$$R^T_{SO_4} = R^0_{SO_4} F^{1-[K_2/K_1]} \tag{77}$$

where K_1 = unidirectional rate constant for $S^{32}O_4$ reduction

K_2 = unidirectional rate constant for $S^{34}O_4$ reduction

$R^T_{SO_4}$ = (S^{32}/S^{34}) sulfate at time T

$R^0_{SO_4}$ = (S^{32}/S^{34}) sulfate at start

$$F = \frac{\text{conc. } SO_4 \text{ at time } (T)}{\text{conc. } SO_4 \text{ at time } (0)} = \frac{C_T}{C_0}$$

This relation may be rewritten:

$$\log R^T_{SO_4} = \log R^0_{SO_4} F^{1-[K_2/K_1]}$$

$$\log R^T_{SO_4} = \log R^0_{SO_4} + (1 - [K_2/K_1]) \log F$$

let $\alpha = K_1/K_2$ and replace $F = \dfrac{C_T}{C_0}$

$$\log R^T_{SO_4} = \log R^0_{SO_4} + \left(1 - \frac{1}{\alpha}\right) \log C_T - \left(1 - \frac{1}{\alpha}\right) \log C_0$$

$$\log R^T_{SO_4} = \left(1 - \frac{1}{\alpha}\right) \log C_T + \left[\log R^0_{SO_4} - \left(1 - \frac{1}{\alpha}\right) \log C_0\right] \tag{78}$$

If α, the instantaneous fractionation factor, is constant, then $[1 - (1/\alpha)]$ is the slope of the plot of $\log R^T_{SO_4}$ versus $\log C_T$, for values measured at different times, and $\{\log R^0_{SO_4} - [1 - (1/\alpha)] \log C_0\}$ is a constant representing the initial condition.

Assuming that increasing depth of burial is equivalent to time in regular increments, the relationship can be used to analyze the sulfate concentration and its isotopic composition for increasing depths in the sediment.

B. Measurements of α in Marine Sediment

JOIDES Leg 4, Sites 27 and 26, Southwest Atlantic Ocean

Dissolved sulfate from interstitial water has been analyzed from a core taken at Site 27 of Leg 4, JOIDES Deep Sea Drilling Project (Table XXI). The site is located off the continental shelf and has a relatively low rate of sedimentation (Bader et al., 1970).

Sulfate reduction, during burial, has occurred to a depth of at least 249 m below the sediment surface (Presley and Kaplan, 1970). Enrichment of S^{34} in the residual sulfate corresponding to depletion in sulfate concentration, is shown according to the Rayleigh plot in Fig. 29. Determination of α from the slope yields a value of 1.026. Projection of the linear slope passes through the value for the concentration of open ocean seawater of $\delta S^{34} = +20‰$ (Thode et al., 1961). This may indicate that the fractionation factor, $\alpha = 1.026$, has been constant during the entire reduction process (Sweeney et al., 1973).

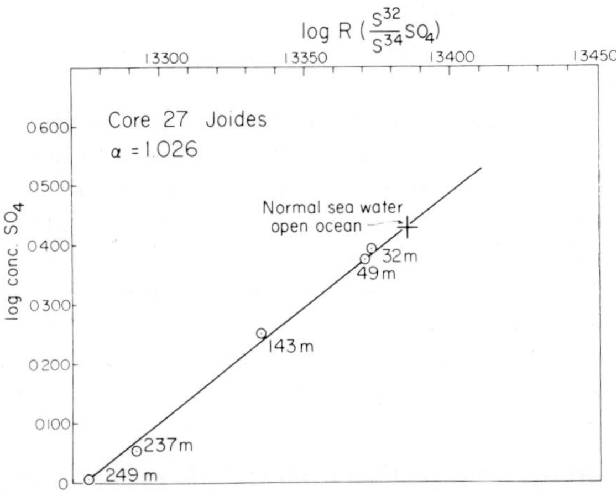

Fig. 29. Site 27 (JOIDES) Southwest Atlantic Ocean. Graphical presentation of the Rayleigh relationship (equation 78) for the interstitial water sulfate data. The calculated fractionation factor, α, from the slope is 1.026. After Sweeney et al. (1973).

Equation 78 is only valid if the porewaters do, indeed, approximate a closed system with respect to diffusive flux of sulfate. Strong evidence in support of this assumption is obtained from closed-system mass and isotope balance calculations on JOIDES cores. This is accomplished by making the assumptions that (1) the initial concentration and δS^{34} of the sulfate trapped at the time of initial burial is the same as seawater sulfate, and (2) all the sulfide formed within the sediment has ultimately been transformed to pyrite at the depth of production. This pyrite sulfur should be equal to the

Table XXI

Sulfide Formation During Burial from Sites 26 and 27, JOIDES

(a) Determination of Sulfide Produced by Sulfate Reduction During Burial for Site 27

Depth (m)	Normal Seawater Sulfate Conc. (g/kg I.W.)	Normal Seawater Sulfate δS^{34}‰	Measured Interstitial Sulfate Conc. (g/kg I.W.)	Measured Interstitial Sulfate δS^{34}‰	Calculated Sulfate Reduced During Burial Conc. (g/kg I.W.)	Calculated Sulfate Reduced During Burial Av. δS^{34}‰
237	2.71	+20.0	1.13	+40.9	1.58	+4.0
249	2.71	+20.0	1.10	+44.7	1.71	+4.5

(b) Comparison of Calculated Sulfide Produced During Burial to Measured Sulfide in the Sediment for Sites 26 and 27 JOIDES

Site/Depth (m)	H_2O Content (% Sediment)	Sulfate Reduced (gm/kg I.W.)	Calculated Sulfate Reduced and Transferred to Sediment %S	Calculated Sulfate Reduced and Transferred to Sediment δS^{34}	Sulfide Measured in Sediment %S	Sulfide Measured in Sediment δS^{34}
27/237	31	1.58	0.023	+4.0	0.015	+3.8
249	28	1.71	0.021	+4.5	0.015	+3.7
26/100	32	1.46	0.023	0	0.020	+2.0
230	26	2.61	0.031	+15	0.025	+13.4

difference between concentration in seawater sulfate (C_0) and the sulfate present in the interstitial water (C_T), taking into account the water content of the sediment (Sweeney et al., 1973).

The results of the calculation for two depths in JOIDES, Hole 27, are shown in Table XXI along with the measurements of the iron sulfide observed in the sediment (which had previously been washed free of any residual porewater sulfate). The agreement of the isotopic ratios between that calculated from sulfate reduction during burial with no diffusion (+4.0 and +4.5‰, respectively) and that measured in the sediment (+3.8 and +3.7‰) are in good agreement, considering analytical errors and approximations used in the calculations. The amount of sulfide measured in the sediment is actually lower than predicted by a closed-system model (0.015 compared to 0.023 and 0.021, respectively) and argues against addition of sulfate by diffusion.

Site 26

Samples were analyzed from depths of 100 and 230 m below the sediment surface (Table XXI). Sulfate reduction had occurred during burial, as shown by decreasing concentration of sulfate in the interstitial water with depth. Knowing the concentration and isotopic ratio of dissolved sulfate at the two depths, the amount and δS^{34} of the sulfide added to the sediment during burial can be calculated by assuming a closed system. The results are shown in Table XXI, along with the concentration and δS^{34} of the pyrite in the sediment. Again, as for Site 27, there is good agreement between the values measured, and the values calculated for a system closed to sulfate diffusion.

The same Rayleigh distillation equation may also be applied to nearshore cores exhibiting strong sulfate gradients, keeping in mind that diffusion may play a relatively more important role in such cases (Table XVIII). This has been done for Santa Barbara Basin sediments using the sulfate data of Sholkovitz (1972), which have been presented previously (Fig. 15) and are reproduced in Table XXII together with δS^{34} measurements of Sweeney et al. (1973) on the same samples.

Graphical presentation of the data following the Rayleigh relationship (equation 78)

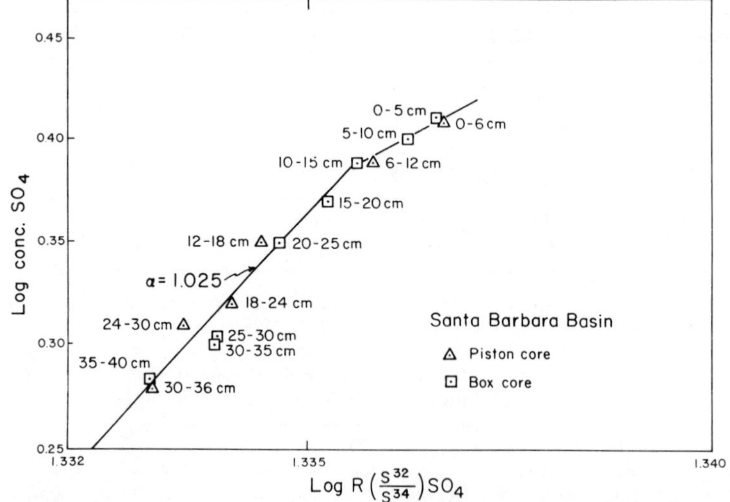

Fig. 30. Santa Barbara Basin. Graphical presentation of the Rayleigh relationship (equation 78) for the interstitial water sulfate data (Table XXII). The calculated α from the slope is 1.042 above 15 cm and 1.025 below 15 cm depth. After Sweeney et al. (1973).

TABLE XXII

Concentration and Isotopic Ratio of Dissolved Sulfate in the Interstitial Water from the Santa Barbara Basin

Core	Depth (cm)	Sulfate (g SO_4/kg I.W.)	Sulfate δS^{34}‰
Piston	Supernatant water	2.70	+20.13
	0–6	2.61	+23.02
	6–12	2.57	+25.11
	12–18	2.23	+28.24
	18–24	2.09	+29.36
	24–30	2.04	+30.48
	30–36	1.88	+31.53
Box	Supernatant water	2.65	+20.47
	0–5	2.65	+20.68
	5–10	2.53	+23.99
	10–15	2.47	+25.33
	15–20	2.35	+26.39
	20–25	2.24	+27.84
	25–30	2.04	+29.80
	30–35	2.03	+29.56
	35–40	1.92	+31.62

is shown in Fig. 30. Below the depth of 15 cm, the calculated isotopic fractionation factor during reduction, α, is 1.025, assuming a closed system. Between the sediment surface and 15 cm, the calculated α, determined from the slope, is 1.042. This would indicate that the sulfide being formed, by sulfate reduction above 15 cm depth in the sediment, will have a δS^{34} value of 42‰ more negative than the δS^{34} of the sulfate being reduced. Table XXIII shows that the average value of reduced sulfur in the surface sediment of the Santa Barbara Basin is $\delta S^{34} = -23$‰, or 43‰ more negative than seawater sulfate. The agreement suggests that the α calculated from isotopic enrichment in the sulfate is an accurate indication of the instantaneous fractionation factor during sulfate reduction. If this conclusion is valid over the entire core, then it may be argued that a two-stage fractionation process occurs during sulfate reduction. The first occurs near the sediment surface, where sulfate ard nutrient reservoirs are large, but reduction is controlled by availability of nutrient and electron sources and

TABLE XXIII

Solid Sulfur Species in Surface 9 cm Sediment from the Santa Barbara Basin

Acid-volatile Sulfide % Sulfur	Acid-volatile Sulfide δS^{34}‰	Pyrite % Sulfur	Pyrite δS^{34}‰	Elemental Sulfur % Sulfur	Elemental Sulfur δS^{34}‰	Total Sulfur % Sulfur	Total Sulfur δS^{34}‰
0.200	−24.0	0.105	−20.9	0.041	−14.5	0.346	−23

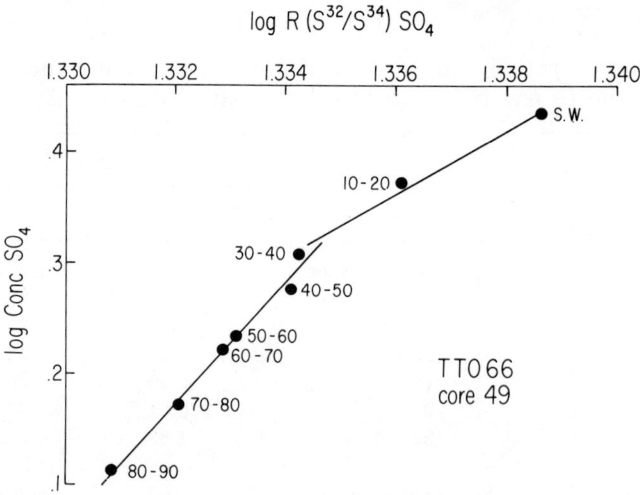

Fig. 31. Graphical presentation of the Rayleigh relationship for interstitial water sulfate from core 49, west coast of Baja California. For depths above 40 cm, the calculated α is 1.034, and for depths below 40 cm, α = 1.019. (Numbered black circles refer to depth in centimeters.) After Sweeney et al. (1973).

is represented by zero-order kinetics with respect to sulfate. The second occurs after burial and significant depletion of sulfate or nutrients.

Additional data from areas of relatively rapid sediment accumulation are available from two cores (numbers 11 and 49) taken on the University of Washington ship, *T. G. Thompson*, cruise TTO66, off the west coast of Baja California in about 500 m of water. Dissolved hydrogen sulfide was present in all samples analyzed. The Rayleigh relationship for core 49 is shown in Fig. 31. Two isotopic fractionation factors can be calculated from the data. Above 40 cm, calculated α = 1.034 and below 40 cm, α is calculated to be 1.019. This again indicates a two-stage fractionation process. The Rayleigh relationship for core 11 is shown in Fig. 32. Unlike the interstitial water sulfate data from the other sediments, there is sufficient scatter in the data points that two separate fractionation factors could not be distinguished in this core. A fractionation factor of 1.032 is calculated for the mean value during burial to 70 cm depth in sediment.

There is a marked similarity between fractionation factors calculated for JOIDES, Hole 27, and for the Santa Barbara Basin below 15 cm as well as core 49 below 40 cm. A good case can be made for the JOIDES samples approximating simple closed-system sulfate reduction. Furthermore, the fractionation factors calculated are quite reasonable when compared to those measured under laboratory conditions (see Section 2). It is therefore tempting to conclude by analogy that closed-system sulfate reduction is also approached in the more rapidly deposited sediments. There is agreement between α calculated assuming a closed system for interstitial sulfate (0 to 15 cm) and $\Delta\,\delta S^{34}$ between pyrite and seawater sulfate in the Santa Barbara Basin. In order for addition of sulfate by diffusion to be of minor importance in Santa Barbara Basin sediments, the effective diffusion coefficient of the sulfate ion would have to be smaller than presently available data indicate. This might imply that factors such as the existence of electrical potential gradients arising from counterdiffusing ions of different mobilities or specific chemical interactions between dissolved and solid components,

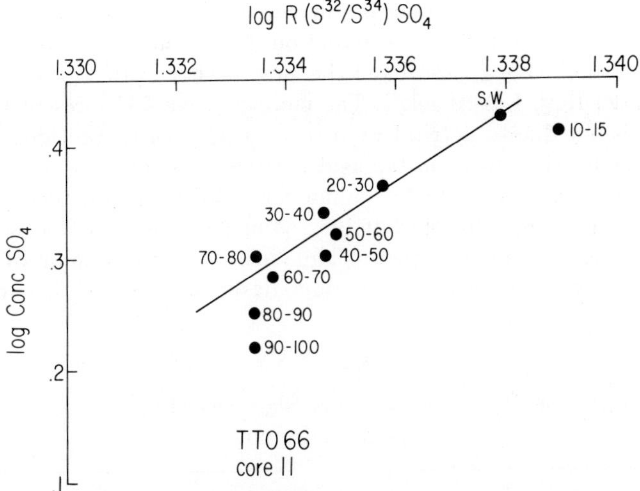

Fig. 32. Graphical presentation of the Rayleigh relationship (equation 78) for interstitial water sulfide from core 11, west coast of Baja California. The calculated α from the slope is 1.032 for depths above 70 cm. (Numbered black circles refer to depth in centimeters.) After Sweeney et al. (1973).

act to reduce the diffusive flux of sulfate into sediments. The open system calculation of α is presently under consideration and the closed system interpretation presented above is viewed as a limiting case which does not rigorously hold everywhere but may be approached in some environments.

C. *Isotopic Tests for the Formation of Pyrite in Neritic Environments*

Sulfur isotope ratios of reduced sulfur in sediment from the California Borderland are shown in Table XXIV from the data of Sweeney and Kaplan (1973b). Differences in the value of δS^{34} occur both between basins and within basins. Correlations between δS^{34} and quantity of sulfur, quantity of organic carbon, and sedimentation rates were

TABLE XXIV

Distribution of δS^{34} in Sulfide from Sediment of the California Borderland

Location	Number Samples	δS^{34}‰ Reduced Sulfur Compounds		Δ‰ ($\delta S^{34}_{SO_4} - \delta S^{34}_{S^{2-}}$)
		Mean	Range	
East Cortez Basin	6	−37	−33 to −41	57
Santa Barbara Basin	11	−26	−18 to −34	46
Santa Catalina Basin	10	−36	−30 to −40	56
Santa Monica Basin	3	−20	−18 to −23	40
San Diego Trough	2	−39	−36 to −42	59
Long Basin	6	−48	−46 to −51	68
Marina del Rey Harbor (Los Angeles)	6	−13	−7 to −19	33

attempted but failed. Geographic variations in δS^{34} with distance from shore do not show consistent relationship, with the exception that the most negative value ($-48‰$) is furthest from shore (Long Basin) and the most positive value ($-7‰$) is nearest to shore (Marina del Rey, Los Angeles). The more positive δS^{34} present in Marina del Rey sediment is not due to detrital pyrite admixing with the authigenic sulfide, as almost all the sulfide is present in the acid-volatile phase and not as pyrite.

As stated earlier, increase in δS^{34} of sulfide formed by *in situ* reduction is generally not reflected in the pyrite fraction of the sediment. This is probably because the amount of pyrite formed at the surface is large relative to the amount of sulfur added after burial. However, in the Santa Catalina Basin, the δS^{34} of the pyrite fraction becomes more negative with depth (Table XXV). This trend cannot be produced by isotope fractionation occurring during burial. It must be concluded, therefore, that the δS^{34} of the pyrite forming at the sediment surface is not constant with time. That is, the average fractionation during reduction of sulfate is not constant for one locality just as it is not between regionally distributed localities.

Table XXV

Content and δS^{34} for Pyrite in Various Size Fractions, from Santa Catalina Basin Sediment

Depth (cm)	Total		> 104 μ	104–74 μ	74–44 μ	< 44 μ	% Sulfate Depleted in I.W.
	%S	δS^{34}‰	δS^{34}‰	δS^{34}‰	δS^{34}‰	δS^{34}‰	
0–10	0.350	−28.0	−27.2	—	−28.0	−28.1	None
18–23	0.370	−30.2	−30.2	—	—	−28.7	None
40–45	0.279	−35.1	−34.1	—	—	−35.8	None
162–167	0.240	−39.3	−45.6	−44.1	−43.6	−35.6	20
248–256	0.231	−38.6	−43.0	−42.1	—	−35.4	—
314–322	0.309	−40.1	−40.5	−43.7	—	−38.5	20
356–361	0.525	−40.6	−40.6	−40.5	−41.6	−35.6	25
415–423	0.276	−37.3	−41.6	−43.4	—	−34.0	30
435–440	0.597	−40.1	—	—	—	—	—

At some depth in the sediment column (corresponding to zone E in Fig. 27), sulfate reduction may have ceased, and all dissolved sulfide reacted to form solid phases. At this depth, the sulfur content and isotopes will reflect the sum total of all processes that add sulfur, including diffusion. Such a situation is approached in the deepest samples analyzed by Kaplan et al. (1963) from the Santa Barbara Basin. The δS^{34} of total sulfur (including all forms) for the Santa Barbara Basin is recorded in Table XXVI. There, a decrease in δS^{34} with depth can only indicate a change in conditions at the sediment-water interface. The sulfate diffusion-reaction model of Berner (1964c) for this basin predicts that 0.13 mol of sulfur per liter of porewater should be reduced to sulfide. If the water content of the sediments is 60% by wet weight, this would correspond to a total of nearly 0.5% sulfur (by dry weight) added. If no sulfur was lost from the sediments, the sulfate added by diffusion must (when fully reduced and precipitated as pyrite) have the seawater isotopic value of $\delta S^{34} \cong +20‰$. This predicted amount of isotopically heavy sulfur constitutes nearly 50% of the maximum

TABLE XXVI

δS^{34} of Total Sulfur from Santa Barbara Basin Sediments

Depth (cm)	δS^{34} of Total Sulfur
0–10	−10.9
90–100	−13.3
260–270	−13.0
360–370	−14.6

total observed sulfur content of the sediment. Such a large input of heavy sulfur by diffusion is inconsistent with the observed isotopic distribution (Table XXVI), which predicts a large proportion of light sulfur. An unreasonably large deposition of isotopically light sulfur at the sediment-water interface would be required to offset such a large input of isotopically heavy sulfate by diffusion.

Diffusion of porewater sulfide would not modify this result if, as was argued in a previous section, such sulfide does not escape from the sediment. There are cases, however, where the dissolved sulfide gradient reaches to the sediment-water interface. If sulfur flows out of the sediment by diffusion, and it is isotopically light (about −25‰ in Table XIX), the result would be to cause a further increase in δS^{34} of the residual sediment sulfur.

Because of nonconstancy of the isotopic ratio of pyrite formed at the sediment surface, it is difficult to quantitatively measure sulfate reduction by changes in the isotopic composition of pyrite with depth, except in the special case where little or no pyrite is formed at the sediment-water interface as in JOIDES samples from Sites 26 and 27. A more qualitative approach, however, may be used by analyzing the isotopic composition of the pyrite present in different size fractions of the sediment (Table XXVII).

The first iron sulfide phase formed from solution is probably not pyrite, but metastable iron sulfide (amorphous $FeS_{0.9}$, mackinawite, $FeS_{0.9}$, or greigite, Fe_3S_4).

TABLE XXVII

Content and δS^{34} of Reduced Sulfur from Various Size Fractions of Surface Marine Sediments

	>104 μ		104–74 μ		74–44 μ		<44 μ	
Location	% S	δS^{34}‰	% S	δS^{34}‰	% S	δS^{34}‰	% S	δS^{34}‰
Marina del Rey 1[a]	0.076	−14	0.028	−13.8	0.015	−13.3	0.182	−14.1
Marina del Rey 2[a]	0.025	−14.6	0.003	−15.0	0.002	—	0.064	−14.1
Santa Barbara Basin[b]	0.048	−31.0	0.011	−29.8	0.076	−29.0	0.288	−29.2
Santa Catalina Basin[b]	0.012	−27.2	0.006	—	0.019	−28.0	0.313	−28.1

[a] Acid volatile + elemental sulfur + pyrite sulfide.
[b] Pyrite only.

Sweeney and Kaplan (1973a) showed that iron sulfide produced during burial (after iron sulfide formed at the surface has already mostly changed to pyrite), should precipitate independently of previously formed pyrite. This follows from the observation made with the aid of scanning electron microscopy that pyrite framboids do not commonly appear to be overgrown by later-formed pyrite. It was also argued that later-formed pyrite might be concentrated in the finer size fraction of the sediment. To check for this effect (Sweeney and Kaplan, 1973b), the sediment samples from the Santa Catalina Basin (Table XXV) were separated into fractions $>104\ \mu$, 104–$74\ \mu$, 74–$44\ \mu$, and $<44\ \mu$. The results show that insignificant differences in δS^{34} exist between size fractions where sulfate reduction has not occurred after burial. Where sulfate reduction has occurred after burial, as evidenced by sulfate depletion in the porewaters, the $<44\ \mu$ fraction has a consistently more positive δS^{34} than the other fractions. This difference, 5 to 9‰, is significant when compared to the range (1‰) in different size fractions of surface sediment, and a range of 1 to 2‰ for pyrite in other size fractions at the same depth.

The change in δS^{34} in the $<44\ \mu$ fraction due to *in situ* sulfate reduction can be calculated as before, assuming no addition of sulfate by diffusion. Using this value, it is possible to calculate back to the δS^{34} of the pyrite, assuming it had formed at the surface from seawater sulfate with $\delta S^{34} \approx +20‰$. The calculated δS^{34} for pyrite is shown for the Santa Catalina Basin to be in good agreement with the average for the other fractions of the sediment (Table XXVIII).

Table XXVIII

Isotopic Correction for Pyrite Sulfur from Santa Catalina Basin Due to Sulfate Reduction During Burial

Depth (cm)	δS^{34}‰ of Pyrite Sulfur in Sediment		
	Average $>44\ \mu$	Measured $<44\ \mu$	Calculated $<44\ \mu$ Sediment Surface
160–167	−44.5	−35.6	−45.1
248–256	−42.5	−35.4	−41.9
314–322	−42.1	−38.5	−42.6
356–361	−40.9	−35.6	−43.3
415–423	−42.5	−35.2	−43.3

A similar study of the pyrite in the sediment from the Cariaco Trench (JOIDES, Leg 15; Hole 147b) showed that at the sediment depth analyzed, sulfate reduction is complete in the interstitial water. Measured δS^{34} values of pyrite from different size fractions of sample 2-6 (54–64), indicate the $<44\ \mu$ fraction to be more positive than the others (Tables XXIX and XXX). Calculation of the initial δS^{34} value of this fraction, assuming complete reduction of sulfate from the interstitial water and 50% water content in the sediment, yields a $\delta S^{34} = -32.7‰$, more consistent with the δS^{34} values (−30.0 and −31.2‰) for the larger size fractions.

It should be noted that there is no direct evidence that interstitial water removed from a sediment layer by squeezing has always been in contact with that particular sediment. Upward displacement of water by compaction of sediment must occur. The effect follows the water loss from the sediment and is therefore exponential (Emery,

TABLE XXIX

Pyrite Distribution in Cariaco Trench Sediment: JOIDES Core 147B

Sample	Depth (m)	Pyrite % Sulfur	Pyrite δS^{34}‰
1-2 (9–18)	2	1.443	−31.8
1-3	4	1.901	−29.4
2-6 (54–64)	20	1.719	−29.4
7-4	66	1.266	−32.1
12-5 (135–143)	112	1.130	−30.4

TABLE XXX

δS^{34} of Pyrite in Different Size Fractions of Cariaco Trench Sediment Sample 2-6 (54–64), and the Calculated Value δS^{34} of Surface-Formed Pyrite in $< 44\ \mu$ Fraction

Total		$> 104\ \mu$		104–74 μ		74–44 μ		$< 44\ \mu$ Measured		$< 44\ \mu$ Calculated	
% S	δS^{34}‰	% S	δS^{34}‰	% S	δS^{34}‰	% S	δS^{34}‰	% S	δS^{34}‰	% S (Sediment)	δS^{34}‰ (Surface)
1.719	−29.4	0.34	−30.0	0.43	−30.0	0.17	−31.2	0.776	−26.9	0.766	−32.7

1960), being most pronounced near the sediment-water interface. In the slowly deposited deep-sea cores from JOIDES, the relative effect of water migration will be small, because the water content of sediment is relatively constant. In the rapidly depositing nearshore basins, depletion of sulfate occurs quickly, and upward migration of water would not influence interaction between the solid and dissolved components. The effect of water displacement has not been taken into account in the preceding calculations, but it does not appear to have any recognizable influence on these calculations.

D. δS^{34} *of Sulfide in Lithified Sediment*

Studies of the isotopic ratio of ancient sedimentary deposits are generally concerned in determining $\Delta\delta S^{34}$ (δS^{34} contemporaneous seawater SO_4 − δS^{34} sulfide), as an environmental indicator. Measured values of δS^{34} in sulfides showing negative readings (< -15‰) are often interpreted as resulting from biological processes under normal marine conditions. Sulfides with values of $\delta S^{34} \geqslant 0$‰ are generally interpreted as resulting from igneous or hydrothermal processes. However, values in the intermediate range present problems in interpretation. Two possible explanations can be offered for marine sulfides with relatively low enrichment in S^{32}.

The first assumes that a significant proportion of the metal sulfides have formed by diffusion of seawater sulfate into the sediment column, without escape of the sulfide produced. In this event, δS^{34} of the sulfide will approach the δS^{34} value for seawater (+20‰ ± 10‰, depending on the geological epoch) (see Holser and Kaplan, 1966). As some sulfide forms near the sediment-water interface, the final δS^{34} of total sulfide in any particular stratigraphic layer will be $< \delta S^{34}$ of seawater sulfate, but may still conceivably be $>0‰$. Although we have not yet recognized areas on the present ocean where this process occurs to any large extent, such areas may not be rare and should be searched out, as isotopically heavy pyrite has been reported (Kaplan, 1962). They would be found in places where organic content is high, rate of sedimentation is relatively low, and the sulfate gradient is steep (equation 57).

A second explanation is that, where the content of pyrite-sulfur in sediment is relatively low ($\leqslant 0.3\%$) the influence of reduced trapped sulfate on δS^{34} is high. This assumes a closed system in which some pyrite formation occurs near the surface and an approximately equal amount is formed from trapped seawater. Assuming this closed system is in operation, a graphical relationship can be constructed between δS^{34} of the sample and the pyrite-sulfur formed, in order to determine δS^{34} of sulfide first deposited near the sediment-water interface. The utility of the method is illustrated in Fig. 33 from Sweeney (1972) for two samples of sediment, one with a relatively high sulfur content (Cariaco Trench) and one with a low sulfur content (San Pedro Martir Basin).

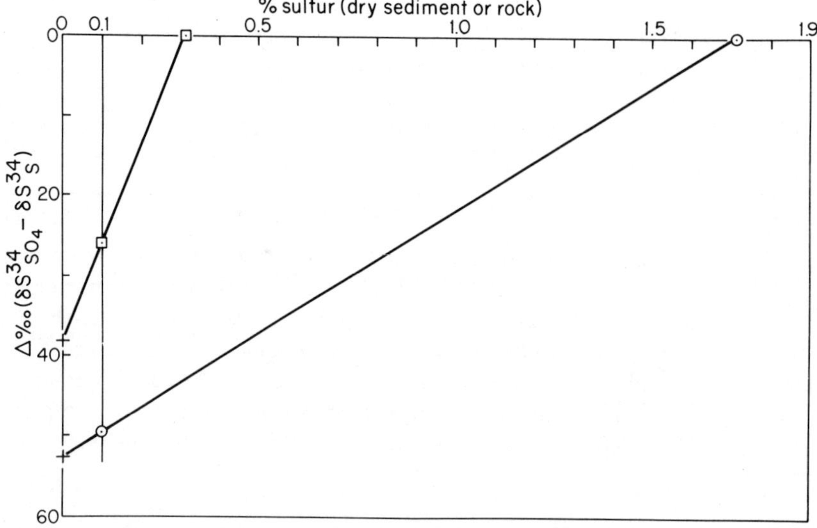

Fig. 33. Approximate determination of $\Delta\ \delta S^{34}$ ‰ between seawater sulfate and pyrite formed at the sediment-water interface. See text for discussion. After Sweeney and Kaplan (1973b).

The effect of sulfate reduction during burial is subtracted from the measured value of δS^{34} of the sulfide in the sediment. This is accomplished by subtracting 0.1% sulfur, with a δS^{34} value of contemporaneous seawater, from the total sulfide measured. For both examples, the δS^{34} of seawater is taken as $+20‰$. The Δ measured is the difference between $+20‰$ and the δS^{34} of the pyrite measured in the sediment.

This value is plotted on the vertical line at % S $= 0.1$. The percent sulfur measured in the sediment is plotted on the $\Delta = 0$ abscissa. Projection of the line connecting these points will intersect the % S $= 0$ ordinate at the approximate Δ value of the pyrite formed at the sediment surface. The δS^{34} of the pyrite formed at the sediment surface is determined by subtracting the Δ values from $+20‰$.

Example 1

San Pedro Martir Basin (501 to 511 cm); % S = 0.3; $\delta S^{34} = -6.1‰$

$\Delta(‰)$ measured sulfide = [+20 − (−6.1)] = 26.1
$\Delta(‰)$ sulfide formed at the sediment surface = 38
δS^{34} (‰) sulfide formed at the sediment surface = −18

Example 2

Cariaco Trench 2-6 (54 to 64 cm), % S = 1.72; $\delta S^{34} = -29.4‰$

$\Delta(‰)$ measured sulfide = +20 − (−29.4) = 49.4
$\Delta(‰)$ sulfide formed at the sediment surface = 52.5
δS^{34} sulfide formed at the sediment surface = −32.5

From these examples, it is obvious that the greatest change during diagenesis occurs in the sediment containing least sulfur.

If extensive ionic diffusion of sulfate occurs during burial, the weighted δS^{34} sulfide formed from dissolved sulfate is unknown. However, if for example 1, one-and-a-half times normal surface concentration (at +20‰) is considered to be added to the sediment during burial, then % S = 0.15 would be used instead of % S = 0.1 in Fig. 33. This would produce a δS^{34} of about −30‰ for the pyrite formed at the sediment surface, which is 12‰ lighter than the value calculated, and 10‰ lighter than actually measured in pyrite from surface sediment of San Pedro Martir Basin. For example 2, if diffusion increases normal seawater concentration by threefold, then the pyrite formed at the sediment surface would be about −40‰, which is 8‰ lighter than calculated for the closed system and 9 to 10‰ lighter than that measured for pyrite in the larger size fractions in the Cariaco Trench (Sweeney, 1972).

For ancient sedimentary deposits, the limits to the interpretation that sulfate reduction during burial is the cause of isotopically heavy pyrite are: (1) the δS^{34} of contemporaneous seawater sulfate, (2) the amount of pyrite present (the smaller the pyrite content, the less enrichment in S^{32}), and (3) an open or closed basin with respect to ocean water circulation, which may control δS^{34} of pyrite first formed at the sediment-water interface.

6. Summary of Sulfur Diagenesis in Sediments

Sulfur in the modern marine environment exists primarily in two forms, dissolved sulfate or pyrite. The former is introduced by rivers during weathering and erosion, the latter is formed *in situ* in sediments. Seawater sulfate can be reduced by bacteria to the oxidation level of sulfide. This reduction can take place in the water column provided that the circulation is greatly restricted. More frequently, the site of sulfate reduction is in the underlying sediments. In either case, the production of sulfide is closely related to the availability of organic matter.

The sulfide so formed may react in several ways, summarized schematically in Fig. 34. The dominant pathway probably involves reaction with iron oxide (e.g., equation 28). In addition to elemental sulfur, the products formed at neutral pH will include an acid-volatile sulfide phase. Of the two acid-volatile iron sulfides presumed to be important in marine sediments (mackinawite, $FeS_{0.9}$ and greigite, Fe_3S_4), only mackinawite has been demonstrated to form in the laboratory by reaction at neutral pH between iron oxide and dissolved sulfide. Nonetheless, greigite is implicated as an intermediate in pyrite formation by its important role in producing the "framboidal" texture commonly observed in sedimentary pyrite (Fig. 9). Therefore, a reaction described by equation 79 probably converts mackinawite to greigite (Berner, 1971b).

$$3\ FeS + S^{\circ} \rightarrow Fe_3S_4 \tag{79}$$

Greigite will then transform to pyrite (equation 80) through further addition of elemental sulfur (Berner, 1971b).

$$Fe_3S_4 + 2\ S^{\circ} \rightarrow 3\ FeS_2 \tag{80}$$

Direct formation of greigite by reaction with iron oxide, at neutral pH, while as yet unsubstantiated by laboratory experiments, is tentatively included as a possibility in Fig. 34. The direct formation of pyrite in marine sediments without prior acid-

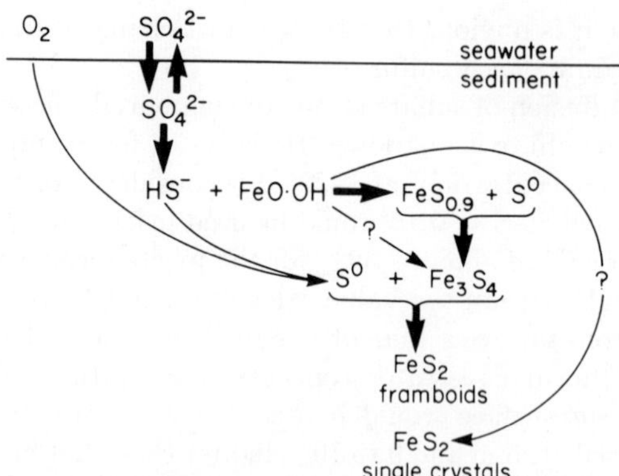

Fig. 34. Summary of pyrite formation in the upper layers of marine sediments. Proposed pathways and intermediates are shown that lead to pyrite framboids and single crystal formation. Sulfate is shown as exchanging rapidly with seawater sulfate. After relatively shallow burial exchange should not occur.

volatile sulfide formation is also shown in Fig. 34, as there is some evidence that this reaction occurs in the laboratory at pH < 7. If a prerequisite to the direct precipitation of pyrite is undersaturation with respect to acid-volatile sulfides, then the low concentrations of dissolved H_2S in sediments compared to laboratory experiments could cause undersaturation even at neutral or slightly basic pH. Direct precipitation of pyrite may be the cause of single crystal as opposed to framboid formation. An alternative source for these single crystals is direct reaction of mackinawite with elemental sulfur to form pyrite without intermediate greigite formation (equation 30). This reaction has been demonstrated by Sweeney and Kaplan (1973a).

The sulfide formed by sulfate reduction will react with other reagents besides iron oxide. Additional sources of iron are present in sediments, for example, as iron bound in crystal lattices of silicate minerals or as organically bound iron. This iron will presumably react to form acid-volatile sulfides, which can then undergo the transformations previously described. Some sulfide will not react with iron or iron-bearing phases, but will be oxidized to elemental sulfur or sulfate ion. This oxidation is indicated in Fig. 34 as occurring by reaction with molecular oxygen from the overlying water, although the process of elemental sulfur formation in sediments is not well understood.

Pyrite formation in nearshore sediments with abundant organic matter is in large part a phenomenon associated with the sediment layers at or immediately below the sediment-water interface. This conclusion is reached from several lines of evidence. When closely spaced samples are available from near the sediment surface, reduced sulfur is abundant in the shallowest sample (e.g., Table XIX). Furthermore, factors relating to pyrite formation show constant values below the top several centimeters. This is the case for the organic carbon-to-sulfur ratio in Kiel Bay (Fig. 12), as well as the "degree of pyritization" determined by Berner (1970) for Connecticut coastal muds (Table XV).

A linear relationship has been demonstrated between organic carbon and reduced sulfur (Fig. 10) when both are measured at various depths in cores from different areas. This correlation is interpreted as indicating that sulfate reducing bacteria rapidly metabolize a preferred fraction of detrital organic matter in the vicinity of the sediment-water interface. Subsequent modifications of this initial carbon-to-sulfur ratio by continuing sulfate reduction are frequently obscured by variations in the rate of deposition of organic carbon (e.g., Fig. 11). The existence of a highly reactive fraction of organic matter at the sediment surface has also been suggested by Berner (1972) to account for rates of sulfate reduction (pyrite formation) in excess of those predicted by a diffusion reaction model.

Sulfur isotope measurements of reduced sulfur in sediments indicate a marked enrichment in S^{32} with respect to S^{34}. These data are interpreted as indicating bacterial sulfate reduction in the presence of an effectively infinite reservoir of sulfate (i.e., seawater). This limits the majority of pyrite formation to a zone near the sediment surface in which relatively rapid exchange with seawater is possible. It is not known to what depth in sediments exchange between porewater and seawater sulfate can occur. The sulfur isotopic data, however, place more stringent requirements on the place of pyrite formation than do the other arguments presented above, which demonstrate measurable addition of reduced sulfur to the solid phases several centimeters deep in the sediment where exchange with seawater is less likely. It may therefore be concluded that in many nearshore sediments, the rate of pyrite formation is most rapid at the sediment surface and decreases very rapidly with depth. This has been stressed by Berner (1972).

Sulfate reduction will in many cases continue (at reduced rates) over sediment thicknesses much greater than the relatively thin layer that supports the majority of authigenic pyrite formation. This is evidenced by decreasing concentration of porewater sulfate with depth. The decrease in rate of sulfate reduction at depth may be associated with the ability of sulfate-reducing bacteria to metabolize only certain compounds that are rapidly depleted near the sediment surface. A lower limit to the amount of sulfur added to the sediments can be calculated by the difference in concentration between seawater sulfate and the observed porewater concentration (i.e., the closed-system amount). For complete reduction, this will amount to between 0.1 to 0.3% S, depending on water content of the sediment. Additional sulfate will flow into the sediments by diffusion, making the closed-system calculation an underestimate of the sulfate actually reduced.

The diffusion of sulfate and sulfide in porewaters is linked by charge balance requirements (equation 76) and will depend, to a first approximation, on the magnitude of ionic diffusion coefficients, the magnitudes of gradients exhibited by diffusing species, and the sedimentation rate. Variations in the latter two quantities in particular imply that diffusion will not assume the same relative importance in all diagenetic regimes (Table XVIII). However, even under circumstances where diffusion could be of large relative importance, available evidence suggests that in the sediments studied, it may be relatively unimportant (below the upper few centimeters) in terms of defining the overall outcome of sulfur diagenesis. This evidence includes the arguments that most of the authigenic sulfides are forming near the sediment-water interface. In addition, isotope and mass balance calculations on pyrite in different size fractions separated from Santa Catalina Basin sediments indicate that reduction of trapped sulfate is sufficient to explain the observed changes. Rayleigh distillation calculations (equations 77 and 78) on dissolved sulfate from several cores are consistent with the assumption of only a minor input of sulfate by diffusion. At relatively large depth in Santa Barbara Basin sediments, where sulfur diagenesis is essentially complete, there is no indication that large amounts of isotopically heavy sulfate has been added, when compared to shallower depths in the same core. Finally, in the top layers of sediments from two shallow cores in the vicinity of the Santa Barbara Basin, the amount of reduced sulfur present was similar, despite the fact that one core exhibited a steep gradient in porewater sulfate, whereas the other showed no such gradient (Table XVI, Fig. 15). If it may be concluded that diffusion of sulfate is of minor importance in sulfur diagenesis, then it follows that diffusion of sulfide will also be minor since the two processes are coupled.

7. Strataform Ore Deposits

Base metal sulfides intermixed with pyrite, found conformably layered within bedding planes of sediments, are referred to as strataform deposits. The metal sulfides always contain iron sulfides (pyrite and/or pyrrhotite), but zinc sulfide (sphalerite), lead sulfide (galena), and copper sulfide (chalcopyrite and bornite) are common associates. Zinc is always more abundant than lead, and copper, if present, may be in higher concentration than zinc. The metal sulfides occur in a variety of marine sediments, very often in association with highly carbonaceous shales and frequently in association with dolomite. Commonly, the sedimentary facies are overlain or underlain by volcanics (often pyroclastic tuffs), or horizontally interfingered with volcanic rocks. The mineralized zones may extend laterally from hundreds of meters to several kilometers or possibly over 100 km, as in the Kupferschiefer ores of Europe. Their thickness may vary from a fraction of a centimeter for individual beds to many tens of meters for a stratigraphic unit. A detailed account of such deposits, together with the prevailing hypotheses concerning their origin, has recently been given by Stanton (1972). As this type of deposit constitutes the most important source for the world's supply of Zn and Pb and a significant source of Cu, it is of interest to briefly examine the mechanism of formation of strataform ores in light of the preceding discussion on metal sulfide deposition in recent marine sediments.

As stated earlier, Fe is the most abundant transition metal in normal marine sediments, the average content of Zn, Pb, and Cu in shale (equivalent to continental shelf sediment) is 80, 20, and 57 ppm, respectively (Krauskopf, 1967). In order to concentrate the ores to the range of 1% metal content of the sediment, it would therefore require concentration factors of approximately 125 for Zn, 500 for Pb, and 176 for Cu. However, even in the most organic-rich normal marine sediment, the concentration factor rarely exceeds three- or fourfold over their average concentration. The actual binding of these metals within the sediment is not known. If they are introduced within detrital minerals, then there is little opportunity for the metal to form sulfides. However, it is probable that a significant proportion of trace metals may be introduced as adsorbants on calcareous and opaline tests (Presley et al., 1972), as well as iron oxide phases. Irrespective of its form, the concentration factor required for ore formation is too great to allow metal sulfide in ore concentration to accumulate from the sediment source alone.

Producing sufficient sulfide in sediment does not present the problem attending metal concentration. If it is accepted, based on a previous discussion, that $\approx 20\%$ of the organic carbon depositing is used for sulfate reduction, sediment containing $\approx 5\%$ organic carbon should provide $>1\%$ reduced sulfur in the sediment. Many areas on the present ocean floor contain considerably higher contents of organic carbon: for example, unnamed fjords in Norway (Strøm, 1939), 23.4% C; Tanner Basin on the southern California continental shelf (Emery, 1960), 11% C; and continental shelf west of Walvis Bay, Africa (Calvert and Price, 1971), 26.5% C. Rates of sedimentation in nearshore environments may range from 50 cm/1000 yr (Emery, 1960), to 400 cm/1000 yr (Gucluer and Gross, 1964, for the Saanich Inlet, and Koide et al., 1972, for the Santa Barbara Basin). Corrected for loss of water by compaction, this would give a range of accumulation of 10 to >100 m/10^6 yr, for lithified sediment with $\approx 1\%$ water content. It is therefore evident, that thicknesses commensurate with known mineralized strataform deposits can form in present-day basins containing sulfide-rich sediments in times measuring $<10^6$ yr.

With the exception of the Red Sea deposits (Degens and Ross, 1969), no other basins on the ocean floor are presently known to be depositing base metal sulfides. Because there are areas on the ocean floor that could generate sulfide contents $>5\%$ of the sediment, it is obvious that a mechanism must exist for transport of metals to the site of deposition. This mechanism must include a source of the heavy metals and a driving force for mobilizing the metals. In the Red Sea, the source of metals could either be submarine basalts associated with sea floor spreading or alternatively large thicknesses of Miocene shales. The carrying fluids are brines formed by solution of Miocene evaporites. The driving energy may be the geothermal gradient of burial of the sedimentary sequences, but more likely, it is heating derived from the convection cell underlying the Red Sea rift. Copper has often been noted as an associate of submarine basalts (for example, British Columbia Karmutsen pillow basalts on N. Vancouver Island) (Carlisle, 1963). It was recently reported in basalt gathered by the Deep Sea Drilling Project from Ninety East Ridge in the Indian Ocean (Von der Borch and Sclater, 1972). Anomalously high content of zinc (as sphalerite) was found in sediment from Site 105 JOIDES (at base of continental rise, eastern United States), at depths of 250 to 304 m, associated with zeolites and altered volcanic ash (Lancelot et al., 1972). The δS^{34} of the sulfide associated with the sphalerite was measured in this laboratory to be $\approx -30‰$, a result consistent with a marine origin for sulfur.

It therefore appears that our present oceans contain sufficient sites for strataform sulfides to deposit if a transport and enrichment mechanism exists for emplacement of the metals. Inland seas, adjacent to areas of high heat flow (by plate movement or convection cells), such as the Gulf of California are obvious candidate locations for this to occur.

Acknowledgments

We wish to thank Dr. R. E. Sweeney for discussion and making available many unpublished data, and Dr. S. Ben-Yaakov for suggestions on how to formulate the discussion on the relative significance of diffusion in sediments. Thanks also to Barrie Wall and George Claypool for editorial suggestions. One of us (I. R. Kaplan) received valuable stimulation from a sojourn at C.S.I.R.O., Laboratory of Mineral Research North Ryde, N.S.W., Australia during 1971 with partial support from the Guggenheim Memorial Foundation. Some of the data presented here were measured on sediment collected in the Gulf of California in 1972 by the Hypogene Expedition, operated by the Institute of Marine Resources, Scripps Institution of Oceanography. Special acknowledgment is made here to Drs. Pat Wilde and William Menard, co-chief scientists for assistance in sampling. The studies were supported by a contract from the Atomic Energy Commission AT(04-3)-34, P.A. 134.

References

Baas Becking, L. G. M., 1925. Studies on the sulfur bacteria. *Ann. Bot.*, Lond., **39**, 613–650.

Bader, R. G., R. D. Gerard, W. E. Benson, H. W. Bolli, W. W. Hay, W. T. Rothwell, Jr., M. H. Ruef, W. R. Reidel, and F. L. Sayles, 1970. Introduction. In *Initial Reports of the Deep Sea Drilling Project.* Vol. IV. U.S. Government Printing Office, Washington, D.C., pp. 3–17.

Ben-Yaakov, S., 1972a. Diffusion of seawater ions. I. Diffusion of seawater into a dilute solution. *Geochim. Cosmochim. Acta,* **36**, 1395–1406.

Ben-Yaakov. S., 1972b. The incremental concentration cell and its application for studying ionic diffusion in seawater. Electrochem. Soc. Am., Fall meeting, Miami Beach, Florida, October 1970. In press.

Ben-Yaakov, S., 1973. pH buffering of pore water of recent anoxic marine sediments. *Limnol. Oceanog.* In press.

Berner, R. A., 1962. Tetragonal iron sulfide. *Science,* **137**, 669.

Berner, R. A., 1964a. Distribution and diagenesis of sulfur in some sediments from the Gulf of California. *Mar. Geol.*, **1**, 117–140.

Berner, R. A., 1964b. Iron sulfides formed from aqueous solution at low temperatures and atmospheric pressure. *J. Geol.*, **72**, 293–306.

Berner, R. A., 1964c. Stability fields of iron minerals in anaerobic marine sediments. *J. Geol.*, **72**, 826–834.

Berner, R. A., 1964d. An idealized model of dissolved sulfate distribution in recent sediments. *Geochim. Cosmochim. Acta,* **28**, 1497–1503.

Berner, R. A., 1967. Thermodynamic stability of sedimentary iron sulfides. *Am. J. Sci.*, **265**, 773–785.

Berner, R. A., 1969a. The synthesis of framboidal pyrite. *Econ. Geol.*, **64**, 383–384.

Berner, R. A., 1969b. Migration of iron and sulfur within anaerobic sediments during early diagenesis. *Am. J. Sci.*, **267**, 19–42.

Berner, R. A., 1970. Sedimentary pyrite formation. *Am. J. Sci.*, **268**, 1–23.

Berner, R. A., M. R. Scott, and C. Thomlinson, 1970. Carbonate alkalinity in the pore waters of anoxic marine sediments. *Limnol. Oceanog.*, **15**, 544–549.

Berner, R. A., 1971a. Worldwide sulfur pollution of rivers. *J. Geophys. Res.*, **76**, 6597–6600.

Berner, R. A., 1971b. *Principles of Chemical Sedimentology.* McGraw-Hill, New York, 240 pp.

Berner, R. A., 1972. Sulfate reduction, pyrite formation and the oceanic sulfur budget. In Nobel Symposium 20; "The Changing Chemistry of the Oceans," D. Dyrssen and D. Jagner, eds. Almqvist and Wiksel, Stockholm, Wiley Interscience Division, pp. 347–361.

Bigeleisen, J., 1949. The relative reaction velocities of isotopic molecules. *J. Chem. Phys.*, **17**, 675–678.

Bischoff, J. L. and T. L. Ku, 1971. Pore fluids of recent marine sediments: II. Anoxic sediments of 35° to 45°N Gibraltar to Mid-Atlantic ridge. *J. Sediment. Petrol.*, **41**, 1008–1017.

Bonatti, E., D. E. Fisher, O. Joensuu, and H. S. Rydell, 1971. Post-depositional mobility of some transition elements, phosphorus, uranium, and thorium in deep sea sediments. *Geochim. Cosmochim. Acta,* **35**, 189–201.

Borodovskiy, O., 1965. Transformation of organic matter in bottom sediment and its early diagenesis. *Mar. Geol.*, **3**, 83–114.

Bostrom, K., 1967. Some pH controlling redox reactions in natural waters. In *Equilibrium Concepts in Natural Water Systems.* A symposium sponsored by DWAWC, Am. Chem. Soc. Publ., Washington, D.C., 344 pp.

Broecker, W. S., 1971. A kinetic model for the chemical composition of seawater. *Quat. Res.*, **1**, 188–207.

Burton, S. D. and R. Y. Morita, 1964. Effect of catalase and cultural conditions on growth of *Beggiatoa. J. Bacteriol.*, **88**, 1755–1761.

Butlin, K. R. and J. R. Postgate, 1954. The microbiological formation of sulphur in Cyrenaican lakes. In *Biology of Deserts*. J. L. Cloudsley-Thompson, ed. Inst. Biology, London, pp. 112–122.

Calvert, S. E. and N. B. Price, 1971. Recent sediments of the Southwest African Shelf. In *The Geology of East Atlantic Continental Margin*. F. M. Delang, ed. Inst. Geol. Sci. Rep. No. 70/16, 171–185.

Carlisle, D., 1963. Pillow breccias and their aquagene tuffs, Quadra Island, British Columbia. *J. Geol.*, **71**, 48–71.

Carroll, D., 1958. Role of clay minerals in the transportation of iron. *Geochim. Cosmochim. Acta*, **14**, 1–27.

Carstea, D. D., 1968. Formation of hydroxy-Al- and Fe interlayers in montmorillonite and vermiculite: influence of particle size and temperature. *Clays and Clay Minerals*, **16**, 231–238.

Caspers, H., 1957. The Black Sea and Sea of Azov. In *Treatise on Marine Ecology and Paleoecology*. Vol. 1. J. W. Hedepeth, ed. Memoir 67, Geol. Soc. of Am., New York, 801 pp.

Challenger, F., 1959. *Aspects of the Organic Chemistry of Sulphur*. Academic Press, New York, 253 pp.

Chave, K. E., 1965. Carbonates: association with organic matter in surface seawater. *Science*, **148**, 1723–1724.

Chave, K. E. and E. Suess, 1967. Suspended minerals in seawater. *Trans. of the N.Y. Acad. of Sci.*, II, Vol. 29, 991–1000.

Chester, R., 1965. Elemental geochemistry of marine sediments. In *Chemical Oceanography*. J. P. Riley and G. Skirrow, eds. Academic Press, New York, pp. 23–80.

Clark, A. H., 1966. Some comments on the composition and stability relation of mackinawite. *Neves Jahrb. Mineral. Monatsh.*, **10**, 300–304.

Clark, A. H. and A. M. Clark, 1968. Electron microprobe analysis of mackinawite from the Ylojarvi deposit, Finland. *Neves Jahrb. Mineral. Monatsh.*, **6**, 259–268.

Cline, J. D., 1969. Spectrophotometric determination of hydrogen sulfide in natural waters. *Limnol. Oceanog.*, **14**, 454–458.

Curtis, C. D., 1967. Diagenetic iron minerals in some British Carboniferous sediments. *Geochim. Cosmochim. Acta*, **31**, 2109–2123.

Degens, E. T., 1965. *Geochemistry of Sediments: A Brief Survey*. Prentice-Hall, Englewood Cliffs, N.J., 342 pp.

Degens, E. T. and D. A. Ross, 1969. *Hot Brines and Recent Heavy Metal Deposits in the Red Sea*. Springer-Verlag, New York, 600 pp.

Dell, C. I., 1972. An occurrence of greigite in Lake Superior sediments. *Am. Min.*, **57**, 1303–1304.

Delwiche, C. C. and P. L. Steyn, 1970. Nitrogen isotope fractionation in soils and microbial reactions. *Env. Sci. & Technol.*, **4**, 929–935.

Doss, B., 1912. Melnkovit, ein neues eisenbisulfid, und seine bedeutung fur die genesis der kieslagerstatten. Zeitschr. prakt. *Geologie*, **20**, 453–483.

Doyle, R. W., 1968. Identification and solubility of iron sulfide in anaerobic lake sediment. *Am. J. Sci.*, **266**, 980–994.

Drever, J. L. 1971a. Magnesium-iron replacement in clay minerals in anoxic marine sediments. *Science*, **172**, 1334–1336.

Drever, J. L., 1971b. Early diagenesis of clay minerals, Rio Ameco Basin, *J. Sediment. Petrol.*, **41**, 982–994.

Duursma, E. K., 1966. Molecular diffusion of radioisotopes in interstitial waters of sediments. In *Disposal of Radioactive Wastes into Seas, Oceans, and Surface Waters*. International Atomic Energy Agency, 355 pp.

Dunham, K., 1961. Black shale, oil, and sulfide ore. *Advan. Sci.*, **18**, 284–299.

Edmond, J. M., 1970. High precision determination of titration alkalinity and total carbon dioxide content of seawater by potentiometric titration. *Deep-Sea Res.*, **17**, 737–750.

Emery, K. O., 1960. *The Sea off Southern California*. Wiley, New York, 366 pp.

Emery, K. O. and S. C. Rittenberg, 1952. Early diagenesis of California basin sediments in relation to origin of oil. *Am. Assoc. Pet. Geol. Bull.*, **36**, 735–806.

Ernst, W. G., 1969. *Earth Materials*. Prentice Hall, Englewood Cliffs, N.J., 143 pp.

Evans, H. T., Jr., C. Milton, E. C. T. Chao, I. Adler, C. Mead, B. Ingram, and R. A. Berner, 1964. Valleriite and the new iron sulfide, mackinawite, U.S. Geol. Surv. Prof. Paper 475-D, D64–D69.

Farrand, M., 1970. Framboidal sulfides precipitated synthetically. *Min. Deposita (Berl.)*, **5**, 237–247.

Feely, H. W. and J. L. Kulp, 1957. Origin of Gulf Coast saltdome sulfur deposits. *Amer. Assoc. Petrol. Geol. Bull.*, **41**, 1802–1853.

Feld, W., 1911. Uber die beldung von eisenbisulfid (FeS_2 in L'bsungen und die entstehung der naturlichen pyritlager, Zeitschr fur anew. *Chemie*, **24**, 97–103.

Fleming, R. A., 1940. The composition of plankton and units for reporting population and production. *Proc. Sixth Pacific Congress California 1939*, **3**, 534–540.

Galliher, E. W., 1933. The sulfur cycle in sediments. *J. Sediment. Petrol.*, **3**, 51–63.

Garrels, R. M. and M. E. Thompson, 1962. A chemical model for seawater at 25°C and one atmosphere total pressure. *Amer. J. Sci.*, **260**, 57–66.

Garrels, R. M. and C. L. Christ, 1965. *Solutions, Minerals, and Equilibria.* Harper and Row, New York, 450 pp.

Garrels, R. M. and F. T. Mackenzie, 1971. Evolution of the sedimentary rocks. Norton, New York, 397 pp.

Garrels, R. M. and F. T. Mackenzie, 1972. A quantitative model for the sedimentary rock cycle. *Mar. Chem.*, **1**, 27–41.

Ghose, T. K. and T. Wiken, 1955. Inhibition of bacterial sulfate-reduction in presence of short-chain fatty acids. *Physiol. Plantarum*, **8**, 116–135.

Golubev, U. S. and A. A. Garibyants, 1971. Heterogeneous processes of geochemical migration. Consultants Bureau, New York, 150 pp.

Goldhaber, M. B. and I. R. Kaplan, 1973. The apparent dissociation constants of H_2S in seawater. In preparation.

Gucluer, S. M. and M. G. Gross, 1964. Recent marine sediments in Saanich Inlet, a stagnant marine basin. *Limnol. Oceanog.*, **9**, 359–376.

Harmsen, G. W., A. Quipsel, and N. R. Otsen, 1954. Observations on the formation and oxidation of pyrite in the soil. *Plant and Soil*, **5**, 324–348.

Harrison, A. G. and H. G. Thode, 1957. The kinetic isotope effect in the chemical reduction of sulphate *Trans. Faraday. Soc.*, **53**, 1648–1651.

Harrison, A. G. and H. G. Thode, 1958. Mechanism of the bacterial reduction of sulphate from isotope fractionation studies. *Trans. Faraday Soc.*, **54**, 84–92.

Hartmann, U. M. and H. Nielsen, 1969. δS^{34} werte in rezenten meeressedimenten und ihre deutung am beispiel einiger sedimentprofile aus der west lichen ostsee. *Geol. Rundschau*, **58**, 621–655.

Hirst, D. M., 1962. The geochemistry of modern sediments from the Gulf of Paria—I. The relationship between the mineralogy and the distribution of major elements. *Geochim. Cosmochim. Acta*, **26**, 309–334.

Hoering, T. C., 1967. Organic acids from the oxidation of recent sediments. Carnegie Inst., Ann. Report Geophys. Lab. 1966–1967, 515–526.

Holser, W. T. and I. R. Kaplan, 1966. Isotope geochemistry of sedimentary sulfates. *Chem. Geol.*, **1**, 93–135.

Hulsemann, J. and K. O. Emery, 1961. Stratification in recent sediments of Santa Barbara as controlled by organisms and water character. *J. Geol.*, **69**, 279–290.

Iya, K. K. and M. Sreenivasaya, 1944. A preliminary study of the bacterial flora associated with sulphur deposits on the east coast (Masulipatam). *Curr. Sci.*, **13**, 316–317.

James, H. L., 1966. Chemistry of the iron-rich sedimentary rocks. U.S. Surv. Prof. Paper 440-W, U.S. Government Printing Office, Washington, D.C.

Jedwab, J., 1967. Mineralization engreigite de debris vegetaux d'une vase recente. *Soc. Belge Geologie Bull.*, **76**, 1–19.

Jones, G. G. and R. L. Starkey, 1957. Fractionation of stable isotopes of sulfur by microorganisms and their role in deposition of native sulfur. *Appl. Microbiol.*, **5**, 111–118.

Kaplan, I. R., 1962. Sulfur isotope fractionations during microbiological transformations in the laboratory and in marine sediments. Ph.D. thesis, University of Southern California, 213 pp.

Kaplan, I. R. and S. C. Rittenberg, 1962. The microbiological fractionation of sulfur isotopes. In *Biogeochemistry of Sulfur Isotopes.* M. L. Jensen, ed. Yale University Press, New Haven, Conn., pp. 89–93.

Kaplan, I. R., K. O. Emery, and S. C. Rittenberg, 1963. The distribution and isotopic abundance of sulfur in recent marine sediments off Southern California. *Geochim. Cosmochim. Acta*, **27**, 297–331.

Kaplan, I. R. and S. C. Rittenberg, 1964. Microbiological fractionation of sulfur isotopes. *J. Gen. Microbiol.*, **34**, 195–212.

Kaplan, I. R. and A. Friedman, 1970. Biological productivity in the Dead Sea: Part I. Microorganisms in the water column. *Israel J. Chem.*, **8**, 513–528.

Kemp, A. L. W. and H. G. Thode, 1968. The mechanism of the bacterial reduction of sulphate and of sulphite from isotope fractionation studies. *Geochim. Cosmochim. Acta*, **32**, 71–91.

Kemper, W. D. and J. C. van Schaik, 1966. Diffusion of salts in clay water systems. *Soil Sci. Amer. Proc.*, **30**, 534–540.

Kobayashi, K. and M. Nomura, 1972. Iron sulfides in the sediment cores from the sea of Japan and their geophysical implications. *Earth and Planet Sci. Letters*, **16**, 200–208.

Koide, M., A. Soutar, and E. D. Goldberg, 1972. Marine geochronology with ^{210}Pb. *Earth and Planet. Sci. Letters*, **14**, 442–446.

Kizak, L. M. and P. M. Huang, 1971. Adsorption of hydroxy-Al by certain phyllosilicates and its relation to K/Ca cation exchange selectivity. *Clays and Clay Min.*, **19**, 95–102.

Krauskopf, K. B., 1967. *Introduction to Geochemistry*. McGraw-Hill, New York, 720 pp.

Kuznetsov, S. I., M. V. Ivanov, and M. N. Lyalikova, 1963. *Introduction to Geological Microbiology*. Translated by P. T. Broneer. McGraw-Hill, New York, 252 pp.

Lamanna, C. and M. F. Mallette, 1953. *Basic Bacteriology*. Williams and Wilkins, Baltimore, 677 pp.

Lancelot, Y., J. C. Hathaway, and L. D. Hollister, 1972. Lithology of sediments from the western North Atlantic: Leg XI, Deep Sea Drilling Project. In *Initial Reports of the Deep Sea Drilling Project*. Vol. 11. Hollister, C. O., Ewing, J. I. et al., eds. U.S. Government Printing Office, Washington, D.C. pp. 901–950.

Langmuir, D. and D. O. Whittemore, 1972. Variations in the stability of precipitated ferric oxyhydroxides. In *Nonequilibrium Systems in Natural Water Chemistry*. Am. Chem. Soc. Publ., 106 pp. 209–234.

Lepp, H., 1957. Synthesis and probable geologic significance of Melnikovite. *Econ. Geol.*, **52**, 528–535.

Love, L. G., 1965. Micro-organic material with diagenetic pyrite from the Lower Proterozoic Mount Isa shale and a carboniferous shale. *Proc. Yorkshire Geol. Soc.*, **35**, 187–202.

Love, L. G., 1967. Early diagenetic iron sulfide in recent sediments of the Wash (England). *Sedimentology*, **9**, 327–352.

Love, L. G., 1969. Sulfides of metals in recent sediments. In *Sedimentary Ores: Ancient and Modern*. Rev. Ed. Proc. of the 15th Inter-University Geol. Cong., 1967. Published by Dept. of Geol., University of Leicester, England, pp. 31–60.

Love, L. G., 1971. Early diagenetic polyframboidal pyrite, primary and redeposited, from the Wenlockian Denbigh Grit group, Conway, North Wales, U.K., *J. Sediment. Petrol.*, **41, 1038–1044.**

Love, L. G. and G. C. Amstutz, 1966. Review of microscopic pyrite. *Fortschr. Miner.*, **43**, 273–309.

Love, L. G. and G. C. Amstutz, 1969. Framboidal pyrite in two andesites. *N. Jahrbuch. f. Mineralogie Monat.*, **3**, 97–108.

Manheim, F. T., 1970. The diffusion of ions in unconsolidated sediments. *Earth and Planet. Sci. Letters*, **9**, 307–309.

Manheim, F. T., K. M. Chan, and F. L. Sayles, 1970. Interstitial water studies on small core samples. Deep Sea Drilling Project, Leg. 5. In *Initial Reports of the Deep Sea Drilling Project*. Vol. V. D. A. McManus et al., eds. U.S. Government Printing Office, Washington, D.C.

McManus, D. A. et al., 1970. *Initial Reports of the Deep Sea Drilling Project*. Vol. V. U.S. Government Printing Office, Washington, D.C.

Mechalas, B. J. and S. C. Rittenberg, 1960. Energy coupling in *Desulfovibrio desulfuricans*. *J. Bacteriol.*, **80**, 501–507.

Menon, K. K., 1967. Origin of diagenetic pyrite in the Quilon Limestone, Kerala, India. *Nature*, 213, 1219–1220.

Miller, L. P., 1950. Tolerance of sulfate-reducing bacteria to hydrogen sulfide. *Contrib. Boyce Thompson Inst.*, **16**, 73–83.

Moore, III., J. R., 1963. Bottom sediments studies, Buzzards Bay, Massachusetts. *J. Sediment. Petrol.*, **33**, 511–558.

Morice, J. A., L. V. C. Rees, and D. T. Rickard, 1969. Mossbauer studies of iron sulfides. *J. Inorg. Chem.*, **31**, 3797–3802.

Morgan, J. J., 1967. Applications and limitations of chemical thermodynamics to natural water systems. In *Equilibrium Concepts in Natural Water Systems*. Am. Chem. Soc., Washington, D.C., pp. 1–29.

Murray, J. and R. Irvine, 1895. On the chemical changes which take place in the composition of seawater associated with blue muds on the floor of the ocean. *Trans. Roy. Soc. Edinburgh*, **37**, 481–508.

Nakai, N., 1963. Biochemical oxidation of sulfur and sulfide minerals by mixed cultures, and the behaviors of stable sulfur isotopes. *J. Earth Sci.*, **11**, Nagoya University, 279–296.

Nakai, N. and M. L. Jensen, 1964. The kinetic isotope effect in the bacterial reduction and oxidation of sulfur. *Geochim. Cosmochim. Acta*, **28**, 1893–1912.

Nathansohn, A., 1902. Uber eine neue Gruppe von Schwefelbakterien und ihren stoffwechsel. *Mitt. Zool. Sta. Neapol.*, **15**, 655–680.

Nicholas, D. J. D., 1967. Biological sulfate reduction. *Mineralium Deposita*, **2**, 169–180.

Nielsen, H., 1966. Schwefelisotope im marinen kreislauf und da sδ^{34}S der Fruherer Meere. *Geol. Rundschou.*, **55**, 160–172.

Nissenbaum, A., B. J. Presley and I. R. Kaplan, 1972. Early diagenesis in a reducing fjord, Saanich Inlet, British Columbia—I. Chemical and isotopic changes in major components of interstitial water. *Geochim. Cosmochim. Acta*, **36**, 1007–1027.

Nissenbaum, A. and I. R. Kaplan, 1972. Chemical and isotopic evidence for the *in situ* origin of marine humic substances. *Limnol. Oceanog.*, **17**, 570–582.

Olsen, S. R. and W. D. Kemper, 1968. Movement of nutrients to plant roots. *Adv. Agron.*, **20**, 91–151.

Ostroumov, E. A., 1953. *Different Forms of Combined Sulfur in the Sediments of the Black Sea.* Trud. Inst. Okeanol., Akad. Nauk S.S.S.R. Vol. 7. pp. 70–90.

Ostroumov, E. A. and V. M. Shilov, 1956. Distribution of sulfides of iron and hydrogen in deep sediments in the Northwestern Pacific Ocean. *Geochemistry*, **7**, 669–683.

Palacas, J. G., V. E. Swanson, and A. H. Love, 1968. Organic geochemistry of recent sediments in the Choctawhatchee Bay area, Florida; A preliminary report. U.S.G.S. Prof. Paper 600-C, C97–C106.

Park R. and S. Epstein, 1960. Carbon isotope fractionation during photosynthesis. *Geochim. Cosmochim. Acta*, **21**, 110–126.

Pettijohn, F. J., 1949. *Sedimentary Rocks*. Harper and Row, New York, 718 pp.

Postgate, J. R., 1951. The reduction of sulphur compounds by *Desulfovibrio desulphuricans*. *J. Gen. Microbiol.*, **5**, 725–738.

Postage, J. R., 1960. On the autotrophy of Desulphovibrio desulphuricans. *Z. Allgen. Microbiol.*, **1**, 53–56.

Postgate, J. R., 1965. Recent advances in the study of the sulfate-reducing bacteria. *Bacteriol. Revs.*, **29**, 425–441.

Presley, B. J. and I. R. Kaplan, 1968. Changes in dissolved sulfate, calcium and carbonate from interstitial water of near-shore sediments. *Geochim. Cosmochim. Acta*, **32**, 1037–1048.

Presley, B. J. and I. R. Kaplan, 1970. Interstitial water chemistry: Deep Sea Drilling Project, Leg. 4. In *Initial Reports of the Deep Sea Drilling Project*. Vol. IV. U.S. Government Printing Office, Washington, D.C., pp. 415–430.

Presley, B. J., M. B. Goldhaber, and I. R. Kaplan, 1970. Interstitial water chemistry: Deep Sea Drilling Project, Leg. 5. In *Initial Reports of the Deep Sea Drilling Project*. Vol. V. D. A. McManus et al., eds. U.S. Government Printing Office, Washington, D.C.

Presley, B. J., Y. Kolodny, A. Nissenbaum, and I. R. Kaplan, 1972. Early diagenesis in a reducing fjord, Saanich Inlet, British Columbia—II. Trace elements distribution in interstitial water and sediments. *Geochim. Cosmochim. Acta*, **36**, 1073–1090.

Price, N. B. and S. E. Calvert, 1970. Sediment accumulation rates and the composition of marine ferromanganeses nodules. *Mar. Geol.*, **9**, 145–171.

Pytkowicz, R. M., 1967. Carbonate cycle and the buffer mechanism of recent oceans. *Geochim. Cosmochim. Acta*, **31**, 63–73.

Redfield, A. C., B. J. Ketchum, and F. A. Richards, 1963. The influence of organisms on the composition of seawater. In *The Sea*. Vol. II. M. N. Hill, ed. Wiley-Interscience, New York, pp. 26–77.

Rees, C. E., 1973. A steady state model for sulphur isotope fractionation in bacterial reduction processes. *Geochim. Cosmochim. Acta*, **37**, 1141–1162.

Rees, D. A., 1961. Enzymic desulphation of porphyran. *Biochem. J.*, **80**, 449–453.

Regnell, U., 1961. On pyrite in deep sea sediments. *Bull. Geol. Inst. Uppsala*, **40**, 305–314.

Rex, R. W., 1969. X-ray mineralogy studies: Leg. I. In *Initial Reports of the Deep Sea Drilling Project*. Vol. I. Ewing, et al., eds. U.S. Government Printing Office, Washington, D.C., pp. 354–367.

Rex, R. W. and B. Murray, 1970a. X-ray mineralogy studies: Leg IV. In *Initial Reports of the Deep Sea Drilling Project*. Vol. IV. R. G. Bader et al., eds. U.S. Government Printing Office, Washington, D.C., pp. 325–369.

Rex, R. W. and B. Murray, 1970b. X-ray mineralogy studies. In *Initial Reports of the Deep Sea Drilling Project*. Vol. V. D. A. McManus et al., eds. U.S. Government Printing Office, Washington, D.C., pp. 441–483.

Richards, F. A. and R. F. Vaccaro, 1956. The Cariaco Trench, an anerobic basin in the Caribbean Sea. *Deep-Sea Res.*, **3**, 214–228.

Richards, F. A., 1965. Anoxic basins and fjords. In *Chemical Oceanography*. Vol. I. J. P. Riley and G. Skirrow, eds. Academic Press, New York, pp. 611–645.

Rickard, D. T., 1969. The chemistry of iron sulfide formation at low temperatures. *Stockholm Contrib. to Geol.*, **20**, 67–95.

Rickard, D. T., 1970. The origin of framboids. *Lithos*, **3**, 269–293.

Riley, J. P. and R. Chester, 1971. *Introduction to Marine Chemistry*. Academic Press, London, 465 pp.

Roberts, W. M. B., A. L. Walker, and A. S. Buchanan, 1969. The chemistry of pyrite formation in aqueous solution and its relation to the depositional environment. *Mineral Deposita*, **4**, 18–29.

Robinson, R. A. and R. H. Stokes, 1970. *Electrolyte Solutions*. Sec. Ed., fifth impression (revised), Butterworth, London, 571 pp.

Roy, A. B. and P. A. Trudinger, 1970. *The Biochemistry of Inorganic Compounds of Sulfur*. Cambridge University Press, 400 pp.

Rozanov, A. G., I. I. Volkov, N. N. Zhabina, and T. A. Yagodinskiy, 1971. Hydrogen sulfide in the sediments of the continental slope, Northwest Pacific Ocean. *Geochemistry International*, 333–339.

Rust, G. W., 1935. Colloidal primary copper ores at Cornwall Mines, Southeastern Missouri. *J. Geol.*, **43**, 398–426.

Sakai, H., 1968. Isotopic properties of sulfur compounds in hydrothermal processes. *Geochem. J.*, **2**, 29–49.

Schneiderhöhn, H., 1923. Chalkoeraphishe untersuchung des mansfelder cupferschiefers. *Neves Jahrb. Mineral. Geol. Paleontol.*, Beilige-B, **47**, 1–38.

Schouten, A., 1946. The role of sulfur bacteria in the formation of the so-called sedimentary copper ores and pyritic ore bodies. *Econ. Geol.*, **41**, 517–538.

Senez, J. C., 1962. Some considerations on the energetics of bacterial growth. *Bacteriol. Revs.*, **26**, 95–107.

Shishkina, O. V., 1958. On the salt composition of the interstitial waters of the Far-Eastern seas and the adjacent part of the Pacific. *Tr. Inst. Okeanologii Akad. Nauk. SSSR*, **27**. pp. 109–180.

Shishkina, O. V., 1964. Chemical composition of pore solutions in oceanic sediments. *Geochemistry International*, **3**, 522–528.

Sholkovitz, E. R., 1972. The chemical and physical oceanography and the interstitial water chemistry of the Santa Barbara Basin, California. Ph.D. thesis, University of California at San Diego, Scripps Institute of Oceanography, pp 110–183.

Siever, R., 1968. Sedimentological consequences of a steady state ocean-atmosphere. *Sedimentology*, **11**, 5–29.

Siever, R., K. C. Beck, and R. A. Berner, 1965. Composition of interstitial waters of modern sediments. *J. Geol.*, **73**, 39–73.

Sillen, L. G., 1961. The physical chemistry of seawater. In *Oceanography*. Am. Assoc. Adv. Sci., Washington, D.C., pp. 549–581.

Singleton, P. C. and M. E. Harward, 1971. Iron hydroxy interlayers in soil clays. *Soil Soc. Amer. Proc.*, **35**, 838–842.

Sisler, F. D. and C. E. Zobell, 1951. Hydrogen utilization by some marine sulfate-reducing bacteria. *J. Bacteriol.*, **62**, 117–127.

Skinner, B. J., R. C. Erd, and F. S. Grimaldi, 1964. Greigite, the thio-spinel of iron; a new mineral. *Amer. Mineral.*, **49**, 543–555.

Skirrow, G., 1965. The dissolved gases—carbon dioxide. In *Chemical Oceanography*. Vol. I. J. P. Riley and G. Skirrow, eds. Academic Press, New York, pp. 227–322.

Smith, S. V., J. A. Dygas, and R. E. Chave, 1968. Distribution of calcium carbonate in pelagic sediments. *Mar. Geol.*, **6**, 391–400.

Sokolova, G. A. and G. I. Karavaiko, 1964. Physiology and geochemical activity of thiobacilli. Trans. from Russian, 1968, E. Rabinovitz, ed. Israel Program for Scientific Translations Ltd., Jerusalem, 283 pp.

Stanier, R. Y., M. Doudoroff, and E. A. Adelberg, 1971. *The Microbial World*. 3rd ed. Prentice Hall, Englewood Cliffs, N.J., 873 pp.

Stanton, R. L., 1972. Ore Petrology. McGraw-Hill, New York, 713 pp.

Starkey, R. L., 1960. Sulfate-reducing bacteria—physiology and practical significance. Lectures Theret. Appl. Aspects Mod. Microbiol. University of Maryland, College Park,

Strakhov, N. M., 1967. *Principles of Lithogenesis*. Vol. II. Consultants Bureau, New York, 609 pp.

Strøm, K. M., 1939. Land-locked waters and the deposition of black muds, in recent marine sediments. Soc. Econ. Paleont. Mineral., No. 4, P. D. Trask, ed., Tulsa, Okla, 356–372.

Stumm, W. and J. J. Morgan, 1970. *Aquatic Chemistry*. Wiley, New York, 575 pp.

Subba Rao, M. S., K. K. Iya, and M. Sreenivasaya, 1947. Microbiological formation of elemental sulphur in coastal areas. *Rep. Proc. IVth Int. Congr. Microbiol.*, 494–495.

Sugawara, K., T. Koyama, and A. Kozawa, 1953. Distribution of various forms of sulfur in muds. *J. Earth Sci.*, **1**, Nagoya University, 17–23.

Sunagawa, I., Y. Endo, and N. Nakai, 1971. Hydrothermal synthesis of framboidal pyrite. *Socl. Min. Geol.*, Japan, Spec. Issue, **2**, 10–14.

Sweeney, R. E., 1972. Pyritization during diagenesis of marine sediments. Ph.D. thesis, Dept. of Geol., University of California, Los Angeles, 184 pp.

Sweeney, R. E. and I. R. Kaplan, 1973a. Pyrite framboid formation: Laboratory synthesis and marine sediments. *Econ. Geol.* In press.

Sweeney, R. E. and I. R. Kaplan, 1973b. Pyrite formation in marine sediments. *Mar. Chem.* In press.

Sweeney, R. E., M. B. Goldhaber, and I. R. Kaplan, 1973. Isotopic fractionation of sulfur during sulfate reduction in marine sediments. In preparation.

Szilagyi, M., 1971. Reduction of Fe^{3+} ion by humic acid preparations. *Soil Sci.*, **3**, 233–235.

Takeno, S., 1965. Thermal studies on mackinawite. *Hiroshima Univ. J. of Sci.*, Ser. C., **4**, 455–478.

Takeno, S. and A. H. Clark, 1967. Observations of tetragonal $(Fe, Ni, Co)_{1+x}S$, mackinawite. *Hiroshima Univ. J. of Sci.*, Ser. C., **5**, 287–293.

Takeno, S., H. Zoka, and T. Niihara, 1970. Metastable iron sulfide—with special reference to mackinawite. *Am. Min.*, **55**, 1639–1649.

Thode, H. G., H. Kleerekoper, and D. McElcheran, 1951. Isotopic fractionation in the bacterial reduction of sulphate. *Research* (London), **4**, 581–582.

Thode, H. G., A. G. Harrison, and J. Monster, 1960. Sulfur isotope fractionation of recent sediments of Northeast Venezuela. *Bull. Amer. Assoc. Pet. Geol.*, **44**, 1809–1817.

Thode, H. G., J. Monster, and H. B. Dunford, 1961. Sulfur isotope geochemistry. *Geochim. Cosmochim. Acta*, **25**, 159–174.

Thode, H. G. and J. Monster, 1965. Sulfur-isotope geochemistry of petroleum, evaporites and ancient seas. *Amer. Assoc. Petrol. Geol., Mem.*, **4**, 367–377.

Thorstenson, D. C. and F. T. Mackenzie, 1971. Experimental decomposition of algae in seawater and early diagenesis. *Nature*, **234**, 543–545.

Thorstenson, D. C., 1970. Equilibrium distribution of small organic molecules in natural waters. *Geochim. Cosmochim. Acta*, **34**, 745–770.

Toerien, D. F. and W. H. J. Hattingh, 1969. Anaerobic digestion I. The microbiology of anaerobic digestion. *Water Res.*, **3**, 385–416.

Toland, W. G., 1960. Oxidation of organic compounds with aqueous sulfate. *J. Am. Chem. Soc.*, **82**, 1911–1916.

Townsend, F. C. and L. W. Reed, 1971. Effects of amorphous constituents on some mineralogical and chemical properties of a Patamanian latosoil. Clays and Clay Minerals, **19**, 303–310.

Trudinger, P. A., 1969. Assimilatory and dissimilatory metabolism of inorganic sulphur compounds by micro-organisms. *Adv. in Microbiol. Enzymol.*, **3**, 111–158.

Trudinger, P. A., I. B. Lambert, and G. W. Skyring, 1972. Biogenic sulfide ores: a feasibility study. *Econ. Geol.*, **8**, 1114–1127.

Turekian, K. K., 1965. Some aspects of the geochemistry of marine sediments. In *Chemical Oceanography*. Vol. 2. J. P. Riley and G. Skirrow, eds. Academic Press, London, pp. 81–126.

Tuttle, J. H. and H. W. Jannasch, 1972. Occurrence and types of Thiobacillus-like bacteria in the sea. *Limnol. Oceanog.*, **17**, 532–543.

Tzur, Y., 1971. Interstitial diffusion and advection of solute in accumulating sediments. *J. Geophys. Res.*, **76**, 4208–4211.

Uda, M., 1965. On the syntheses of greigite. *Am. Min.*, **50**, 1487–1489.

Vallentyne, J. R., 1963. Isolation of pyrite spherules from recent sediments. *Limnol. Oceanog.*, **8**, 16–30.

Van Andel, T. H., 1964. Recent marine sediments of the Gulf of California. In *Marine Geology of the Gulf of California*. T. H. Van Andel and G. G. Shor, Jr. eds., Am. Assoc. of Petrol. Geol., Mem. 3, 216–310.

van Niel, C. B., 1931. On the morphology and physiology of the purple and green sulphur bacteria. *Arch. Microbiol.*, **3**, 1–112.

van Niel, C. B., 1941. The bacterial photosyntheses and their importance for the general problem of photosynthesis. *Adv. Enzymol.*, **1**, 263–328.

van Straaten, L. M. J. U., 1954. Composition and structure of recent marine sediments in the Netherlands. *Leidse Geol. Mededel.*, **19**, 1–108.

von der Borch, C. C. and J. G. Sclater, 1972. Deep Sea Drilling Project—Leg 22. *Geotimes, 17,* 15–17.

Vaughn, D. J., and M. S. Ridout, 1971. Mossbauer studies of some sulfide minerals. *J. Inorg. Nucl. Chem.*, **33**, 741–746.

Vinograd, J. R. and J. W. McBain, 1941. Diffusion of electrolytes and of the ions in their mixtures. *J. Amer. Chem. Soc.*, **63**, 2008–2015.

Vinogradov, A. P., V. A. Grineko, and V. I. Ustinov, 1962. Isotopic composition of sulphur compounds in the Black Sea. *Geokhimiya*, **10**, 973–997.

Volkov, I. I., 1961. *Iron Sulfides, Their Interdependence and Transformation in the Black Sea Bottom Sediments*. Trudy Inst. Okeanol. Akad. Nauk SSSR, Vol. 50, pp. 68–92.

Volkov, I. I., A. G. Rozanov, and Skaya Yagodin, 1971. *Pyrite Microconcretions in Black Sea Sediments*. Doklady Akad. Nauk SSSR, Vol. 197, pp. 202–205.

Wainright, T., 1970. Hydrogen sulfide production by yeast under conditions of methionine, pantothenate or vitamin B_6 deficiency. *J. Gen. Microbiol.*, **61**, 107–119.

Ward, J. C., 1970. The structure and properties of some iron sulfides. *Rev. of Pure and Appl. Chem.*, **20**, 175–206.

Weyl, P. K., 1967. The solution behavior of carbonate materials in seawater. *Stud. Trop. Oceanogr. Miami*, **5**, 178–228.

Wyrtki, K., 1962. The oxygen minima in relation to ocean circulation. *Deep-Sea Res.*, **9**, 11–28.

Zemmels, I., H. E. Cook, and J. C. Hathaway, 1972. X-ray mineralogy studies: Leg. XI. In *Initial Reports of the Deep Sea Drilling Project*. Vol. XI. C. D. Hollister et al., eds. U.S. Government Printing Office, Washington, D.C., pp. 729–789.

ZoBell, C. E., 1958. Ecology of sulfate-reducing bacteria. *Producers Monthly*, **22**, 12–29.

IV. THE IMPACT OF LIFE PROCESSES EXCLUDING MAN

18. PRIMARY PRODUCTIVITY, DISSOLVED AND PARTICULATE ORGANIC MATTER, AND THE SITES OF OXIDATION OF ORGANIC MATTER

DAVID W. MENZEL

1. Introduction

Apart from presumably small contributions to the carbon pool by both attached and pelagic macrophytes and matter of terrestrial derivation, all organic matter in the oceans is ultimately derived from CO_2 fixed by unicellular algae. Unlike vegetation in the terrestrial environment, the abundance of these plants is controlled primarily by grazing organisms. A major distinction between the two ecosystems is that usually less than 10% of the plant matter is eaten on land and, thus, most directly enters the cycle of decomposition. Contrarily, in the ocean 90% or more of the plant matter produced is eaten. By-products of this production, which enter the biochemical cycle in altered form, are composed of the solid and soluble residues of animal metabolism (Steele, 1972).

If the floor of the ocean is considered analogous to the earth's surface, the water in between, since it is actively moving, causes lateral displacement of matter settling from the surface so that materials may be deposited at some distance from the site of origin. It is in the water column that most plant and animal remains are recycled, with the consequence that relatively minor quantities of organic matter reach the sediments. Existing in the intervening water column and sediments are organisms, all of which ultimately derive their energy in one form or another from the surface layers.

In spite of considerable research effort, it has been difficult to relate in time and space the distribution of particulate and dissolved organic matter in the deep sea to biological events at the surface. A number of theories have evolved to explain observed distributions, all based to a greater or lesser extent on conjecture and all based entirely on empirical observation. This situation has arisen primarily because of our inability to assign rates to any phase of the cycle of organic matter except that related directly to the measurement of primary production. Particularly lacking is information on the rates of input, utilization, and decomposition of organic matter to and in the deep sea, and the extent to which these processes may influence the chemistry of seawater. This chapter will test various concepts applicable to the above problems. These will be discussed by first examining the zonation of primary production and gross carbon budgets of the ocean and later testing hypotheses relating to the distribution and cycling of organic matter.

2. Primary Production and Carbon Budget

Commencing with the round-the-world expedition of the *Galathea* in 1950–1952, numerous measurements of primary production have been made throughout most of the world's oceans. The results of this expedition (Steeman-Nielson and Jensen, 1957), the first on which the ^{14}C tracer method was used, were based on diagonal sections across the Atlantic, Pacific, and Indian Oceans. As might have been predicted, it was determined that various areas of the seas differ greatly in production levels that may be achieved and sustained therein. These spatial variations in production are controlled by physical and chemical factors regulating the rate of photosynthesis, namely, the supply of light and nutrients. In general, light limits growth at the surface only in polar regions, at depth in the open ocean, and in turbid coastal waters. Because light is rapidly attenuated by water and its included particles, production is usually limited to the upper 120 m, this in the clearest or most unproductive waters. The depth to which actively growing plants may be limited is reduced to the upper several meters in highly productive or turbid areas.

Outside the polar regions, rates of production are controlled by the supply of nutrients alone and this, in turn, is influenced by the rates of *in situ* recycling and circulation that replenish or remove these supplies from the euphotic zone. In simplest definition, the ocean may be hydrographically divided into areas of upwelling, coastal zones, convergences, and central gyres in order of decreasing productivity. Using similar frontal features, Sverdrup (1955) prepared a chart of the distribution of primary production, the concept of which has been little modified except in detail where configurations are markedly altered by coastlines that he neglected.

Comprehensive attempts to map and assign specific levels and ranges of production on a global scale have subsequently been attempted by Koblentz-Mishke et al. (1968) and Ryther (1969) and to the Antarctic areas south of 35°S latitude by El-Sayed (1970). Tables I and II, which compare production in these various regimes, also provide estimates of total world production. In spite of the different approaches of the former two authors, and the different absolute values assigned to specific oceanic regions, the

TABLE I

Primary Production Values of Various Types of Water of the World Ocean. Modified from Koblentz-Mishke et al. (1968)

Type of water	Percentage of ocean	Area (km^2)	Mean Productivity ($gC/m^2/yr$)	Total Productivity (10^9 tons C/yr)
Oligotrophic waters of central parts of subtropical halistatic areas	40.3	148×10^6	25.6	3.79
Transitional waters between subtropical and polar zones; extremities of equatorial divergences	22.7	83×10^6	51.1	4.22
Waters of equatorial divergence and oceanic regions of subpolar zones	23.4	86×10^6	73.0	6.31
Inshore waters	10.6	39×10^6	124.1	4.80
Neritic waters	3.0	11×10^6	365.0	3.90
Total				23.0

Table II

Division of the Ocean into Provinces According to Their Level of Primary Organic Production. From Ryther (1969)

Province	Percentage of ocean	Area (km^2)	Mean Productivity (g of $C/m^2/yr$)	Total Productivity (10^9 tons of C/yr)
Open ocean	90	326×10^6	50	16.3
Coastal zone[a]	9.9	36×10^6	100	3.6
Upwelling areas	0.1	3.6×10^5	300	0.1
Total				20.0

[a] Includes offshore areas of high productivity.

estimates of total carbon production vary little, being 23 and 20×10^9 tons C/yr, respectively.

Incrementing the input of carbon to the oceans by phytoplankton production are contributions of matter produced on land. These materials may enter the sea by two routes, through fluvial input and by atmospheric transport. Estimates of dissolved and particulate materials entering the ocean from rivers are based on many assumptions, and major uncertainties arise from the lack of globally comprehensive measures of the concentration of carbon included in the water. Where such values are available, realistic rates of input to the open ocean are still difficult to determine, since significant fractions of the organic matter may be precipitated or decomposed within relatively short distances of the river mouth. Data from the Mississippi, Hudson, and Amazon Rivers (Menzel, unpublished data) indicate that dissolved carbon concentrations range between 4 to 5 g C/m^3 and that these concentrations are reduced to about 2 g C/m^3, near the value of surrounding waters at salinities in excess of 12‰. Thus, if 2 g C/m^3 is assumed to represent a minimum and 5 g C/m^3 a maximum average value for river systems in general, the annual contribution of carbon to the oceans can be estimated at between 0.8 to 1.9×10^8 tons/yr, based on an average river flow of 3.8×10^{13} tons/yr (Nace, 1967). Remarkably, in spite of the reservations expressed above, independent calculations by Skopintsev (1972) from other river systems yielded a net input of 1.8×10^8 tons C/yr, suggesting that some confidence may be placed on these estimates. Additional contributions to the dissolved carbon pool undoubtedly are associated with rainfall directly on to the sea surface. The task of calculating this input is formidable, and will not be attempted because measured values (2.5 to 3.5 mg C/L) undoubtedly include carbon produced in the ocean. The fractionation of carbon of terrestrial and oceanic derivation in precipitation is not technically feasible at this time. Skopintsev (1972), in his treatment of the problem, assumed contributions from this source negligible.

Estimates of the contribution of particulate organic matter to the ocean from land sources are also subject to large errors. While it might be expected that major input may be derived from rivers, it seems highly unlikely that significant fractions are transported off the continental shelves into the deep sea. This reasoning is based in part on recent work (Gardner, unpublished) where specific tracers (degradation compounds of lignins) were used in an attempt to trace particulate organic input from land onto the continental shelves off Georgia and Texas. Assuming that lignin by-products, which are produced only by higher plants, do not behave differently from other particulate organic materials entering the ocean, data indicate a maximum detectable seaward transport of approximately 60 mi. Thus, while particulate organic material transported to the sea by rivers may play an important role in the bioenergetics of nearshore environments it seems unlikely that significant effects are evidenced in offshore oceanic waters.

The total input of particulate carbon from the world's rivers may be calculated, as in the case of dissolved materials, by assigning an average value for carbon from the limited number of observations available. In the Mississippi, commencing at the city of New Orleans, values decrease systematically in a seaward direction from ~2.5 g C/m^3 to 1 g C/m^3 at a point where seawater intrusion (salinity 1‰) is first detected. The same general range of values applies to the Hudson and Amazon Rivers. Again, assuming that these rivers represent reasonable global averages, the total input of particulate carbon to the ocean, probably much of it living phytoplankton, can be estimated at 0.40 to 0.68 $\times$ 10^8 tons C/yr.

Summing the above calculations it can be seen that in comparison to organic production by photosynthetic organisms, two orders of magnitude less material is delivered to the carbon pool of the seas from terrestrial sources. For the purposes of this exercise, the annual rate of input to the sea can be considered 20 $\times$ 10^9 tons C/yr from photosynthetic activity with an additional 0.2 $\times$ 10^9 tons C/yr and 0.06 $\times$ 10^9 tons C/yr contributed in the form of dissolved and solid materials, respectively, from terrigenous sources.

Of the approximately 20 $\times$ 10^9 tons C being produced at the sea surface annually, most is eaten (Steele, 1972) and substantial fractions of the residues of animal metabolism and ungrazed plants are decomposed at the sea surface. The extent to which algae and plankton are biologically decomposed at the surface is critical in assessing the input of organic materials to the deep sea. There are some indications that remineralization may be 100% (Strickland, 1965), this conclusion is based primarily on field observations. Experiments in the laboratory, where the rate of remineralization of mixtures of dead planktonic organisms was measured, have given results markedly different from those above. Under aerobic conditions, Skopintsev (1947, 1964, 1971) estimated that 70% of the original materials were oxidized within 60 days and that an additional 10% was remineralized over a 5-yr period. Of the 20% refractory residual from living matter, it was further calculated that approximately 25% entered solution and 75% remained in particulate form. In other studies (Jewell and McCarty, 1971) refractory residues ranging from 12 to 87% (X 40%) were obtained, with the higher values derived for every young or very old cultures. Otsuki (1968) calculated that 7% of a mass of mixed plankton was degraded to stable, nondecomposable dissolved compounds. Remineralization in all three studies relied solely on bacterial degradation since active grazers and predators were excluded from the mixture. This fact obviously results in a large overestimate of potential contributions to the deep sea if the results are applied indiscriminately. If all phytoplankton are consumed, 20% of the ingested material is excreted by zooplankton, the remainder either being respired or incorporated into tissue (Butler et al., 1970). Thus, only the resulting metabolic debris from plant matter is subjected to bacterial degradation. This can be accomplished with 80% efficiency, leaving as a refractory residual 4% of the total plant production.

If a value of 4% of gross production is accepted as a reasonable estimate of produced carbon added to the carbon pool each year, a total increment of 0.8 $\times$ 10^9 tons C/yr (4% of 20 $\times$ 10^9 tons C/yr) may be expected. Of this amount, 0.2 $\times$ 10^9 and 0.6 $\times$ 10^9

tons may be in the form of dissolved and particulate materials, respectively. Thus, if these materials are as refractory as implied by Skopintsev (1971, 1972) it may be assumed that 3% of the annual production of plants reaches and is incorporated into the organic matter of the abyssal oceanic sediments in particulate form. Other more direct estimates range from 4 to 12% (Trask, 1939; Datsko, 1959; Bogdanov et al., 1971). Obviously these estimates cannot apply to shallow coastal regions where varying fractions of decomposable and stable compounds may be deposited on the bottom depending on the depth, *in situ* rates of remineralization, grazing pressure, and current velocity and direction.

The extent to which the above implied rates of input influence the total amount of organic matter occurring in the oceans, now presumably in steady state, may be inferred by calculating their respective turnover times. While the concentration of both dissolved and particulate fractions is highly variable in the upper layers of the ocean, at depths below 200 to 500 m little variation is found over most of the world's oceans (discussed later). In general, dissolved organic carbon occurs in the range of 0.5 to 0.8 mg C/L in deep water with values seldom exceeding 1.5 mg/L in the top 100 m. Concentrations measured by Russian workers (e.g., Skopintsev et al., 1966) are approximately double that value and are currently not reconciled with most published data. Therefore, an average value of 0.5 mg C/L will be taken as an oceanic mean (see also Williams, 1969).

Also unreconciled are a wide range of values reported for deep-water particulate carbon, sometimes when measurements were made at the same geographical sites. In my opinion, values predating 1967 must be questioned because of inadequate technique and unrecognized contamination problems. Approximately 2000 samples spread over the Atlantic and E. Pacific, which have been analyzed since that time (Menzel and Ryther, 1970; Hobson and Menzel, 1969; Menzel, 1967), range in concentration from 3 to 10 μg C/L with very few exceptions. Similar values have been reported (Gordon, 1971; Williams, 1969; Kinney et al., 1971; and others) from the Pacific suggesting the likely possibility that such values are a common feature of deep waters. Riley (1970), however, argues against such a narrow range of concentration and questions the validity of a seemingly nonvariant distribution. Yet, values accepted by him do not commonly exceed 50 μg C/L. As in the case of dissolved organics concentrations vary greatly in surface waters ranging from 10 to 1000 μg C/L and depend largely on the concentration of living plants, most of which are decomposable or are eventually grazed. In establishing an estimate of the total ocean reservoir of particulate carbon, an average concentration of 10 μg C/L will be used.

Using a value of 0.5 mg C/L and 10 μg C/L for dissolved and particulate carbon, respectively, the total amount of each in an ocean volume of 1.37×10^{18} m^3 (Sverdrup, Johnson, and Fleming, 1942) may be calculated at 665×10^9 and 14×10^9 tons of carbon, respectively. It can thus be seen that the annual increment of stable dissolved carbon (0.2×10^9 tons) probably does not exceed 0.03% of the total present and that the production of refractory particulate carbon by plants (0.6×10^9 tons) and that added by rivers (0.06×10^9 tons) is approximately 20 times less than that present at any one time. The latter may be increased by as much as a factor of 5 if average values higher than 10 μg C/L for particulate carbon (discussed later) are verified. Similarly, a turnover time of 3300 yr may be calculated for dissolved compounds, a value that is twice that of the estimate of 1000 to 1500 yr (Skopintsev, 1972) and equal to the average age of dissolved carbon of 3400 yr determined by ^{14}C dating (Williams et al., 1969). Major errors in the above calculations may result from overestimating refractory residuals or by underestimating the amount of materials in the ocean.

3. Regional Variations

A. *Particulate Carbon*

As far as the surface layers are concerned, large seasonal and regional variations in particulate carbon can be expected, since in these layers living phytoplankton are included in the measurement. It is highly probable that regional differences correlate closely with bands and areas of high productivity and that these can be related to the general oceanic regions defined by Koblentz-Mishke et al. (1968; see Table I). Within each area, however, large variations may also be expected, depending on the seasonal cycles of plant growth. It may further be expected that, at the height of blooms, a greater fraction of the total particulate matter is associated with living plants and less with nonliving detritus. All attempts to correlate particulate carbon with the rate of primary production have yielded a great deal of scatter so that no direct relationship between the two can be assumed (e.g., Ryther and Menzel, 1965). This is so because detrital carbon may also vary widely and its concentration is superimposed on the amount of living matter. As no direct estimate of the relative amounts of these two components is possible, the most common approach has been to measure chlorophyll as indicative of living plants, assume a carbon/chlorophyll ratio, and subtract the obtained value from total carbon to estimate detritus. Significant error may be associated with such an approach since the ratio of carbon/chlorophyll is known to vary seasonally and with depth (Steele, 1964). Furthermore, in estimating living fractions by this technique, the included microzooplankton are neglected. Regardless of the actual value assigned living carbon however, the approach has its use and when applied in the Arabian Sea indicates that living phytoplankton represent no more than 10 to 20% of the total particulate matter in areas of low production. In a few instances where phytoplankton blooms were evident, up to 60% of the carbon in the euphotic zone was living and at the surface, virtually 100% (Ryther and Menzel, 1965). The same general conclusions apply to the upwelling areas of Peru and S.W. Africa, using both the technique described above and that of Hobson et al. (1973). In the latter, all living components (phytoplankton and microzooplankton) were usually counted, their volume determined, and carbon calculated from formulas for equivalent geometric solids. Here phytoplankton carbon was calculated at 20 to 55% and microzooplankton at 2 to 30% of the total particulate carbon respectively. In areas of high phytoplankton standing crops 70 to 90% of the total carbon consisted of plant matter.

Considering the uncertainty of the above calculations Holm-Hansen (1969) refined biomass estimates using ATP as a measure of living cells and found excellent agreement between that method and those outlined above. In general, these studies show that the proportion of living to detrital materials at the surface of the sea is highly variable, within the probable range of 10 to at least 90%, and that these percentages are inversely related to the standing crop of plant matter.

Below the surface of the sea there is invariably a decrease in particulate carbon. Particles that sink or are transported below the euphotic zone are subject to bacterial oxidation and to consumption by predators and/or detritivores. It may be assumed that essentially all particulate carbon in deep water is nonliving (Riley, 1970). A feature common to the oceans is a rapid vertical demarkation in the concentration of carbon, these perturbations either decreasing systematically or abruptly to deep-water values at depths not exceeding 400 m. Below a depth of 400 m there are no further systematic decreases or increases, so that in any given water column variations are small.

The absolute concentration of carbon in the deep seas and regional and temporal variations that may occur therein are, in my opinion, not reconcilable within the published data. Riley (1970) in his recent review of the subject, has documented many cases (Wangersky and Gordon, 1965; Menzel and Ryther, 1970; Riley et al., 1965; Gordon, 1970; DalPont and Newell, 1963; Holm-Hansen et al., 1966; Hobson, 1967; Sziekelda, 1967; Fredricks and Sackett, 1970; and others) where a considerable range in variations (8 to 1000 μg C/L) has been detected in the deep waters of the Pacific, Indian, and Atlantic Oceans. Averaging all values below 1000 m from the Atlantic, a range in concentration from 13 to 74 μg C/L was described, this varying both regionally and seasonally at at least one location. These data are hardly compatible with, in general, more recent equally widespread observations where variations were far less pronounced and the actual values determined significantly lower, these seldom exceeding 10 μg C/L (Menzel, 1967; Menzel and Ryther, 1970; Williams, 1969; Kinney et al., 1971; Hobson and Menzel, 1969; Gordon, 1971; Holm-Hansen, 1969; Handa, 1970).

In connection with the former series of observations, explanations have been advanced that suggest correlation between surface production and deep-water values, although this may not be obvious because of displacements caused by circulatory processes. Second, other studies, or both, have attempted to relate deep-water concentrations to the advection of water masses containing higher or lower levels of carbon (Hobson, 1967; Sziekelda, 1967; Newell and Kerr, 1968; Riley, 1970; Gordon, 1971). These alternate means of treating the problem of variations, although not mutually exclusive, are partly contradictory. Advective processes require considerable periods of time and if integrity is to be preserved in a water mass the assumption must be made that the material transported at depth is biochemically stable and of the same density of the water in which it is entrained. Contrarily, deep-water changes that are influenced by surface production require relatively rapid sinking rates and when concentration gradients are lacking (Riley, 1970; Gordon, 1970) a rapid averaging process must be imposed that increases the concentration in all water below a given depth (400 m) almost simultaneously with fresh input from the surface. This is not to say that the two processes cannot operate together, a "refractory, buoyant" fraction being transported laterally at given density surfaces and a second, heavier fraction settling relatively rapidly throughout the water column. In either case, accepting the simplest explanation that carbon is utilized and should thus decrease in time wherever its source, decreases in concentration should be apparent, the first in longitudinal section originating at the site of deep-water formation and the second in vertical profile from the surface to the bottom. Neither have been observed, although the first assumption has not been adequately tested. Almost all available observations are within restricted geographical areas and have been obtained by many workers, not always with compatible results. If the processes of sinking and advection operate together, the relative importance of each would be nearly impossible to separate.

The differentiation between advective and sinking processes has been attempted by Riley et al. (1965, 1970), Newell and Kerr (1968), and Gordon (1970, 1971). Riley (1965) and Gordon (1970) observed large temporal changes in particulate carbon in the Sargasso Sea, which, because of the magnitude, could not be associated with processes occurring in the immediate surface. Since the total accumulated carbon in the water column was greater than that produced annually at the surface, an advective process whereby all water from the surface to the bottom is displaced seasonally and simultaneously was postulated, higher carbon concentrations probably originating at more northern latitudes (Riley, 1970). Temporal changes were also studied by Gordon (1971) at a location off the Hawaiian Islands. Here, during 1 yr, variations in concentration were detected above and below, but not at 1000 m. This result obviously makes it difficult to propose an active sinking of particles to depths below 1000 m, and, therefore, advective processes originating at the site of formation of Pacific Deep Water (60°S) were employed to account for seasonal variation at greater depths. The "age" of this water has been estimated at some 2000 yr (Craig, 1971a), indicating that if the observed differences in carbon were real, its "age" must be the same as the water in which it is included. Furthermore, it must be implied that seasonal pulses in production at the site of deep-water formation are reflected in the vicinity of the Hawaiian Islands some 2000 yr later.

The above discussion is based on acceptance of the fact that the deep waters of the ocean may contain significantly different and variable quantities of particulate carbon, these varying both temporally and spatially (references above). As noted earlier, these observations are not reconcilable with other data that together demonstrate singularly uniform and homogeneous distribution over much of the world's oceans. Contrary to proposed regional and temporal variations, the work of Kinney et al. (1971) in the Amerasian Basin, Holm-Hansen (1969) in waters off California, Menzel and Ryther (1971) and Hobson and Menzel (1969) in the Atlantic, Menzel (1967) in the S.E. Pacific, Handa (1970) in the Japan Sea, and Newell and Kerr (1968) in the Indian Ocean show variations in the range of 3 to 10 μg C/L (4 to 15 μg C/L in the case of Newell and Kerr), these not associated with readily identifiable physical or biological processes. Other pertinent data are those of Williams and Gordon (1970) who showed that $^{13}C/^{12}C$ ratios for both particulate and dissolved carbon are strikingly constant (-22.0 to -24.4) with depth in the northeast Pacific. The authors postulated, on the basis of these observations, that subsurface carbon is derived from a singular and common source and that it is stable to biochemical fractionation.

Summarizing, whatever the true concentration and absolute variability of particulate carbon in deep water, recent data (see Riley, 1970) supports the premise that below given depths (200 to 500 m) concentrations are relatively homogeneous in vertical profile at any given location. When such homogeneity is lacking, no further consistent decreases in concentration with depth are apparent. Therefore, presuming that carbon is utilized by organisms in the deep sea, a replenishment mechanism must be postulated to maintain the given concentrations. Opinions differ as to how this might be achieved, one theory suggesting that particulate matter sinks slowly and is subject during its transit to both utilization and accretion, the two processes being in dynamic equilibrium (Riley et al., 1965). A second theory (Menzel and Goering, 1966; Menzel and Ryther, 1970) proposed that particles measured in deep water are neutrally buoyant and refractory, neither sinking out of the water column nor being utilized *in situ*. Either or both hypotheses may explain measured concentrations equally well, the first if regional and temporal variations in underlying water are supported and the latter if contrarily, concentrations are relatively homogeneous in time and space over much of the world's oceans.

As pointed out in the introduction to this chapter, markedly lacking is a realistic assessment of the rate of input of organic particles to the deep sea or its relation to concentrations occurring at the surface. Newell and Kerr (1968) noted that surface production had no influence on the concentration of particles at depth supporting the earlier observations of Menzel (1967), who had postulated that essentially all is recycled in the upper 400 m.

In my opinion, it is likely that significant fractions of particulate matter, that which is consumed by both zooplankton and benthic organisms, and that which may be oxidized in transit, are not amenable to collection with current sampling gear. These particles, which one would expect to be primarily fragile fecal pellets (Steele, 1972), and the carcasses of larger dead organisms are probably unevenly distributed and sink rapidly. That fraction retained by water samplers is homogeneously distributed, probably refractory, and may have no significant role in the biochemical cycle of organic matter. To answer this question, large traps moored at middepths or near the ocean floor will be required to provide input rates and to assess the magnitude of materials presently not sampled. Such attempts, when they have been made, indicate that in water only 25 m deep significant fractions of settling material are undetected by conventional water sampling techniques. Material collected in traps consisted almost exclusively of fecal material. No phytoplankton or zooplankton carcasses were detected except during a short spring bloom when some plant cells apparently reached the bottom (Steele and Baird, in press).

B. Dissolved Organic Carbon

Dissolved organic compounds in the sea may originate from several sources or processes, including excretion by plants and animals, bacterial decomposition, and the autolysis of dead organisms. Additional increments are evolved from river drainage and precipitation. Any or all of these sources may be expected to add to the concentration of compounds more in surface layers than in deep water, and all may be expected to influence given areas of the ocean far more than others. In spite of this, the absolute amount of carbon in both surface and deep water is remarkably similar in all areas of the ocean studied.

Concentrations measured at any given instance at the sea's surface, except under unusual circumstances, vary between 0.8 to 2.0 mg C/L. The causative relationship between biological activity and these concentrations is not readily apparent, but probably relates to the phasing between the onset and decline of phytoplankton and microbial populations. When these populations increase simultaneously organic materials in solution are decomposed as rapidly as they are produced. Contrarily, dissolved compounds may accumulate in the water when the production of decomposer organisms is delayed relative to the availability of substrate. The latter situation most likely arises when sudden bursts in plant production occur. In the open ocean the concentration of dissolved organic carbon is infrequently related to primary productivity and, in fact, may be inversely correlated (Menzel and Ryther, 1970). Holmes et al. (1967) also obtained values that could not be directly associated with production at distances as close as 5 to 10 km off the Scripps Institution pier. Markedly higher concentrations, however, were observed by these authors in large blooms of dinoflagellates and by Barber (1967) in recently upwelled water. No correlation between particulate and dissolved carbon, on the other hand, existed in upwelling areas off S.W. Africa (Hobson et al., 1973).

When high values of dissolved carbon have been obtained, these are usually rapidly reduced to normal baseline levels with the progression of the bloom (Barber, 1967; Holmes et al., 1967). However, serial observations at a single position (Duursma, 1963) provided a positive correlation between the accumulation of carbon and primary production in the North Sea. Other observations (Morris and Foster, 1971) demonstrated regular annual cycles in dissolved carbon in the Menai Strait, these directly related to the seasonal cycle of production but lacking direct correlation with the spring bloom. The latter authors postulated that annual ranges of 1 mg C/L in winter to ranges of 3 to 4 mg C/L in summer result from a rapid rate of production associated with a relatively small standing crop. Thus, the rates of supply during seasons of active plant growth presumably exceeded the capacity of organisms to decompose them with dissolved carbon rapidly returning to basal levels when production ceased.

It is likely that rates of remineralization of newly produced material vary greatly depending on temperature, and, as pointed out earlier, the phasing of production with the activity of decomposing organisms. It seems a rather common occurrence that fresh input of dissolved materials due to pronounced bursts in production are reduced within no more than 1 yr to levels (ca 1 mg C/L) that occur over much of the ocean. Because of the observed rapidity of decomposition, it is highly likely that increments, when observed, are transitory in nature. These markedly influence biological activity in the surface layers but play little, if any, role in the metabolism of the deep sea to which the materials in solution must be transported by convective processes.

The relative amounts of dissolved organic carbon in surface and deep waters have been measured by many workers, often resulting in contradictory interpretations of the data (Duursma, 1961; Skopintsev and Timofeyeva, 1962; Menzel, 1964; Holm-Hansen et al., 1966; Skopintsev et al., 1966; Williams, 1968, 1969; Menzel and Ryther, 1968, 1970; Barber, 1967; Ogura, 1970a; Kinney et al., 1971; and others). As stated above, these studies and others indicate average concentrations in surface waters of approximately 1 to 2 mg C/L, although greater quantities may be associated with plankton blooms in some areas. At depths below 300 m, concentrations range between 0.3 to 0.7 mg C/L (average 0.5). Contradictory values have been reported by Skopintsev and his co-workers who assign values some two to three times higher in deep water than those reported above. Variability, however, was much less ($\pm 30\%$). All data, irrespective of the absolute values reported, fail to show predictable decreases or increases below a depth of about 300 m.

Several attempts have been made to relate the concentration of dissolved carbon to the position and movement of deep-water masses (Duursma, 1961, 1965; Holm-Hansen et al., 1966; Menzel, 1964; Barber, 1967; Fredricks and Sackett, 1970), these interpretations based largely on otherwise unexplainable observed irregularities in vertical profile, or to varying concentrations at various locales, or both. There appears to be no reason why such relationships should not exist if production rates at the surface are variable, a constant relative proportion of the produced matter is chemically and biologically stable, and the compounds are transported to depth at the time of mid- and deep-water formation. If this were so, concentrations in slowly moving subsurface waters should maintain their integrity over considerable periods of time and vertical perturbations should correlate with discontinuities in physical parameters.

Clearly, dissolved carbon concentrations in deep water vary regionally but probably to a lesser extent than is indicated in the massed data. Yet, most recent data that suggest seasonal (Williams, 1969) or geographical (Menzel and Ryther, 1968, 1970) differences have failed to correlate these differences with clearly identifiable water mass structure or movement. Sections in the S.E. and S.W. Atlantic (Menzel and Ryther, 1970), which were designed to observe possible correlation of dissolved carbon with the northerly transport of water originating at the subtropical convergence, failed to demonstrate significant latitudinal differences. Markedly lacking in any data are correlations between dissolved or particulate carbon concentrations and the position or magnitude of the oxygen minimum layer or the concentration of nitrate and phosphate, each of which is influenced by decomposition processes (Williams, 1969; Ogura, 1970b). The vertical distribution of carbon in deep water is thus relatively homogeneous, even though other nonconservative properties have well-defined minima and maxima and are in themselves interrelated. Vertical profiles from the

Atlantic (Menzel and Ryther, 1970; Barber, 1968) and Pacific (Williams, 1969) all demonstrate this homogeneity, although, within some of the same data, the absolute concentrations of carbon appear to vary spatially. The reasons for these apparent spatial variations are not known, but, in any case, cannot be easily related to readily identifiable physical or biological processes.

The above observations, along with estimated turnover times of 1000–3500 yr for dissolved carbon (see introduction) indicate that the bulk of the material is constituted of stable compounds that may be considered biologically refractory. This concept is not new, having originally been postulated by Krogh (1934). Apart from the empirical observations noted above, this contention is further supported by the fact that deep-water carbon has been chronologically dated at 3400 yr and that $^{13}C/^{12}C$ ratios are constant, the latter suggesting that the bulk of the associated compounds are "humic" type materials. The ratios, furthermore, are significantly different from those of the plankton organisms from which they are derived (Williams, 1968, 1969). Additionally, attempts have been made to decompose concentrated deep-water carbon under conditions favorable to microorganisms. After storage for 50 days, the concentration of carbon in deep samples was unchanged, while that at the surface was reduced about 50% (Barber, 1968). All of these arguments support the hypothesis that the bulk of dissolved deep-water carbon is biochemically and biologically inert. No direct evidence is available to contradict this premise.

In summary, the vertical homogeneity of dissolved carbon below a depth of about 300 m is a feature common to the oceans. Possible regional differences throughout the water column cannot be explained at present. While it is presumptuous to assume that these concentrations should, in fact, be everywhere constant, there is no evidence to suggest that the included compounds are decomposed at depth or that they in any way influence the concentration of nonconservative properties.

4. Sites of Oxidation of Organic Matter

Observations on the distribution of carbon discussed earlier in this chapter suggest that a great proportion of the organic matter produced at the sea's surface is recycled within the immediate surface layers. Only if this is the case can sharp vertical discontinuities in concentration be established and maintained. However, if concentrations do not decrease with depth below a given discontinuity layer (generally 200 to 500 m), some method of maintaining an equilibrium between utilization and accretion must be postulated, since organisms reside and metabolize at all depths. Earlier it was postulated that particulate fallout, which provides the energy requirements for deep residing animals, may not be represented in the homogeneously distributed matter that is retained in conventional water samples and that has commonly been reported as "particulate carbon." Estimates of the sinking rates of various sizes and components of the living system are complex, since these rates depend on the density and organic constitution of the specific particle. The depth to which organic matter may penetrate the deep sea by sinking is further dependent on the relative rate of *in situ* decomposition, a rate that will vary widely with temperature and depend on how often the matter is ingested and reingested by organisms living below the euphotic zone. Extrapolations that estimate the relative depth of penetration of any given material to depth must, therefore, be interpreted with caution, since the number of assumptions required to establish these estimates largely invalidate meaningful conclusions. Arguments, therefore, must be circuitous, and these will be developed later.

The situation with respect to dissolved organic carbon is considerably simpler, since materials produced at the sea's surface are transported to depth largely by convection. Thus, significant contributions to dissolved components in the deep sea are almost exclusively restricted to surface biological activity at or near sites of deep-water formation. These contributions will be measurable at remote locations only if the included compounds are not decomposed within the time frame required for latitudinal transport to the point of measurement. The period of time required to reduce organics to essentially refractory base levels is not likely to exceed 1 yr (Otsuki, 1968; Skopintsev, 1972) and, therefore, marked changes in deep-water concentrations due to the decomposition of the included labile dissolved carbon are geographically restricted. Additional contributions to the dissolved fraction of carbon in deep water are from the solubilization of the sinking remains of detritus and excretion at depth by organisms. These fractions, when released, may form a labile pool that may be used by other organisms at depth to support life functions, that consequently, are decomposed and, thus, may influence the chemistry of the surrounding water. Such contributions are not likely to be reflected in measured carbon since in a steady-state system, such as that in the deep sea, limiting nutrients are utilized as quickly as they are made available. Again, the lack of decreasing carbon concentrations with depth may be used to support the argument that particulate input (thus, solubilization) whatever its magnitude and animal abundance (thus, excretion) are both greater in shallow than in deep water. The amount of measured dissolved carbon being essentially invariant below 200 m at depth, therefore, cannot be correlated with processes affecting its rate of addition and loss.

Considering that confusion exists relative to estimating the absolute variability in the concentration of particulate and dissolved carbon, it is apparent that only the crudest type of estimate can be made from analytical data regarding the long-term cycling rates of these compounds (see earlier parts of this chapter). It makes little difference in this context whether the absolute values reported are correct, for it is only through variability that rates can be established. Thus, a comparison of data from Russian workers (e.g., Skopintsev et al., 1966), although ranging from 1.4 to 1.7 mg C/L at depths below 500 m when compared to other values ranging from 0.3 to 0.7 mg C/L (e.g., Menzel and Ryther, 1970), indicates that if oxidation does occur at depth the amount of organic matter involved is comparable. In estimating the impact that such changes may exert on the chemistry of the deep sea, it is useful to utilize the stoichiometric equations of Redfield (1942), which predict that O:C:N:P changes are interdependent at a ratio of 260:106:16:1 by atoms. Those ratios have subsequently been verified by many workers including Redfield, Ketchum, and Richards (1963), Ptykowicz (1968), and many others and may be used with some confidence. Accepting 0.4 mg C/L as the maximum variability in deep water, the equation predicts that oxygen differences throughout the world's oceans at depths in excess of 500 m, if attributed solely to the decomposition of measured carbon, can amount to no more than 1.32 O_2 ml/L and that NO_3–N and PO_4–P differences could be no more than 5 and 0.3 μg A/L, respectively. Real differences in fact are 6.8 ml O_2; 20 μg $ANO_3{}^{-N}$, and 2.0 μg $APO_4{}^{-P}$: (from Sverdrup, Johnson, and Fleming, 1942). Furthermore, it has been demonstrated that carbon concentrations in vertical profile cannot be related to the oxygen minimum or the position of phosphate and nitrate maxima (Ogura, 1970b). Since carbon data are not compatible with the interpretation of deep-sea processes, and errors in measurement are larger than is permissible to establish rate processes, interrelated and dependent factors must be examined. The easiest and most directly related measure is oxygen.

Redfield (1942) in his study of the influence of decomposition on the distribution of oxygen postulated that water sinking at the subtropical convergence (50°S) flowed northward, losing oxygen in the process and forming the oxygen minimum. The extent of oxygen depletion was directly correlated to increases in phosphate, except at equatorial regions, where additional increments due to sinking materials had to be imposed. Subsequent studies have failed to support two postulates necessary to support this argument if the sole mechanism controlling O_2 depletion and PO_4–P additions are attributed solely to *in situ* decomposition within the transported water. The first, verified only in recent years, is that the rates of production at the surface in the convergences is nowhere near sufficient to supply the amount of organic matter necessary to produce the observed changes in oxygen once water is removed from the surface and, in fact, is no higher than most subtropical oceanic waters (El-Sayed, 1970). A second observation is that oxygen changes along the trajectory of northern flowing waters from the convergence, while showing marked changes in oxygen, shows no concomitant changes in dissolved or particulate carbon (Menzel and Ryther, 1968). Phosphate and nitrate, on the other hand, were interrelated with oxygen as observed by Redfield and later verified for other oceanic regions by many workers. Menzel and Ryther (1968, 1970), in an attempt to clarify this situation, used the core method of Wüst (1935) to show that oxygen, phosphate, and nitrate could be plotted against salinity at the salinity minimum and that deviations from a straight line were within the limits of accuracy of oxygen and salinity measurements. This observation was verified in two areas of upwelling and along the East coast of South America. Supplemented by data demonstrating essentially invariant dissolved carbon concentrations within the area studied, the authors postulated that oxygen minima are formed in a few restricted areas of the ocean, primarily those of upwelling, and that oxygen concentration in areas remote from these locations was controlled by mixing of waters with equal carbon but unequal oxygen content.

To maintain the observed oxygen/salinity correlations it is obvious that alterations in oxygen due to the oxidation of sinking particles or the respiration of organisms must be essentially invariant over much of the area studied. Such is obviously not the case under areas of high production or in adjacent regions to which organisms or their residues are transported by water movement. It was essential, therefore, to obtain an estimate of the effect of production on the concentration of particles at depth and to survey further the immediate surrounding areas to determine the extent of lateral transport. Studies in an area of upwelling off Peru suggested that while the concentration of particles in the surface increased by a factor of 10 during a five-day period, no concomitant increase in particulate carbon was observed below a depth of 75 m. Thus, particulate carbon at depth was not related to surface production (see also Newell and Kerr, 1968). Regions immediately surrounding the area and extending 600 mi seaward failed to demonstrate that lateral displacement had an effect on particulate carbon levels below a depth of 200 m (Menzel and Ryther, 1970). It was therefore concluded that newly produced organic matter is rapidly recycled in the upper 200 m of the water column. This observation, based entirely on analytical data, fails to explain the fact that zooplankton, which must rely on sinking particles for food, whether detrital or living, are significantly less abundant in areas of low production than in deep waters underlying areas of high production (Banse, 1964; Vinogradov, 1970).

Before pursuing this apparent paradox farther, it is important to note that two recent studies suggest that processes or mechanisms operating in the deep sea, with respect to biological balances, differ significantly from those in the upper 500 m. Ogura (1970b), studying the relationship between dissolved organic carbon and apparent oxygen utilization (AOU) in the North Pacific, noted a linear relationship between the two to a depth of several hundred meters. At depths in excess of several hundred meters oxygen decreased further but carbon maintained a constant value of around 0.5 mg C/L. Packard (1969), using the new technique of measuring respiratory potential from the activity of electron transport systems, demonstrated an exponential decrease in activity to a depth of 500 m below which the oxygen utilization rate was nearly constant, although regression analysis indicated a slight linear decrease with depth. The change in equations (Packard, 1969) and relationships described above (Ogura, 1970b) suggests that processes by which carbon is supplied and consumed above about 500 m differ from like processes in deeper waters. Packard (1969) suggested that these differences might be accounted for by a steady supply of moribund phytoplankton in waters above 500 m and a supply of fecal pellets or other debris below that depth.

Based largely on laboratory experiments, Skopintsev (1971) constructed a graph basing his estimates on the rate of oxidation of the partially decomposed remains of plankton and their sinking rates. His model predicts that nannoplankton (0.05 mm diameter) decompose completely in the upper 100 m, microplankton (0.1 to 0.2 mm diameter) decompose (90%) in the upper 2000 m, and that larger organisms (1 mm) reach maximum depths in a 50% state of decomposition. As suggested earlier, these estimates cannot be taken too seriously since the main constraint on significant vertical transport, ingestion by higher organisms, is neglected in the approach and decomposition estimates are based solely on the role of bacteria. All these studies, however, support the contention that most surface-produced matter is recycled in the upper layers of the ocean and that the physical size, character and/or composition of materials reaching the deep sea differ from those recycled at the surface.

Having established the above base, further estimates of cycling rates and their relation to oxygen depletion will be restricted to processes below 500 m. Geographical variations in the distribution of oxygen and the modes of formation of oxygen minima will not be reviewed except in direct context to establishing the mechanism by which oxygen is depleted in deep water. Broader aspects of this subject have been adequately reviewed (Sverdrup, 1938; Richards, 1957; Wyrtki, 1962; Menzel and Ryther, 1970; and others). As demonstrated earlier, the lack of adequate analytical data on carbon distribution and its variation over the world's ocean precludes using this information to establish oxidation rates. All evidence, in my opinion, suggests that measurable fractions of the dissolved materials are refractory and inert. If oxygen levels are influenced by the oxidation of these compounds, such influence would be restricted to rapidly cycled, nonmeasurable increments that may result from the excretion of organisms or solution of sinking particles.

Craig (1969, 1971a, 1971b) developed a one-dimensional diffusion-advection model that required a continuous particulate flux from the surface and further suggested that part of the CO_2 increase in deep water must be due to the *in situ* oxidation of dissolved organic matter. In order to balance the requirements for input to his model, Craig attempted to demonstrate that differences in dissolved carbon, based on the scattered measurements (Barber, 1967; Williams and Gordon, 1970; Menzel and Ryther, 1970), were sufficient to account for approximately 35% of the carbon requirement necessary to achieve predicted oxygen depletion rates. The effect that an oxygen utilization rate of 0.004 ml/L/yr in Pacific Deep Water (Craig, 1971a) and 0.002 ml/L/yr in the North Atlantic Deep Water (Arons and Stommel, 1967) would exert on the concentration of dissolved carbon can be estimated using again the ratio of -2.60 atoms $O_2 = -1$ atom C (Redfield, 1942). These calculations predict that a rate of utilization of 0.004 ml/L/yr would require 0.0012 mg C/L/yr, or a period of 200 yr before analytical precision (± 0.1 mg C/liter) would allow detection of a significant change in carbon. In the case of the North Atlantic, the time requirement for detection of change would be doubled (400 yr). Residence times for these waters, respectively, based on ^{14}C data, are about 2000 and 570 yr (Craig, 1971a), indicating that use of dissolved carbon data in the case of the N. Atlantic situation is clearly questionable. In the case of the Pacific, a residence time of 2000 yr, with a rate of oxygen depletion of 0.002 ml/L/yr (given that the rates are in fact equal between the two ocean basins) would require the utilization of 4 ml O_2/L. This, in time, would require that over the same period the input of carbon to the deep waters in whatever form (dissolved or particulate) would be 1.2 mg C/L, or integrated through a 4000-m water column, approximately 2.4 g C/m^2/yr. This rate of influx appears quite reasonable and is almost identical to other estimates discussed in the concluding parts of this chapter.

In developing the argument that oxygen concentration at depths in excess of 200 to 300 m is controlled by mixing (Menzel and Ryther, 1970), it was pointed out that the observed linear relationship between salinity and oxygen could be maintained if the respiration rate of organisms at depth were essentially invariant within the time frame that the water was removed from the surface. If this were so, the slope of the regression would depend on mixing processes plus respiration, linearity, and fit would be maintained, and oxygen would appear conservative. The question remaining, then, was not whether oxygen is consumed at depth but whether this consumption can be attributed to the *in situ* oxidation of measurable organic carbon. The object in further discussion of this problem will be to demonstrate that the respiratory requirements of zooplankton and microplankton are sufficient to explain measured oxygen utilization rates in the deep sea. In short, it is not necessary to impose the decomposition of dissolved carbon (Craig, 1971a, 1971b) as a requirement for explaining these rates. Particulate flux is required only to satisfy the metabolic requirements of deep-residing organisms. This flux could be direct (particles) or may result from the mechanism of overlapping vertical links in the food chain (Vinogradov, 1962). Data that are relevant may be summarized as follows. (1) The vertical distribution of zooplankton can everywhere be described by an exponential curve decreasing with depth generally by 1 to 1.5 orders of magnitude from the surface to 1000 m and another order of magnitude from 1000 to 4000 m (Banse, 1964; Vinogradov, 1970). (2) Electron transport activity decreases in an exponential manner to approximately 500 m below which depth it decreases in a linear fashion (Packard, 1969). (This method provides an estimate of the respiratory potential of the included microorganisms and can be used to establish respiration rates.) (3) The abundance of benthic organisms at depth decreases in a fashion similar to zooplankton (Rowe, 1971).

The third observation cannot be assumed to influence oxygen utilization rates within the water column but is used in conjunction with observations 1 and 2 and to demonstrate that observed vertical profiles of particulate matter, which are essentially invariant with depth below about 500 m, cannot be postulated as a food source for organisms in the deep sea or its concentration would also decrease with depth.

According to Vinogradov (1970) the range in biomass (wet weight) of net zooplankton throughout vast reaches of the Pacific, Atlantic, and Indian Oceans is 5 to 10 mg/M^3 at 500 m and 0.1 to 1.0 mg/M^3 at 4000 m. Exceptions are Pacific subarctic and, therefore, presumably other near polar regions where abundances are higher. These may be disregarded here since they border areas of deep-water formation and effects on oxygen concentration in deep waters do not apply to most of the ocean.

These biomasses may be translated into carbon equivalents by assuming that carbon represents 10% of the wet weight, thus yielding 0.5 to 1.0 mg C/m^3 and 0.01 to 0.10 mg C/m^3 at 500 and 4000 m, respectively. The respiratory requirement of various copepods has been established by Conover (1964) at 1% (5°C) and by Mullin and Brooks (1970) at about 2% (10°C). The former value is used here because the temperature more closely approximates that in the deep sea, although, for the purpose of this discussion, either value could be applied. Translated to volume and based on standing crop estimates the metabolic needs of zooplankton would require an input of 0.005 to 0.010 at 500 m and 0.0001 to 0.001 mg C/m^3/day at 4000 m. In the former case, assuming an R.Q. of 0.8 (Mullin and Brooks, 1970) respiration in oxygen equivalents would require 4.2 to 8.4 μl/liter/yr and in the latter 0.085 to 0.850 μl/liter/yr (Table III). At a depth of 4000 m, this rate is 4 to 40% of the rate of oxygen utilization predicted by the model of Arons and Stommel (1967) for North Atlantic Deep Water (2 μl/liter/yr).

Table III

Summary of Estimated Carbon and Oxygen Requirements of Zooplankton and Microorganisms at 500 and 4000 m

	500 m	4000 m
Zooplankton wet weight (mg/m^3)[a]	5–10	0.1–1.0
Zooplankton carbon (mg/m^3)[a]	0.5–1.0	0.01–0.10
Zooplankton respiration (mg C/m^3/day)[b]	0.005–0.010	0.0001–0.0010
Annual zooplankton C requirement (mg C/m^3/yr)[b]	1.83–3.65	0.0365–0.365
Oxygen requirement (μl/L/yr)[b]	4.2–8.4	0.085–0.850
ETS activity (μl/L/yr)[c]	5.0	2.0
Total O_2 requirement (μl/L/yr)	9.2–13.4	2.09

[a] From Vinogradov (1970).
[b] From Conover (1964).
[c] From Packard et al. (1971).

Packard et al.'s (1971) estimates of respiration must be added to those above since they do not include net plankton but only microorganisms trapped in water bottles. These rates varied from 0.5 to 4 μl O_2/L/yr at depths below 500 m with an average of 2 μl/L/yr at 3000 m. Added to the above estimates of 0.09 to 0.9 μl O_2/L/yr for net plankton, the rate of oxygen consumption that can be attributed to organisms at 3000 to 4000 m ranges between 2.1 to 2.9 μl/L/yr (Table III) is certainly sufficient to satisfy the models of Craig (1971a), Arons and Stommel (1967), and others who have developed physical and chemical models and estimated oxygen consumption rates from these.

Extrapolating this exercise one step further, with specific reference to the oxygen minimum layer, an O_2 depletion rate of 9 to 13 μl/L/yr at 500 m (Table III) or a variation of 4 μl/L/yr would require that approximately 25 yr lapse before a significantly measurable (0.1 ml/L) difference in oxygen due to variable respiration rates therein could be analytically detected. Small regional differences within the 4 μl/L/yr would not be detectable for considerably longer periods of time. This factor can easily explain the observation that oxygen at middepths when compared to salinity appears conservative (Menzel and Ryther, 1970), for if respiration is constant within small limits, only effects due to mixing will be obvious.

Packard et al. (1971) further calculated that in order to supply adequate carbon to meet the respiratory requirement of microorganisms at depth, a flux of 2.1 g C/m^2/yr is required below 500 m. The requirement for larger zooplankton can also be estimated and in order to keep the comparisons valid with that of Packard et al., a profile of biomass is taken from the productive region of the eastern equatorial Pacific (Vinogradov, 1970). (This profile shows standing crops slightly higher than average for the Central Pacific.) The concentrations of zooplankton are shown in Table IV, where a

TABLE IV

Zooplankton Biomass and Respiratory Carbon Requirements in the Productive Eastern Tropical Pacific (from Vinogradov, 1970)

Depth	Biomass		Respiratory Requirement	
(m)	(mg/m^3)	Mg C/m^3	mg C/m^3/day	mg C/m^3/yr
500	10	1.0	0.01	3.65
1000	2	0.2	0.002	0.73
2000	0.8	0.08	0.0008	0.29
3000	0.13	0.013	0.00013	0.047
4000	0.11	0.011	0.00011	0.040
Integrated total carbon requirement 1.80g C/m^2/yr				

respiratory requirement of 1% of the body carbon per day has again been used. These calculations predict the requirement for a total flux of energy of 1.8 g C/m^2/yr, which, when added to Packard et al.'s (1970) 2.1 g C/m^2/yr totals 3.9 g, or approximately 1 to 2% of the surface production. Assuming that this material is equally distributed throughout a water column of 3500 m, the resulting concentration would be 1.11 mg C/m^3 or 1.1 μg C/l. This value, an annual requirement, is at least 3 times lower than the lowest reported value for particulate carbon (Menzel and Ryther, 1970) and 50 times lower than some values reported by Riley (1970).

Extrapolations such as those made above and throughout this chapter are tenuous and subject to compound errors. They are necessary for several reasons: (1) available analytical estimates of carbon in other than the euphotic zone are not in agreement and are in themselves subject to inconsistencies that do not permit estimates of the rates of carbon cycling; (2) irrespective of how accurate analyses are, concentrations in themselves cannot be used to establish rates, since, unlike oxygen and other nonconversative properties, carbon input to deep water is continuous and may vary from one site to another; and (3) virtually nothing is known of the mechanisms by which organic matter is transported to depth and how the energy requirements of the deep sea are met. The latter, in the opinion of the author, is the single most important unresolved problem in the fields of marine biology and chemistry, for these processes not only influence life systems but play an important role in the interpretation of chemical data.

References

Arons, A. B. and H. Stommel, 1967. On the abyssal circulation of the world ocean. III. *Deep-Sea Res.*, **14**, 441–457.

Banse, K., 1964. On the vertical distribution of zooplankton in the sea. In *Progress in Oceanography.* Vol. 2. Permagon Press, New York, pp. 56–125.

Barber, R. T., 1967. The distribution of dissolved organic carbon in the Peru Current system of the Pacific Ocean. Ph.D. thesis, Stanford University, Palo Alto, California.

Barber, R. T., 1968. Dissolved organic carbon from deep waters resists microbial oxidation. *Nature*, Lond., **220**, 274–275.

Bogdanov, Y. S., A. P. Lisitsyn, and Y. A. Romankwich, 1971. Organic matter in suspensions and bottom sediments of seas and oceans. In *Organic Matter in Recent and Fossil Sediments.* Nauka Publishing House, Moscow.

Butler, E. I., E. D. S. Corner, and S. M. Marshall, 1970. On the nutrition and metabolism of zooplankton. VII. Seasonal survey of nitrogen and phosphorus excretion by *Calanus* in the Clyde sea-area. *J. Mar. Biol. Ass. U.K.*, **50**, 525–560.

Conover, R. J., 1964. Food relations and nutrition of zooplankton. Proc. Symp. on Exp. Mar. Ecol., Occas. Pub. 2, Grad. School of Oceanogr. University of Rhode Island. 81–91.

Craig, H., 1969. Abyssal carbon and radiocarbon in the Pacific. *J. Geophys. Res.*, **74**, 5491–5506.

Craig, H., 1971a. The deep metabolism: oxygen consumption in abyssal ocean water. *J. Geophys. Res.*, **76**, 5078–5086.

Craig, H., 1971b. Son of abyssal carbon. *J. Geophys. Res.*, **76**, 5133–5139.

DalPont, G. and B. Newell, 1963. Suspended organic matter in the Tasman Sea. *Austral. J. Mar. Freshwat. Res.*, **14**, 155–163.

Datsko, V. G., 1959. Organic matter in the southern seas of the USSR. Izd. AN SSSR.

Duursma, E. K., 1961. Dissolved organic carbon, nitrogen and phosphorus in the sea. *Netherl. J. Sea Res.*, **1**, 1–148.

Duursma, E. K., 1963. The production of dissolved organic carbon in the sea as related to the primary production of organic matter. *Nethl. J. Sea Res.*, **2**, 85–94.

Duursma, E. K., 1965. The dissolved organic constituents of sea water. In *Chemical Oceanography.* J. P. Riley and G. Skirrow, eds. Academic Press, New York, pp. 433–475.

El-Sayed, S. Z., 1970. Phytoplankton production of the South Pacific and the Pacific section of the Antarctic. Sci. Eplor. of the South Pacific, Natl. Acad. Sci., Wash., D.C. Book No. 309–01755–6, 194–210.

Fredricks, A. D. and W. M. Sackett, 1970. Organic carbon in the Gulf of Mexico. *J. Geophy. Res.*, **75**, 2199–2206.

Gordon, D. C., 1970. Some studies on the distribution and composition of particulate organic carbon in the North Atlantic Ocean. *Deep-Sea Res.*, **17**, 233–243.

Gordon, D. C., 1971. Distribution of particulate organic carbon and nitrogen at an oceanic station in the Central Pacific. *Deep-Sea Res.*, **18**, 1127–1134.

Handa, N., 1970. Dissolved and particulate carbohydrates. In *Organic Matter in Natural Waters.* D. W. Hood, ed. Inst. Mar. Sci., University of Alaska, Pub. No. 1, 129–152.

Hobson, L. A., 1967. The seasonal and vertical distribution of suspended particulate matter in an area of the Northeast Pacific Ocean. *Limnol. Oceanog.*, **12**, 642–649.

Hobson, L. A. and D. W. Menzel, 1969. The distribution and chemical composition of organic particulate matter in the sea and sediments off the east coast of South America. *Limnol. Oceanog.*, **14**, 159–163.

Hobson, L. A., D. W. Menzel, and R. T. Barber, 1973. Primary productivity and sizes of some pools of organic carbon in the mixed layer of the ocean. *Mar. Biol.* **19**, 298–306.

Holm-Hansen, O., 1969. Determination of microbial biomass in ocean profile. *Limnol. Oceanog.*, **14**, 740–747.

Holm-Hansen, O., J. D. H. Strickland, and P. M. Williams, 1966. A detailed analysis of biologically important substances in a profile off southern California. *Limnol. Oceanog.*, **11**, 548–561

Holmes, R. W., P. M. Williams, and R. W. Eppley, 1967. Red water in LaJolla Bay, 1964–1966. *Limnol. Oceanog.*, **12**, 503–512.

Jewell, W. J. and P. L. McCarty, 1971. Aerobic decomposition of algae. *Envir. Sci. Technol.*, **5**, 1023–1031.

Kinney, P. J., T. C. Loder, and J. Groves, 1971. Particulate and dissolved organic matter in the Amerasian Basin of the Arctic Ocean. *Limnol. Oceanog.*, **16**, 132–136.

Koblentz-Mishke, O. J., V. V. Volkovinsky, and J. G. Kabanova, 1968. Plankton primary production of the world ocean. In *Symp. Sci. Eplor. South Pacific*. W. S. Wooster, ed. Scripps Institution of Oceanography, pp. 183–193.

Krogh, A., 1934. Condition of life in the ocean. *Ecol. Monogr.*, **4**, 421–439.

Menzel, D. W., 1964. The distribution of dissolved organic carbon in the Western Indian Ocean. *Deep-Sea Res.*, **11**, 757–765.

Menzel, D. W., 1967. Particulate organic carbon in the deep sea. *Deep-Sea Res.*, **14**, 229–238.

Menzel, D. W. and J. J. Goering, 1966. The distribution of organic detritus in the ocean. *Limnol. Oceanog.*, **11**, 333–337.

Menzel, D. W. and J. H. Ryther, 1968. Organic carbon and the oxygen minimum in the South Atlantic Ocean. *Deep-Sea Res.*, **15**, 327–337.

Menzel, D. W. and J. H. Ryther, 1970. Distribution and cycling of organic matter in the oceans. In *Organic Matter in Natural Waters*. D. W. Hood, ed. Inst. Mar. Sci., University of Alaska, Pub. No. 1, 31–54.

Morris, A. W. and P. Foster, 1971. The seasonal variation of dissolved organic carbon in the inshore waters of the Menai Strait in relation to primary production. *Limnol. Oceanog.*, **16**, 987–989.

Mullin, M. M. and E. R. Brooks, 1970. Growth and metabolism of two planktonic, marine copepods as influenced by temperature and type of food. In *Marine Food Chains*. J. H. Steele, ed. University of California Press, pp. 74–95.

Nace, R. L., 1967. Water resources: a global problem with local roots. *Envir. Sci. Technol.*, **1**, 550–560.

Newell, B. S. and J. D. Kerr, 1968. Suspended organic matter in the south-eastern Indian Ocean. *Austral. J. Mar. Freshwat. Res.*, **19**, 129–138.

Ogura, N., 1970a. Dissolved organic carbon in the equatorial region of the Central Pacific. *Nature*, Lond., **227**, 1135–1136.

Ogura, N., 1970b. The relation between dissolved organic carbon and apparent oxygen utilization in the Western North Pacific. *Deep-Sea Res.*, **17**, 221–230.

Otsuki, A., 1968. Biochemical studies on the production of dissolved organic matter in relation to food chain of hydrosphere. Ph.D. thesis, Tokyo Metropolitan University, Tokyo.

Packard, T. T., 1969. The estimation of the oxygen utilization rate in seawater from the activity of the respiratory electron transport system in plankton. Ph.D. thesis, University of Washington, Seattle.

Packard, T. T., M. L. Healy, and F. A. Richards, 1971. Vertical distribution of the activity of the respiratory electron transport system in marine plankton. *Limnol. Oceanog.*, **16**, 60–70.

Pytkowicz, R. M., 1968. Water masses and their properties at 160°W in the southern ocean. *J. Oceanogr. Soc. Japan*, **24**, 21–31.

Redfield, A. C., 1942. The processes determining the concentration of oxygen, phosphate and other organic derivatives within the depths of the Atlantic Ocean. *Pap. Phys. Oceanogr. Meteor.*, **9**, 22 pp.

Redfield, A. C., B. H. Ketchum, and F. A. Richards, 1963. The influence of organisms on the composition of sea water. In *The Sea*. Vol. 2. M. N. Hill, ed. Wiley-Interscience, New York, pp. 26–77.

Richards, F. A., 1957. Oxygen in the ocean. In *Treatise on Marine Ecology and Paleoecology*. J. Hedgepath, ed. Geol. Soc. Mem. I, **67**, 185–238.

Riley, G. A., 1970. Particulate organic matter in sea water. In *Advances in Marine Biology*. Vol. 8. F. S. Russell and M. Yonge, eds. Academic Press, London and New York, pp. 1–118.

Riley, G. A., D. Van Hemert, and P. J. Wangersky, 1965. Organic aggregates in surface and deep waters of the Sargasso Sea. *Limnol. Oceanog.*, **10**, 354–363.

Rowe, G. T., 1971. Benthic biomass and surface productivity. In *Fertility of the Sea*. J. D. Costlow, ed. Gordon and Breach Science Publishers, New York, London, Paris, pp. 441–454.

Ryther, J. H., 1969. Photosynthesis and fish production in the sea. *Science*, **166**, 72–76.

Ryther, J. H. and D. W. Menzel, 1965. On the production, composition, and distribution of organic matter in the Western Arabian Sea. *Deep-Sea Res.*, **12**, 199–209.

Skopintsev, B. A., 1947. Concerning the rate of decomposition of organic matter from dying plankton. *Dokl. Akad. Nauk. SSSR*, **58**, 1797.

Skopintsev, B. A., 1964. Calculation of organic matter formation and oxidation in seawater. *Okeanol. issled.*, **13**,

Skopintsev, B. A., 1971. Recent advances in the study of organic matter in the oceans. *Okeanologiya*, Akad. Nauk. SSSR, **11**. Translated into English, *Oceanology*, **11**, 775–789.

Skopintsev, B. A., 1972. On the age of stable organic matter—aquatic humics in oceanic waters. In *The Changing Chemistry of the Oceans*. D. Dryssen and D. Jagner, eds. Nobel Symp. 20. Wiley, New York, London, pp. 205–207.

Skopintsev, B. A. and S. N. Timofeeva, 1962. *Organic carbon content in the Baltic and North Sea, and tropical and subtropical regions of the North Atlantic*. Vol. 25. Trudy Morsk. Gedrofiz. Inst., Akad. Nauk. SSSR, **25**, pp. 110–117.

Skopintsev, B. A., S. N. Timofeeva, and O. A. Vershinina, 1966. Organic carbon in the equatorial and southern Atlantic and Mediterranean. *Okeanologiya*, Akad. Nauk. SSSR, **6**. Translated into English, *Oceanology*, **6**, 201–210.

Steele, J. H., 1964. A study of production in the Gulf of Mexico. *J. Mar. Res.*, **22**, 211–222.

Steele, J. H., 1972. Factors controlling marine ecosystems. In *Changing Chemistry of the Oceans*. D. Dryssen and D. Jagner, ed. Nobel Symp. 20. Wiley, London, New York, pp. 209–221.

Steele, J. H. and I. E. Baird. Sedimentation of organic matter in a Scottish sea loch. Mem. Ist. Ital. Idrobiol., 29. Suppl. In press.

Steeman-Nielsen, E. and E. A. Jensen, 1957. Primary oceanic production. The autotrophic production of organic matter in the oceans. *Galathea Rep.*, **1**, 49–135.

Strickland, J. D. H., 1965. Production of organic matter in the primary stages of the marine food chain. In *Chemical Oceanography*. J. P. Riley and G. Skirrow, eds. Academic Press, New York, pp. 477–610.

Sverdrup, H. U., 1938. On the explanation of the oxygen minima and maxima in the oceans. *J. Cons. Int. Explor. Mer.*, **13**, 163–172.

Sverdrup, H. U., 1955. The place of physical oceanography in oceanographic research. *J. Mar. Res.*, **14**, 287–294.

Sverdrup, H. U., M. Johnson, and R. Fleming, 1942. *The Oceans*. Prentice-Hall, Englewood Cliffs, N.J., 1087 pp.

Szekielda, K. H., 1967. Some remarks on the influence of hydrographic conditions on the concentration of particulate carbon in sea water. In *Chemical Environment in the Aquatic Habitat*. H. G. Golterman and R. S. Clymo, eds. N. W. Noord-Hollandsche Uetgevers Maatschappij, Amsterdam, pp. 314–322.

Trask, P., 1939. Organic content of recent marine sediments. In *Recent Marine Sediments*. P. Trask, ed. Amer. Assoc. Pet. Geol., Tulsa, Oklahoma, 428–453.

Vinogradov, M. E., 1962. Feeding of deep sea zooplankton. *Rapp. Proc. Verb. Cons. Perm. Int. Explor. Mer.*, **153**, 114–119.

Vinogradov, M. E., 1970. Vertical distribution of oceanic zooplankton. Akad. Nauk. SSSR. Inst. Okeanologii. Translated into English by the Israel Program for Scientific translations, Jerusalem for U.S. Dept. Interior and National Science Foundation, 339 pp.

Wangersky, P. J. and D. C. Gordon, 1965. Particulate carbonate, organic carbon and Mn^{++} in the open ocean. *Limnol. Oceanog.*, **10**, 544–550.

Williams, P. M., 1968. Stable carbon isotopes in the dissolved organic matter of the sea. *Nature*, Lond., **219**, 152–153.

Williams, P. M., 1969. The distribution and cycling of organic matter in the ocean. Proc. Rudolfs Conf., Rutgers University.

Williams, P. M. and L. I. Gordon, 1970. Carbon-13:carbon-12 ratios in dissolved and particulate organic matter in the sea. *Deep-Sea Res.*, **17**, 19–28.

Williams, P. M., H. Oeschger, and P. Kinney, 1969. Natural radiocarbon activity of dissolved organic carbon in the north-east Pacific Ocean. *Nature*, Lond., **224**, 256–258.

Wyrtki, K., 1962. The oxygen minimum in relation to ocean circulation. *Deep-Sea Res.*, **9**, 11–23.

Wust, G., 1935. Schichtung and Zirkulation des Atlantischen Ozeans. Die Stratosphere. *Wiss. Erg. dt. atlant. Exped. Meteor*, **6**, 109–288.

19. NATURAL PRODUCTS CHEMISTRY OF THE MARINE ENVIRONMENT

D. John Faulkner and Raymond J. Andersen

It is a mystery why so many natural-products chemists have concentrated their investigations on terrestrial sources when those who have studied marine organisms have been rewarded with such an exotic array of compounds. It is understandable that chemists have overlooked those organisms that require collection by SCUBA, but the neglect of intertidal species is inexcusable. Since marine and terrestrial organisms exist in such different environments, one must expect the secondary metabolites to differ considerably. The higher pressures and lower temperature encountered in the marine environment may be expected to cause some changes in the rates of biochemical reactions; therefore, some compounds that might normally be regarded as unstable could exist in marine organisms. The lack of light beneath the surface of the oceans may also be expected to cause the formation of unusual natural products. In particular, the apparent need for organisms to produce light in the darkness of the abyss has created a vast though relatively inaccessible source of organisms for the chemical studies of bioluminescence. Nearer the surface, the competition for sunlight has given rise to a spectrum of pigments resulting in a more efficient utilization of solar energy. Perhaps the greatest divergence in the two environments lies in the high ionic concentrations encountered in the sea, which undoubtedly accounts for the unusually large proportion of halogen containing marine natural products.

Although the discovery of a unique natural product is often ample reward for the chemist's efforts, investigations of the marine enviroment offer many opportunities to combine structural elucidation with more pragmatic research, such as the search for new drugs and environmental studies. Preliminary pharmacological screening has indicated that many marine organisms contain physiologically active compounds, yet few of these have been isolated and identified. The study of chemical communication in the marine environment is in its infancy, but if it parallels the study of chemical communication in insects, it will become a fascinating field of research. In related environmental studies, the marine natural-products chemist will undoubtedly make vital contributions to studies of marine chemistry and marine pollution through an investigation of the organic chemicals in seawater. Use of the terms "dissolved organic carbon" and "particulate organic carbon," currently employed to describe organic chemicals in the ocean, indicates an almost complete lack of knowledge of individual components. Without a basic knowledge of the natural constituents of the oceans, who can say which industrial products are pollutants? In particular, some industrial chemicals that might be considered as pollutants may be among the natural compounds from marine organisms. To know which chemicals had existed before the industrial age will allow the pollution researchers to identify man's chemical input to the oceans.

Whatever the chemist's objective, his first task is to ensure a reliable supply of starting materials. Since few marine organisms can be obtained commercially, the investigator is usually dependent on his own efforts as a collector. Ironically, it is at this stage that the chemist usually encounters most of the problems involved in natural-products studies. Many marine organisms cannot be identified in the field, particularly during SCUBA collections. Additionally, many areas lack a taxonomic guide to marine species, and, in some cases, classification is still a matter of debate. Under these circumstances, it is often difficult to obtain a homogeneous sample of an identified species. When such a collection is possible, however, the chemist must ensure that his ravages cause minimal ecological disruption. Laboratory culture, the logical alternative to field collection, is currently possible for only a few species, and it appears that mariculture will be economically feasible only when natural products of great value are isolated from marine organisms.

In this chapter, we have reviewed major contributions to the literature of secondary metabolites from marine sources. Although we were limited to secondary metabolites by the prejudices of the natural-products chemist, we have included references to a few compounds of biochemical and physiological significance where the structures had been elucidated.

As a basis for a discussion of future research in marine natural products, we have catalogued the known marine natural products, grouping them in accordance with their probable biosynthetic origins. Some subjects, such as marine pharmaceuticals, marine toxins, and chemical communication among marine organisms, where marine biological research far exceeds chemical studies, defy such classification and have been presented according to biological action.

It is fitting to begin a review of marine natural products with sterols and their derivatives, since this is the most heavily studied area of research. An indication that organisms contained sterols other than cholesterol came in the first decade of this century, when novel sterols were found in sponges (Henze, 1908; Doree, 1909), insects (Menozzi and Moreschi, 1940), and starfish (Doree, 1909). This early research indicated that a variety of sterols were to be found in the invertebrates, setting the stage for Bergmann's authoritative studies. Bergmann provided an excellent review of his own research and related studies, with an exhaustive literature coverage up to 1958 (Bergmann, 1962). We can only abstract some of the more important of Bergmann's conclusions in this chapter.

Before the structure of cholesterol (**1**) was elucidated in 1932 (Rosenheim and King, 1932) the literature contained a confused multiplicity of trivial names that had been derived from the biological sources and bore no relationship to the chemical structures. Moreover, most of the "compounds" consisted of mixtures of sterols, which are renowned for their tendency to cocrystallize. This is not in itself surprising, since most of the sterols found in the invertebrates differ from cholesterol only in the nature of their side chains. When Bergmann began his investigations of the sterols from sponges, it appeared that every sponge contained a unique sterol. After a detailed investigation of some 50 species of sponge, Bergmann (1949) concluded that the "unique sterols" comprised mixtures of sterols, consisting mainly of known structures but containing a sprinkling of novel compounds such as clionasterol (**2**) (Valentine and Bergmann, 1941), poriferasterol (**3**) (Valentine and Bergmann, 1941), neospongosterol (**4**) (Bergmann et al., 1945), and chondrillasterol (**5**) (Bergmann and McTigue, 1948). The Δ^7 sterol, chondrillasterol, is unique among sponge sterols, which are usually Δ^5 sterols. Bergmann attempted to use his analyses of the sterol contents of sponges to aid the taxonomist in the difficult task of classifying sponges. In one case, the sterol mixture from the sponge known as *Suberites distortus* (*S. tuberculosus*) gave an optical rotation of opposite sign to the sterol mixtures from all other *Suberitae*. Subsequent reexamination of this sponge led to its reclassification into the family *Choanitidae* under the name *Anthosigmella varians* (Bergmann et al., 1950). Despite this success, it appears that chemical arguments will only serve to detect incorrect classification rather than form the basis of a taxonomic system.

Bergmann also studied the sterols from other invertebrate phyla, although in less detail. Among the coelenterates, he found two sterols having unusually high melting points, gorgosterol from the gorgonian, *Plexaura flexuosa*, and an unnamed sterol from the coral, *Madrepora cervicornis* (Bergmann et al., 1943). Gorgosterol (**6**), whose structure was recently elucidated by X-ray crystallography of 3β-bromogorgostene (Ling et al., 1970), was the first sterol found to have a cyclopropane ring in the side chain (Hale et al., 1970). A second cyclopropane-containing sterol, 23-dimethylgorgosterol (**7**), was isolated along with gorgosterol from *Gorgonia flabellum* or *G. ventilina* (Schmitz and Pattabhiraman, 1970). Even more unusual was the isolation of a related seco-gorgosterol derivative (**8**) from the gorgonian, *Pseudopterogorgia americana* (Weinheimer et al., 1970). These three examples indicate that the gorgonians may be a source of further related sterols having a 22,23-cyclopropane ring.

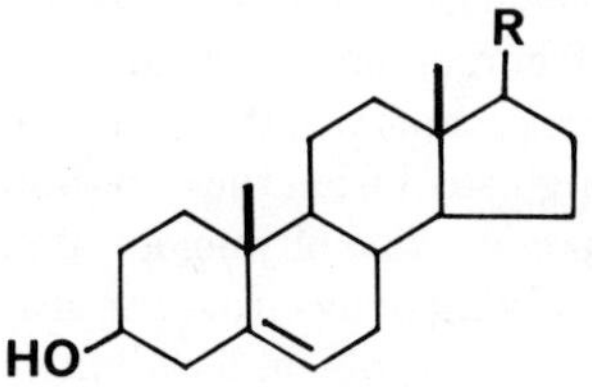

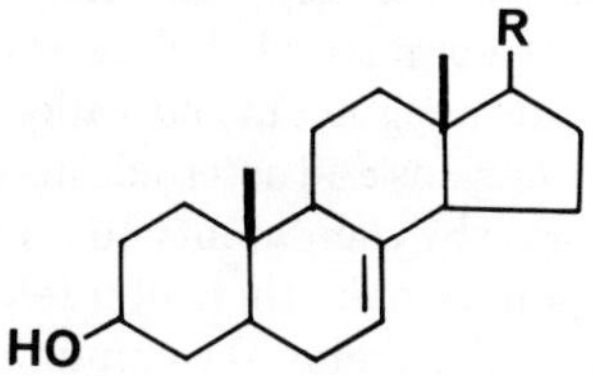

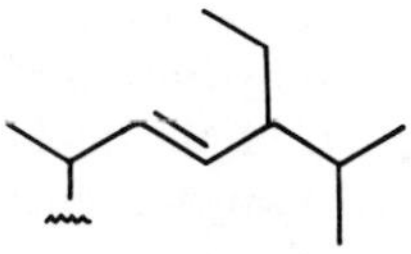

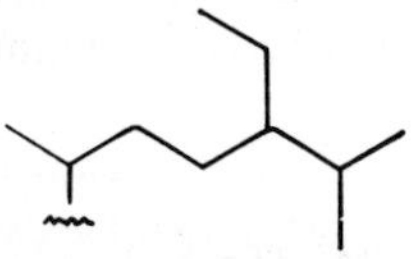

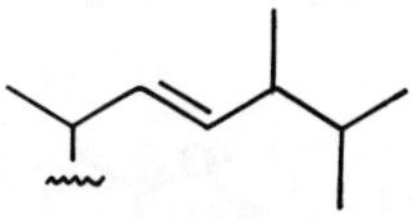

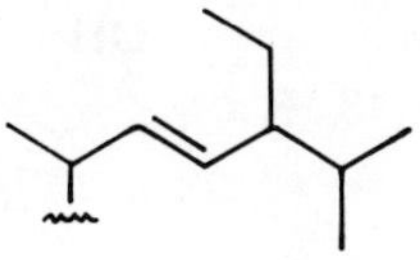

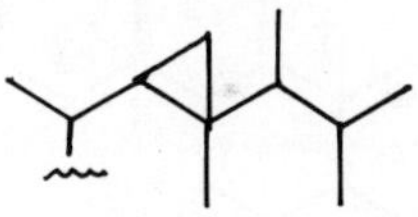

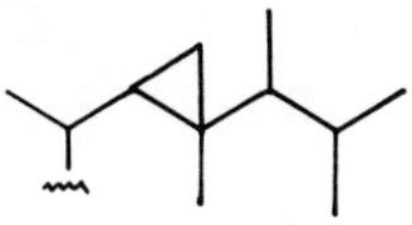

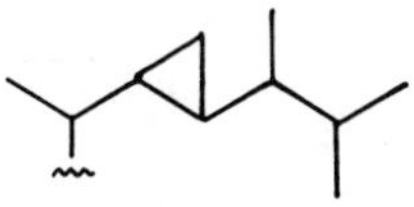

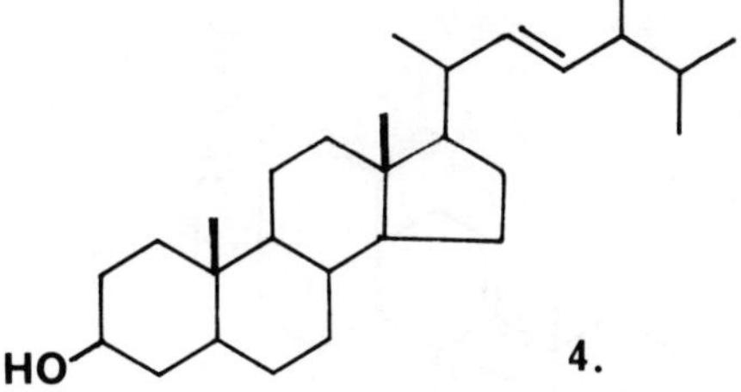

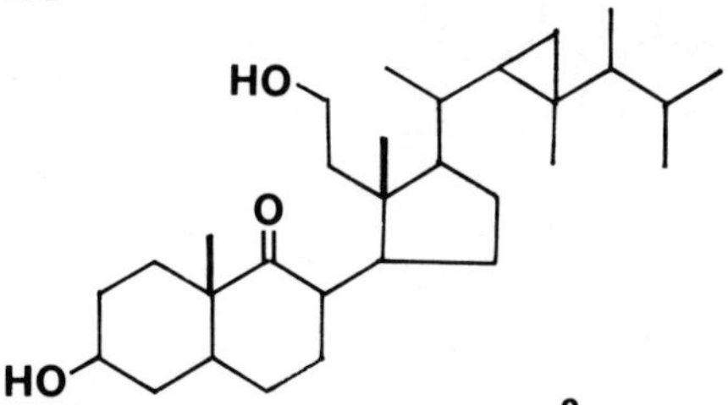

Sterol analyses have been performed on each of the five classes of the phylum *Echinodermata*. The phylum may be divided into two major groups according to the dominant type of sterol (Bergmann, 1962). Asteroids (sea stars) and holothurians (sea cucumbers) both contain the relatively rare Δ^7 sterols, while echinoids (sea urchins), ophiuroids (brittle stars), and crinoids (sea lilies) contain Δ^5 sterols. This relationship appears independent of the nature of the sterol content of the echinoderm food source.

A careful study of echinoderm sterols, using gas chromatography to separate the sterols as their trimethylsilyl ethers, confirmed the pattern of Δ^5 and Δ^7 sterols in this phylum (Gupta and Scheuer, 1968). The major sterol from *Acanthaster planci* was found to be 24-methyl-Δ^7-cholesterol (**9**) (stellasterol). A minor sterol, which Scheuer called acanthasterol (**10**), was isolated from *A. planci*. This sterol was identified as the Δ^7 analog of gorgosterol, before the structure of gorgosterol was known. Djerassi confirmed this assignment but called the same sterol acansterol (Sheikh et al., 1971).

The holothurians and asteroids may also be distinguished from the remaining classes of echinoderms by their ability to produce toxic saponins. The physiological properties of these saponins make them of interest to those studying drugs from the sea and also to those studying chemical communication. The greatest problem for all investigators has been the purification of saponins. Preparations that appeared relatively pure by conventional criteria often gave complex mixtures of sterols and carbohydrates on acid-catalyzed hydrolysis. As a result, most investigators have preferred to study the sterol portion of the molecule without reference to the structure of the original saponin of the saponin mixture.

A number of sapogenins (the sterol portions) have been isolated after acid hydrolysis of crude saponin mixtures. Holothurian sapogenins have a common feature, the

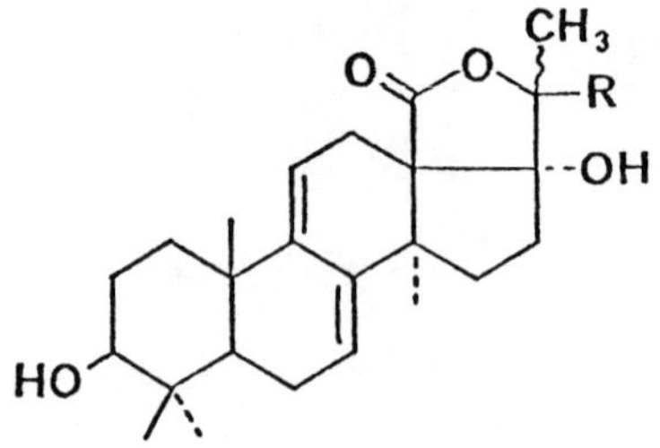

CH$_3$ O O R OH HO

11. R = 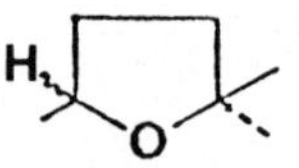
13. R = 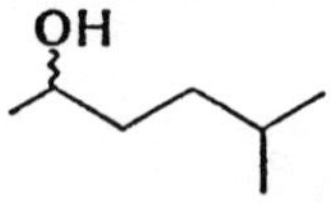
14. R = 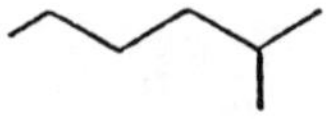
15. R = OCH$_3$

CH$_3$ O O R H HO

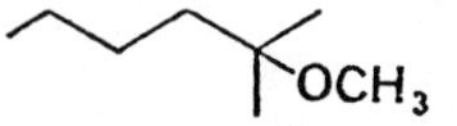

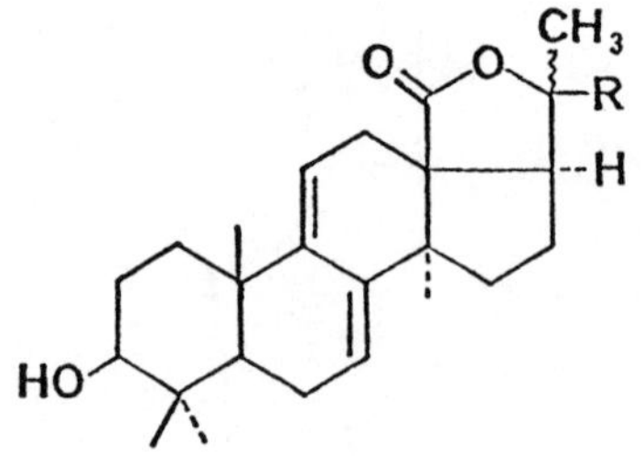

12. R = 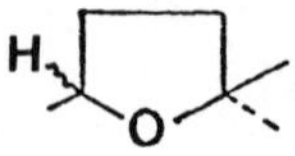
16. R = OCH$_3$
17. R =  OH
18. R =

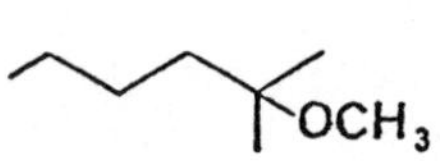

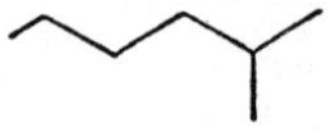

7,9-diene system, which allowed them to be located by UV spectroscopy during chromatographic separation. Since the saponin mixtures do not contain a UV chromophore, the sapogenins must be artifacts of the true sterol fragments.

Chanley et al. (1966) showed that the crude saponin extract from *Actinopyga agassizi*, called holothurin, was a mixture of glycosides of at least six sterols. On acid hydrolysis, holothurin yielded one equivalent of sulfate, four carbohydrates, and an aglycone fraction, consisting of at least six triterpene alcohols. Two components of the mixture were identified as 22,25-oxidoholothurinogenin (**11**) and its 17-deoxy analog (**12**). The principal sapogenins from *Halodeima grisea* have been identified as 22,25-oxidoholothurinogenin (**11**) and griseogenin (**13**) (Tursch et al., 1967). It seems probable that griseogenin was one of the unknown aglycones obtained from holothurin. The parent compound, holothurinogenin (**14**) and praslinogenin (**15**), have been isolated from *Holothuria poli* (Habermahl and Volkein, 1967). Ternaygenin (**16**), koellikerigenin (**17**), seychellogenin (**18**), and praslinogenin (**15**) have been isolated from *Bohadshia koellikeri* (Roller et al., 1969; Tursch et al., 1970). The methoxy groups in ternaygenin and praslinogenin and the oxido-ring in 22,25-oxidoholothurinogenin appear to have been formed during the acid catalyzed methanolysis.

Elyakov et al. (1969) have isolated two saponins, stichoposide A and C, from *Stychopus japonicus*, one of which may be identical with Shimada's holotoxin (Shimada, 1969), an antifungal compound. Stichoposide A was hydrolyzed with hydrocholoric acid to obtain stichopogenin A_4 (**19**) and its dehydration product stichopogenin A_2 (**20**), both of which contain a nonconjugated diene system.

Yasumoto and Hashimoto (1966) demonstrated that the toxic principle of *Asterias amurensis* was separable into six components. Two components designated asterosaponin A and asterosaponin B were isolated (Yasumoto and Hashimoto, 1967). Hydrolysis of these compounds both gave sulfate ion, a mixture of carbohydrates, and a complicated mixture of sterols. The sterols have not been identified.

The most complete study of a starfish saponin has been performed by Mackie and his collaborators (Mackie and Turner, 1970; Turner et al., 1971). They were able to purify a saponin from *Marthasterias glacialis* because of the presence of a UV chromophore in the steroidal portion. On acid hydrolysis of the purified saponin, they

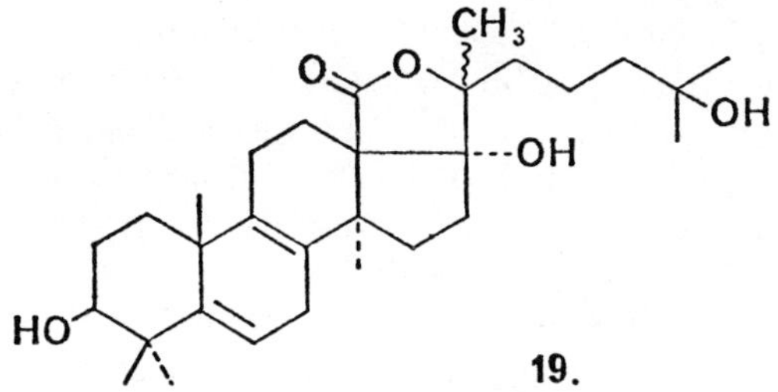

CH3 O O OH OH HO

19.

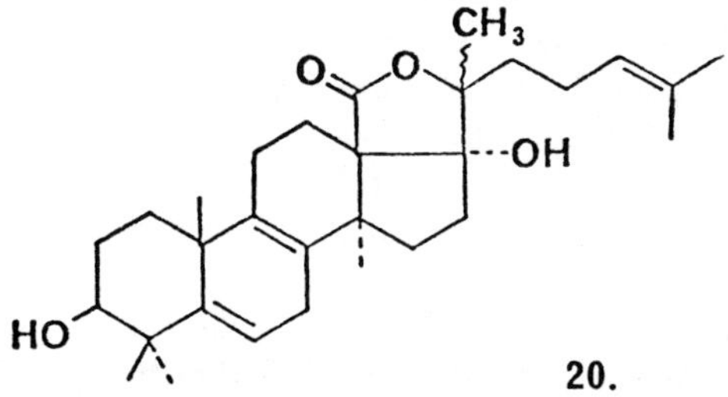

CH3 O O OH HO

20.

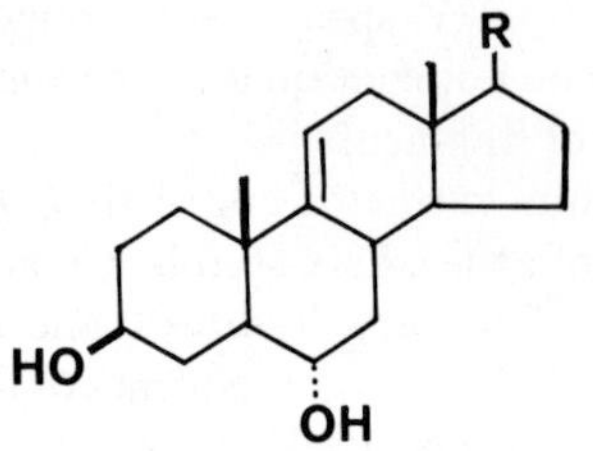

R

HO

OH

21. R =

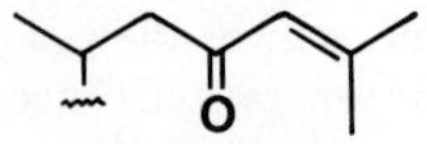

22. R =

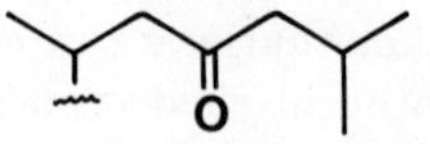

23. R = $-COCH_3$ 24. R =

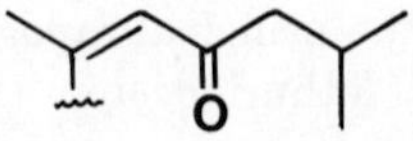

isolated two steroidal molecules, marthasterone (**21**) and 24,25-dihydromarthasterone (**22**), which differed only in the side chain (Mackie and Turner, 1970). After studying the order in which sugars appeared during hydrolysis, Mackie suggested that the saponin contained four carbohydrate units in the order fucose-quinovose-quinovose-glucose-steroid-sulfate. Shimizu (1971) has recently reported the isolation of an aglycone from *Acterina pectinifera* having the molecular formula $C_{27}H_{46}O_4$, but no chemical studies have followed.

Three groups have recently reported the major sapogenin from *Acanthaster planci* (Sheikh et al., 1972a; Shimizu, 1972) and *Asterias amurensis* (Ikegami et al., 1972a) to be 5α-pregn-9(11)-ene-3β,6α-diol-20-one (**23**). Each group has reported a different melting point and optical rotation for this compound, indicating, as is known for one sample (Faulkner, unpublished), that the samples were contaminated with the 17α-acetyl isomer to a greater or lesser extent. We have shown by gas chromatographic analysis of the trimethylsilyl ethers that the pregnane derivative is the major sapogenin from many other starfish. One of the groups found a second sapogenin (**24**) from *A. planci* (Sheikh et al., 1972a). Since the saponin mixture shows no UV chromophore, it is imperative that future work be carried out on intact saponins so that the true identity of the sterol portions may be determined.

In contrast with green and red algae, which usually contain sterols more characteristic of terrestrial plants, the brown algae have provided a source of several interesting sterols. The characteristic sterol of brown algae is fucosterol (**25**) (Miller, 1962), while its C-20 epimer, sargasterol (**26**) has been isolated from *Sargassum ringgoldianum* and *Eisenia bicyclis* (Tsuda et al., 1958). Recently, some unique sterols have been isolated as minor constituents of brown algae. The vinyl alcohol (**27**), derived by oxidation of fucosterol, has been isolated from *S. ringgoldianum* (Ikekawa et al., 1966) and *Fucus evanescens* (Ikekawa et al., 1972). In addition *F. evanescens* contained the diol (**28**) derived from fucosterol by allylic oxidation and the dienone (**29**), formed by dehydration of the corresponding 7-keto-alcohol.

The sterols of molluscs present a relatively confused picture with many trivial names having been assigned to complex mixtures of sterols. Nevertheless, it is safe to make some general observations about this phylum. The chitons differ from all other molluscs by having Δ^7 rather than Δ^5 sterols. Some marine molluscs, particularly bivalves, contain relatively large quantities of $\Delta^{5,7}$ sterols.

The crustaceans have not provided the chemist with new sterols, but they are the source of several important molting hormones. Shortly after the structure of ecdysone had been determined, Horn reported crustecdysone (20-hydroxyecdysone) (**30**) to be the principal molting hormone of the crayfish, *Jasus lalandei* (Hampshire and Horn, 1966). A second crustacean molting hormone (**31**), lacking the 2-hydroxy group, has been isolated from the shrimp *Crangan vulgans* (Galbraith et al., 1968). In addition to

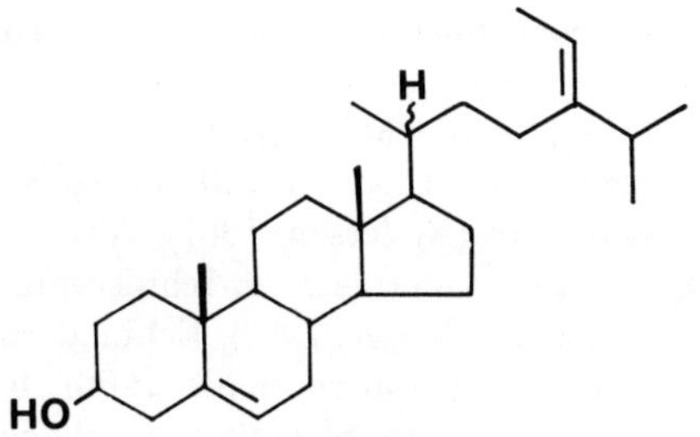

25, 26

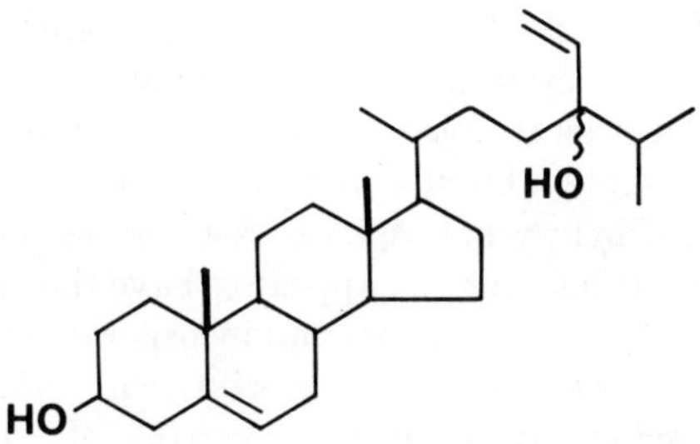

27

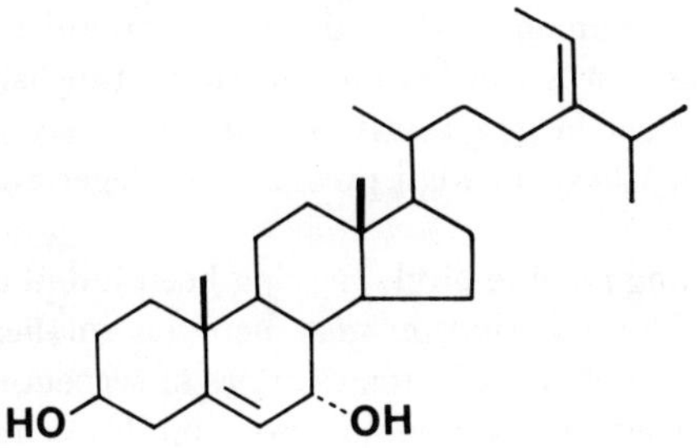

28

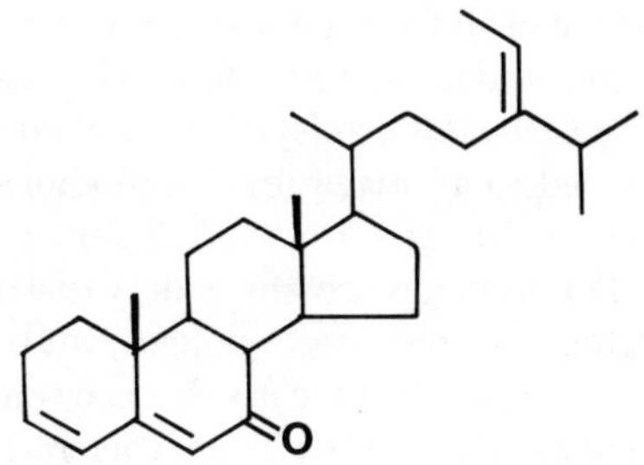

29

crustecdysone, two ecdyones called callinecdysone A (**32**) and callinecdysone B (**33**) have been isolated from the crab, *Callinectes sapidus* (Faux et al., 1969).

The biosynthesis of sterols and particularly cholesterol has been studied in a few marine species with mixed results. The acyclic precursor of sterols, squalene (**34**), is one of the more important marine natural products. First isolated from the liver of the shark (squalidae) in 1906 by Tsujimoto (1906, 1916), the structure defied definition until Karrer (1931) showed that squalene consisted of two farnesyl units, linked in a

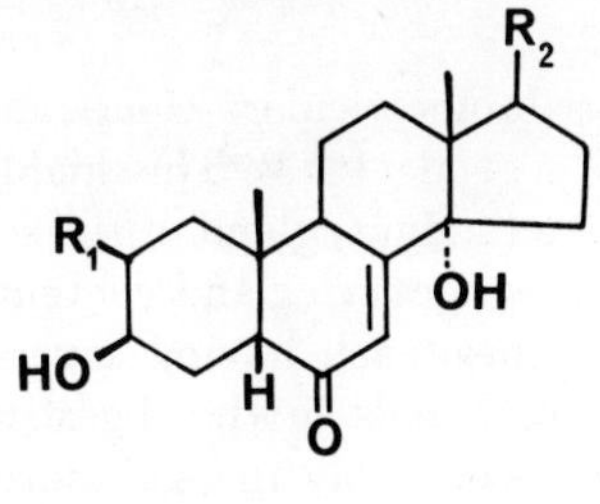

30. R_1 = -OH

31. R_1 = -H

R_2 =

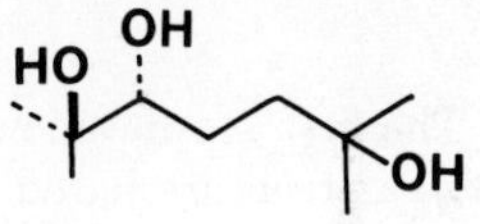

32. R_1 = -OH R_2 =

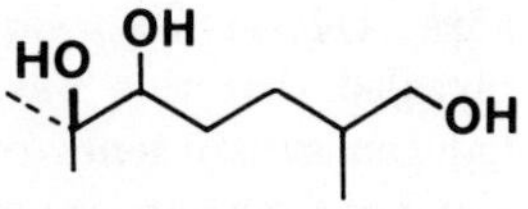

33. R_1 = -OH R_2 =

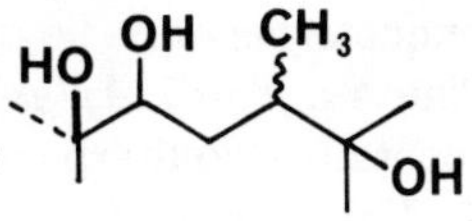

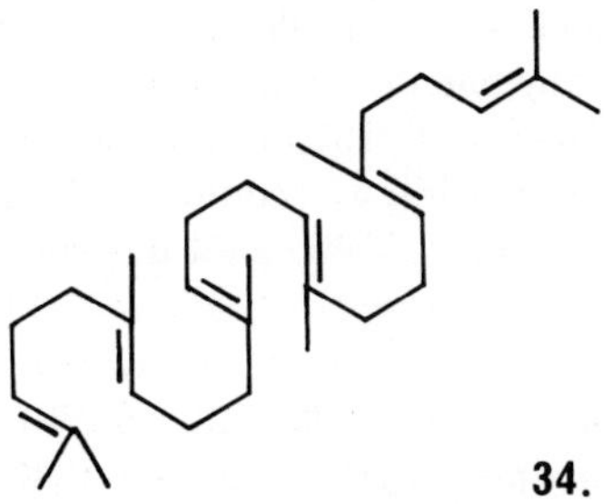

34.

"tail-to-tail" manner. The important all-*trans* stereochemistry was determined using X-ray crystallography (Nicolaides and Laves, 1954). The biosynthesis of cholesterol and other sterols from acetate cannot be accomplished by all marine invertebrates. For example, the zooxanthellae isolated from *Pseudoplexaura porosa* will incorporate farnesyl pyrophosphate, but not acetate or mevalonate (Andersen, 1967). Although crustaceans do not appear to have the ability to synthesize sterols (Shin-Ichi-Teshima, 1971), some molluscs can incorporate acetate into sterols (Voogt, 1969). Echinoderms are reported unable to synthesize sterols from acetate (Salaque et al., 1966), but starfish have been shown capable of rearranging cholesterol to Δ^7-cholestenol (Fagerlund and Idler, 1966).

One of the unique features of the marine environment is the existence of organisms living under high pressure. The discovery that the swim-bladder of the rattail fish, *Corphaenoides acrolepis*, from 2000 m contain very large quantities of free cholesterol has led to an investigation of cholesterol biosynthesis at high pressures (Phleger and Benson, 1971).

The terpenes are not widely distributed among marine phyla, having been found in algae, coelenterates, sponges, and molluscs. The distribution may be even smaller, however, since there is evidence that algal symbionts are the true sources of terpenoid compounds isolated from coelenterates and that the terpenoids from molluscs are derived from ingested algae. Nevertheless, the variety of structures that have already been described suggest that all structural types of terpenoids found in plants may eventually be found algae. In addition, the algal metabolites contain halogen substituted terpenes not found in plants.

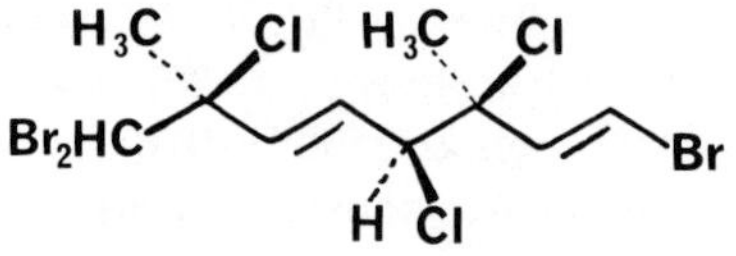

35

The first marine monoterpene to be described was a tribromotrichloro compound (**35**), a structure based on the geraniol skeleton (Faulkner et al., 1973). This highly halogenated monoterpene was extracted from the digestive (midgut) gland of the sea hare, *Aplysia californía*. A GC-mass spectral analysis of the digestive gland contents revealed that this was the first of a series of monoterpenes, each having several halogen substituents (unpublished results). Since the compounds in the digestive gland of a sea hare appear to be derived from its food, there is probably an algal source of monoterpenes to be discovered.

The sea hare, *Aplysia kurodai*, was among the first marine organisms shown to contain sesquiterpenes, namely aplysin (**36**), debromoaplysin (**37**), and aplysinol (**38**) (Yamamura and Hirata, 1963). This discovery would have been quite remarkable had Irie et al. not discovered a series of related compounds in several species of the genus *Laurencia*, a red alga. The phenols, laurinterol (**39**) and debromolaurinterol (**40**), isolated from *L. intermedia* (Irie et al., 1970b) were clearly related to aplysin (**36**) and debromoaplysin (**37**). This relationship was confirmed by the conversion of laurinterol (**39**) into aplysin (**36**) using toluenesulfonic acid in glacial acetic acid (Suzuki et al., 1969). A third metabolite of *L. intermedia*, iso-laurinterol (**41**), could also be converted into aplysin (**36**) under similar acidic conditions. Examination of the metabolites of *L. okamurai* revealed the coexistence of laurinterol (**39**) and aplysin (**36**), debromolaurinterol (**40**) and debromoaplysin (**37**), together with aplysinol (**38**) (Irie et al.,

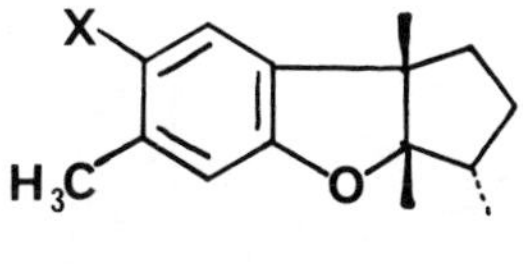

36 X=Br
37 X=H

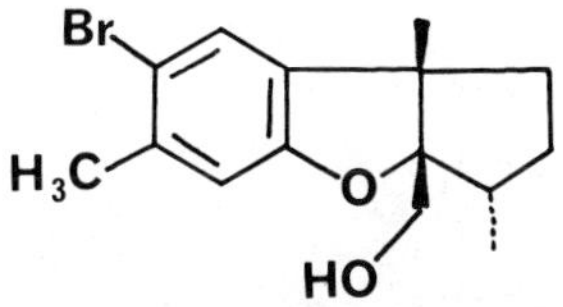

38

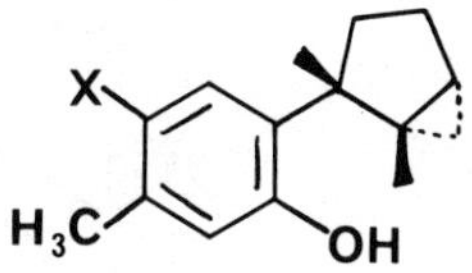

39 X=Br
40 X=H

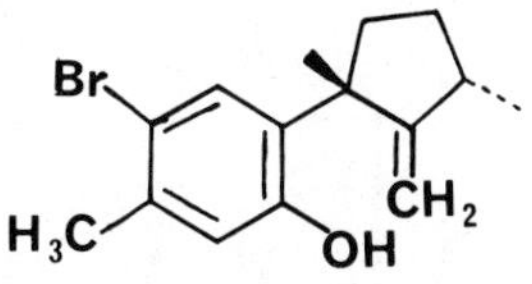

41

1969b). There now seemed no reason to doubt that the terpenes from *Aplysia kurodai* had been derived from *Laurencia*, a common food of the sea hare.

The parent hydrocarbon of this group of sesquiterpenes, laurene (**42**), has been isolated from *L. glandulifera* and *L. nipponica* (Irie et al., 1969c). The suggestion (Irie et al., 1965b) that laurene (**42**) was a biosynthetic precursor of the series of sesquiterpenes appeared unlikely after the discovery of new metabolites, such as spirolaurenone (**43**) from *L. glandulifera* (Suzuki et al., 1970), and was omitted from the later publication (Irie et al., 1969a). A related vinyl bromide, laurenisol (**44**), has been isolated from *L. nipponica* (Irie et al., 1969a).

A recent investigation (Sims et al., 1971) of metabolites from *L. pacifica* resulted in the discovery of a new class of sesquiterpenes containing both bromine and chlorine, the first of which was pacifenol (**45**). A closely related sesquiterpene, johnstonol (**46**), was then isolated from *L. johnstonii* (Sims et al., 1972), while the precursor to pacifenol, prepacifenol (**47**), has been isolated from *L. filiformis* (Sims et al., 1973). The presence of these three compounds alongside laurinterol (**39**) and isolaurinterol (**41**) led to the suggestion that both groups were derived from a common biosynthetic precursor, the ion (**48**). We have recently isolated pacifidiene (**49**) and a hydrogen chloride addition product (**50**), as well as pacifenol (**45**) and johnstonol (**46**), from the sea hare. *A. californica* (Faulkner and Stallard, unpublished). This array of products

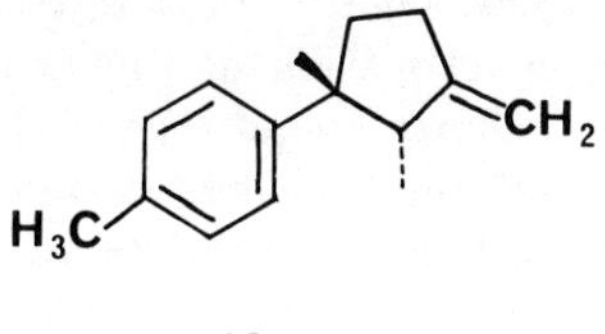

42

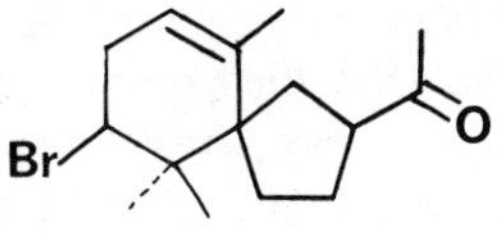

43

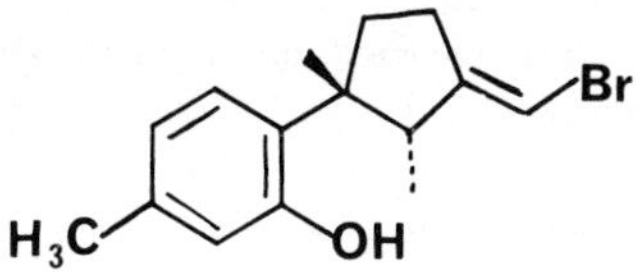

44

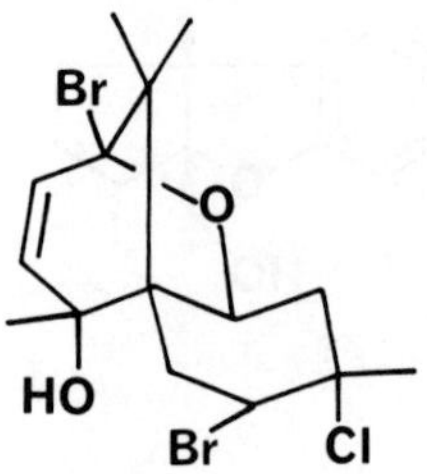

strongly suggests that the sea hare carries out acid-catalyzed reactions on compounds from its algal foodstuffs within the digestive gland.

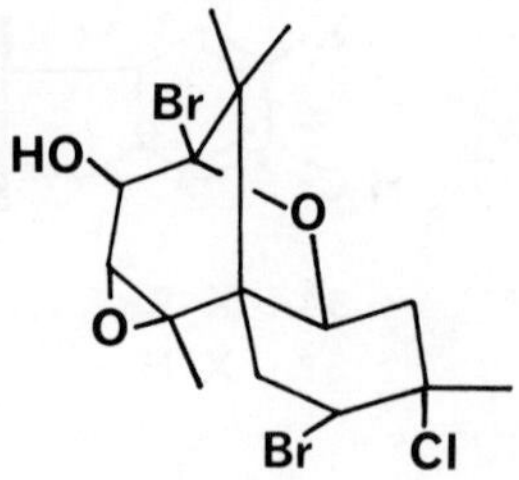

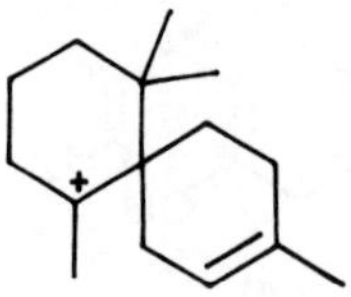

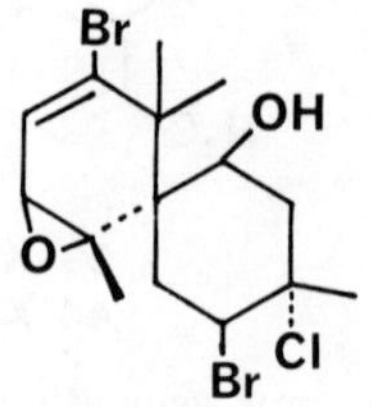

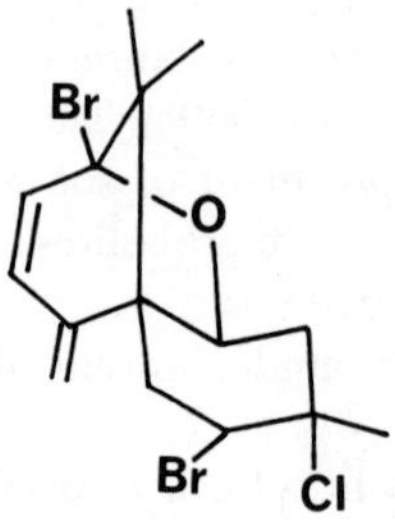

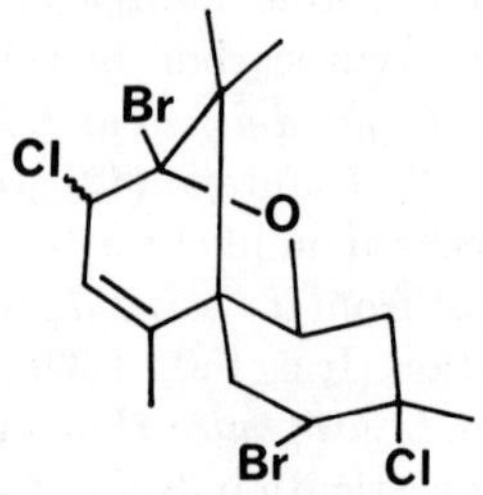

The discovery in 1951 of an unknown sesquiterpene alcohol from the brown alga, *Dictyopteris divaricata*, prompted the first extensive study of sesquiterpenes in a marine alga (Takaoka and Ando, 1951). Subsequent investigations showed that *D. divaricata* contained (−)-copaene (**51**), cadalene (**52**), (−)-γ,-cadinene (**53**), and (−)-δ-cadinol (**54**), and a new hydrocarbon, which was identified as (+)-β-elemene (**55**) (Irie et al., 1967). β-Elemene had been isolated previously from a terrestrial source but as the opposite optical antipode. Further investigation of the metabolites of *D. divaricata* revealed that dictyopterol, the unknown sesquiterpene alcohol from the previous paper, was an inseparable mixture of α- and β-isomers of selinen-lβ-ol (**56** and **57**) (Kurosawa et al., 1966). A corresponding ketone, dictyopterone (**58**), was also isolated from the essential oil.

Recently, a new sesquiterpene hydrocarbon, zonarene (**59**), was isolated from *Dictyopteris zonaroides* (Fenical et al., 1972). From the same source came a fungicidal compound, zonoral (**60**), having a sesquiterpene skeleton linked to a hydroquinone residue (Fenical, et al., 1973a). The corresponding double bond isomer, isozonarol (**61**), has also been found in *D. zonaroides*.

The hydrocarbon, (+)-β-elemene (**55**), has been isolated from a gorgonian, *Eunicea mammosa* (Weinheimer et al., 1968). Because (+)-β-elemene had been isolated after distillation (100°), cold extracts of *E. mammosa* were examined (Weinheimer et al., 1970). The hydrocarbon fraction was shown to contain both (−)-germacrene (**62**) and

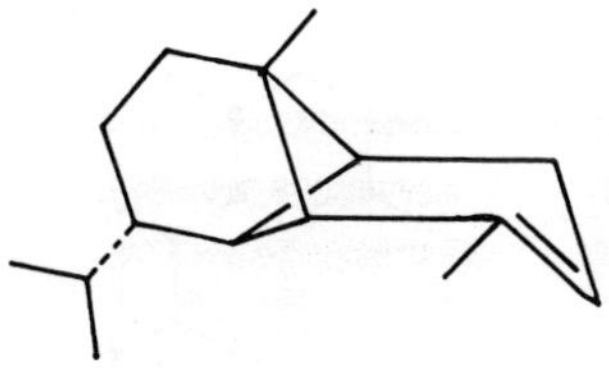

51

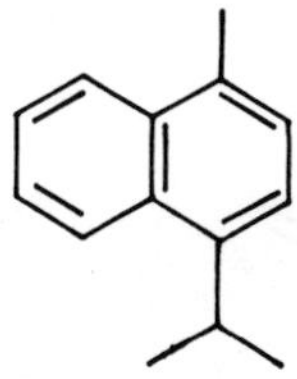

52

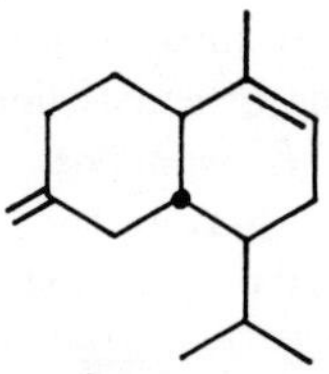

HO

53

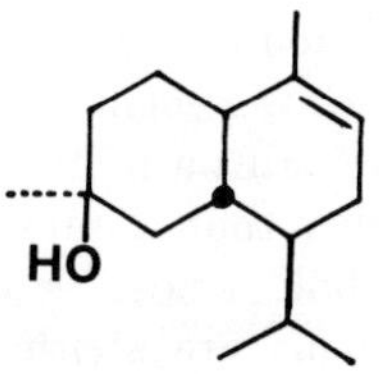

54

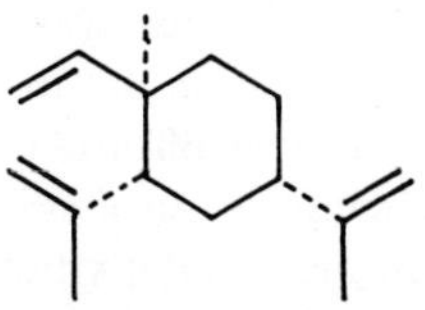

HO

55

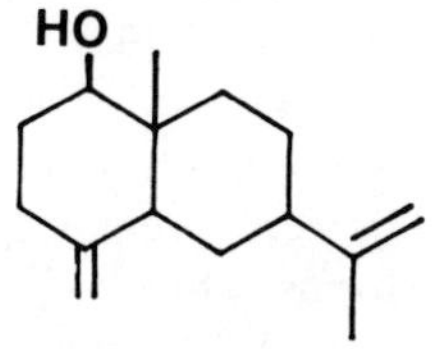

56

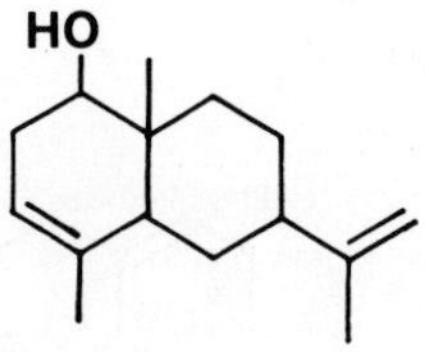

HO

O

57

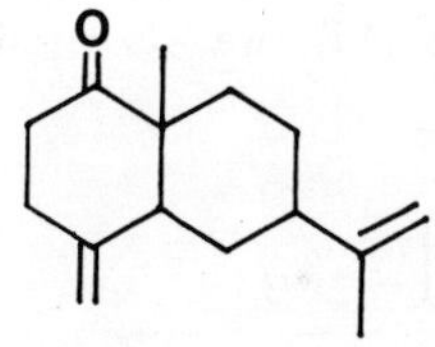

58

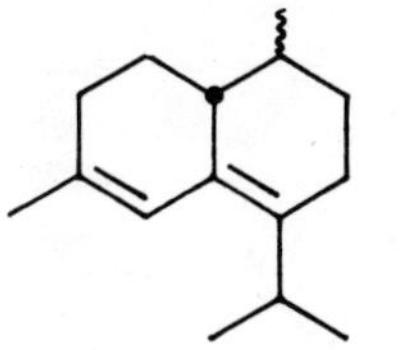

59

HO

OH

HO

OH

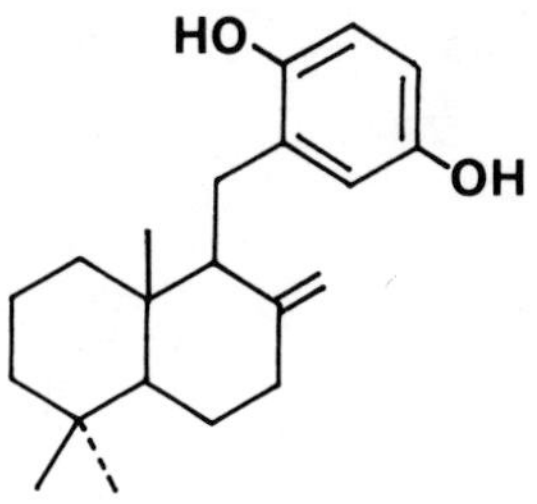

60

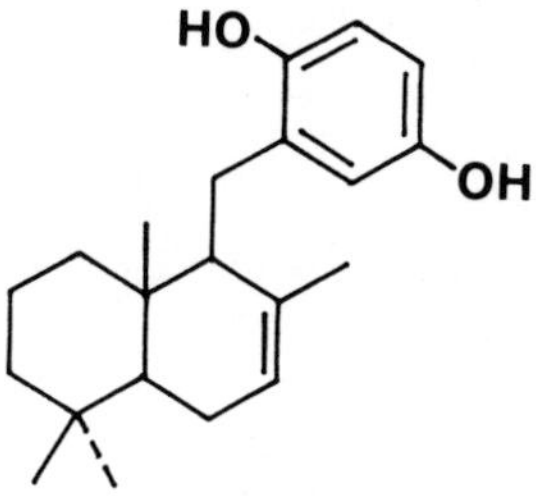

61

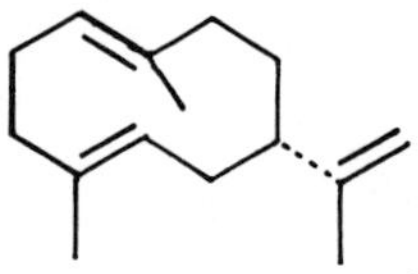

62 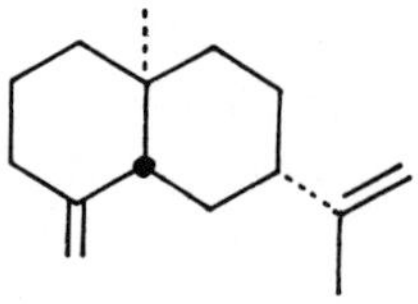 63 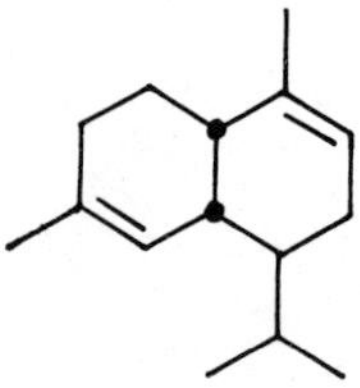 64

(+)-β-elemene (**55**) in a 3:2 ratio with (−)-β-selinene (**63**) as a minor component. There can be no doubt that (−)-germacrene was converted into (+)-β-elemene through a Cope rearrangement. Whether (+)-β-elemene is a major constituent of the living gorgonian remains a matter of conjecture. A sample of *E. mammosa* obtained from Jamaica rather than Bimini contained (+)-α-muurolene (**64**) as the principal sesquiterpene alcohol. A possible explanation of this irregularity is that the sesquiterpene hydrocarbons are synthesized by the zooxanthellae associated with the gorgonians, rather than the coral itself.

The gorgonian coral, *Pseudopterogorgia americana*, contained a mixture of four sesquiterpene alcohols, the major component of which was the previously unknown compound β-gorgonene (**65**) (Weinheimer et al., 1968d). β-Gorgonene was the first example of an eudesmane-derived nonisoprenoid sesquiterpene with a "displaced" isopropenyl residue. Of the remaining constituents, (+)-9-aristolene (**66**) and (−)1(10)-aristolene (**67**) were previously known from terrestrial sources, although as the enantiomeric forms, while (+)-γ-maaliene (**68**) had been obtained by dehydration of a related alcohol. (+)-β-Ylangene (**69**), (+)-α-cubebene (**70**), and (+)-calamenene (**71**) were obtained from *Pseudoplaxaura porosa*, while (+)-β-bisabolene (**72**) was found in *Plexaura dichotoma* (Weinheimer et al., 1968c). The nonisoprenoid benzofuran, furoventalene (**73**), was isolated after steam distillation of extracts of *Gorgonia*

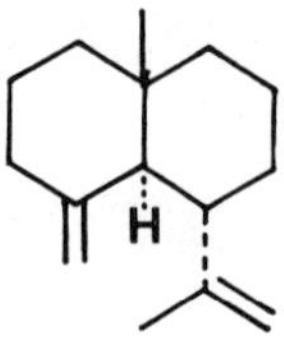

H 65 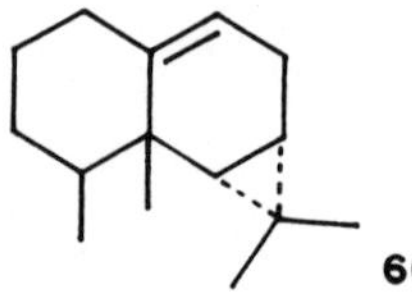 66 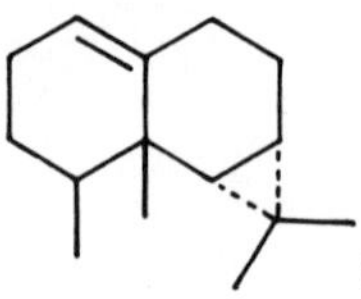 67

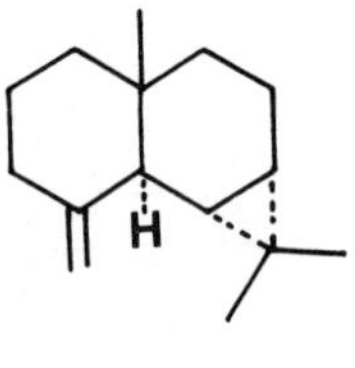

H 68 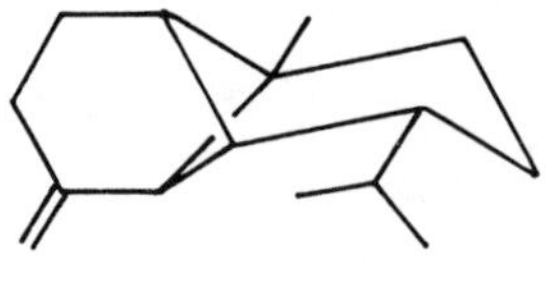 69 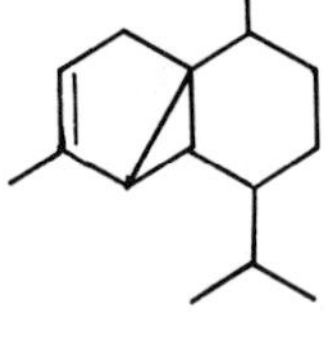 70

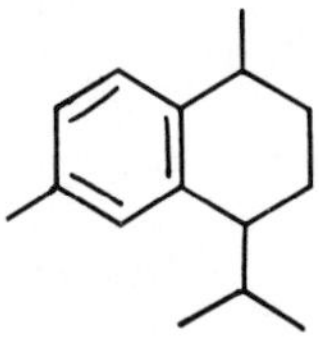

71 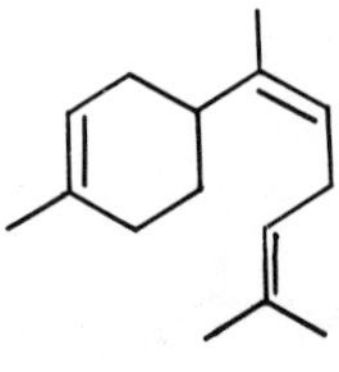 72 O 73

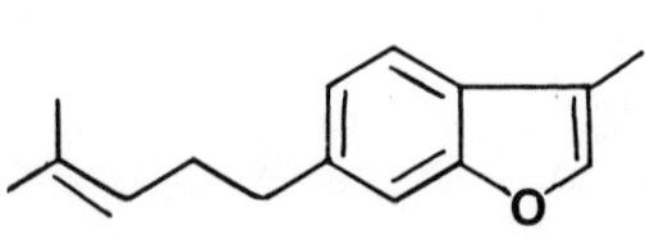

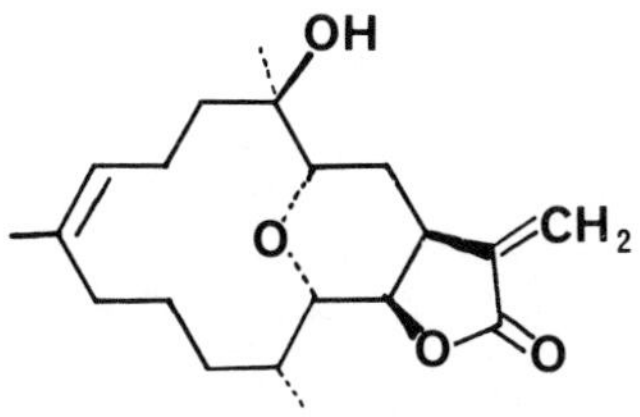

74

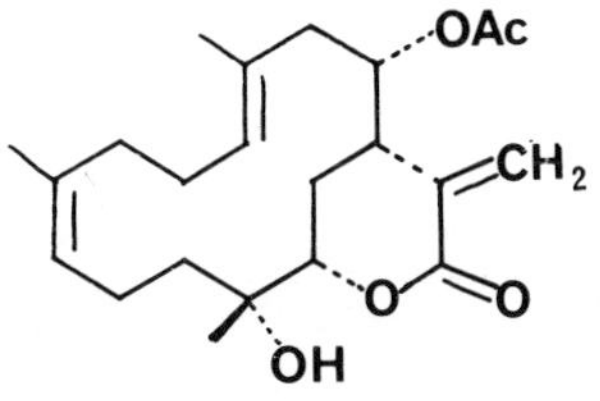

75

ventalina (Weinheimer and Washecheck, 1969). One cannot therefore be certain that furoventalene was a natural constituent of the gorgonian.

The diterpenes found in gorgonians have all been large ring lactones. The diterpene lactones, eunicin (**74**), from *Eunicea mammosa* (Weinheimer et al., 1968b) and crassin acetate (**75**), from *Pseudoplexaura* species (Weinheimer et al., 1968a; Houssain and Helm, 1969), both showed antibacterial activity. A third lactone, jeunicin, was isolated from *E. mammosa* (Weinheimer et al., 1968c) but has not been fully characterized.

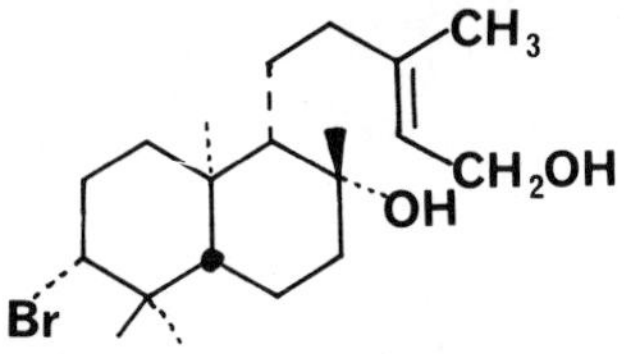

76

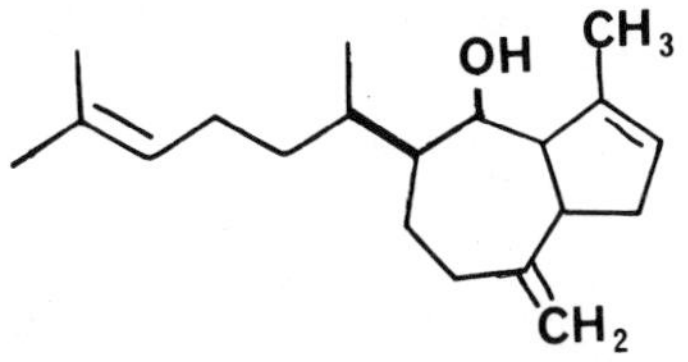

77

The first marine diterpene to be described was a aplysin-20 (**76**), a brominated compound from *A. kurodai* (Matsuda et al., 1967). The structure of aplysin-20 is of biosynthetic significance, since it may formally be regarded as produced by bromonium ion-initiated cyclization of geranylgeraniol. The only other diterpene whose structure has been elucidated was pachydictol A (**77**), a diterpene alcohol from *Pachydictyon coriaceum*. Ciereszko's group has announced the discovery of a family of five "Briariins" from a coelenterate source, but the structures of these "highly oxygenated diterpenes containing chlorine" have not been revealed.

Among the most unusual terpenes isolated from marine organisms are the sesterterpenes isolated from sponges (Cimino et al., 1972a). The sesterterpenes ircinin-1 (**78**) and ircinin-2 (**79**) from *Ircinia oros* both contain five isoprene units joined head to tail; they differ only in the position of the olefinic linkage. A third sesterterpene, fasciculatin (**80**), has been isolated from *Ircinia fasciculata* (Cafieri et al., 1972). All three sesterterpenes contain a tetronic acid function together with one or two furan groups. They represent a unique series of sesterterpenes that are themselves a relatively unknown group of compounds (Nozoe et al., 1965).

A group of C-21 furanoterpenes, believed to be oxidized sesterterpenes, has been isolated from sponges. *Spongia nitens* was shown to contain nitenin (**81**) and dihydronitenin (**82**) (Fattorusso et al., 1971b), while *Spongia officinalis* and *Hippospongia communis* both yielded furospongin-1 (**83**) as the major terpenoid compound (Cimino et al., 1971) and a series of related compounds as minor components (Cimino et al., 1972d). The same group has recently described a series of prenylated benzoquinones (**84**) together with the corresponding quinols from *Ircinia spinosula* (Cimino et al., 1972b).

The carotenoid pigments from marine organisms would provide sufficient material for a separate chapter. We are content to leave such a review to a specialist (Isler, 1971) and list only two important marine pigments. Fucoxanthin (**85**) is the principal pigment in brown algae (*Fucus* sp.) and has also been isolated from diatoms. Its structure contains an allenic function, the first example of this functionality in a carotenoid (Bonnett et al., 1969). The principal carotenoid of dinoflagellates is peridinin (**86**), which is again an allenic carotenoid (Strain et al., 1971).

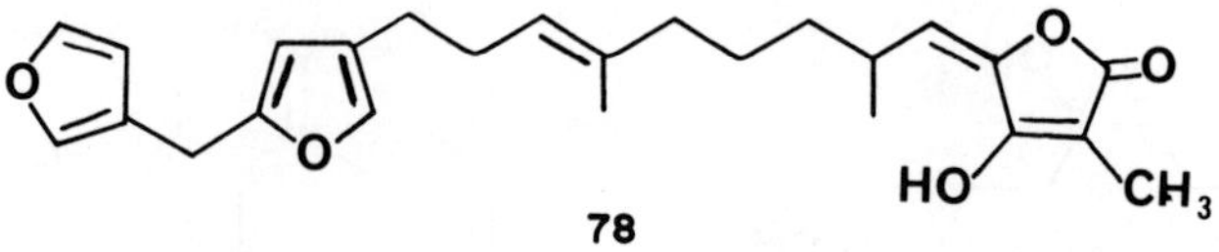

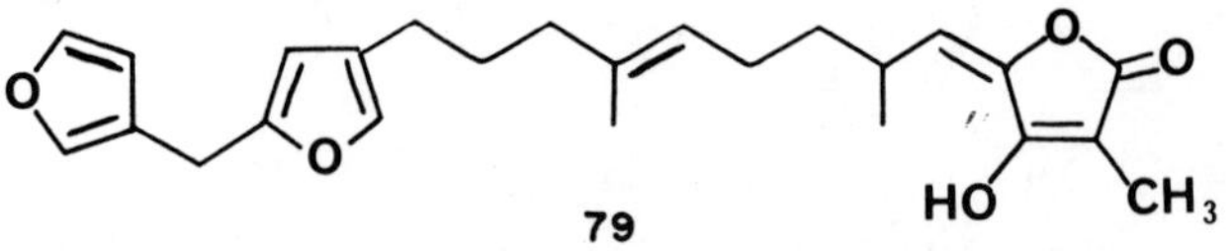

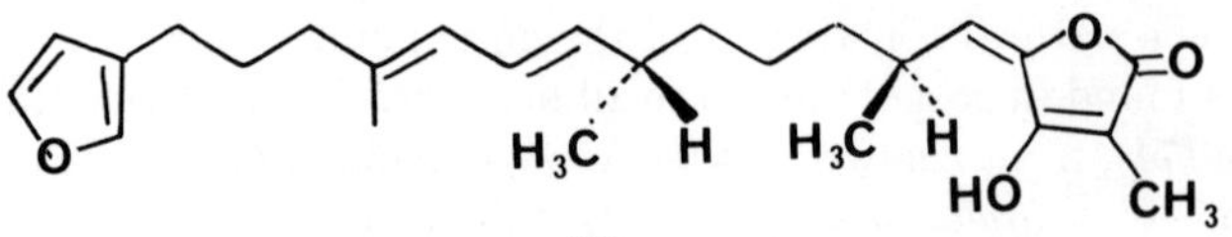

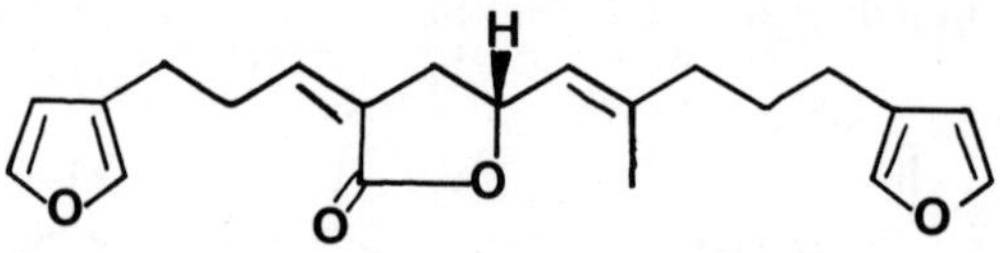

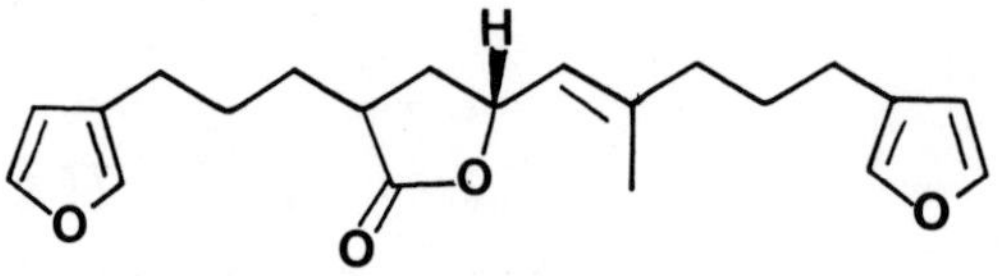

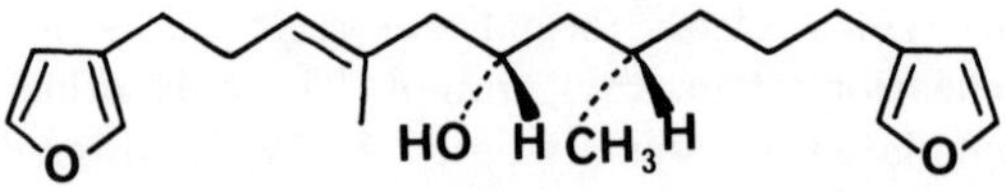

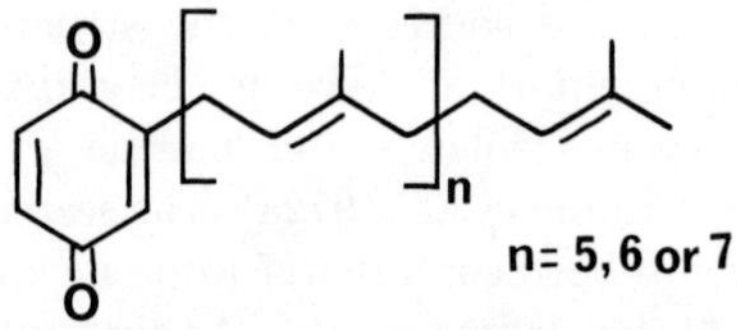

It becomes particularly difficult to distinguish a boundary between natural-products chemistry and biochemistry when one examines the literature on marine hydrocarbons. We have made an arbitrary decision to term all comparative studies of *n*-alkanes, *n*-alkenes, fatty acids, and fatty alcohols as biochemistry and are left with a relatively small number of studies where major concern has been the structural elucidation. Some recent studies straddle both fields but are of interest, since they describe unusual natural polyenes. The brown alga, *Fucus vesiculosus*, was shown to contain two

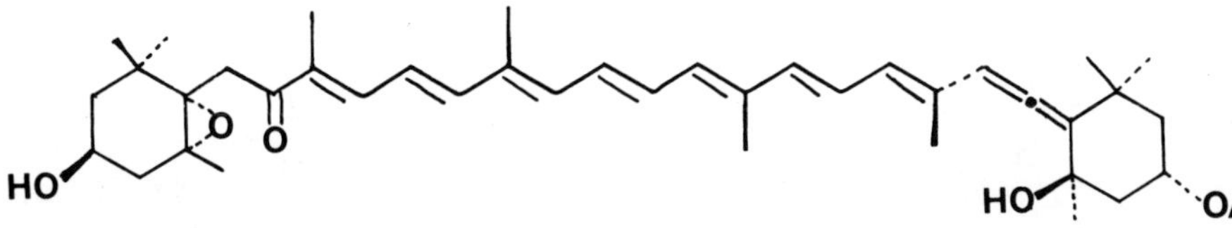

85

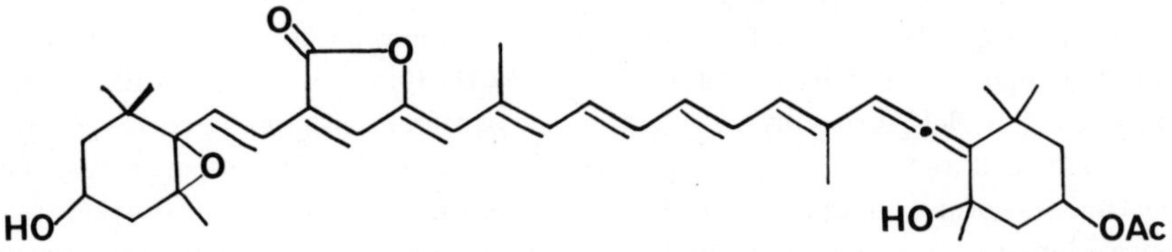

86

new C_{21} polyolefinic hydrocarbons, heneicosa-1,6,9,12,15-pentaene (**87**) and heneicosa-1,6,9,12,15,18-hexaene (**88**) (Halsall and Hills, 1971). Two laboratories have independently reported the presence of heneicosa-3,6,9,12,15,18-hexaene (**89**) in marine phytoplankton (Blumer et al., 1970; Lee et al., 1970; Lee and Loeblich, 1971).

87

88

89

Algae of the genus *Dictyopteris* produce unusual C_{11} hydrocarbons, some containing a cyclopropane ring (Moore et al., 1968). Dictyopterene A (**90**) and dictyopterene B (**91**) have been found in *Dictyopteris australis*, together with *trans,cis,cis*-1,3,5,8-undecatetraene (**92**) (Pettus and Moore, 1970). Moore has postulated that both dictyopterene B (**91**) and the tetraene (**92**) may be formed from the same intermediate, *cis,trans,cis*-1,4,6,8-undecatetraene, the former through a "photochemical" di-π-methane rearrangement and the latter through a "thermal" 1,5-sigmatropic proton shift. Further examination of *Dictyopteris* metabolites revealed that *trans,trans,cis*-undeca-1,3,5,8-tetraene (**93**), *trans,trans*-undeca-1,3,5-triene (**94**), and *trans,cis*-undeca-1,3,5-triene (**95**) were also present (Pettus and Moore, 1971).

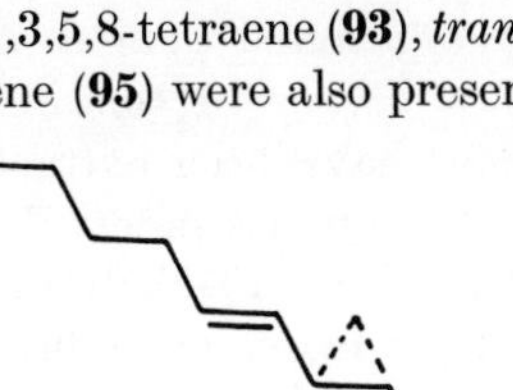

90

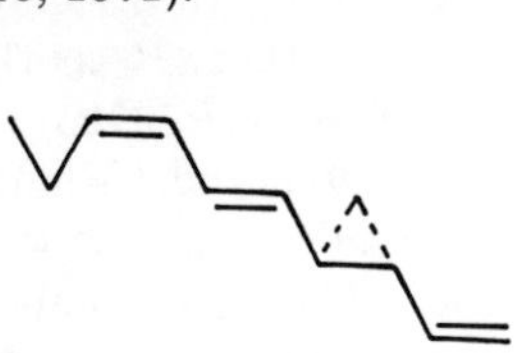

91

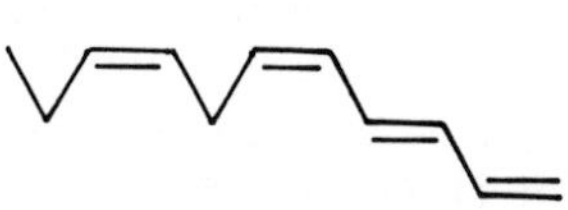

92

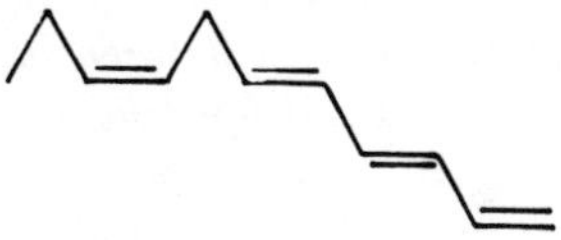

93

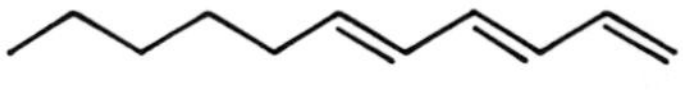

94

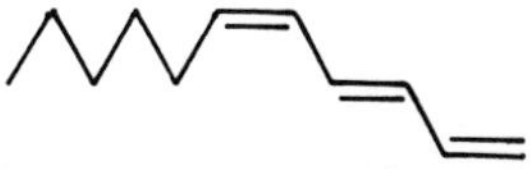

95

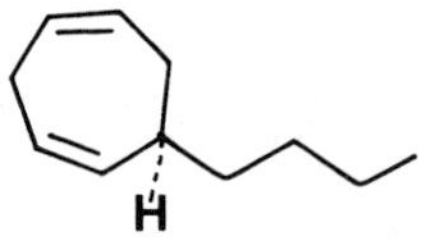

96

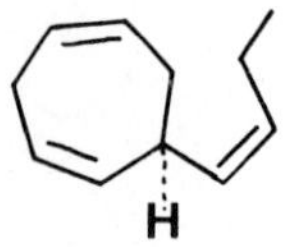

97

Two cyclic compounds, dictyopterene C′ (**96**) and dictyopterene D′ (**97**) were also obtained from *Dictyopteris* sp. The enantiomeric compounds could be obtained by Cope rearrangement of the *trans*-cyclopropanes so that it seemed most likely that dictyopterenes C′ and D′ arose by *in vivo* Cope rearrangements of the corresponding *cis*-cyclopropanes, a rearrangement that would occur at lower temperatures. The discovery that the gamete attractant of the brown alga *Ectocarpus siliculosus* possessed a structure identical to dictyopterene D′ (optical properties unknown) has created further interest in these unusual compounds (Müller et al., 1971).

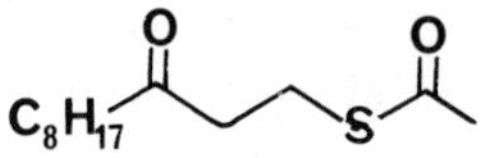

C_8H_{17} 98

C_6H_{13} 99

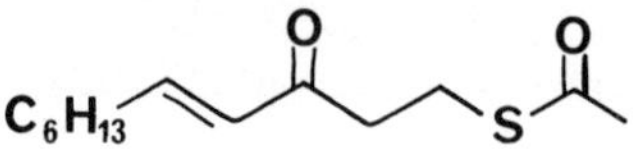

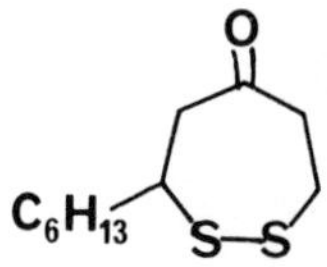

C_6H_{13} 100

C_8H_{17} C_8H_{17} n = 1 - 3 101

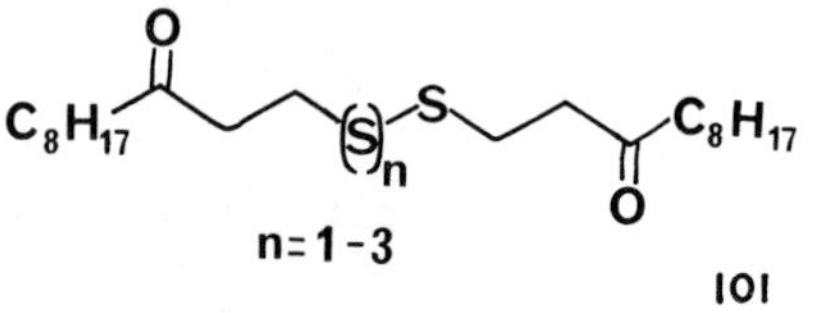

Dictyopteris sp. have also yielded some unusual sulfur-containing lipids (**98**–**101**) (Roller et al., 1971). They each contain an 11-carbon chain and may therefore be related, possibly as precursors, to the previous series of compounds. The polysulfides (**101** $n = 2$ or 3) represent only the second instance of polysulfides in nature (Moore, 1971).

Apart from being a rich source of brominated terpenes, the genus *Laurencia* has also yielded a series of brominated acetylenes. *Laurencia glandulifera* was shown to contain laurencin (**102**), whose structure was confirmed by X-ray analysis (Irie et al., 1968). Soon after, laureatin (**103**) and iso-laureatin (**104**) were isolated from *L. nipponica* (Irie et al., 1970). Of these, laureatin is most unusual because it contains a four-membered cyclic ether. Recently four new acetylenes have been extracted from *L. nipponica*; laurefucin (**105**), acetyl-laurefucin (**106**) (Fukuzawa et al., 1972a), *trans*-laurediol (**107**), and *cis*-laurediol (**108**) (Kurosawa et al., 1972). Irie suggested that all compounds in this series were derived from *trans*-laurediol by bromination and cyclization. The latest compound in this series, chondriol (**109**), not only contains both chlorine and bromine but also an unusual carbon-carbon cyclization (Fenical et al., 1973b). Rather surprisingly, chondriol was isolated from *Chondria oppositiclada* rather than a species of *Laurencia*. There seems good reason for the taxonomist to take a second look at *Chondria*.

The gorgonian, *Pterogorgia anceps*, contains two *bis*-butenolides, ancepsenolide (**110**) (Schmitz et al., 1966) and hydroxyancepsenolide (**111**) (Schmitz et al., 1969). (+)-Ancepsenolide was isolated from *Pt. guadalupensis*, while *Pt. anceps* gave only the racemate. A third related compound, guadalupensic acid (**112**), has recently been found.

Of all the compounds recently found in marine organisms, the prostaglandins

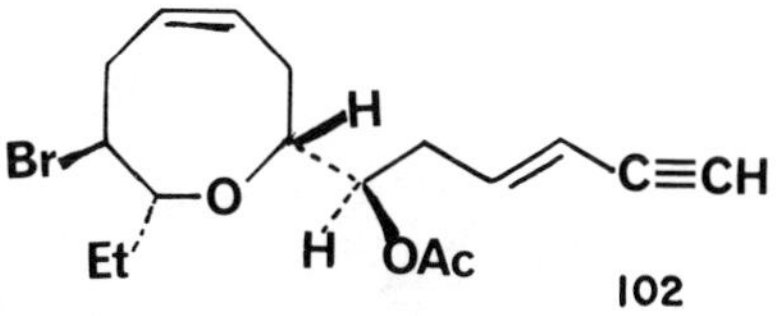

102

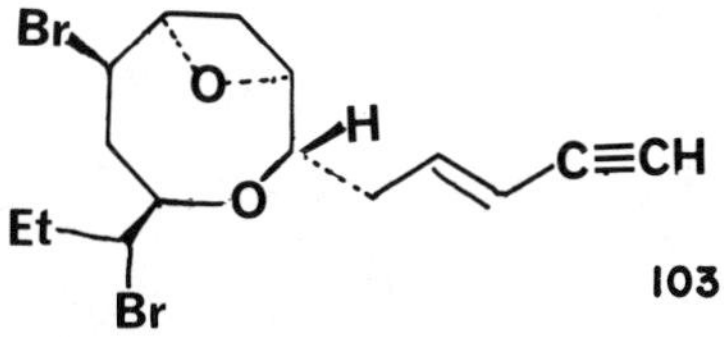

103

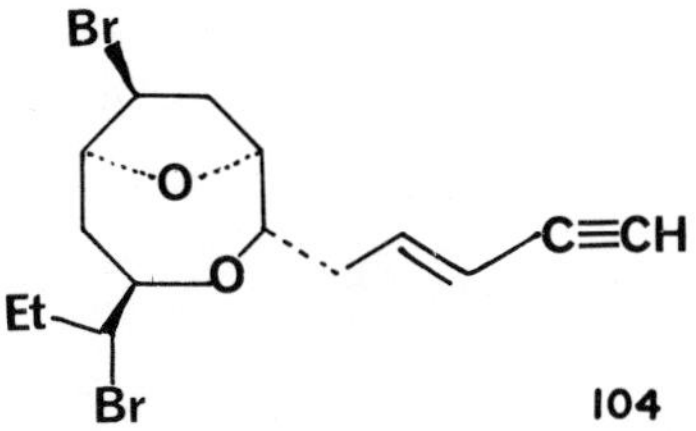

104

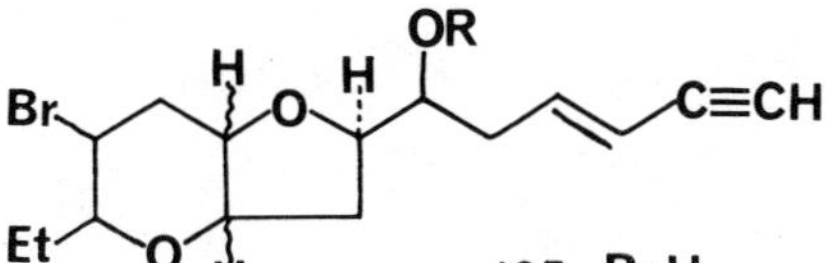

105 R=H

106 R=Ac

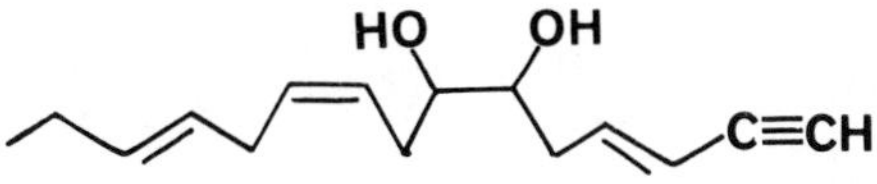

6R,7R & 6S,7S

107

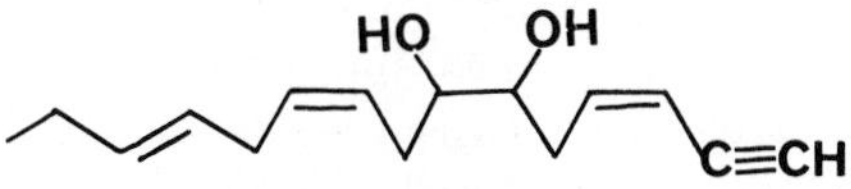

6R,7R & 6S,7S

108

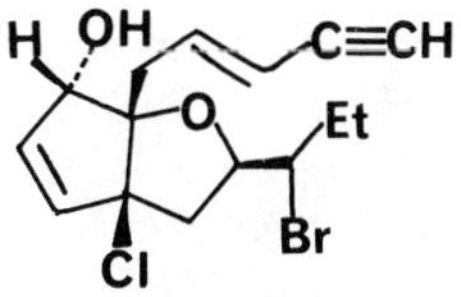

109

promise to be the most important. In 1969, Weinheimer and Spraggins surprised the natural-products community by announcing the discovery of prostaglandin derivatives in *Plexaura homomalla* (Weinheimer and Spraggins, 1969). The derivatives, 15-epi-PGA_2 (**113**) and its diester (**114**), found in remarkably high concentrations in

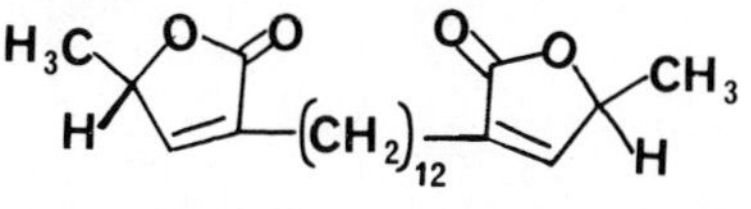

110

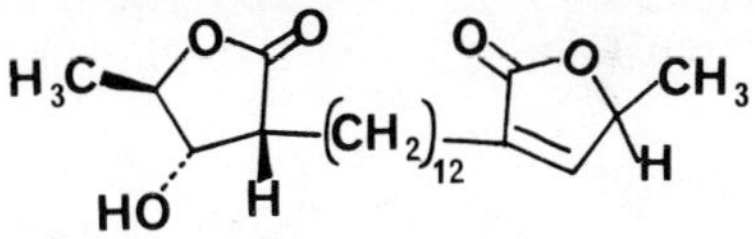

111

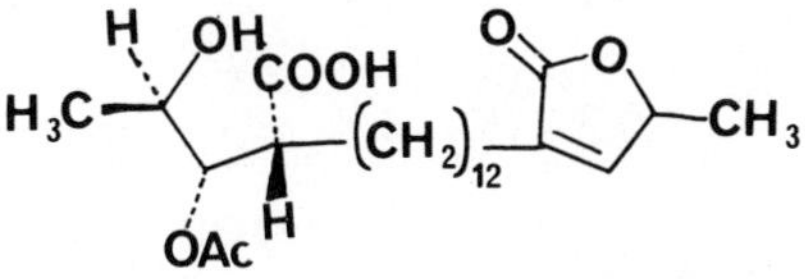

112

the corals, were devoid of biological activity. This problem has largely been overcome by two recent developments. The prostaglandins from corals may be chemically modified to obtain biologically active materials (Bundy et al., 1972a, 1972b; Spraggins, 1971). A more interesting development was the discovery of esters of PGA_2 (**115**) and PGE_2 (**116**) having the correct configuration at C-15 from certain samples of *P. homomalla*, which may be identified using a thin layer chromatography system (Schneider et al., 1972). A novel prostaglandin, 5-*trans*-PGA_2 (**117**), has also been isolated after hydrolysis from the same source (Bundy et al., 1972a).

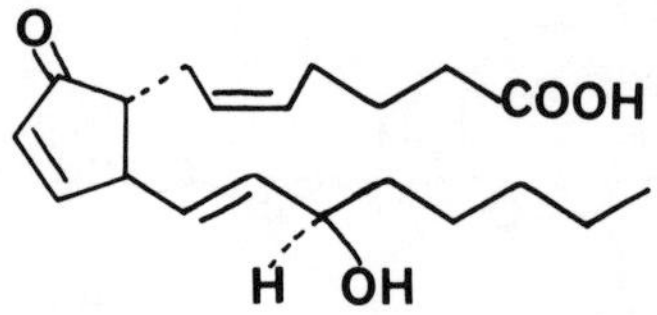

113

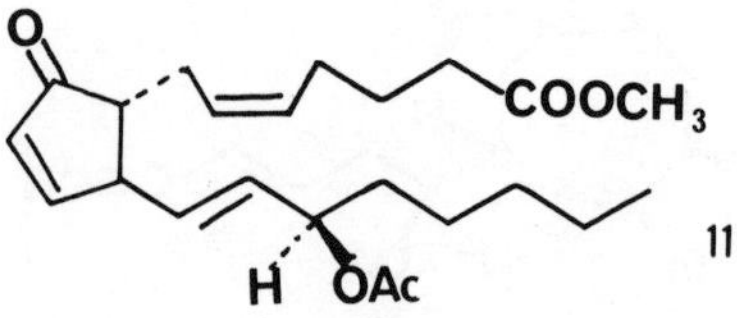

114

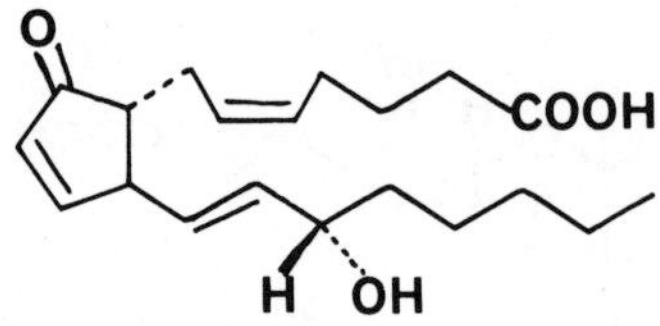

115

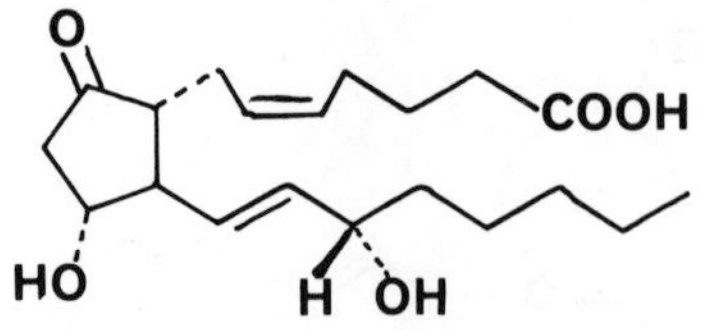

116

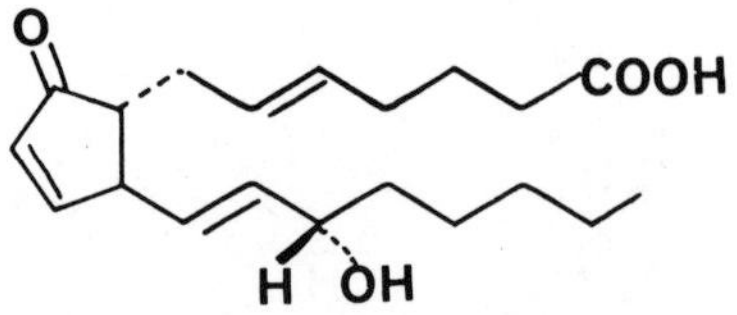

117

The medicinal properties of several α-amino acids from marine algae have recently been investigated. The simplest of these, laminine (**118**), isolated (Takemoto et al., 1964) from *Laminaria sp.*, has been studied for its hypotensive properties (Ozawa et al., 1967). Two antihelminthic agents, kainic acid (**119**) and domoic acid (**122**), were discovered as a result of scientific investigations of Japanese folk medicine. Kainic acid (**119**) (Murakami et al., 1955a) was isolated from *Digena simplex* along with allo-kainic acid (**120**) (Murakami et al., 1955b) epimeric at carbon 4, and kainic acid lactone (**121**), (Morimoto, 1955b) a byproduct of the isolation procedure. Domoic acid (**122**), with its closely related chemical structure, was obtained from *Chondria armata*, an alga of the same family (*Rhodomalaceae*) (Takemoto et al., 1966).

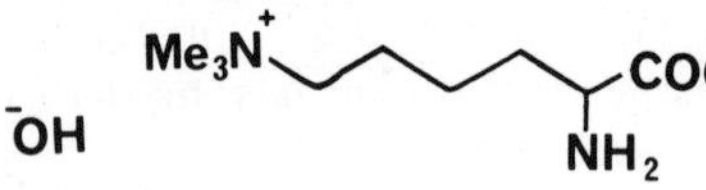

118

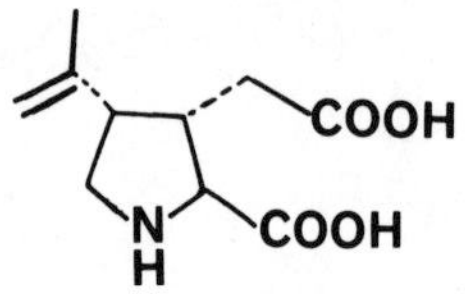

119

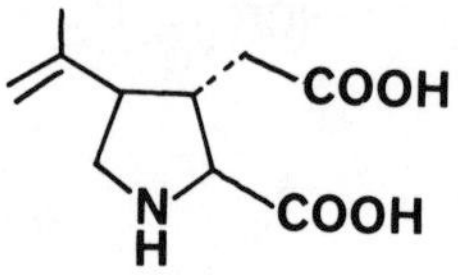

120

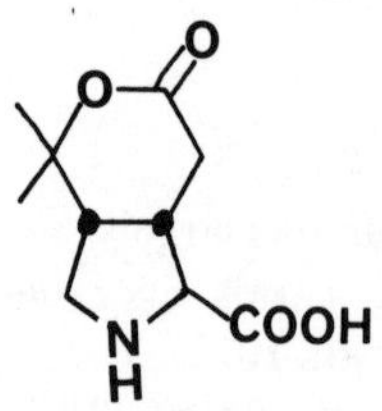

121

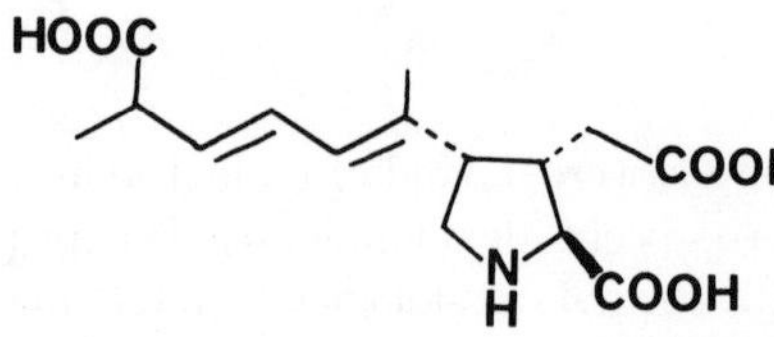

122

The unusual dextrorotatory amino acid derivative, D-octopine (**123**), has been isolated from both octopus and squid (Irrine and Wilson, 1939). β-Phosphonoalanine (**124**), containing a direct carbon-phosphorus bond, has been reported from extracts

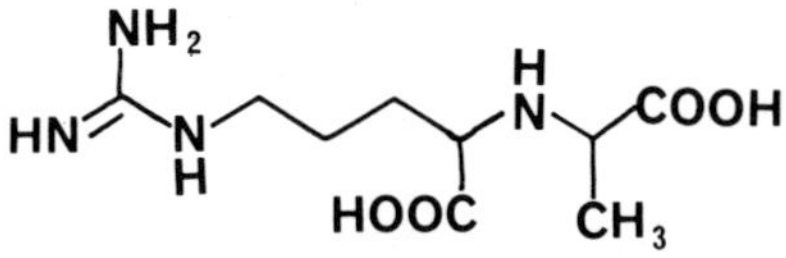

123

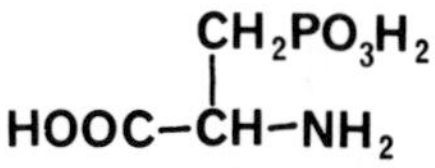

$HOOC-CH(CH_2PO_3H_2)-NH_2$

124

$CH_2PO_3H_2$
|
CH_2NH_2

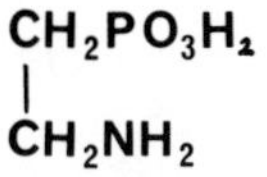

125

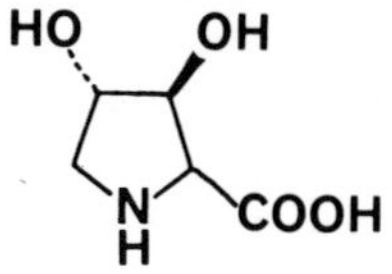

126

of the anemone, *Zoanthus sociatus* (Kittredge and Hughes, 1964), while its decarboxylation product, 2-aminoethylphosphonic acid (**125**), was found in the anemones *Anthopleura elegantissima* (Kittredge et al., 1962) and *Metridium dianthus* (Quin, 1964). 3,4-Dihydroxyproline (**126**), another new amino acid, was recently isolated from the diatom, *Navicula pelliculosa* (Nakajima and Volcani, 1969).

Halogenated aromatic amino acids were found in a number of marine organisms. 3,5-Diiodo-tyrosine (**127**) from the coral, *Gorgonia carolinni*, was among the first of the marine natural products to be identified (Dreschel, 1907). This report was followed by the discovery of 3,5-dibromotyrosine (**128**) from a number of *Gorgonia* species of coral (Morner, 1913). The fibrous protein, spongin, from the sponges of the class *Demospongia*, was hydrolyzed to obtain both diiodo- and dibromotyrosine (Ackermann and Burchard, 1941). Later studies revealed that the bath sponge, *Spongia officinalis obliqua*, also contained mono-iodotyrosine (**129**) and mono-bromotyrosine (**130**) (Low, 1951). Monochloromonobromotyrosine, presumably having the structure (**131**), has been obtained from the scleroprotein constituting the operculum of the mollusc, *Buccinum undatum* (Hunt and Breuer, 1971).

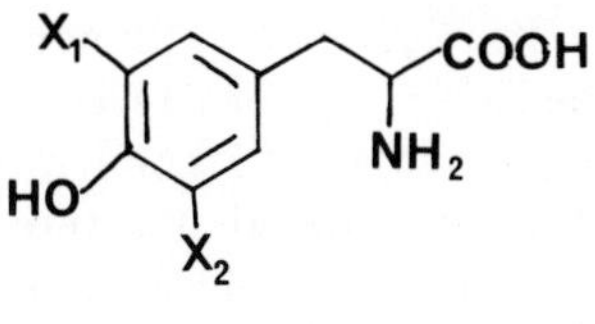

127 $X_1 = X_2 = I$
128 $X_1 = X_2 = Br$
129 $X_1 = H, X_2 = I$
130 $X_1 = H, X_2 = Br$
131 $X_1 = Cl, X_2 = Br$

One of these amino acids, dibromotyrosine (**128**), was suggested as the biosynthetic precursor of all the secondary metabolites isolated from sponges of the genus *Verongia*. As a consequence of the worldwide distribution and the potential pharmaceutical value of the compounds derived from the sponges of this genus, the chemistry of at least six species has been studied. In 1967 Burkholder and Sharma discovered the broad spectrum antibiotic activity of extracts of *V. fistularis* and *V. cauliformis* (Sharma and Burkholder, 1967a). From both sources they isolated two antibiotics, the dienone (**132**) (Sharma and Burkholder, 1967b) and the corresponding dimethyoxy ketal (**133**) (Sharma et al., 1970). An examination of the Mediterranean sponge, *Verongia aerophoba*, revealed the presence of the related compounds aeroplysinin I (**134**) (Fattorusso et al., 1972) and aeroplysinin II (**135**) (Minale et al., 1972). Aeroplysinin I (**134**) was also found in *V. archeri* (Stempien et al., 1972a), while its enantiomer was reported from a sponge of the genus *Ianthella* (Fulmor et al., 1970), which also contained aeroplysinin II (**135**) as the racemate (Minale et al., 1972). A possible precursor or degradation product of these compounds (3,5-dibromo-4-hydroxyphenyl)-acetamide (**136**) was isolated from *Verongia archeri* (Stempien et al., 1972a). An undescribed species of *Verongia* from the Gulf of California has yielded the dienone (**132**), the lactone (**135**), and a new antibiotic substance (Andersen and Faulkner, 1972). This new antibiotic was assigned the mixed ketal structure (**137**). Since the ketal (**137**) was isolated as a mixture of diastereoisomers, the arene oxide (**138**) was proposed as a naturally occurring precursor.

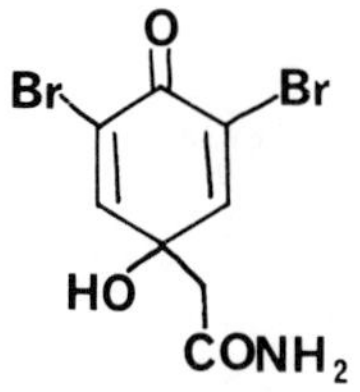

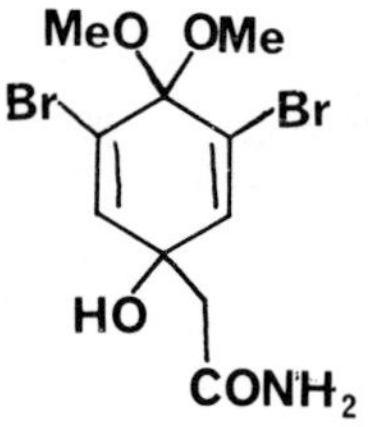

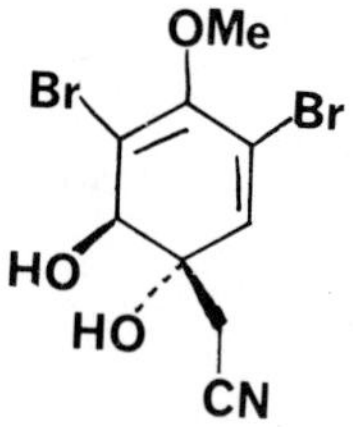

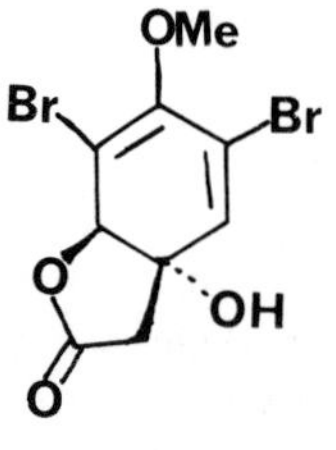

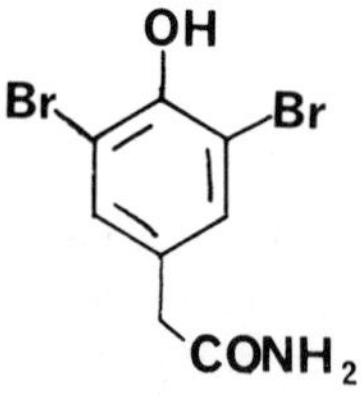

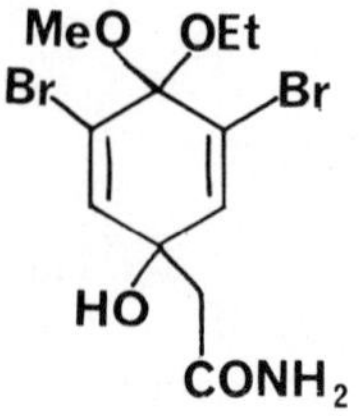

The dimeric compounds, aerothionin (**139**) and homoaerothionin (**140**), were first isolated from *V. aerophoba* (Moody et al., 1972) but were later found in *V. thiona* and the unidentified *Verongia* from the Gulf of California. Another species of *Demospongia* that contains brominated antimicrobial compounds is *Dysidea herbacea*, obtained from the western Caroline Islands, from which 1-(2′,4′-dibromophenoxy)-2-hydroxy-4,5,6-tribromobenzene (**141**) and 1-(4′-bromophenoxy)-2-hydroxy-5-bromobenzene (**142**) were obtained (Sharma and Vig, 1972).

A series of closely related bromophenols has recently been isolated from several species of marine algae. The first of this series, 5-bromo-3,4-dihydroxybenzaldehyde (**143**), was found in the red alga, *Polysiphonia morrowii* (Saito and Ando, 1955, 1957). The first naturally occurring aromatic compound containing bromine atoms on adjacent carbons was the dipotassium salt of 2,3-dibromobenzyl alcohol 4,5-disulfate

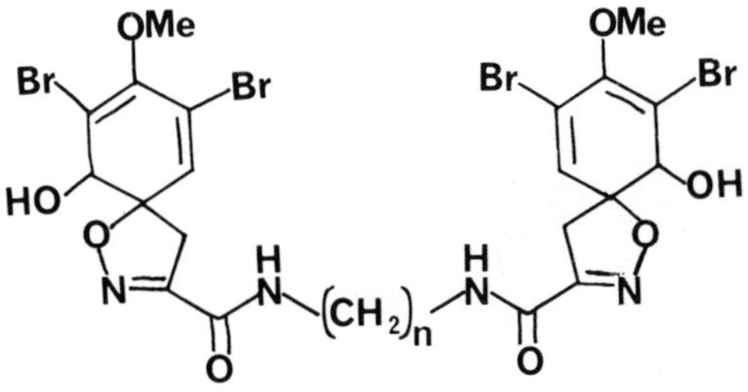

139 n=4 140 n=5

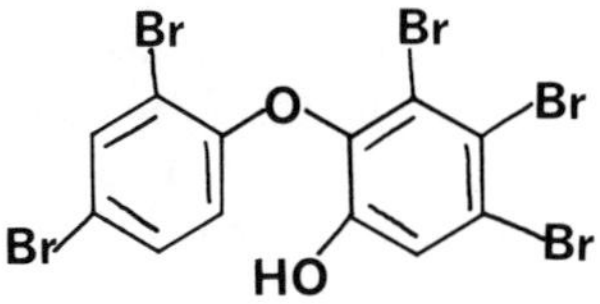

141

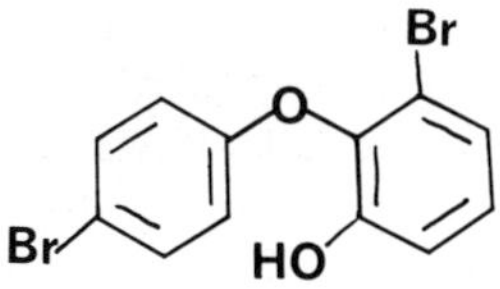

142

(**144**) from the red alga, *Polysiphonia lanosa* (Hodgkin et al., 1966). Later, 2,3-dibromo-4,5-dihydroxybenzyl alcohol (lanosol) (**145**) was shown to be the major bromo-phenol of *Odonthalia dentata* and *Rhodomela confervoides* (Craigie and Guenig, 1967). Coexisting with it in both algae was 3,5-dibromo-4-hydroxybenzyl alcohol (**146**). From extracts of the red alga, *Rhodomela larix*, 5,6-dibromoprotocatechualdehyde (**147**) and the corresponding 2,3-dibromo-4,5-dihydroxybenzyl methyl ether (**148**) were both obtained in high yield (Katsui et al., 1967). This accounts for the use of *R. larix* as a source of bromine during World War II (Scagel, 1961). The methyl ether has also been found in the alga, *Odonthalia corymbifera* (Matsumoto and Kagawa, 1964).

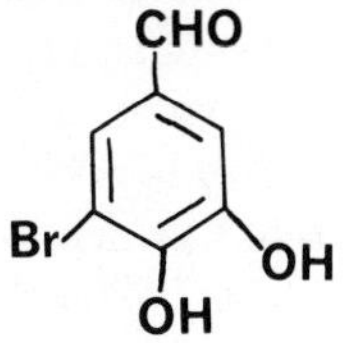

143

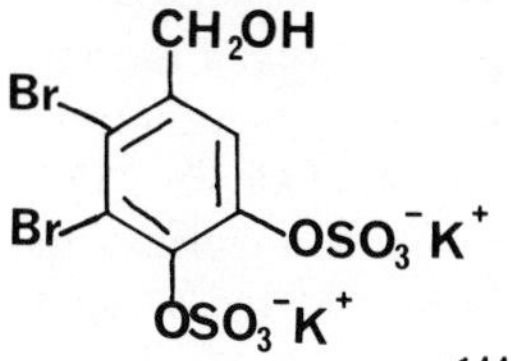

144

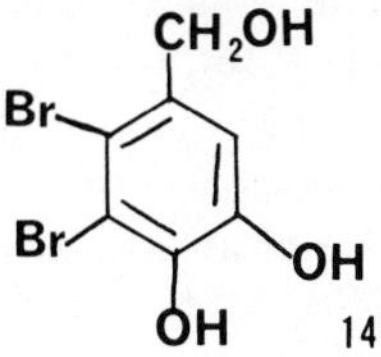

145

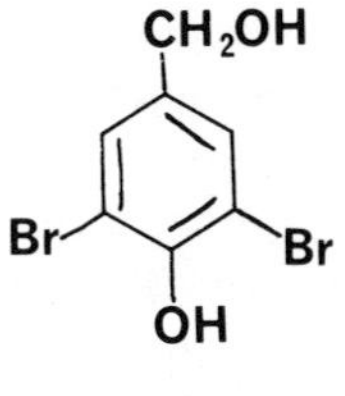

146

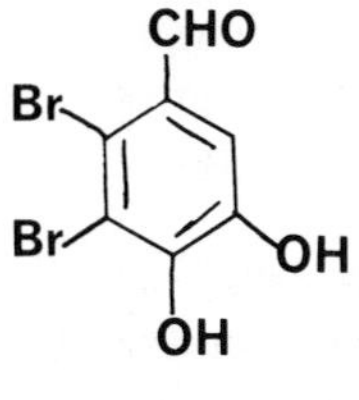

147

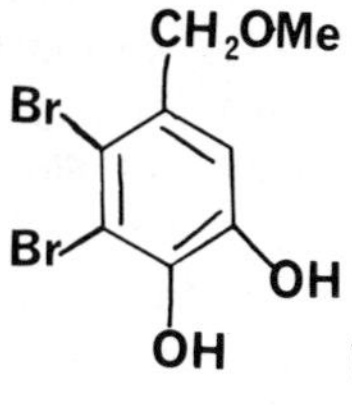

148

Only one marine hemichordate has been shown to contain bromo-phenols. Large quantities of 2,6-dibromophenol (**149**) were isolated from the bioluminescent acorn worm, *Balanoglossus biminiensis*, and may account for the characteristic iodoform-like smell of the worm (Ashworth and Cormier, 1967).

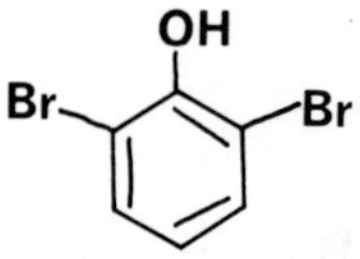

The ancient Tyrian purple dye, obtained from the molluscs, *Murex brandaris*, *M. trunculus*, *Purpura aperta*, and *P. lapillus*, was characterized as 6,6′-dibromoindigotin (**150**) (Baker and Sutherland, 1968). Tyrian purple does not exist as such in the hypobranchial gland of the live molluscs, but was formed by the action of sunlight on glandular smears. A salt of tyrindoxyl sulfate (**151**) has been isolated from the mollusc, *Dicathais orbita*, and is believed to be the actual tissue component of the mollusc which yields Tyrian purple upon irradiation with sunlight in the presence of the required enzymes (Salagne et al., 1966).

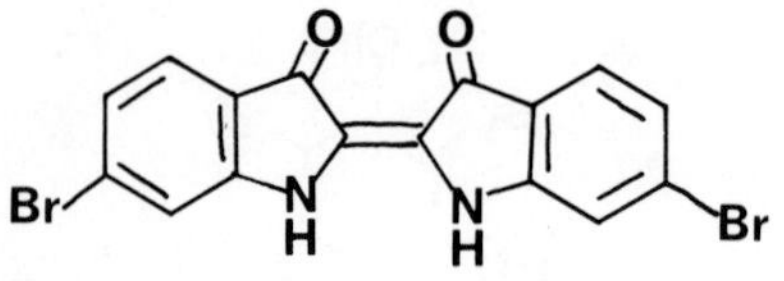

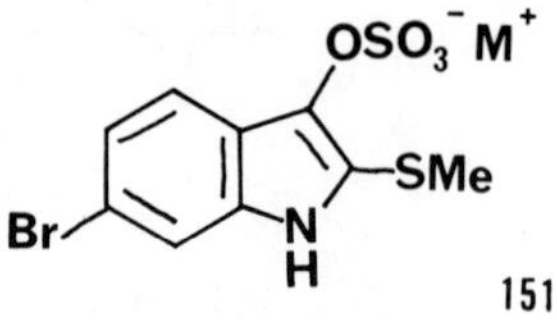

A unique brominated antibiotic was obtained from the marine bacterium *Pseudomonas bromoutilis* (Burkholder et al., 1966). Synthetic (Hanessian and Kaltebroun, 1966) and X-ray studies (Lovell, 1966) showed the antibiotic to be 2-(3,6-dibromophenyl)-3,4,5-tribromopyrrole (**152**). This remarkable antibiotic contains over 70% of its weight as covalently bound bromine.

A series of biogenetically related bromo-pyrroles has been isolated from the sponges *Agelas oroides* (Forenza et al., 1971), and *Phakellia flabellata* (Sharma and Burkholder, 1971). Although dibromophakellin (**153**), the brominated alkaloid from *P. flabellata*, contained a guanidino group, it is interesting that it did not have the high basicity usually associated with that functionality. 4-Bromophakellin (**154**) was also obtained from the same source. *A. oroides* was shown to contain 4,5-dibromopyrrole-2-carboxylic acid (**155**), together with the corresponding nitrile (**156**) and amide (**157**). Oroidin (**158a**), a complex, highly nitrogenated metabolite of *A. oroides*, was shown to have the same molecular formula as dibromophakellin (**153**), but the relationship between the two is not at all obvious. We wish to suggest that the structure (**158b**), which is not excluded by the data given, be considered as an alternative to allow a biosynthetic correlation between oroidin and dibromophakellin.

Five Jamaican sponges of the genus *Agelas* were shown to contain the same antibiotic which has been partly characterized (Stempien, 1966). The data indicated that the structure was either 4,6-dihydroxyindole (**159a**) or 6,7-dihydroxyindole (**159b**). The sponge, *Verongia aerophoba*, was shown to contain 3,4-dihydroxyquinoline-2-carboxylic acid (**160**), for which no biological activity was reported (Fattorusso et al., 1971a).

An interesting pigment, caulerpin (**161**), was obtained from three *Caulerpa* species (Aguilar-Santos and Doty, 1967). This dimeric structure is unusual in that it appears completely unrelated to any other algal products. A general review of marine pigments is not appropriate within this chapter, since the topic has been adequately covered elsewhere (Singh et al., 1967; O'nEocha, 1958; see also Isler, 1971).

Man first became interested in marine natural products because of their toxicity. Early medical records, often contained in the folklore of mariners and fishermen, cite

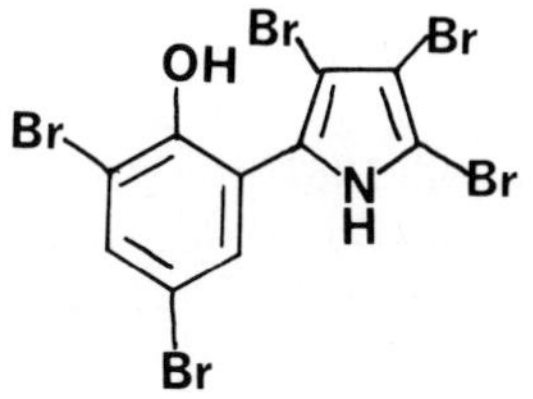

152

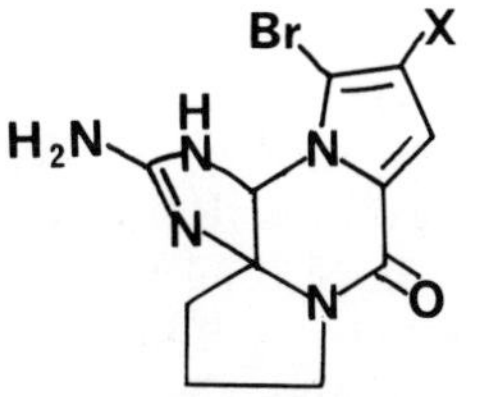

153 X=Br

154 X=H

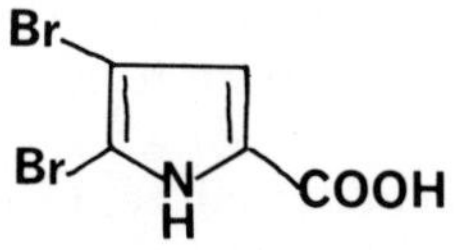

155

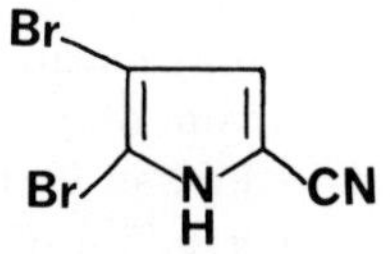

156

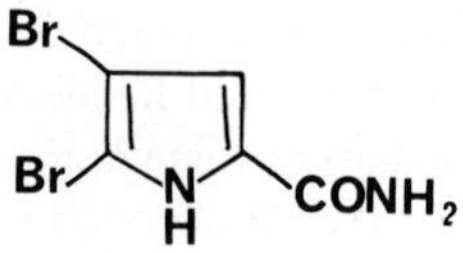

157

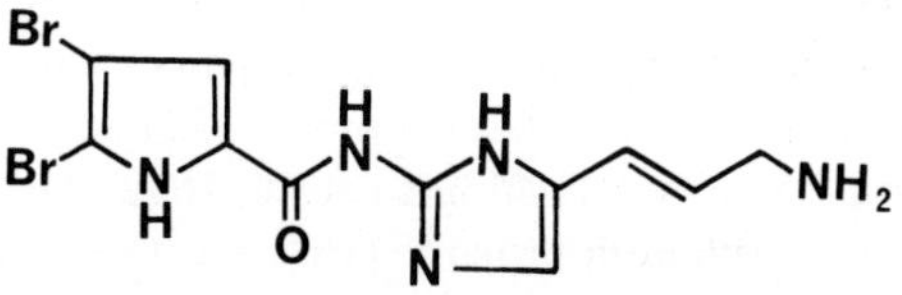

158a

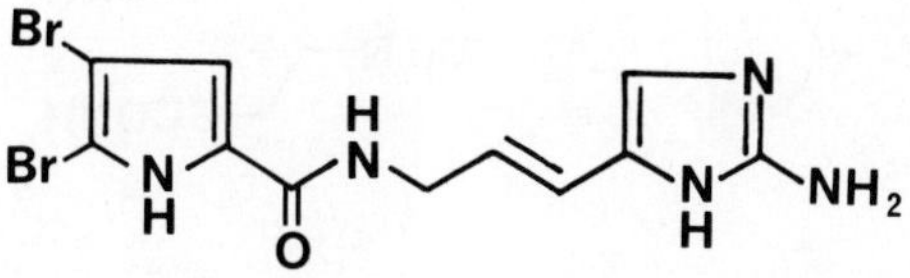

158b

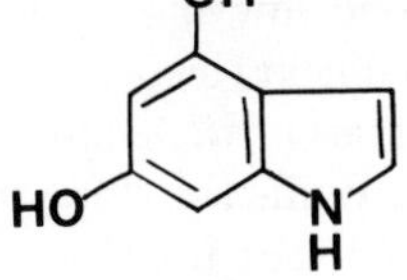

159a

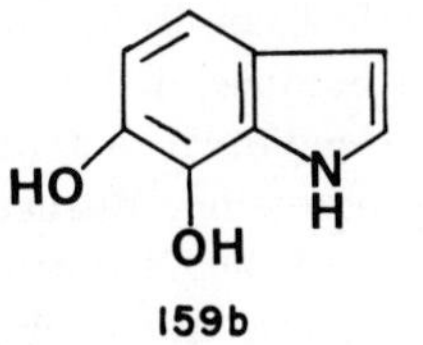

159b

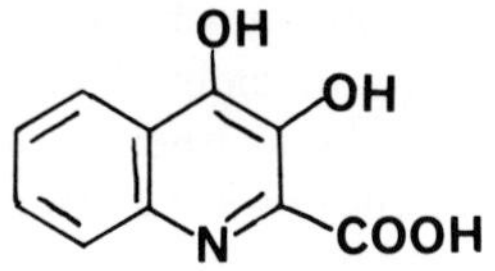

160

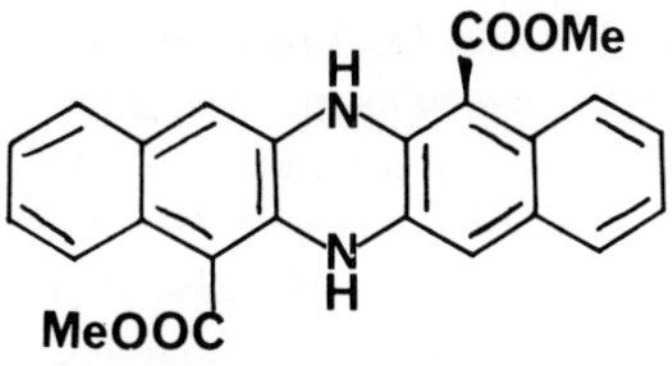

161

many reports of dangerous and toxic marine organisms. Following the leads provided by these early reports, marine biologists have accumulated an impressive array of scientific accounts of the toxicology of many of the approximately 1000 species of toxic marine organisms (Halstead, 1965, 1967; Russell, 1967; Russell, 1965; Scheuer, 1969). Chemists have been very slow to follow the marine biologists into this field. Despite Biblical reports of marine toxins, the first structural elucidation of a marine toxin was that of murexine, reported as recently as 1953 (Ersparmer and Benati, 1953). Since then, fewer than a dozen marine toxins have received serious chemical investigation. This is very surprising in light of the fact that two toxins, nereistoxin and tetrodotoxin, both of which have unusual chemical structures, have also found commercial and medical applications. Could it be that natural-products chemists have become discouraged on finding that many marine toxins turned out to be proteins or polypeptides and hence outside their realm of interest?

The structural elucidation of nereistoxin was part of a study that began with a fisherman's tale and ended with the commercial use of a derivative of nereistoxin as an insecticide. Japanese fishermen who used the annelid worm *Lumbriconereis heteropoda* as bait noticed that insects that fed on the worm usually died. These observations led to the isolation and partial characterization of a powerful toxin from the worm (Nitta, 1934). Further chemical studies led to the structure 4-N,N-dimethylamino-1,2-dithiolane (**162**) for nereistoxin (Hashimoto and Okaichi, 1960; Okaichi and Hashimoto, 1962). A variety of derivatives of nereistoxin have been synthesized and tested for insecticidal activity and toxicity (Hashimoto et al., 1972). One derivative, 1,3-*bis*-(carbamoyl thio)-2-N,N-dimethylaminopropane (**163**) was found to be a very effective insecticide and is now marketed in Japan.

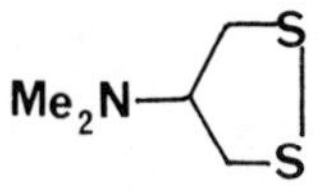

Me_2N—(dithiolane, S—S)

162

Me_2N—CH(CH_2SCONH_2)$_2$

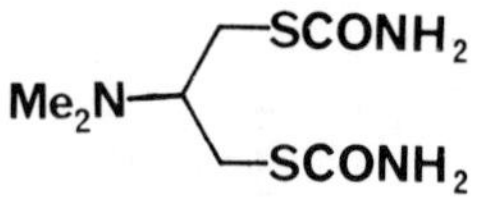

163

Some of the earliest records of fish poisoning were associated with ingestion of tetraodontoid fish. Such poisonings still occur in Japan where the puffer fish, *Spheroides rubripes* and *S. vermicularis*, are a prized culinary delight. The toxic principle of these fish, tetrodotoxin, is one of the most toxic among low molecular weight poisons. Attempts to isolate the toxin from puffer fish started near the beginning of this century (Tahara, 1909), but because of the unusual properties of the compound, a crystalline sample was not obtained until 1950 (Yokuo, 1950). While the structural elucidation of tetrodotoxin was progressing, Mosher demonstrated that tarichatoxin, isolated from the eggs and embryos of the California newt, *Taricha torosa*, was identical to tetrodotoxin (Mosher and Brown, 1963; Mosher et al., 1964). Three groups independently elucidated the structure of tetrodotoxin (**164**), which contained several unique structural features (Woodward, 1964; Goto et al., 1965; Tsuda, 1966). Most striking among these was the hemi-lactal function, which had not previously been encountered. Since few small molecules possess such a highly functionalized carbon skeleton, tetrodotoxin has become an ideal target molecule for the synthetic organic chemist. The challenge has been successfully met by Kishi, whose total synthesis led to the development of some novel chemistry (Kishi et al., 1972c). Tetrodotoxin has been used as a research tool in neurophysiology and may yet find limited clinical use as a muscle spasm relaxant or as a palliative in terminal cancer treatment.

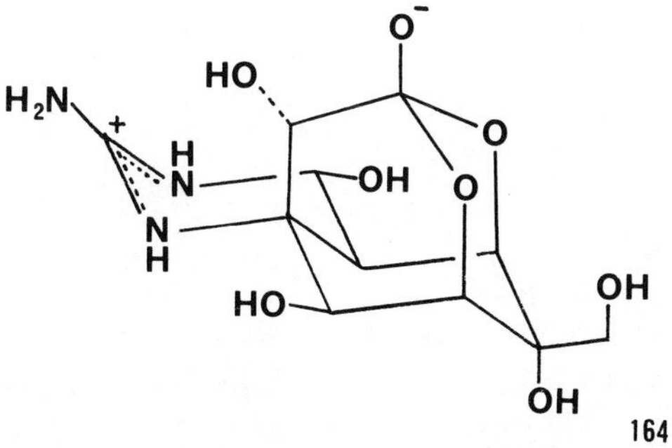

164

When the boxfish, *Ostracion lentiginosus*, was placed in a small tank, it secreted a toxin that killed other fish in the tank (Brock, 1956). The toxin, pahutoxin, was obtained in copious quantities by immersing the boxfish in fresh water. A crystalline toxin was isolated and identified as a choline ester of β-acetoxypalmitic acid (**165**) (Boylan and Scheuer, 1967). Two other choline esters have been isolated: murexine (**166**) from *Murex trunculus* (Esparmer and Benati, 1953) and the choline ester of 14-methyl-4-pentadecenoic acid (**167**) from a Japanese oyster (Nakazawa, 1959). Both pahutoxin and murexine are toxic to fish but not to man.

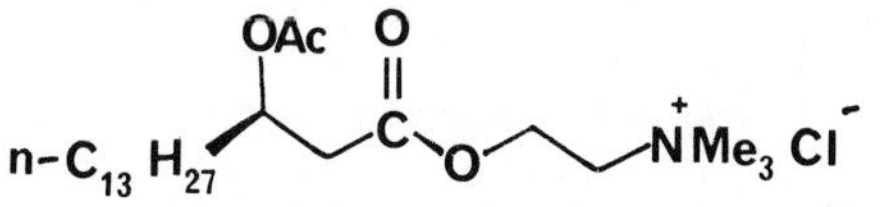

165

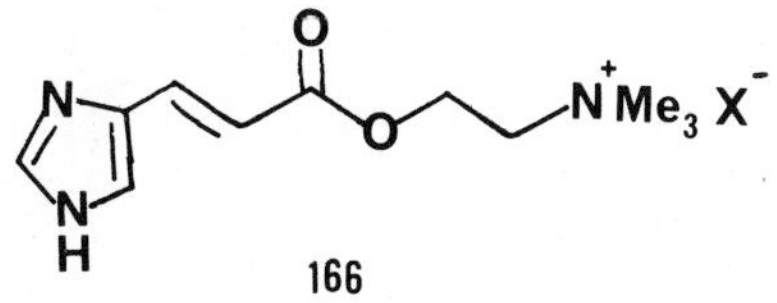

166

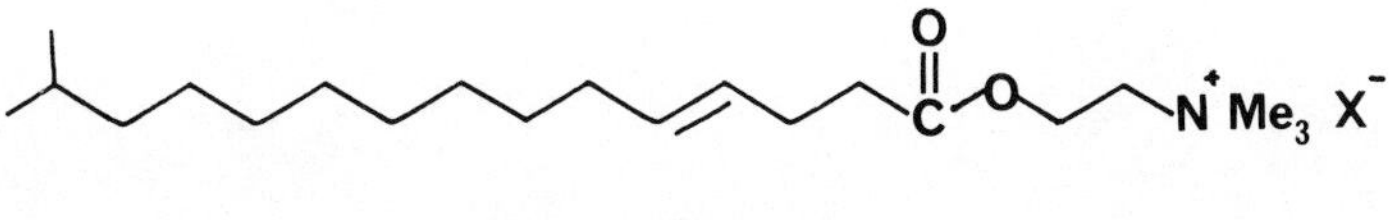

167

Paralytic shellfish poisoning was traced to the dinoflagellate, *Gonyaulax catenella*, whose toxin, saxitoxin, was concentrated unchanged by the California mussel and the Alaskan butter clam. The structural elucidation of saxitoxin has been hampered by the lack of crystalline derivatives, but the structure (**168**) was eventually proposed on

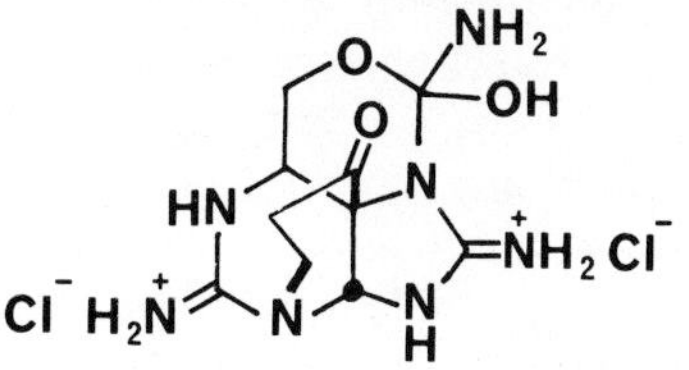

168

the basis of spectroscopic data and degradation studies (Wong et al., 1971a, b). This structure, which contains two guanadino groups and a cyclic hemi-urea function, must certainly be confirmed by synthesis. A similar but different toxin may be found in *G. tamarensis* (Rapoport, personal communication).

It is fortunate that the macroalgae cannot rival the unicellular organisms in toxin production. A single example of a toxin from *Caulerpa* species, caulerpicin (**169**), has been identified as a mixture of homologues (Aguilar-Santos and Doty, 1967; Doty and Aguilar-Santos, 1970).

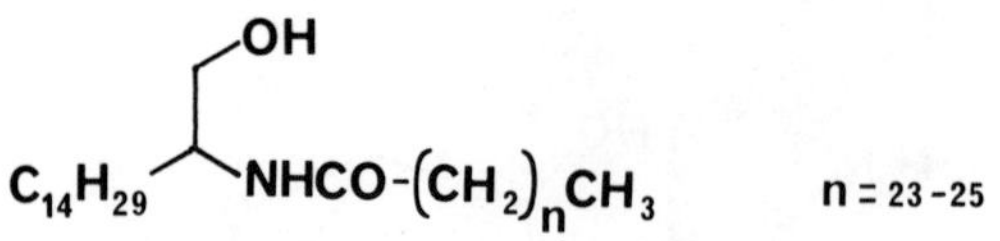

OH
$C_{14}H_{29}$ $NHCO-(CH_2)_nCH_3$ $n = 23-25$

169

When the carnivorous gastropod, *Babylonia japonica*, was taken from a limited area of Suruga Bay, Japan, it was found to contain a toxin in the midgut gland (Hashimoto et al., 1967). The structure of surugatoxin (**170**) was determined by X-ray crystallography (Kosuge et al., 1972). The molecule contained a bromo-indanone residue, characteristic of residues found in molluscs (cf. Tyrian purple), but the limited occurrence of the toxin points to a dietary source. The "mixed biosynthesis" of surugatoxin indicates how readily toxic compounds may be manufactured by molluscs given an unusual dietary component.

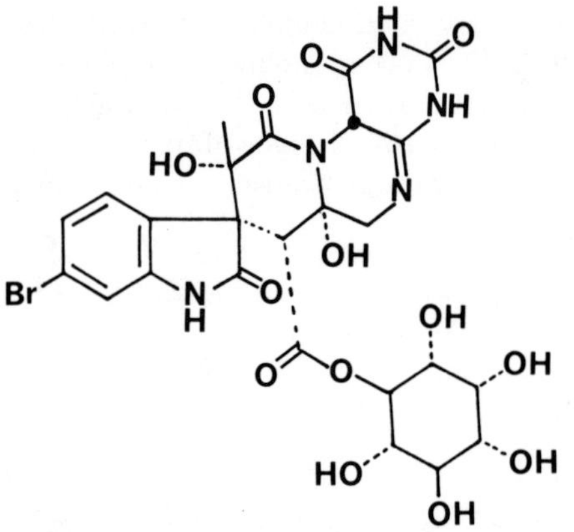

170

Of the five classes of echinoderms, only holothurians (sea cucumbers) and asteroids (sea stars) produce toxic saponins. Holothurin A from the Cuvier organ of *Actinopyga agassiza*, the first saponin from a nonplant source, was shown to be toxic against mice, fish, and protozoa as well as exhibiting cytotoxic activity (Nigrelli et al., 1955). A saponin preparation from starfish caused severe lesions in mice when injected subcutaneously. The chemistry of both holothurin and starfish saponins has been retarded because the saponin mixtures cannot readily be separated. The saponins consist of at least four sugar units joined to a sterol portion, with a sulfate unit attached to the molecule. Most chemical studies have concentrated on the sterol portion of the molecule, since pure saponins could not be obtained.

Use of the name ciguatera poisoning to classify all illnesses that result from eating fresh reef fish (except puffer fish) can only serve to complicate the toxicology and chemistry. Concentrating on a single species of moray eel, *Gymnothorax javanicus*, Scheuer isolated a single toxin called ciguatoxin, for which the empirical formula $C_{35}H_{65}NO_8$ was obtained (Scheuer et al., 1967). A chromatographically identical material has been isolated from the stomach of the surgeon fishes, *Ctenochaetus* and *Acanthurus lineatus*, suggesting that the toxin has a dietary source (Yasumoto et al., 1971).

Several other toxins are currently under investigation: palytoxin, from a coelenterate of the genus *Palythoa* (Sheikh, 1970), grammistin, a skin secretion of soapfish (Randall et al., 1971), maculotoxin, a neurotoxin found in the posterior salivary gland of the blue ringed octopus, *H. maculosa* (Freeman and Turner, 1970), and an unnamed toxin from the dinoflagellate, *Gymnodinium breve* (Sasner et al., 1972).

Marine pharmacology (Baslow, 1969), together with the related natural-products chemistry, is a subject that has held "great promise" for a number of years. However, the promised "drugs from the sea" have been slow to materialize. From the information now available, it seems unlikely that commercial quantities of pharmaceuticals, with a few possible exceptions, will be obtained from marine sources. This does not mean that this research should be abandoned since the novel structures of marine pharmaceuticals can provide the starting point from which new drugs may be developed.

Although the prostaglandins[1] originally found in *Plexaura homomalla* were not physiologically active, this fact did not discourage further research. Since they provided a large potential source of compounds having the correct carbon skeleton, a method of chemical modification to obtain active prostaglandins was quickly developed. This progress places the drug industry in a dilemma, as it could be ecologically and economically disasterous to harvest the gorgonian before mariculture techniques have been established. At present, "wild" gorgonians are being collected by hand, but it must be only a matter of time before this primitive method is superceded.

A better example of the development of a drug having marine origins is found in the case of D-arabinosyl cytosine (**171**), an important synthetic antiviral agent. The nucleosides spongosine (**172**), spongothymidine (**173**), and spongouridine (**174**) were isolated from the sponge, *Cryptotethya crypta*, during the late 1950s (Bergmann and Burke, 1955, 1956). They remained for some years as marine curiosities until it was shown that the D-arabinosyl nucleosides possessed useful activity against leukemia and viral infections (Cohen, 1966). This led to the testing of synthetic D-arabinosyl nucleosides, from which D-arabinosyl cytosine appeared as the most effective agent. Three derivatives of spongouridine (**175** to **177**) have been patented as antiviral and anticancer drugs (Mirata et al., 1968).

The antihelminthic drugs, kainic acid (**119**) and domoic acid (**122**), owe their discovery to Japanese folk medicine, as did the antihypertensive, laminine (**118**). The suppression of folk medicine in the United States and parts of Europe has left most laboratories without the required local observations on which to base a similar study.

Two polysaccharides from macroalgae have shown useful physiological activity and provide an instance where harvest of the organism is already a commercial operation. Apart from its normal use as an emulsifier, alginic acid, obtained commercially from *Macrocystis pyrifera* and other algae, has recently been shown to preferentially remove radiostrontium from the human gastrointestinal tract. Perhaps the best use for alginic acid is in the science of tablet making, where it is used as a tablet-disintegrating agent. *Laminaria colousoni* and other species yield a sulfated polysaccharide, laminarin. Highly sulfated laminarin derivatives have anticoagulant properties, while low-sulfate laminarin derivatives have antilipemic properties.

The majority of marine pharmaceuticals whose structures have been elucidated are antibiotics. This is not surprising, since the chemist finds antibiotic assays to be simple to interpret and convenient to perform. The comparatively large number of known marine antibiotics indicates that the process of structural elucidation is considerably accelerated by having a handy bioassay. There appear to be two methods to accelerate marine pharmacology in general: one may form interdisciplinary groups or simplify bioassay procedures to the point where any competent person can perform them. The

[1] See p. 694–6.

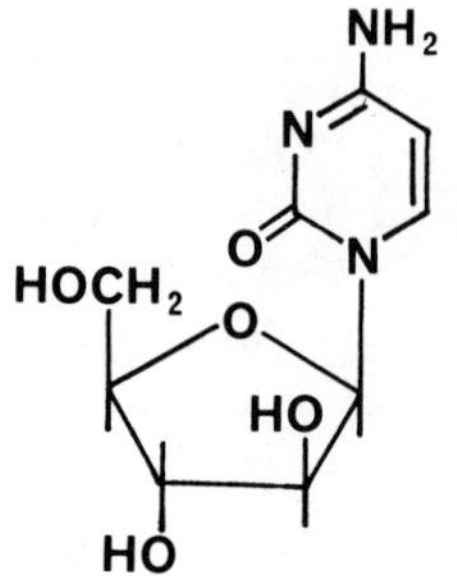

171

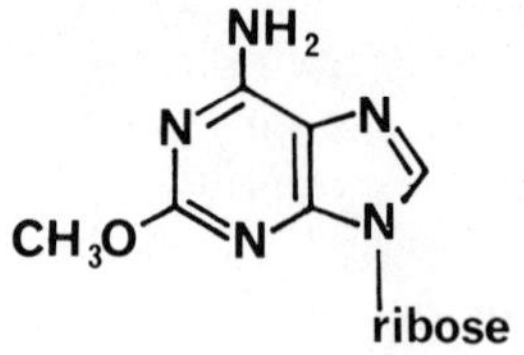

172

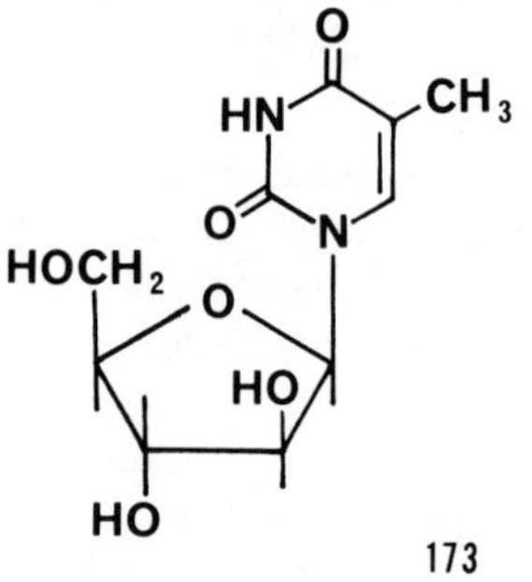

173

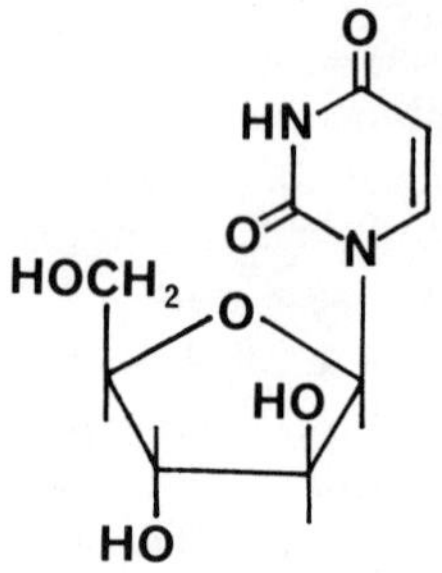

174

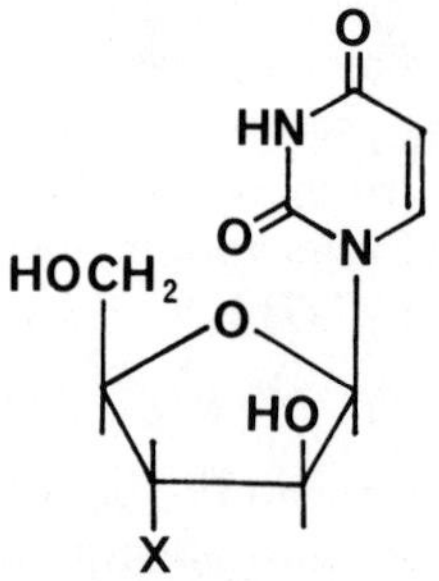

175 X = N_3
176 X = Cl
177 X = Br

latter possibility would exclude the traditional animal assays in favor of biochemical screens such as enzyme assays, possibly in kit form. Assay kits would certainly be ideal for shipboard screening, which can conveniently be arranged to cause minimal ecological disturbance.

We are uncertain whether the cephalosporins should be included as marine products. The fungus, *Cephalosporium acremonium*, was isolated from water in the vicinity of a sewage outfall off Sardinia leaving its marine or terrestrial origin in doubt (Crawford et al., 1952). The antibiotic principle of *C. acremonium* was identified as cephalosporin C (**178**) (Abraham and Newton, 1961; Hodgkin and Maslen, 1961). The cephalosporins, produced by synthetic modification of cephalosporin C, have found wide use as broad spectrum antimicrobials.

There are many more reports of pharmacologically active extracts from marine

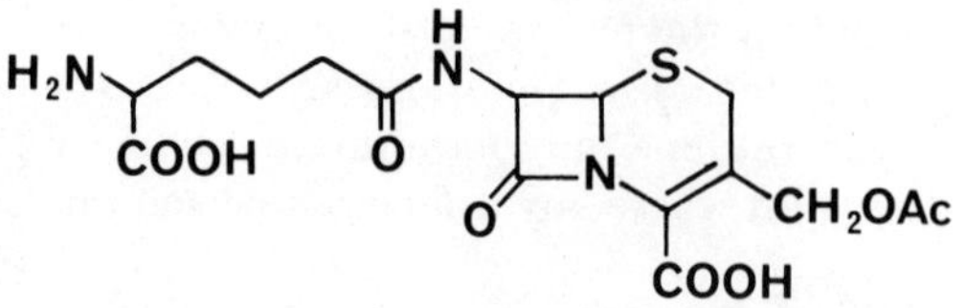

178

organisms, but few of these studies have passed the stage of initial screening. The natural-products chemist, unable either to obtain the active organism or to perform a complex assay, has been obliged to ignore these reports. It is apparent that successful studies to obtain new drugs from these sources will require the interdisciplinary approaches of the pharmaceutical industry.

Among the more useful indicators of potential physiological activity are the observations of marine biologists and behaviorists concerning the complex interactions of marine organisms. Many of these behavior patterns, particularly those involving predator-prey relationships, have been attributed to chemical communication. The most graphic examples of chemical communication are found among the chemical defense systems involving marine toxins. The toxins, which act on a wide variety of other organisms, have obvious physiological activity. A second group of chemicals that deserves investigation are those that do not kill but cause an avoidance reaction between two species. For example, many intertidal and subtidal gastropods, pelycipods, and individuals of other marine phyla show specific and stereotyped avoidance responses to the chemical secretion from starfish (Bullock, 1953). The active constituent was shown to be a complex mixture of saponins whose physiological and toxicological properties are under investigation (Mackie et al., 1968; Faulkner, unpublished research).

Studies of chemical communication between two members of the same species are unlikely to produce compounds of widespread physiological activity. However, these studies may yield information concerning the effect of sublethal levels of pollutants on the ability of a species to survive!

Only three studies of intraspecies chemical communication have resulted in the identification of the active compound. The male-attracting substance produced by the female gametes of the brown alga, *Ectocarpus siliculosus*, was identified as the cycloheptadiene derivative (**96**) (Müller et al., 1971). A second example of a gamete attractant, although historically first (Macklis, 1958), is sirenin (**179**) (Nutting et al., 1968), a gamone from the freshwater slime mold, *Allomyces*.

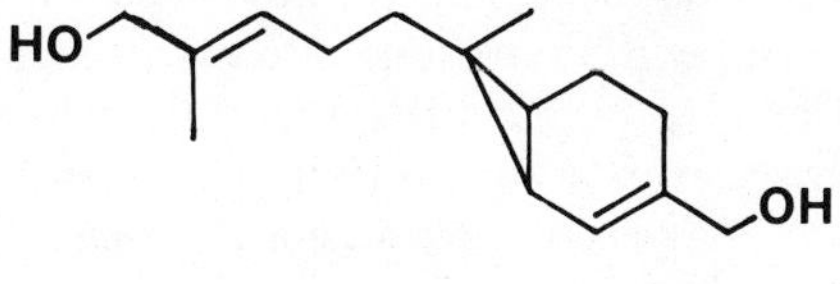

HO OH

179

A more interesting report of pheromone research concerns the crustaceans. Male crabs of the species *Portunus sanginolentus* were reported to display a mating response when immersed in water in which a premolt female had been kept (Ryan, 1966). This report prompted Kittredge et al. (1971) to investigate the action of small amounts of molting hormone, crustecdysone, on male crabs. He found that the mating behavior could be induced by concentrations of crustecdysone as low as $10^{-13}M$ for *Pachygrapsus crassipes*, $10^{-10}M$ for *Cancer antennarius*, and $10^{-8}M$ for *Cancer anthonyi*. Kittredge has also shown that chemoreception in the crab was masked by very low concentrations of oil in seawater (Kittredge, personal communication). The implications of this research are frightening. If sublethal concentrations of a chemical inhibited reproduction in a marine organism by blocking reception of a chemical sex attractant, the effect after several generations would be the same as if a lethal concentration had originally been present.

In a recent study of the action of potential insecticides on a barnacle larvae, we found the insecticide, ZR-512 (**180**) to be a useful research tool to study barnacle metamorphosis (Gomez et al., 1973). The ZR-512 caused premature metamorphosis of the cyprid larva of the acorn barnacle, *Balanus galaetus*, in concentrations as low as 10 ppb in filtered seawater.

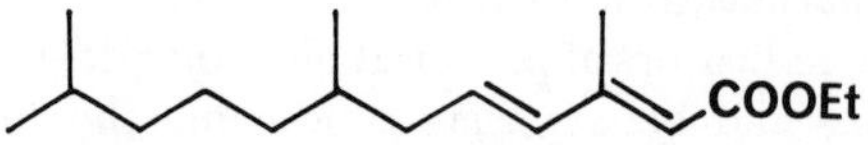

COOEt

180

In many research areas, particularly in chemical communication in the marine environment and in marine pharmacology, the research of the biologist has failed, often by a single factor, to produce a bioassay that can be used by the natural-products chemist. We have set up a series of criteria, all of which must be satisfied, for tackling the chemistry of a biological phenomenon. The most critical requirement is a guaranteed supply of organisms, the collection of which should not alter the ecological balance in the collection area. The organisms must be able to accept laboratory conditions without altering their behavior patterns and must exhibit the behavior for long periods of the year. The bioassay should be accepted by the biological community but at the same time be simple enough to allow easy repetition. In this respect, the ideal bioassay is one that has a short time lapse and easily classified positive or negative results. Furthermore, there should be some indication that the chemist has sufficient expertise and equipment to elucidate the structure of the active chemical and that the information, once obtained, will stimulate further biological research. In fact, once the dose-response relationship has been determined for a pure chemical in a given bioassay, every attempt should be made to establish the effect of pollutants on the natural system.

Having shown how the marine biologist may help the natural-products chemist, we must examine how the biologist may be repaid. Studies of the marine food chain may certainly be enhanced by substituting an inert natural product for the pollutants, such as DDT, which have been used as tracers. Chemical taxonomy, another possible source of aid to the biologist, does not seem to be too successful at present. Although the echinoderms may be conveniently separated into two groups by chemical methods, there seems little hope of making taxonomic classifications based on natural-product analysis down to the species or even the genus level. The most that should be expected is that a natural-products analysis may occasionally suggest that a species had originally been assigned to the wrong genus and is worthy of reexamination by the systematist.

Marine natural-products chemistry may even be enjoyed for its own sake. Each novel structure encountered among marine natural products, many of which contain unusual assemblages of functional groups, may be regarded as a target for synthesis. Marine organisms will be used to study the biosynthesis of bromine-containing compounds, which occur in such profusion among their metabolites. The possibility of "mixed" origins for compounds such as surugatoxin adds a new dimension to biosynthetic studies. Yet the real impact of marine natural products lies in the unique structures that have stimulated fundamental research in organic chemistry.

Addendum (March 12, 1973)

During the few months since completion of our review, the structures of several novel marine natural products have been announced.

The sterols arising from starfish saponins have been subjected to close scrutiny.

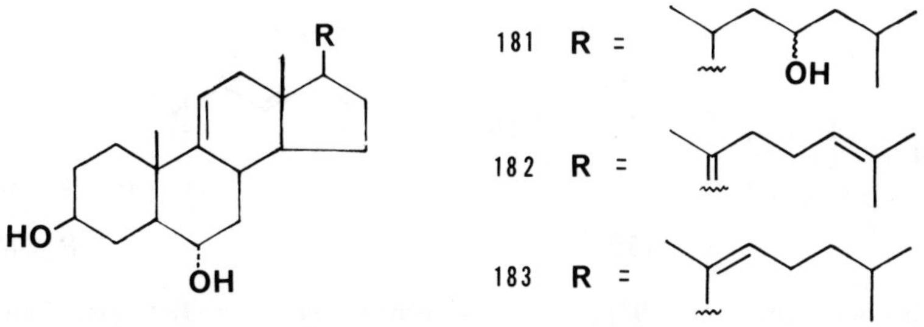

181 R =
182 R =
183 R =

Two groups have announced the synthesis of the pregnane derivative (**23**)(Smith and Turner, 1972; Gurst et al., 1973) while three new sapogenins (**181** to **183**) have been described (Ikegami et al., 1972b; Sheikh et al., 1972b).

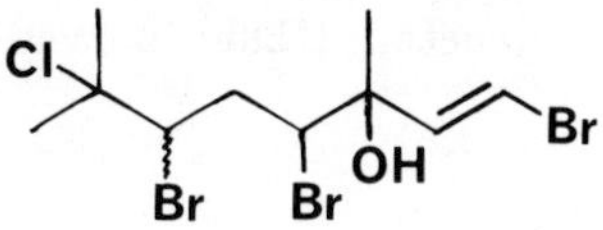

184

A second halogenated monoterpene, the alcohol (**184**), was isolated from the sea hare, *Aplysia californica* (Faulkner and Stallard, 1973). Examination of the algae on which *A. californica* was known to graze revealed that both the alcohol (**184**) and the original halogenated monoterpene (**35**) had originally been fabricated by the red alga, *Plocamium coccineum.*

The sponges continue to yield an array of furanoterpenes (Cimino et al., 1972c). The latest additions to this group are two sesquiterpenes, dehydrodendrolasin (**185**) and pleraplysillin (**186**), from *Pleraplysilla spinifera.* The formation of the six-membered ring in pleraplysillin (**186**) is of biosynthetic interest, since the resultant

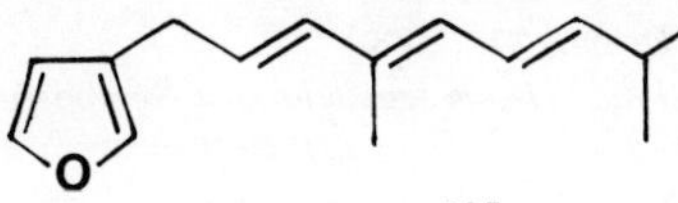

185

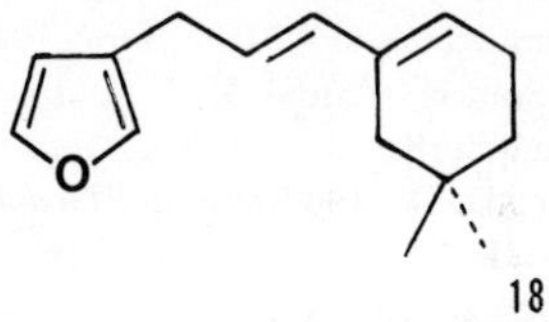

186

sesquiterpene ring system was unknown. The prenylated quinone (**187**), the corresponding hydroquinone (**188**), and the carboxylic acid derivative (**189**) have all been isolated from *Ircinia spinosula* (Cimino et al., 1972c). The phenol (**190**), obtained from the alga, *Taonia atomaria* may be formally related to the hydroquinone (**188**)

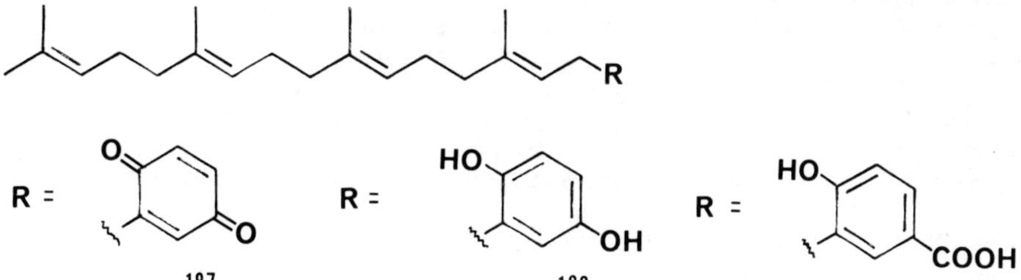

R =

187

188

189

by a biosynthetic cyclization similiar to that found in triterpene and sterol biosynthesis (Gonzalez et al., 1971). An analogous cyclization has been suggested to account for the formation of zonarol (**60**) and isozonarol (**61**).

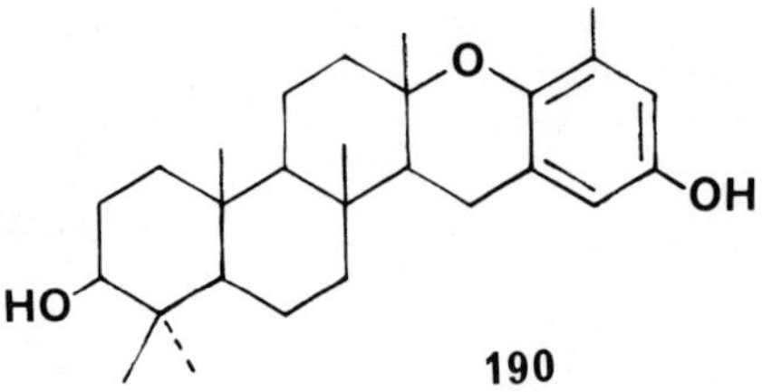

190

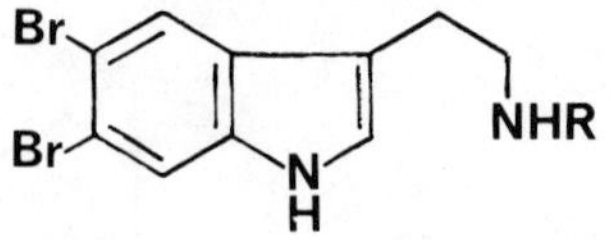

191 R = H

192 R = Me

5,6-Dibromotryptamine (**191**) and its N-methyl derivative (**192**) were found to be responsible for the antibacterial properties of the sponge, *Polyfibrospongia maynardii* (Van Lear et al., 1973). A sponge of the genus *Agelas* has yielded a new antibiotic, the bromopyrrole (**193**), having a structure reminiscent of that assigned to oroidin (**158a**) (Stempien et al., 1972b). A synthetic study of compounds related to oroidin suggests the assignment of the structure (**158b**) to oroidin (Garcia et al., 1973).

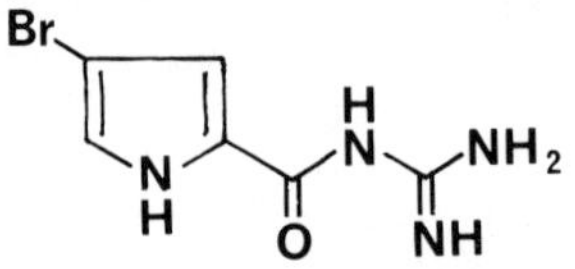

193

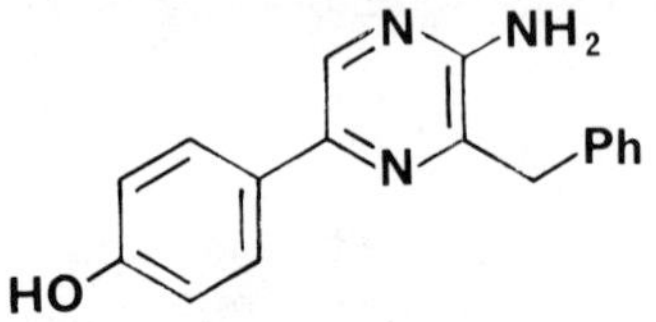

194

Further details of the synthesis of tetrodotoxin (**164**) have recently been reported by Kishi et al. (1972a). The same group has also reported a synthesis of the light-emitting moiety (**194**) of the bioluminescent jellyfish, *Aequorea* (Kishi et al., 1972b).

References

Abraham, E. P. and G. G. F. Newton, 1961. *Biochem. J.*, **79**, 377.

Ackermann, D. and C. Burchard, 1941. *Z. Physiol. Chem.*, **271**, 183.

Aguilar-Santos, G. and M. S. Doty, 1967. *Transactions, Drugs from the Sea Symposium*, Rhode Island, 173.

Andersen, D. G., 1967. *Plant Physiology, Supp.*, S45.

Andersen, R. J. and D. J. Faulkner, 1972. *Third Food and Drugs from the Sea Conference*, Kingston, Rhode Island, August.

Ashworth, R. B. and M. J. Cormier, 1967. *Science*, **155**, 1558.

Baker, J. T. and M. D. Sutherland, 1968. *Tetrahedron Letters*, 43.

Baslow, M. H., 1969. *Marine Pharmacology*. Williams and Wilkens, Baltimore.

Bergmann, W., 1949. *J. Mar. Res.* (*Sears Foundation*), **8**, 137.

Bergmann, W., 1962. *Comparative Biochemistry*. M. Florkin and H. S. Mason, eds. Academic Press, New York, **3**, 103.

Bergmann, W. and D. C. Burke, 1955. *J. Org. Chem.*, **20**, 1501.

Bergmann, W. and D. C. Burke, 1956. *J. Org. Chem.*, **21**, 226.

Bergmann, W., D. H. Gould, and E. M. Low, 1945. *J. Org. Chem.*, **10**, 570.

Bergmann, W., M. J. McLean, and D. Lester, 1943. *J. Org. Chem.*, **8**, 271.

Bergmann, W. and F. H. McTigue, 1948. *J. Org. Chem.*, **13**, 738.

Bergmann, W., F. H. McTigue, E. M. Low, W. M. Stokes, and R. J. Feeney, 1950. *J. Org. Chem.*, **15**, 96.

Blumer, M., M. M. Mullin, and R. R. L. Guillard, 1970. *Mar. Biol.*, **6**, 226.

Bonnett, R., A. K. Mallams, A. A. Spark, J. L. Tee, B. C. L. Weedon, and A. McCormick, 1969. *J. Chem. Soc., C*, 429.

Boylan, D. B. and P. J. Scheuer, 1967. *Science*, **155**, 52.

Brock, V. E., 1956. *Copeia*, **3**, 195.

Bullock, T. H., 1953. *Behavior*, **5**, 130.

Bundy, G. L., E. G. Daniels, F. H. Lincoln, and J. E. Pike, 1972a. *J. Amer. Chem. Soc.*, **94**, 2124.

Bundy, G. L., W. P. Schneider, F. H. Lincoln, and J. E. Pike, 1972b. *J. Amer. Chem. Soc.*, **94**, 2123.

Burkholder, P. R., R. M. Pfister, and F. M. Leitz, 1966. *Appl. Microbiol.*, **14**, 649.

Cafieri, F., E. Fattorusso, C. Santacroce, and L. Minale, 1972. *Tetrahedron*, **28**, 1579.

Chanley, J. D., T. Mezzetti, and M. Sobotka, 1966. *Tetrahedron*, **22**, 1857.

Cimino, G., S. de Stefano, L. Minale, and E. Fattorusso, 1971. *Tetrahedron*, **27**, 4673.

Cimino, G., S. de Stefano, L. Minale, and E. Fattorusso, 1972a. *Tetrahedron*, **28**, 333.

Cimino, G., S. de Stefano, and L. Minale, 1972b. *Tetrahedron*, **28**, 1315.

Cimino, G., S. de Stefano, and L. Minale, 1972c. *Experientia*, **28**, 1401.

Cimino, G., S. de Stefano, L. Minale, and E. Fattorusso, 1972d. *Tetrahedron*, **28**, 267.

Cimino, G., S. de Stefano, L. Minale, and E. Trivellone, 1972e. *Tetrahedron*, **28**, 4761.

Cohen, S. S., 1966. *Progress in Nucleic Acid Research and Molecular Biology*. J. N. Davidson and W. E. Cohen, eds. Academic Press, New York, **5**, 1.

Craigie, J. S. and D. E. Gruenig, 1967. *Science*, **157**, 1058.

Crawford, K., N. G. Heatley, P. F. Boyd, C. W. Hale, B. K. Kelly, G. A. Miller, and N. Smith, 1952. *J. Gen. Microbiol.*, **6**, 47.

Doree, C., 1909. *Biochem. J.*, **4**, 72.

Doty, M. S. and G. Aguilar-Santos, 1970. *Pacific Science*, **24**, 351.

Dreschel, E., 1907. *Z. Biol.*, **33**, 96.

Elyakov, G. B., T. A. Kuznetsova, A. K. Dzizenko, and Y. N. Elkin, 1969. *Tetrahedron Letters*, 1151.

Ersparmer, V. and O. Benati, 1953. *Science*, **117**, 161.

Fagerlund, U. H. M. and D. R. Idler, 1966. *Can. J. Biochem. Physiol.*, **38**, 997.

Fattorusso, E., S. Forenza, L. Minale, and G. Sodano, 1971a. *Gazz. Chim. Ital.*, **101**, 104.

Fattorusso, E., L. Minale, G. Sodano, and E. Trivellone, 1971b. *Tetrahedron*, **27**, 3909.

Fattorusso, E., L. Minale, and G. Sodano, 1972. *J.C.S. Perkin I*, 16.

Faulkner, D. J. and M. O. Stallard, 1973. *Tetrahedron Letters*, 1171.

Faulkner, D. J., M. O. Stallard, J. Fayos, and J. C. Clardy, 1973. *J. Amer. Chem. Soc.*, **95**, 3413.

Faux, A., D. H. S. Horn, E. J. Middleton, H. M. Fales, and M. E. Lowe, 1969. *Chem. Comm.*, 175.

Fenical, W., J. J. Sims, R. M. Wing, and P. C. Radlick, 1972. *Phytochem.*, **11**, 1161.

Fenical, W., J. J. Sims, D. Squatrito, R. M. Wing, and P. Radlick, 1973a. *J. Org. Chem.*, **38**, 2383.

Fenical, W., J. J. Sims, and P. Radlick, 1973b. *Tetrahedron Letters*, 313.

Forenza, S., L. Minale, R. Riccio, and E. Fattorusso, 1971. *Chem. Comm.*, 1129.

Freeman, S. E. and R. J. Turner, 1970. *Toxicol. Appl. Pharmacol.*, **16** (3), 681.

Fukuzawa, A., E. Kurosawa, and T. Irie, 1972. *Tetrahedron Letters*, 3.

Fulmor, W., G. E. Van Lear, G. O. Morton, and R. D. Mills, 1970. *Tetrahedron Letters*, 4551.

Galbraith, M. N., D. H. S. Horn, R. J. Hackney, and E. J. Middleton, 1968. *Chem. Comm.*, 83.

Garcia, E. E., L. E. Benjamin, and R. I. Fryer, 1973. *Chem. Commun.*, 78.

Gomez, E. D., D. J. Faulkner, W. A. Newman, and C. Ireland, 1973. *Science*, 813.

Gonzalez, A. G., J. Darias, and J. D. Martin, 1971. *Tetrahedron Letters*, 2729.

Goto, T., Y. Kishi, S. Takahashi, and Y. Hirata, 1965. *Tetrahedron*, **21**, 2059.

Gupta, K. C. and P. J. Scheuer, 1968. *Tetrahedron*, **24**, 5831.

Gurst, J. E., Y. M. Sheikh, and C. Djerassi, 1973. *J. Amer. Chem. Soc.*, **95**, 628.

Habermahl, G. and G. Volkein, 1970. *Annalen*, **731**, 53.

Hale, R. L., J. Leclercq, B. Tursch, C. Djerassi, R. A. Gross, Jr., A. J. Weinheimer, K. Gupta, and P. J. Scheuer, 1970. *J. Amer. Chem. Soc.*, **92**, 2179.

Halsall, T. G. and I. R. Hills, 1971. *Chem. Comm.*, 448.

Halstead, B. W., 1965 and 1967. *Poisonous and Venomous Marine Animals of the World*. Vol. I, II, III, U.S. Government Printing Office.

Hampshire, F. and D. H. S. Horn, 1966. *Chem. Comm.*, 37.

Hanessian, S. and J. S. Kaltenbronn, 1966. *J. Amer. Chem. Soc.*, **88**, 4509.

Hashimoto, Y. and T. Okaichi, 1960. *Ann. N.Y. Acad. Sci.*, **90**, 667.

Hashimoto, Y., K. Miyazawa, A. Kamiya, and M. Shibota, 1967. *Bull. Jap. Soc. Sci. Fish.*, **33**, 661.

Hashimoto, Y., M. Sakai, and K. Konishi, 1972. *Third Food-Drugs from the Sea Conference*, Kingston, Rhode Island, August.

Henze, M., 1904 and 1908. *Z. Physiol. Chem. Hoppe Seyler's*, **41**, 109 and **55**, 427.

Hodgkin, J. H., J. S. Craigie, and A. G. McInnes, 1966. *Can. J. Chem.*, **44**, 74.

Hodgkin, D. C. and E. N. Maslen, 1961. *Biochem. J.*, **79**, 393.
Houssain, M. B. and D. van der Helm, 1969. *Rec. Chim. Pays, Bas.*, **88**, 1413.
Hunt, S. and S. W. Breuer, 1971. *Biochim. Biophys. Acta*, **252**, 401.
Ikegami, S., Y. Kamiya, and S. Tamura, 1972a. *Tetrahedron Letters*, 1601
Ikegami, S., Y. Kamiya, and S. Tamura, 1972b. *Tetrahedron Letters*, 3725.
Ikekawa, N., K. Tsuda, and N. Morisaki, 1966. *Chem. Ind.*, 1179.
Ikekawa, N., M. Morisaki, and K. Hirayama, 1972. *Phytochem.*, **11**, 2317.
Irie, T., K. Yamamoto, and T. Masamune, 1964. *Bull. Chem. Soc., Japan*, **37**, 1053.
Irie, T., Y. Yasunari, T. Suzuki, N. Imai, E. Kurosawa, and T. Masamune, 1965. *Tetrahedron Letters*, 3619.
Irie, T., M. Suzuki, and T. Masamune, 1968. *Tetrahedron*, **24**, 4193.
Irie, T., A. Fukuzawa, M. Izawa, and E. Kurosawa, 1969a. *Tetrahedron Letters*, 1343.
Irie, T., M. Suzuki, and Y. Hayakawa, 1969b. *Bull. Chem. Soc., Japan*, **42**, 843.
Irie, T., M. Suzuki, Y. Yasunari, E. Kurosawa, and T. Masamune, 1969c. *Tetrahedron*, **25**, 459.
Irie, T., M. Izawa, and E. Kurosawa, 1970a. *Tetrahedron*, **26**, 851.
Irie, T., M. Suzuki, E. Kurosawa, and T. Masamune, 1970b. *Tetrahedron*, **26**, 3271.
Irrine, J. L. and D. W. Wilson, 1939. *J. Biol. Chem.*, **127**, 565.
Isler, O., ed., 1971. *Carotenoids*, Birkhäuser Verlag, Basel.
Karrer, P. and A. Helfenstein, 1931. *Helv. Chim. Acta*, **14**, 78.
Katsui, N., Y. Suzuki, S. Kitamura, and T. Irie, 1967. *Tetrahedron*, **23**, 1185.
Kishi, Y., T. Fukuyama, M. Aratani, F. Nakatsubo, T. Goto, S. Inoue, H. Tanino, S. Sugiura, and H. Kakoi, 1972a. *J. Amer. Chem. Soc.*, **94**, 9219.
Kishi, Y., H. Tanino, and T. Goto, 1972b. *Tetrahedron Letters*, 2747.
Kishi, Y., M. Aratani, H. Tanino, T. Fukuyama, T. Goto, S. Inoue, S. Sugiura, and H. Kakoi, 1972c. *The 8th International Symposium on the Chemistry of Natural Products*, New Delhi, India, and private communication.
Kittredge, J. S. and R. R. Hughes, 1964. *Biochemistry*, **3**, 991.
Kittredge, J. S., E. Roberts, and D. G. Simonsen, 1962. *Biochemistry*, **1**, 624.
Kittredge, J. S., M. Terry, and F. T. Takahashi, 1971. *Fish. Bull.*, **69**, 337.
Kosuge, T., H. Zenda, A. Ochiai, N. Masaki, M. Noguchi, S. Kimura, and H. Narita, 1972. *Tetrahedron Letters*, 2545.
Kurosawa, E., M. Izawa, K. Yamamoto, T. Masamune, and T. Irie, 1966. *Bull. Chem. Soc., Japan*, **39**, 2509.
Kurosawa, E., A. Fukuzawa, and T. Irie, 1972. *Tetrahedron Letters*, 2121.
Lee, R. F. and A. R. Loeblich III, 1971. *Phytochem.*, **10**, 593.
Lee, R. F., J. C. Nevenzel, G. A. Paffenhofer, A. A. Benson, S. Patton, and T. E. Kavanagh, 1970. *Biochim. Biophys. Acta.*, **202**, 386.
Ling, N. C., R. L. Hale, and C. Djerassi, 1970. *J. Amer. Chem. Soc.*, **92**, 5281.
Lovell, F. M., 1966. *J. Amer. Chem. Soc.*, **88**, 4510.
Low, E. M., 1951. *J. Mar. Res.*, **10**, 239.
Mackie, A. M. and A. B. Turner, 1970. *Biochem. J.*, **117**, 543.
Mackie, A. M., R. Lasker, and P. T. Grant, 1968. *Comp. Biochem. Physiol.*, **26**, 415.
Macklis, L., 1958. *Physiol. Plant.*, **11**, 181.
Matsuda, H., Y. Tomiie, S. Yamamura, and Y. Hirata, 1967. *Chem. Comm.*, 898.
Matsumoto, T. and S. Kagawa, 1964. *Abstracts of the Annual Meeting of the Chemical Society of Japan*, 278.
Menozzi, T. and A. Moreschi, 1940. *Atti. Accad. Nazl. Lincei. Rend. Classe Sci., Fis. Mat. Nat.*, **19**, 126.
Miller, J. D. Z., 1962. *Physiology and Biochemistry of Algae*. R. A. Lewin, ed. Academic Press, New York, p. 365.
Minale, L., G. Sodano, W. R. Chan, and A. M. Chen, 1972. *J.C.S. Chem. Comm.*, 674.
Mirata, S., T. Kobayashi, and T. Naito, 1968. *C.A.*, **68**, 87501g, 87502r.
Moody, K., R. H. Thompson, E. Fattorusso, L. Minale, and G. Sodano, 1972. *J.C.S. Perkin I*, 18
Moore, R. E., 1971. *Chem. Comm.*, 1168.
Moore, R. E., J. A. Pettus, and M. S. Doty, 1968. *Tetrahedron Letters*, 4787.
Morimoto, H., 1955. *J. Pharm. Soc. Japan*, **75**, 916.
Morner, C. T., 1913. *Z. Physiol. Chem. Hoppe. Seyler's*, **88**, 138.

Mosher, H. S. and M. S. Brown, 1963. *Science*, **140**, 295.
Mosher, H. S., F. A. Fuhrman, H. D. Buckwald, and H. G. Fischer, 1964. *Science*, **144**, 1100.
Müller, D. G., L. Jaenicke, M. Donike, and T. Akintobi, 1971. *Science*, **171**, 815.
Murakami, S., T. Takemoto, Z. Tei, and K. Diago, 1955a. *J. Pharm. Soc. Japan*, **75**, 866 and 869.
Murakami, S., T. Takemoto, Z. Tei, and K. Diago, 1955b. *J. Pharm. Soc. Japan*, **75**, 1255.
Nakajima, T. and B. E. Volcani, 1969. *Science*, **164**, 1400.
Nakazawa, Y., 1959. *J. Biochem., Tokyo*, **46**, 1579.
Nicolaides, N. and F. Laves, 1954. *J. Amer. Chem. Soc.*, **76**, 2596.
Nigrelli, R. F., J. D. Chanley, S. K. Kohn, and H. Sobotka, 1955. *Zoologica*, **40**, 47.
Nitta, S., 1934. *J. Pharmacol. Soc. Japan*, **54**, 648.
Nozoe, S., M. Morisaki, K. Tsuda, Y. Iitaka, N. Takahashi, S. Tamura, K. Ishibashi, and M. Shirasaka, 1965. *J. Amer. Chem. Soc.*, **87**, 4968.
Nutting, W. H., H. Rapoport, and L. Machlis, 1968. *J. Amer. Chem. Soc.*, **90**, 6434.
Okaichi, T. and Y. Hashimoto, 1962. *Agr. Biol. Chem.*, **26**, 224.
O'nEocha, C., 1958. *Arch. Biochem. Biophys.*, **73**, 207.
Ozawa, H., Y. Goni, and I. Otsuki, 1967. *J. Pharm. Soc. Japan*, **87**, 935.
Pettus, J. A. and R. E. Moore, 1970. *Chem. Comm.*, 1093.
Pettus, J. A. and R. E. Moore, 1971. *J. Amer. Chem. Soc.*, **93**, 3087.
Phleger, C. F. and A. A. Benson, 1971. *Nature*, **230**, 122.
Quin, L. D., 1964. *Science*, **144**, 1133.
Randall, J. E., K. Aida, T. Hibiya, N. Mitsuura, H. Kamiya, and Y. Hashimoto, 1971. *Seto Marine Biological Lab., Kyoto, Japan Publi.*, **19** (2–3), 157.
Roller, P., C. Djerassi, R. Cloetens, and B. Tursch, 1969. *J. Amer. Chem. Soc.*, **91**, 4918.
Roller, P., K. Au, and R. E. Moore, 1971. *Chem. Comm.*, 503.
Rosenheim, O. and H. King, 1932. *Nature*, **130**, 315; H. Wieland and E. Dane, 1932. *Z. Physiol. Chem.*, **210**, 268.
Russell, F. E., 1965. *Adv. Marine Biology*, **3**, 255.
Russell, F. E., 1967. *Fed. Proc.*, **26**, 1206.
Ryan, E. P., 1966. *Science*, **151**, 340.
Saito, T. and Y. Ando, 1955, 1957. *J. Chem. Soc. Japan*, **26**, 478; *C.A.* **51**, 17810i.
Salaque, A., M. Barbier, and E. Lederer, 1966. *Comp. Biochem. Physiol*, **19**, 45.
Sasner, J. J., M. Ikawa, F. Thurberg, and M. Alam, 1972. *Toxicon*, **10**, 163.
Scagel, R. F., 1961. *Fisheries Research Board of Canada Bull.* No. 127.
Scheuer, P. J., 1969. *Forschr. Chem. Organ. Naturstoffe*, **27**, 322.
Scheuer, P. J., W. Takahashi, J. Tsutsumi, and T. Yoshida, 1967. *Science*, **155**, 1267.
Schmitz, F. J. and T. Pattabhiraman, 1970. *J. Amer. Chem. Soc.*, **92**, 6073.
Schmitz, F. J., K. W. Kraus, L. S. Ciereszko, D. H. Sifford, and A. J. Weinheimer, 1966. *Tetrahedron Letters*, 97.
Schmitz, F. J., E. D. Lorance, and L. S. Ciereszko, 1969. *J. Org. Chem.*, **34**, 1989.
Schneider, W. P., R. D. Hamilton, and L. E. Rhuland, 1972. *J. Amer. Chem. Soc.*, **94**, 2122.
Sharma, G. M. and P. R. Burkholder, 1967a. *J. Antibiot. (Tokyo), Ser. A*, **20**, 200.
Sharma, G. M. and P. R. Burkholder, 1967b. *Tetrahedron Letters*, 4147.
Sharma, G. M. and P. R. Burkholder, 1971. *Chem. Comm.*, 151.
Sharma, G. M. and B. Vig, 1972. *Tetrahedron Letters*, 1715.
Sharma, G. M., B. Vig, and P. R. Burkholder, 1970. *J. Org. Chem.*, **35**, 2823.
Sheikh, M. Y., 1970. University of Hawaii Dissertation: *Dissertation Abs. B.*, **30**(12), 5438.
Sheikh, Y. M., C. Djerassi, and B. M. Tursch, 1971. *Chem. Comm.*, 217.
Sheikh, Y. M., B. M. Tursch, and C. Djerassi, 1972a. *J. Amer. Chem. Soc.*, **94**, 3278.
Sheikh, Y. M., B. Tursch, and C. Djerassi, 1972b. *Tetrahedron Letters*, 3721.
Shimada, S., 1969. *Science*, **163**, 1462.
Shimizu, Y., 1971. *Experientia*, **27**, 1188.
Shimizu, Y., 1972. *J. Amer. Chem. Soc.*, **94**, 4052.
Shin-Ichi-Teshima, 1971. *Comp. Biochem. Physiol.*, **39B**, 815.
Sims, J. J., W. Fenical, R. M. Wing, and P. Radlick, 1971. *J. Amer. Chem. Soc.*, **93**, 3774.
Sims, J. J., W. Fenical, R. M. Wing, and P. Radlick, 1972. *Tetrahedron Letters*, 195.
Sims, J. J., W. Fenical, R. M. Wing, and P. Radlick, 1973. *J. Amer. Chem. Soc.*, **95**, 972.
Singh, H., R. E. Moore, and P. J. Scheuer, 1967. *Experientia*, **23**, 624.

Smith, D. S. H. and A. B. Turner, 1972. *Tetrahedron Letters*, 5263.

Spraggins, R. L., 1971. *Abstracts, Food-Drugs from the Sea Conference*, Rhode Island, August.

Stempien, M. F., 1966. *Amer. Zool.*, **6**, 363.

Stempien, M. F., Jr., J. S. Chib, R. F. Nigrelli, and R. A. Mierzwa, 1972a. *Third Food and Drugs from the Sea Conference*, Kingston, Rhode Island, August.

Stempien, M. F., R. F. Nigrelli, and J. S. Chib, 1972b. *Abstracts, ACS National Meeting*, New York, August.

Strain, H. H., W. A. Svec, K. Aitzetmüller, M. C. Grandolfo, J. J. Katz, H. Kjøsen, S. Norgard, S. Liaaen-Jensen, F. T. Haxo, P. Wegfahrt, and H. Rapoport, 1971. *J. Amer. Chem. Soc.*, **93**, 1823.

Suzuki, M., Y. Hayakawa, and T. Irie, 1969. *Bull. Chem. Soc., Japan*, **42**, 3342.

Suzuki, M., E. Kurosawa, and T. Irie, 1970. *Tetrahedron Letters*, 4995.

Tahara, Y., 1909. *J. Pharmacol. Soc. Japan*, 587.

Takaoka, M. and Y. Ando, 1951. *J. Chem. Soc. Japan, Pure Chem. Sec.*, **72**, 999.

Takemoto, T., K. Diago, and N. Takagi, 1964. *J. Pharm. Soc. Japan*, **84**, 1176.

Takemoto, T., K. Diago, Y. Kondo, and K. Kondo, 1966. *J. Pharm. Soc. Japan*, **86**, 874.

Tsuda, K., 1966. *Naturwiss*, **53**, 171.

Tsuda, K., R. Hayatsu, Y. Kishida, and S. Akagi, 1958. *J. Amer. Chem. Soc.*, **80**, 921.

Tsujimoto, M., 1906, 1916. *J. Chem. Ind. Japan*, **9**, 953; see also *J. Ind. Eng. Chem.*, **8**, 889.

Turner, A. B., D. S. H. Smith, and A. M. Mackie, 1971. *Nature*, **233**, 209.

Tursch, B., I. S. De Souza Guimaraes, B. Gilbert, R. T. Aplin, A. M. Duffield, and C. Djerassi, 1967. *Tetrahedron*, **23**, 761.

Tursch, B., R. Cloetens, and C. Djerassi, 1970. *Tetrahedron Letters*, 467.

Valentine, F. R., Jr. and W. Bergmann, 1941. *J. Org. Chem.*, **6**, 452.

Van Lear, G. E., G. O. Morton, and W. Fulmor, 1973. *Tetrahedron Letters*, 299.

Voogt, P. A., 1969. *Comp. Biochem. Physiol.*, **31**, 37.

Weinheimer, A. J. and R. L. Spraggins, 1969. *Tetrahedron Letters*, 5185.

Weinheimer, A. J. and P. H. Washecheck, 1969. *Tetrahedron Letters*, 3315.

Weinheimer, A. J., T. K. B. Karns, D. H. Sifford, and L. S. Ciereszko, 1968a. Abstracts from 155th National Meeting, Amer. Chem. Soc., San Francisco.

Weinheimer, A. J., R. E. Middlebrook, J. O. Bledsoe, Jr., W. E. Marsico, and T. K. B. Karns, 1968b. *Chem. Comm.*, 384.

Weinheimer, A. J., F. J. Schmitz, and L. S. Ciereszko, 1968c. *Drugs from the Sea.* Trans of Drugs from the Sea Symposium, Marine Technology Society, 135.

Weinheimer, A. J., P. H. Washecheck, D. van der Helm, and M. B. Houssain, 1968b. *Chem. Comm.*, 1070.

Weinheimer, A. J., W. W. Youngblood, P. H. Washecheck, T. K. B. Karns, and L. S. Ciereszko, 1970. *Tetrahedron Letters*, 497.

Weinheimer, A. J., R. L. Spraggins, and N. S. Bhacca, 1970. Abstracts, Western Regional A.C.S. Meeting, San Francisco, October.

Wong, J. L., M. S. Brown, K. Matsumoto, R. Oesterlin, and H. Rapoport, 1971a. *J. Amer. Chem. Soc.*, **93**, 4633.

Wong, J. L., R. Oesterlin, and H. Rapoport, 1971b. *J. Amer. Chem. Soc.*, **93**, 7344.

Woodward, R. B., 1964. *Pure Appl. Chem.*, **9**, 49.

Yamamura, S. and Y. Hirata, 1963. *Tetrahedron*, **19**, 1485.

Yasumoto, T. and Y. Hashimoto, 1965 and 1967. *Agr. Bio. Chem.*, **29**, 804 and **31**, 368.

Yasumoto, T., M. Tanaka, and Y. Hashimoto, 1966. *Bull. Jap. Soc. Sci. Fish.*, **32**, 673.

Yasumoto, T., T. Hashimoto, R. Bagnis, J. E. Randall, and A. H. Banner, 1971. *Bull. Jap. Soc. Sci. Fish.*, **37**, 724.

Yokuo, A., 1950. *J. Chem. Soc., Japan*, **71**, 590.

20. IMPACT OF LIFE ON CHEMICAL AND PHYSICAL PROCESSES

H. A. LOWENSTAM

1. Introduction

The marine biomass affects chemical and physical processes in the oceans in a multitude of ways, directly as well as indirectly. The effects on seawater constituents, required as nutrients and critical for maintaining and propagating life, have been thoroughly scrutinized. Those produced by metabolic waste products, decaying organic matter, and animal excreta, as they concern recycling and scavenging of seawater components, have received increasing attention. Similarly, the effects of life on physical processes have been widely studied.

A large segment of the marine biomass precipitates inorganic constituents in their hard parts. The significance of the impact of biologic mineral fixation on chemical and physical processes in the sea has long been acknowledged on the basis of the mass fixation of carbonate minerals and opal, and of small volumes of phosphatic minerals. For some time, a few other kinds of inorganic constituents have been recognized or suspected to be hard-part precipitates of marine organisms. Search for still other kinds of inorganic constituents precipitated in hard parts of the marine biomass seemed pertinent but did not stimulate research until quite recently. However, within the last decade, a total of 16 inorganic compounds has been added to the list of previously known biologic hard-part precipitates. Of these, some are widely distributed in marine life and some are found in large volume. They establish for the first time that a variety of iron oxide compounds are tied up in hard parts of numerous organisms and that previously known phosphates and several formerly unrecognized phosphatic compounds are precipitated by a large segment of marine life. For this reason, the main consideration concerning the impact of life on chemical and physical processes in the sea will be given to the inorganic constituents of hard parts now known to be biologic precipitates of marine organisms, including those in the deep sea.

The treatment of this subject matter will be extended to the geologic past, as documented by the fossil record.

This chapter points to many problems, which can be answered only by future studies, based on better quantitative data than are presently available.

2. Inorganic Constituents in Hard Parts of Marine Life

Considerable progress has been made recently in extending our knowledge of the kinds of inorganic constituents that are precipitated by marine life in their mineralized hard parts. A number of inorganic substances have been identified in hard-part precipitates, which in the past were thought to be formed solely by inorganic, that is, magmatic, metamorphic, and hydrothermal processes at elevated temperatures and pressures. They include some substances that had been inferred long ago from determinations of their major chemical constituents. Until recently, they remained unsubstantiated for lack of further study, clarifying their structures with the aid of modern techniques. Progress has been made also on the phyla distribution of earlier identified inorganic precipitates, which before were known only from hard parts of some groups. Some newly discovered inorganic constituents are amorphous, hydrous substances. Infrared spectra of untreated aliquots of the same substances indicate that they are hydrogels with highly disordered to poorly ordered PO_4 molecules. The other cations are present for charge compensation purposes. They do not indicate

	Bacteria	Bacillariophyceae	Chlorophyta	Rhodophyta	Phaeophyta	Coccolithophorida	Protozoa	Porifera	Coelenterata	Bryozoa	Brachiopoda	Sipunculida	Annelida	Mollusca	Arthropoda	Echinodermata	Chordata
Carbonates																	
Calcite	?			+		+	+	+	+	+	+		+	+	+	+	+
Aragonite	+		+	+	+	?	+	+	+	+		+	+	+	+		+
Calcite & Aragonite									+	+		+	+	+	+		+
Vaterite						?											+
Monohydrocalcite														+			+
Amorphous									+				+	+	+		+
Phosphates																	
Dahllite													+	+	?		+
Francolite											+			+			+
Amorphous calcium phosphatic hydrogels							?						+	+	+		+
Amorphous ferric phosphatic hydrogels													+	+		+	
Silica																	
Opal		+					+	+						+			
Fe-Oxides																	
Magnetite														+			
Goethite														+			
Lepidocrocite								+						+			
Amorphous hydrates							+						+	+			
Sulfates																	
Celestite							+										
Barite							+										
Gypsum									+								
Halides																	
Fluorite														+	+		
Oxalates																	
Weddellite														+		+	

Fig. 1. Inorganic constituents found in hard parts of marine organisms and their phyla distribution.

cation ordering (Lowenstam and Rossman, 1973). Although inorganic constituents of biologic hard parts have been investigated in recent decades, largely with the aid of X-ray or electron diffraction techniques, the presence of amorphous hydrogels has been commonly overlooked, where crystalline compounds were part of the precipitates. The increasing number of reported occurrences of amorphous substances in hard parts indicates that they may be of equal if not greater importance than crystalline compounds as biologic precipitates in the marine biomass. The growing diversity of newly discovered crystalline compounds makes it abundantly clear that our present knowledge of the kinds and diversity of the inorganic substances that are synthesized by marine life is still very incomplete.

Figure 1 shows all but two of the different kinds of inorganic constituents that have been firmly established as precipitates in hard parts of marine life and their distribution in the spectrum of bacteria, plant, and animal phyla where they have been located. Those not included in the chart are a crystalline calcium phosphate mineral, likely $Ca_3Mg_3(PO^4)_4$, which has been recently discovered in a polychaete species

(Neff, 1971) and the oxalate mineral whewellite ($Ca[C_2O_4]H_2O$), which has just been reported to occur in marine codiacean algae (Friedman et al., 1972).

Carbonates are precipitated by species of bacteria in algal and animal hard parts. They are found throughout the range of major biochemical systems, which are involved in skeletal metabolism in the sea. They constitute the most common inorganic constituents of biologic precipitates in the oceans. Crystalline compounds, either in the form of calcite or aragonite, have long been known to be common inorganic constituents of skeletal hard parts. There are many phyla with species that precipitate either calcite or aragonite. In some classes, both mineral phases are found in the same species, but each is confined to a separate architectural component of the skeletons. As shown in Fig. 1, recent additions to the precipitating agents of these two mineral phases are all of the newly discovered Sclerospongia among the Porifera (Hartman and Goreau, 1970), the sipunculids (Rice, 1969; Lowenstam, unpublished), and several groups of polychaete worms and tunicates (Lowenstam, unpublished). Other biologic carbonate precipitates are shown to consist of vaterite, monohydrocalcites, and amorphous forms of calcium carbonate (Carlström, 1963; Lowenstam, 1972; Lowenstam and Abbott, 1973).

Previously, vaterite had been found among the initial precipitation products, for example, in regeneration of artificially injured aragonitic mollusc shells and in laboratory cultures of some coccolithophorids, which normally do not precipitate $CaCO_3$ (Wilbur and Watabe, 1963). The aragonitic shells of molluscs collected from the sea commonly show areas of repair of mechanically or predator-produced breakage. The carbonate of the repaired portions is always composed of aragonite, indicating that if vaterite was initially laid down or coprecipitated with aragonite, in the rapid healing process of the shells it was shortly thereafter converted to aragonite. The recently discovered vaterite, in tunicate spicules, remains stable as the calcification product throughout the life of the organisms (Lowenstam and Abbott, 1973) and hence differs materially from the short-lived existence of this metastable phase prior to aragonite conversion reported in the literature.

The phosphates of mineralized hard parts are shown to be considerably more diverse in mineralogic form than was thought earlier and more widely distributed in the marine biomass. Among the crystalline compounds, calcium magnesium phosphate (Neff, 1971) has been added to the already known carbonate apatites, dahllite and francolite. We are currently investigating others, still poorly structurally defined. The major extension of phosphatic substances as biologic precipitates is the discovery of an increasing number of amorphous forms. They include hydrous, amorphous phases of calcium phosphates and ferric phosphates, which are either rich in calcium, magnesium, or barium (Lowenstam, 1972, 1973). Heat-treated samples of the calcium phosphatic hydrogels indicate from their X-ray diffraction patterns that some are originally hydrous, disordered dahllites and others are originally hydrous, disordered whitlockites (Lowenstam, 1972, 1973). Small to moderate concentrations of phosphorus, reported as P_2O_5 in chemical analyses of some ashed sponges, octocorallia, bryozoa, and crustaceans, indicate the possible presence of phosphatic substances in these groups of organisms (Clarke and Wheeler, 1922; Schopf and Manheim, 1967; Vinogradov, 1953). "Iron phosphate" cements have been mentioned to occur in some arenaceous foraminifera (Carpenter, 1879). It remains to be determined whether discrete phosphatic substances are precipitated by any of these forms, and, if so, whether they are crystalline or amorphous substances.

Inorganically precipitated silicates, including authigenic minerals in the sea, are highly diverse in their chemical composition. By contrast, biologic systems synthesize only opal in skeletal hard parts. Few taxonomic groups of organisms are involved in this process in the oceans. As shown in Fig. 1, four of the six phyla, known to precipitate opal, are unicellular algae and Protozoa, and of the Eumetazoans, the Porifera are of the cellular grade. The only tissue grade invertebrates, where opal precipitation in hard parts has been confirmed, are Patellacean gastropods, where every species that I have examined so far, deposit the opal at homologous sites (Lowenstam, 1971). Silica has been reported also, enclosed in vacuoles of the gastropod, *Onchidella celtica* (Labbé, 1933; Kahane and Antoine, 1935). We have investigated the soft bodies of many species of this naked gastropod, including samples of that from which silica has been reported. We have been unable to find opal in any of these forms. Quartz grains, recovered from these samples, were in all cases well-rounded and of detrital origin.

It is worth noting that silicon concentrates at active bone-forming sites in the preosseous tissue of rats and mice prior to dahllite nucleation and then becomes rapidly released (Carlisle, 1970). Hence, silicon, in the form of an as yet unknown organic compound, may be a factor in the process of bone mineralization. Silicon is becoming increasingly recognized as a stimulus for growth and development of plants and vertebrates (Lewin and Reimann, 1969; Carlisle, 1972). It is of interest to inquire why silicon is a trace constituent of the soft parts of most organisms, plays a definite role in vital processes and possibly bone mineralization, and yet is precipitated, and then only as opal, in a few groups of algae and invertebrates in their mineralized hard parts.

The most noticeable advances in our knowledge of inorganic constituents in biologic hard parts are exemplified in iron oxide compounds. They include three crystalline minerals, magnetite, goethite and lepidocrocite, not previously known to be biologic precipitates (Lowenstam, 1962a, b, 1967; Carefoot, 1965; Towe and Rützler, 1968). Others are insoluble, amorphous, hydrous ferric oxides, which have been extended in their distribution to species in a number of invertebrate classes (Towe, 1967; Lowenstam, 1972). The precipitating agents of the crystalline compounds, magnetite and goethite, are limited to the Mollusca, and only lepidocrocite, also synthesized by one group of them, has been located in species of one other phylum, the Porifera. In all, the known iron oxide precipitating agents are found so far among species of only a few animal phyla. As in the case of the amorphous phosphatic hydrogels, it is likely that as more information on hard-part precipitates becomes available, the distributional range of amorphous ferric hydrogels will extend to other groups of organisms. One of these concerns the microbial formation, where limited information suggests rather than establishes uniquely, that they are involved in these processes, possibly even in the formation of ferromanganese concretions (Kalinenko et al., 1962; review by Silverman and Ehrlich, 1964). Mörner (1902) suggested that part of the ferric iron in the "phosphatic" bodies of certain holothurians is present in the form of a ferric hydrate $Fe(OH)_3$. Infrared spectra of these bodies from many holothurian species indicates that the ferric iron is an integral part of a calcium, magnesium-rich hydrogel (Lowenstam, 1972; Lowenstam and Rossman, 1973). Hence, it has been excluded from the list of iron oxide substances shown in Fig. 1.

Sulfate minerals include the long-known skeletal celestite precipitation by one group of animal protozoa (Odum, 1951), the recently confirmed earlier suggestion of gypsum (Spangenberg and Beck, 1968) in one group of tissue grade organisms, and barite, present in all species of one animal protozoan group (Arrhenius, 1957, 1963; Tendal, 1972). There is still major disagreement as to whether the abundant barite crystals in pelagic sediments are authigenic minerals with biologic activity and organic material, playing only an indirect role in their formation or growth, or whether a fraction of them is the direct precipitate in the bodies of the protozoan group, the Xenophyophorids (Arrhenius, 1963; Tendal, 1972; Church, unpublished thesis). Arguments put forth by Tendal (1972) favor the biologic synthesis of the barite crystals found in large concentrations in the Xenophyophorids. Hence, barite is listed in Fig. 1 among direct biologic precipitates. Each of the sulfate minerals is known so far to be precipitated only by a single group of lower invertebrates.

Known biologic precipitates of halides in their hard parts are represented by fluorite (CaF_2) in species of two phyla. Those deposited by the arthropod representatives, the mysids, were earlier suggested on grounds of chemical analyses (Hensen, 1863; Bethe, 1895), but only recently confirmed by means of modern techniques (Lowenstam and McConnell, 1968). The recent identification of these minerals in hard parts of a group of gastropods extends the range of fluorite-precipitating agents among the marine invertebrates (Lowenstam and McConnell, 1968). High fluorine contents, up to 20% by weight, were reported in amorphous hard parts of some gastropods (McCance and Masters, 1937; Lowenstam and McConnell, 1968). Recent studies by us indicate that these hard parts are composed of two or three separate substances, amorphous, hydrous, calcium carbonate, rarely monohydrocalcite, and an amorphous phase of calcium fluorite (Lowenstam, 1973). We have just found an amorphous phase of calcium fluorite in small quantity, associated with calcite in certain hard parts of another invertebrate group. These forms of amorphous fluorine-bearing substances, not listed in Fig. 1, further underline the earlier voiced conviction that amorphous substances of various chemical composition may be more widespread among inorganic constituents of biologic hard parts than crystalline compounds.

Oxalates are by now represented among hard-part precipitates of marine organisms by monohydrates and dihydrates, whewellite and weddellite (Lowenstam, 1968, 1972; Friedmann et al., 1972). The utilization of weddellite as a strengthening agent of hard tissues by two groups of marine invertebrates is interesting in that this mineral is usually precipitated only pathologically in animals.

A variety of still other inorganic constituents have been mentioned or suggested in the early literature dealing with the anatomy of marine organisms. However, definitive identifications are lacking to justify their inclusion among the inorganic constituents listed in Fig. 1.

Some data show that certain inorganic constituents in mature hard parts differ from their initial precipitation products elaborated on their organic matrices in mineral phases, chemical composition, and structural ordering. Phase transformations from vaterite to aragonite or calcite have been reported in early growth stages and growth expansion of mollusc shells and in the carapace of some crustaceans (Mayer, 1931, 1932; Dudich, 1929; unspecified quotes by Vinogradov, 1953). Vaterite is the most metastable polymorph of carbonate minerals. The initial precipitation product of the carbonate mineral, dahllite, in mammalian bones has been found in some cases to consist of amorphous, hydrous, calcium phosphate (Trautz, 1960). Magnetite (Fe_3O_4) is found in the mature teeth of all chiton species (Lowenstam, 1962, 1967, 1972). The mineralization products of the first one or two tooth rows are chemically similar to the micelle of the iron storage protein ferritin (Towe and Lowenstam, 1967). The ferritin micelle is either a ferric oxyhydrate (Harrison et al., 1967) or, more likely, a colloidal, hydrous ferric oxide (Towe and Bradley, 1967). The changes in the maturing of the precipitation products involve dehydration, transformation from ferric to ferric-ferrous iron oxide, and structural ordering.

It would appear that metastable mineral phases and, more commonly, amorphous, hydrous phases are the initial nucleation products of crystalline compounds in biologic mineral precipitates. Amorphous, hydrous substances were shown to persist in the mature mineralized hard parts of many marine organisms. This raises the question what kinds of biochemical processes lead to their dehydration, transformation to crystalline compounds in many groups of organisms, rather than why there are amorphous, hydrous substances persisting as strengthening agents of hard parts.

Present data on inorganic constituents precipitated by marine life indicate that at the unicellular level, organisms precipitate a wide range of minerals. They include some minerals such as celestite ($SrSO_4$), or possibly barite ($BaSO_4$), not known in more complex biochemical systems. Yet all unicellular species are known to precipitate only one kind of mineral. Starting with the cellular grade of invertebrates, as many as two minerals may be synthesized by a single organism, as recently shown by the Sclerospongia. At the more advanced grade of tissue differentiation, animals are able to develop hard tissues at various anatomical sites, although this is not always the case. In animals with several hard-tissue sites, a variety of several different minerals, or at least several mineral phases, may be precipitated by the same individual. Each depositional site usually contains different inorganic constituents. Individual, mature hard tissues may consist of a number of distinct microarchitectural units, each containing a different crystal phase of the same mineral or an entirely different mineral species. Some molluscan classes and the Molpadiidae among the holothurians seem to have gone further in mineral diversification of their inorganic precipitates than any other known group of marine organisms. Examples are tropical chiton species, where the inorganic precipitates at different girdle sites are composed of aragonite, and the mature major lateral teeth contain magnetite, lepidocrocite, and francolite, each confined to a discrete architectural unit of the teeth (Lowenstam, 1967). Or among the Patellaceans, the shell contains separate layers of calcite and aragonite and the radular teeth are mineralized with opal and goethite (Lowenstam, 1962, 1971). Among some molpadian holothurians, the calcareous ring consists of calcite, and the body wall contains sclerites composed of calcite and an amorphous calcium fluorite compound, mineralized bodies composed of weddellite and granules of amorphous, hydrous ferric phosphate.

Of the 21 different kinds of inorganic precipitates known from hard parts of marine life, 16 are crystalline compounds. The balance is represented by amorphous substances, which, except for opal, are so far defined primarily by their chemical composition. It is of interest to note that the distribution of different biologic precipitates decreases in diversity from 21 in the benthos to 10 in the necton and 4 in the plankton.

The chemistry of specialized cells or cell complexes controls the precipitation of the inorganic constituents where these are cell enclosed. Hard parts form a brick and mortar structure, where the inorganic constituents represent the "bricks" and the enclosing organic matrices the "mortar." Specialized cells in contact with the growing hard parts elaborate the organic matrices and supply the ions for the inorganic mineral precipitates. The chemical composition and structures of the organic matrices are considered to control the types of inorganic constituents that are elaborated on them and act as templates of their crystallographic orientation. Aside from dahllite-bearing bone formation, the template concept of the matrices is suggestive but as yet unproven. The sequence of elaboration of different minerals and the alteration in form of the initial to the final mature mineral precipitates strongly suggests that the cell complexes in contact with hard-tissue sites must undergo changes in their chemistry and chemical functions. This may involve changes in the permeability of their cell walls to resorb water expelled from the hydrous nucleation products in the process of transformation to crystalline anhydrous minerals.

The foregoing considerations point to the basic differences that control specificity and the precipitation of inorganic substances by organisms versus inorganic processes in the sea. The diverse mineral suites partitioned between different hard parts found in a single tissue grade organism are the most spectacular manifestation that distinguishes the organic from the inorganic precipitation process. Biochemical systems are basically semiclosed systems that have the ability to modify their fluid chemistry from that of the external medium by various means. They can further differentiate their chemistry within cells and in cell complexes. Specificity of membrane permeability and transport mechanisms serve to screen, reject or retain, concentrate, and channel chemical constituents to particular sites where the inorganic substances are to be precipitated. These biochemical processes are responsible for the prevalence in specificity of the kinds of inorganic constituents, which are elaborated by a particular biochemical system at a particular cell or tissue site. Ecologic factors induce changes in mineral phase in some biochemical systems. In some cases, they lead to subtraction or addition of minerals. More commonly, they affect the volume of fixation of mineral precipitates. This subject will be treated later in this chapter. Through these mechanisms, organisms are able to elaborate a variety of inorganic substances that would not be precipitated inorganically from seawater in many parts of the present oceans and some minerals, for example, magnetite, would not be precipitated at all.

The basic differences and complexity in interference of the mineral-precipitating biomass to inorganic processes become fully apparent once one considers the various marine ecosystems. All encompass communities composed of highly diverse organisms with mineralized hard parts. Of these, most precipitate different inorganic substances, irrespective of whether the waters in which they live are saturated or undersaturated with reference to the mineral species that they precipitate. The inorganic constituents, precipitated by their mineral precipitating biomass, tie up a wide range of trace constituents. The concentrations of the trace constituents in the same minerals or the same crystal phases elaborated by different members of the community in the same macroenvironment usually differ widely according to species. Hence, biochemical controls extend past the determination of the mineralogy to the trace constituents incorporated in the inorganic substances. Given the same environmental conditions, the fraction of the mineral precipitates that could be precipitated inorganically from seawater if life would not be present would have uniform trace element concentrations.

All of these attributes of biologic systems are the roots of the impact of life on processes regulating the chemistry of the oceans today as far as they are determined by the inorganic constituents of the mineral-precipitating biomass.

3. Biologic Factors Affecting Their Mineral Productivity and Selectivity

Biologically precipitated inorganic substances and their trace constituents affect the chemistry of seawater in various ways. Some, like biogenic opals, are primarily responsible for the changes in depth distribution of the concentration levels of silica in the oceans, and biogenic carbonates affect in a major way the degree of saturation with reference to their mineral phases to varying depths in the sea. Phosphatic substances in hard parts should also influence the distribution of those chemical constituents in seawater which are tied up in these biologic precipitates. However, for reasons pointed out later, their effects on the phosphate budget in the oceans are as yet ill-defined. In other cases, as for example, biologic iron oxide precipitates, there is so far no evidence of their effect on the distribution of dissolved, colloidal, and particulate iron in seawater.

The impact of life on the chemistry of seawater, as determined by its hard-part fixed inorganic substances, is initially dependent on the sizes of the standing crops and turnover rates of the biomass constituents that are involved in these processes. The sizes of the standing crops and hence their mineral productivity are governed by the trophic levels the various organisms occupy in the food chain. Modes of life of the component parts of the mineral precipitating biomass determine their spatial and depth distribution and, in turn, the extent, modes, and differences in their effect on the chemistry of the water masses in the oceans. The selectivity in mineral precipitates found in organisms occupying key trophic levels in the marine biomass needs an explanation. Speculations concerning this phenomenon will be advanced later in the analyses of the existing situations in the oceans today.

We are concerned here only with biologic attributes that determine or may contribute to the differences in magnitudes of the mineral productivity by the marine biomass.

The largest volume of inorganic constituents precipitated by marine life today are the carbonate mineral phases, calcite, aragonite, and silica in the form of opal. As noted earlier, biomass fixation of carbonates extends all the way from bacteria through primary producers to all levels of the consumer chain. This is true for shallow-shelf sea areas, and their combined volume of carbonate fixation, predominantly by benthic organisms, is large and, to a considerable extent, enhanced by animal members of their communities. These members have zooxanthellar and chloroxanthellar symbionts, as most strikingly shown by the volume of carbonate fixation of reef-building corals. Shelf sea areas today are very small compared to the deep, open oceans, making up only 5.5% of the total surface area of the sea (Kuenen, 1950). Based on data from the Northwest Pacific, the benthic biomass decreases on the average 2000 to 3000 times in quantity from the littoral zone to the central parts of the oceans and diminishes most rapidly past the continental slope (Zenkevich, 1956, quoted in Graham and Edwards, 1962). Hence, even though a large segment of the deep-sea benthos precipitates carbonate, its total volume of fixation is negligible compared to the benthic communities on the shelves, particularly in the photic zone. Without the enormous volume of carbonate fixation and rapid turnover rates in the surface waters of the oceans by planktonic coccolithophorids, foraminifera, and to a much lesser extent, by the nectonic pteropods and heteropods (which undergo diurnal migrations from slightly deeper to surface waters) (McGowan, 1960; Chen and Bé, 1964), only a small fraction of the total volume of present-day carbonate fixation in the oceans would be precipitated by marine life. The large productivity of the pelagic carbonate-secreting plankton stems from the fact that they occupy key trophic levels in the food web. The coccolithophorids, of which some are heterotrophic, are primary producers in the photic zone but are able at subphotic levels to utilize particulate organic matter and probably free amino acids and other organic breakdown products of organic material present in seawater. Some of the planktonic foraminifera have zooxantellae. As yet, little is known about their food sources. They appear to be grazers that supplement their food by nannoplankton, bacteria, and particulate organic material and its breakdown products. Whatever their food requirements, their large population justifies assignment to a key trophic level in the pelagic communities (Lipps and Valentine, 1970). The pteropods and heteropods have significantly smaller populations (1 to 10 individuals per square meter), and despite their larger size as compared to micro- and nannoplankton, they are comparatively weakly calcified (aragonite). Their diurnal vertical migration and limited data on their stomach content suggest that they are largely plankton feeders (Pelseneer,

1887, 1888; Morton, 1954; Wormelle, 1962). Phytoplankton and zooplankton have been found in their food, but in other cases, their stomachs were found to be empty. Since their population sizes are smaller than those at key trophic levels, they cannot be assigned to those levels.

The population in the trophic structures of ecosystems, unless inverted, decreases in size from the level of primary producers to the highest level of the consumers. Primary producers may have enormous population sizes and rapid turnover rates. Primary consumers usually have smaller size populations, particularly if they supplement their food from other sources. At the higher consumer levels, the population sizes are small and decrease exponentially the higher the level they occupy in the food chain. Short life-spans are a common feature of many primary producers and primary consumers. Planktonic habits further contribute, most decidedly in the vast expanse of the open oceans, to enhance the population size of organisms in the sea, where they become widely dispersed by the movement of the water masses.

The planktonic coccolithophorids and foraminifera meet all of these optimal requirements to assure enormous populations and huge volumes of carbonate mineral fixation.

The silica-precipitating biomass differs in certain respects from that of the carbonate-secreting biomass. Benthic constituents on the shelves and in the open oceans are considerably less taxonomically diverse, and their volume of opal fixation is relatively smaller. The planktonic constituents are responsible for the far greater tieup of silica in their skeletons as compared to the carbonate-precipitating plankton. This is due first to the enormous population sizes and turnover rates of the primary producers in the surface waters by diatoms, silicoflagellates, and ebridians. Second, it is accentuated by the planktonic opal-precipitating radiolarians that are most populous in the surface waters but have sizable populations ranging to depths of between 5000 to 8000 m (Reshetniak, 1966). The food sources of radiolarians are still little known. Likely, they are largely bacterial, nannoplankton, and particulate organic detritus feeders, although at shallow depths, live and dead phytoplankton may contribute a major part of their diet. Their overall population size would certainly place them into a key trophic level, also. Insofar as the radiolarian constituents of the opal precipitating biomass have a greater depth range, between 4000 and 8000 m, they extend materially mass fixation of opal to a larger cross section of the open oceans than carbonate-precipitating plankton. This points to still another factor that potentially enhances major biogenic volume fixation of their inorganic constituents.

It is of interest to note that only celestite ($SrSO_4$) has been found, in addition to carbonate and opal, as an inorganic substance in the microplankton and nannoplankton. The primary reasons for this phenomenon may be found in the biochemistry of the unicellular groups of organisms that are part of the oceanic plankton. The absence of phosphate-precipitating plankton may be explained by considering that phosphate is a basic nutrient in primary producers. One can speculate that if phosphate was ever utilized in any mutation of the phytoplankton, negative selection pressure might have suppressed its spread to tie up large volumes of phosphatic substances. The dependence of population size of grazers on the phytoplankton population could be explained if this hypothesis were true. For, in the intertidal zone of the tropics, where enmeshing and endolithic algae are more abundant per square meter than is phytoplankton on the average in the open sea, at least one common grazer, the chitons, precipitate francolite in one of the microarchitectural units of their mature teeth (Lowenstam, 1967). Another area worth exploring is why only some of the known biogenic inorganic precipitates are found in skeletal hard parts of the necton and plankton. To stay in suspension, as in silica- and carbonate-precipitating plankton, buoyancy can be maintained only by the development of light gas and and organic compounds such as fatty acid inclusions, aside from enlargement of their surface areas, to counterbalance the weight increase produced by the skeletal hard parts. The specific gravity of opal is 2.1 to 2.3, of calcite 2.71, and of aragonite 2.85 to 2.94. For dahllite it ranges from 3.15 to 3.27, for celestite 3.84 to 3.97, for the iron minerals, lepidocrocite 4.1, goethite 4.2, and magnetite 4.97 to 5.18, and for barite 4.3 to 4.6. Logistic problems in accommodating large-sized counterbalancing mechanisms in nanno- and microplanktonic cells may be the limiting factors in precipitating heavier compounds, even sparingly in hard parts or with increased surface area such as long spines and increased fenestration of the skeletons. This does not explain why a variety of other substances, lighter or close in specific gravity to opal and carbonate minerals, are not known from the plankton. Nor is it known in the Acantharia with celestite skeletons, which are the only exception among heavier substances. They may be of interest to investigate whether they have developed highly specialized hydrodynamically counterbalancing mechanisms, or compared to opaline- and carbonate-precipitating plankton, if they maintain suspension by volume reduction and by selective employment of $SrSO_4$ in the mineralized hard parts, aside from the enlargement of their surface area. If the volume of celestite precipitation should equal that, for example, of the opal in radiolarians, this whole approach would seem in doubt, and an explanation would have to be sought solely in the area of the biochemistry of the plankton, including those that precipitate carbonate and silica. In the case of the diatoms, there are already data to show that silica is vital to cell growth and other vital processes (Lewin and Reimann, 1969). Among the active plankton, only gypsum has been identified in one species and, hence, one cannot as yet tell how widespread and what volume of this mineral is tied up in the sea. Concerning the more energetic necton, aside from the common fixation of the carbonate apatite mineral phases, dahllite, francolite, and fluorite, carbonate minerals are found as major or minor mineralization products in sizable populations. None precipitate inorganic constituents with specific gravities in excess of 3.3. All of these organisms occupy higher trophic levels in the food chain, and their population sizes and volumes of fixation of the minerals they precipitate are commonly smaller than those at key trophic levels.

Turning to the benthic organisms, all but gypsum of the currently known kinds of inorganic substances are represented. Here specific gravity of minerals is of no concern. Carbonates are found in constituents at all trophic levels. Grossly, phosphates and iron oxide minerals are found as precipitates of primary consumers, filter and deposit feeders. Deposit feeders also seem to precipitate barite. At higher trophic levels, carnivores such as those with zooxanthellae and zoochlorellae precipitate carbonate minerals; those without symbionts precipitate, in addition, oxalates, amorphous ferric phosphatic, and calcium phosphatic hydrogels; some also precipitate fluorite in hard tissues, separate from those where the carbonate is laid down.

A guess, and in some cases, gross estimates of the volumes of mineral fixation, indicate again that they are largest among primary producers, followed by primary consumers, and, on the average, smallest at the higher levels of the consumer chain. There are some exceptions among the carbonate-secreting constituents at higher trophic levels, most conspicuous in the case of the hermatypic corals. However, like other less conspicuous examples, they have zooxanthellar or zoochlorellar symbionts, which readily accounts for the higher carbonate productivity of the consortium of primary producers and higher level consumers.

Although the biologic factors and ecologic adaptations indicated or speculated on, contribute to accounting for the relative abundance and distribution of mineral precipitates by the marine biomass, most critical gaps in our knowledge are apparent concerning the biochemistry that determines why some inorganic constituents are limited in their phyla distribution, whereas others are not. Also, there are questions concerning the reason for the selectivity of the mineral precipitates in the plankton and data on the food supplies for properly placing them in the food web.

4. Ecology and Its Relation to Biogenic Minerals and Their Trace Element Chemistry

A number of minerals are unstable and become dissolved prior to or following transfer to the sediments of the oceans at nearly all depths or at depths varying with their saturation levels in seawater with reference to the mineral species. This is best documented in the mineral phase of carbonate, calcite, and silica, in the form of opal and celestite ($SrSO_4$) (Berger, 1967, 1968; Peterson, 1966). Hence, the mineralogy of the inorganic compounds found in skeletal hard parts of marine organisms and the water chemistry at the depths at which the organisms live or their hard parts are post-mortem transferred becomes important as to whether the minerals will be stabilized in the sediments. Data on various ecologic effects on the kinds of mineral or crystal phases of a mineral precipitated in single species or species in the same genus occupying different environments have a bearing on this question. The best-documented examples are provided by the carbonate precipitates of marine organisms. In a number of benthic invertebrates from the intertidal to shallow bathyal depths in phyla ranging from Coelenterata to the Arthropoda, the ratios of aragonite to calcite in their hard parts increases with elevation in environmental temperatures. Or, mineralization by aragonite is limited to warmer waters, as indicated by a Ciripedian species, many calcified red and green algal species, and a brown algal species (Lowenstam, 1954, 1964; Schopf and Manheim, 1967). The changes of the aragonite-calcite ratios in individual species and between species in the same genus or at higher taxonomic levels differ in the same temperature environment, indicating that the biochemistry of the organisms acts as a filtering mechanism of the temperature response on the aragonite-calcite ratio. Salinity has also been indicated to affect in a few species the ratio of the two mineral phases. Where this has been found, decrease in salinity affects the aragonite-calcite ratio inversely to that by temperature. Possible effects on the mineralogy of changes in water chemistry and increase in ambient pressures with depth have as yet not been uniquely identified, or where they are indicated, as in the case of increase in depth, may be temperature rather than pressure induced. In the case of the local subspecies of the polychaete *Salmacina disteri* in Bermuda, where the surface water populations precipitate tubes mineralized by aragonite, individuals ranging to depths of the shallow aphotic zone precipitate small percentages of calcite in addition to aragonite. Recent investigations of the inorganic constituents of the gizzard plates in samples of individual cosmopolitan species and species in the same genus of some tectibranchs have been found to change either with temperature or with depth. Samples of the shallow water species *Philine aperta* show that monohydrocalcite is precipitated as one of the inorganic constituents in the gizzard plates in colder waters, whereas in the tropics an amorphous carbonate phase is found instead. In *Cylichna* species, weddellite is found as a constituent of the inorganic precipitates in the gizzard plates from colder waters only at depths in excess of 20 to 30 m. In chitons examined from cold to cold temperate waters, the mature radular teeth are sheathed with magnetite and an amorphous ferric phosphatic hydrogel, whereas in the tropical waters, magnetite plus lepidocrocite and francolite are found instead (Lowenstam, 1972). The magnetite percentage of the tooth enamel also decreases with elevation in environmental temperatures. The observed reduction in the magnetite fraction and the unmixing of the amorphous iron phosphate to form separate crystalline compounds of ferric and carbonate apatite minerals appears to be related to a temperature effect on the biochemistry of the epithelial cells of the radular sac and possibly to resultant changes on the organic matrix on which the inorganic compounds are elaborated (Lowenstam, 1972). In species assigned to the tectibranch gastropod genus, *Scaphander*, the gizzard plates of those ranging from the surface waters into the aphotic zone to a depth of about 1000 m are mineralized by fluorite and an amorphous, calcium phosphatic hydrogel. In species recovered from 3500 m, weddellite and a ferric barium-rich phase of an amorphous, hydrous compound are found instead. In the deep-water holothurian species *Ceraplectana trachyderma*, individuals from 3800 m depth precipitate weddellite in addition to calcite, and amorphous calcium and magnesium-bearing iron phosphates at two hard tissue sites. The individuals from 6600 m depth do not precipitate weddellite and the mineralization by the amorphous ferric phosphatic hydrogel of one mineralization site is volumetrically greatly reduced. In species of another holothurian genus, *Molpadia*, the samples examined to date from the surface waters to a depth of about 3500 m precipitate, aside from the calcareous ring and mesodermal sclerites composed of calcite, amorphous "phosphatic bodies" similar in chemical composition to those in *Ceraplectana trachyderma* at the same tissue sites. When one compares the phosphate-calcite ratios from about 30 m to 3600 m, the ratio decreases from about 95% irregularly with increase in depth to an average value of a fraction of one percent to at most 10% by volume (Lowenstam, in preparation). These data indicate that not only the carbonate minerals, calcite and aragonite, but also the noncarbonate minerals precipitated by marine invertebrates may be affected by environmental temperatures and, as yet undefined, ecologic factors with increase in depth occupation. The question of whether the depth changes in mineralogy cited are related in part, at least, to changes in temperature, water chemistry, or hydrostatic pressure effects remains to be determined. The data presented here are primarily to call attention to the need for further mineralogic studies of deep-water invertebrates in conjunction with precise determinations of the ecologic factors that control their precipitation at the sites where they have been recovered.

The mineral phases of carbonate, calcite, and aragonite are widely synthesized by marine organisms in their hard parts (Fig. 1). Studies of their chemistry have shown that the calcite phase contains in many species between 10 to nearly 20% of magnesium carbonate, whereas in the aragonite phase the magnesium contents range from a trace to at most half a mol percent. $SrCO_3$ contents in many biogenic aragonites range from 1 to 1.2 mol %, whereas in the calcite phase the range extends from less than 0.1 to at most 0.4 mol %. These differences in Sr and Mg substitutions for Ca ions in the two mineral phases are readily explained on crystal chemical grounds.

There are, however, numerous species where the calcites are very low in Mg as well as other trace constituents and aragonites, with trace amounts to at most 0.3 mol % of $SrCO_3$. The low magnesium calcites are volumetrically important in consideration of the carbonate budget of the oceans, as they include the major carbonate contributors to pelagic sediments, namely the planktonic coccolithophoridae and foraminifera. The same is true to a lesser extent for the low strontium aragonites, which include the pteropods that form a fair-sized contributor to pelagic sediments at bathyal depths. Data on the magnesium and strontium in the calcitic and aragonitic skeletons of all carbonate-secreting species in the same benthic habitat show limited differences on the genus level and major ones between species of different phyla, statistically more commonly in the magnesium contents of the calcites than in the strontium contents of the aragonites. In the benthic tissue-grade invertebrates with coexisting calcite and aragonite in their skeletons, there is a tendency for the ratios of strontium carbonate contents of the aragonites to calcites to decrease with increase in structural grade (Lowenstam, 1964). It has been shown further that the magnesium carbonate contents of the aragonites precipitated by the constituents of the same communities decrease with increase in structural grade (Lowenstam, 1963). The average Sr and Mg contents of the different layers found in bivalve shells composed entirely of aragonite or calcite have been shown to differ markedly. The tendency is toward higher values in the inner as compared to the outer layers. The different layers are elaborated by the cells of different mantle lobes (Lowenstam, 1964; Hallem and Price, 1968). Cellular control of the differentiation of average Sr and Mg contents in component parts of aragonitic shells is strengthened further by data on the shell of the bivalve *Chama macerophyla*. The myostracal layer deposited by the epithelial cells of the connective tissue of the adductor muscle is similar to mantle-deposited shell layers composed of aragonite. The average Mg and Sr contents of the myostracal aragonite are lower than the lowest values of the shell layers (Lowenstam, 1964).

These data illustrate the significance of biochemical controls on the Sr and Mg uptake by the carbonate-secreting biomass in the sea. The complexity of these effects ranges from varying degrees of modifying and even masking crystal chemical effects. In individuals of tissue grade, it extends its influence all the way down to the chemistry of the cells and tissue complexes that are involved in the elaboration of hard tissue matrices and mineral precipitates.

Ecologic factors have been reported to be superimposed on the crystal chemical and biochemical effects of the uptake of Mg and Sr in a variety of carbonate-secreting organisms. The most convincing evidence is for a widespread ecologic effect of temperature (reviewed by Dodd, 1967; Gibbs and Bryan, 1972). In calcite and aragonite precipitates there is a positive correlation in Mg uptake with temperature, whereas in Sr, positive and inverse relations with temperature have been reported for calcitic and aragonitic skeletons (reviewed by Dodd, 1967; Gibbs and Bryan, 1972). Increment studies of shell layers in some bivalve species have shown that there is a positive correlation of Sr uptake with temperature, whereas in the inner layer the correlation is inverse (reviewed by Gibbs and Bryan, 1972). The distribution coefficient between the Sr/Ca ratio in aragonite precipitates to the Sr/Ca ratio in seawater with elevation in temperature has been recently determined experimentally in the laboratory (Kinsman and Holland, 1969; Kinsman, 1969). Two approximate values on the distribution coefficient, defined similarly to that for aragonite in relation to temperature, have been determined also for calcite precipitation from seawater by the same investigators. Applying the distribution coefficients for the Sr/Ca values of calcite and aragonite in biologic precipitates, Kinsman found that in some groups the Sr/Ca ratios are close to or precisely the values one would expect at the temperature at which the carbonates were precipitated. However, in many other groups biochemical controls were found to be dominant, resulting in higher or lower Sr/Ca ratios, even in one or the other mineral phase where calcite and aragonite coexist. The modifying effect by biochemical controls on biologic carbonate precipitates explains further why the Sr/Ca ratios in such groups as the calcareous brachiopod and some echinoderms show in their calcitic precipitates a positive instead of a negative correlation with temperature. No comparable experimental data on the distribution coefficient for magnesium in calcites and aragonites exist, and hence the answer to the question of to what extent biochemical controls modify the temperature effects on Mg uptake remains to be determined.

It has been suggested that salinity may also affect the Mg and Sr contents of skeletal carbonate minerals in a few bivalves, some articulate brachiopods, and one echinoid species (Dodd, 1966; Pilkey and Hower, 1960; Lowenstam, 1954). The Mg/Ca and Sr/Ca ratios are stated to show an inverse relationship with salinity as compared to temperature. Eisma (1966) and Hallam and Price (1968) have argued that in the case of bivalves, temperature instead of salinity is responsible for the supposed salinity effects, whereas Dodd (1966) supports his argument in favor of salinity control in the case of the *Mytilus* populations that he studied along the west coast of North America. In the case of the articulate brachiopods, the samples from the insulated waters of the Mediterranean show higher values in Mg contents of their calcitic shells as compared to samples from the same temperature regime from the open oceans. As the Mg/Ca ratios were shown to be the same in both cases, it appears that a salinity effect accounts for the noticeable differences in the magnesium contents of these samples. Further studies on samples from nature and also on samples grown in waters of different salinities under uniform temperature conditions should provide a clearer understanding of the possible influence of salinity on the Mg/Ca and Sr/Ca ratios of species from different phyla.

There are a few data to suggest that local differences in the Sr/Ca ratios in seawater may be monitored by the Sr/Ca ratios of skeletal carbonates (Lowenstam, 1961). The inshore waters of Auke Bay, Alaska, were determined to have a Sr/Ca ratio that is 7% higher and those from a Mediterranean station have a Sr/Ca ratio 15% higher compared to the average values in the surface waters of the open oceans. The Sr/Ca ratios of the calcitic shells of articulate brachiopods from the Auke Bay and Mediterranean stations were higher than those in samples from open oceanic environments. Unpublished data by the author on the Sr/Ca ratios from waters at Palau taken along a traverse from outside the barrier reef across the lagoon into the interisland waterways show a decrease by about 7%. The salinity of the waters in the interisland waterways was found to be up to 0.5% lower than on the outer reefs and in the open lagoon. The islands bordering the waterways consist of low strontium calcite and are characterized by karst topography. The decrease in the Sr contents of the waters across the outer reef barrier and the fringing reefs around the lagoonal islands can be related principally to the mass fixation of high strontium aragonites of the reef populations and lagoonal fauna. The depletion may be slightly accentuated in the interisland waterways by a slight dilution of Sr-depleted fresh water from the islands. The year-round water temperatures at Palau are 28°C, and over a 50-yr period show maximum deviations of ± 1°C (Lowenstam, 1964). Temperatures in the interisland waterways may exceed the mean annual temperature by 2°C at slack tide. Sr determinations of the aragonitic plates of the chiton, *Acanthopleura spiniger*, show a decrease of about 15% in the samples taken from the seaward side of the barrier reef across the lagoon to within the inshore waterways. As the changes in Sr contents in the chiton plates are in the same direction as those in the waters of their habitats, it would appear that the biologically fixed strontium concentrations reflect primarily, if not entirely, those in the seawater. The $MgCO_3$ contents of the chiton plates do not change along the traverse from outside the reef across the lagoon to the inshore waters, and there is also an indication that the Mg/Ca ratio in the waters does not change (Fig. 2).

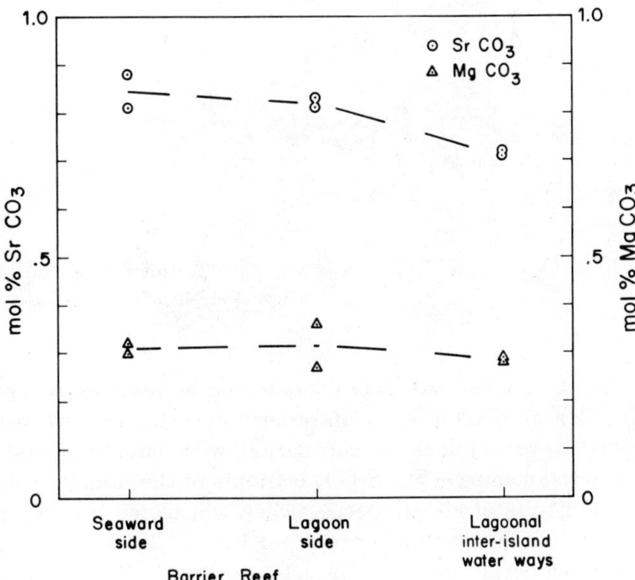

Fig. 2. $SrCO_3$ and $MgCO_3$ contents of aragonite in valves of the chiton *A. spiniger* from Palau, Caroline Islands.

High-pressure experiments have shown effects on various biochemical reactions and genetic coding of bacteria and cell and tissue cultures under laboratory conditions (Arnold and Albright, 1970; Albright and Henigman, 1971). Hence, the question whether hydrostatic pressure effects also find an expression in the biogeochemistry of skeletal carbonates in deep-sea organisms becomes relevant. A preliminary survey has been conducted on some eurybathial holothurian species obtained from museum collections (Lowenstam, 1973). Samples of the calcitic sclerites of the subspecies of *Elpida glacialis* from depths of 610 to between 8780 and 8830 m were analyzed for their magnesium and strontium contents and in selected samples also for manganese, iron, barium, copper, and boron concentrations. Environmental data were available only for temperature. In the absence of data on the temperature relations of Sr and Mg uptake by the calcitic precipitates of the shoal water holothurians, samples of species from the shallow water genus, *Psolus*, were initially investigated from temperature environments between 0 to 16°C. The $MgCO_3$ and $SrCO_3$ contents in the calcitic hard parts of *Psolus* showed a positive correlation with temperature. The environmental temperature of the samples from the eurybathial *Elpida glacialis* subspecies cover a narrow range between -1.1 to $+2.8$°C. Plots of the Mg contents against temperature for samples of all subspecies showed a random distribution of the experimental points (Fig. 3). Analyses of the data by subspecies revealed that magnesium carbonate contents of the North Atlantic subspecies *glacialis* showed decided positive correlation with temperatures. The samples of the other subspecies, each derived from a different trench in the Indo Pacific, were found to show no correlation with reference to temperature. A plot of the magnesium values of all samples against depths shows a very gross negative correlation (Fig. 4). The experimental points over the depth range from 600 m to 2400 m are based on samples from the subspecies *glacialis*, and hence the decrease in the Mg contents with increase in depth is solely a reflection of the decrease in temperature with depth. On the other hand, the

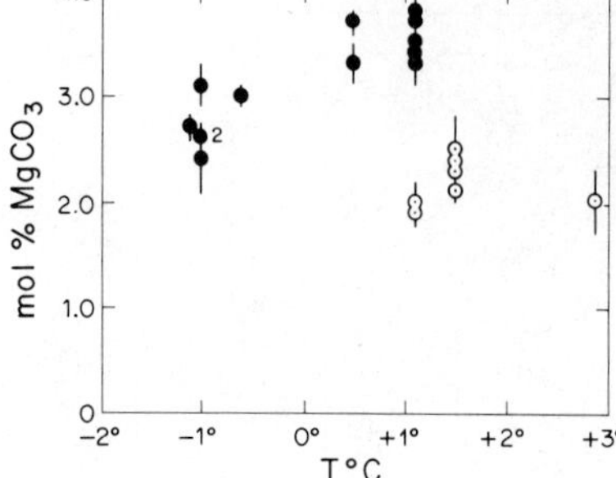

Fig. 3. $MgCO_3$ content of calcitic sclerites of *Elpidia glacialis* subspecies in relation to temperature.

experimental points for the subspecies *sundensis*, *kermadecensis*, and *solomonensis* from depths of 7200 to 8800 m show an orderly decrease with increase in depths in contrast to their apparent lack of correlation with environmental temperatures. Examining the relationships of the $SrCO_3$ contents of the samples with temperature, the experimental points of all subspecies, when considered jointly, indicate a large scatter in the range of temperature between -1.1 to $+1.1$°C and well-defined negative correlation with temperatures between $+1.5$ to 2.8°C (Fig. 5). The experimental points in the lower temperature range are based on samples of the subspecies *glacialis*, whereas those at higher temperatures (above 1.1°C) represent samples of the four other subspecies. Closer inspection of the experimental points from the samples of the subspecies *glacialis* alone indicate a poorly defined positive correlation between $SrCO_3$ contents and temperature. This contrasts sharply with the negative correlation of the $SrCO_3$ contents from the interpretation of samples from the four other subspecies of *E. glacialis*. Plotting the $SrCO_3$ contents from the sample of all subspecies against depth shows a greatly improved negative correlation as compared to that with temperature (Fig. 6). This is because the experimental points for the subspecies *glacialis* conform with the trend indicated for those of the other subspecies.

The present, limited data indicated that in *Elpidia glacialis*: (1) the ultraabyssal subspecies are biochemically more closely related to each other than to the bathyal

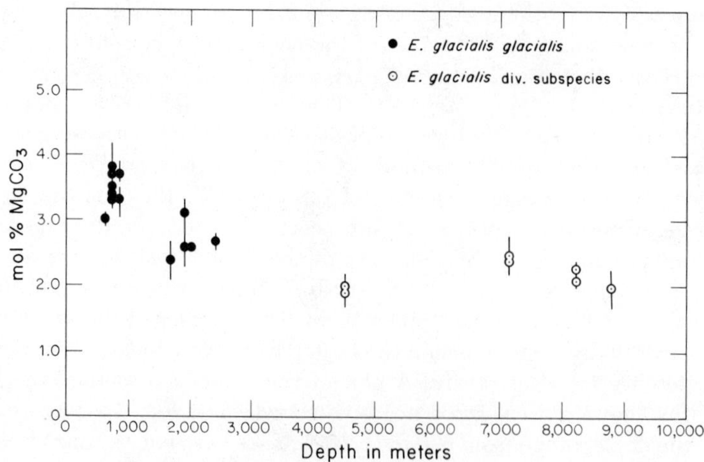

Fig. 4. $MgCO_3$ content of calcitic sclerites of *Elpidia glacialis* subspecies in relation to depth.

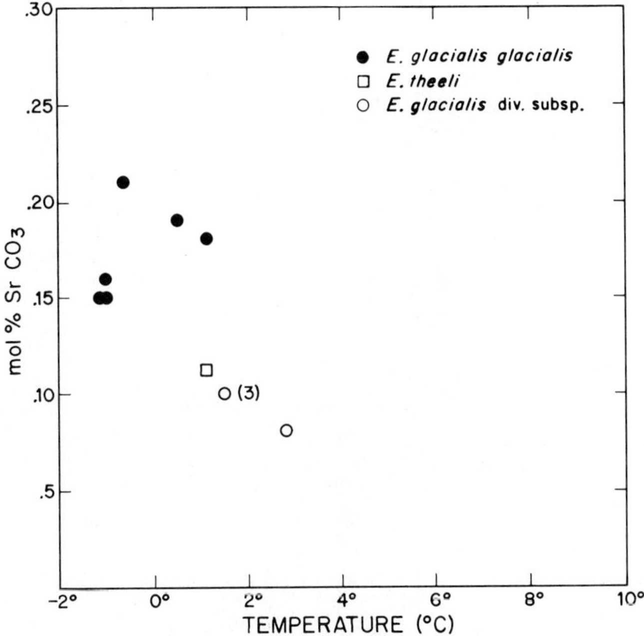

Fig. 5. $SrCO_3$ contents of calcitic sclerites of *Elpidia glacialis* subspecies in relation to temperature.

subspecies *glacialis*; (2) within the depth range covered by the samples of the subspecies, *glacialis*, the $SrCO_3$ contents are more strongly controlled by a depth-related factor than by temperature, whereas their $MgCO_3$ contents are primarily dependent on environmental temperatures; and (3) in the ultraabyssal subspecies their $MgCO_3$ contents appear to be more clearly affected by an undefined depth factor than by temperature, whereas in their $SrCO_2$ contents the reverse seems to be in evidence.

Considering three samples of the deep-water holothurian species *Oneirophonta mutabilis*, the $MgCO_3$ contents between the depths of 3570 to 4500 m indicate a temperature effect, whereas between 4500 and 5850 m, a depth-related factor seems to control the Mg uptake in this species.

Studies of the trace element contents of several noncarbonate mineral precipitates in hard parts of eurybathyal species are in progress. Based on as yet few samples, changes in concentrations of several trace constituents seem to be indicated. In the francolite-hardened shells of the cosmopolitan deep-water brachiopod *Pelagiodiscus atlanticus*, samples from depths of 1500 to nearly 5200 m show an increase in iron and manganese contents and a decrease in magnesium contents with increase in depth. A decrease in magnesium contents accompanied by an increase in manganese is also indicated for amorphous iron phosphate granules precipitated by the holothurian *Molpadia musculus* in a few samples from 1200 to nearly 3600 m. Temperature data available for some of the sample locations indicate differences in water temperatures of 1 to at most 2°C, and in salinity a few tenths of ‰ between the shallowest and greatest depth from which the samples were recovered. Hence, temperature and salinity seem unlikely to be ecologic variables to account for the depth-related changes in concentration levels of the trace constituents in the inorganic precipitates of the hard parts under consideration. Where the changes in the trace element chemistry uptake

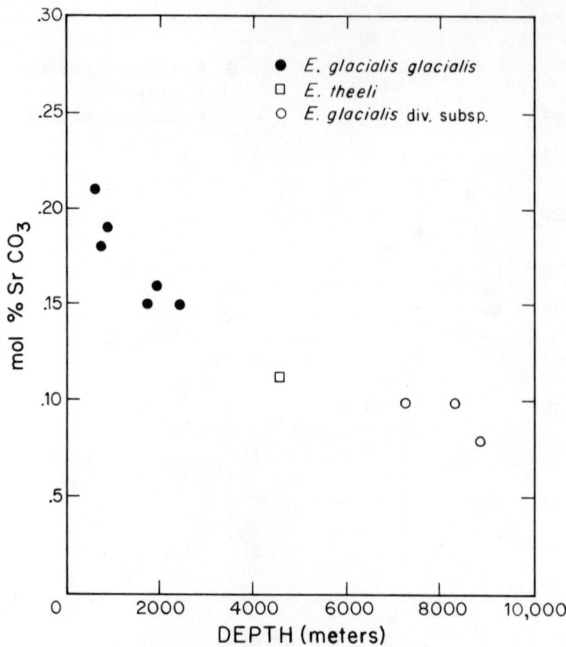

Fig. 6. $SrCO_3$ contents of calcitic sclerites of *Elpidia glacialis* subspecies in relation to depth.

are small with increase in depth, as in the case of iron, these could be related to differences in iron contents of the environmental waters. In the case of the manganese contents, the values increase with depth from a trace to 0.5% and can be as high as 0.8% by weight. These differences are too large to be accounted for by Mn concentration differences in seawater in dissolved and particulate form, and the systematic change indicated so far in the depth range between 1200 and 5200 m, even in deposit feeders such as the holothurians, are likely to be related or at least greatly accentuated by biochemical processes in the organisms, and the same would seem to apply to the changes in Mg contents of their hard-part minerals.

It is tempting to correlate the depth-related concentration changes in Sr, Mn, possibly Fe, and in some cases those in Mg in hard tissue minerals to the effect of increase in hydrostatic pressure on the biochemistry of the organisms. However, more data are needed on the relationships of the seawater chemistry and various ecologic factors to determine whether known high-pressure effects are thus also translated by the biochemistry of the organisms to the chemistry of their hard-part mineral precipitation.

5. Effects of Some Biogenic Mineral Precipitates on the Chemistry of the Oceans

The significance of inorganic constituents in hard parts of marine life on chemical processes in the sea is most apparent and best documented for carbonate minerals and opal. They are briefly treated here to illustrate two different modes of major biologic interference with physicochemical precipitation processes in the oceans. As has been shown for fluorine, minor concentrations of trace elements incorporated in biogenic carbonates and opals are transferred in sizable quantities to the marine sediments by these two major biogenic mineral precipitates (Carpenter, 1969). Hence, fluorine is included here to stimulate similar studies of other constituents of these and other major biologically precipitated inorganic substances. Such investigations should aid in assessing more precisely the impact of life on a wider range of ionic species in seawater. Other examples to be treated in this section are phosphatic substances and iron oxides, since more data have become available on the former, and hardly anything had been known earlier with respect to biogenic hard-part fixation of the latter. Finally, we shall examine briefly barium fixation by biologic agents and its possible effects on the chemistry of seawater.

Precipitation and sediment accumulations of calcium carbonate minerals in all oceans is essentially the product of biologic agents. A highly diverse carbonate-secreting biomass is found in shallow-shelf seas. High and low magnesium calcites and aragonites are their precipitation products. Higher aragonitic percentages and higher magnesium contents in calcites are found in the carbonate-secreting biomass in warm water regions than in the temperate to cold water areas. In the open oceans, shallow water pelagic nanno- and microplankton, represented by coccolithophorids and foraminifera, constitute the principal precipitation agents of calcium carbonate in the form of low-magnesium calcite. Pteropods, heteropods, species of the gastropod genus *Janthina* and of the cephalopod genus, *Spirula*, are also part of the pelagic organisms that lay down carbonate minerals. All of these organisms precipitate low strontium aragonites, but *Janthina* also has a low-magnesium calcite shell layer. The pteropods outrank noticeably in population size the other last-mentioned groups of pelagic organisms, but including the pteropods, their combined volume of carbonate fixation is small compared to that of the coccolithophorids and planktonic foraminifera, which occupy key trophic levels in the pelagic. Carbonate-secreting benthos extends on the ocean floors all the way to the deepest trenches (Wolff, 1960, 1970). Data on their carbonate mineralogy that I obtained in a study still in progress (unpublished), from samples to a maximum depth of 9000 m show the presence of calcites with low to medium magnesium contents and of aragonites that have very low to occasionally medium strontium concentrations. The volume of carbonate fixation by the benthos of the deep-sea floor is negligible when compared to that of the shelf sea communities and the pelagic surface water populations in the open oceans. Carbonate productivity per unit area is higher in shelf sea communities, particularly in the photic zone, as compared to that of the carbonate-secreting biomass in the open oceans. However, since the shelf sea expanse today represents only about 5.5% of the total surface area of the oceans (Kuenen, 1950), the volume of carbonate fixation by the marine biomass is largely embodied in the plankton population of the open oceans.

Although the number of reported occurrences of carbonate-cemented submarine sediments and coral reefs is increasing, it appears that physicochemically-precipitated carbonate is unimportant, as it involves mostly local redistribution of originally biologically-precipitated carbonate, and moreover, its precipitation may be controlled by bacterial action (Taft et al., 1968; Fischer and Garrison, 1967; Land and Goreau, 1970). Other reasons for considering the inorganically precipitated fraction of total carbonate fixation as being negligible are that the locally observed clouds of aragonite needles in a few shallow water areas of the tropics may be suspension products of algal precipitates (Cloud, 1962; Lowenstam and Epstein, 1957), and there is increasing doubt that the precipitation of oolites is entirely controlled by inorganic precipitation processes. Hence, although the surface waters of the oceans are supersaturated with reference to calcite and aragonite, biologic agents almost entirely suppress physicochemical precipitation of carbonate minerals in the sea.

The significance of biologic fixation by organisms became fully apparent from the study of pelagic sediments, where it was found that carbonate-rich and pure carbonate accumulations cover about 65% of the Atlantic Ocean floor and about 40% of that of the Pacific and Indian Oceans (Sverdrup et al., 1942). The average maximum depth for carbonate-rich sediments are found between 4000 and 5000 m in low latitudes and become shallow toward high latitudes, more conspicuously in the North Pacific than in the North Atlantic (Berger, 1971). The deepest carbonate-rich sediments are composed of the low magnesium calcitic skeletal remains of planktonic foraminifera and coccolithophorids, and at shallower depth may locally contain and be rich in aragonitic pteropod shells. The pelagic carbonate accumulations between the arctic and antarctic convergences have been estimated to contain on the average 30% coccolith (McIntyre and McIntyre, 1971). Data on the degree of saturation of seawater with respect to carbonate minerals and solubility studies of calcite spheres and planktonic foraminifera shells have shown that seawater starts to become undersaturated with reference to aragonite in the Atlantic at about 2000 m, and in the Pacific at about 500 m (Li et al., 1969). The more extensive data obtained by various methods on calcites show considerable divergence in results but agree, in principle, that the rate of dissolution of this more stable carbonate phase starts at greater depths, considerably deeper in the Atlantic as compared to the Pacific (Peterson, 1966; Berger, 1967; Ruddiman and Heezen, 1967; Li et al., 1969). The actual compensation depths for calcite accumulations, which vary from ocean to ocean and within them, largely by latitude, regions of upwelling, and of oceanic currents, then represent the depths at which the supply of calcitic skeletons is compensated by dissolution.

Data on the total initial supply of the pelagic carbonate skeletons in the surface waters are still very incomplete. This is partly due to the complexity introduced by the wide variations and patchiness of skeletal supplies in the oceans and seasonal variations in standing crops, indicated by the longer and more extensive efforts to obtain quantitative data for foraminifera shells by numerous workers in this field (Bradshaw, 1959; Belyaeva, 1964; Bé and Tolderlund, 1971). Similar studies on coccolithophorids, or more often surface water-suspended coccoliths, have been started only recently and, hence, are still very incomplete. To indicate the complexity confronting reasonable estimates for foraminifera, one specimen per cubic meter occurs on the average in central waters, more than 10 specimens per cubic meter have been counted in transitional waters, 25 specimens per cubic meter in equatorial waters, and a maximum of 30 specimens per cubic meter in subpolar transitional waters (Bé and Tolderlund, 1971). In the case of coccoliths, 800 to 50,000 platelets per square meter have been found in suspension in the surface waters of a limited number of sampling stations (Uschakova, 1971). As in the case of the foraminifera, maximum numbers came from zones of divergence of water masses. Precise global average accumulation rate distributions for carbonate accumulations are still incomplete. The average rate of accumulation in the Atlantic has been estimated to amount to 0.10 ± 0.03 mol $CaCO_3/m^2$ yr, and for the Pacific and Indian Oceans 0.05 ± 0.02 mol $CaCO_3/m^2$ yr (Broecker, 1971). Only about 15% of the skeletal calcites precipitated in the surface waters today are thought to survive in deep-sea sediments (Broecker, 1971). Considering that the carbonate cycle in the sea has been under extensive scrutiny, matched only by that for silica, it is apparent that even in this case more data are needed. Nevertheless, this is one of the most spectacular examples of the displacement of physicochemical processes by skeletal mineral fixation by marine life. Low-magnesium calcites are more stable than aragonite, and this mineral phase is more stable than high-magnesium calcites. One wonders what the depth distribution patterns of calcite accumulations in the pelagic areas would have been like if the coccolithophorids and planktonic foraminifera would have precipitated high-magnesium calcites instead. As high-magnesium calcites are common in inorganic carbonate precipitates, one may extend this question to the geologic past, when in the open oceans physicochemical processes controlled carbonate precipitation entirely.

Turning to silica, seawater is undersaturated with reference to opal. The undersaturation is greatest in the photic zone, and although markedly decreasing with depth, extends all the way down to the deepest trenches. Mass fixation of opal, principally by phytoplankton (mostly diatoms) and to a lesser extent by silicoflagellates, takes place in the euphotic zone and by the planktonic protozoan representatives, the radiolarians, extends to a depth between 5000 and 8000 m. However, most of the radiolarian production of silica occurs in the upper 200 m (Lisitzin, 1971). Extensive belts and localized areas of pelagic sediments composed in excess of 50% by weight of opaline skeletal remains are found at depths below the compensation point for calcite stability in the oceans. Lower percentages of skeletal opals are found at all oceanic depths, indicating a lack of opal compensation depth. Comparison of the opal volumes in the standing crop, estimated as 8×10^{10} to 1.6×10^{17} tons and in suspension above as well as in the pelagic sediments, indicates dissolution losses in the course of settling opaline skeletons of $\frac{1}{20}$ to $\frac{1}{50}$ of the initial supply (Lisitzin, 1971). The annual opal accumulations on the sea floor are estimated to amount to 3×10^8 tons. As shown in Fig. 7, there are two other opal-precipitating groups of organisms

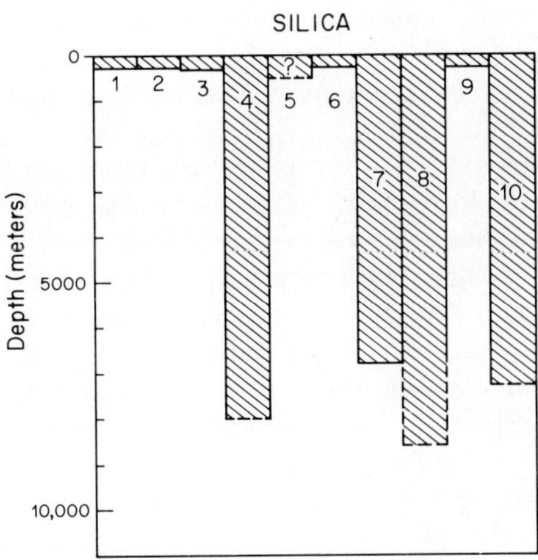

Fig. 7. Opal precipitating agents and their known depth ranges. (1) Diatoms; (2) silicoflagellates; (3) ebridians; (4) radiolarians; (5) foraminifera; (6) Sclerospongia; (7) Hyalispongia; (8) Demospongia; (9) acmaeid and patellid gastropods; (10) lepetidian gastropods.

that have wide distribution in space and in depth in the oceans. The first includes the sponges with opaline spicules, which have been traced to 7000 m depth in the Hyalispongia and 8500 m depth for the Demospongia (Lévi, 1964; Wolff, 1970). Siliceous spicules have been located also in a number of shoal water Sclerospongia (Hartman and Goreau, 1969). The second group is represented by the gastropod superfamily, Patellacea, where opal is precipitated in their mature teeth, and is found further in two families as plates in the radular sheath (Lowenstam, 1971). The species of two of the families (Acmaeidae and Patellidae) have large populations on rocky shores of the intertidal zone and smaller ones in the subtidal shallow waters, whereas the third family, Lepetidae, have, on the average, small populations that range from subtidal shallow water to depths of 6850 m (Knudsen, 1964). Spicules of silica sponges are commonly encountered in bathyal and abyssal sediments and locally have been reported as major constituents in patches bordering the equatorial belt of radiolarian oozes (Lisitzin, 1971). There are as yet no estimates of the volume of silica fixation, the standing crop of sponges nor of the volume contributed to the sediments. In the case of the patellacean gastropods, minimum estimates of the amount of opal in the standing crop on a worldwise basis gives values of 6.5×10^6 g, and 4×10^7 g contributed annually to the shoal water sediments by the anterior teeth and tooth bases, which are continuously shed (Lowenstam, 1971). More realistic estimates would likely double the volumes of the silica in the standing crop and that contributed to the sediments. In the Sclerospongia, the siliceous spicules, incorporated into the aragonitic skeletons in the process of growth, become dissolved. There is the possibility that all or most of the opal from gastropod teeth, transferred to the nearshore sediments, may be dissolved also by the silica-depleted surface waters. If this should turn out to be the case, the silica skeletally fixed by these and other silica-precipitating organisms would undergo a rapid turnover in shallow subtidal waters of the shelf areas. If not, the volume of silica deposition from biologic sources in marine sediments would be slightly in excess of that estimated in pelagic sediments from data based on diatom, silicoflagellates, and radiolarian skeletons alone. The recent discovery that silicon is temporarily enriched in preosseous tissues of mammals may indicate that silicon may be widely involved in vital processes, not only in diatoms, but in a wide array of biochemical systems that do not precipitate silica in their hard parts. As advocated by several investigators, there is by now little doubt that the silica distribution in seawater passes through biologic systems and today is principally, if not entirely, controlled by biologic processes rather than by inorganic processes (Harriss, 1966; Calvert, 1968; Lisitzin, 1971).

Phosphates are a basic requirement of life as nutrients of primary producers and a variety of vital processes of the consumers in the food chain. In the photic zone of the oceans, this accounts for the low average phosphate concentrations in seawater and the well-known seasonal variations that are roughly inversely proportional to the standing crops of its phytoplankton populations. The highest phosphate concentrations in the sea are found largely in a narrow segment of the water column in the subphotic zone, indicating rapid turnover of a major fraction of the organically bound phosphorus by plants and animals through rapid degradation from the photic zone of the organically bound phosphates by the animal populations in the surface waters. Estimates on the phosphate content of the oceans as a whole suggest that it is 100 times greater than the amounts annually tied up in the phytoplankton populations. The volume of their uptake exceeds the input of phosphate from external sources, and loss to sediments has to be regenerated by recycling of degraded organic matter (Emery et al., 1955). Calculations suggest that the waters of the Pacific Ocean are saturated or supersaturated with reference to the carbonate apatite mineral, dahllite (Kramer, 1964). There is also a tieup of phosphate in the inorganic fraction of hard tissues in marine animals. It has long been established that skeletal hard parts of most marine fishes and marine mammals are strengthened by the carbonate apatite mineral, dahllite (summarized by Vinogradov, 1953). More recently, it has been shown that the phosphate in the enamel of the teeth and skin denticles of sharks and the shells of some inarticulate brachiopods is a fluorine-bearing phase of carbonate apatite, called francolite (McConnell, 1963; Büttner, 1966).

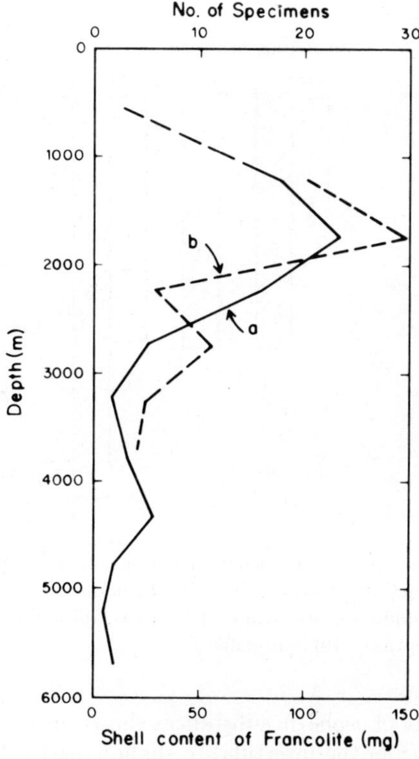

Fig. 8. Francolite contents (in milligrams) of *P. atlanticus* shells in number of specimens: (*a*) from 500-m depth intervals per dredge haul in all oceans; (*b*) per square meter on seafloor bordering Antarctica. Data minus francolite contents from Zezina (1964).

Remains of skeletal debris of fishes have been reported from shallow water and pelagic sediments (Murray, 1897; Helms and Riedel, 1971). Francolite-bearing shells and shell fragments of the cosmopolitan deep-water brachiopod *Pelagiodiscus atlanticus* have been located in pelagic sediments recovered in dredge hauls (Zezina, 1964) (Fig. 8). Identifiable fish remains, principally of teeth, are known to be common in most types of pelagic sediments and have been traced back in them through geologic time to the Cretaceous (Helms and Riedel, 1971). Comminuted debris of skeletal phosphates, assigned to fish, but possibly derived from other biologic sources, has also been reported from pelagic sediments (Arrhenius, unpublished). These data are significant in that they show that some of the phosphate taken up from seawater by the primary producers in the photic zone is being lost to the sediments through links in the food chain that precipitate crystalline carbonate apatites in their hard tissues.

Figure 9 shows the mineralogic forms of the phosphates presently known to strengthen hard parts in marine organisms, the groups of organisms that are the precipitating agents of each of the kinds of phosphatic substances and the known depth ranges of the precipitating agents. The inorganic precipitation products are divided into three groups, crystalline compounds, amorphous calcium phosphates, and amorphous ferric phosphatic hydrogels. There are some species that precipitate in one hard tissue site calcium phosphate and in another ferric phosphatic hydrogels (Sternaspidae). Furthermore, there are some classes where some species harden homologous hard tissues by francolite and others by amorphous ferric phosphatic hydrogels (Chitons). In one annelid species among the Serpulidae, certain collar cells enclose two different crystalline carbonate apatites, of which one is dahllite and the other is a calcium magnesium phosphate (Neff, 1971). (The latter is not shown on the graph, Fig. 9.)

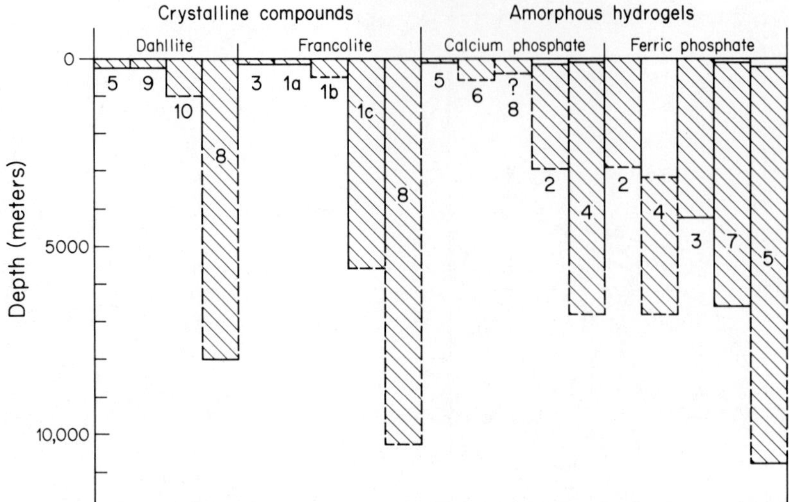

Fig. 9. Organisms precipitating phosphatic substances and their depth distributions. (1–3) Inarticulate brachiopods: (1a) *Lingula*, Discinisca sp., (1b) *Glottidia* sp., (1c) *P. atlanticus*; (2) annelid: *Sternaspis* sp.; (3) chitons; (4) cephalaspidian gastropods; (5) bivalves; (6) arthropods; (7) molpadian holothurians; (8) fish; (9) reptiles; (10) mammals.

Among the precipitating agents of the different phosphatic substances shown in the graph, seven are bathymetrically known only from the intertidal to shallow bathyal zones. Numerically, this is more commonly the case among biologic agents that precipitate crystalline compounds than among those that synthesize amorphous hydrogels. Seven biologic groups with phosphatic hard parts extend bathymetrically into waters of the abyssal zone in excess of 3000 m; of these, three range into the ultraabyssal or hadal zone. Hesitation to state categorically that these two groups alone are the most important agents of phosphate fixation in the hard parts in the sea stems from lack of adequate data on the abundance of several invertebrate groups that are known to occur in all oceans to depths of at least 3000 m, and some to nearly 11,000 m. These groups include the Molpadiidae among the holothurians, the Sternaspidae among polychaete worms, and the Cephalaspidae among the gastropods. Better data exist for a common cosmopolitan constituent of bathyal to abyssal depths, found largely along the borders of continents, islands, and seamounts. This is the inarticulate brachiopod species, *Pelagiodiscus atlanticus* (Zezina, 1965). There are still others of the groups listed where their distributional abundance cannot be assessed at present, or where they are known only locally from limited areas and their significance in this context has not been considered. The inarticulate brachiopod species of the genus *Glottidia* is a case in point. A survey of the distribution of *G. alba* was made on the mainland shelf off Southern California (Jones and Barnard, 1963). Recovery of this species from about half the number of stations (382) sampled between Point Conception and Northern Baja California, Mexico amounted to 10,142 individuals.

The lack of reliable data on the world populations of the groups that are involved in hard-tissue fixation of phosphatic compounds severely limits a meaningful estimate of the magnitude of their effects on the phosphate contents of seawater and on the volume of loss to the bottom sediments. There are further questions about the fate of biologically tied up phosphate in crystalline compounds of inhabitants of shallow waters and of those in phosphatic hydrogels at any depth, once transferred to the bottom sediments.

Attempts have been made here to estimate grossly the volumes of fixation and of the sediment contribution of some groups involved in hard-part fixation of phosphates, where some data on population density per square meter exist. Where the groups of organisms are worldwide in distribution through the oceans, as in the case of fish, or concentrated primarily in the intertidal to shallow subtidal zone of nearly all rocky shores, such as chitons, calculations of average minimum volumes of tieup and loss of phosphates for all oceans have been carried out here. Similar estimates for groups with worldwide but discontinuous distributions among annelids, brachiopods, gastropods, and holothurians had to be limited either to their average bathymetric range in the oceans, local vertical profile, or limited bottom areas. For most members of the cephalaspidian gastropods, data on population densities in space and depth are so inadequate that it seemed advisable to present in almost all cases only weights of the phosphatic hard parts for single individuals from different depths, presented to convey the possible significance of this group once better information becomes available on standing crops for inclusion in future calculations of the phosphate budget in the sea.

The annual production of fish (fresh weight) in the sea has been estimated by Schaeffer (1965) to amount to about 2×10^{13} to 2.3×10^{13} g by Graham and Edwards (1965) (of bony fish only) and 2.4×10^{13} g by Ryther (1969). Let us take Ryther's estimate and assume that the phosphorus content given by Hutchinson (1952) for the annual fish harvest is based essentially on the mineral content of the hard parts. One then finds that fishes tie up annually about 2.4×10^{11} g/P, which is equivalent to about 3.2×10^{11} g of dahllite. No data could be found on the biomass of marine mammals to estimate their volume of phosphorus fixation.

Considering the chitons, the phosphatic compounds precipitated in their mature major lateral teeth consist, as noted earlier, in warm temperature to tropical species of francolite and in the colder water range of an amorphous ferric phosphatic hydrogel. Taking an average-size chiton and assuming 30 individuals per square meter in the intertidal zone of rocky shores in the warm water and 10 in cold water with 3 m in depth of intertidal exposure normal to the shore line, and finally assuming that one-half of the estimated detailed shore lines of the continents and islands are about five times greater than the linearly estimated values, one arrives at a value of 4.5×10^{8} g of francolite in the standing crops of chitons of the warmer waters and 5.6×10^{7} g of their iron phosphate hydrogel fraction in the colder water on a worldwide basis. A chiton studied in detail (Nesson, 1968) shed daily 0.5 to 0.7 tooth rows. This is equivalent to an average unabraded tooth per day. Making the same assumptions for the standing crop, one arrives at an annual loss of shed teeth of 2.5×10^{9} g of francolite and 2.0×10^{8} g of ferric phosphatic hydrogel to the sediments.

For the cosmopolitan bathyal to abyssal inarticulate brachiopod, *P. atlanticus*, Zezina (1964) summarized data from the USSR and earlier expeditions on the distribution depth ranges of this species, numbers of live specimens taken per dredge haul, and dead shells recovered per square meter. We have studied the biogeochemistry, mineralogy, and weights of limited numbers of the mineral fraction in shells from depths of 1480 m to 5160 m. An average-size shell was determined to contain 5 mg of francolite. Figure 8 is a graph published by Zezina on the depth distributional abundance of *P. atlanticus* from dredge hauls per square meter, to which we have added a coordinate on average shell weights in milligrams of francolite for estimating its volume by the number of individuals at different depths. Converting the average numbers of live individuals reported at different depth intervals, francolite is precipitated in excess of 100 mg between depths of 1500 to 2000 m, 200 to 250 mg between 1500 to 2500 m, and about 25 mg at depths greater than 3500 m. Stations where live specimens were recovered are located at the foot of continents, islands, and seamounts. We have also obtained live specimens from transported cobbles and from manganese nodules between 1500 and 3500 m depth. The discontinuous distribution, controlled by the availability of hard substrates, and the variability in population sizes, a function of available food, make it hazardous at this stage of limited knowledge to estimate the volume of francolite tied up by the standing crop in the oceans as a whole. Dead shells per square meter ranged on the average from 12 to 76 shells or 60 to 380 mg of francolite per square meter. The largest number of dead shells was found at the foot of seamounts, with the largest haul near a seamount containing 480 shells, equivalent to 2.4 g of francolite. Dead shells were commonly found at depths in excess of those for living individuals. The greatest depth at which dead shells were recovered in the Indian Ocean was 5300 m, and in the Pacific, 5800 m. These data are important in that they show that phosphate, originally tied up from seawater, is lost to the sediments in the form of francolite, even though we cannot yet estimate the total volume of loss for reasons pointed out concerning the standing crop of this deep-water species. The maximum depth at which dead shells have been found preserved further indicates that in the Indian Ocean the waters are saturated, if not supersaturated to at least 5300 m, and in the equatorial Pacific to at least 5800 m depths. The greatest depth at which phosphatic fish remains were recovered was 5550 m in the Pacific, which falls within the range of the recorded maximum depths for dead shells of *P. atlanticus*.

Sampling of the benthic communities on the mainland shelf of Southern California provides some data on the abundance of some of the other groups of organisms that precipitate phosphatic minerals in the form of the crystalline phase, francolite and amorphous, hydrous calcium and ferric phosphates in localized hard parts (Barnard and Hartman, 1959; Jones and Barnard, 1963; Barnard, Jones, and Hartman, 1965). The phosphate precipitating agents, for which some data on abundance per 0.2 to 0.25 m^2 per station were recorded, include the inarticulate brachiopod, *Glottidia albida*, the polychaete worm, *Sternaspis fossor*, samples of cephalaspidia, gastropods of the genus *Cylichna* and the holothurian, *Molpadia intermedia*. With the exception of *G. albida*, they are representatives of phosphate-precipitating groups, which are widely but discontinuously represented by different species in all oceans recorded to depths of 3000 m to nearly 7000 m (Wolff, 1960, 1970). To gain a gross measure of the volume of the phosphatic minerals that is tied up in standing crops and possibly transferred postmortem to marine sediments, the data obtained for these organisms from the Southern California survey are tabulated in Table I. Column 1 gives the names of the species; column 2 gives the number of stations where the samples were sorted and species identified; column 3 gives the number of stations where a particular species was found; column 4 gives the average number of individuals per species recalculated to a surface area of 1 square meter; column 5 gives the average number of individuals from all stations where sorting of the benthic organisms either showed or did not show the presence of a given phosphate-precipitating species; column 6 gives the phosphatic substances precipitated by the species listed; column 7 gives the average weights of the hard-part minerals of the individuals found per square meter for stations where they were found; and column 8 gives average weight for all stations sampled, including those where the species was absent.

The data indicate that the representatives of the holothurians far outstrip all other agents among those listed in Table I in terms of phosphate fixation. Considering that the other species with lesser volume fixation of phosphate are similarly worldwide in distribution, they must be included in the consideration of future calculations of the biologic fixation of phosphates in hard-parts by the marine biomass in toto. These must take into account that (1) the holothurians precipitate markedly lower volumes of ferric phosphatic granules in their body wall with increase in depth occupation, and (2) the cephalaspidians with mineralized gizzard plates that contain phosphates, usually in the form of calcium phosphatic and less commonly ferric phosphatic amorphous hydrogels, differ widely in the amounts of the phosphates tied up by adult individuals in different species. Our data show that the phosphatic compound in the gizzard plates range from 0.06 mg per individual to 1 g per individual, depending on the species. Our samples come from surface waters to depths up to 5400 m. As in the holothurian, Molpadiidae, there is a gross tendency toward decrease in size and volume fixation of phosphatic compounds in the cephalaspidian gizzard plates with increase in depth.

Placing them in perspective, the data show that hard tissue fixation of phosphatic substances is more widespread among marine animals, more diversified in mineralogic forms, and encompasses a larger volume than was thought in the past. Loss of skeletally-derived crystalline phosphate minerals to pelagic sediments has been extended from fish to a deep-water brachiopod (*P. atlanticus*). Estimates on volumes of phosphate minerals contained in the standing crops of various groups of animals, except for the chitons, are limited to small areas. They focus attention on the need for extensive quantitative surveys of this sort for all oceans. There is the added question of the postmortem fate of the mineral precipitates in crystalline form in sediments on the shelves, and for the amorphous, hydrous phases, in general. The concept that the phosphate cycle in the sea is affected by organisms through skeletal fixation processes is materially strengthened for standing crops and pathways of loss to the sediments, but the magnitude of the effect remains to be determined.

Biologic processes have been shown to affect the iron contents, principally the particulate fraction, in seawater through uptake in vital processes in the food chain of the upper layers of the sea. Incorporation of the iron in organic compounds in the food chain assures rapid turnover in the shallower parts of the oceans (Goldberg, 1952, 1965; Lewis and Goldberg, 1954; Riley, 1965). We have called attention here to the precipitation of iron compounds among the inorganic constituents of the hard tissues in a variety of forms among species of a number of invertebrate classes.

Iron occurs in the sea in dissolved, colloidal, and particulate forms. Colloidal and particulate iron is taken up by phytoplankton populations, particularly in the diatoms, stimulates their growth, and has been indicated as a limiting factor of their standing crop. The iron transferred from the phytoplankton through the food chain is involved in a variety of vital processes in herbivores and carnivores. Iron is incorporated in organic compounds and, hence, it appears that there is rapid turnover of this ionic species in the upper layers of the oceans and likely to a lesser degree to depths occupied in daytime by the organisms that make up the "scatter layer."

It has been noted above that iron is also incorporated in the inorganic constituents of hard-parts in species of several invertebrate phyla. The iron occurs in the form of crystalline compounds, a variety of amorphous, hydrous phases of which many are ferric phosphates. These hard-tissue precipitates signify a greater diversity in pathways and localization of biologic iron fixation, a wider range of precipitating agents, and a more extensive volume of iron incorporation into biologic systems in the sea. Most important, the iron-bearing compounds include mineralogic forms that are

Table I

Weight Percentages of Phosphatic Substances in Hard Parts of Some Marine Invertebrates Calculated for Individuals per square meter

Species	Number of Stations Sampled	Number of Stations Where Species Was Found	Average Number of Individuals Collected per Square Meter of Surface Area for All Stations Where Individuals Were Found	Mean Number of Individuals per Square Meter for All Stations With or Without Individuals	Mineralogy of Principle Hard Parts	Weight Percent Average of Mineral Content per Square Meter: Where Found	Weight Percent Average of Mineral Content per Square Meter: For All Stations Sampled
Glottidia albida	382[a]	189	54	21	Francolite	~140 mg[b]	~54 mg[b]
Sternaspis fossor		5[c]	16	—	Amorphous ferric-phosphate hydrogel	40 mg	—
	352[d]	160[d]	29	13	Amorphous ferric-phosphate hydrogel	72.5 mg	32.5 mg
		6[d]	~14	—		~35 mg	—
Cylichna sp.	9[d]	8[d]	~18	~16	Amorphous calcium-phosphate hydrogel	~470 mg	~320 mg
Molpadia intermedia	12[c]	5	5.6	2.3	Ferric-phosphate hydrogel	25 g	10 g
	315[e]	63	6.2	1		28 g	4.5 g

[a] Jones and Barnard (1963).
[b] Estimates of average size and weight of shell minerals from data in Jones and Barnard (1963).
[c] Barnard and Hartman (1959) Santa Barbara shelf area.
[d] Barnard, Jones, and Hartman (1965) for shelf sampling from within Baja California to Point Conception.
[e] Ibid., from stations with Echinoderm samples that had been sorted and *M. intermedia* was counted per 0.25 m^2.

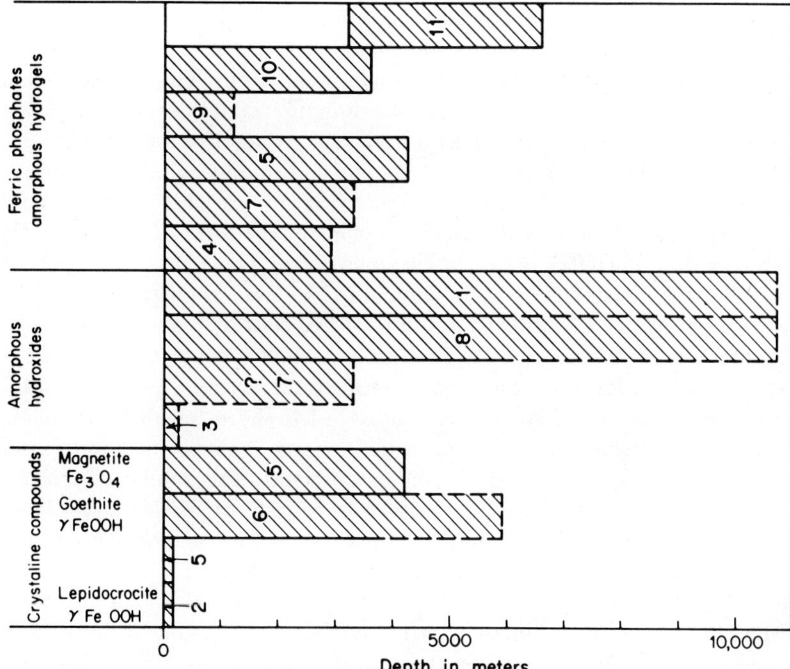

Fig. 10. Organisms precipitating iron oxides and iron-rich phosphatic substances and their known depth distributions. (1) Foraminifera; (2) sponges; (3) polychaete norms; (4) Annelida: *Sternaspis* div. sp.; (5) chitons; (6) patellacean gastropods; (7) cephalaspidean gastropods; (8) bivalves; (9–11) genera of molpadian holothurians.

known to occur in marine sediments where their formation has been attributed to inorganic processes. Hence, there is the possibility that a biologically precipitated fraction of these minerals may be transferred to the marine deposits.

To determine the role played by these hard-tissue precipitates of iron compounds on the iron budget in the oceans, one would like to know the total spectrum of their precipitating agents, their standing crops, and volume of fixation and turnover rates of the iron in the precipitated compounds. Figure 10 shows the present state of our knowledge of the "mineralogic" forms in which the iron is tied up, the groups of organisms in which they have been located, and their known depth ranges. A total of 11 taxonomic groups are shown to be involved in the fixation of iron-bearing compounds. Of these, four precipitate crystalline iron oxide minerals in the range from the intertidal zone to a maximum depth of nearly 7000 m. Amorphous ferric hydrogels have been located in four groups, of which two are known to range in depth to the deepest trenches in the oceans. The remaining groups of organisms, which include some that also synthesize crystalline iron oxide minerals or ferric phosphatic hydrogels, range from the surface waters to a maximum depth of 6600 m.

As far as is known at present, chitons and patellacean gastropods have large populations in the intertidal and shallow subtidal zones on rocky bottoms of all oceans and small populations, ranging to depths between 4000 to almost 7000 m. Species of the holothurian family, Molpadiidae, and of the polychaete genus, *Sternaspis*, are known to be cosmopolitan in their distribution in the oceans, the former with known precipitates of iron phosphate hydrogels to a maximum depth of 6200 m and the latter to nearly 3000 m. There is only scant information on their population sizes, but these suggest that the amounts of iron tied up in their hard tissues may be sizable once better data become available on their worldwide populations. Large local populations are indicated also for species of the other ferric oxide mineral and iron phosphate-precipitating agents, but no data exist on their worldwide distribution.

There are some data on the average size of the chiton and patellacean populations per square meter in the intertidal zone of rocky shores. In chitons, the iron in the mature major lateral teeth, as noted earlier, exists in the form of magnetite (Fe_3O_4) plus lepidocrocite (γFeOOH) or an amorphous ferric phosphate hydrogel. In the Patellacea, the iron occurs in the tooth enamel in the form of goethite (αFeOOH). In both groups of mollusca, the anterior tooth rows are continuously shed and approximate rates of daily tooth loss are known for some of their species. The amounts of iron have been determined for a few individuals of medium-sized chitons and patellacean gastropods. Let us assume that half of the detailed shore lines of continents and islands have a rocky substrate and have on the average 3 square meters of intertidal exposure. Based on these assumptions, one can estimate the volume of fixation and the turnover rates of iron in the inorganic compounds of chiton and patellacean gastropod teeth. The calculations indicate that the volume of fixation of iron on a worldwide basis in the standing crop of chitons amounts to 2.7×10^8 g and of the patellaceans to 1.17×10^9 g, totalling 1.4×10^9 g. The annual loss of iron to the sea through shedding of teeth in chitons is estimated to amount to 3.9×10^9 g, and from patellaceans to 3.3×10^{10} g, totalling about 3.72×10^{10} g.

In species of the holothurian family, Molpadiidae, it was noted earlier that the body wall contains amorphous, hydrous iron phosphatic granules in varying concentrations, depending on the depth at which they live. The largest individuals and the largest concentrations of these granules are found in species in the near-surface waters to about 300 m in depth. In *Molpadia intermedia*, which is common off the West coast of the Americas, adult individuals contain by weight 4.5 g of these granules. A survey in the bay off Santa Barbara, California, to a depth of about 100 m, found in samples taken from a surface area of 0.25 square meters large individuals of this species in 9 out of 27 stations, dominated by *Listriolobus* communities (Barnard and Hartman, 1959). Taking the number of individuals listed for only four stations, given an average of 1.5 individuals per square meter, assuming an average of 4.5 g of granules per individual, and an iron content of about 30% by weight, the total amount of iron tied up in the granules by *M. intermedia* is about 2.1 g/square meters.

The same report contains data also on the number of *Sternaspis fossor* individuals taken from four stations, each on bottoms "subdominated" by immature *Listriolobus pelodes* communities and from four additional stations where *Molpadia intermedia* were recovered. The average number of *Sternaspis* specimens in the first named habitat was found to be 48 individuals, whereas in the latter there were close to two individuals per square meter. The sternal shields of an individual of this species are mineralized by an amorphous ferric phosphatic hydrogel, chemically similar to that of *M. intermedia* (Lowenstam, 1972). The mineralization product of these shields for averaged-size individuals from Southern California waters weigh on the average 2.5 mg, of which 0.75 mg are represented by iron. Hence, the volume of iron in the precipitated shields of the standing crop of *S. fossor* amounts, in the habitat with two individuals per square meter to 0.75 mg, and in that with 48 individuals to 34.5 mg. These data on local population densities of *Molpadia intermedia* and *Sternaspis fossor* are so limited that it is impossible to estimate the volume of fixation in the standing crops of the Molpadiidae and *Sternaspis* species on a worldwide basis in the oceans. The same is true for the remaining groups of organisms shown in Fig. 10, which in single individuals tie up iron in the range from five to several hundred milligrams, as no data exist at all on their population densities even in limited areas per square meter. Another unknown is the volume of iron precipitation by bacteria in the sea. There are some data to indicate that trace amounts of iron are tied up also in the mineral phases, calcite and aragonite, of calcareous skeletons in species of many phyla, and similarly in those with carbonate apatite hard parts. The values for iron reported are in part for total dry matter of the organisms or given as oxides, combined with aluminum (reviewed in Vinogradov, 1953).

Another unknown at present is the postmortem fate of the biologically-precipitated iron oxide minerals and amorphous iron and iron phosphatic hydrogels, and of the iron incorporated in carbonate and carbonate apatite skeletons. Considering the crystalline iron oxide minerals, magnetite, goethite, and lepidocrocite, individual crystals have, as investigated so far, less than 1 μ to slightly more than 1 μ diameters. Once exfoliated, through degradation of their organic matrices, the magnetite fraction may be oxidized to ferric oxide and all of these iron oxide crystals could be, depending on the burial environment, either stabilized in the sediments or incorporated or absorbed by clay minerals, organic matter, or recycled through ingestion by deposit feeders. If preserved in their original state, their presence in the mineralogic analyses of the submicroscopic fraction of marine sediments would be readily recognized, and similarly their biologic derivation, since their crystal habits, as determined by the constituents of the organic matrices in the teeth, differ from those of inorganic origin (Towe and Lowenstam, 1967; Lowenstam, unpublished data). The hydrous phases of iron oxides and iron phosphates remain to be determined also. If stabilized, they may not have been recognized in the sediments in the past as they are in an amorphous state.

All of the presently known agents with hard-part precipitates of iron or iron phosphate are benthic organisms that are either grazers, filter feeders, or deposit feeders. The total volume of fixation of iron in their hard parts remains to be determined, but it is clear from the few data on partial fixation of their iron contents that their widespread occurrence must be taken into account in considering pathways, recycling rates, and possibly at least local effects on the colloidal and particulate fractions of the iron contents of seawater. Very few vertical profiles of iron concentrations have been extended to the waters close to the ocean floors. Those that exist indicate more commonly a slight increase of the total soluble and particulate iron, while a few show a decrease. Without data on the standing crops of the benthic community segments that deposit iron minerals in their hard parts, these data cannot be evaluated in terms of their possible influence on the iron contents of the near-bottom waters. Quantitative studies, taking into account the iron concentrations in both the organisms and environmental waters, should aid in clarifying possibly existing relationships. The need for more data is indicated on the kinds and sources of iron-bearing compounds in the biomass, in sediments, of the concentrations of colloidal and particulate iron in porewaters of sediments and in the waters in contact and close to the ocean bottoms to aid in clarifying the questions raised.

Barium is known from the granellae of the Xenophyophoriidae (Rhizipodae, Protozoa) where it occurs in the form of barite crystals ($BaSO_4$), and as a trace constituent of skeletal carbonate, phosphate, and $SrSO_4$ minerals from many marine organisms. It is considered possible that the high barium contents of localized water masses and their increase with depth in the Pacific and Indian Oceans may be tied up with the dissolution phenomena of biogenic organic matter and minerals in their transfer from the surface waters to the deep sea. The apparent lack of correlation of high organic productivity in the surface waters with localized high barium concentrations of the deeper waters raises questions concerning the magnitude of biologic effects on the barium distribution in marine waters as compared to those from inorganic processes (Turekian and Johnson, 1966).

Arrhenius (unpublished) reported 700 ppm of barium from a composite sample of calcitic tests of common pelagic foraminifera, which are major constituents of deep-sea carbonate accumulations on the ocean floors. He further found 5400 ppm of barium in the $SrSO_4$ skeletons of pelagic acantharid radiolarians and in the carbonate apatite minerals of fish debris in recent pelagic sediments. Arrhenius was the first to report that barite crystals, which are common in certain pelagic sediments, initially have a central hole, which becomes progressively filled in with barite. Earlier reports had indicated that barite crystals are concentrated in the granellae of xenophyophorids (Schulze and Thierfelder, 1905). Arrhenius and coworkers (unpublished) confirmed by means of modern techniques that the barite crystals concentrated in the granellae of a deep-water sample of the xenophyophorids are similar in shape to those found in pelagic sediments. However, he favored the view that the crystals in the sediments were of inorganic origin. In a comprehensive treatment of the xenophyophorids, Tendal (1972) showed that members of this group have been found in all oceans from the littoral to the hadal zone (at least to 7700 m). The samples made available to Tendal suggest that this group is poorly represented in the Atlantic and around Antarctica, but as he points out, specimens that could have been reduced by sample treatment to unrecognizable fragments commonly remained unidentified as sponge remains. According to Tendal, the concentration, as well as release of large numbers of the barite crystals from the plasma of the xenophyophorids and, when checked, the paucity of the crystal in proximity to individuals, strongly suggest that the barite crystals are precipitated by them. Our studies of the previously unknown precipitation of amorphous calcium and ferric phosphatic hydrogels in gizzard plates of cephalaspidian gastropods show that average barium concentrations in the range from 0.1 to as high as 4.0% by weight occur in the nonhydrous fractions of the plates in samples of five specimens recovered from the subtropical to abyssal depths (3500 m) (Lowenstam, 1972, unpublished to date). Values of 0.1 to 0.2% by weight of barium were determined also for the nonhydrous fraction of the amorphous ferric-phosphatic hydrogels of the sternal shields from shallow water species of the polychaete genus *Sternaspis* in samples from all oceans and similarly in the ferric phosphatic bodies of deep-sea holothurian species *Ceraplectana trachyderma*, taken at depths of 3800 and 6600 m (Lowenstam, unpublished).

These data indicate that appreciable amounts of barium are incorporated in carbonate and phosphatic skeletal minerals of planktonic, nectonic, and benthic animal groups from the surface waters to depths close to 8000 m. Of the organisms noted, the pelagic foraminifera should have a noticeable effect on the barium distribution in seawater despite the low average value of about 900 ppm in the calcite of their tests. Increased selective dissolution of settling tests from the surface waters toward the compensation depths for calcite should release progressively greater barium concentrations to the water column with increase in depths, whereas the surviving fractions of the tests, which accumulate on the ocean floor, should lead to loss of barium to the sediments. The complete dissolution of the barium-rich tests of the acantharid radiolarians, suspended at regular intervals for a period of months to a depth of 5000 m by Berger (1967), points to another transfer agent of biogenically fixed barium to the water column with increase in depth in the Pacific and Indian

Oceans. The low barium contents of the skeletal hard parts of bathypelagic fishes and shallow water fish debris (6 to 75 ppm of Ba) versus the high concentrations reported in pelagic fish debris (5000 ppm) may indicate scavenging of barium from the bottom waters in the deep sea by the biologically precipitated carbonate apatite skeletal debris.

Of the remaining groups noted to concentrate or contain high barium contents, the Xenophyophoria are of particular interest. The dramatic increase in our knowledge of their spatial and depth distribution in the oceans by Tendal (1972) would suggest that they may be common constituents of the benthic communities in the oceans. If it can be uniquely shown that the accumulation of the barite crystals in their granellae are precipitated by these organisms, they may turn out to be a major biologic extracting agent of barium from seawater and a major contributor of barite to marine sediments. Determination of their distribution relations to pelagic sediments high in barite content and in turn to areas where the bottom waters show anomalous high barium concentrations should be of particular interest. Concerning the amorphous phosphatic hydrogels, data are needed on their stability relations in sediments in relation to sediment types and depth, the distribution and population densities of the species known to precipitate barium, and further search for others likely to be present before their possible role in the barium cycle can be properly assessed.

There is increasing evidence that fluorine is incorporated in the mineral fraction of hard parts by a wide range of marine organisms. Fluorite has been positively identified as the sole hardening agent of the statoliths of mysid species from the suborder, Mysida, and as a major inorganic constituent of the gizzard plates of some cephalospidian gastropods (Lowenstam and McConnell, 1968). The fluorite-bearing statoliths of mysids are discarded in the molts as often as 40 times during the lifetime of the individual. This indicates that some biologic systems have a highly efficient fluorine transport system to enable them to concentrate and stabilize as well as discard this ionic species in the form of fluorite. As shown in Table II, 9 to 20% of fluorine is found in the spicules of certain nudibranch gastropods. The inorganic constituent containing these high fluorine concentrations is an amorphous hydrous, calcium-rich substance that requires further structural characterization. Biologic carbonate apatite minerals are shown to contain from 0.13 to nearly 4% of fluorine by weight. Of these, the values in the range of 2.0 to 4% are found only in the mineral phase, francolite. Amorphous calcium phosphatic hydrogels, precipitated by species of the gastropod genus, *Philine*, have fluorine contents of 0.4 to 1.4%. The biogenic carbonates, as shown by recent fluorine determination for some groups (Carpenter, 1969), contain on the average from 280 to about 900 ppm of this ionic species, of which the higher volumes were found in the aragonitic phase.

The question to what extent biologic fixation of fluorine in the inorganic fraction of hard parts may affect the marine geochemistry of this ionic species has been investigated recently by Carpenter (1969). The principal agents of mass fixation and postmortem transfer of carbonate to geologic sediments are coccolithophorids and pelagic foraminifera. Carpenter calculated that they transfer annually 4.0×10^{11} g of fluorine from seawater to the sediments. The annual transfer rate of fluorine in calcium phosphatic minerals of fish and taken up by phosphorite nodules was considered to equal about 2.0×10^{11} g fluorine. No data were presented on the fluorine contents of fish skeletons and on their fraction of the calculated volume of phosphates annually lost to the ocean floors. Phosphorite nodules are generally found on the continental shelf and the shallower parts of continental slopes (Bezrukow et al., 1961). Kolodny and Kaplan (1970) reported that the nodules they examined from the Atlantic,

TABLE II

Fluorine Contents of Skeletal Minerals from Marine Organisms

Biologic Group	Mineralization Site	Mineral Form	Fluorine Contents	Sources of Information
Gastropods:				
Scaphander div. sp.	Gizzard plates	Fluorite	~49%	Lowenstam and McConnell (1968)
Gastropods:				
Dorids	Spicules	Amorphous Ca, F-bearing substance	9–20%	Ibid.
Brachiopods:				
Lingula div. sp.	Shells	Francolite	2.0–2.4%	McConnell (1963); Rhodes and Bloxom (1971)
Glottidia div. sp.	Shells	Francolite	2.7%	Lowenstam (unpublished)
Pelagiodiscus atlanticus	Shell	Francolite	2.7–3.0%	Lowenstam (1972); and unpublished
Fishes				
Sharks	Durodentin of teeth	Francolite	2.4–3.7%	Büttner (1966)
	Skin denticles	Francolite	2.4%	Lowenstam unpublished
Polyplacophora:				
Chitonidae	Mature teeth	Francolite	2.3%	Lowenstam (1967)

Gastropods:				
Philine div. sp.	Gizzard plates	Amorphous calcium phosphate hydrogel	0.4–1.4%	Lowenstam (1972); and unpublished
Malacostraca:				
Pseudosquilla sp.	Carapace		0.4%	Lowenstam (1972)
Fishes:				
Minus sharks	Ashed bones and scales	Dahllite	0.13–0.14%	Quoted in Vinogradov (1953)
Coelenterates:				
Corals (unidentified)	Skeletons	Aragonite	~900 ppm	Carpenter (1969)
Algae:				
Coccolithophorids div. sp.	Hard parts	Calcite	160–350 ppm	Ibid.
Protista:				
Globigerinidae div. sp.	Tests	Calcite	75–505 ppm	Ibid.
Diatoms, radiolarians siliceous sponge spicules	Hard parts	Opal	8–120 ppm	Ibid.

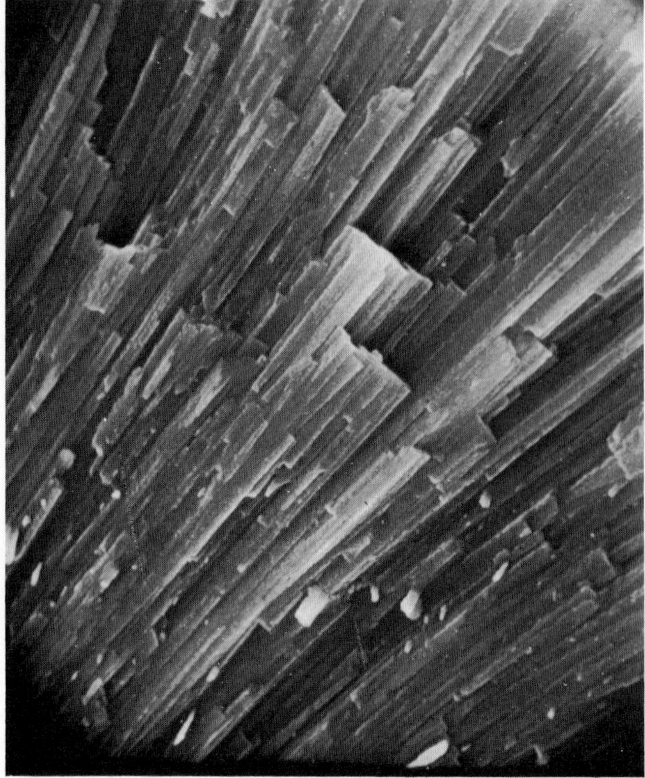

Fig. 11. Scanning electron microscope picture of the shape of the fluorite crystals in the statolith of the mysid *P. flexuosus*. Magnification × 5250.

Pacific, and Indian Oceans showed signs of present-day erosion rather than accretion. Radiometric ages determined by them by U^{234}/U^{238} activity ratios indicated that the nodules had a minimum age of 8×10^5 yr, and were probably older. It was considered possible that some marine phosphorite deposits at low latitudes, not studied by these authors, may be accreting today. If so, the volume of fluorine taken up by marine phosphorites today relative to that by phosphatic minerals in animal skeletons would be greatly reduced as compared to the Tertiary.

Considering the organisms listed in Table II, other biologic agents are indicated as contributors to removal of fluorine to marine sediments. Mysid statoliths, composed of fluorite, were encountered in almost all shelf sediments in the Northwest Pacific (Enbysk and Linger, 1966). Shelf sediments there contained from one to two statoliths and in some areas of known high population densities, five statoliths per gram of dry total samples. An average-sized statolith contains about 0.01 mg of fluorite.

My scanning electron microscope studies of the fluorite crystals in mysid statoliths have shown that they are prevalently acicular in shape with a tendency to taper (Fig. 11). An average-size crystal is tens of microns long and averages 0.1 μ in width. Acicular-shaped, inorganically-precipitated fluorite crystals are exceedingly rare (R. Jahns, personal communication). Hence, it should be possible to determine mysid-derived fluorite crystals in the ultrafine fraction of marine sediments. Such studies would determine whether the shelf and upper continental slope sediments contain a larger fluorite contribution from mysids than indicated by skeletally preserved statoliths. The common encounter of dead shells of the deep-water brachiopod, *P. atlanticus*, in oceanic sediments between 1000 to almost 6000 m was noted earlier. The francolite of their shells contains from 2.7 to 3.0% fluorine by weight. The largest volume of fluorine tied up by dead shells of this species should be found in sediments between 1500 m to 2500 m, averaging about 5 mg fluorine per square meter. A major potential contributor of fluorine to the sediments is the warm water chiton. The volume of fluorine fixation in the mature teeth of the standing crops on a worldwide basis is estimated to amount to 1.0×10^7 g fluorine, and the volume of loss through tooth shedding to the shallow-shelf sediments should yield about 5.8×10^7 g fluorine per year. As noted earlier, the question remains to be answered whether the tooth minerals of the chitons, which include the francolite, become stabilized in shallow-shelf sediments. There are too few data on the other organisms that precipitate phosphatic minerals, as shown in Table II, to determine their volumes of fluorine tie-up in the standing crops and of their postmortem recycling rates.

Aside from the principal carbonate-secreting agents, estimates on the volumetric tie-up of fluorine by the inorganic fractions of the other even major biologic agents involved in the process remain to be determined. The same applies to the question of the total loss of skeletally fixed fluorine to the oceanic sediments. Yet, considering the large standing crops of coccoliths, pelagic foraminifera, chitons, mysids, and fish in the shallower waters of the oceans, one would expect lower fluorine values in the near surface as compared to the deeper waters of the oceans. Some anomalous high fluorine values have been noted from deep waters in local areas (Brewer et al., 1970; Greenhalgh and Riley, 1963). Warner (1971) reported that the F/Cl ratios determined in samples of shallow and deep waters along a traverse from the western Atlantic to the central Pacific was constant. More data are needed on the fluorine distribution in the oceans. All one can say at present is that there is little question that the marine geochemistry of fluorine is affected by incorporation of this ionic species in skeletal mineral precipitates and through their partial loss to sediments. However, the magnitude of the effect remains to be determined, particularly through studies of the submicroscopic fractions of marine sediments.

6. History of Mineralized Hard Parts and Its Implication

The oldest fossils with skeletal hard parts are of early Cambrian age. This indicates that mineralized tissue formation goes back 6.0×10^8 yr. The early Cambrian skeletal remains belong to benthic marine invertebrates ranging from sponges to echinoderms. Their mineralization products as preserved today consist of calcite, quartz, fluorapatite, and ilmenite. The iron titanium oxide mineral, ilmenite, forms the hardening agent of the radular teeth of a mollusc not yet assigned to a particular class (Durham, 1971). It is as yet uncertain whether the ilmenite is a diagenetic alteration product of magnetite as found in the teeth of extant chitons or an original mineralization product. In the case of calcite, crystal habits and fabric studies of the crystals indicate in many groups that this mineral phase was the original precipitation product, whereas in others aragonite may have been present instead. With these qualifications one can show that biologic carbonate, silica, phosphate, and iron oxide mineralization occurred as early as 6.0×10^8 yr ago. Recent studies of Precambrian rocks have yielded unquestionable biologic remains in deposits as old as 3.2×10^9 yr. All of the fossils occur in water-layered deposits. Hence, the organisms were aquatic and inferred to have been marine. 2.0×10^9 to 3.2×10^9 yr-old fossils consist of bacteria, spherical-celled and filamentous blue-green algae, and a variety of unicellular forms of uncertain biologic affinities (Schopf, 1969). The fossils from about 1.4×10^9 to approximately 1.0×10^9 yr show a greater diversity of blue-green algae and possibly include representatives of green algae, fungi, and dinoflagellates, but no animal-type protista. The oldest records of animal life are found in late Precambrian rocks estimated to cover the period between 7.0×10^8 to 6.0×10^8 yr. In the earlier part of this time interval, trails and burrows indicate their presence; in the later part, these trace fossils are associated with detailed body impressions of invertebrates ranging from coelenterates to echinoderms (Glaessner, 1966). Except for two questionable cases, there is no evidence for cell or tissue-confined mineralization sites in fossils older than 6×10^8 yr. The possible exceptions are reported occurrences of fragmentary siliceous sponge spicules in cherts estimated to be between 1.2×10^9 to 1.4×10^9 yr old (Wetzel, 1940) and orderly distributed pits in body impressions of an invertebrate in very late Precambrian deposits, considered by Cloud (1968) to be Eocambrian in age. Glaessner and Daily (1959) and Glaessner (1961) referred these fossils to pennatulid coelenterates and attributed the pits to depressions left by dissolved spicules. There are still questions on the biologic affinities of these fossils (Cloud, 1968) and the origin and meaning of the pits. However, if pennatulid affinities can be confirmed, there is the possibility that the pits were originally the sites of calcitic spicules, as in recent pennatulids, or the spicules may have been composed of a resilient organic compound such as gorgonine. The much older suggested occurrences of siliceous sponge spicules (Wetzel, 1940) is intriguing. If a biologic origin of these siliceous objects can be verified, it would extend the inception of hard-part mineralization by marine organisms past 1.0×10^9 yr and further indicate that silica fixation preceded biologic hard-part fixation by other mineral species by 6×10^8 to 8×10^8 yr.

Although life in the oceans appeared more than 3×10^9 yr ago, only in the last 6.0×10^8 yr did biologic mass fixation of diverse minerals come into existence, an astonishingly recent development. Prior to this event, physicochemical precipitation would appear to have regulated mineral precipitation processes in the sea. There are some indications that organisms may have indirectly participated in and, in some cases, even activated these precipitation processes. Extensive limestone accumulations are found in sedimentary rocks of Precambrian ages ranging as far back as 2.8×10^9 yr. Stromatolithic structures, some still preserving filaments of blue-green algae, are common and in some sequences found throughout huge limestone accumulations (Hoffman, 1967; Glaessner et al., 1969; Schopf, 1969). Present-day blue-green algae form mats and buildups of various shapes by trapping detrital mineral grains on their mucilaginous filaments (Ginsburg, 1955; Logan, 1961). They are not known to precipitate carbonate minerals on their filaments, although claims to the contrary have been made. In areas of restricted circulation in hypersaline environments where they became intertidally exposed, some carbonate may be indirectly precipitated from seawater. There is no conclusive evidence that the blue-green algae in Precambrian time were direct carbonate-precipitating agents. In the absence of biologic mass fixation of carbonate minerals in hard parts, as occurred later, indirect precipitation of carbonate minerals from seawater should have been induced in the Precambrian oceans over shelf areas in the photic zone where the bottoms were densely veneered by blue-green algae due to effects of reduction of pCO_2 by their photosynthetic activity. Prior to effective shielding from ultraviolet radiation by ozone, this process was limited in the photic zone to depths in excess of 10 m, whereas after the ozone shield was formed, it could reach upward into the intertidal zone.

Greenfield (1963) has shown in laboratory cultures that certain bacteria precipitate actively aragonite. Little is known about how many types of bacteria are engaged in this process in the present shelf seas. It is conceivable that since bacteria inhabited the Precambrian oceans, some of them may have been engaged in carbonate fixation from seawater, possibly on a major scale in the absence of the later-evolved competitors in performing this function. Plated out on particulate suspended organic material would have allowed extension of their range to the surface and near-surface waters of the open oceans, where otherwise physicochemical precipitation should have prevailed. Intriguing as a speculation at present, criteria will have to be found to determine whether there is any substance to it.

Bacteria, similar to recent iron-precipitating types, are common in the widespread banded iron formation in the Precambrian prior to 2×10^9 yr. Cloud (1965) visualizes that they were formed in the period of a highly reducing atmosphere, since under these conditions the solubility of the iron becomes greatly enhanced. Ocean water must have been greatly enriched in dissolved iron compared to the present seas. If so, most of its precipitation must have been facilitated by physicochemical processes in the oceans. The origin of the siliceous deposits commonly associated with the banded iron formation is not clear. Most Precambrian fossils have been located in cherts, where they are preserved in three-dimensional form. This suggests that they were engulfed in inorganically-precipitated silica gel. Metabolic waste products, dissolved organic compounds, and organic debris of the organisms may have locally changed the water chemistry to trigger the silica precipitation.

Organismic utilization of phosphate from seawater for vital processes had its modest beginning somewhere in the period between about 3.2×10^9 to about 1.9×10^9 yr ago. Procaryotic organisms that existed during this time interval are interpreted to have shifted gradually from utilizing largely inorganically-formed organic compounds for their energy requirements to primary producers in the form of blue-green algae and bacterial decomposers of their organic remains. The localized oxygen oases postulated to account for the mass precipitation of the banded iron ores suggest marked differences in population densities of oxygen-producing photosynthetic agents and hence limited phosphate utilization by primary producers even in the later part of this period. In the absence of effective shielding by ozone from ultraviolet radiation, the sphere of photosynthetic activity, hence biologic phosphate uptake from seawater, was limited to depths in excess of 10 m in the photic zone. The transition period between roughly 1.9×10^9 yr to 7×10^8 yr shows major advances in biochemical evolution. It is marked initially by the inception of Eucaryotes, implying aside from the ability of cell division, improvement in enzyme chemistry and greater efficiency of photosynthetically-produced free oxygen by a more diversified algal population. This was followed by the inception and rapid diversification of animal life. The higher oxygen yields from photosynthesis led to a gradual yet still slow buildup of the pO_2 in the oceans and in the atmosphere. The initiation and increase in effectiveness of the ozone shield against UV radiation allowed algae and algal consumers to occupy progressively shallower depths in the photic zone. The immediate consequence of these phenomena may have resulted in a noticeable volume increase in phosphate extraction by the primary producers in the photic zone. Rapid recycling of algally-fixed phosphate in the photic zone of the open oceans was likely prior to the inception of multicellular animal life. This is implied by considering that only naked, single-celled algae of minute size, found among Precambrian fossils, would qualify to have been planktonic in habit. In the presence of bacterial decomposers there may have been ample time to degrade slowly sinking cells of low molecular weights within or at a short distance below the photic zone. Prior to the existence of life and even after it came into existence, until photosynthesizing agents evolved, the distribution of phosphate in the oceans must have been fairly uniform, and precipitation of phosphate minerals in the sea was likely entirely controlled by physicochemical processes. The depth stratification in concentration levels of dissolved and particulate phosphate is, in the present oceans, primarily related to primary productivity in the photic zone, and large-scale regeneration from decaying organic matter takes place at shallow depth in the subphotic zone. A modest beginning of depth differentiation in phosphate concentrations in the oceans must have come into existence after photosynthetic organisms and bacterial decomposers originated. Thereafter, as the primary productivity increased, a gradual, greater tie-up of phosphate should have led to progressive lowering of the phosphate concentrations in the photic zone. The fossils, as young as about 1.0×10^9 yr, indicate that the food chain was limited to primary producers and bacterial decomposers. If decomposition of algally derived organic matter occurred in the photic zone and at shallow depth in the subphotic zone, phosphate depletion in the surface waters would have been considerably less than at present and, similarly, enrichment in the shallow subphotic zone may have been less extensive than in the present oceans. A tendency toward enrichment in the shallow subphotic zone might have triggered inorganic mineral precipitation of phosphate minerals that were transferred to the ocean floors. Primary productivity is controlled largely by the availability of nitrogenous compounds. If, as Holland (quoted in Fischer, 1972) suggests, the buildup of nitrate was slow, primary productivity was initially small and may not have reached proportions comparable to that of today, even when the first animal metazoans appeared somewhere between 8.0×10^8 to 7.0×10^8 yr ago. Even then, the magnitude of depletion of phosphate in the surface waters and enrichment in the shallow subphotic zone was likely considerably dampened as compared to today.

These are at best speculations based on inferred functions, efficiencies, and standing crops of Precambrian life. Geijer (1962) investigated the phosphorus contents of sedimentary iron deposits and the distribution of phosphorite deposits through geologic time. In his survey of iron ores, he distinguished between phosphorus percentages of banded and oolithic deposits. The phosphate contents of banded iron ores show an increase from deposits, presumably all of early Precambrian age to early Paleozoic (Ordovician to Devonian) deposits, or an average of 0.02 to an average of 0.25% of phosphorus. Oolitic iron deposits are common in the Phanerozoic but only a few are known from the late Precambrian. The phosphorus content of Phanerozoic deposits show a wide scatter of values. However, the average phosphorus content shows a marked increase from 0.06% in the Precambrian to about 0.7% in the Phanerozoic. Maximum values for the early Paleozoic occurrences are 1.0%, for Mesozoic 1.3% and for Cenozoic 1.7% of phosphorus. Phosphorite nodules are apparently rare in early Precambrian deposits, slightly more common in late Precambrian younger than 1.0×10^9 yr, and common starting with the Cambrian. Geijer relates the phosphorus distribution in iron ores including those of the Precambrian to inorganic precipitation processes possibly aided by decomposition products of organic matter of soft-bodied organisms. Taken on face value, most of the dissolved phosphate bypassed the shallow seas in Precambrian time, suggesting that the deep oceans became the principal sink of phosphatic mineral precipitation.

The data serving for the foregoing interpretations on the marine geochemistry of the Precambrian are based on records of water-layered deposits of which some are considered likely to be shallow-shelf sea records. During the enormous time span preceding biologic mineral precipitation, the initially highly reducing atmosphere enabled life to come into existence, and until biochemical systems evolved that began to produce free oxygen through photosynthesis, physicochemical processes prevailed in regulating the marine geochemistry, with the open oceans providing the sink for the inorganically precipitated minerals. In the following period, when photosynthetically-produced oxygen yields were still low and largely kept low to satisfy inorganic oxidation processes, a shelfward shift of large sedimentary iron fixation was apparently facilitated by biologically created "oxygen oases," and there, through interaction with iron-precipitating bacteria and silica fixation, possibly by their degration products. Similarly, such biologically created oxygen oases seem to account for shelf deposits of carbonates, possibly, but yet to be proven, aided by bacterial agents of carbonate fixation. Further buildup of biologically-produced oxygen yields, above concentration levels required to satisfy oxidation requirements of inorganic minerals, affected inorganic processes to varying degrees. Mass transfer of soluble ferrous iron to the oceans became spectacularly reduced in the presence of oxygen in the aqueous media. Inorganic carbonate and silica fixation became more common in the shelf seas; also, some phosphate deposition occurred there. The iron, now in the ferric stage, became more widely disseminated in shelf sea areas. It appears that physicochemical precipitation processes were still the principal mechanisms to precipitate minerals from seawater.

The period thereafter, bracketed by an astonishingly short time interval of at most 7×10^8 yr, witnessed a major expansion in the diversity of life, and its influence may be reflected in the increasing volumes, particularly of carbonate precipitation, probably still by indirect means.

Tracks and trails and shortly thereafter the first appearance of a wide range of diverse naked invertebrates are found within 2×10^8 yr prior to what is conveniently considered the beginning of the Cambrian epoch. This suggests that biochemical evolution led to the development of the consumer chain and thereafter solved logistic problems to aggregate and maintain cell complexes and differentiate them into tissues with divided functions. This apparently took place in an astonishingly short period of time, probably less than 3×10^8 to 4×10^8 yr prior to the onset of the Cambrian epoch. This occurred assuming that the currently known fossil record for this critical time interval is reliable. Accepting it on face value, all of the explosive diversification of life to extend to advanced invertebrate groups appears to have occurred in localized areas of the shelf seas, while free O^2 was building up to levels estimated, at most, at 1% of today.

Most of the early naked Eumetazoans appear to have been grazers and deposit feeders. Some must have been primary consumers and others were possibly carnivores feeding on animal protozoans and deposit feeders. Larger contents of organic matter in the sedimentary rocks suggests more extensive productivity of primary producers and hence, a greater tie-up of seawater constituents, vital to primary producers, and great contributions of their metabolic waste products and organic matter to the water column. Animals started to compete very modestly in oxygen uptake, at least locally, with oxygen-consuming degradation processes by bacteria. In all, there is as yet little evidence as to what extent all of these biological processes affected the chemical composition of seawater and indirectly affected physicochemical precipitation processes of minerals in the shelf sea areas. In the open oceans, biologic influence on inorganic mineral precipitation processes was likely still limited to indirect effects, unless bacterial precipitation, for example, of carbonate, increased due to a likely greater population of phytoplankton. Hence, within the span of time documented for the existence of life, namely about 3.2×10^9 yr, processes regulating the chemistry of the oceans seem to have been hardly affected by life except for oxygen buildup before the last 6×10^8 yr. Only in the last 6×10^8 yr, life displaced progressively a variety of physicochemical precipitation processes, reaching its climax for the oceans as a whole only in the last 2×10^8 yr.

The evolution of the mineral-precipitating biomass in the oceans shows over the last 6×10^8 yr a succession of extinctions compensated by adaptive radiation of surviving or newly evolved stocks at different trophic levels and new niche occupations in the oceans. During this time interval, biochemical evolution trended toward increase in mineral diversity, modification of the mineral chemistry, and expanded depositional sites in hard tissues. This indicates increasing departure of the internal from the external fluid chemistry, improvement in transport systems, and increased efficiency in chemical potentials of the cells that elaborated the organic matrices and mineral precipitates at different hard-tissue sites. Although some groups of organisms abandoned hard-tissue mineralization in the course of their evolution, the overall trend over the last 6×10^8 yr is that of increase in diversity and volume fixation of hard tissue-confined minerals.

The principal differences between biologic and physicochemical mineral fixation are: (1) increased diversity of mineral precipitates by a single organism as compared with inorganic precipitation under identical environmental conditions; (2) the ability of organisms to differentiate the trace element composition in the same minerals precipitated by coexisting species compared to inorganic precipitates in the same environment; and (3) the ability of organisms to elaborate minerals, which would not be precipitated by physicochemical processes in the oceans as time progressed, or in segments of water masses where the water chemistry would inhibit or even dissolve certain inorganic precipitates.

The earliest groups of organisms known to precipitate minerals in discrete hard parts consisted of diverse Eumetazoan groups with benthic habits in shallow water environments on the inundated marine areas of the continents. Although unevenly distributed, their skeletal remains commonly constituted a major fraction of bottom deposits and entirely made up sediments over wide areas. Skeletal sediment accumulations consisted principally of carbonates, of a considerable although smaller fraction of apatites, and a minor contribution of silica in many facies types. The noted fixation of ilmenite, or its iron oxide precursor, is known so far only in minor quantities in hard parts from a few localities of a limited area. The possibility remains that weak carbonate and phosphate mineralization may have extended to protozoans and algae and indirect precipitation of a variety of minerals by bacteria. Thin section studies of early sedimentary rocks, always diagenetically altered to varying extent, have so far been negative in indicating their presence in the form of recognizable crystal aggregates.

There is considerable uncertainty as to whether the early Cambrian biomass, as known from shelf deposits, encompassed nectonic and planktonic constituents with mineralized hard parts. Those that appear either of minute size and, on grounds of comparative functional morphology, resemble recent pelagic necton, have in nearly all cases thick, calcareous- or carbonate-strengthened skeletons. Possibly some spinose trilobites may have been nectonic in habits, but whether their ecologic range extended to the open oceans cannot be ascertained.

No mineral-precipitating plankton is known from early Cambrian time, but planktotrophic larvae with mineralized hard parts of some of the benthic and possibly nectonic shelf sea dwellers may have extended to the surface waters of the open oceans (Fig. 12).

In early Cambrian time, physicochemical carbonate precipitation was the primary

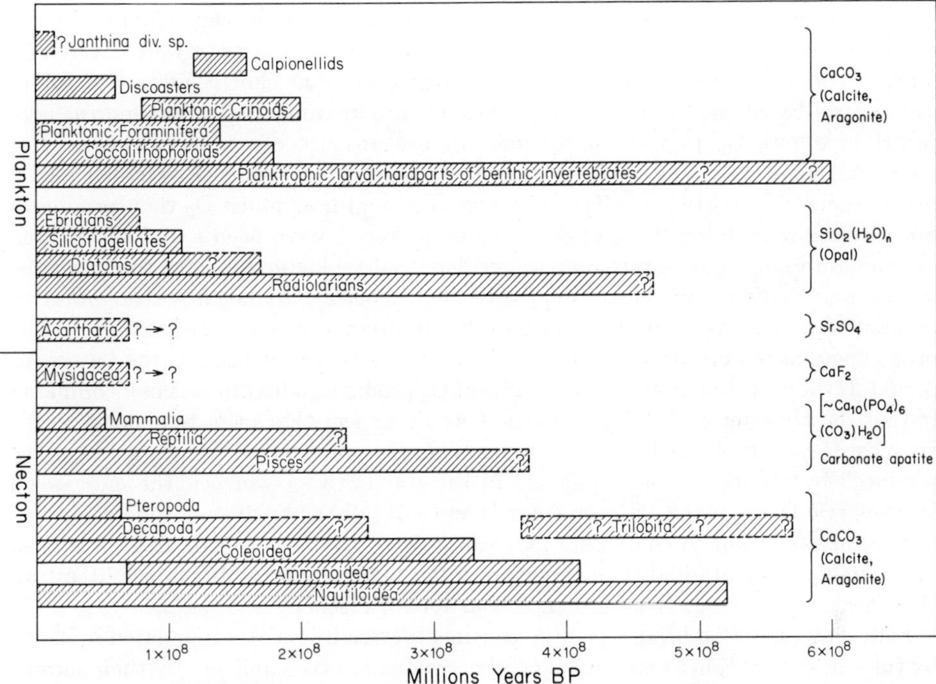

Fig. 12. Age ranges of major groups of pelagic organisms with mineralized hard parts during the last 6×10^8 yr.

target of biologic mineral metabolism. Most carbonate was tied up in skeletons of benthic Eumetazoa, which inhabited the inundated continental borderlands and their slopes to depths of ample organic detritus. The accumulation of their skeletal carbonates was centered along the shallow ocean margins, defining the sphere of principal substitution by organisms of physicochemical carbonate fixation and deposition in sediments. As indicated by extensive oolite and structureless carbonate accumulations even there, physicochemical precipitation was only reduced and in the open oceans still prevailed even if the few shelf sea elements, possibly with nectonic and planktonic habits, ranged far out to sea. The relatively small volumes of skeletally fixed phosphates and the negligible tie-up of silica and iron oxide minerals by benthic Eumetazoa in shallow water habitats indicate that precipitation of these minerals was still essentially controlled by inorganic processes.

The subsequent history of marine life with mineralized hard parts, its consequences on biologic mineral precipitates in kinds and volumes, and their disposition on the ocean floors as they affected inorganic processes is conveniently traced by a sequence of four consecutive stages.

The first covers the time interval between the beginning of the Mid-Cambrian and the end of the Devonian, spanning a period of about 2.3×10^8 yr. The significant changes in environmental setting that occurred during this time interval concern the rapid buildup of free O_2 in the atmosphere and the areal extent of continental inundations by the oceans. Concerning free O_2, it is widely held that in the course of this time interval its concentrations in the atmosphere rose rapidly to near present-day levels. The oldest vascular land plants are found in 4×10^8-yr-old deposits. Rapid diversification and increase in population density of tree-sized land plants followed and in the course of about 2×10^7 yr, large parts of the land surfaces were covered by forests. Therefore, there is convincing documentation that shortly after 4×10^8 yr ago, a land-based source of photosynthetic O_2 production existed and increasingly contributed free O_2 to the atmosphere. In the absence of unquestionable, older terrestrial plant fossils prior to this time, it is uncertain when O_2-producing land plants came into existence, what they were like, and how much O_2 they produced. Spore coats, resembling those of land plants, however, have been found as far back as the Cambrian. Since algae, represented largely by blue greens, live today on the surface and shallowly in soils to depths of light penetration and, from the maturity of many sediments as far back as the late Precambrian, it has been suggested that O_2-producing plants were present on land, at least locally, as far back as the Cambrian period. If they existed at all, their volume of O_2 production had to be small compared to that shortly after 4×10^8 yr. Hence, it would appear that prior to about 4×10^8 yr, most if not all of the O_2 in the atmosphere was still derived from evasion of O_2, produced by photosynthesizing agents in the sea. If this is correct, the increase in atmospheric O_2 from the Pasteur point level ($\sim 1\%$ PAL) until such time when terrestrial plants began to contribute materially O_2 to the atmosphere may have been considerably more gradual than the exponential increase postulated in the literature (Berkner and Marshall, 1965; Cloud, 1968a, 1968b; Fischer, 1965, 1972).

Following early Cambrian time, the continents were frequently inundated in depth by the sea, several times approaching and occasionally exceeding 50% of their surface area. Large areas covered by the sea were shallowly submerged to depths within and shallowly below the photic zone. Combined with either marked shallowing or possibly effective elimination of high UV radiation intensity within the upper 10 m of the photic zone, the areal extent of shelf sea floors, which could be densely populated by benthic algae, and of the water column, which could be occupied by planktonic ones, became greatly expanded. Close to nutrient-providing land sources was a marked increase of the standing crops of primary producers with the result of high yields of O_2 production due to the greatly extended shelf sea areas. Thus, more O_2 could have evaded the shelf sea-covered continents, allowing a more rapid increase in atmospheric O_2 contents as compared to the previous period, although the rates and volume increase may have been far lower than widely assumed.

Let us consider next the major consequences of the vastly extended shelf sea areas occupied by a greatly increased standing crop of primary producers on the mode of inroads biologic effects made on processes regulating the chemistry of the oceans during this time interval. In general, there occurred a noticeable expansion of mineralized hard parts in classes and phyla of the Eumetazoa to include fish between 5.5×10^8 to roughly 4.5×10^8 yr ago. Within this time span, it extended further to members of animal Protozoa and benthic algae. Documented hard-part fixation of inorganic compounds encompassed carbonates, carbonate apatites, and silica. Preferential fixation of carbonates, initiated prior to this time, extended to most groups that developed hard parts for the first time in the period under discussion. Fabric studies of the skeletal carbonates indicate that calcite was the common mineral phase of the precipitates. Aragonite, inferred from consistent sparry calcite preservation of skeletal carbonates in a number of groups and of discrete microarchitectural units in carbonate skeletons of others, was apparently less commonly the mineral phase precipitated by the carbonate-secreting biomass. The spread in carbonate fixation occurred principally among benthic organisms and extended to some new groups with nectonic modes of life. Evidence for the existence of carbonate-secreting plankton in this time interval remains as enigmatic as was indicated for the early Cambrian. There is certainly no convincing evidence for calcareous nannoplankton.

Phosphate mineral fixation among members of the benthos became sharply reduced prior to 5×10^8 yr either through extinction of groups or substitution of carbonate in all or parts of their mineralized skeletons. Further reduction in diversity among benthic groups, which continued to precipitate phosphatic skeletons, was brought about by extinction of one lineage among the inarticulate brachiopods about 4.5×10^8 yr ago and shifted to total carbonate fixation by the bryozoa close to 4×10^8 yr ago. Starting about 4.5×10^8 yr ago, fish appeared in the fossil records and in the course of their adaptive radiation compensated by about 3.5×10^8 yr for the continued reduction of phosphate fixation by invertebrate groups. The shift from exclusive uptake of skeletal phosphates by invertebrates to predominant fixation by fish involved transfer of its tie-up from benthic to largely nectonic Metazoans.

Silica fixation initiated earlier by sponge members of the benthos was extended to a plantonic element of the Protozoa, the radiolarians. Questionable records indicate their appearance in the Cambrian, but their presence and silica-fixing ability can be traced back only to roughly between 5 to 4.5×10^8 yr ago.

The marine deposits from roughly 5.8×10^8 to 3.5×10^8 yr show generally increasingly greater percentages of mineralized skeletons. Limestone deposits, entirely or largely composed of calcareous skeletons, became more frequent and more extensive in thickness and areal extension. Reefs built by calcareous encrusting algae, by Sclerospongia, tabulate, and rugose corals locally attained dimensions similar to large-sized reefs of today.

Siliceous sponges, bedded and nodular cherts, largely composed of their skeletons and spicules or formed from sponge-derived silica syn- or epigenetically in the sediments, became increasingly more common in the shallow shelf seas from about 4.5×10^8 yr on. Other chert deposits, largely laid down in mobile belts and tectonically active basins from the same time interval, contain mostly or only recognizable skeletal remains of radiolarians, suggesting that silica was derived from their skeletal accumulations. A short marine incursion of silica-precipitating algae (Desmidacea) may have taken place near the close of this episode (Bashnagel, 1942).

Phosphatic skeletons from benthic invertebrates were on the average minor constituents of the shelf sea deposits and only very rarely attained densities to become rock-forming constituents of thin beds with limited areal extent, up to roughly 4.5×10^8 yr ago. Thereafter, skeletal phosphates became negligible in shelf sea deposits except in nearshore areas until close to the end of this time interval, when fish extended their range far out into the open shelf seas.

It follows that during this episode the vastly extended shelf sea areas became increasingly the sites of mass fixation and accumulation grounds of biologically-precipitated carbonates and silica and small volumes of phosphate minerals. Therefore, on the shelves, physicochemical precipitation of carbonate and silica became progressively reduced. In the case of the carbonates, a rough guess of biologic substitution for physicochemical precipitation was likely in excess of 50% of the total precipitation, starting about 4.2×10^8 yr ago. Criteria are lacking as yet to establish to what extent silica, not preserved in skeletal form, was derived from biologic fixation agents, now found in the form of unfossiliferous cherts. One would also need to know more about autigenically formed clay minerals and silica uptake of land-derived clay minerals from seawater before one can assess the extent of biologic substitution of silica fixation for physicochemical precipitates.

Being confined to shelf sea geosynclinal sources of information woefully limits the assessment of biologic interference with physicochemical precipitation processes in the open oceans below shallow-shelf sea slopes. One is on safer ground to infer that the silica-precipitating radiolarians became integral constituents of the pelagic nannoplankton around 4.5×10^8 yr ago. This implies that aside from limited fixation of silica by benthic sponges, a potentially far more effective biologic agent to reduce physicochemical precipitation processes of silica was injected into the water column of the open oceans.

In the case of carbonate, most nectonic elements until near the close of the time interval under consideration can be shown on grounds of (1) skeletal designs, (2) heavy mineralized armor, and particularly (3) limited niche occupation in the shelf seas, to be disqualified for pelagic modes of life in the open oceans. Up to about 3.7×10^8 yr, some species of the trilobites continued to occur intermittently with skeletal designs, which on grounds of comparative functional morphology suggest that they had either planktonic or nectonic habits. Skeletal remains of some of these species were widely distributed in shelf sea sediments. Burial remains of their exoskeletons form mostly a minor fraction of skeletal carbonates. Considering further that parts of their burial records were discarded molts, their population densities even in the shelf areas must have been small. Considering the rapid increase in diversity and population density of benthic Eumetazoa with calcareous hard parts, it would appear that planktotrophic larvae with calcareous skeletons became commensurately more common. Those with long planktotrophic larval stages among benthic organisms near shelf sea margins and from deeper water ocean floors should have skeletally tied up and contributed carbonate to the sediments in the open oceans. Lacking adequate data on the volume of fixation and postmortem fate of their carbonate skeletons in the plankton today, it is as yet impossible to guess their share of carbonate fixation in the open oceans during this time interval. Another possible carbonate-precipitating element, again unknown in quantity, may have been represented by bacteria plated out on particulate organic material in suspension. Logistic problems to stay afloat and extend their radius of activity are suggested for some of the cephalopod groups that evolved within the last 5×10^7 yr of this period. If they ranged into the open oceans their volume of carbonate fixation was likely also small. Hence, it would appear at present that physicochemical processes seem to have controlled carbonate mineral precipitation in the open oceans.

Sharks and bony fish hydrodynamically similar in design to modern oceanic occupants evolved and diversified rapidly within the last 5×10^7 yr of this period. Their wide distribution in the shelf seas makes it likely that their range extended into the open oceans. Thus, aside from some phosphate-precipitating benthic invertebrates, there is the possibility that in the course of this short time interval, fish may have started to reduce inorganic precipitation of phosphate minerals in the open oceans.

The major features discernible during this time interval as they pertain to the history of the impact of life on inorganic processes regulating the chemistry of seawater indicate the following. The concentrations of free O_2 in the oceans appear to have risen modestly although at higher rates than in the preceding period between roughly 5.7×10^8 yr to shortly after 4×10^8 yr and exponentially in the course of the next 5×10^7 yr. It reflects a net gain in the standing crops of primary producers, which enabled rapid expansion of oxygen-consuming animal life.

Continuous rapid diversification of the marine biomass was accompanied by widespread development of mineralized hard parts. Sessile and vagrant benthic Eumetazoa made up most of the mineral-precipitating biomass. The enormous expansion of shoal water habitats, developed during repeated deep inundations of the continental surfaces, accommodated enormous standing crops of mineral-precipitating benthos and provided the depositional ground for retention of their mineralized skeletons and disaggregation products. Euxinic basin deposits show that highly diversified nectonic and planktonic populations existed at that time. However, only a very small segment of these developed mineralized hard parts.

Biologic mineral precipitates, laid down on the shelf sea floor, were principally derived from benthic organisms. They consisted overwhelmingly of carbonates, a considerably less amount of silica and a decreasingly minor volume of phosphates. Fractions of biogenic mineral accumulations derived from plankton are indicated to have been considerable for silica from radiolarians from about 4.5×10^8 yr on, on the average negligible for carbonates and nonexistent for phosphates. Necton-derived contributors to the sediments were limited to carbonates and phosphates. Their fraction in the carbonate increased in the course of this episode but remained very small compared to that from benthic organisms. Concerning phosphates, their contribution, limited to fish, was negligible until about 4×10^8 yr ago but increased in the next 5×10^7 yr to equal if not exceed the volume fraction from benthic organisms.

Qualified by the assumption that the shelf sea plankton and necton ranged or was representative of that in the open ocean, there should have been extensive silica fixation by planktonic radiolarians from roughly 4.5×10^8 yr on and increasing although still modest phosphate fixation by nectonic fish after about 3.5×10^8 yr ago. As to biologic carbonate precipitation, if one combines evidence from likely planktonic and nectonic shelf sea dwellers and an increased contribution from planktotrophic larvae of shelf and oceanic benthic constituents, it appears that the volume of their carbonate fixation was minor if not negligible unless bacteria, as yet not demonstrable, played a major role.

Translated into biologic effects on processes regulating the chemistry of the oceans, the depth distribution in concentration levels of free O_2 and CO_2, and the basic nutrients of primary producers at least for nitrogenous products and phosphate, must have been progressively modified to approach the average patterns in the present oceans. Silica uptake solely for vital processes must have increased in consequence of the increasingly larger standing crops of primary producers and consumers in the photic and subphotic zones. Their effects alone would seem to have remained still negligible on the concentration levels of dissolved and colloidal silica in the surface and nearsurface levels of the oceans. Increasing biologic infringement on physicochemical precipitation of carbonate, silica, and phosphate minerals from seawater occurred in the course of this time interval. The magnitude of the inroads of substituting biologic for inorganic precipitation processes differed generally but most conspicuously for carbonate and phosphate minerals and silica between the shelf areas and open oceans. The shelf sea areas, significantly larger than today, were densely populated by benthic organisms mostly with massive calcareous, some siliceous and limited phosphatic hard parts. The pelagic segment of the shelf sea biota with mineralized hard parts, which probably extended to the open oceans, secreted silica principally with smaller volumes of carbonate and phosphate minerals. Hence, on the shelves carbonate fixation by organisms substituted increasingly for inorganic precipitation processes, likely exceeding 50% of the total volume of its fixation, whereas in the open oceans physicochemical precipitation was at best little affected. In the case of silica, considerable although proportionately smaller volumes were biologically precipitated on the shelf and most likely sizable volumes in the open oceans. Hence, inorganic silica precipitation became volumetrically reduced throughout the oceans. Skeletal phosphate fixation, always minor in proportion to carbonate and even silica, was until the last 5×10^7 yr of this episode limited to the shelf seas. Hence, inorganic phosphate precipitation was hardly impeded throughout the oceans until near the end of the time interval under consideration.

The extensive shelf seas were not only the sites of proportionately larger volumes of carbonate and silica fixation as compared to the open oceans, but what is more important, a considerably larger proportion of the biologic and inorganic mineral precipitates became locked up in their shoal water sediments. The shallow waters of the present oceans, despite severe biologic drain by organisms, remain supersaturated with reference to calcite and aragonite, and hence the same situation must have prevailed in the oceans in the past. There is widespread preservation of even small fragile skeletons, originally composed of silica, and extensive chert deposits are widely distributed in shelf sea sediments in the time interval under discussion. This would suggest that the surface waters of the oceans at that time were saturated or even supersaturated with reference to silica. Therefore, the volume of biologic and inorganic fixation of silica during this time interval must have been considerably smaller than that supplied by the rivers to the sea. Judging from the preservational records of skeletal phosphates, the same seems to apply to the phosphate contents of the surface water at that time.

The transition from the Paleozoic to the Mesozoic eras witnessed extinction and decimation of a number of groups followed by the appearance of new groups and the adaptive radiation of descendants of preexisting groups with mineralized tissues. Environmentally, it was preceded by formation of extensive evaporites, phosphate deposits, and, mostly in the southern hemisphere, by widespread glaciations. Increasing continentality, reaching its climax close to the Paleozoic-Mesozoic boundary and continuing through the early Triassic, reduced documentation of marine life during this time interval almost entirely to geosynclinal records, similar to the early Cambrian. The major changes in constituents and proportionate volumes of the mineral-secreting biomass in the oceans in mid- through late Triassic time accentuated rather than altered the pathways and inroads of biologic effects on processes regulating the chemistry of seawaters, which can be traced back to late Devonian time. Hence, they are included in the characterization of the next episode, which spanned the time interval between about 3.5×10^8 to roughly 1.8×10^8 yr prior to the present.

The rapid expansion of a plant cover on land within a few tens of millions of years increased the content of free O_2 in the atmosphere early during this time interval to about that of today followed by fluctuations around the mean of the present-day level. Resultant higher levels of free O_2 made it possible in the photic zone for the consumer chain to diversify in trophic levels. This became most noticeably reflected in nectonic predators such as cephalopods and fish, which required elevated oxygen respiration for increasing speeds and extending their operational ranges. Diversification in both groups is noticeable and accompanied in the ammonites by solving logistic problems in shell and internal chamber wall designs and in fish by increased streamlining and a tendency to reduce or abandon mineralized hard parts, particularly in body scales. Starting with the Permian, they were joined by reptilian representation, the turtles, and thereafter, by a variety of paddling, diving, and fish-shaped species. Aside from O_2, the depth distribution of CO_2, NO_3/NO_2, and phosphate in the oceans must have been similar if not the same as today, whereas in the case of silica it remains uncertain. The areal extent of submergence of the continents by the sea became on the average progressively reduced, becoming minimal in the late Permian through the early Triassic. Sedimentary accumulations of carbonates, silica, and phosphates tied up in skeletons increased noticeably in proportion to those of physicochemical origin and in diagenetically altered sediments, which may have been derived from other sources. This mirrors a further step in the progression of inhibiting physicochemical precipitation of these minerals in the shelf seas by biologic agents, which elaborated them in their hard parts.

Carbonates continued to be the principal biogenic mineral precipitates. Although calcite remained the dominant crystal phase of the precipitates, aragonite greatly increased in proportion as compared to the previous period. The progressive increase of the aragonite-calcite ratios for total biologically-precipitated carbonates resulted primarily from (1) the decline in population sizes of most of the major calcite-depositing agents in the course of this period, (2) extinction of decimated stocks of groups that were prominent calcite depositors in the preceding period as, for example, rugose and tabulate corals and trilobites, and (3) diversification, niche, and population expansions of aragonite-precipitating gastropods, bivalves, and ammonites and replacement in the Anthozoa of rugose by scleractinian corals at the Permo-Triassic boundary. The reduction in volume fixation of biogenic calcite, resulting from decline of previously major contributors, was partially compensated by the rise and major population expansions of carbonate-secreting benthic foraminifera.

High to medium magnesium contents are mostly indicated for the biogenic calcites, based on very limited data from species of major precipitating agents of this mineral phase in samples of Carboniferous age. Except for crinoids, the magnesium contents are lower than for recent species in the same classes that precipitate high magnesium calcites. No significance can be attached at this time to these differences, as high magnesium calcites are diagenetically unstable in most sedimentary facies even in near recent sediments of a few hundred thousand years in age. The strontium contents of these calcitic fossils are low and within the range of recent species in the same classes. The few gastropod and cephalopod shells still composed of original aragonite from the Carboniferous and Triassic have, with few exceptions, noticeably higher strontium contents than extant descendants or species in related groups. The differences in strontium contents have been attributed to lesser biochemical discrimination in strontium relative to calcium in the late Paleozoic to early Mesozoic as compared to recent descendants (Lowenstam, 1963; Hallam and Price, 1968).

The silica-precipitating agents were represented as in the preceding period by benthic sponges and pelagic radiolarians. There is better documentation for radiolarian oozes now in the form of radiolarites composed of their densely packed skeletal remains. The same is true for sponge-bearing cherts, yet there are many chert deposits known to be unfossiliferous or largely not investigated for their fossil contents. Hence, the data are too poor to tell whether the ratios of the biogenic fixations to those of physicochemical origins were equal or greater than during the preceding episode. The uncertainty of the size of the standing crops of radiolarians in the surface waters explains our present inability, noted earlier, to assess the depth distribution of silica in the oceans at that time.

The expansion of the marine phosphate-precipitating biomass in the shelf sea was due to major diversification and larger population sizes of sharks, rays and bony fish, and in the Triassic by the addition of reptiles. Among the increasing number of diverse arthropods other than trilobites, some seem to have precipitated phosphatic substances in their carapaces, but their distribution and volume secretion is poorly documented. All of these groups were nectonic in habits. The benthic constituents were composed of inarticulate brachiopods and coelenterate representatives, the conularids. The minute, toothlike structures, called conodents, of as yet uncertain biologic affinities and unknown habits, were part of biologically-fixed phosphate minerals throughout this time interval. The organisms that formed the conodents, and the conularids even more so, became progressively insignificant as phosphate-precipitating agents. The benthic inarticulate brachiopods were on the average minor contributors of phosphatic shells to the shelf sea deposits. However, during the Carboniferous, deposits near the strandline, particularly in euxinic basins, show large accumulations of acrotididians with shell shapes similar to those of the extant deep-water dwellers *Pelagiodiscus*. I found that large populations of these species were pseudoplanktonic, forming a dense overgrowth on drift logs of terrestrial trees. Similar modes of life have been described for Devonian crinoids. Terrestrial forests came into existence only in Devonian time and formed, during the Carboniferous, dense covers in coastal swamps of huge areal extent. Hence, starting during Devonian time, increasingly large populations of benthic organisms with mineralized tissues were rafted out to sea by tree trunks. Their planktotrophic larvae also settled out on them and could develop into sizable populations, which postmortem or by sinking of their water-logged substrate would contribute to at least marginal segments of open ocean sediments. Hence, the contributions of carbonate, silica, and phosphatic skeletons derived from benthic biologic sources to open oceanic sediments must have increased over the previous period due to megascopic, benthic algae set adrift, and through driftwood decay, thus extending the radius of their dispersion in the open oceans.

The distinguishing feature of the biologic effects on processes regulating the chemistry of seawater during this episode can be summarized as follows. Increasing continentality reduced the volume of carbonate, silica, and phosphorus accumulations tied up in shelf sea deposits except for a short time during the Permian for phosphorus. The shelf sea carbonates were increasingly derived from biogenic skeletal sources, largely from the benthos, progressively reducing the fraction of the physicochemical precipitates, as a guess, to probably less than 30% of the total. The increase in biologic fixation of carbonates was accompanied by an increase in the aragonite-calcite ratios. Magnesium and strontium contents appear to have been similar to extant biogenic calcites. In biogenic aragonites of certain mollusc groups, the Sr/Ca ratios were higher than those in their present-day representatives, whereas the Mg/Ca ratios appear to have been generally low, as in recent species. Group representation of silica-precipitating agents was the same as in the preceding time interval. However, for lack of data one cannot tell whether the volume of silica fixation by organisms changed relative to that from inorganic precipitation processes in the shelf seas. Phosphate mineral fixation by biologic agents rose in the shelf seas due to increase in nectonic vertebrates. Fluorine fixation in biogenic carbonate apatite minerals must have increased as the volume of the fish populations rose. The biologic inroads on phosphate mineral precipitation by inorganic processes remain uncertain in view of the possibility that microorganisms may have been directly or indirectly involved in their fixation.

In the open oceans, nectonic ammonites, possibly some planktonic crinoids and tree-plus algally-rafted benthos, added to biologic carbonate fixation of benthic community constituents and planktotrophic larvae from benthic organisms from the shelf sea to deeper waters. Yet the volume precipitated by all these organisms must have remained still small compared to inorganic precipitation of carbonate in the open oceans, and their fractions incorporated into pelagic sediments must have been above the then existing compensation levels for calcite and aragonite stability. Concerning silica, it remains uncertain whether the ratios in volumes of inorganic to biogenic fixation had undergone changes as compared to the previous time interval. Noticeable diversification of fish, morphologically streamlined to make them potential occupants of the open sea, and indications that their populations had become larger, suggest an increase in the volume of fixation of phosphate minerals and fluorine tie-up by these biologic constituents. Hence, fish would appear to have contributed greater volumes of skeletal phosphates and fluorine to pelagic sediments. Aquatic reptiles appeared in Permian time and became more diversified, morphologically better adapted to nectonic life and more widespread in the mid- to late Triassic shelf seas. Compared to fish, their populations seem to have been small, and whether their range extended to the open oceans is uncertain. Tree-rafted benthic brachiopods were likely contributors of very small amounts of phosphatic shells to the oceanic sediments near the continental shelf borders, noticeably during the Carboniferous and particularly during the interval of maximum continentality in late Permian to early Triassic time. Some phosphate larval shells from planktotrophic larvae of benthic organisms may have further added minute amounts of fluorocarbonate and carbonate apatites derived from hard tissues to the pelagic deposits.

An increase in biologic fixation and sedimentary contribution of skeletally-fixed phosphate minerals to pelagic sediments, at least close to the continental shelf margins, appears likely. However, compared to physicochemical precipitation and accumulation of phosphate minerals and phosphorites, the share of these biologic fixation products likely remained small in the open oceans unless phosphorites were microbially precipitated.

The episode between 1.8×10^8 and roughly 6.5×10^7 yr traces a sequence of steps in cumulative expansion of the mineral-precipitating biomass, which extended its influence to affect significantly for the first time processes regulating the chemistry of seawater throughout the oceans. The single most profound change that occurred in the course of this time interval was the massive expansion of biologic mineral fixation in hard parts among an increasing number of diverse taxa in the nannoplankton and microplankton in the photic and shallow subphotic zone. It occurred chiefly among micro- and nanno- constituents of the phytoplankton and zooplankton, represented by diatoms, coccolithophorids, silicoflagellates, pelagic foraminifera, and possibly *Nannoconus*, which occupy key trophic levels in the planktonic food chain today. This assured vast standing crops and rapid turnover rates of their populations, which in turn tied up and released to the water column and to pelagic sediments enormous volumes of their mineralization products. Hence, irrespective of whether the epicontinental shelf seas were small or large, mineral precipitation processes in the surface waters of the entire oceans during this time interval became progressively subject to biologic controls reaching proportions close, if not similar, to those of today. Therefore, in the course of this episode, the foundation was laid to shift the center of gravity of biologic mineral fixation and of its influence on various processes regulating the chemistry of seawater from the shelf areas to the pelagic realm. Their mass fixation of these minerals indicates that the principal targets of massive displacement of physicochemical precipitation processes by biologic agents in the open sea involved carbonates and silica and the trace constituents of these minerals.

The history of the mineral-precipitating plankton in the course of this episode is complex. The first planktonic organisms to appear were calcite-precipitating crinoids, which came into existence about 2×10^7 yr prior to the beginning of the episode under consideration. They underwent considerable diversification, were repeatedly represented locally by large populations, but became extinct at about the end of the episode under consideration. They are known so far only from the plankton of the shelf seas. It remains uncertain whether they ever became an important planktonic constituent on the shelf seas throughout this period, and whether they extended their range to the surface waters of the open oceans. Calcareous calpionellids and problematic calcareous nannofossils are common in geosynclinal deposits ranging in ages between about 1.6×10^8 to roughly 1.2×10^8 yr ago. The calpionellids are thought to be the mineralized tests of tintinnids, a group of cilliated animal Protozoa that were always part of the plankton since about 5.5×10^8 yr ago (Chennaux, 1968). Aside from the short time interval, when they developed calcareous tests (the calpionellids), they were either naked or they agglutinated mineral particles to their gelatinous body walls. The calpionellids were conspicuous rock-forming constituents in geosynclinal deposits in the short time span of their existence. Again, we do not know whether they or other calcareous nannoplankton constituents were at that time part of the pelagic plankton. Of the plankton members, which continued to exist past this episode to the present and increasingly dominated the mineral-precipitating plankton, the coccolithoporids apparently originated close to or even shortly before about 1.8×10^8 yr ago. They became populous enough 2×10^7 yr later in the plankton so that their calcareous coccolith remains were major sediment-forming constituents. The oldest siliceous diatoms appeared about the same time as the coccolithophorids, but remained obscure until about the close of this episode when they began spectacular diversification and mass fixation of silica in the plankton. The planktonic foraminifera originated roughly 1.6×10^8 yr ago and 4×10^7 yr later their calcareous remains, together with coccolith remains, started to form accumulations of extensive chalk oozes on shelf sea floors and in the open oceans to the compensation depth of calcite stability. The silica-precipitating silicoflagellates appeared in the plankton shortly prior to 1.1×10^8 yr. At the close of this episode they were joined by the silica-depositing ebridians. Together they increased rapidly thereafter, although they never reached a comparable proportion in silica fixation to the diatoms.

The calcites and opals precipitated by the planktonic constituents that continued to exist past the episodes under consideration to the present are characterized by low trace element contents.

Throughout the time interval under consideration, parts of the continental surfaces were repeatedly inundated by the sea, particularly in midlate Cretaceous time. The extensive epicontinental shelf sea floors were widely populated by densely crowded benthic communities with mineralized hard parts. Nectonic elements and the progressively diversified plankton populations with mineralized hard parts were common in the waters of the shallow shelf seas, particularly in the last 3×10^7 yr of this episode.

As indicated by their skeletal accumulations, which were sizable in the epicontinental shelf sea deposits, carbonates were the principal biologic precipitation products. At the beginning of the episode, the carbonate-precipitating biomass resided principally in constituents of benthic communities. Thereafter, the necton played a small but conspicuous role, and the newly evolved carbonate-precipitating planktonic constituents became progressively and increasingly the important components of the carbonate precipitators, particularly in the last 3×10^7 yr of the episode, even in the shallow epicontinental shelf seas. Silica-precipitating sponges in the benthic communities were minor although conspicuous throughout this episode. Opal became increasingly tied up by the plankton through addition to the preexisting radiolarians of diatoms, silicoflagellates, and ebridians in the course of the last 3×10^7 yr of this episode, largely in the deeper water areas of the shelf seas. Phosphate minerals became increasingly tied up in hard parts of the shelf sea biomass. Nectonic fish and to a lesser extent nectonic reptiles account principally for the increase in skeletal phosphate fixation. Sedimentary records indicate greater diversification and larger standing crops of bony fish. Deep-sea remains of Cretaceous age document conclusively for the first time the suspected earlier extension of the range of fish to the open oceans. Phosphate mineral fixation by members of the benthic communities were small by comparison with that by the necton. Yet, aside from the fluorcarbonate apatites tied up in inarticulate brachiopod shells, it is too early to tell if phosphates in the form of calcium phosphate and iron phosphatic hydrogels were not also deposited already during this time interval by other benthic constituents. The earliest noted occurrence of calcitic spicules of a holothurian group, which today precipitates, in addition, large volumes of ferric phosphatic hydrogel granules, indicates present ignorance on this subject. The same is true for iron oxide minerals such as magnetite, goethite, and lepidocrocite, where we have fossil records of the groups that precipitate these minerals not only from this period but for several hundred million years earlier. Skeletal remains of mysidacea from the episode under discussion also raise questions about whether biologic fluorite precipitation by these nectonic arthropods had not been initiated at this time, but again, for lack of search for their statoliths, it remains at present only a possibility.

Considering biologic carbonate fixation in the epicontinental shelf seas, the aragonite-calcite ratio increased further as a result of changes in community structures, population sizes, and to a very minor extent, through newly added aragonite-precipitating organisms. The major expansion of principally aragonite-precipitating scleractinian corals, bivalves, and gastropods, possibly including Sclerospongia, continued reduction of calcite-precipitating brachiopods and crinoids, larger population sizes of ammonites with aragonitic shells, and aragonite-precipitating algae in benthic communities were primarily responsible for increased biologic aragonite fixation. The appearance of a small group of foraminifera with aragonitic tests (Robertinacea) contributed in a minor way to this trend and probably, as is true today, mostly in deeper water communities. The magnitude of the shift to greater aragonite-calcite ratios in the shelf sea was partially dampened by a noticeable increase in calcite-precipitating benthic foraminifera and nectonic belemnites with only minor aragonite fractions in their skeletons. At times of major invasions of calcitic plankton, particularly during the last 3×10^7 yr of this episode, the volume of aragonite relative to calcite in the carbonate-secreting biomass of the shelf seas was temporarily smaller.

This episode is most instructive in showing the dichotomy that arose among some of the biologic mineral-fixation products and resultant effects on biogenic mineral accumulations between shallow shelf seas and the open oceans. Considering carbonates, aragonite became more prominent, and calcites, largely with high magnesium contents, were characteristic of a large segment of the shelf sea-precipitating agents and their depositional records. In the open oceans low magnesium calcites from newly evolved, unequivocal planktonic constituents made up nearly all of the biologic carbonate precipitates, considering that the volume of aragonite and high magnesium calcites from constituents of initially small benthic communities had to be negligible for reasons of limited food sources similar to today. Even if high magnesium calcite-bearing crinoids, together with planktonic- and aragonite-precipitating nectonic ammonites, did extend into the open oceans, their volume of carbonate fixation compared to that tied up in the key trophic levels of the plankton had to be small if not negligible. Hence, biologic carbonate fixation in the open oceans consisted almost entirely of low magnesium calcite and was definitely dominant in the last 2×10^7 yr of this episode, following extinction of planktonic crinoids and major decline of nectonic ammonites.

In the case of silica, the volume of biologic fixation by the shelf community became increasingly negligible compared to the open oceans, following the exponential increase in silica fixation toward the end of this episode, by the additions to the pre-existing radiolarians of diatoms, silicoflagellates, and ebridians in the plankton. It would be interesting to know whether the volume of silica fixation in the open oceans simply increased in proportion to the addition and population increases of the newly added extracting agents in the surface waters, or whether it was slightly compensated by a reduction in radiolarian populations and siliceous sponges. One may also ask if the strongly silicified radiolarians may have extended their range to deeper silica-rich water levels as a result of the competition for silica in the surface waters, and if they were also responsible for an increase in poorly silicified groups in the radiolarian populations.

As to phosphatic minerals, skeletal fixation increased. However, the ratio of the volumes precipitated by biologic agents in the shelf seas compared to that in the open oceans remains uncertain until better data from pelagic sediments become available. Since fish were the major phosphate-precipitating agents, it seems unlikely that there were significant differences in proportions of fluorcarbonate apatites and carbonate apatites between the populations in the shelf seas and open oceans.

The most significant events that occurred in the course of this episode as they concern the progression of the impact of the mineral-precipitating biomass on the chemistry of seawater and the processes of regulating it are related to the spectacular extension of the sphere of biologic mineral fixation from the shelf seas to the open oceans. In the case of biologic carbonate fixation, the appearance and rapid proliferation of constituents at key trophic levels in the nanno- and microplankton increasingly reduced physicochemical carbonate precipitation in the open oceans. Considering further that the large volumes of carbonate minerals were still tied up by a wide spectrum of the shelf sea communities, physicochemical precipitation of carbonate minerals from seawater in the oceans as a whole must have become negligible at the end of this episode, similar to today. Pelagic calcite deposits toward the close of this episode must have been composed already largely, if not entirely, of coccolith and plankton foraminifera tests to the compensation depths for low magnesium calcites. Their depth distribution, areal extent, and accumulation rates as compared to today remain uncertain for reason of the interaction of several unknowns. These concern (1) lack of knowledge of the standing crops of the low magnesium calcite-secreting populations, (2) absence or at best small volumes of aragonite-precipitating agents that would have added through dissolution of their skeletons at shallower depths to the carbonate saturation of the waters, (3) considerably higher temperatures of oceanic deeper waters as compared to today (based on δO^{18} data of skeletal carbonates), and (4) likely differences in mixing rates of oceanic waters and in cross sections of oceanic currents. Probably they only slightly modified the basic pattern of surface water supersaturation with reference to calcite and aragonite and the rates of dissolution of carbonate minerals due to increased undersaturation with increase in depth of the water column of the open oceans as we find it today. Let us assume that the trace elements and their concentration levels, tied up in the low magnesium calcites of the planktonic contributors to pelagic carbonate oozes, were similar to today. If so, the uncertainties of the fraction of the standing crops of these planktonic elements that were dissolved in transport through the water column and those incorporated in the sediments make it impossible to even guess distribution patterns in the water column and the magnitudes of loss of the trace constituents to the sediments. It would be interesting to know whether high strontium aragonites and high magnesium calcites were part and possibly the major precipitation products of physicochemical carbonate precipitates, which were dominant prior to biologic displacement in the open oceans. Hence, it is too early to speculate whether the progressive shift from inorganic to primarily biologic carbonate fixation during this episode was accompanied by significant changes in trace element tie-up in the carbonate budget of the open oceans.

In the case of silica, biologic fixation carried out in the oceans primarily by sponges in the shelf sea areas and by radiolarians in the open oceans as far back as Cambro-Ordovician times increased exponentially very late in the episode under discussion through acquisition and mass fixation of siliceous skeletons in key trophic levels of the oceanic plankton and to a minor extent in the shelf sea by diatoms. Concerning their effects on the chemistry of seawater, the silicon contents of the photic and shallow subphotic zone must have been materially reduced and accompanied by seasonal changes. Thus, for the first time, silica was added to the list of chemical constituents that are significantly reduced by primary producers in the surface-waters of all oceans today. However, the magnitude of its depletion may have been less drastic compared to today if the standing crops of its extracting agents were smaller at that time compared to the present. The distribution pattern of silica concentration in the deeper waters of the open oceans toward the end of this episode must have approached similarity to today. Drastic changes must have occurred in the sedimentary composition of silicon-bearing minerals of pelagic sediments after biologic agents began mass fixation of opal in the open oceans. In the first roughly 6×10^7 yr of this episode, inorganic silicate minerals must have taken up most of the dissolved silica from seawater, and biogenic opals formed a minor fraction. In the course of the next roughly 4×10^7 yr, the biogenic opal fraction exponentially increased and substituted largely for inorganically formed silicon-bearing compounds on the deep-sea floors.

As indicated for phosphates and other minerals precipitated today by the marine biomass, the present data for this time interval are too incomplete to assess their possible effects on the chemistry of seawater.

The final phase, between about 6.5×10^7 yr to the present, witnessed progressive reduction of the shelf sea areas to that of today. Hence, in the analyses of the progression and pathways of the inroads of biologic mineral fixation on the chemistry of seawater and the processes regulating it, the plankton and necton in the open oceans acquire greatest significance. Among constituents at key trophic levels of the nanno- and microplankton, there occurred further diversification and increasingly greater standing crops of the carbonate- and silica-precipitating groups. Mineral diversification is indicated by the appearance of a radiolarian group with celestite ($SrSO_4$) in their hard parts. In the carbonate-precipitating plankton, the coccolithoporids and planktonic foraminifera, which made their appearance in the preceding episode, maintained their key position in the standing crops and huge volume fixation of low magnesium calcites. They were joined by a group of problematic, nannoplanktonic organisms represented by low magnesium calcitic hard parts, called Discoasters. These made their appearance about 6×10^8 yr ago and apparently died out close to 1 million years ago. *Janthina* species were the last addition to the calcareous plankton in late Cenozoic time. The shells of this constituent are composed of aragonite and calcite. Their combined population sizes and sedimentary contribution were considerably smaller than those of the coccolithophorids and pelagic foraminifera and, in the case of *Janthina*, negligible. Thus, there occurred further expansion of contributors and of volume fixation of low magnesium calcite and a very minor addition of aragonite fixation in the calcareous plankton.

The silica-precipitating plankton expanded in group representation by the addition of a nannoplanktonic algal constituent, the ebridians, at or shortly prior to the beginning of this episode. Volume fixation of the silica-precipitating planktonic biomass expanded enormously. The silica-secreting diatoms, which, like the silicoflagellates, had made their appearance in the plankton only late in the preceding episode, were primarily responsible for the enormous increase in silica fixation.

The celestite-secreting Acantharia are today widespread in the oceanic plankton and are locally represented by large populations. Skeletal remains are scarce in the fossil records and limited to species of one superfamily. The oldest fossils are of Eocene age, close to 5×10^7 yr. As was noted earlier, skeletons of Acantharia, suspended from about 500 m to a depth of about 5000 m in the central Pacific for four months, dissolved at all levels (Berger, 1968). The rare fossil records of Acantharian skeletons suggest that the seawater was undersaturated with reference to $SrSO_4$, at least during the last 5×10^7 yr. Moreover, Acantharia may have come into existence in the oceanic plankton considerably earlier than is suggested by their oldest fossils if seawater, prior to the Eocene, was already undersaturated with reference to $SrSO_4$.

During this episode, the pelagic necton underwent major compositional changes in its mineral-precipitating constituents. Of the marine reptiles only the turtles survived and increased further in importance. Marine mammals began early to substitute for marine reptiles; they diversified in types, acquired large populations, and extended their range in the open oceans. Fish regrouped and expanded significantly in importance throughout the open oceans and in their depth ranges. Bathypelagic fish can be traced back to at least 2×10^7 yr. Following the extinction of the ammonites and belmnites, prior to this episode, nectonic constituents that survived, such as the nautiloids, became a minor element and furthermore, became restricted to a small area of the Indo-Pacific. The squids and related forms, which also continued to survive and expanded in density and population sizes in the main were characterized by reduced mineralized tissues. Moreover, except for *Spirula*, they were populous largely in the shelf sea and the bordering segments of open oceans. Their skeletal remains, however, were widely distributed through rafting in the open oceans. A significant addition to the pelagic necton were representatives of the gastropod. These were the carbonate-secreting pteropods and heteropods. They appeared close to the onset of this episode and rapidly increased in population size, which acquired significant proportions in the oceanic necton at least as far back as about 2.5×10^7 yr ago. Statolith records in marine sediments as far back as about 5×10^7 yr indicate that Mysidacea became more important as a constituent of the necton at least in the shelf bordering segments of the open oceans, aside from developing large populations in the shelf seas starting about 2×10^7 yr ago.

Of the constituents of the pelagic necton, reptiles, mammals, and fish precipitated in their hard-tissue sites carbonate apatites and some of the fish laid down fluorcarbonate apatite also. The cephalopods, pteropods, and heteropods deposited aragonitic hard parts, and the mysids precipitated fluorite (CaF_2) in their statoliths. To judge from the fossil record, major increase in the volume of mineral fixation by the planktonic necton occurred in the open oceans during this episode. It principally involved major expansion of phosphate minerals, sizable, although lesser volumes of aragonite, and apparently fluorite to a minor degree.

Hardly anything is known about the composition of benthic communities of the deep sea of the Cenozoic, nor of the mineral that they precipitated, except for the carbonate-precipitating foraminifera. This is particularly unfortunate concerning the presence of skeletal fixation of the iron oxide minerals, calcium and ferric phosphatic hydrogels, barite, fluorite, and calcium oxalates, known among the inorganic substances in hard parts of recent deep-water constituents of the benthic communities.

In the progressively restricted shelf sea areas, skeletal carbonates continued to prevail in the benthic communities, particularly on shallow shelf sea floors. The aragonite-calcite ratios continued to increase largely through major expansion of aragonite-precipitating, warm water algae, the fixation of aragonite, solely or substituting partly for calcite in skeletons of a variety of bryozoa and octocorallia, and further expansion of the aragonite fraction in the mollusca. Data are insufficient to determine whether the proportions of high to low magnesium calcites changed in the benthic shelf sea communities on a world-wide basis.

The volume of silica fixation by siliceous sponges seems to have become progressively smaller compared to that of the preceding periods. The continuing decrease in occurrence and volume of cherts in shallow water sedimentary records could be related to this phenomenon. Causally, the impression of lesser opal fixation by shoal water sponges may reflect the progressively increased tie-up of silica from seawater by opal-precipitating micro- and nannoplankton, chiefly by the diatom. Support for this interpretation comes from observation that some recent silica sponges develop the organic framework of newly formed spicules during the period of diatom blooms, but silicify them only after the diatom populations decline (Stone, 1970). On the other hand, a large volume of silica is precipitated in the teeth of intertidal patellacean gastropods, whose source is primarily the silica fixed by the benthic algae on which they feed. Because of the scarcity of geologic records of rocky shore and bordering subtidal areas of pre-Pleistocene ages, it remains uncertain when silica fixation of these gastropods, with a long geologic history, came into existence. The decreasing occurrence and volume of cherts in shoal water deposits during this time interval may imply that it occurred rather recently. Another more likely interpretation of all the phenomena cited may be that there was no major reduction in the volume of biologic opal precipitation in shelf sea communities. The undersaturation of the surface waters with reference to opal brought about by the exponential increase in silica-precipitating plankton during this episode may have produced sufficient undersaturation of the shelf sea waters over the depositional grounds to cause dissolution of the siliceous skeletal remains on the surface and in the accumulating shoal water sediments.

Phosphate fixation by the shelf communities increased during this time interval due to progressively larger standing crops of fish and mammals and perhaps turtles.

Possible volume changes in fluorite fixation by shelf sea organisms in the course of the entire episode are as yet poorly understood due to very limited data on the occurrence of mysid statoliths. Large accumulations of the latter in about 2×10^7-yr-old deposits indicate that from this time onward sizable fixation of fluorite by mysids occurred. The group of gastropods that deposits fluorite in their gizzard plates evolved near the beginning of this episode. However, lack of published records of their gizzard plates make it impossible to determine when they acquired fluorite fixation.

Concerning the large number of other mineral species that are today precipitated by benthic constituents of the shelf seas, there are as yet no fossil records to trace the history of their volumetric biologic tie-up in the course of this recent time span!

The history of the mineral-precipitating biomass of the last roughly 6.5×10^7 yr shows for carbonate, silica, and phosphate that the inroads of their skeletal fixation rapidly reached proportions and affected the chemistry of seawater in a way similar to that of today. With the reduction in shelf sea areas, which principally tied up carbonate in the past in sizable volumes by their large benthic populations, mass transfer of biologic mineral fixation, not only of carbonate but also of silica and phosphates, to the pelagic organisms continued, and the open oceans became the focal point of the enormous increase of the impact of life on the chemistry of the oceans. Biologic carbonate and silica fixation reduced inorganic precipitation to insignificant proportions and phosphate mineral fixation considerably. The vast volumes and enormous extent of biogenic carbonates that today blanket the oceanic floor above the compensation point for aragonite and for calcite stability must have progressively attained proportions similar to those found today. The effects on silica were even more dramatic. Biologic mass fixation led to major undersaturations in the surface waters. Its influence extended further throughout the water column. Yet in contrast to the shallow depth ceiling for biogenic carbonates (accumulations that escaped dissolution), biologic silica probably became incorporated in the sediments clear down to the deepest trenches in the oceans.

The occurrence of phosphatic skeletal remains of fish and to a lesser extent of marine mammals in nearly all types of pelagic sediments during the Tertiary indicate loss of phosphate to the depositional grounds, but the volume changes in time remain to be determined. The sedimentary fraction of inorganically precipitated phosphate minerals, mostly in the form of phosphorites, decreased and possibly ceased about 2×10^7 yr ago. As was noted earlier, data exist on some of the trace constituents of biogenic carbonates, silica, and phosphate minerals precipitated by the plankton and necton, which exponentially took over their fixation in the open oceans, reaching its climax within the last 6.5×10^7 yr. These forcefully demonstrate that the increasing impact of life as it concerns these minerals alone vastly extended its influence on processes regulating the distribution of a variety of other ionic species in seawater, as for example, was recently indicated for fluorine.

A variety of other mineral species was shown earlier to be precipitated by constituents of the extant marine biomass. They include other carbonate mineral phases, a variety of iron oxide minerals in the crystalline and amorphous state, gypsum, and most likely barite and oxalates. All but gypsum are hard-part precipitates of benthic organisms from the intertidal zone to abyssal and some even to hadal depths. Gypsum is deposited by a scyphozoan member of the plankton. The biologically precipitated iron oxide and iron phosphate minerals are of particular importance as the volumes of their fixation and possible stabilization in sediments, in particular of magnetite and goethite, were shown to be sizable. Although modification of the mineralogic form may take place once these biologically precipitated minerals become incorporated in the sediments, their contribution to and likely tie-up in marine sediments has to be reckoned with. To what extent this modifies earlier concepts on the distribution of iron in seawater, particularly in the cell of the water masses over the shelves, which are loosely coupled with that of the open oceans, remains to be seen.

It is unfortunate that so far nothing is known, not even for the last period, about the influences on the chemistry of seawater that were exerted by all of the biologically precipitated minerals other than carbonates, opal, and apatites. Nor is anything known about the distribution of the elements that were tied up by these minerals nor about the volumes of their losses to the sediments.

7. Impact of Marine Life on Physical Processes

There is increasing evidence of the significance of biologic interference with physical processes in the present oceans. Biochemical and biomechanical action, carried out by marine life, is responsible for modifying, retarding, or even reversing physical processes if these were unimpeded by biologic activity. Benthic fungi, plants, and animals most extensively affect inorganic processes. Marine plants and certain animal groups or species, in particular, those with zoochlorellar or zooxanthellar symbiosis, are limited to the photic zone. Shallow water communities affecting physical processes are more diversified, and their standing crops are vastly greater than on the deep-sea floors. Hence, several of the most striking biologic effects on rates of sedimentation and on physical processes are limited and others vastly accelerated in the shelf sea areas. The visible manifestations of biologic interference with physical processes primarily involve diversion and changes of the depositional sites of the suspended loads of marine sediments, mixing of unconsolidated sedimentary sequences, changes in grain size of sedimentary constituents, velocity changes of water movement on the macro- and microscale, erosion, varying degrees of retardation of unimpeded physical erosion caused by wave action off rocky shores, and construction and expansion of rocky bottoms and islands by organisms in the range of the "energy gradient" of water movement, where, in the absence of life, physical erosion and levelling to effective wave base would occur instead. To consider only the extremes of major biologic interference with physical processes, those produced by plants and grazers among the benthic animals are limited to the photic zone, whereas all others are effective at all levels in the subphotic zone, although the extent of their interference may vary at certain depth levels in the oceans.

Mechanical and biochemical action affecting physical processes may be constructional or destructional in nature. Some of the biologic effects result in geomorphologic features of the bottom and rocky shore topography, which in the same environments would not be produced by physical processes, and others are accentuated noticeably by them.

Examples of biologic interference with the depositional sites of water-suspended sedimentary particles and sediment distribution are provided by mat-forming, filamentous, largely blue-green algae that agglutinate saltating sedimentary particles on their mucilaginous sheets and stabilize considerable volumes of sediments by entrapment and binding by vertical and horizontal expansion of the filamentous mats. This occurs on tidal flats and supratidal depressions behind beach ridges. Wave-dislodged mat fragments tend to acquire biscuit-shaped forms in the process of movement and rolling action in the turbulent waters on bottoms of unconsolidated sediments at shallow depths (Ginsburg, 1955, 1960). In Shark Bay, Western Australia, they form a series of isolated, although densely spaced, vertically raised structures, which are low and tubular near the high-tide level and tall and mushroom-shaped near the low-water mark (Logan, 1961). Those continually subjected to rougher water on the outside of the bay tend to be conical in shape and inclined, facing into onshore moving waters (P. Hoffman, personal communication). Carbonate precipitates from entrapped seawater at low tide leads to cementation of all these structures (Logan, 1961; Logan et al., 1970).

This is the oldest, hence the first, of the recognizable inroads of marine life interfering with physical processes in the sea in the geologic past, documented as far back as roughly 2.7×10^9 yr. All of the basic growth forms, called stromatolites, tubular and oncolitic in shape, are found in the geologic records thereafter, characterized by accretion of fine laminae of the entrapped sediments, whereas commonly the algal filaments, responsible for the localized accretions, have been diagenetically removed. The widespread occurrence and commonly enormously thick accumulations over huge areas of stromatolites entirely and later largely made up of Cyanophytes until about 4.5×10^8 yr indicate that they were of major significance in the trapping and stabilization of sediments during the early history of marine life. Their influence in this capacity and their environmental range declined thereafter, most noticeably since Mesozoic times until today, where it is of minor significance, limited largely to tropical tidal flats and extreme hypersaline water, such as in Shark Bay. They were thus restricted to environments with very stringent ecologic conditions, where other algal types and vascular marine plants are kept out or greatly reduced in population size, and for similar ecologic reasons, animal grazers are limited or nonexistent. It appears that most Cyanophytes occupied the photic zone in their early history to a depth of about 10 m below the water surface until an ozone shield was established. Thereafter, they extended their depth range en masse upward into the intertidal zone and became progressively confined to it (Fischer, 1965). Hence, their sphere of effective sediment-trapping activity was further subject to a shift in depth range on shelf sea bottoms.

The vascular marine grasses, represented in tropical waters (largely by Thallassia), illustrate another mode of sediment-trapping by marine life. They form usually densely crowded, tall submarine lawns at shallow depth and support a sizable epifaunal community, largely composed of animals with carbonate hard parts. The bottom, covered by dense growth of these grasses, traps the skeletal remains of their epiphytes and the winnowed, clay-sized fraction of the unsorted sediments from outside their habitat range, thrown into suspension in the waters during the heavy periodic storms (Ginsburg and Lowenstam, 1958). The differentially greater buildup of sediments by the grasses leads to the development of mounds or banks, which crest conspicuously above the level of their surrounding bottoms. The entwined, deep root masses of these vascular plants aid materially in resisting effective surface erosion by tidal currents that sweep through gaps between the grass bank, as shown by overhanging borders, to the depth of their penetration. Bacterial breakdown of the grasses or root mats alone, buried in the process of mound-building, gives the impression of unstratified sedimentary bodies, usually composed of biogenic carbonate, free of their sediment-trapping agents. Similar lenticular, carbonate structures are common in the sedimentary rocks in epicontinental shelf sea sequences as far back as the early Paleozoic. The earliest geologic records of marine grasses are about 8×10^7 yr in age (Voigt, 1956). Hence, trapping action, similar to that producing grassbanks, may account for some, if not most, of the unstratified lenticular structures, at least in younger sedimentary rocks. Other organisms, for example, tall, densely crowded, soft-bodied algae and carbonate-secreting organisms such as bryozoa (Pray, 1958), may have performed the same functions of sediment-trapping to account for similar older structures. Possible approaches to trace the history of the sediment-trapping agents of the structureless moundlike structures, usually called bioherms, have been pointed out elsewhere (Lowenstam, 1967).

Sequences of sediments accumulating on the shelf and deep-sea floors show widespread reworking by deposit feeders, burrowing organisms of which some pile up excavated sediment to form mounds, even to considerable height, around the surface entrances of the burrows. Tracks and trails of vagrant benthos furrow deeply, at occasions, the accumulating sediments. Where thin layers of different grain size and mineralogic composition are affected by these processes, complex inhomogeneity and poor sorting of the sediments are the result. These processes are so well known and so widely discussed that they require no further elaboration beyond mentioning their gross physical expressions.

The fecal pellets, produced by mucus binding of the excreted sediments by the deposit feeders, are commonly preserved intact. In environments with large populations of deposit feeders, the sediments, particularly fine-grained deposits, become largely or entirely peleted. Where these processes continue for long times without radical changes in hydrodynamic conditions, thick accumulations of pelleted sediments are produced, most noticeably in fine-grained carbonates. Most freshly produced pellets can be mechanically easily disaggregated. There are indications that in the process of prolonged undisturbed accumulation, some cementation may occur. Changes in chemical composition and finally total removal of the binding mucus through bacterial action and hydrolysis by interstitial waters may be responsible for the various degrees of cementation of certain types of pellets. Physically, the effect of pelleting results in large grain-sized aggregates of the originally fine-grained sediments. If cementation occurs, these aggregates will resist water transport during episodes of slightly increased wave intensity to other depositional sites as compared to the unconsolidated, fine-grained constituent grains.

The extensive burrows of many infaunal invertebrates are maintained in unconsolidated sediments by excretions of hardening agents to prevent their collapse. In most cases, "mucus" excreted by the burrowers is considered to form the hardening material. A brown cement, apparently composed of amorphous calcium phosphate (collophanite) has been reported to bind tightly the loose sand grains of the burrows of the decapod crustacean *Callianassa major* (Weimer and Hoyt, 1964). Systematic studies of the materials that cement and support burrows produced by a diversity of animals may lead to further discoveries of other inorganic substances secreted directly by them or precipitated from their organic excretions once in contact with seawater and/or bacteria breaking them down. There is no information on the precise composition of the various types of "mucus" secretions by deposit feeders left behind in moving through and on the surface of sediments and active as binding agents of fecal pellets. The various mucus types may affect differentially constituent grains of the mineral suites of sediments. Depending on the resistivity to them, some kinds of mineral grains may be dissolved peripherally or to a considerable extent, and others may be chemically altered, at least surficially. Still others may act as protective coatings long enough to decellerate dissolution by interstitial and bottom waters, in all cases in combination with bacterial actions. It may well be that the "mucus" secretions may have a far greater effect on modifying marine sediments and their depositional processes at all depths than the various noticeable modifications brought about by biologic activity in the oceans.

Tracks and trails of marine invertebrates can be traced back in marine sedimentary rocks to slightly in excess of 6.5×10^8 yr in age. Together with burrows and fecal pellet accumulations, they became increasingly abundant in sedimentary rocks from 6×10^8 yr up to the present. Hence, with the appearance of Eumetazoa, the impact of life on physical processes in the oceans became greatly extended and diversified as compared to earlier initiated activities by bacteria, fungi, and Cyanophyte algae.

Mineralized exoskeletons of life organisms are commonly invaded surficially by algal, fungal, and a variety of invertebrate borers and biomechanically eroded by grazers with tooth "enamel" harder than the minerals in the exoskeletons affected by them in the photic and algae-free subphotic zone. Biochemical and biomechanical borings by a variety of predators produce large excavations that usually penetrate the exoskeletal shields. Carnivores dismember exo- and endoskeletons of their prey biomechanically. Most of these biochemical and biomechanical weakening and break-up processes of mineralized hard parts occur and usually are intensified and deposited on the sea floor after the death of the organisms. A recent symposium on "Penetration of Calcium Carbonate Substrates by Lower Algae and Invertebrates" presents data on the diversity of organisms involved in these processes, which extend their range of activity also to carbonate rocks from the intertidal zone to some depth below (Carriker et al., eds., 1969). It documents the present state of knowledge on biologic erosion processes biomechanically by unmineralized cell complexes and on the, as yet, very limited understanding of the chemistry of biochemical erosion unaided or combined with hard-tissue action.

Mineralized hard parts, their fragmental remains, and breakdown products range from clay to large cobble size. Their shapes and their macro- and microarchitectures differ largely and significantly from sedimentary constituents of terrigenous, submarine, volcanic, and autigenic origin. Quiet to rough water environments are inhabited by organisms with skeletal hard parts encompassing all sizes and shapes. Barring volcanic ejectives, ice-rafted sediments, and intrusion of turbidity currents, given a quiet water environment without mineralized hard parts, as existed prior to roughly 6×10^8 yr, the accumulating sediments would be composed almost entirely of well-sorted microparticles of minerals that settled out of the water column. Following the event of the development of mineralized hard parts, unsorted sediments were deposited instead, due to the contributions of variously-sized skeletal remains from benthic and later through increasingly larger contributions from nectonic organisms. If located at depths where heavy storms only occasionally churn up the bottom sediments, graded beds or sequences of coarse to fine-grained beds would be found interbedded with unsorted sediments, denoting undisturbed, quiet water deposition. Within reach of frequent storms and slow sedimentation rates, only the coarser fractions would accumulate locally. The degree of differences in sorting of skeletal-free and skeletal-bearing sediments decreases as depositional environments become subject to greater frequency of increasing wave energies. Yet, even in the intermediate range of the energy gradient, sorting and transport would differ between equally heavy but differently-shaped and sized skeletal remains and inorganically derived rock fragments. Therefore, since the beginning of the formation of mineralized skeletons, sorting processes of accumulating sediments became significantly modified by life over a wide range of the energy gradient in depositional environments.

The crystals of mineralized hard parts are almost in all cases minute, ranging on the average from less than 0.1 μ to a few tens of microns. The crystal shapes are determined by the constraints of the morphology of the organic matrices that enclose them. Acicular, "needle-shaped" crystals have been found among a variety of carbonate and noncarbonate minerals precipitated in hard tissues. These and other shapes, dictated by the organic matrix forms, are found rarely or not at all among the crystals of the same minerals formed inorganically in the cooling melts of magmas by metamorphic processes and precipitated from hydrothermal solutions. Moreover, inorganically precipitated minerals produced by these processes usually have a considerably greater size range, and crystals measuring millimeters to several centimeters in diameter are common. The uniformly microscopic to submicroscopic sizes and the differences in shapes of the crystals from hard tissues, once freed from their organic matrices, should behave differently from the hard parts in which they occur and, in particular, from identical crystals or crystal fragments of inorganic origin in water transport, settling velocities, and the depositional sites where they became stabilized.

Fluorite crystals, precipitated by nectonic mysids in their statoliths, serve to illustrate likely differences of this sort. The statoliths are dish- to crucible-shaped and, on the average, sand sized. The crystals in the statoliths are acicular in shape, on the average about 30 μ long and 1 μ in diameter (Fig. 11). Inorganically formed fluorite crystals are commonly large, cubic, less frequently octahedral, and rarely dodecahedral in shape. Acicular crystal habits have been observed but are so rare that they are not mentioned among crystal habits of fluorite (R. Jahns, personal communication). The usual forms of the crystals fracture flat-conchoidal to splintery or unevenly. Hence, detrital fragments of inorganically formed crystals, when transported to the sea or derived from ejections of marine volcanoes, depending on their size, weight, and shape, could be incorporated in sediments over a wide range of the energy gradient. Mysid statoliths, settling with or without the shed molts, because of their shape and organic content, would settle likely at a different rate than inorganic fluorite crystals and, because of their size-controlled low weight, would be deposited only in quiet semirough water-bottom environments. Once their acicular crystals become freed through degradation of their organic matrices, the crystals could then go back into suspension in semirough water environments and during storms in the quiet water ones, would stay longer in suspension and hence disperse more widely than inorganic fluorite crystals or their fragments of equal weight. Their final depositional site would be limited to extreme quiet water bottoms.

There are two phenomena in subtropical and tropical shallow water environments that illustrate most dramatically the impact of life on physical processes in the sea: "coral" reefs and intertidal to low subtidal nips or undercut level formations of rocky shores composed of limestone.

Biologic reefs are carbonate structures that fringe shorelines and platform margins, form pinnacles, archipelagos, and, in the open sea, atolls. They owe their existence to constructional processes of carbonate-secreting coralline algae, zooxanthellae-bearing scleractinian corals, hydrozoans, encrusting bryozoa, and Sclerospongia. Their skeletons construct rigid frameworks, commonly in the form of an open-meshed room and pillar structure, and in part of the structures, by massive compact accretions. They support or provide ecologic conditions for large, highly diverse benthic and nectonic populations of algae and animals. Of these, a very large segment secretes similarly carbonate skeletons. Some of the sessile benthos aid in reinforcing the structural framework. All of the carbonate-secreting biomass, including the reef builders, provide skeletal debris that partially or entirely fills the interstitial spaces of the rigid framework, accumulates in depressions on the reef surfaces, contributes to lagoonal deposits, and makes up most of the debris of the talus slopes, which flank the structures when these are located on shallow water bottoms. Large-scale cementation by fine-grained carbonate of the skeletal debris in the interstices of the framework has been discovered recently in a number of recent to-near-recent buildup parts of the reef framework (Land and Goreau, 1970). It is as yet unclear whether the carbonate cements are of inorganic origin, directly or indirectly precipitated by biologic activity such as by bacteria. Frame building and areal extent of the rigid structures resulting from it may form only a small segment of the entire reef complex. Yet it owes in its entirety its existence and maintenance to the constructional agents of the complex, ecologically-zoned ecosystem.

Reef-building organisms are capable of constructing their own hard substrate, even on unconsolidated sediment accumulations, where scattered cobble-sized skeletal debris or volcanic ejectives serve as nucleation centers for their colonization. The maximum depth at which corals are active in reef building is 46 m, and most reef building takes place between 30 m and the surface waters (Vaughan and Wells, 1943). Once a hard substrate is constructed by them, even at depths up to 45 m, the reef-building organisms are capable of raising it into the turbulent surface waters and maintaining it there through their exceptional power of large-scale skeletal carbonate secretion. One of the most impressive features of reef-building processes is their ability to expand peripherally the reef surface in the wave-swept surface waters and most extensively on the windward side in the wake of greatest water turbulence. Under the same hydrodynamic conditions, rocky platforms, including those composed of limestone, would be instead rapidly eroded and leveled to the depth of the effective wave base. Leeward-transported bioclastic debris on reef surfaces commonly accumulates and builds up to form islands above the water surface, which become consolidated by freshwater-precipitated carbonate cements and colonized by land vegetation. While these island-forming processes are similar to those produced by wave transport of sediments in shoal water areas of continental shelves and island borders, they would not take place in large parts of the open oceans where their sources of the sediments and their formation and their maintenance are entirely due to biologic reef and atoll formation.

The power of skeletal carbonate fixation by reef-building corals is indicated by measured increases in coral colonies in height up to 8 cm/yr and annual weight increases of their carbonate up to 1200% (Boschma, 1936; Tamura and Hada, 1932). Measurements of areal expansion of some coral colonies have been recorded for a period of 29 weeks by increases from 16 to 320 square centimeters (Stephenson and Stephenson, 1933). However, growth and expansion differ widely between individual colonies of the same species and between species of different reef builders and accessories, depending on macro- and microenvironmental conditions and competition for nutrients, food, and space.

Maintenance and expansion of reef complexes is materially aided by large-scale retention of bioclastic carbonate debris, generated by reef builders and reef dwellers. One of the modes of retention is infiltration and later incorporation by overgrowth of skeletal debris in the initially open mesh of the expanding framework of the reef builders. Another is provided by colonization of coralline algae and reef-building corals of unconsolidated bioclastic debris accumulations in depressions surrounded by the elevated rims of frame-building activity, laid down in lagoons and forming the talus slopes, particularly on the lee side of the reef complex. This leads to pinpoint, patchy, and areally extensive cementation of unconsolidated sediments. Filamentous medium to tall, rhizome-rooted, calcareous and uncalcified algae, seagrasses, and a variety of gorgonians and alcyonarians also aid considerably in reducing losses of reef-generated bioclastic debris by reducing wave energy. In shoal water reefs, the extensive talus slopes on the leeward side are commonly densely carpeted by seagrasses such as *Thallasia*, performing the same functions in sediment retention and accretion as was earlier shown to be performed by isolated grass banks. These various processes that aid in retaining a large volume of bioclastic debris on the reefs are initially made possible by reducing fetch and wave energy over the reef surface by large-scale dissipation on the reef front. However, during occasional heavy storms of hurricane strength, particularly when these hit the lee side of the reef, there is major destruction of reef portions and major loss of their unconsolidated sediments.

Biologic destructional forces are also at work by an extensive, highly diversified segment of the reef biota. They are biomechanical and biochemical in nature. Biochemical processes are more extensive, and in overall effects, more effective than the biomechanical ones. They take the form of microscopic and megascopic borings and tunnelings of hard substances, including skeletal structures of life organisms of reef builders. Densely crowded, microscopic borings by endolithic algae, mostly blue greens and fungi, are most extensively developed shallowly below the surface of the substrates in the intertidal zone and to a short distance below. They lead to weakening of carbonates, which they permeate, and cause local dislodging of mineral grains.

Medium- to large-sized borings, produced by representatives of bryozoa, polychaetes, sipunculids, echiurids, barnacles, gastropods, bivalves, and, in part, possibly by echinoids, occur at all levels and in all habitats on the reef. Greater diameters and depths of penetration, particularly by bivalves and sipunculids, weaken the physical strength of the skeletons of the reef builders, which when intensely bored become more readily subject to wave destruction and wave erosion. Biomechanical processes carried out singly or in combination with biochemical ones cause surface erosion. Soft parts and mineralized hard tissues are effective in biomechanical erosion. The most widespread destruction is produced by boring sponges, gastropods, and certain reef fish, but members of polychaete worms and decapod crustaceans, and possibly echinoids, are also involved in this process. This subject matter will be elaborated on further in considering biologic effects in nip formation. The net effect of biologic destruction reduces the net gain of growth and expansion of reef complexes produced by constructional processes. The net gain of biologically produced carbonate has been estimated to raise reef surfaces in the process of upgrowth between 0.5 to 5 cm/yr with a likely average of 1 cm/yr (Kuenen, 1950). Chave et al (1972) have estimated that the annual average potential production of biogenic carbonate on reef surfaces is close to 10^4 g/m^2, the gross production between 4×10^2 and 6×10^4 g/m^2 and the net production about 10^3 g/m^2. There are very few known drowned reefs. This attests to the exceptional power of reef growth expansion owing to their constructional agents, which provide them with considerable latitude to cope usually with subsidence of their substrate in tectonically active areas. Drilling operations on a number of oceanic atolls have provided the most impressive evidence of the ability of reef-building processes to cope successfully with substrate subsidence in combination with rapid, glacially-controlled eustatic sea level changes, to which they were subjected during the Pleistocene, throughout millions of years. Submarine bottom profiling has shown that many growing atolls in the Eastern Pacific Ocean form pinnacles or broader structures perched on the flat tops of seamounts or guyots, whose surfaces are located as deep as 1800 m below sea level (Ladd et al., 1950). The guyots are the submerged remnants of submarine volcanoes, whose tops were truncated while they were located in the zone of effective wave erosion. Other atolls have been found adjoining guyots or on volcanic lavas belonging to them (Ladd and Schlanger, 1960).

The estimated average rate of vertical expansion of coral-algal reefs of 1 cm/yr and under optimal conditions of 4 cm/yr, as observed by Sluiter on Krakatau (cited in Kuenen, 1950), provide considerable latitude to cope with subsidence of their substrate, even in tectonically active areas and with rapid rise in sea level, as occurred repeatedly during interglacial stages of the Pleistocene. Where reef foundations are located on unconsolidated sediments, subsidence through settling, induced by the increased load of the growing reef mass, may result from their own activity (Kuenen, 1950). As long as subsidence and rise in sea level do not exceed the rates of upgrowth of reefs over the depth range of their average-to-optimal development, reef surfaces can maintain contact with the water surface or rapidly rise again to this level. The carbonates recovered by drilling operations on various atolls consist entirely or largely of biofacies found in recent reef complexes and their lagoons. Most drillings to depths of about 400 to 800 m recovered reef rocks of Neogene ages without reaching the base of the reef structures. However, on Eniwetok atoll, two borings penetrated the entire carbonate sections and bottomed shallowly in the basaltic rocks of the volcanic substrate at depths of about 1250 and 1300 m. The carbonate rocks, showing zones of diagenetic alterations, including dolomite formation, range in geologic ages from the recent to the Eocene. The sequence in the 1250 m thick section is composed of reef rocks, reef talus, and shallow lagoonal deposits. The 1300 m drilling recovered reef and apparently lagoonal-type deposits only to a depth of about 880 m, followed by globigerina oozes and, in turn, by shoal water bioclastic debris. This sequence indicates that reef expansion reached this location only shortly prior to the Eocene epoch. These drilling records establish that reef building of oceanic atolls have been essentially continuous for periods between more than 1×10^7 to as long as about 5×10^7 yrs (Ladd and Schlanger, 1960). This, more than anything else, attests to the spectacular power of withstanding, overcoming, and modifying physical processes, including conspicuous changes in submarine topography in the open oceans by biologic forces through the mass fixation and deployment of the skeletally-precipitated carbonate by reef ecosystems.

Shelf reef development, particularly in the form of reef barriers at platform margins, acquires further significance in that they defend the platforms, islands, and land masses by greatly retarding their rates of mechanical erosion through wave action.

The history of skeletally-constructed reef structures may go back to close to the beginning of the invention of skeletal mineral metabolism, about 6×10^8 yr ago. This remains to be determined by whether the taxonomically problematical Archaeocyathids were frame-builders or not. The earliest unquestionable reefs are of mid-Ordovician age (about 4.5×10^8 yr ago). As in all reefs thereafter, their constructional agents precipitated carbonate, with the possible exception of some of the stromatoporoids, which are now considered to be taxonomically assignable to the extant Sclerospongia (Hartman and Goreau, 1970). These reef builders today precipitate aragonitic or calcitic skeletons and a small fraction of opaline spicules. Stromatoporoids, as far back as 3.5×10^8 yr ago, occasionally also show evidence of siliceous spicule formation. Reef-dwelling organisms with mineralized hard parts that, as today, played a major role in the development of ancient reef complexes, also precipitated carbonate skeletons, with rare exception. Contributions of phosphatic skeletons to the bioclastic debris, even by bony fish, which started to occupy reef niches only roughly 3.7×10^8 yr ago, were always insignificant. Silica-precipitating agents, such as siliceous sponges, may have been minor contributors also to reef sediments. However, as indicated by the dissolution of the siliceous spicules of recent Sclerospongia, in the course of skeletal carbonate accretion, opal may not have been stable in the alkaline interstitial waters of the carbonate buildups and, hence, was likely solution-removed during the growth or in the course of diagenetic alterations of the reefs. Major turnover and changes in dominance occurred among reef builders and sediment-contributing reef dwellers in the history of reef building in the course of geologic time. Those of concern here involve resultant changes in their carbonate mineralogy and skeletal construction, which had a bearing on rates of reef growth in relation to the latitude of physical environmental conditions under which it could take place.

Before considering these aspects, let me point out that beginning with the late early Silurian, about 4.2×10^8 yr ago, reef development started to become widespread in the shallow epicontinental shelf seas on the submerged craton. By mid-Silurian time, reef archipelagos, similar in extent if not larger than the extant Great Barrier Reef, came into existence. Constructional agents were able to raise and maintain reefs in the turbulent surface waters, as best illustrated by the horseshoe-shaped Marine Reef in Illinois (Lowenstam, 1950), which is similar in shape to extant reefs growing into the prevailing wind and wave direction on the Sahul shelf of Western Australia (Teichert and Fairbridge, 1948). Reefs developed during this time covered a range of present-day reef forms, attained similar areal extents and vertical dimensions, and were able to cope with subsidence similar to extant shelf reefs. Reef segments, dislodged during heavy storms and transported to the surrounding deeper-lying bottoms remained rigid, including the framework-filling bioclastic debris, exposed on the reef blocks, indicate that cementation processes similar to those recently found in extant reefs were already operative in the early Paleozoic. One apparent difference between ancient reefs in general and early Paleozoic reefs in particular, as compared to present-day shelf reefs, was the enormous development of talus slope accumulations of bioclastic debris, which frequently exceeded the areal extent of the framework-enclosed reef portions. This could be attributed to less effective skeletal growth and slower expansion rates of the Paleozoic reef builders that, with the exception of the surviving Sclerospongia, were composed of algal and anthozoan constituents that became extinct at the end of this era. However, the lack of comparable extensive reef flank development of extant shelf-sea reefs can be more reasonably attributed to the very short time elapsed since sea level reinundated the present-day shelf sea bottoms in post-Winconsin time. Only after sea level rose again to reestablish and enable reefs to grow up again during the last 5×10^3 yr B.P. could reef talus accumulate on their periphery. By contrast, during tens of millions of years of shallow submergence, wave-resistant reefs in the cratonic shelf seas, as during the Silurian, could shed bioclastic debris for a hundred thousand years or more, as long as they remained active and the sea floor was located below effective wave base. Hence, their huge talus slope expanse cannot be attributed *per se* to less effective frame building of Paleozoic reef builders, although it may have been slightly less as compared to extant reef builders. However, criteria are lacking to verify this possibility. Pinnacle-shaped, wave-resistant reefs with little talus scree up to 300 m in height, found only along margins of a subsiding basin in the Silurian reef archipelago, indicate that reef builders as far back as the Silurian were already able to keep pace in upgrowth with subsidence of their substrate, although the rate of compensational growth cannot as yet be assessed (Lowenstam, 1957). Hence, all basic potentials of modern reef-building communities to cope with physical processes had their origin at least as far back as 4.2×10^8 yr, although the extent to which they could respond to some, such as rates of subsidence in particular, cannot as yet be fully assessed.

Let us return to consider the major discernible changes that occurred in the mineral phases and trace element chemistry of skeletal carbonates during the geologic history of reef-building processes. Of the principal reef builders in the Paleozoic, the coralline algae, tabulate, and rugose corals had calcitic skeletons on grounds of the preservation of their crystal fabric. The Sclerospongia, wherever I have examined them so far, are composed of sparry calcite, suggesting that their skeletons may have been originally composed of aragonite, as in most of the recent species. Sclerospongia were commonly a major constituent of the Silurian and Devonian reef builders. There are no data on whether the algae and tabulate corals precipitated low or high magnesium calcites, whereas scanty data for rugose corals indicate at least medium magnesium contents and were likely originally high magnesium calcite (Lowenstam, 1963). Scleractinian corals, which replaced the Paleozoic Antozoa and became major reef builders since Triassic time, were as recent ones, composed of aragonite. The coralline algae, which continued to be major frame-building agents and increased in importance in this capacity starting about 1.5×10^8 yr ago, precipitated calcite. Sclerospongia, reappearing in the fossil records including reefs about 1.5×10^8 yr B.P., were reduced in importance to minor constituents in reef-building processes. Whether they were calcite- or aragonite-precipitating agents remains to be determined. During the mid- to late-Cretaceous time, caprinids and rudistids with skeletons composed of calcite and aragonite were reef-building constituents. Among the sediment contributors of the reef dweller, crinoids, and, next in abundance, the articulate brachiopods, were of primary significance. They, like nearly all minor sediment contributors, had calcitic skeletons. A few biogeochemical data of Paleozoic crinoids indicate that they precipitated high magnesium calcites similar to recent species, and the brachiopods low-to-medium magnesium calcites. Beginning with the Mesozoic era, crinoid and brachiopod populations steadily declined, until today they are insignificant among the reef dwellers. They were progressively replaced by high Sr-bearing, aragonite-precipitating algae and foraminifera with low and high magnesium calcite skeletons. Molluscs with predominantly aragonitic skeletons, cirripedia, echinoids, asteroids, and ophiuroids with high magnesium calcitic hard parts, and polychaete worms with aragonitic tubes are of secondary importance among reef dwellers as sediment contributors. The overall trend one finds in the carbonate mineral phases in the evolution of reef-forming organisms in the course of geologic time is an increase in the volumes of fixation of aragonite relative to calcite, more pronounced in the carbonate precipitates of the reef dwellers, the major contributors to reef sediments, than among the frame-building agents. The very limited biochemical data on Paleozoic carbonate-secreting agents, which are represented also on reefs, at best suggest that high Sr-bearing aragonites increased with time among builders and dwellers of reefs, whereas it remains uncertain whether high magnesium as compared to low magnesium calcites remained unchanged, increased, or decreased. The changes in the calcite-aragonite ratios among the constructional agents and dwellers in the course of the history of reef-building processes were accompanied by changes in size, shape, weight, crystal fabric, and degrees of crystal aggregation. Hence, changes in abrasion, disaggregation, and sorting in water transport and depositional sites on and off the reef structures of the bioclastic debris must have occurred, similar to those indicated by Chave (1960) for shoal-water carbonate accumulations in general. For example, the aragonite-precipitating green, red, and brown algal populations became important reef dwellers, although not limited to reef habitats, starting about Cretaceous time. Their aragonite precipitates are, with the exception of *Halimeda*, so poorly aggregated that they disintegrate into individual crystals postmortem. The size of the crystals ranges from fractions of a micron to several hundred microns. The crystals precipitated by many species that deposit aragonite are acicular in shape, including those in *Halimeda*, which also loses crystals that are locally poorly aggregated (Lowenstam, 1955; Stockman et al., 1967; Perkins et al., 1972). Easily transported even by low wave energy, they become stabilized on the reefs only in quiet water areas and particularly in lagoons of atolls. However, a considerable fraction is lost to depositional grounds outside the reefs (Lowenstam, 1957). In the Paleozoic, particularly in Silurian and Devonian time, calcite-precipitating crinoids occupied the niches now held by these algae and were equal, if not larger, in population sizes on and at the periphery of the reefs. Their disarticulated skeletal elements were, on the average, centimeters in circumference. Hence, because of their larger size and heavier weight, nearly all of them became stabilized on the reefs and their talus slopes over a considerably wider range of the energy gradient of wave action than most of the aragonitic precipitation products of the algae, which substituted for the crinoids in geologically younger reefs.

Considering changes in skeletal construction, those that occurred in the course of evolution of reef-building corals appear of major significance. Most of the groups of scleractinian corals form massive aragonitic skeletons. However, porous or vesicular skeletal formation characterizes species of the Acroporidae, Poritidae, and many of the Pocilloporidae, which are major reef-building agents. Species of the first two groups mentioned are most diversified today in Indo-Pacific reefs and the last one named is confined to them. Branching types are common or are most commonly developed among these species. Experimental and observational studies in nature show that the porous corals grow at vastly greater rates, and despite their conservation of carbonate fixation per cubic area, accrete considerably larger volumes of aragonite because of their accelerated growth rates per unit of time than massive corals. Annual increases in height in porous corals are at the minimum doubled and may be 10 times greater than in massive corals, and percentage gain in weight increases may differ between the two types by as much as 1200% versus 20% (summarized in Vaughan and Wells, 1943; Wells, 1956).

Species with porous skeletons within the groups where they are found today originated between mid- to late-Cretaceous time. They were minor reef-building constituents through the Paleogene, increased slightly in importance in the early Neogene, and expanded exponentially since the onset of the Pleistocene, in particular, the Poritidae and Acroporidae, to become the dominant reef builders, principally in the Indo-Pacific thereafter (Vaughan and Wells, 1943). A possible explanation to account for the explosive expansion of the porous types among the reef-building corals in the Pleistocene, which apparently escaped notice by students of corals and reef-building processes, was advanced by Gerth (1930). He suggested that this phenomena may be linked to exceptional, rapid, glacially-controlled eustatic sea level changes during the Pleistocene. This would certainly explain why porous types, because of their exceptional power of upgrowth, could break out of their previous confinement in intercommunity competition with massive corals when sea level rose particularly rapidly following lowering during glacial stages. One can also speculate under what environmental conditions selection pressure would favor the origin and subsequent survival and spread of porous corals prior to the onset of the Pleistocene. These would be areas of moderate tectonic subsidence in mobile belts. Because such conditions were localized time, and perhaps because their annual upgrowth increments were initially smaller than those that evolved shortly prior to and during the Pleistocene, their selective advantage in reef-building processes was not large enough to effectively displace even locally massive coral types on a large scale. The glacially controlled rapid shifts in sea levels on a worldwide scale provided the threshold for their phenomenal expansion and put a premium on selection pressure for species with accelerated upgrowth potential. Thus, physical environmental conditions were responsible for the phenomenal expansion of these critical building agents in present-day reef building, and these, in turn, reduced materially the power of destruction of such physical forces as high wave turbulence. This does not explain, however, why the porous types among the reef-building corals declined prior to the Pleistocene in the Atlantic oceans, even though they were never a major constituent of the constructional agents as far as I have been able to ascertain from personal studies of pre-Pleistocene reefs. A moderate increase in population size relative to massive corals seems to be in evidence in certain ecologic zones on some Atlantic reefs, but why they did not expand proportionately during the Pleistocene to those in the Indo-Pacific Ocean remains to be determined. However, it may explain the markedly less luxurious and extensive reef development in the Atlantic and eastern Pacific as compared to the Indo-Pacific Ocean.

The last conspicuous phenomenon of biologic effects on physical processes to be considered here concerns the origin of the deeply incised nips on subtropical and tropical limestone islands and raised reefs in the intertidal zone, and less frequently and then only locally, a short distance underneath in the subtidal zone. Shallow to moderately deep nips are found in many parts of the land masses all over the oceans on coastal cliffs that are subjected to continuous heavy surf action and lie in the path of frequent heavy storms. These affect indiscriminately all rock types, but differ in intensity depending on the physical strength of the rocks attacked by wave action. Even in these cases, boring algae, fungi, and bacteria may contribute to the physical notching process, weakening the bonding strength of the constituent mineral grains.

The most noticeable distinction of the nips on warm-water limestone islands from those produced by wave action is that they increase noticeably in depth of excavation as one proceeds from the open ocean side with greatest wave action to the sheltered side of an individual island. This becomes even more noticeable in closely spaced islands strung out over greater distances parallel to a longer gradient of decreasing fetch and wave action. There is a tendency in more protected areas for the nips to develop near horizontal roof structures.

Although surface waters are supersaturated with reference to calcite and aragonite, the possibility of physicochemical solution by seawater was considered early in the investigations of the origin of these nips. Diurnal temperature changes, coupled with nightly lowering of the alkalinity of the waters through respiration of both animals and plants, were cautiously suggested to be responsible in part at least as the solution mechanisms (Kuenen, 1950; Revelle and Fairbright, 1957). Data have accumulated to show that rocky shores, mostly composed of limestones, are subject to intense biomechanical and biochemical erosion in the intertidal and may extend to subtidal levels and the supratidal spray zone (Otter, 1937; Emery, 1962; Ginsburg, 1953; North, 1954; Ranson, 1955; Hodgekin, 1964; McLean, 1967). Studies extended in some cases to nips and a few specifically concerned with biologic activity in relation to nip formation have indicated that biomechanical and biochemical processes are the primary forces, if not the only ones, to account for their origin (Newell, 1954, 1956; Emery, 1962; Neumann, 1966; McLean, 1964, 1967). The large populations of grazing gastropods and surface-enmeshing and endolithic algae, which are their primary food sources, have been given special attention and have led to the conclusion that they are of major significance in the biologic erosion that leads to nip formation (Newell, 1954, 1956; Emery, 1962). In conjunction with studies of the mineralization products of gastropod and chiton teeth, I have made extensive observations on a large number of organisms engaged in the destructional processes that lead to nip formation in Barbados, Fiji, and, in particular, at Palau. The results of these unpublished studies modify previous concepts on the methods of erosion for some of the biologic agents engaged in this process and show further that the composition of rock-destroying organisms differs in niche occupation and population density in the range from quiet to rough water nips formed in limestone cliffs and, more conspicuously, in those shallowly formed in volcanic breccias. Table III is based on a tabulation of all known biologic erosional agents and their activity, amended by data obtained from personal observations and some new literature data. Figures 13 and 14 show the results of my personal study on the nip-forming agents at Palau.

Three distinct biologic activities are involved in intertidal nip formation, weakening and partially disintegrating the substrate to varying depths by boring, biochemical erosion, and biomechanical erosion. The organisms involved in boring activity are listed in Table III and Figs. 13 and 14. The precise nature of the biochemistry producing these borings is poorly established or unknown. Biochemical and biomechanical erosion is commonly produced separately by different organisms. However, some species dissolve as well as mechanically abrade the substrate.

Patellacean gastropods are the most noticeable species that dissolve as well as

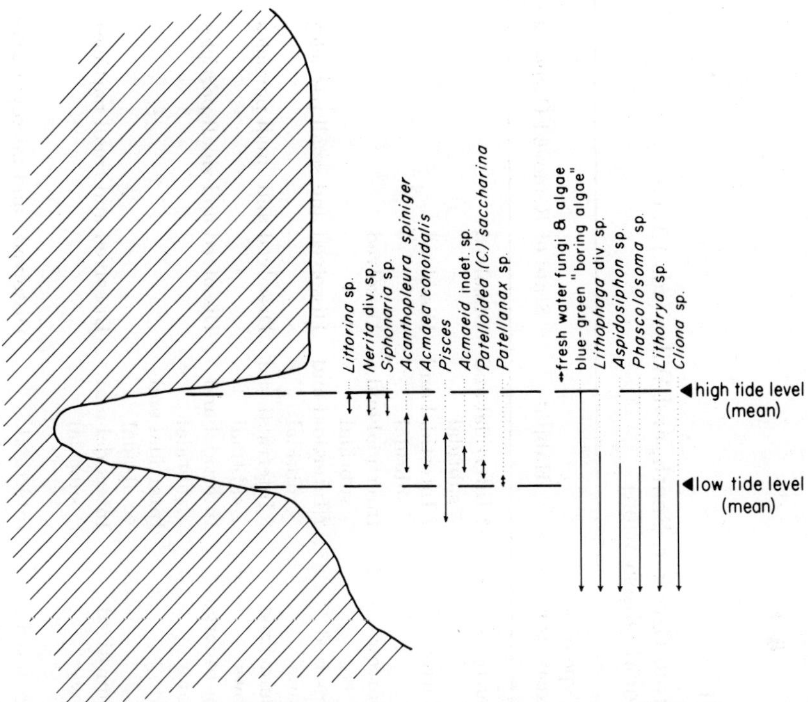

Fig. 13. Vertical distribution of substrate weakening and destroying organisms in nips at Palau, Caroline Islands. Vertical ranges approximate.

Species	Biomechanical eroding agents: Scraping mechanism	Mineralogy	Hardness relative to limestone*	Biochemical eroding agents: Surface depression	Subsurface borings	Distribution & relative abundance on: limestone substrata (quiet, semi-rough, rough water)	volcanic breccia substrata (quiet, semi-rough, rough water)
Acanthopleura spiniger	Denticle capping of teeth	$FeO \cdot Fe_2O_3$	+ 3	~			
Acmaea conoidalis	"	$\alpha FeOOH$ $SiO_2(H_2O)_n$	+ 2.5	✓			
Patellanax sp.	"	"	"	~			
Patelloida (C.) saccharina	"	"	"	✓			
Acmaeid indet. sp.	"	"	"	✓			
Pisces	"	$Ca_{10}(PO_4)_6$ CO_3H_2O	+ 2				
Nerita div. sp.	"	Organic compounds	- 1	~			
Siphonaria sp.	"	"	"	~			
Littorina sp.	"	"	"	~			
"blue-green" algae	—	—	—		✓		
Lithophaga div. sp.					✓		
Aspidosiphon sp.	—	—	—		✓		
Phascolosoma sp.	—	—	—		✓		
Lithotrya sp.	—	—	—		✓		
Cliona sp.					✓	—?—	

* (on Mohs hardness scale)

Fig. 14. Mechanisms, distribution, and relative abundances of rock weakening and destroying organisms in hips formed in limestones and volcanic breccias; Palau, Caroline Islands.

TABLE III

Carbonate Substrate-Destroying Organisms (Data from Carriker, Smith, and Wilce (eds.) 1969; Neumann, 1968; and Personal Observation)

Penetrants	Type of Excavator	Mechanism of Penetration	Type of Excavator	Habitat	State of Removed Carbonate
Bacteria	Burrower	Chemical	Microburrows	? Intertidal and subtidal	Dissolved
Fungi	Burrower	Chemical	Microburrows	? Intertidal and subtidal	Dissolved
Algae	Burrower	Chemical	Microburrows	Intertidal and subtidal	Dissolved
Porifera: *Cliona* div. sp.	Burrower	Chemical and mechanical	Medium-sized burrows	? Intertidal and subtidal	Dissolved and small particles
Bryozoa	Burrower	Chemical and mechanical ?	± Medium-sized burrows	? Intertidal and subtidal	Dissolved and small particles
Sipunculoidea	Burrower	Chemical and mechanical ?	Medium-to-large burrows	Intertidal and subtidal	Dissolved and small particles
Brachiopoda: Articulata	Burrower	Chemical ?	Burrows	Intertidal and subtidal	?
Annelida: Polychaeta	Burrower	Chemical some + mechanical	± Medium-sized burrows	Intertidal and subtidal	Dissolved and small particles
Mollusca:					
Polyplacophora	Scraper Burrower	Mechanical and Chemical ?	scrape-marked burrows, oval-shaped depressions	Intertidal Subtidal	Dissolved ? and microparticles

Gastropoda:					
Patellacea	Scraper Burrower	Mechanical and chemical	Scrape-marked burrows, oval-shaped depressions	Intertidal Subtidal	Dissolved and microparticles
Other diverse Gastropoda	Scrapers Burrowers	Mechanical and chemical ?	Scrape-marked burrows, oval-shaped depressions	Supratidal Intertidal Subtidal	Dissolved ? and microparticles
	Borer	Chemical and some mechanical	Medium-to-large burrows or bore-holes	Intertidal ? Subtidal	Dissolved microparticles
Bivalvia	Burrower Borer	Mechanical some chemical	Medium-to-large burrows or bore-holes	Intertidal ? Subtidal	Microparticles ? Dissolved
Crustacea:					
Cirripedia	Burrower Borer	Chemical-mechanical ?	Burrows Boreholes	Intertidal Subtidal ?	Dissolved microparticles ?
Deapoda	Burrower	Mechanical	Scrape marks	Supratidal Intertidal	Microparticles and dissolved
Isopoda	Burrower	Mechanical ?	Burrows	Intertidal ? Subtidal	?
Echinodermata:					
Echinodea	Burrower	Chemical ? Mechanical	Boreholes Burrow	Intertidal Subtidal	Dissolved ? microparticles
Pisces	Burrower	Mechanical	Scrape marks	Intertidal Subtidal	Microparticles and dissolved

mechanically abrade the substrate. While grazing, their opal and goethite-sheathed teeth, harder than the substrate, scrape the rock surfaces. The site to which most individuals usually return to rest during low tide is marked by a depression of the same size and shape as the base of their shells. Emery (1962) found that the pH measured of the sole of their foot ranged from 5.7 to 7.5 with a mean of 7.2. From this, he concluded that the depressions were formed by biochemical dissolution. Microscopic studies by us of the depressions at Palau show that they are covered by radular scrape marks similar to those produced by the same species when grazing. Hence, the depressions are the products of both mechanical scraping action and biochemical dissolution. The depth of the depressions vary widely for different Acmaeid species. Also, the scrape marks of the feeding trails differ between species. Their depth of substrate penetrations are shallow and because of the small size of the teeth, minute in diameter. They become clearly visible under the microscope at low power when illuminated at a low angle. Nearly all rock samples where I found the Acmaeids were completely crisscrossed by their scrape marks. As shown in Fig. 13, none of the four species occupy the nips located in quiet waters. All occupy those in semirough water, and only two extend into those in the turbulent waters. One of the species is also found in the shallow nips formed in volcanic breccias. Populations of the Acmaeids are large wherever they occur. Hence, in the habitats that they occupy, they are more important as agents of biomechanical erosion than of biochemical erosion. The other gastropod species, which are grazers in the limestone nips, have protenaceous teeth. Their vertical range of niche occupation is shown in Fig. 12. They mechanically remove considerable volumes of the substrate mostly because its physical strength is weakened shallowly, largely by the enmeshing and endolithic algae. Their feeding marks are on the average shallower than those of the Acmaeids and their resting places are poorly marked. Hence, they appear to be principally engaged in mechanical erosion. The chitons are limited to the nips in limestones, where they are most abundant in the quiet water areas free of Acmaeids, and decrease in population size toward the rough water end of the wave energy spectrum. Their teeth, sheathed with magnetite, lepidocrocite, and francolite (Lowenstam, 1967) are considerably larger than those of the Acmaeids. Hence, their feeding marks are deeper and megascopically visible. Their resting places are poorly delineated. The chitons are major biomechanical eroders and are most effective in this capacity in quiet water-located nips. The only other biomechanical degrading agents are bony, herbivorous fish, whose teeth are composed of francolite and dahllite and, hence, are also harder than the calcareous substrate that they scrape for algae. Among the invertebrates, all but *Clione* produce medium to large deep borings by biochemical means, although where rigid papillae and calcareous hard parts are developed, which are either high magnesium calcites or aragonite, these may possibly mechanically aid in the boring process (Rice, 1969). The sipunculids, limited to semirough water to rough water environments, where they have large populations, are major biochemical borers in weakening the substrate strength. *Clione*, as recently shown (Cobb, 1969) bore by means of biochemical etching of amoebocytes around the edges of cells, freeing small chips of carbonate by undercutting. This sponge plays a considerably lesser role at Palau in the nip formation than do the sipunculids. The same is true for the biochemically boring bivalve, *Lithophaga*, which aids biomechanically by its shell to clean out the bore holes.

The shallowing of the nips in limestone cliffs from quiet to rough water can be readily explained by the increase in coralline algal sheathing, the rougher the water. The growth of these algae reduces biochemical and biomechanical erosion effect, although not sufficiently to eliminate notching altogether.

Data from depths of wall recession by the erosional processes summarized for several of the biologic agents by Neumann (1968) and the volumes of carbonate found in the fecal pellets of some of the gastropods by McLean (1967) clearly show that the nips and their depths, formed in carbonate rocks in the intertidal zone, can be satisfactorily attributed entirely to biologic erosion. The limiting factor in depth development of the nips is roof failure, which, as shown widely on notched islands, leads to collapse and rock slides.

Absence of or exceedingly shallow notching of volcanic breccias adjoining calcitic rocks with deep notches may be related to limited algal and fungal growth supporting fewer grazers and a less suitable substrate for boring invertebrates. Very extensive notching of limestone subtidally is locally produced almost entirely by *Clione* as shown in Bermuda (Neumann, 1966). Echinoids, aided by *Clione*, in many areas subtidally form a second deep nip a few meters below the intertidal notch, for example, as found at Barbados, again in a limestone substrate.

The nips produced by biologic agents are most extensive where wave action would be ineffective and less developed where it could be effective. Moreover, biologically developed nips exceed in depth those caused by wave action and also differ in the geometry of inorganically produced notches.

Biologic erosion-producing nips can be traced back in geologic time only to the late Neogene, as far as I am aware. This may be simply because preservation of rocky coasts of earlier seas are a rarity and always lack, through later erosion, the intertidal to subtidal segments. Hence, so far, the beginning and early history of this mode of the impact of life on physical processes seems to remain indeterminable.

A variety of other kinds of biologic effects on physical processes in the sea are known, but the more spectacular examples presented suffice to indicate some of these phenomena.

One of the major problems, repeatedly touched on, concerns the question of the importance and the various forms of biochemical solution and erosion, their contributing agents, particularly among bacteria and fungi, and the precise nature of the biochemical processes, even where we deduce them from their physical expressions.

8. Concluding Remarks

The data on newly discovered inorganic fixation products by organisms have contributed largely to the formulations of questions rather than to providing answers to the elucidation of the impact of life through mineral fixation on chemical and physical processes in the oceans.

Looking to the future one would like to know more about the biochemical processes that enable organisms to concentrate chemical constituents and the mechanisms used to stabilize them in the form of inorganic substances in their hard parts. This further involves the question of why some forms of inorganic constituents are widely precipitated by members of the marine biomass, whereas others are deposited less commonly and still others seem to be avoided.

Life has succeeded in largely substituting or displacing to varying extent inorganic precipitation processes in the sea in the course of the last 6×10^8 yr. It has affected the chemistry of seawater by other means. There are some indications that life processes accelerate recycling rates of some chemical constituents of seawater and decellerate others by large-scale removal to oceanic sediments. A better evaluation of selectivity and of the length of time biologically precipitated sediments are retarded in being recylced in the oceans will come from better data on their chemical stability in accumulating sediments and of the turnover rates produced by plate tectonics. Some biologic processes modify sedimentation processes. Others retard and even produce the opposite effect by erosion processes subject to wave and current action if they were unimpeded by biologic activity. Still others affect movement of water masses locally and also oceanic circulation. The question remains, what is basically unique about life and its impact on processes in the oceans as compared to how oceans would have developed totally subject to control by inorganic processes alone.

Acknowledgment

I wish to thank my colleagues who have generously contributed to my research in permitting me to use their unpublished data and literature references, and providing me with specimens for biogeochemical studies, as well as the opportunity to participate in dredging operations. They include D. P. Abbott, G. Arrhenius, G. A. Cooper, J. W. Durham, K. Evans, the late T. G. Goreau and N. Goreau, B. Hansen, O. Hartman, W. D. Hartman, P. Hoffman, C. L. Hubbs, R. Jahns, J. B. Kirkegaard, J. Knudsen, L. Land, L. Lemche, E. Marcus, J. H. McLean, R. J. Menzies, W. K. Ockelmann, G. H. Peterson, E. Rasmussen, W. R. Riedel, M. Stevens, K. Towe, G. Voss, R. J. Weimer, J. Westphal, and T. Wolff.

Unpublished biogeochemical data in this chapter are based on studies supported by NSF grants GB-8261, GB-6707X, and GB-6707XI, and parts of the ecologic studies were carried out with the financial aid of the Division of Geological and Planetary Sciences, California Institute of Technology.

References

Albright, L. J. and J. F. Henigman, 1971. Seawater salts—Hydrostatic pressure effects upon cell division of several bacteria. *Can. J. of Microbiol.*, **17**, 1246–1248.

Arnold, R. M. and L. J. Albright, 1970. Hydrostatic pressure effects on the translation stages of protein synthesis in a cell-free system from *Escherichia coli*. *Biochimica et Biophysica Acta*, **238**, 347–354.

Arrhenius, G., M. N. Branlette, and E. Picciotto, 1957. Localization of radioactive and stable heavy nuclides in ocean sediments. *Nature*, **180**, 85–86.

Arrhenius, G. and E. Bonati, 1965. Neptunism and vulcanism in the ocean. *Prog. in Oceanog.*, **3**, 7–22.

Arrhenius, G., 1964. Sedimentary record of long-period phenomena. In *Advances in Earth Science*. Cambridge, Mass., MIT Press, pp. 55–174.

Arrhenius, G., 1963. Pelagic sediments. In *The Sea*. Vol. 3. M. N. Hill, ed. New York, Wiley-Interscience, pp. 655–727.

Arrhenius, G. Oceanic barite and associated phases. Unpublished.

Arrhenius, G. Selected biogeochemical data. Unpublished.

Barnard, J. L., G. L. Jones, and O. Hartman, 1965. *An Oceanographic and Biological Survey of the Southern California Mainland Shelf*. State Water Quality Contr. Board, Publ. 27.

Barnard, J. L. and O. Hartman, 1959. The sea bottom off Santa Barbara, California: Biomass and community structure. *Pac. Nat.*, **1**, 3–15.

Bashnagel, R. A., 1942. Some microfossils of the Onondaga Chert of central New York. *Bull. Buffalo Soc. Nat. Sci.*, **17**, 1–8.

Bé, A. W. H. and D. S. Tolderlund, 1971. Distribution and ecology of living planktonic foraminifera in surface waters of the Atlantic and Indian Oceans. In *The Micropalaeontology of Oceans*. Cambridge University Press, pp. 105–149.

Belyaeva, N. V., 1964. *Distribution of Planktonic Foraminifera in the Water and on the Floor of the Indian Ocean*. Vol. 68. Trudy Inst. Okean, Akad. Sci., USSR. pp. 12–83. In Russian.

Berger, W. H., 1967. Foraminiferal ooze: solution at depths. *Science*, **156**, 383–385.

Berger, W. H., 1968. Radiolarian skeletons: solution at depth. *Science*, **159**, 1237–1238.

Berger, W. H., 1971. Sedimentation of planktonic foraminifera. *Mar. Geol.*, **11**, 325–358.

Berkner, L. V. and L. Marshall, 1965. On the origin and rise of oxygen concentrations in the earth's atmosphere. *J. Atm. Sci.*, **22**, 225–261.

Bethe, A., 1895. Die Otocyste von *Mysis*. *Zool. Jahrb. Anat.*, **8**, 544–564.

Bezrukov, P. L., A. P. Lisitsyn, V. P. Petelin, and N. S. Skornyakova, 1961. Map of oceanic bottom sediments. In *Recent Sediments of Seas and Oceans*. N. M. Strakov, ed. Moscow.

Boschma, H., 1936. Sur la croissance de quelques coraux des récifs de Île. d'Edam (Baie de Batavia). Mus. Roy. Hist. Belgique. Mem. 3, pp. 101–115.

Bradshaw, J. S., 1959. Ecology of living planktonic foraminifera of the North and Equatorial Pacific Ocean. Cushman Found. Foram. Res., Contr. 10, No. 2, pp. 25–64.

Brewer, P. G., D. W. Spencer, and P. E. Wilkness, 1970. Anomalous fluoride concentrations in the North Atlantic. *Deep-Sea Res.*, **17**, 1–7.

Bricker, O. P., R. N. Ginsburg, L. S. Land, and F. T. Mackenzie, eds., 1969. *Carbonate Cements*. Sp. Pub. No. 3, Bermuda Biological Station. 325 pp.

Broeker, W. S., 1971. Calcite accumulation rates and glacial to interglacial changes in oceanic mixing. In *The Late Cenozoic Glacial Ages*. Yale University, pp. 239–265.

Büttner, W., 1966. Konzentration und Verteilung von Fluorid in Haifischzähnen. In *Advances in Fluorine Research and Dental Caries Prevention*. Vol. 4, pp. 193–200.

Calvert, S. E., 1968. Silica balance in the ocean and diagenesis. *Nature*, **219**, 919–920.

Carefoot, T. H., 1965. Magnetite in the radula of the Polyplacophora. *Proc. Malac. Soc. Lond.*, **36**, 203–213.

Carlisle, E. M., 1970. Silicon: A possible factor in bone calcification. *Science*, **167**, 279–280.

Carlisle, E. M., 1972. Silicon: An essential element for the chick. *Science*, **178**, 619–621.

Carlström, D., 1963. A crystallographic study of vertebrate otoliths. *Biol. Bull.*, **125**, 441–463.

Carpenter, R., 1969. Factors controlling the marine geochemistry of fluorine. *Geochim. Cosmochim. Acta*, **33**, 1153–1167.

Carpenter, W. B., 1879. Foraminifera. *Encyclopedia Britannica*. Ninth ed. Vol. 9, pp. 371–387.

Carriker, Smith, and Wilce, eds., 1969. Penetration of calcium carbonate substrates by lower plants and invertebrates. *Am. Zool.*, **9** (3) edit. 2.

Chave, R. E., 1960. Carbonate skeletons to limestone problems. Trausac, New York. *Acad. Sci.*, **23**, 14–24.

Chave, R. E., S. V. Smith, and R. J. Roy, 1972. Carbonate production by coral reefs. *Mar. Geol.*, **12**, 123–410.

Chen, C. and A. W. H. Bé, 1964. Seasonal distributions of euthecosomatous pteropods in the surface waters of five stations in the Western North Atlantic. *Bull. of Mar. Sci. of the Gulf and Caribbean*, **14**, 186–220.

Chennaux, G., 1968. Presence de tintinnoidiens dans l'ordovicien du Sahara. *Compt. Rend. Acad. Sci. Paris*, **266D**, 86–87.

Church, T. M., 1970. Marine barite. Unpublished thesis.

Clarke, F. W. and W. C. Wheeler, 1922. The inorganic constituents of marine invertebrates. U. S. Geol. Surv. Prof. Paper 124.

Cloud, P. E., 1962. Environment of calcium carbonate deposition west of Andros Island, Bahamas. Geol. Surv. Prof. Paper 350. U.S. Government Printing Office, Washington, D.C.

Cloud, P. E., Jr., 1965. Significance of the Gunflint (Precambrian) microflora. *Science*, **148**, 27–35.

Cloud, P. E., Jr., 1968. Pre-metazoan evolution and the origin of the Metazoa. In *Evolution and Environment*. Yale University Press, New Haven and London, pp. 1–72.

Cloud, P. E., Jr., 1968. Atmospheric and hydrospheric evolution of the primitive earth. *Science*, **160**, 729–736.

Cobb, W. R., 1969. Penetration of calcium carbonate substrates by the boring sponge, *Cliona*. *Am. Zool.*, **9**, 783–790.

Dodd, J. R., 1966. The influence of salinity on mollusc shell mineralogy: a discussion. *J. Geol.*, **74**, 85–89.

Dodd, J. R., 1967. Magnesium and strontium in calcareous skeletons: a review. *J. Paleon.*, **41**, 1313–1329.

Dudich, E., 1929. Die Kalkeinlagerungen des Crustaceenpanzers in polarisiertem Licht. *Zool. Anzeig.*, **85**, 257.

Durham, J. W., 1971. A possible molluscan radula from the earliest Cambrian of the White-Inyo Mountains, California (abstract). Geol. Soc. America, *Cordilleran Sec.*, **3** (2), 114.

Eisma, D., 1966. The influence on mollusk shell mineralogy: a discussion. *J. Geol.*, **74**, 89–94.

Emery, K. O., W. L. Orr, and S. C. Rittenberg, 1955. Nutrient budgets in the ocean. In *Essays in Natural Sciences in Honor of Capt. Allan Hancock*. USC Press, Los Angeles, pp. 299–309.

Emergy, K. O., 1962. Marine geology of Guam. U.S.G.S. Prof. Paper 403-B, U.S. Government Printing Office, Washington, D.C.

Enbysk, B. J. and F. I. Linger, 1966. Mysid statoliths in shelf sediments off Northwest North America. *J. Sediment. Petrol.*, **36**, 839–840.

Fischer, A. G., 1965. Fossils, early life and the atmospheric history. *Proc. Nat. Acad. Sci.*, **53**, 1205–1215.

Fischer, A. G. and R. E. Garrison, 1967. Carbonate lithification on the seafloor. *J. Geol.*, **75**, 488–496.

Fischer, A. G., 1972. Atmosphere and the evolution of life. Main currents in modern thought. Vol. 28, 4 pp.

Friedmann, E. I., W. C. Roth, and J. B. Turner, 1972. Calcium oxalate crystals in the aragonite-producing green alga *Penicillus* and related genera. *Science*, **177**, 891–892.

Geijer, P., 1962. Some aspects of phosphorus in Precambrian sedimentation. *Arch. Min. and Geol. Kungl. Svenska Vet.*, **3**, 165–186.

Gerth, H., 1929. The evolution of reef corals during the Cenozoic period. 4th Pac. Sci. Cong. vol. 11A, Physical papers, pp. 333–350.

Gibbs, P. E. and G. W. Bryan, 1972. A study of strontium, magnesium and calcium in the environment and exoskeleton of decapod crustaceans, with special reference to *UCA Burgersi* on Barbuda, West Indies. *J. Exp. Mar. Biol. Ecol.*, **9**, 97–110.

Ginsburg, R. N., 1953. Intertidal erosion on the Florida Keys. *Bull. Marl Sci, Gulf and Carib.*, **14**, 55–58.

Ginsburg, R. N., 1955. Recent stromatolitic sediments from Southern Florida. *J. Paleo.*, **29**, 723–724.

Ginsburg, R. N., 1960. Ancient analogues of recent stromatolites. 21st Internat. Geol. Congress, Copenhagen, pt. 22, 26–35.

Ginsburg, R. N. and H. A. Lowenstam, 1958. The influence of marine bottom communities on the depositional environment of sediments. *J. of Geol.*, **66**, 310–318.

Glaessner, M. F. and B. Daily, 1959. The geology and late Precambrian fauna of the Ediacara fossil reserve. *Rec. South. Australian Mus.*, **13**, 369–401.

Glaessner, M. F., 1961. Precambrian animals. *Sci. American*, **204**, 72–78.

Glaessner, M. F., 1966. Precambrian paleontology. *Earth-Science Rev.*, **1**, 29–60.

Glaessner, M. F., W. V. Preiss, and M. R. Walter, 1969. Precambrian columnar stromatolites in Australia: Morphological and stratigraphic analysis. *Science*, **164**, 1056–1058.

Goldberg, E. D., 1952. Iron assimilation by marine diatoms. *Biol. Bull.*, **102**, 243–248.

Goldberg, E. D., 1957. Biochemistry of trace metals. Geol. Soc. of Amer., Mem. 67, **1**, 345–357.

Goldberg, E. D., 1963. The Oceans as a chemical system. In *The Sea*. Vol. 2. M. N. Hill, ed. Wiley-Interscience, New York and London, pp. 3–25.

Goldberg, E. D., 1965. Minor elements in seawater. In *Chemical Oceanography*. Vol. 1. Pp. 163–194 (Chapter 5).

Graham, H. W. and R. L. Edwards, 1962. The world biomass of marine fishes. In *Fish in Nutrition*. Fishing News (Books), London, pp. 2–8.

Greenfield, L. J., 1963. Metabolism and concentration of calcium and magnesium and precipitation of calcium carbonate by a marine bacterium. *An. N. Y. Acad. Sci.*, **109**, 23–45.

Greenhalgh, R. and J. P. Riley, 1963. Occurrence of abnormally high fluoride concentrations at depth in the oceans. *Nature*, **197**, 371–372.

Hallam, A. and N. B. Price, 1968. Environmental and biochemical control of strontium in shells of *Cardium edule. Geochim. Cosmochim. Acta*, **32**,

Hallam, A. and N. B. Price, 1968. Further notes on the strontium contents of unaltered fossil cephalopod shells. *Geol. Mag.*, **105**, 52–55.

Harrison, P. M., F. A. Fischbach, T. G. Hoy, and G. H. Haggis, 1967. Ferric oxyhydroxide core of ferritin. *Nature*, **216**, 1188–1190.

Harris, R. C., 1966. Biological buffering of oceanic silica. *Nature*, **212**, 275–276.

Hartman, W. D., and T. F. Goreau, 1970. Jamaican coralline sponges: their morphology, ecology, and fossil relatives. *Symp. Zool. Soc., London*, **25**, 205–243.

Helms, P. B. and W. R. Riedel, 1971. Skeletal debris of fishes. In *Deep Sea Drilling Project*. Vol. 7, part 2, 1709–1720.

Hensen, V., 1863. Studien über das Gehörorgan der Decapoden. In *Zeitsch. f. wiss. Zool.* Vol. 13, p. 395.

Hodgkin, E. P., 1964. Rate of erosion of intertidal limestone. *Z. Geomorphol.*, **8**, 385–392.

Hoffman, P., 1967. Algal stromatolites: Use in stratigraphic correlation and paleocurrent determination. *Science*, **157**, 1043–1045.

Hutchinson, G. E., 1952. The biogeochemistry of phosphorus. In *The Biology of Phosphorus*. Michigan St., Coll. Press.

Jones, G. F. and J. L. Barnard, 1963. The distribution and abundance of the inarticulate brachiopod *Glottidia albida* (Hinds) on the mainland shelf of Southern California. *Pacific Naturalist*, **4**, 27–61.

Kahane, E. and G. Antoine, 1935. Sur la nature de la silice chez, les etres vivants. Silice de constitution et silice d'interposition. *Bull. Soc. Chimie Biol.*, **18**, 1769–1782.

Kalinenko, V. O., O. V. Belokopylova, and G. Nikolaeca, 1962. The bacteriogenic formation of ferro-manganese concretions in the Indian oceans. *Okeanologia*, **2**, 1050–1059.

Kinsman, D. J. J., 1969. Interpretation of Sr^{2+} concentrations in carbonate minerals and rocks. *J. Sediment. Petrol.*, **39**, 486–508.

Kinsman, D. J. J. and H. D. Holland, 1969. The co-precipitation of cations with $CaCO_3$-IV. The co-precipitation of Sr^{2+} with aragonite between 16–95°C. *Geochim. Cosmochim. Acta*, **33**, 1–17.

Knudsen, J., 1964. Scaphopoda and Gastropoda from depths exceeding 6000 meters. *Galathea Report*, **7**, 125–136.

Kolodny, Y. and I. R. Kaplan, 1970. Uranium isotopes in sea-floor phosphorites. *Geochim. Cosmochim. Acta*, **34**, 3–24.

Kramer, J. R., 1964. Seawater: saturation with apatites and carbonates. *Science*, **146**, 637–638.

Kuenen, Ph. H., 1950. *Marine Geology*. Wiley, New York.

Labbe, A., 1033. Les oncidiades, mollusques a silice. C. R. Acad. Sci., Paris, **135**, 1003.

Ladd, H. S., J. I. Tracey, Jr., J. W. Wells, and K. O. Emery, 1950. Organic growth and sedimentation on an atoll. *J. Geol.*, **58**, 410–425.

Ladd, H. S. and S. O. Schlanger, 1960. Drilling operations on Eniwetok atoll. Geol. Surv. Prof. Paper-260-Y, 863–903.

Land, L. S. and T. F. Goreau, 1970. Submarine lithification of Jamaican reefs. *J. Sediment. Petrol.*, 457–462.

Lévi, Claude, 1964. Spongiaires des zones bathyale abyssale et hadale. *Galathea Report*, **7**, 63–113.

Lewin, J. and B. E. F. Reimann, 1969. Silicon and plant growth. *Annual Rev. of Plant Physiol.*, **20**, 289–304.

Lewis, G. J., Jr., and E. D. Goldberg, 1954. Iron in marine waters. *J. Mar. Res.*, **13**, 183–197.

Li, T. H., T. Takahashi, and W. S. Broecker, 1969. The degree of saturation of $CaCO_3$ in the oceans. *J. Geophys. Res.*, **74**, 5507–5525.

Lipps, J. H. and J. W. Valentine, 1970. The role of Foraminifera in the trophic structure of marine communities. *Lethaia*, **3**, 279–286.

Lisitzin, A. P., 1971. Distribution of siliceous microfossils in suspension and bottom sediments. In *Micropaleontology of Oceans*. Cambridge University Press, pp. 173–195.

Logan, B. W., 1961. Cryptozoan and associated stromatolites from the Recent, Shark Bay, Western Australia. *J. Geol.*, **69**, 517–533.

Logan, B. W., G. R. Davies, J. F. Read, and D. E. Cebulski, 1970. Carbonate sedimentation and environments, Shark Bay, Western Australia. AAPG Memoir 13, 223 pp.

Lowenstam, H. A., 1950. Niagaran reefs of the Great Lakes area. *J. Geol.*, **58**, 430–487.

Lowenstam, H. A., 1954. Factors affecting the aragonite-calcite ratios in carbonate-secreting marine organisms. *J. Geol.*, **62**, 284–322.

Lowenstam, H. A., 1955. Aragonite needles secreted by algae and some sedimentary implications. *J. Sediment. Petrol.*, **25**, 270–272.

Lowenstam, H. A., 1957. Niagaran reefs of the Great Lakes Area: Treatise Marine Ecology and Paleoecology, G.S.A. Memoir 67, 215–2448.

Lowenstam, H. A., 1960. Paleocology (geochemical aspects). *McGraw-Hill Encyclopedia of Science and Technology*, pp. 516–518.

Lowenstam, H. A., 1961. Mineralogy, O^{18}/O^{16} ratios, and strontium and magnesium contents of recent and fossil brachiopods and their bearing on history of the oceans. *J. Geol.*, **69**, 241–260.

Lowenstam, H. A., 1962. Magnetite in denticle capping in recent chitons (Polyplacophora). *G.S.A. Bull.*, **73**, 435–438.

Lowenstam, H. A., 1962. Goethite in radular teeth of recent marine gastropods. *Science*, **137**, 279–280.

Lowenstam, H. A., 1963. Sr/Ca ratio of skeletal aragonites from the recent marine biota at Palau and from fossil gastropods. In *Isotopic and Cosmic Chemistry*. North Holland Publ., Amsterdam, pp. 114–132.

Lowenstam, H. A., 1964. Coexisting calcites and aragonites from skeletal carbonates of marine organisms and their strontium and magnesium contents. Reprinted from *Recent Researches in the Fields of Hydrosphere, Atmosphere and Geochemistry*. Editorial Committee of Sugawara Festival, Volume, 373–404.

Lowenstam, H. A., 1967. Adaptive traits in skeletal morphology: Short Course Lecture Notes. *Paleoecology*. American Geol. Inst., 12 pp.

Lowenstam, H. A., 1967. Lepidocrocite, an apatite mineral, and magnetite in teeth of chitons (Polyplacophora). *Science*, **156**, 1373–1375.

Lowenstam, H. A. and D. McConnell, 1968. Biologic precipitation of fluorite. *Science*, **162**, 1496–1498.

Lowenstam, H. A., 1968. Weddellite in a marine gastropod and in Antarctic sediments. *Science*, **162**, 1129–1130.

Lowenstam, H. A., 1971. Opal precipitation of marine gastropods (Mollusca). *Science*, **171**, 487–490.

Lowenstam, H. A., 1972. Phosphatic hard tissues of marine invertebrates: Their nature and mechanical function and some fossil implications. *Chem. Geol.*, **9**, 153–166.

Lowenstam, H. A. and D. Abbott, 1973. Tunicate spicules composed of vaterite. To be published.

Lowenstam, H. A. and S. Epstein, 1957. On the origin of sedimentary aragonite needles of the Great Bahama Bank, *J. Geol.*, **65**, 364–375.

Lowenstam, H. A. and G. R. Rossman, 1973. Iron and phosphatic hydrogels and amorphous, hydrous fluorite. To be published.

Lowenstam, H. A., 1973. Biogeochemistry of hard tissues, their depth and possible pressure relationships. Will appear in Symposium Volume. Duke University Press.

Mayer, F. K., 1931. Röntgenographische Untersuchugen an Gastropoden-schalen. *Jena Zeitsehr. Naturwiss.*, **65**, 487–512.

Mayer, F. K., 1932. Über die Modifikation des Kalzium-karbonates in Schalen und Skeletten rezenter und fossiler Organismen. *Chem. d. Erde*, **7**, 346.

McCance, R. A. and M. Masters, 1937. The chemical composition and the acid base balance of *Archidoris britannica*. *J. Mar. Biol.*, **22**, 273.

McConnell, D., 1963. Inorganic constituents in the shell of the living brachiopod *Lingula*. *Geol. Soc. Am. Bull.*, **74**, 363–364.

McIntyre, A. and R. McIntyre, 1971. Coccolith concentrations and differential solution in oceanic sediments. In *Micropaleontology of Oceans*. Cambridge University Press, pp. 253–261.

McGowan, J. A., 1960. The systematics distribution and abundance of the Euthecosmata of the north Pacific. Ph.D. dissertation, University of California, San Diego, La Jolla, California.

McLean, R. F., 1964. Mechanical and biological erosion of beachrock in Barbados, W.I. Ph.D. thesis, McGill University, Montreal, Canada, 266 pp.

McLean, R. F., 1967. Measurements of beachrock erosion by some tropical marine gastropods. *Bull. Mar. Sci.*, **17**, 550–561.

Mörner, C. T., 1902. Kleinere Mittheilungen 3: Die sogennaten weinrothen Körper der Holothurain. *Hope-Seyler's Z. Physiol. Chem.*, **37**, 89–93.

Morton, J. E., 1954. The pelagic mollusca of the Benguela Current. *Discovery Rpt.*, **27**, 165–199.

Murray, J., 1897. On the distribution of the pelagic Foraminifera at the surface and on the floor of the ocean. *Nat. Sci.*, **11**, 17–27.

Neff, J. M., 1971. Ultrastructure of calcium phosphate-containing worm *Pomatoceros caerulus*. *Calc. Tiss. Res.*, **7**, 191–200.

Nesson, M. H., 1968. Studies on radula tooth mineralization in the Polyplacophora. Ph.D. thesis, California Institute of Technology, Pasadena, California.

Neumann, A. C., 1966. Observations on coastal erosion in Bermuda and measurements of the boring rate of the sponge, *Cliona lampa*. *Limnol. and Oceanog.*, **11**, 92–108.

Neumann, A. C., 1968. Biological erosion of limestone coasts. *Encycl. of Geomorphology*. Vol. 3. R. W. Fairbridge, ed.

Newell, N. D., 1954b. Reefs and sedimentary processes of Raroia. *Atoll Res. Bull.*, **36**, 35 pp.

Newell, N. D., 1956. Geological reconnaissance of Raroia (KonTiki) atoll, Tuamoto archipelago. *Bull. Am. Mus. Nat. Hist.*, **109**, 372 pp.

North, W. J., 1954. Size distribution erosive activities and gross metabolic efficiency of the marine intertidal snails. *Littorina planaxis* and *L. scutulata*. *Biol. Bull.*, **106**, 185–197.

Odum, H. T., 1951. Notes on the strontium content of seawater, celestite Radiolaria and strontianite snail shells. *Science*, **114**, 211–213.

Otter, G. W., 1937. Rock-destroying mechanisms in relation to coral reefs. Great Barrier Reef Exped. 1928–29, Sci. Rept., 323–352.

Pelseneer, P., 1887. Report on the Pteropoda collected by H.M.S. "Challenger." I. The Gymnosomota. Sci. Repts. "Challenger." *Zoology*, **19** (4), 1–69.

Pelseneer, P., 1888. Report on the Pteropoda collected by H.M.S. "Challenger." II. Thecosomata; III. Anatomy. Sci. Repts. "Challenger." *Zoology*, **13**, 1–132.

Perkins, R. D., M. D. McKenzie, and P. L. Blackwelder, 1972. Aragonite crystals within codiacean algae: distinctive morphology and sedimentary implications. *Science*, **175**, 624–626.

Peterson, M. N. A., 1966. Calcite: rates of dissolution in a vertical profile in the central Pacific. *Science*, **154**, 1542–1544.

Pilkey, O. H. and J. Hower, 1960. The effect of environment on the skeletal magnesium and strontium in *Dendraster*., *J. of Geol.*, **68**, 203–214.

Pray, L. C., 1958. Fenestrate bryozoan core facies, Mississippian biotherms, Southwestern U.S. *J. Sediment. Petrol.*, **28**, 261–273.

Ranson, G., 1955b. Observations sur les principaux agents de la dissolution du calcaire sous-marine dans la zone côtiere des îles coralliennes de l'Archipel des Tuamotu. *Compt. Rendus Seances Acad. Sci. Paris*, **240**, 806–808.

Reshetniak, B. B., 1966. Deep water Radiolarian Phaeodaria of Northwestern part of Pacific Ocean. *Fauna of U.S.S.R.*, **94**, 55–56.

Revelle, R. and R. W. Fairbridge, 1957. Carbonates and carbon dioxide. G.S.A. Memoir 67, **1**, 239–296.

Rhodes, F. H. T. and T. W. Bloxam, 1971. Phosphatic organisms in the Paleozoic and their evolutionary significance. Proc. North Am. Paleont. Conv. Pf.K., Allen Press, Lawrence, Kansas, 1489–1513.

Rice, M. E., 1969. Possible boring structures of sipunculids. *Am. Zool.*, **9** (3), edit. 2, 803–812.

Riley, G. A., 1965. Theory of food chain relations in the ocean. In *The Sea*. Vol. 2. M. N. Hill, ed. Wiley-Interscience, New York, pp. 438–455.

Ruddiman, W. F. and B. C. Heezen, 1967. Differential solution of planktonic Foraminifera. *Deep-Sea Res.*, **14**, 801–808.

Ryther, J. H., 1969. Photosynthesis and fish production in the sea. *Science*, **166**, 72–76.

Schaeffer, M. B., 1965. The potential harvest of the sea. *Trans. Amer. Fish. Soc.*, **94**, 123.

Schopf, T. J. M. and F. T. Manheim, 1967. Chemical composition of Ectoprocta (Bryozoa). *J. Paleon.*, **41**, 1197–1225.

Schopf, J. W., 1969. Recent advances in Precambrian paleobiology. *Grana Polynologica*, **9**, 147–168.

Schulze, F. E. and H. Thierfelder, 1905. Über Baryumsulfat im Meerestieren (Xenophyophoren). Sber. Ges. naturf. Freunde, Berl. 2–4.

Silverman, M. P. and H. L. Ehrlich, 1964. Microbian formation and degradation of minerals. *Appl. Microbiol.*, **6**, 153–205.

Spangenberg, D. B. and C. W. Beck, 1968. Calcium sulfate dihydrate statoliths in *Aurelia*. *Trans. Amer. Microsc. Soc.*, **87**, 329–335.

Stephenson, T. A. and A. Stephenson, 1933. Growth and asexual reproduction in corals. Gr. Barrier Reef Exped., Sci. Rept. 3, 219–245.

Stockmann, K. W., R. N. Ginsburg, and E. A. Shinn, 1967. The production of lime mud by algae in South Florida. *J. Sediment. Petrol.*, **37**, 633–648.

Stone, A. R., 1970. Seasonal variations of spicule size in *Hymeniacidon perlev*. *J. Mar. Biol. Ass. U. K.*, **50**, 343–348.

Sverdrup, H. A., M. W. Johnson, and R. H. Fleming, 1942. *The Oceans, Their Physics, Chemistry and General Biology*. Englewood Cliffs, N.J., Prentice-Hall.

Taft, W. H., F. Arrington, A. Haimouitz, C. MacDonald, and C. Woolheater, 1968. Lithification of modern marine carbonate sediments at Yellow Bank, Bahamas, *Bull. Mar. Sci.*, **18**, 762–828.

Tamura, T. and Y. Hada, 1932. Growth rate of reef building corals, inhabiting in the South Sea Island, Tōhoku Imp. Univ., Sci. Rept. 7, 433–455.

Teichert, C. and R. W. Fairbridge, 1948. Some coral reefs of the Sahul shelf. *Geog. Rev.*, **38**, 222–249.

Tendal, O. S., 1972. A monograph of the Xenophyophoria (Rhizopodea, Protozoa). *Galathea Report*, **12**, Copenhagen.

Towe, K. E., H. A. Lowenstam, and M. H. Nesson, 1963. Invertebrate ferritin: Occurrence in Mollusca. *Science*, **142**, 63–64.

Towe, K. M. and W. F. Bradley, 1967. Mineralogical constitution of colloidal "Hydrous ferric oxides." *J. Colloid. and Interface Sci.*, **24**, 384–392.

Towe, K. M., 1967. Wall structure and cementation in *Haplophragmoides canariensis* Contrib. from Cushman Foundation for Foram. Res., **18**, 147–151.

Towe, K. M. and H. A. Lowenstam, 1967. Ultrastructure and development of iron mineralization in the radular teeth of Cryptochiton stelleri (Mollusca). *J. Ultramicroscop. Res.*, **17**, 1–13.

Towe, K. M. and K. Rützler, 1968. Lepidocrocite iron mineralization in keratose sponge granules. *Science*, **162**, 268–269.

Trautz, O. R., 1960. Crystallographic studies of calcium carbonate phosphate. Ann. N.Y. Acad. Sci., **85**, 145–160.

Turekian, K. K. and D. G. Johnson, 1966. The barium distribution in sea water. *Geochim. Cosmochim. Acta*, **30**, 1153–1174.

Uschakova, M. G., 1971. Coccoliths in suspension and in the surface layer of sediment in the Pacific Ocean. In *Micropaleontology of Oceans*. Cambridge, Cambridge University Press, pp. 245–251.

Vaughan, T. W. and J. W. Wells, 1943. Revision of suborders, families, and genera of Scleractinia. G.S.A. Spec. Paper 44 (15), 363 pp.

Vinogradov, A. P., 1953. The elementary chemical composition of marine organisms. Sears Found. Mar. Res. Mem. 2.

Voigt, E., 1956. Der Nachweis des Phytals durch Epizoen als Kriterium der Tiefe vorzeitlicher Meere. *Geol. Rundschau*, **45**, 97–119.

Warner, T. B., 1971. Normal fluoride content of seawater. *Deep-Sea Res.*, **18**, 1255–1263.

Weimer, R. J. and J. H. Hoyt, 1964. Burrows of *Callianassa major* Say, geologic indicators of littoral and shallow neritic environments. *J. Paleon.*, **38**, 761–767.

Wells, J. W., 1956. Scleractinia. Treatise on Invert. Paleont., ed. Moore, F. Coelenterata. G.S.A., pp. F329–F444.

Wetzel, O., 1940. Micropalaeontologische Untersuchungen an eozoischen und palaezoischen Kieselgesteinen aus Nordamerika (U.S.A. und Kanada). Zentralbl. Min. Geol. Palaeont., Abt. B, 60–85.

Wilbur, K. M. and N. Watabe, 1963. Experimental studies on calcification in molluscs and the alga *Coccolithus* huxleyi. *Ann. N.Y. Acad. of Sci.*, **109**, 82–111.

Wolff, T., 1960. The hadal community, an introduction. *Deep-Sea Res.*, **6**, 95–124.

Wolff, T., 1970. The concept of the hadal or ultra-abyssal fauna. *Deep-Sea Res.*, **17**, 983–1003.

Wormelle, R. L., 1962. A survey of the standing crop of plankton of the Florida current. VI. A study of the distribution of the pteropods of the Florida current. *Bull. Mar. Sci. of Gulf and Caribbean*, **12**, 95–136.

Zezina, O. N., 1964. Distribution of the deepwater brachiopod *Pellagiodiscus atlanticus* (King). *Oceanography*, **5**, 127–131. Transl. from the Russian.

California Institute of Technology Contribution No. 2288.

V. THE IMPACT OF MAN ON THE CHEMISTRY OF THE OCEANS

21. HEAVY METALS, METALLOIDS, AND SYNTHETIC ORGANICS

ARNE JERNELÖV

1. Introduction

At least in theory it can be stated that all compounds used and released by man will occur as marine contaminants. The total number of compounds to be included in the list of marine contaminants could thus be counted in tens of thousands. There is no way to cope with such a number of compounds, nor is it really necessary. Most of the synthetic compounds have never actually been demonstrated to be present or even looked for in the marine environment. Most of them are, luckily, nonpersistent, so that their survival in the oceans is quite limited. Even out of those that have been looked for and shown to be present, there is only a small number of compounds of which we have more than isolated or scattered data, more or less all of them belonging to the groups of heavy metals, of metalloids or of chlorinated hydrocarbons. Our ignorance is thus monumental and our ability to evaluate the present situation and future trend regarding total marine contamination is close to nonexistent.

In this situation, evidently, we desperately need methods to identify those compounds that involve the largest hazards to enable us to concentrate our resources most effectively. During the last decade, many individual research workers as well as working groups convened by national or international organizations have made attempts to identify the properties of chemicals that are likely to have deleterious edge concerning the impacts of these chemicals.

The bases for some of these hazard evaluations from physicochemical and biological properties will be discussed at the end of this chapter after the presentation of some case studies, where behavior and effects of a small number of comparatively well-studied compounds are described. As will be seen, there are large gaps in our knowledge concerning the impacts of these chemicals.

2. Case Studies

A. DDT

DDT and its metabolites are in many ways the classical biocides, first, because they comprised the first group of synthetic compounds that came into widespread use to control (insect) pests, second, because they are the most widely used ones, and third, because many of the problems connected with the use of biocides were first observed in the DDT group.

Some of these classical observations of problems that are quite familiar today were originally made on organisms in terrestrial or limnological ecosystems. However, they are of a basic nature and subsequently were seen in marine ecosystems.

The first use of DDT compounds was for antilice powdering of soldiers and refugees during World War II. Shortly after, the practice of spraying settlements and villages for sanitary purposes and mosquito-breeding areas for the control of disease-carrying insects was introduced.

Within a few years of DDT use (as early as 1946), the first insect strain resistant to DDT was observed in a small Italian village. This finding was made on the common housefly (Musca domestica). During the 25 yr that elapsed a large number of insects and of other invertebrate species have been described that show decreased sensitivity to DDT and its metabolites. When a systematic review was made in 1960, one or more DDT-resistant strains were found to have been reported in 137 species. Today, the number far exceeds 500 and notices of resistant strains of new species can be found weekly, if not daily, in scientific journals.

Another classical example, involving the DDT-metabolite DDE, is commonly referred to as the Clear Lake Case. Clear Lake, despite the name, is a muddy California lake that appears to be an ideal breeding group for Chironomus midges. After consultations with leading biologists, DDE was sprayed in the lake in repeated attempts to control population of midge larvae. The success initially achieved turned out only to be temporary. The main lesson that made Clear Lake classic was the continued enrichment from water to organisms and further along the food chain that caused death and reproductive failure among the highest predators in the system—the fish-eating birds.

DDT reaches the marine environment in two main ways, from local sources such as runoff waters from agricultural areas treated with substantial amounts of chlorinated insecticides, as direct discharges from DDT-producing industries, or from the atmosphere in connection with atmospheric precipitation or as a direct fallout. Most of the intensively studied areas such as the southwest coast of the United States, the Japanese Sea, or the Baltic Sea are likely to receive the main part of their DDT and metabolites from local sources, while for the oceans as a whole, the atmospheric route seems to be by far the most important.

No exact figures are available on the world production of DDT. Most estimates are based on the production in the United States (Table I), and an inspection of production and utilization figures suggesting that the total world production is not more than 150% of the one in the United States. According to this, the total integrated world production of DDT should be in the order of 2×10^{12} g, with a present production of $\sim 1.5 \times 10^{11}$ g. Other sources, however, estimate the present world production to $(2.25–3) \times 10^{11}$ g. There is closer agreement on accumulated world production.

From the United States data, it is evident that the peak production was reached during the early 1960s and that production there since has decreased. The use within the United States (on an average $\sim 30\%$ of the production) has also been substantially reduced during the last decade. The main reason for this is the high number of resistent species and the thereby reduced effectiveness of DDT as an insecticide. During the last few years (not reflected in Table I), legal actions and bans enforced on some uses in some states have further contributed to the trend. It is likely that the world production and use of DDT, too, has decreased during the last decade or at least during the last years, but not to the same extent as in the United States.

The existing data on DDT transport to the oceans and amounts present in different phases of the marine ecosystem was collected and evaluated in 1970 (NAS, 1971). The transport of DDT and its metabolites to the seas by surface runoff was estimated

TABLE I

Production of DDT in the United States 10^9 g/yr[a]

Year	DDT	Year	DDT
1944	4.4	1956	62.6
1945	15.1	1957	56.6
1946	20.7	1958	66.0
1947	22.5	1959	71.2
1948	9.2	1960	74.6
1949	17.2	1961	77.9
1950	35.5	1962	75.9
1951	48.2	1963	81.3
1952	45.4	1964	56.2
1953	38.4	1965	64.0
1954	44.2	1966	64.2
1955	59.0	1967	47.0
		1968	63.4

Accumulated production 1944 to 1968: 1220.0×10^9 g

[a] From *Chemical Economics Handbook*, 1969.

to be about 0.1% of the annual production in the United States. There are no reasons to believe that the percentage should be markedly different in other parts of the world.

It seems likely that the main part of the DDT entering the atmosphere evaporates from plants and soils, but other routes, such as aerial drift during application and rapid vaporization from water surfaces, could also be important. No reliable figures exist on the rate of transport of DDT and its metabolites to the atmosphere from different sources under different conditions. Once in the atmosphere, DDT residues may travel very long distances before they are washed out with precipitation or fallout.

The extent to which dry fallout of DDT residues over the oceans occurs is unknown. An attempt has been made to calculate the washout of DDT with precipitation over the oceans using an average concentration of DDT of 80 parts per trillion and an estimated precipitation of water over the oceans of 3×10^{22} cc indicated that 2.4×10^{10} g of DDT and its metabolites corresponding to about one-quarter of the annual production could reach the sea through this route (NAS, 1971). No information is presently available on the actual concentration of DDT residues in seawater. In marine plankton the concentration—disregarding occasional high values due to local contamination—ranges from 0.001 to 0.2 ppm with an estimated average of 0.01 ppm. Marine fish frequently contain 0.2 to 2 ppm of DDT residues, giving an average of $\sim$1 ppm. Marine mammalians such as seals, porpoises, and whales have been reported to contain levels of $\sim$100 ppm in the Baltic, North Sea, and Gulf of St. Lawrence, while reports from the American West Coast indicate concentrations of up to 1000 ppm. Body lipids of marine birds have frequently been reported to contain up to and even above 1000 ppm in areas where fish concentration ranges from 1 to 10 ppm of DDT residues.

Assuming a standing crop of plant and animal plankton of 3×10^{15} g (a yearly production of 2×10^{16} g) and a standing crop of fish of 6×10^{14} g, the total amount of DDT and its metabolites in marine organisms will be about 600 tons. Fish will evidently be the main biotic reservoir of DDT residues, with plankton containing only $\sim$3 tons, and birds and mammalians having insignificant amounts. The part of DDT residues in the marine biota thus is a very small part of the calculated annual input (10^5 tons). This could mean that the seawater and sediment contain the principal part of the DDT residues present in the marine environment. If the accumulated production of DDT to date would be dissolved in the upper 100 m of the sea, the resulting concentration would be in the order of 0.1 ppb.

However, concentration of DDT residues in the oily surface film may cause a very uneven distribution in the water mass and may affect the rate of exposure of different organisms. Only a very few figures on DDT concentrations in marine sediments are available. They indicate concentrations in the range of 0.04 to 0.6 ppb in the top centimeters.

In marine organisms DDT residues generally consist of at least 80% of DDE. The rest are mainly p,p′-DDT and p,p′-DDD. From an ecological point of view, the concern is centered about DDE being the most persistent member of the DDT family.

Until recently, food-chain accumulation of DDT residues have generally been regarded as an important mechanism in the marine environment leading to the observed high levels in fish as well as it was for DDE in the classical Clear Lake Case referred to above. Lately, however, several independent reports have stressed that concentrations of DDT residues do not increase with trophic level in marine organisms if correction is made for lipid content. This indicates that fish and planktonic organisms may take up and lose DDT residues both from and to the water. This would mean that they should be in an equilibrium with their surrounding media and that this process could compensate for differences in intake of DDT residues with food related to their trophic level. If this hypothesis is accepted, knowledge of the equilibrium relation between DDT concentrations in the organism and the surrounding water could provide an indirect way of estimating the amounts present in water. Under the speculative assumption that organisms and seawater (upper 100 m) are in equilibrium and that relative concentrations of DDT residues in the two phases correspond to the relation between fat and water solubility of DDE, the water concentration would be in the order of 10^{-4} of that found in fish (0.2 ppm) or $\sim$0.02 ppb or $\sim$20% of the estimated accumulated world production.

The assessment of the ecological impact of DDT is derived from a combination of laboratory tests and field observations.

Concern has been expressed about possible changes in the oxygen concentration of the atmosphere as a result of the inhibition of photosynthesis in marine algae by DDT, observed in laboratory experiments. The effects, however, were observed at concentrations far exceeding those that can be expected in seawater and also exceeded by 10 times the solubility of DDT in water. Furthermore, with known interspecies variations in toxicity and with the ability of some lower animals and terrestrial plants to develop resistant strains, it seems much more likely that species composition rather than total production will be affected if DDT-residue levels in the sea should reach the point where photosynthesis is affected. Comparing the sensitivity of different ecological groups, it also appears that serious disturbances can be expected at higher trophic levels before primary production is effected.

From their relation to insects, it is not surprising that crustaceous have been shown to be comparatively sensitive to DDT and its metabolites. Significant mortality among calinoid copepods have been reported at concentrations in seawater as low as 5 parts per trillion of DDT, and the development of adults from nauplear stages was completely blocked when hatched from eggs from egg-bearing females maintained at 10 parts per trillion.

Shrimps, crabs of commercially valuable species as well as zooplankton are killed if exposed to DDT in the parts per billion range. On the United States West Coast, the decline in production of Dungeness crabs is associated with high DDE levels in developing larvae.

Molluscs are well-known concentrates of chlorinated hydrocarbons as well as of many other pollutants. Even low concentrations in water may therefore lead to high tissue concentrations and thereby cause biological effects. Characteristically, DDT interferes with growth of oysters at water concentrations down to 0.1 ppb. The resultant tissue levels are around tens of parts per million.

Reproductive failure has been reported for some species of marine fish in coastal areas heavily contaminated with DDT. Sea trout from Laguna Madre in Texas show DDT residues in the ripe eggs of up to 8 ppm. Experiments with freshwater trout have demonstrated that DDT residues of 5 ppm may cause complete failure in the development of sac fry or young fish.

From 1964 to 1969 there was a progressive decline from 30 to 0.2 fish per acre. Furthermore, no juvenile fish have been observed in the Laguna Madre in recent years. In a control area 100 mi away, the year class distribution of sea trout is and has been normal during the period of observation.

Reproductive failure associated with thin eggshells has been reported for a large number of fish-eating and other birds from many parts of the world and several species have disappeared from large parts of their formal habitat. In experimental studies, DDE in the diet at concentrations similar to those observed in nature have resulted in thin eggshells and reduced hatching success.

Good negative correlation between eggshell thickness and DDE content has also repeatedly been reported.

Several different physiological effects of DDT and its metabolites have been described that could contribute to the shell thinning in birds and abnormal behavior observed in contaminated populations. Inhibition of ATP ase (myosine) leads to an energy deficiency, thereby blocking the ion transport in nerve membranes and thus nerve impulses. Also other energy-requiring membrane transports such as ionic calcium in shell glands in birds can be affected. DDE has also been demonstrated to increase the concentration of multifunction oxidase enzymes in livers of mammalians and birds.

A certain resemblance between compounds in the DDT family and steroid hormones is believed to cause the hormone sensors to overestimate the actual hormone concentration in the body. The production of estrogen, testosterone, and thyroxine metabolizing enzymes is therefore stimulated, resulting in too low concentrations of these hormones to allow them to fulfil their pertinent function in different phases of reproduction.

This structural resemblance has also been suggested as the cause for the observed interaction with photosynthesis described above. Obviously, the existing levels of DDT residues in the marine environment have an effect on some species of fish and fish-eating birds. Should the levels increase, it is obvious that the effects would become more severe. As our knowledge of ecological effects in general is very limited, and we have to make our predictions from extrapolations of laboratory studies and field observations in a situation where the only safe statement is that the ecosystem response is neither linear nor continuous, the only reasonable conclusion today is that we must halt the buildup of DDT residues in the marine environment and aim at a lowering of the present levels.

B. PCB's

Polychlorinated biphenyls (PCB's) are a group of compounds with several unique or rare properties such as noninflammability, high boiling temperature (dependent on the degree of chlorination), temperature independent viscosity, and water insolubility. These properties render them very suitable for a wide range of uses such as cooling media at high temperature ranges, softener in plastics, additives in printing ink, paints, and noncarbon copypaper. The degree of leakage of PCB's to the environment connected with the different uses is unknown. In many instances, for example, in connection with the use of PCB's in transformers, there appear to be good possibilities to retain and reuse the polychlorinated biphenyls and avoid environmental contamination.

The accumulated production of PCB's is not accurately known to the scientific community. Available estimates suggest that the total world production can be estimated to be about $\sim 1.0 \times 10^{12}$ g.

Most of our knowledge of PCB in the environment, and especially in the marine environment, is obtained together with information on DDT residues. It is common to present PCB levels in relation to those for DDT residues. In comparing the two groups of compounds, it is generally found that in coastal zones, especially near agricultural areas, the DDT concentrations are higher than those of the PCB's. In open sea areas, on the other hand, the contents of PCB's are frequently higher than the DDT ones.

In marine plankton, the average concentration of PCB's has been estimated to be about 0.3 ppm. Unlike DDT, the levels of PCB's in fish do not seem to be higher on an average than those in plankton.

Making a calculation similar to the one made for DDT residues on the amounts of PCB's present in marine biota, one gets $\sim 1 \times 10^9$ g, or 0.1% of the estimated accumulated world production. No results are available from analyses on seawater concentrations of PCB's. Information is also lacking on the persistence of PCB's in the marine environment. It is likely, however, that it is longer than for DDT residues. There are some confusing circumstances in connection with the occurrence of PCB's in the marine environment.

The pattern of PCB occurrence in marine organisms suggests that atmospheric transport is an important route of injection of PCB's into the sea. In organisms from the upper layer of the oceans, the PCB gas chromatographic patterns match quite well one of the commercially available PCB formulations, mostly Arochlor 1254, and some other Arochlors manufactured in the United States by Monsanto.

It seems quite unlikely that the "fingerprint" of the PCB's could remain the same if the individual PCB compounds evaporated to the atmosphere, precipitated to the ocean surface, and were accumulated individually in marine organisms. A possible explanation is that PCB is introduced into and transported in the atmosphere as an aerosol, which would mean that the PCB unit for transport in the environment is a droplet of a single commercial formulation instead of an individual PCB molecule.

Observations in seals and certain bottom-feeding organisms, however, show that these organisms contain spectra of elution peaks that differ considerably from the commercial formulations, indicating that a degradation of PCB's occur at a significant rate. The lack of corresponding degradation products in organisms from the upper layer of the oceans can be explained in one of the following two ways: (1) degradation of PCB's does not occur in the surface layer of the ocean but only in the vicinity of the bottom. Such an idea is not in agreement with our general understanding of degradation processes; and (2) there is a mechanism for quick removal of PCB residues from the surface layers of the oceans either through a rapid total degradation or through a vertical transport mechanism. The concept of a very fast complete degradation in the surface waters—or the one with a fast down transport—does not agree with the calculations, indicating that a noticeable fraction of the PCB's produced is currently present in marine biota. Furthermore, it would be somewhat surprising to find a mechanism for a fast vertical PCB transport that does not affect DDT in a similar way.

To overcome these apparent contradictions, it has been suggested that the total output of PCB's to the environment are much higher than the calculated ones. Another suggestion has been that PCB's could be formed during the process of pulp-bleaching with chlorine. So far, however, these ideas have not been substantiated.

Our ideas on biological properties of and ecological risks with PCB's have generally been derived from analogies with DDT. The acute toxicity of PCB's on lower organisms is generally lower than that of DDT, while the reverse is the case for higher organisms, such as most vertebrates. Most of the physiological effects on enzymes and hormones that have been demonstrated for DDT and its metabolites have also been indicated for PCB's.

C. Aliphatic Chlorinated Hydrocarbons

Besides the comparatively well-known aromatic chlorinated hydrocarbons such as DDT and PCB, there have been some reports during the last few years showing that large amounts of chlorinated compounds are produced and used for a variety of purposes, among them, dry cleaning (chemical washing). Many of these "new" compounds are manufactured in quantities surprisingly large to anyone who has not followed the subject closely. Most of them are short-chained aliphatic hydrocarbons, and from the uses and their properties, it is obvious that they will occur to some extent as marine contaminants.

One group of short-chain aliphatic hydrocarbons that has been studied as a marine contaminant is the one that forms the so-called EDC tar, a by-product from vinyl-chloride production. Some of the compounds in this group are chemically identical to those mentioned above.

The constituents in the EDC tar occur before chlorination as impurities in the ethylene that is to be converted to vinyl chloride for further polymerisation to PVC plastic. The amount of such impurities varies from factory to factory and from time to time within one factory. After chlorination, they are separated from the vinyl chloride. The total amount of such EDC tar produced in northern Europe is estimated to ~75,000 tons/yr and the amounts are increasing with the use of PVC plastics. The total world production can be estimated to at least 300,000 tons/yr. Chemically, the EDC tar consists of about 25 different compounds.

Most of the EDC tar formed to date has been dumped into the oceans. After dumping—due to its density of 1.25 to 1.40—the EDC tar starts to sink. However, the tendency to disperse is great and the rate of sinking will rapidly decrease as the drops get smaller. Furthermore, EDC tar has shown a tendency to adhere to a large variety of substances, and after contact with floating or suspended material, the droplets of the tar rapidly form a film or layer surrounding the particle.

These tendencies to dispersion and adherence contribute to keep the EDC tar in the upper layers of the oceans. They also tend to keep the individual compounds in the EDC tar together, thereby conserving to some extent the "fingerprint" developed by gas chromatography of the mixture.

An acute effect of dumping of EDC tar has been a massive fish kill. Most fish specimens that were caught in the North Sea or along the Norwegian coast and analyzed for these chlorinated hydrocarbons were shown to contain them. Analyses of water samples demonstrated their presence in patches of water from different places scattered over the North Atlantic.

Biologic accumulation has been shown to occur both from water and food, giving concentration factors ranging from 15 to 3000 for different species of organisms. The biological half-time in cod liver was found to be about a few days for the low-boiling compounds in the EDC tar and about a few weeks for the less volatile ones.

Experiments with acute toxicity demonstrated LC_{50} 48h values from 2.5 to 25 ppm for different species. Sublethal effects on barnacles and polychaetas were observed at concentrations around 2 ppm.

D. Mercury

The first incidence that drew attention to mercury as an environmental pollutant occurred in the coastal marine environment of Minamata Bay, Japan. Although this tragic event had the positive consequence that we became aware of the hazards that could be connected with mercury pollution, we now know that from most points of view it was not typical for the marine mercury contamination problems.

The Minamata case was very localized, where methyl mercury was discharged directly to a river and the bay. Around the coasts of the world we have many areas with local mercury pollution, but in most cases mercury is or has been discharged in inorganic form or as organo mercurials other than methyl mercury. This means that before the mercury becomes a hazardous contaminant in fish or shellfish, it has to undergo methylation. Compared to bioaccumulation, biological methylation is a slow process. Some conditions do exist, however, under which the rate of biological methylation of mercury is considerably enhanced, and they will be discussed below.

For the open ocean the mercury problem is quite different. No local sources can affect the mercury levels in organisms in the open sea. The mercury content in them results from natural processes or to man-affected changes of global significance.

Of the total mercury present in an aquatic ecosystem, only a small proportion is generally found in the methylated form. This fraction, however, is the important one from a fish-contamination point of view, as the biological half-time of methyl mercury in fish can be measured in years, while that for inorganic mercury is a matter of weeks. Furthermore, for man as a consumer of marine organisms, methyl mercury is by far more dangerous than inorganic mercury. From what has been said above, it is evident that there are two principal ways in which methyl mercury levels in marine organisms, notably fish, can be increased: (1) through an increase in the total amount of mercury; and (2) through an increase in the proportion of the total mercury that exists in the form of methyl mercury. This would be the result of an increased rate of biological methylation of mercury.

Mercury both from man-made and natural sources may reach the ocean in two principal ways: through surface runoff and through the atmosphere. Mercury in fresh water is generally found attached to particles of organic or inorganic origin. The size of these particles can naturally show a wide range, some of them being extremely small. As their mercury-binding ability is more dependent on surface area than on mass, the smaller particles play a more important role than should be expected from their relative weight.

When entering the sea, the formation of soluble tetrachloride complexes results in an extraction of mercury from some of the inorganic particles such as clay, while the bond strengths between most organic substances and mercury allow persistence of the complexes. The net result of this is a relocation of particle-bound mercury into association with organic ligands.

Methylation of mercury takes place as a detoxification when the microorganisms, while consuming organic substances, happen to come into contact with the mercury ions.

When the organic particles settle, predominantly in nearshore areas, the attached mercury is incorporated in the deposits. Should the sediments become anaerobic during the degradation of the organics with the production of sulfide ions, mercury will be bound as sulfide. The result of these processes is that mercury transported to the marine environment by surface runoff will have but a small impact on the open sea. Most of it will be retained in the coastal zone.

The mercury that reaches the upper mixed layer of the open oceans through rivers or through the atmosphere will eventually be accumulated by organisms. Attached to or incorporated in dead organisms or fecal pellets, it will then be transported vertically toward the deeper parts of the oceans. In connection with the final decomposition of the carrier material, the mercury is released again into a soluble form, from which it may either be transported back up to the surface with upwelling currents or incorporated in the authigenic minerals forming on the sea bottom.

In the coastal zone itself, industrial discharges frequently give rise to elevated concentration of mercury in marine organisms. In some instances, where methyl mercury is discharged as such or where mercury-rich organic sediments are partially exposed to air as a result of tidal motions, very high levels of methyl mercury (>10 ppm) may occur in marine organisms.

Volatile mercury, such as its elemental form, or dimethyl mercury, will evaporate into the atmosphere. Industrial sources handling mercury as such, the burning mercury-containing fuels, or washing mercury-containing minerals, will contribute to the atmospheric load.

Dimethyl mercury is unstable in the atmosphere. In contact with acids it will be degraded to water-soluble monomethyl mercury and in contact with UV light to elementary (inorganic) mercury.

The world production of mercury is in the order of 1×10^{10} g/yr. To losses from the subsequent usage should be added direct release of mercury in connection with burning of fossil fuels, heating of mercury-containing minerals, and so on. At the very most, these sources could account for a release of mercury of the same order of magnitude as the "intentional" production.

Estimates of mercury transports to the sea indicate that the rivers may contribute with $\sim 10^{10}$ g/yr while the washout with precipitation from the atmosphere could be $(2.5 - 15) \times 10^{10}$ g/yr. The last figure is based on an estimated atmospheric load of 4×10^{9} g, a close to complete washout in connection with precipitation and an average time between rain of 10 days. The estimate of the atmospheric burden of mercury has been questioned and it has been suggested that it represents a tenfold or greater overestimate.

The alternative figure (2.5×10^{10} g) is derived at by multiplying the amount of rain falling over the oceans with a conservative estimate of the average mercury concentration in precipitation of 0.06 ppb derived from mercury content in apparently uncontaminated glacial ice. Accepting the concept that 1.5×10^{11} g/yr represents an underestimate, a compromise of 5×10^{10} g may be a reasonable estimate for calculation purposes.

Analyses of the Greenland ice sheet have demonstrated a tendency to an increase in mercury concentrations during the last decades. When the estimated atmospheric flux of mercury is related to the human production—of which not all is released to the atmosphere—it is apparent that the observed increase, perhaps with a factor of two, that seems to have occurred during the last decades cannot be accounted for by the mercury released from mercury-handling industries, fossil-fuel burning and so on.

The "natural" flux of mercury—"degassing from the earth crust"—appears to be of dominating importance. Weiss et al. has estimated it to be in the order of $(2.5–44) \times 10^{10}$ g/yr.

It is possible that man, through his activities, has affected this degassing during the last decades. This enhancement of the process may have occurred through the changed agricultural practice involving more effective plowing, the use of fertilizers, and so forth. Should this be the case, it is possible that the degassing involves a biological dimethylation of mercury forming a volatile mercury compound that, after introduction to the atmosphere, will be degradated as described above. If that is the case, the mercury case study would have provided us with another example of ecological interaction of a hard-predicted type.

Surface water in the oceans has been found to contain ~ 0.13 μg/g of mercury while the few available analyses from deep water from both the Atlantic and Pacific Oceans indicate higher figures (~ 0.30 μg/g). In their classical work from the 1930s, Stock and Cucuel reported concentrations in sea surface water of 0.03 to 0.04 ppb. Several later reports have also indicated similar figures. The total amount of mercury in seawater would thus amount to $\sim 2.1 \times 10^{14}$ g. Evidently, man has not so far been able to affect this amount measurably.

Marine plankton frequently contains mercury levels of 2 to 10 ppb, most of which is in the inorganic form, while fish concentrations vary considerably from 0.01 to 2 ppm, with a substantial fraction of their mercury in the form of methyl mercury. The (methyl) mercury in the fish is bound to the protein and is not dissolved in the fat as are the chlorinated hydrocarbons. Unlike them, the mercury content in fish is consequently not very fat-dependent but much more related to trophic level, size, and age of the fish. The highest mercury content is found in large predators like swordfish and tuna. The fact that many of these fish have mercury levels above the permissible levels in North America (0.5 ppm) has during the last years had a clear negative impact in the fishing industry.

Analyses of museum specimens of tuna and swordfish have not indicated any notable change in mercury content during the last 150 yr. A surprising finding during these analyses was the large variation in mercury content in these fishes, both in the old specimens and the recent ones, in view of the common understanding among ecologists that these species should be among the best integrators over large areas that we have.

If the existing data are closely examined to find a pattern in these variations, it appears as if the tuna caught in areas with upwelling currents—the most productive fishing areas—tended to have a higher mercury level than those from other parts of the oceans.

A possible explanation of this could be that the higher mercury content in the deep water in connection with the high (micro) biological activity in these superproductive zones results in a higher rate of biological methylation of mercury. The phenomena could thus be a natural one. Some of the marine mammals, notably the seals, have been found to contain very high amounts of mercury, especially in the liver. Despite the fact that most of the mercury they consume in fish is in the form of methyl mercury, the seal liver contains predominantly inorganic mercury. It has been suggested that the seals may have an enzyme that breaks the covalent bonds between the mercury and carbon atoms in methyl mercury.

From laboratory experiments with methyl mercury chloride or other salts, effects on photosynthesis of algae and on behavior of freshwater organisms have been reported at very low concentrations of methyl mercury. Acute toxicity on fish has been found to occur at methyl mercury concentrations in the tissues of $\sim$20 ppm.

Except for a few incidences such as Minamata Bay, however, there are no field reports from the marine environment describing effects of existing mercury levels on the organisms. The mercury problem is commonly considered as a problem for the fish consumer, not as a problem for fish production. In some instances, the national standards on permissible levels of mercury in fish—enforced to protect public health—prevent the use of certain fishing resources.

Specialized fish eaters—such as the seals mentioned above—may have developed certain protective mechanisms through evolution.

Recently it has been suggested that selenium may have an antagonistic effect to the toxicity of mercury, and that there may be an uptake regulating process leading to stoichiometric relations between mercury and selenium in marine organisms that render both elements less toxic than if they had occurred independently. So far, this is a matter for further research.

E. Cadmium

High concentrations of cadmium have been found in marine organisms in some coastal areas. Cadmium concentration in seawater near the coast has been reported to be within the range of 0.05 to 1 ppb. In the open sea the levels are reported to be from 0.01 to 0.05 ppb. Probably the true range is much narrower.

Analyses of cadmium contents in North Atlantic deep-sea sediment have shown average concentrations of 225 ppb with somewhat lower levels in areas rich in shell debris.

In freshwater, cadmium has been found to bind strongly to organic substances, especially in chlorophyll-containing plants. In marine water, however, cadmium appears in complexes to a higher degree than mercury does. In comparative studies, $\sim$80% of cadmium has been found to go through a 0.22 μ membrane that will retain 80 to 90% of the mercury.

The concentration factors from seawater to marine organisms for cadmium are commonly 100–1000. Certain marine mammalians (sea otters) have been reported to contain up to 500 ppm of cadmium in their kidneys. Corresponding concentrations in man would cause severe kidney damage. The biological effects of cadmium in these sea otters and those of the levels found in other marine organisms are unknown.

F. Lead

The behavior of lead in the marine environment is to a high degree dependent on the properties of the individual lead species in question. Like most other elements and compounds described as case studies here, lead enters the oceans both through runoff water from land and through the atmosphere. It is believed that in prehistoric times, the rivers were the main source of lead for the oceans. The lead thus transported to the sea could be as insoluble forms attached to organic or inorganic particles, as soluble chelates, or as soluble inorganic complexes. Naturally there was some exchange taking place between the soluble and insoluble phases. The particle-bound lead settled in the near-coast areas similar to the way described for mercury, with smaller fractions entering the deeper parts of the oceans. Of the lead entering the oceans in a soluble form, a large part was accumulated in organisms of the photic zone.

Out of the lead reaching the oceans each year in prehistoric time, it is believed that only about 1.8×10^{10} g reached the open sea.

The residence time for lead in the upper mixed layers of the ocean has been estimated to be only a few years.

The smelting of lead and production of alkyl leads from 1750 to 1966 is presented in Table II.

The amount of lead aerosols estimated to have been produced per year during 4 yr chosen within the time interval is presented in Table III.

A substantial part of the $\sim 1.5 \times 10^{11}$ g of lead aerosols that are produced today will fall out over the ocean.

The present injection of lead to the sea through surface runoff has been estimated to 5×10^{11} g/yr. A very large part of this is estimated to be retained in the coastal zone.

Table II

10^3 Tons of Lead Smelted or Burned as Alkyl Lead per Year 1750 to 1966[a]

	Northern Hemisphere			Southern Hemisphere
Year	Primary Smelting	Secondary Smelting	Burned Alkyl Lead	Primary Smelting
1750	60			40
1800	90			50
1860	220			
1880	400			
1890	520			40
1900	750	0		80
1910	940	60		100
1920	880	200	0	110
1930	1200	400	4	170
1940	1300	400	36	230
1950	1300	550	110	240
1960	1900	600	180	360
1966	2400	700	310	350

[a] From Murozumi et al. (1969).

Analyses of lead in the Greenland ice sheet have shown an increase in lead fallout of about 500 times over the last 2800 yr. A substantial part of this increase occurred after the introduction of ethyl lead in gasoline.

Analyses of lead in seawater support the idea of a recent increase due to fallout. "Young" surface water contains variable and high concentrations of lead ranging from 0.07 to 0.35 ppb, while "old" deep seawater contains 0.02 to 0.04 ppb.

When this picture is compared with that found for chemically similar metals such as

TABLE III

Estimated Lead Aerosol Production During Four Years in the Time Period 1750 to 1970[a]

Year	Estimated Amount ($g \times 10^{10}$)
1753	0.2
1815	0.4
1933	1
1966	10

[a] From *Impingements of Man on the Oceans.* Wiley-Interscience, London, 1972 (Chapter on Lead, by Pattersson).

barium and radium, which tend to have relatively high concentrations in "old" deep seawater and relatively low ones in "young" surface water, the indications of a recent increase due to higher fallout are further strengthened. This is even more likely as the lead distribution is similar to those of radioactive debris from nuclear explosions.

The levels of lead in marine organisms and the biological and ecological effects of the environmental contamination is practically unknown. There are, however, reasons for considerable concern.

G. Copper

Extremely high concentrations of copper have been found in water, sediment, and biota in some coastal areas. To a very large extent, however, the copper appears to remain in the nearshore area. Studies of long-term changes in copper content of seaweed in a coastal area without any known direct discharge have not revealed any notable change during the last decade.

The suggestion that atmospheric transport of copper to the open ocean should occur to a significant extent is yet to be verified and quantified.

There are at present no indications of a food-chain magnification of copper.

H. Zinc

In connection with substantial local discharge, highly elevated levels of zinc have been found in sediment and biota in some coastal waters. Nothing is known about zinc contamination in the open sea. From heavy contaminated coastal areas, it is known that zinc content generally decreases when going up the food chain.

I. Selenium

Selenium is found in a variety of marine organisms. Especially in livers of seals and penguins, the reported concentrations are very high ($\sim$100 ppm). To what extent this is due to man's impact is unknown. The theory of interdependence of mercury and selenium concentrations in marine organisms is treated in the mercury section.

J. Arsenic

Reports of high concentrations of arsenic in the biota in general have been confined to coastal areas with known discharge. In the Baltic, the concentrations of arsenic in fish have been found to be well correlated with salinity. Even extremely high local contamination in the northern low-salinity part does not render the arsenic concentration in fish much higher than those commonly found in the oceans.

Some marine invertebrates such as crabs and lobsters have long been known to contain high concentrations of arsenic. As stated already in the 1930s, "the concentrations of arsenic in some marine organisms are so high that if it had been arsenic as As^{3+} one single meal would have been toxic to man. As no effects are observed, it has to occur in the heptavalent form (As^{5+})."

During the 1960s, some further light was thrown on the form of arsenic in marine organisms. In fish oil, arsenic was observed to occur as an organo-arsenic compound. Further investigations showed that marine algae accumulate arsenic, probably mistaking it for phosphates and converting it into organic compounds, one type of which seems to be lipids with phosphorus replaced by arsenic. Some other organo-arsenic compounds have not yet been identified in the form in which they occur in marine biota. After conversion into organic compounds in the algae, arsenic is further accumulated along the food chain.

K. Vanadium

In connection with burning of some petroleums, large amounts of vanadium are entering the atmosphere. Open ocean surface water has been found to contain more vanadium than does subsurface water. This could be due to atmospheric fallout but also to surface contamination from oil spills or to a natural accumulation process in the surface film.

Vanadium is known to have very high accumulation factors from seawater to some marine organisms. The extent of man's impact on vanadium concentrations in marine organisms is unknown and so are the biological and ecological effects of vanadium contamination.

L. Manganese and Iron

In connection with mining operations, large amounts of iron and manganese are discharged to the marine environment. Compared to the natural flux, however, the amounts released and discharged by man are small. Elevated concentrations of iron and manganese are only found locally in coastal areas.

The natural transport of iron and manganese involves release from minerals on the continents, transport with surface runoff to the oceans, solubilization as complex ions in contact with saline water, or precipitation with mineral particles on the continental shelves.

Bioaccumulation provides a mode for vertical transport in dead organisms or fecal pellets. In the bottom water, iron and manganese are released and precipitated as oxides. In this process of precipitation of iron and manganese, heavy metals such as mercury, cadmium, copper, and zinc may be incorporated.

Manganese and iron are not mentioned here because of their biological significance as man-made contaminants, which is believed to be small, but because they demonstrate a special problem of transport and because of their impact on mercury and other heavy metals during the formation of ferromanganese minerals.

3. Future Trends and Hazard Evaluation

Looking at these case studies, it is evident that our knowledge is quite limited. Yet, the compounds discussed here are the most extensively studied. There are many others that may turn out to be as hazardous as those considered here. Presently, for example, concern has arisen about the effects of phthalates a group of compounds used to soften plastics some bleaching agents in detergents that appear to be biologically persistent despite the fact that they do not contain any halogens, and the effects of an antibiotic produced by man. Neither of these have been dealt with here, as the available information both on concentrations in the marine environment and biological effects is too scarce.

The case study on aliphalic chlorinated hydrocarbons provides an example of how the scientific community and the public, more or less accidentally, can become aware of a new pollutant produced and discharged in hundred thousands of tons per year.

An elementary requirement necessary as a step toward a clearer understanding of the whole problem of marine contamination is a worldwide registry on production and use of chemical compounds.

The present situation where we, through decades of investigations, have collected a reasonable amount on information of only tens of elements and compounds while thousands of new ones are synthesized and are being used each year is unacceptable if we are to maintain the ecological conditions required for man's existence.

The positive factor in the last years' development is the new general awareness of the problem. The health of the oceans—as we can measure it—is continuously becoming poorer and is likely to continue to do so for the next years to come.

One general illustration of this, complementary to the information given in the case study on DDT on the recently reduced use of that compound, is the overall figures on pesticide use in relation to agricultural productivity.

Based both on geographical and time comparisons, it appears as if the use of biocides increased with a factor of 10 when yield per surface area is doubled (Table IV).

The green revolution during the last year with the successful introduction in many

TABLE IV

Pesticide Use and Agricultural Yield in Some Areas of the World[a]

Geographical Area	Pesticide Use: Grams per Hectare	Pesticide Use: Rank	Yield: Kilograms per Hectare	Yield: Rank
Japan	10,790	1	5,480	1
Europe	1,870	2	3,430	2
United States	1,490	3	2,600	3
Latin America	220	4	1,970	4
Oceania	198	5	1,570	5
India	149	6	820	7
Africa	127	7	1,210	6

[a] From *FAO Production Yearbook*, 1963.

countries of high-yield crops have further underlined this trend and increased man's dependence of pesticides.

Looking at industrial pollutants, the long-term trend may be more encouraging, but of the case studies cited here rapid improvement can be expected only for lead and aliphatic chlorinated hydrocarbons. Also here the economic implications may make many governments hesitant to ban the use of alkyl lead in gasoline and demand destruction instead of dumping of by-products from vinyl-chloride production.

Concerning the risks connected with contaminants in the marine and general environment, the following environmental characteristics and properties should be known to allow an evaluation of potential undesirable inputs.

1. Human production and release in relation to natural flux.

2. Persistency in the environment (residence time in waters, sediment-soil, atmosphere and organisms).

3. Bio-accumulation.

(*a*) The relation between fat and water solubility may give an indication of "passive" accumulation.

(*b*) If "active" accumulation is known to occur, the concentration factor should be estimated.

4. Properties affecting the dispersion of the compound (e.g., volatility, tendency to adhere to or form complexes with organic and inorganic particles; tendency to form soluble complexes with chlorides or other abundant ions in seawater; tendency to form oxides or sulphides with low solubility).

5. Toxicity to aquatic organisms.

6. Toxicity to man (or other mammalian).

7. Biological effects such as selective enhancement or retardation of metabolic activities of certain organisms that may have long-term effects on the balance of the ecosystem.

8. Transformation reaction that may change the properties of the compound. Most such reactions performed by organisms increase water solubility of the compound, thereby making it possible to excrete them. Some notable exceptions, such as the biological formation of methyl mercury and organo-arsenic compounds, are known, however.

From the case studies, several examples can be found of the importance of one or more of these factors for the behavior and effects of a compound. The mercury case study, however, has already provided us with examples of new principles and reactions not anticipated. Any evaluation of hazard has, of course, the limitations that it is based on existing knowledge. In the history of environmental pollution, there are to date numerous examples of underestimated effects and damage and few with excess cautionary measure. It is for all of us to hope that the future will show that the Jeremiahs of today will add to that small group, although the present perspectives are not encouraging.

Our hope lies in the growing awareness and the belief that man will be able to use his intelligence to protect the future of his own species, thereby demonstrating the intelligence is of long-term selective advantage and not something that enhances the process of rise and fall of the species.

References

Hood, D. W., ed. 1971. *Impingement of Man on the Oceans*. Wiley-Interscience, London.

Baseline Studies of Pollutants in the Marine Environment and Research Recommendations. The IDOE Baseline Conference, May 24–26, 1972, New York, 1972.

Chlorinated Hydrocarbons in the Marine Environment. A report prepared by Panel on Monitoring Persistent Pesticides in the Marine Environment. U.S. National Academy of Sciences, Washington, 1970.

Man's Impact on the Global Environment. Report of the Study of Critical Environmental Problem SCEP. M.I.T. Press, Cambridge, Mass., 1970.

22. ARTIFICIAL RADIOACTIVITY IN THE SEA

A. Preston

Since the last chapter on this subject was prepared for Vol. 2 of *The Sea* (Miyake, 1963), the picture has been altered by the very large extra input of artificial radionuclides from nuclear weapon testing following the temporary moratorium of 1959 to 1961, and by the increased input of waste from civil and military nuclear operations. Furthermore, the scale and variety of research activities has increased in relation to waste disposal control, and the greater awareness of the opportunities that radioactive labelling of the marine environment presents for many aspects of oceanographic research—physical, chemical, and biological. Several good reviews of marine radioactivity in various contexts have recently been produced (National Academy of Sciences, 1971; Duursma, 1972; Preston, 1972). This chapter will concentrate on areas of current interest to pollution control and supporting research fields.

1. Global Inventory of Artificially Produced Radionuclides

To provide a general perspective to the levels of artificial radioactivity in the oceans, it is instructive to consider briefly the total inventory of artificial radionuclides in the world ocean. The data, which are displayed in Table I, are taken from a recent FAO report (FAO, 1971) and show the order of magnitude of the total radionuclide content of the world ocean in 1970, the only significant sources being weapon-test fallout and controlled disposal of radioactive waste. The total figure of 10^9 Ci should be compared with the total oceanic content of the naturally occurring radionuclide potassium-40, which approximates to 5.10^{11} Ci. Artificially produced radioactivity is thus about one-thousandth of the total natural radioactivity in the oceans.

This comparison suggests that artificial radioactivity from nuclear power programs is only one-hundredth of that from the weapon-testing programs, and thus a very small fraction of the natural radioactivity inventory. However, the significance of the two situations pertaining to artificial radioactivity is quite different from that suggested by these proportions. Fallout radioactivity is widely and relatively uniformly

Table I

Total Inventory of Artificial Radionuclides Introduced into the World Oceans (Preston, 1972)[a]

	Year 1970	Year 2000
Nuclear explosions (worldwide distribution)		
Fission products (exclusive of tritium)	2–6 × 10^8 Ci	? × 10^8 Ci[a]
Tritium	10^9 Ci	? × 10^9 Ci[a]
Reactors and reprocessing of fuel (restricted local distribution)		
Fission and activation products (exclusive of tritium)	3 × 10^5 Ci	3 × 10^7 Ci
Tritium	3 × 10^5 Ci	? × 10^8 Ci
Total artificial radioactivity	10^9 Ci	10^9 Ci
Total natural ^{40}K	5 × 10^{11} Ci	5 × 10^{11} Ci

[a] Assumed that atmospheric nuclear testing will continue at about the rate of 1968 to 1970.

distributed and at comparatively low concentration (Table II), except in the immediate vicinity of ocean weapon-test areas for short times after the explosions, whereas the contamination from waste disposal is severely restricted in its distribution and somewhat higher (sometimes very much higher) in concentration (Table III).

The second column of Table I outlines the situation that may exist toward the end of this century, assuming that the present level of nuclear weapon testing continues and that the disposal rate of low-level radioactive waste grows in proportion to the growth in nuclear power. However, the trends of the last decade or so suggest that improvements in radioactive waste management will achieve a reduction in the amount of radioactive material reaching marine environments per unit of fuel burnt and

TABLE II

Radionuclide Concentrations from Global Fallout, as pCi/l for Seawater, pCi/kg for Dry Sediments, and pCi/kg for Wet Biological Material (FAO, 1971)

			Biological Materials			
Radionuclide	Water	Sediments	Seaweeds	Mollusca	Crustacea	Fish
^{3}H	$1–10^{2}$					
^{54}Mn	(1)	$10^{3}–10^{4}$	10^{3}			
^{90}Sr	$10^{-1}–1$	$1–10^{2}$	1–10	$10^{-1}–10$	1–10	1–10
$^{95}Zr/Nb$	$10^{-1}–10$	$10^{2}–10^{5}$	$10^{3}–10^{4}$			
^{106}Ru	$10^{-2}–1$	$10^{2}–10^{5}$	$10–10^{4}$	$10–10^{2}$	$1–10^{2}$	$1–10^{3}$
137Cs	$10^{-1}–1$	$10–10^{4}$	1–10	1–10	1–10	$1–10^{2}$
^{144}Ce	$10^{-2}–1$	$10^{2}–10^{5}$	$10–10^{4}$	$10–10^{3}$	$1–10^{2}$	$1–10^{2}$
^{239}Pu	$10^{-5}–10^{-3}$	$10^{-1}–1$	1	10^{-1}		10^{-3}

TABLE III

Radionuclide Concentrations Resulting from the Controlled Disposal of Radioactive Wastes from Nuclear Power Production, as pCi/l for Seawater, pCi/kg for Dry Sediments, and pCi/kg for Wet Biological Material (FAO, 1971)

			Biological Materials			
Radionuclide	Water	Sediments	Seaweeds	Mollusca	Crustacea	Fish
^{3}H	$10^{1}–10^{3}$					
^{32}P	1–10			$10^{2}–10^{3}$		
^{55}Fe	$10^{-1}–10$		10^{2}	$10^{2}–10^{3}$		
^{60}Co	$10^{-2}–1$	$10^{2}–10^{3}$	$10^{2}–10^{3}$	$10–10^{3}$		
^{65}Zn	$10^{-3}–1$	10^{3}	$10^{2}–10^{3}$	$10^{2}–10^{5}$		
^{90}Sr	$1–10^{2}$		$10–10^{2}$	$10^{2}–10^{3}$	10^{3}	1
$^{95}Zr/Nb$	$1–10^{3}$	$10^{5}–10^{7}$	$10^{4}–10^{6}$	$10^{4}–10^{6}$	$10^{3}–10^{4}$	
^{106}Ru	$1–10^{3}$	$10^{5}–10^{8}$	$10^{4}–10^{6}$	$10^{4}–10^{6}$	$10^{3}–10^{5}$	10^{3}
^{110m}Ag	$10^{-3}–10^{-2}$			$10^{2}–10^{3}$		
^{134}Cs	1–10	10^{3}				10^{3}
^{137}Cs	$1–10^{2}$	$10^{2}–10^{4}$	10^{3}	$10^{2}–10^{3}$		$10^{3}–10^{4}$
^{144}Ce	$1–10^{3}$	$10^{5}–10^{7}$	$10^{4}–10^{6}$			
^{239}Pu		$10^{2}–10^{5}$	$10^{2}–10^{4}$			1–10

reprocessed. There is, therefore, every possibility that a lower inventory than that indicated for nuclear power will be realized.

2. Radioactivity as a Potential Pollutant

The major impact of artificial radioactivity on the oceans has been as a potential pollutant, and, in particular, concern has centered on the public health problem that might ensue following human exploitation of contaminated marine environments. This public health problem has been a most important stimulus to marine pollution methodology, and the development and deployment of critical path analysis techniques to the environmental management of these materials (Preston, 1969; Slansky, 1971; Foster, Ophel, and Preston, 1971) provides an exemplary basis for the control of a chemical pollutant (Preston and Wood, 1971).

Radionuclides have long been recognized as highly toxic materials as a consequence of their emitted radiation and damage to biological systems following absorption of energy from this radiation. Two distinct types of damage are recognized, according to whether the consequences arise in the individual—somatic effects—or in future generations following damage to genetic material. At the levels of radiation obtaining in the environment, somatic effects are most likely to be limiting and to manifest themselves as malignant disease whose appearance will be very infrequent and often long delayed. Other nonmalignant effects, such as life shortening, are less easy to distinguish, and genetic effects may show up only generations later as characteristic abnormalities.

Because of the existence of these potentially damaging effects, strict controls are set on waste disposal so as to limit public exposure to a level that carries with it a very minute degree of risk. The basic radiation standards employed in control are those of the International Commission on Radiological Protection (ICRP, 1966).

In 1958 the United Nations Conference on the Law of the Sea, under Article 25 of its "Convention on the High Seas," required every state to take measures to prevent pollution of the seas from radioactive waste. The Conference adopted a resolution recommending that the International Atomic Energy Agency (IAEA) should take such action as might be required to assist member states in achieving adequate control over the introduction of radioactive wastes to the sea. In response to this initiative, IAEA set up a panel of experts under the chairmanship of H. Brynielsson (Sweden) to study the scientific and technical aspects of radioactive waste disposal to the sea. The panel reported in 1960 (IAEA, 1961) and concluded that low- and intermediate-level radioactive wastes might be safely disposed of into the sea under properly controlled and specified conditions, which they enumerated.

The basis of the control recommended was the application to environmental situations of ICRP dose limits through the use of critical path techniques. These techniques had been in use since the early 1950s (Dunster, 1958) and have since been extensively developed (Morgan, 1964a; Preston, 1966, 1969; Slansky, 1971). The model used in this approach provides a means of evaluating environmental capacity for a specified composition of radioactive waste and of establishing limits within which discharges may be controlled (Slansky, 1971). At the same time it provides a basis for optimal deployment of resources on environmental monitoring (Preston, 1969) from which the actual degree of human or resource radiation exposure can be assessed.

The model depends on a critical evaluation of the environmental behavior of the discharged radionuclides and the identification of the limiting pathway(s) to public exposure. This identification is achieved by the use of data from habits surveys that yield basic information on the working, eating, and recreational habits of the exposed population. From all this information, together with hydrographic data, various critical pathways can be identified in accordance with a scheme as outlined below:

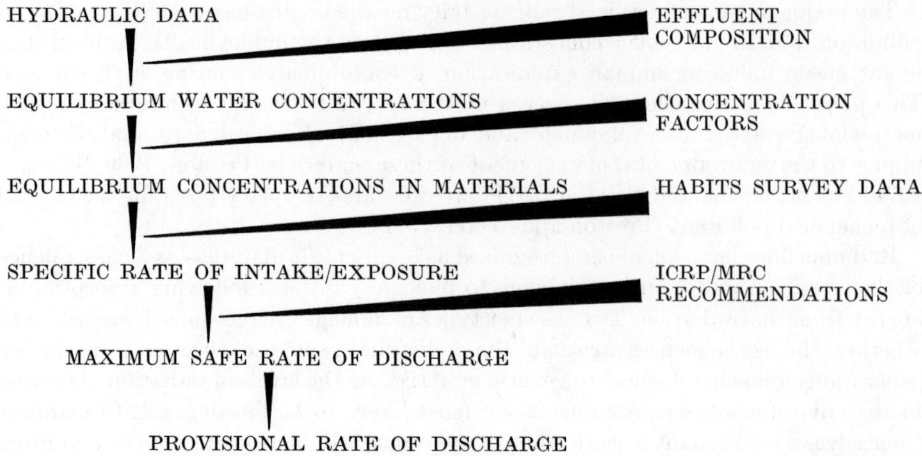

The data are then used in establishing discharge limits, and, when the site has been operational long enough to generate measurable contamination in the environment, the habits data are again used, in conjunction with monitoring data, to refine the estimates of the original evaluation and to provide a basis for estimating public radiation exposure.

In terms of worldwide population dose, the major contribution has been from weapon-test fallout that, including terrestrial and freshwater routes, will contribute 0.075 mrem/person/yr up to the year 2000 (UNSCEAR, 1966; Foster, Ophel, and Preston, 1971) or about 0.1% of natural background radiation levels. Thirty years of controlled radioactive waste disposal have had a very much smaller global impact, although local dose rates have in some instances been greater than local fallout dose rates. However, in no case have the ICRP dose limits been exceeded. Examples of marine disposals are given in Table IV, together with data on individual exposure where available. The value of worldwide population dose from waste disposal can already be estimated from data relating to the United Kingdom, where, in spite of the largest per capita production of nuclear power, the dose from marine disposals is less than 0.003% of the per capita natural background dose (Mitchell, 1971).

Detailed consideration of the United Kingdom (Preston and Mitchell, in press) shows that the major consideration in terms of human radiation dose will remain with the discharge of waste from fuel reprocessing, with individual nuclear power stations contributing only a very small fraction of this dose. Furthermore, even in the case of fuel reprocessing, it is the individual somatic dose consideration that will prove limiting (Table V), and in meeting criteria in relation to individual dose commitments, population dose will be held to a very low level. A similar exercise conducted by the UN Scientific Committee on the Effects of Atomic Radiation (UNSCEAR) for the global situation indicates that the per capita dose to individuals per megawatt electrical year will be more limiting than the average per capita dose to the population (UNSCEAR, 1972).

TABLE IV

Public Health Implications of Discharges of Liquid Radioactive Waste to the Marine environment from Selected Sites (Preston, Woodhead, Mitchell, and Pentreath, 1972)

Site	Critical Group	Material	Radionuclide(s)	Organ	Percentage of ICRP Dose Limit	
Windscale, United Kingdom	Laverbread eaters in South Wales	*Porphyra* seaweed	^{106}Ru	GI tract	6	1970
Bradwell, United Kingdom	Local oyster fishermen	Oyster flesh	^{110m}Ag	GI tract	0.2	1970
Hanford, United States	Oyster fishermen, Willipa Bay	Oyster flesh	^{65}Zn, ^{32}P	Total body	0.6	1969
Tokai Mura, Japan	Local fishing communities	Fish flesh		No information available		
Trombay, India	Local fishing communities	Fish flesh		No information available		
La Hague, France	Local fishing communities	Fish flesh and seaweed		No information available		

TABLE V
Estimates of Public Radiation Exposure from Marine Radioactive Waste Disposal in the United Kingdom

Source	Percentage of recommended Dose Limits	
	Somatic Dose	Genetic Dose
Nuclear fuel production and reprocessing	10	$< 10^{-4}$
Nuclear generation of electricity	10^{-1}	—

3. Radiation Dose Commitment to Marine Organisms

The limiting consideration in controlling radioactive waste disposal to the sea is the radiation dose commitment to man, and it is implicit that the commitment to marine organisms is negligible by comparison. The evidence for this assumption has recently been extensively reviewed (Templeton, Nakatani, and Held, 1970; Woodhead, 1971); it supports the established view that fish are the most radiosensitive component of the marine ecosystem and that damage to resources, if it occurred, would most likely stem from the direct effects of radiation on fish rather than on effects produced in organisms at lower levels in the food webs. Moreover, the elements most at risk in the life cycle of a fish are the radiosensitive mature gametes and developing embryos.

A detailed consideration of radiation doses experienced by marine organisms has recently been made (Woodhead, 1973a) on the basis of idealized models and rather incomplete data on radionuclide tissue concentrations and distributions. However, it has been possible to derive reasonable estimates of dose for five groups of organisms—phytoplankton, zooplankton, mollusca, crustacea, and fish. Within the limitations imposed by the data and the simplified dosimetry models, these estimates show that in a global context the dose rates from artificial radionuclides are of the same order as those due to natural background radiation (Table VI). The major contribution to the artificial component is from fallout. Locally, high doses are produced in the vicinity of waste disposal operations, but even here, in population terms or on a global scale, the dose-rate contribution is negligible.

In the case of fish in a waste disposal area, the estimated doses have been confirmed by *in situ* measurements using thermoluminescent dosimetry techniques (Woodhead, 1973b). In the case of developing fish embryos, it has been the possibility of significant dose rates from activity accumulated on or within the egg that has generated concern (Polikarpov, 1966). Even here, however, experimental investigation of the accumulation of radionuclides by the eggs of the plaice shows that the radiation doses experienced by eggs in a waste disposal area are much lower than those that have been found necessary to produce significant effects in laboratory experiments. In fact the dose to the developing embryo is much less than that due to natural background (Woodhead, 1970).

4. The Spectrum of Artificially-Produced Radionuclides in Marine Environments and Their Overall Distribution

The control of radioactive waste disposal has depended on a steadily improving knowledge of the behavior of radionuclides when released to the environment, the

TABLE VI

Summary of Dose Rates (μrad h^{-1}) to Marine Organisms from Environmental Radioactivity (Woodhead, 1973a)

Source	Phytoplankton 20 m Depth, Remote from Sea Bed	Zooplankton 20 m Depth, Remote from Sea Bed	Mollusca 20 m Depth, on the Sea Bed	Crustacea 20 m Depth, on the Sea Bed	Fish	
					20 m Depth, Remote from Sea Bed	20 m Depth, on the Sea Bed
NATURAL BACKGROUND						
Cosmic radiation	0.5	0.5	0.5	0.5	0.5	0.5
Internal activity	1.9–7.3	2.6–15.7	7.4–14.9	7.9–21.4	2.7–4.2	2.7–4.2
Water activity	0.4	0.2	0.1	0.1	0.1	0.1
Sediment activity, γ	—	—	1.5–16.0	1.5–16.0	—	1.5–16.0
β	—	—	1.6–21.0	1.6–21.0	—	1.6–21.0
Total	2.8–8.2	3.3–16.4	9.5–31.5	10.0–38.0	3.3–4.8	4.8–20.8
FALLOUT						
Internal activity, ^{3}H, ^{14}C, ^{90}Sr, ^{137}Cs, ^{239}Pu	0.01–0.88	0.23–13.4	0.06–0.32	0.004–0.097	0.02–0.06	0.02–0.06
Other nuclides	0.25–24.6	1.2–134	0.04–7.7	0.36	0.12–1.7	0.12–1.7
Water activity	5×10^{-5}–0.016	4×10^{-5}–0.011	$(0.2–32) \times 10^{-4}$	$(0.2–32) \times 10^{-4}$	$(0.3–65) \times 10^{-4}$	$(0.2–32) \times 10^{-4}$
Total	0.26–24.5	1.4–147	0.10–8.0	0.36–0.46	0.14–1.8	0.14–1.8
WASTE DISPOSAL						
Windscale						
Internal activity	200–2100	530–6900	15.3–58.9	6.9–67.9	0.5–1.5	0.5–1.5
Water activity	0.2–3.3	0.2–3.0	0.05–1.2	0.05–1.2	0.09–2.4	0.05–1.2
Sediment activity, γ	—	—	36.4–3340	36.4–3340	—	36.4–3340
β	—	—	207–5380	207–5380	—	207–5380
Total	200–2100	530–6900	51.8–3400	43.3–3410	0.6–3.9	37.0–3340
Bradwell						
Internal activity	—	—	1.37–1.81	—	—	—
Sediment activity, γ	—	—	1.69	1.69	—	1.69
β	—	—	1.32	1.32	—	1.32
Total	—	—	3.1–3.5	1.7	—	1.7

mechanisms effecting their distribution, and, in particular, those determining their interaction with biological materials, especially their entry into the marine food chains. The remainder of this chapter will be devoted to an examination of these factors and a consideration of the problems still to be confronted.

Virtually the whole range of fission products must at some time or other have been introduced to segments of the marine environment, following test explosions conducted under water. Many of these radionuclides will have been of extremely short

TABLE VII

Artificially Produced Radionuclides That Have Been Detected in the Marine Environment

Mode of Production					
Fission			Neutron Activation		
Radionuclide	Half-Life	Type of Decay	Radionuclide	Half-Life[a]	Type of Decay
^{3}H[b]	12.26 y	β^-	^{14}C[b]	5.76×10^3 y	β^-
^{89}Sr	51 d	β^-	^{32}P[b]	14.3 d	β^-
^{90}Sr[b]	28 y	β^-	^{35}S	87.2 d	β^-
^{90}Y[b]	64.2 h	β^-	^{45}Ca	165 d	β^-
^{91}Y	59 d	β^-	^{46}Sc	84 d	$\beta^-\gamma$
^{95}Nb[b]	35 d	$\beta^-\gamma$	^{51}Cr[b]	27.8 d	Kγ
^{95}Zr[b]	65 d	$\beta^-\gamma$	^{54}Mn[b]	314 d	Kγ
^{99}Mo	67 h	$\beta^-\gamma$	^{55}Fe[b]	2.7 y	K
^{99}Tc	2.1×10^5 y	β^-	^{59}Fe	45 d	$\beta^-\gamma$
^{103}Ru[b]	40 d	$\beta^-\gamma$	^{57}Co	270 d	Kγ
$^{106}Ru/^{106}Rh$[b]	1.0 y	$\beta^-\gamma$	^{58}Co	71 d	K$\beta^+\gamma$
^{125}Sb	2.7 y	$\beta^-\gamma$	^{60}Co[b]	5.26 y	$\beta^-\gamma$
^{131}I	8.04 d	$\beta^-\gamma$	^{65}Zn[b]	245 d	K$\beta^+\gamma$
^{132}Te	78 h	$\beta^-\gamma$	^{76}As	26.5 h	$\beta^-\gamma$
^{137}Cs[b]	30 y	$\beta^-\gamma$	^{108m}Ag	127 y	Kγ
^{140}Ba	12.8 d	$\beta^-\gamma$	^{110m}Ag[b]	253 d	$\beta^-\gamma$
^{140}La	40.2 h	$\beta^-\gamma$	^{113m}Cd	14 y	β^-
^{141}Ce	32.5 d	$\beta^-\gamma$	^{115m}Cd	43 d	$\beta^-\gamma$
$^{144}Ce/^{144}Pr$[b]	285 d	$\beta^-\gamma$	^{124}Sb	60 d	$\beta^-\gamma$
^{147}Pm	2.6 y	β^-	^{134}Cs	2.1 y	$\beta^-\gamma$
^{155}Eu	1.81 y	$\beta^-\gamma$	^{181}W	30 d	Kγ
			^{185}W	73 d	β^-
			^{187}W	24 h	$\beta^-\gamma$
			^{207}Bi	28 y	Kγ
			^{239}Np	2.35 d	$\beta\gamma$
			^{238}Pu	86 y	α
			^{239}Pu[b]	2.44×10^4 y	α
			^{240}Pu	6.6×10^3 y	α
			^{241}Pu[b]	13.2 y	β
			^{241}Am[b]	458 y	$\alpha\gamma$
			^{242}Cm	163 d	α

[a] Half-life: y (years), d (days), h (hours).

[b] Major occurring radionuclides.

half-life and will therefore only have had a transitory existence and have been of local importance over short time scales. It is the longer-lived activities, and particularly those isotopes of elements of biological significance, that have been the most widely distributed and have received the greatest attention.

The list in Table VII covers all artificially produced radionuclides reported as detected in the marine environment, together with their radioactive half-lives and principal radiation components. The data include those for neutron-activation products as well as fission products, and indicate what a wide variety of materials is involved.

Radionuclides such as tritium, when introduced to the sea, are truly conservative in their behavior with respect to seawater, because they are largely in the form of tritiated water. On the other hand, highly refractory materials such as zirconium-95 and niobium-95 are nonconservative with respect to seawater and are rapidly removed to suspended matter and to bed sediments. Between these two extremes are radionuclides that are partially removed both by surface adsorption to physical materials and by biological accumulation, such as caesium-137, zinc-65, and cobalt-60, and those that are very highly reconcentrated in biological systems by processes of true "bioaccumulation," although not necessarily for essential metabolic requirements, for example, silver-110m in oyster flesh, and manganese-54 in clams and scallops.

In general, even those radionuclides that are concentrated to high degrees by biological systems are not, in total budgetary terms, held to any large extent in such systems (Preston, Jefferies, and Mitchell, 1971), and the two major marine compartments are nearly always water and bed sediments, except perhaps for suspended matter and large macrophytes in some highly silted river estuaries or coastal embayments (Wolfe, Cross, and Jennings, 1973). However, recent studies of fish populations subject to fallout contamination have shown that although this compartment may well be small in absolute terms, the residence time of, for example, caesium-137 in tuna populations (Hodge, Folsom, and Young, 1973) and in cod and plaice populations (Preston and Jefferies, 1969) is long enough, in relation to rate of decline of fallout inputs, to ensure only a very slow decline in radionuclide concentrations over periods approaching a decade (Table VIII).

Table VIII

Mean Concentrations of Casesium-137 in Fish Muscle Tissue, pCi kg^{-1} (wet weight), and total cumulative deposition on the northern hemisphere

Year	Pacific Albacore	Icelandic Cod	North Sea Cod	Total Cumulative Deposition[a]
1964	160	18	80	100
1965	90	28	78	104
1966	88	30	48	105
1967	81	25	51	105
1968	58	28	53	105
1969	78	40	60	103
1970	64	30	80	102
1971	58	10	50	101

[a] Corrected for decay and normalized to 100 in 1964.

Attention has frequently been focused on the biological transport of radionuclides, but on a geochemical scale, this is not a significant contributory factor in terms of the oceanic distribution of radioactivity. The most important considerations in the context of distribution are the method of introduction, that is, diffuse source, as in atmospheric fallout, or point source, as in waste disposal, and whether the source is continuous or discontinuous. Thereafter, the controlling factors are dispersion by the water mass itself, including diffusion and advection, and removal to suspended matter and its subsequent transport or sedimentation.

However, small as the total biological inventory may typically be, it is often the most significant in terms of the impact of radioactivity as a pollutant.

5. Distribution of Radionuclides in Seawater

A great deal of work has been accomplished concerning the distribution of fallout radionuclides in seawater, and in particular strontium-90 and caesium-137 in open ocean systems, and, in the context of pollution, knowledge of their behavior is adequate, although studies of their distribution have revealed big gaps in our knowledge of ocean mixing patterns. A review of the oceanic data appeared in 1971 (Volchok et al., 1971), but the authors were unable to resolve conflicting interpretations of the data on deep-water strontium-90 concentrations. If the view is taken that strontium-90 has penetrated to great depth as a result of vertical mixing, then the oceanic inventory would appear to be very much larger than that calculated from the known nuclear-test explosions (Table IX), and vertical mixing rates would need to be very much higher than those generally accepted. The extrapolation of land-derived weapon-test radionuclide fallout contours to the sea surface also suggests a much smaller oceanic inventory than that demanded by the proponents of deep-water vertical penetration, or, alternatively, the latter's propositions imply very different fallout mechanisms over the ocean than over the land. The whole area of atmospheric transport, as a pathway to ocean surface water, is one now receiving extensive examination, and not only in the context of radioactivity.

Other radionuclide distributions in seawater, including carbon-14 and tritium, have also been used as a basis for studying water movements both on local and oceanic scales (Münnich and Roether, 1967). In the medium and long term they hold

TABLE IX

Oceanic Inventory of ^{90}Sr in 1966, Megacuries (Preston, 1969)

	Alternative values for deep-water concentration, dpm/100 liters		
	0		3
Surface-water component	14.3		13.1
Deep-water component	0		18.4
Total	14.3		31.5
Value from extrapolated overland deposition		7.6	

much promise for the study of oceanic circulation patterns, particularly tritium with its enhanced inventory from nuclear power production (see Table I). Data from studies of weapon-test fallout tritium penetration show that there is significant penetration in the northern latitudes of the Atlantic, but that in equatorial latitudes, it is largely restricted to waters above the thermocline. On the other hand, carbon-14 studies in the northeast Pacific show that this radionuclide is entirely restricted to the surface 200 m.

The radionuclides of cerium, ruthenium, zirconium, and niobium, which are known to be associated with suspended matter, show very similar profiles with respect to depth. Studies of the distribution of cerium, in particular, show considerable penetration, and sedimentation may be the controlling factor here.

The distribution of caesium-137 in coastal and shelf water has been studied both in relation to waste disposal (Preston, Jefferies, and Mitchell, 1971; Preston, Jefferies, and Pentreath, 1972) and weapon-test fallout (Feldt, 1966; Kautsky, 1971; Preston, in press) and has produced interesting confirmatory evidence of the overall circulation pattern of shallow sea areas such as the Irish Sea (Preston, Jefferies, and Pentreath, 1972) and the North Sea, including tentative estimates of turnover time. The distributions of zinc-65 and chromium-51 discharged to the North Pacific through the Columbia River have provided an interesting picture of the contrasting distributions of a nonconservative, biologically active nuclide, such as zinc, and those of a conservative nuclide exhibiting little biological involvement, such as chromium (Forster, 1972a).

In general, the distribution of conservative or semiconservative radionuclides conforms to the known pattern of water circulation and mixing, and this is especially true of the situations that have been examined in shallow sea areas such as the Irish Sea, North Sea, Baltic, and the mouth of the Columbia River, where extensive data were available from conventional hydrographic studies on which to base a probable model of water circulation patterns. In the deeper oceanic waters, the distribution of radionuclides presents a somewhat more conflicting picture, which probably reflects the comparatively inadequate nature of our present knowledge in relation to deep-water circulation and mixing patterns. The difficulties are compounded in some instances by doubt over input rates from the troposphere and their latitudinal variation in relation to the probable rates of horizontal and vertical mixing of the water masses. Radiotracer studies themselves may yet make a major contribution to the elucidation of some of these problems.

6. Distribution of Radionuclides in Sediment

In the context of marine pollution, the adsorption or absorption of pollutants to sediments or suspended matter, whether or not this is subsequently deposited on the sea bed, may markedly modify the distribution in time and space of a potential pollutant, and may be a prime factor in determining its eventual biological fate. Modification of a pollutant's distribution through sedimentation may have other important consequences in the sense that high concentrations may be maintained over restricted areas with, in some cases, direct adverse consequences either to man or to elements of the marine source.

Sediment, including suspended matter eventually reaching the bed, has been of prime interest in the context of the behavior of artificial radionuclides and heavy metals, in the sense of interactions of a physicochemical nature, and particularly as they may affect food-chain contamination.

The exchange capacity of a sediment is determined by its composition; it is well established, for instance, that finely divided sediments show higher concentrations of radionuclides and metals per unit weight than do coarse sediments (the smaller the particle size the greater the surface area available for exchange or adsorption), and adsorbed material per unit of surface area appears to be constant for mineral fractions so far as radionuclides are concerned. Together with particle size, mineralogy is perhaps the most important factor determining exchange capacity. Of the finely divided mineral fraction in sediments, the clays (montmorillonite, illite, chlorite, and kaolinite) have greater ion-exchange capacity than other minerals (Table X), so that the higher the fraction of these, the greater the ion-exchange capacity of the sediment. The removal of or enrichment of cations from the interstitial waters of sediments appears also to be largely determined by these parameters of mineralogy and particle size.

TABLE X

Cation-Exchange Capacity of the Mineral Constituents of Marine Sediments for 10 Selected Radionuclides (Duursma and Eisma, unpublished) in Milliequivalents per 100 g (Duursma and Gross, 1971)

Montmorillonite	100
Chlorite	25
Illite	25
Kaolinite	10
Other minerals	0

The chemical exchange between mineral particles and water is accomplished by ion exchange and, to a lesser extent, adsorption. Exchange occurs, of course, at the sediment-water interface. Texture, structure, organic content, pH, oxidative state, pressure, temperature, and salinity are all capable of modifying the exchange capacity of sediments. The organic detrital matter of deposited sediment may modify the exchange capacity directly or indirectly. Organic matter may be deposited in sediments directly or by sedimentation after attachment to clays, particularly illite, and this may cause flocculation and increase the sedimentation of suspended matter under some conditions. Bed sediments of high organic matter content may be virtually anaerobic, and some metals and other constituents may be held firmly to particles under such conditions, only to be released under oxidative conditions. It is interesting to speculate whether or not the safe dumping of mercurial wastes at sea might not be best accomplished by arranging to introduce them to the bottom sediments of anaerobic basins where they might be held indefinitely as mercuric sulphide, perhaps even until such time as concentrations made recovery operations worthwhile!

The total sorptive capacity of a dry sediment is often expressed in terms of a dimensionless ratio, the distribution coefficient, which expresses the quantity of a radionuclide or metal, for example, per unit volume of dry sediment to the amount per unit volume of seawater. The larger the distribution coefficient the stronger the binding to the sediment. Equilibrium values for distribution coefficients have been determined experimentally by Duursma and co-workers (Duursma and Gross, 1971).

They are reached very rapidly for caesium, strontium, and zinc, whereas iron, cobalt, and zirconium/niobium appear to be much slower; ruthenium, cerium, and manganese are intermediate. Some of these observations are in direct conflict with field observations, where the concentration versus distance distributions on the sea bed around an outfall suggest that zirconium-95/niobium-95 are very rapidly removed, as are cerium-141/144, and that ruthenium-103/106 are somewhat intermediate, with caesium-134/137 relatively slowly removed (Preston, Jefferies, and Mitchell, 1971; Jefferies and Hetherington, to be published). In contrast, the depth profiles observed in the field show this increasing order of depth penetration: zirconium-95/niobium-95, cerium-141/144, plutonium-239, ruthenium-106, caesium-134/137. To some extent this is a reflection of radioactive decay, but the long-lived plutonium, one of the most rapidly adsorbed, is one of the most slowly penetrating in depth. This is, however, borne out by experimental evidence that shows that the relative order of penetration determined experimentally is, in fact, the reverse of the order of experimentally determined distribution coefficients, that is, the stronger and more rapid the binding of a radionuclide, or metal, to a sediment, not only the larger the distribution coefficient but also the slower the depth penetration.

This has interesting biological implications, since it might be inferred that those substances bound most strongly to sediments and largely confined to superficial layers, where the majority of biological activity occurs, might be least available to organisms ingesting the sediment. Bryan and Hummerstone (1971) have recently reported increased copper body burdens in polychaetes in copper-rich sediments, but see no similar trend for zinc, which they infer is strictly regulated by the organism. Another interpretation may be that zinc simply is not available to the worm if its primary source is sediment and not water. This type of result has been obtained with zinc, manganese, and iron (Cross, Duke, and Willis, 1970).

Perhaps the area meriting greatest attention in terms of the interactions that occur between dissolved and solid phases is that of river estuaries in the transition from fresh to saline water. In such situations, among those factors that must be judged to be important are:

1. The forms in which chemical pollutants are introduced.

2. The relative roles of organic and inorganic matter in determining interaction between phases.

3. The role of microbiological activity in the suspended and sedimented material in the estuary.

Some of these problems have recently been examined by De Groot, De Goeij, and Zegers (1971) in the estuaries of the Rhine and the Ems, where the "solubilization" of metals associated with suspended load in the river has been examined in the estuary and in coastal water. In sharp distinction to the experimental findings of Duursma and co-workers (Duursma and Gross, 1971) and the observations in the mouth of the Columbia River (Forster, 1972b) and northeast Irish Sea (Preston, Jefferies, and Mitchell, 1971) in relation to radionuclides, De Groot finds substantial removal of most metals from suspended matter as judged by the metal content of very freshly sedimented material, until under coastal water conditions (Wadden Sea) virtually all the mercury, for example, is in solution. He suggests as a possible mechanism the breakdown of organic detrital material with the formation of organic complexing agents capable of stripping metals from the mineral material in suspension. However, there are no complementary determinations of the metal content of the water, and the few measurements carried out on the suspended matter reveal, grain size for grain size, very high concentrations of metals compared with those found in sedimented material.

The picture of sediment-water interaction in general thus appears to be a very complex one, with conflict between some experimental observations and field experience and even between different field situations, and with very little understanding of the significance of water, suspended matter, and bed sediment pools as sources of pollutants to the food chain. However, in spite of this complexity, satisfactory models have been derived for pollution control in some situations. Jefferies, for example, has from field observations described the distribution of gamma-emitting radionuclides with respect to surface deposition and depth penetration (Jefferies, 1968, 1970; Jefferies and Hetherington, to be published), and from this has constructed a model that allows the computation of the gamma radiation dose rate to within 10% of the observed dose rate (Fig. 1). It has also been possible, from field observations in two contrasting situations, to describe the outcome of interactions, in that the overall size of water, bed sediment, and biota as compartments for radionuclides of differing behavior have been estimated. What is required now, perhaps, is a carefully thought-out field research program in a few contrasting situations (deltaic and nondeltaic estuaries, estuaries with and without a large fraction of organic matter in suspension or in the bed) and to choose elements showing extreme tendencies in behavior (e.g., conservative hexavalent chromium and nonconservative manganese) and examine their budgets and distributions in these situations. Specific problems for experimental resolution will be introduced by such studies.

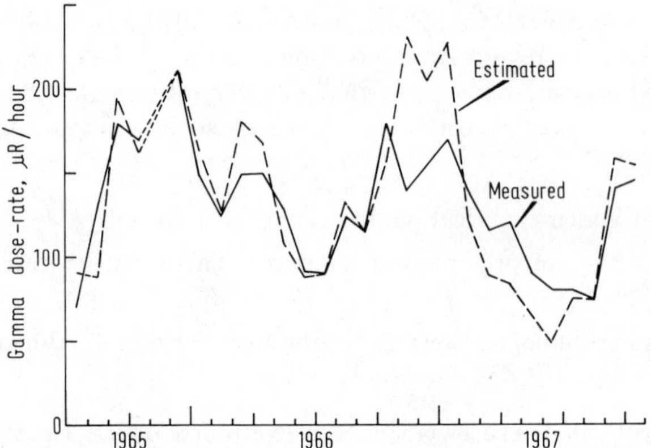

Fig. 1. Comparison of measured and predicted gamma dose rates over mud flats in the Ravenglass Estuary, Cumberland, England. Jefferies (1970).

7. Bioaccumulation

The problems of bioaccumulation of radionuclides have been of central concern to the evaluation of the potential radioactive pollution problem from the very beginning, and radiotracers have provided a means to study more accurately the kinetics of trace element turnover, including the development of mathematical models. The measurement of stable and radioactive nuclide concentrations of the same element in seawater and in biological materials has revealed in some cases, notably the heavy metals, differences in the ratio of the two isotopes in the two media that are indicative of differences in biological availability, related presumably to differences in chemical or physical state. These problems have in turn highlighted the need to know more of the physicochemical state of trace metals in seawater and of the role of complexing agents and their significance in the biological cycling of metals. This need extends also to the role of suspended matter, both physical and organic, in mediating the introduction of metals and their radionuclides to biological systems, or in acting as reservoirs essentially unavailable to living matter.

Simple mathematical models employing linear differential equations with constant coefficients have been used for many years to describe in approximate terms the turnover of mineral components in human metabolism and in particular in relation to radionuclides (ICRP, 1959). Their application to marine organisms in the context of radionuclide turnover is, also, of recent origin (Davis and Foster, 1958; Morgan, 1964b; Reichle, Dunaway and Nelson, 1970; Hiyama and Shimizu, 1969; Jefferies and Hewett, 1971). Using such equations, accumulation with respect to time may be described as:

$$C_t = C_{ss}e^{-\lambda t}(1 - e^{-kt})$$

where C_t = concentration of nuclide at time t
C_{ss} = steady-state concentration
λ = decay constant of radionuclide
k = excretion rate of $0.693/t_{1/2}$, $t_{1/2}$ being biological half-time

This simplified model has recently been used to make a theoretical examination of the relative contributions of food and water as sources of radionuclides and metals to fish (Pentreath and Jefferies, 1971; Preston, Jefferies, and Pentreath, 1972). From a consideration of the drinking rates in fish, 4 to 7% of body weight per day (Pentreath, Jeffereies, and Preston, 1972), and water flux across other body surfaces, such as the gill, it is concluded that only a very small fraction of the observed body burdens of several metals can be turned over by absorption from the water, especially where the concentration ratio of the metal as between unit weight of water and fish is high, as it is in the case of the transition metals.

When considering food as a pathway, and assuming a concentration ratio between food and water of 10 for a particular nuclide, then those fish that exhibit steady-state concentration ratios of the order of 10, and biological half-times of the order of 10 days, could, it is calculated, meet their requirements with a food intake of 6.9% of body weight per day, assuming 100% assimilation of the metal from the food. This is a credible rate of food intake. However, many essential metal metabolites exhibit concentration ratios over water of 10^3 with biological half-times of 10^2 days or less; moreover, assimilation rates from food are not likely to reach 100%, so that the prey of these fish will need to exhibit concentration ratios in relation to the water of at least the same order as the predator, and often higher. Indeed, evidence from some radionuclide studies does indicate a decrease in concentration ratio, with respect to water, with ascent of the trophic pyramid.

Extending this type of argument successively downward in the trophic chain leads to the postulation that at some basic level in the food chain there must be rapid and very high concentration of those trace metals that appear at high concentrations in the upper levels of the food web. This process is too rapid and of too great a magnitude to be a metabolic requirement at the level at which it occurs, but it sets the scene for the rest of the food web. The most probable mechanism for this concentration is surface adsorption to finely divided matrices such as phytoplankton, and detrital and sediment material in suspension. Radionuclide studies have indeed shown very high concentrations in phytoplankton (Rice and Willis, 1959; Chipman, Rice, and Price, 1958), and trace element analyses have revealed very high concentration factors for some trace metals (Bowen et al., 1971). Recently some of these propositions have been examined experimentally for zinc, manganese, cobalt, and iron in fish (Pentreath, 1973a), and it has indeed been shown that only small fractions (less than 5%) of the metal body pool are turned over by the metals in the water. Indeed, the direct accumulation from water of the nuclides examined represents a water input of only 12% of body weight per day, whereas the total water flux is of the order of 300% or more of body weight per day as determined by experiments with ^3H_2O, so that metal uptake from water is, in fact, severely restricted, emphasizing the even greater importance of food as a source of metals. Further studies conducted with the molluscan bivalve *Mytilus* [Pentreath, in press (a)] have shown that although the role of water in metal accumulation does not fall into the same pattern as that proposed for teleosts, it nevertheless is a minor pathway compared with food.

In fact, by the time the upper levels of the trophic pyramid are reached, the whole business of metal accumulation is of considerable embarrassment to the organism in a metabolic sense (Pequegnat, Fowler, and Small, 1969). The animal is dealing effectively in combating the entrance of metals through the water, but is absorbing far greater quantities across the gut surface and is excreting all that it can, binding much of the remainder into sites that will not permit interference in the normal chemical cycles (Romeril, 1971).

The rapid accumulation of metals by phytoplankton proposed in this theoretical examination has also been examined experimentally (Davies, in press), and it has been found that zinc builds up rapidly on the outside of the organism by surface adsorption, and then diffuses into the cell down the concentration gradient so established. The amounts of zinc involved greatly exceed any metabolic requirement on the part of the phytoplankton organism. The study also suggests that the metal-binding capacity of the cells is related to their protein content and since this in turn is limited by the availability of the nutrient salts of phosphorus and nitrogen, the metal-binding capacity of the cells will be affected by nutrient availability. If this is so, will the contrary be true, and will phytoplankton in areas of eutrophication be richer in metals, and will this be reflected in higher metal concentrations further up the food web?

The study of the physicochemical states of zinc in seawater in relation to biological availability has been the most interesting one of recent years. Studies have shown that zinc occurs in different states in seawater, some 30 to 50% being particulate; the ionic fraction is relatively small at 10 to 20% (Piro, Verzi, and Papucci, 1969; Piro et al., in press; Branica, Bernhard, and Piro, 1973), probably in the form of Zn^{2+} with some $ZnOH^+$ (Báric and Branica, 1967). An organically complexed fraction has also been identified (Slowey and Hood, 1971; Piro et al., 1973; Branica, Bernhard, and Piro, in press), comprising some 40 to 50% of the total zinc pool in seawater. During investigations of the behavior of zinc-65 when added to seawater, it was found that after more than 100 days, the radionuclide had not equilibrated with all the fractions of the stable element pool and remained essentially in the ionic state with some particulate (Piro et al., 1973). This may provide an interesting explanation of the differences found, during experimental studies, in the relative accumulation of zinc-65 and zinc by diatoms (Bernhard and Zattera, 1969), where higher specific activities were found in diatoms than in water, suggesting preferential uptake of the radioactive zinc, which is essentially from the ionic pool in seawater.

Thus, in the case of zinc we have a situation where rapid surface adsorption from a small ionic pool in seawater, and with negligible biological requirements on the part of the organism, nevertheless sets the scene for the whole food web up to fish, and presents successive predators with difficult situations requiring special mechanisms to deal with metallic ions that would otherwise seriously interfere with normal metabolism.

Interesting as this story is, many other questions remain to be answered. Is the chelated zinc fraction available to phytoplankton or other organisms, even if only on a long time scale? How is the ionic pool regenerated when it is depleted under natural conditions? In experimental investigations (Piro et al., 1973), lowering of pH of seawater to pH6 leads to particulate zinc becoming ionic, whereas under normal pH or at pH6 the chelated zinc, except for a small labile fraction, does not become ionic. Is it the particulate zinc, then, that regenerates the ionic pool under natural conditions? However, if the normal ionic fraction is removed by electrolysis at pH6 and the seawater then returned to pH8, the chelated fraction is able to regenerate the ionic pool.

The continued development of experimental approaches using radioactive tracers will answer many of these questions and lead toward a better understanding of the behavior of heavy metals in seawater, thus contributing to the evaluation of the significance of high metal concentrations in the marine environment.

8. Conclusions

The behavior of artificial radionuclides in the marine environment is better understood than the behavior of any marine pollutant. Ease of detection and measurement with increasingly sophisticated equipment, the fact that the wastes, generated by an advanced technology, were of known high toxicity, the increasing concern of a world public introduced to them in the context of nuclear weapon testing, and world tension were all factors conducive to a rapid evaluation of their significance. However, the major factor leading to control was a good quantitative understanding of their toxicity and an early and sound foundation for acceptable radiation exposure standards, a major element lacking in our assessment of many other pollutants.

The use of critical path techniques defined the gaps in knowledge essential for evaluation and control, and many of these are still bridged in a less than perfect manner. For example, although the use of concentration factors affords a perfectly sensible engineering-type approach for assessing concentrations in given materials in relation to specified water concentrations, it tells nothing of the mechanisms by which concentration is effected. However, we do not need to know the mechanism in order to control, although clearly a thorough understanding of all the factors at play might well improve our control methods, as, for example, in the choice of chemical form in which to discharge a radionuclide in order to minimize its impact in a specified environmental situation.

The exploitation of nuclear power is vital to a world where overpopulation and underfeeding are problems of major concern. The development of such power inevitably implies some radioactive contamination of the environment, including the seas. The principles and procedures for limiting the introduction of artificial radioactivity to the seas and oceans are well founded, and environmental dispersion of radionuclides should and will play a part in waste management practices in the future. Application of similar methodologies to the control of other pollutants will be rewarding, and radioactively labelled marine environments will also play an important part in elucidating the mechanisms controlling their distribution.

References

Báric, A and M. Branica, 1967. Polarography of sea water. I. Ionic state of cadmium and zinc in sea water. *J. Polarogr. Soc.*, **13**, 4–8.

Bernhard, M. and A. Zattera, 1969. A comparison between the uptake of radioactive and stable zinc by a marine unicellular alga. Pp. 389–398 in *Symposium on Radioecology*. D. J. Nelson and F. C. Evans, eds. Proc. 2nd Nat. Symp., Ann Arbor, Michigan, 1967. U.S. Atom. En. Comm., Conf.-670503 (TID-4500), 774 pp.

Bowen, V. T., J. S. Olsen, C. L. Osterberg, and J. Ravera, 1971. Ecological interactions of marine radioactivity. Pp. 200–222 in *Radioactivity in the Marine Environment*. Nat. Acad. Sci., Washington, D.C., 272 pp.

Branica, M., M. Bernhard, and A. Piro, in press. Zinc in seawater. II. Determination of physico-chemical states of zinc in seawater.

Bryan, G. W. and L. G. Hummerstone, 1971. Adaptation of the polychaete *Nereis diversicolor* to estuarine sediments containing high concentrations of heavy metals. I. General observations and adaptation to copper. *J. Mar. Biol. Ass. U.K.*, **51**, 845–863.

Chipman, W. A., T. R. Rice, and T. J. Price, 1958. Uptake and accumulation of radioactive zinc by marine plankton, fish and shellfish. *Fishery Bull. Fish Wildl. Serv. U.S.*, **58**, 279–292.

Cross, F. A., T. W. Duke, and J. N. Willis, 1970. Biogeochemistry of trace elements in a coastal plain estuary: distribution of manganese, iron and zinc in sediments, water, and polychaetous worms. *Chesapeake Sci.*, **11**, 221–234.

Davies, A. G., 1973. The kinetics of and a preliminary model for the uptake of radio-zinc by *Phaeodactylum tricornutum* in culture. Pp. 403–420 in *Radioactive Contamination of the Marine Environment*. Proc. Symp., IAEA, Vienna, 1973, 784 pp.

Davis, J. J. and R. F. Foster, 1958. Bioaccumulation of radioisotopes through aquatic food chains. *Ecology*, **39**, 530–535.

Dunster, H. J., 1958. The disposal of radioactive liquid wastes into coastal waters. *Proc. 2nd Int. Conf. peaceful Uses of atom. Energy*, **18**, 390–399.

Duursma, E. K., 1972. Geochemical aspects and applications of radionuclides in the sea. *Oceanogr. & Mar. Biol.*, **10**, 137–223.

Duursma, E. K. and M. G. Gross, 1971. Marine sediments and radioactivity. Pp. 147–160 in *Radioactivity in the Marine Environment*. Nat. Acad. Sci., Washington, D.C., 272 pp.

FAO, 1971. *Report of the Seminar on Methods of Detection, Measurement and Monitoring of Pollutants in the Marine Environment*. Panel 7. Radioactivity. Fish. Rep. F.A.O., No. 99, Suppl. 1, 87–96.

Feldt, W., 1966. Radioactive contamination of North Sea fishes. Pp. 739–752 in *Radioactive Wastes into Seas, Oceans and Surface Waters*. Proc. Symp., IAEA, Vienna, 1966, 898 pp.

Forster, W. O., 1972a. Radioactive and stable nuclides in the Columbia River and adjacent northeast Pacific Ocean. Pp. 663–700 in *The Columbia River Estuary and Adjacent Ocean Waters*. A. T. Pruter and P. L. Alverson, eds. University of Washington Press, Seattle and London, 868 pp.

Forster, W. O., 1972b. Radionuclide distribution in Columbia River and adjacent Pacific Shelf sediments. Pp. 701–735 in *The Columbia River Estuary and Adjacent Ocean Waters*. A. T. Pruter and D. L. Alverson, eds. University of Washington Press, Seattle and London, 868 pp.

Foster, R. F., I. L. Ophel, and A. Preston, 1971. Evaluation of human radiation exposure. Pp. 240–260 in *Radioactivity in the Marine Environment*. Nat. Acad. Sci., Washington, D.C., 272 pp.

Groot, A. J. de, J. J. M. de Goeij, and C. Zegers, 1971. Contents and behavior of mercury as compared with other heavy metals in sediments from the Rivers Rhine and Ems. *Geologie Mijnb.*, **50**, 393–398.

Hiyama, Y. and M. Shimizu, 1969. On the uptake of radioactive nuclides by aquatic organisms: the application of the exponential model. Pp. 463–476 in *Environmental Contamination by Radioactive Materials*. Proc. Seminar, Vienna, 1969. Publ. FAO/IAEA, 726 pp.

Hodge, V. F., T. R. Folsom, and D. R. Young, 1973. Retention of fall-out constituents in upper layers of the Pacific Ocean as estimated from studies of a tuna population. Pp. 263–276 in *Radioactive Contamination of the Marine Environment*. Proc. Symp., IAEA, Vienna, 1973, 784 pp.

IAEA, 1961. Radioactive Waste Disposal into the Sea. *Saf. Ser. Int. atom. Energy Ag.*, No. 5, 174 pp.

ICRP, 1959 Report of Committee II on Permissible Dose for Internal Radiation. Recommendations of the International Commission on Radiological Protection. *ICRP Publ.* (*2*). Pergamon Press, Oxford, 233 pp.

ICRP, 1966. Recommendations of the International Commission on Radiological Protection (Adopted September 17, 1965). *ICRP Publ.* (*9*). Pergamon Press, Oxford, 27 pp.

Jefferies, D. F., 1968. Fission-produced radionuclides in sediments from the north-east Irish Sea. *Helgoländer wiss. Meeresunters.*, **17**, 280–290.

Jefferies, D. F., 1970. Exposure to radiation from gamma-emitting fission-product radionuclides in estuarine sediments from the north-east Irish Sea. Pp. 205–216 in *Environmental Surveillance in the Vicinity of Nuclear Facilities.* W. C. Reinig, ed. Charles C Thomas, Springfield, Ill., 465 pp.

Jefferies, D. F. and J. A. Hetherington, in preparation. The distribution of some fission-product radionuclides in sea and estuarine sediments. To be submitted to *Limnol. Oceanog.*

Jefferies, D. F. and C. J. Hewett, 1971. The accumulation and excretion of radioactive caesium by the plaice (*Pleuronectes platessa*) and the thornback ray (*Raia clavata*). *J. Mar. Biol. Ass. U.K.*, **51**, 411–422.

Kautsky, H., 1971. Untersuchungen über die Verteilung des radioaktiven Fallout im Bereich der Nordsee, des Skagerraks under der westlichen Ostsee. *Dt. hydrogr. Z.*, Band 24, Heft 6, 262–267. (Eng. Summ.)

Mitchell, N. T., 1971. Radioactivity in Surface and Coastal Waters of the British Isles 1970. *Tech. Rep. Fish. radiobiol. Lab., Lowestoft,* FRL 8, 35 pp.

Miyake, Y., 1963. Artificial radioactivity in the sea. Pp. 78–87 in *The Sea: Ideas and Observations on Progress in the Study of the Seas.* Vol. 2. M. N. Hill, ed. Wiley-Interscience, New York and London, 554 pp.

Morgan, F., 1964a. Design and development of marine monitoring programs. *Agricultural and Public Health Aspects of Radioactive Contamination in Normal and Emergency Situations.* FAO atom. Energy Ser., No. 5, pp. 239–244.

Morgan, F., 1964b. The effects on marine foodstuffs of a large release of radioactivity into the sea. Pp. 153–161 in *Nuclear Detonations and Marine Radioactivity.* S. H. Small, ed. Proc. Conf., Norwegian Defence Research Establishment, Kjeller, 1963, 721 pp.

Münnich, K. O. and W. Roether, 1967. Transfer of bomb ^{14}C and tritium from the atmosphere to the ocean. Internal mixing of the ocean on the basis of tritium and ^{14}C profiles. Pp. 93–104 in *Radioactive Dating and Methods of Low-Level Counting.* Proc. Symp., IAEA, Vienna, 1967, 744 pp.

National Academy of Sciences, 1971. *Radioactivity in the Marine Environment.* Nat. Acad. Sci., Washington, D.C., 272 pp.

Pentreath, R. J., 1973. The roles of food and water in the accumulation of radionuclides by marine teleost and elasmobranch fish. Pp. 421–436 in *Radioactive Contamination of the Marine Environment.* Proc. Symp., IAEA, Vienna, 1973, 784 pp.

Pentreath, R. J., in press (a). The accumulation from water of zinc-65, manganese-54, iron-59 and cobalt-58 by the mussel, *Mytilus edulis.*

Pentreath, R. J. and D. F. Jefferies, 1971. The uptake of radionuclides by I-group plaice (*Pleuronectes platessa*) off the Cumberland coast, Irish Sea. *J. Mar. Biol. Ass. U.K.*, **51**, 963–976.

Pequegnat, J. E., S. W. Fowler, and L. F. Small, 1969. Estimates of the zinc requirements of marine organisms. *J. Fish. Res. Bd Can.*, **26**, 145–150.

Piro, A., M. Verzi, and C. Papucci, 1969. L'importanza dello stato fisico-chimico degli elementi per l'accumulo negli organismi marini. 1. Lo stato chimico-fisico dello zinco in aqua di mare. *Pubbl. Staz. zool. Napoli,* **37**, 298–310. (Eng. Summ.)

Piro, A., M. Bernhard, M. Branica, and M. Verzi, 1973. Incomplete exchange reaction between radioactive ionic zinc and stable natural zinc in seawater. Pp. 29–45 in *Radioactive Contamination of the Marine Environment.* Proc. Symp., IAEA, Vienna, 1973, 784 pp.

Polikarpov, G. G., 1966. *Radioecology of Aquatic Organisms.* North Holland Publishing Co., Amsterdam, 314 pp.

Preston, A., 1966. Site evaluation and the discharge of aqueous radioactive wastes from civil nuclear power stations in England and Wales. Pp. 725–737 in *Disposal of Radioactive Wastes into Seas, Oceans and Surface Waters.* Proc. Symp., IAEA, Vienna, 1966, 898 pp.

Preston, A., 1969. Aquatic monitoring programmes. Pp. 309–324 in *Environmental Contamination by Radioactive Materials.* Proc. Seminar, IAEA, Vienna, 1969, 746 pp.

Preston, A., 1972. Contamination of the seas and oceans by artificial radioactivity. *Underwat. J.*, **4**, 49–58.

Preston, A., in press. Radioactivity in the marine environment. Chapter to be published in *Sea Fisheries Research*, Logos Press, London.

Preston, A. and D. F. Jefferies, 1969. Aquatic aspects in chronic and acute contamination situations. Pp. 183–211 in *Environmental Contamination by Radioactive Materials*. Proc. Seminar, IAEA, Vienna, 1969, 746 pp.

Preston, A. and N. T. Mitchell, in press. The evaluation of public radiation exposure from the controlled marine disposal of radioactive waste (with special reference to the United Kingdom). *Interaction of Radioactive Contaminants with the Constituents of the Marine Environment*, IAEA/SM-158/36, IAEA, Vienna.

Preston, A. and P. C. Wood, 1971. Monitoring the marine environment. *Proc. R. Soc. B*, **177**, 451–462.

Preston, A., D. F. Jefferies, and N. T. Mitchell, 1971. Experience gained from the controlled introduction of liquid radioactive waste to coastal waters. Pp. 629–644 in *Nuclear Techniques in Environmental Pollution*. Proc. Symp., IAEA, Vienna, 1971, 810 pp.

Preston, A., D. S. Woodhead, N. T. Mitchell, and R. J. Pentreath, 1972. The impact of artificial radioactivity on the oceans and on oceanography. *Proc. R. Soc. Edinb.*, (*B*), **72**, 411–423.

Preston, A., D. F. Jefferies, and R. J. Pentreath, 1972. The possible contributions of radioecology to marine productivity studies. *Symp. zool. Soc. Lond.*, No. 29, 271–284.

Reichle, D. E., P. B. Dunaway, and D. J. Nelson, 1970. Turnover and concentration of radionuclides in food chains. *Nucl. Saf.*, **11**, 43–55.

Rice, T. R. and V. M. Willis, 1959. Uptake, accumulation and loss of radioactive cerium-144 by marine planktonic algae. *Limnol. Oceanog.*, **4**, 277–290.

Romeril, M. G., 1971. The uptake and distribution of ^{65}Zn in oysters. *Mar. Biol.*, **9**, 347–354.

Slansky, C. M., 1971. Principles for limiting the introduction of radioactive waste into the sea. *Atom. Energy Rev.*, **9**, 853–868.

Slowey, J. F. and D. W. Hood, 1971. Copper, manganese and zinc concentrations in Gulf of Mexico waters. *Geochim. Cosmochim. Acta*, **35**, 121–138.

Templeton, W. L., R. E. Nakatani, and E. Held, 1970. Effects of Radiation in the Marine Ecosystem. *FAO Technical Conference on Marine Pollution and its Effects on Living Resources and Fishing, Rome, 1970*. FIR: MP/70/R-10, 19 pp.

UNSCEAR, 1966. Report of the United Nations Scientific Committee on the Effects of Atomic Radiation. *General Assembly Official Records: Twenty-first Session, Suppl. No. 14 (A/6314)*, 153 pp.

UNSCEAR, 1972. Report of the Scientific Committee on the Effects of Atomic Radiation, Annexe A.

Voipio, A. and A. Salo, 1971. On the balances of ^{90}Sr and ^{137}Cs in the Baltic Sea. *Nord. Hydrol.*, **II**, 57–63.

Volchok, H. L., V. T. Bowen, T. R. Folsom, W. S. Broecker, E. A. Schuert, and E. S. Bien, 1971. Oceanic distributions of radionuclides from nuclear explosions. Pp. 42–89 in *Radioactivity in the Marine Environment*. Nat. Acad. Sci., Washington, D.C., 272 pp.

Wolfe, D. A., F. A. Cross, and C. D. Jennins, 1973. The flux of iron, manganese and zinc in an estuarine ecosystem. Pp. 159–175 in *Radioactive Contamination of the Marine Environment*. Proc. Symp., IAEA, Vienna, 1973, 784 pp.

Woodhead, D. S., 1970. The assessment of the radiation dose to developing fish embryos due to the accumulation of radioactivity by the egg. *Radiat. Res.*, **43**, 582–597.

Woodhead, D. S., 1971. The biological effects of radioactive waste. *Proc. R. Soc. B.*, **177**, 423–437.

Woodhead, D. S., 1973a. Levels of radioactivity in the marine environment and the dose commitment to marine organisms. Pp. 499–525 in *Radioactive Contamination of the Marine Environment*. Proc. Symp., IAEA, Vienna, 1973, 784 pp.

Woodhead, D. S., 1973b. The radiation dose received by plaice *Pleuronectes platessa* in the north-east Irish Sea from the fuel reprocessing plant at Windscale. Hlth. Phys. 25, 115–121.

VI. ORIGIN OF THE OCEAN

23. ORIGIN OF THE OCEAN

GUSTAF ARRHENIUS, BIBHAS R. DE, AND HANNES ALFVÉN

1. Sources of New Information

Our records of the early history of the ocean and of the composition and evolution of the interior of our planet are fragmentary. Inquiries based on modern geophysical and geochemical data were made in the classical studies by Rubey (1951, 1955) and Urey (1952) and in other important papers related to this subject and referred to in context below.

Lars Gunnar Sillén's interest was drawn to the early phase of the Earth's history as a logical extension of his fundamental work on the chemical dynamics of the ocean. The question of how the controlling chemical processes differed from now at the time when life was possibly absent was one of the last scientific problems that he embarked on (Sillén, 1965, 1966). He also began to devote his interest to the primordial condensation processes in space, using thermodynamic equilibrium considerations as a first, although admittedly unrealistic, approximation. The usefulness of such an approach in guiding necessary disequilibrium considerations (Arrhenius, 1972; Arrhenius and Alfvén, 1971) has subsequently been demonstrated by Lord (1965), Larimer (1967), Anders (1971), and most recently by Grossman (1972).

In the last 5 yr, experimental data have been obtained which are of great significance in shaping our ideas about the origin and evolution of the Earth's ocean and atmosphere. New insights have been gained from theoretical developments inspired largely by the exploration of space. Among materials that cast new light on the early history of the planet are the oldest known preserved sedimentary rocks from South Africa ($\sim$3.0 Gy; Engel et al., 1968) and preserved crustal sections as old as 3.9 Gy recently found in Greenland (Black et al., 1971). The intensified studies of meteorites have also given important clues to the sources of the Earth's atmosphere and ocean. (Wasson, 1969; Fanale, 1971). Most importantly, the exploration of the Moon has placed the planetary evolution and the history of the Earth in an entirely new perspective. This is being further broadened by missions to still more primitive objects in the solar system: comets, asteroids, and planetary satellites.

The new facts accumulating from measurements on the lunar surface and on samples returned from the Moon are providing perhaps the most important guidance in assessment of the various possibilities for the evolution of the Earth. These observations have drawn attention to circumstances of crucial importance in the early history of the planet that now appear straightforward but that were nonetheless largely ignored in the Earth-limited era of earth sciences. In general, these results emphasize the fact that the problems of the origin and evolution of the ocean and the atmosphere cannot be resolved realistically without referring to the processes by which the Earth itself formed. The observational data pertinent to these problems do not support the previously common notion that the differentiation took place and the ocean and the atmosphere developed only after the Earth had already formed. On the contrary, the processes leading to the formation of the Earth must themselves play a decisive role in producing the differentiation and in giving rise to the precursors for the present ocean and atmosphere while the Earth was still in a state of formation.

2. Formation of the Solar System

It is now generally believed that the creation of planets can only take place by accumulation of small solid bodies (planetesimal accretion). Formation of planets from individual contracting gas clouds is excluded because of insufficient gravitation; such a process seems impossible even for a giant planet such as Jupiter (Hattori et al., 1969; Kumar, 1972). Hence, it is likely that the Earth has accumulated from a large number of small bodies in space. Considerations of orbital and spin characteristics of the Earth and other planets and their satellites place stringent requirements or limitations on the assumed dynamic state of these building blocks referred to here as grains, aggregates, embryos, and planetesimals (Alfvén, 1942 to 1945; Schmidt, 1944; Safronov, 1954; Alfvén, 1954; Levin, 1972; Alfvén and Arrhenius, 1970a, 1973).

When the formation of our solar system began, matter in the form of gas and dust must somehow have become emplaced in the circumsolar region. Several different explanations of this emplacement have been suggested; reviews of these are given by ter Haar (1967) and Hartmann (1972). Most theories attempt an explanation of the present properties of the planetary system but ignore the three well-developed satellite systems.

In an evolutionary scheme that attempts to account for the present state of both planetary and satellite systems (Alfvén and Arrhenius, 1970a, b, 1973), the Sun at the outset attracted gas and dust by gravitation. The history of formation of the Sun itself is highly uncertain; it could have been formed by collapse of a gas cloud, but equally well could have been formed by a stellesimal accretion process similar to the planetesimal process. None of these processes have been observationally verified. In contrast, the processes that can realistically be invoked to explain the late evolution of the solar system and, with less certainty, the formative state, can all be identified with processes observable today.

The neutral gas particles in the circumsolar region presumably became ionized upon reaching their critical velocity for ionization by gravitational acceleration toward the Sun. The same process occurred around the magnetized protoplanets (Jupiter, Saturn, and Uranus) after their formation. The resulting plasma was stopped by the magnetic field at various distances from these central bodies, determined by the atomic mass and the ionization potential of the controlling chemical species in the neutral gas. The plasma was brought into its necessary rotational state by magnetohydrodynamic transfer of angular momentum from the central bodies.

Under the combined action of the gravitational and the magnetic fields, the plasma acquired a state of motion referred to as partial corotation. The plasma rotating around the Sun provided the material that, after condensation to small particles, aggregated to larger bodies that ultimately gave rise to the planets. The theory draws on the similarity between the planetary system and the three regular satellite systems (Jovian, Saturnian, and Uranian) and stresses that the regular satellites must have formed around the planets by the same series of processes by which the planets formed around the Sun. The existence of four analogous systems thus removes the constraint of relying solely on the Sun-planet system for relevant information.

3. Occlusion of Volatiles in Solid Condensates

Condensation from the partially corotating plasma around the Sun led to the formation of solid grains, which, by inheriting the momentum of the parent plasma, assumed eccentric Kepler orbits. Such grains appear to have been preserved to this day in space as aggregates; some fragments of these are dense and strong enough to survive passage through the atmosphere and are known to us as meteorites.

Individual grains of this kind are abundant components of certain types of meteorites (carbonaceous chondrites). Such grains often form isolated crystals and twins of high regularity (Fig. 1) or rounded crystalline aggregates with cavities preserving the crystal-vapor interface and showing delicate growth features such as freely grown calcium silicate fibers (Fuchs, 1969).

This meteoritic material, believed to represent a primordial condensate but not necessarily to be identified with the material that formed the Earth, also has chemical features indicative of the conditions of growth. Among these is the incorporation of volatile components such as noble gas atoms and halogen and hydroxyl ions in some types of crystals. The noble gas components are particularly useful for the study of the mode of incorporation, since they do not develop strong chemical bonds with the host structure.

Aside from surface implanted and radiogenic components, which have different and characteristic signatures and will not be discussed here, the noble gas component of particular interest to the problems of the Earth is the component that is strongly bound through the volume of the crystals and requires high-activation energies for release. This indicates that the noble gas atoms were incorporated as impurities in crystal imperfections at growth from the vapor phase.

The fact that the occluded noble gas component is strongly bound internally in the crystals shows that the incorporation took place as a part of the crystallization process and not by subsequent surface adsorption or other low-energy processes. Furthermore, it is well known from experiments that for such noble gas occlusion to be significant, the temperature of the crystals has to be below the range 400 to 600°K. The vapor phase temperature, however, must have been an order of magnitude higher for several reasons. One such reason is the requirement for sufficient concentration of vapor components to permit growth; at the low vapor pressures of silicates and oxides, this is not possible if the vapor were in temperature equilibrium with the grains at the temperature indicated (Arrhenius and Alfvén, 1971). Another reason is the need for the gas particles to provide sufficient kinetic energy to heat the grains at the relevant plasma densities ($\lesssim 10^{12}/\text{cm}^3$). These maximum densities are required to permit the momentum transfer process to operate. In this density range, gas temperatures of the order 10^4°K are required (Lehnert, 1970; Arrhenius, 1972; De and Arrhenius, 1973) to maintain grain temperatures in the range of 300 to 900°K indicated by the chemical record (Larimer, 1967; Larimer and Anders, 1967, 1970; Grossman, 1972).

Hence we are concerned with a thermal steady state that must be common in gas-solid systems in space and where crystallizing grains at comparatively low temperature are immersed in, and exchange matter and energy with, a hot, optically thin, partially ionized gas.

4. Primordial Grains as Carriers of Atmospheric and Oceanic Components

The composition of the occluded noble gas component in primordial condensates gives useful clues to the origin of the atmosphere of the Earth and the formation of its ocean. Measurements on meteorites show that this component characteristically

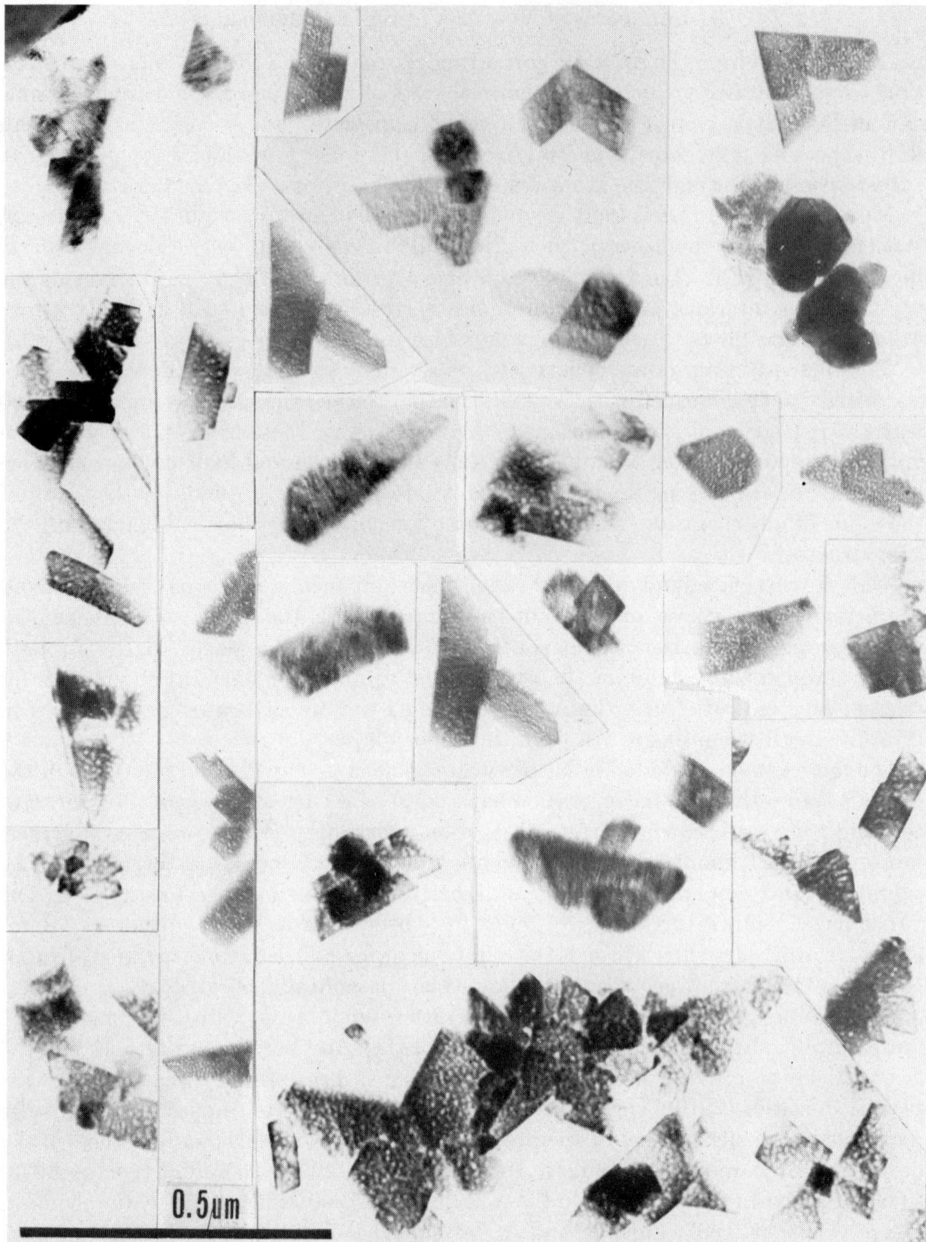

Fig. 1. Delicate, leafy crystals of the magnesium-iron silicates of olivine and pyroxene, frequently twinned, and loosely adhering to each other. These crystals form a characteristic component of the porous regions of the carbonaceous chondrite Allende. The thickness of the crystal leaves is of the order of 100 Å, tapering off toward the edges. The crystal habit and the lack of significant adhesion show that the crystals and twinned aggregates grew from a vapor phase. The preservation of their delicate features indicates their relative velocities at aggregation must have been low, perhaps in the range of meters per second or lower. From Arrhenius and Asunmaa (1973).

has a relative abundance distribution of primordial noble gas species that is closely similar to that of the Earth's atmosphere (Signer and Suess, 1963). In contrast, the solar abundances more or less accurately represented by solar wind, and by the components implanted in the surface skin of lunar rocks and meteorite grains were realized to be markedly different with a much higher abundance of light noble gases.

These facts suggest that the special noble gas composition, as found in meteorites and in the terrestrial atmosphere, was established in the gas phase from which the primordial condensates grew, both in the region of space where the parent materials of meteorites formed, and in the region where the parent material of the Earth condensed. Several mechanisms may have contributed to the observed noble gas fractionation in the circumsolar region (see reviews in Arrhenius, 1972; Black, 1972a, b).

The Earth could then have acquired its atmosphere and ocean as it grew from primordial grains and aggregates similar to, but not necessarily identifiable with those found in meteorites, by the release of the volatiles mainly during the accretion process into a primordial atmosphere from which the present one has gradually developed (Aston, 1924).

Although the important discovery of the "planetary" component of noble gases in meteorites was made over a decade ago, the full implications of a genetic relationship was not realized until recently (Wasson, 1969; Fanale, 1971). Fanale aptly ascribes this delay to a climate of opinion that for a long time fostered a belief that the primordial atmosphere of the Earth must have been entirely removed by some *ad hoc* process. The present atmosphere would under these circumstances have evolved entirely by degassing the interior of the planet, which then would need from the outset to have retained a sufficient mass of volatile components.

As demonstrated by Fanale, this is not likely to have been the case; the primordial noble gases with the possible exception of xenon must at accretion onto Earth have been largely transferred to the atmosphere where they still reside. They do not appear to play a significant role in the present gas flux from the Earth's interior, where the noble gas component is dominated by radiogenic species, nor do they occur in measurable quantities in igneous rocks. Other chemically reactive volatiles show a more complex partition between the atmosphere and the solid Earth, as discussed below.

The component of primordial solids of major importance as a source of oceanic water is hydroxyl ion. This ion forms a regular structural element in magnesium and iron hydroxysilicates with sheet structure, which form the major mass of carbonaceous chondrites of Type I (Wiik, 1956). (Crystal hydrates of magnesium and sodium sulfates found in carbonaceous chondrites are probably not generated in space where they are unstable; they are likely to be forming by reaction with water vapor in terrestrial museums.)

It was previously believed (on the basis of geological experience) that the hydroxysilicates in meteorites must be understood as a secondary reaction product between anhydrous silicates and water in vapor form, or even as liquid water in rivers and swamps on a planet from which the sediments would subsequently have been removed as meteorites. It is now known from experiment (Meyer, 1969, 1971) that magnesium hydroxysilicates, analogous to those in meteorites, crystallize directly from partially ionized gas containing magnesium, silicon, hydrogen, and oxygen species and at grain temperatures below about 500°K. Furthermore, substitution with hydroxyl occurs also in the terrestrial varieties of silicates, common in space, such as olivine and pyroxene (Martin and Donnay, 1972). Such partial hydroxylation is likely to occur also at the growth of these silicates in free space, particularly in vapor crystallization at high relative pressure of atomic and ionic species of oxygen and hydrogen.

In view of the small mass of the hydrosphere compared to the mantle (1/3000) concentrations as small as 300 ppm of available hydroxyl in the accreting silicates are sufficient to generate the total mass of the hydrosphere, considering also the initial loss process discussed in Section 9. Thus the space condensates that we know from meteorites fallen on the Earth and on the Moon (Gibson and Moore, 1973a; Apollo 16 PET, 1973) would provide ample sources for both the ocean and the atmosphere.

This should not be taken to mean that the Earth formed from any of these specific materials, which represent different condensation regions and events in space. But the observations imply that primordial condensates in different parts of the solar system, although varying markedly in chemical composition (Alfvén and Arrhenius, 1973, Part IV), have incorporated substantial amounts of volatiles, which were subsequently released in the accretional heat front at the formation of planets (Alfvén and Arrhenius, 1970b).

An important related question concerns the chemical composition of the Earth's total store of primordial volatiles, determined by the average composition of the planetesimals from which the Earth was built and modified by the loss processes discussed in the following material. In the case of the primordial noble gases, the observations previously mentioned indicate relative elemental and isotopic proportions similiar to those found in meteorites and concentrations within the range of those in meteorites.

The content and proportion of reactive volatiles in the Earth's source material (primarily species of H, C, N, O, S, and the halogens) is obscured by the fact that the fraction of each one of these, hidden in the Earth's interior, is totally unknown. Analyses of crustal rocks and extrusions from the upper mantle are not informative on this point since they are likely to be contaminated by the ocean's atmospheric reservoir. Extraterrestrial materials do not provide much quantitative guidance on this point either, since their absolute and relative contents of reactive volatiles are extremely variable (Gibson and Moore, 1973b; Gibson and Johnson, 1971, 1972; Gibson, 1973).

5. The Immediate Precursor Stages

As shown above, we can trace the Earth's ocean and atmosphere with some certainty into the plasma phase, which preceded the formation of solid grains around the Sun. We shall now turn our attention to those stages of the protoplanetary development that have a most immediate effect on the formation of the ocean.

The first problem we must solve is that of the orbital evolution of a large number of grains born in eccentric Kepler orbits around the Sun and undergoing mutual collisions that result in loss of orbital energy. The result of analysis of this many-body problem (Alfvén, 1970; Baxter and Thompson, 1971, 1973; Trulsen, 1971) is contrary to intuitive application of experience from scattering of particles in a stationary frame of reference. If the particles are orbiting in a gravitational field, and if the collision time is long compared to the orbital period, the particle orbits, instead of spreading increasingly widely in space, contract into a torus (Fig. 2) whose thickness decreases with time until a state is reached where the collision velocity is low.

The exchange of energy at the particle collisions tends to equalize eccentricity, orbital inclination, and orbital radius for all particles in the assemblage. Particle

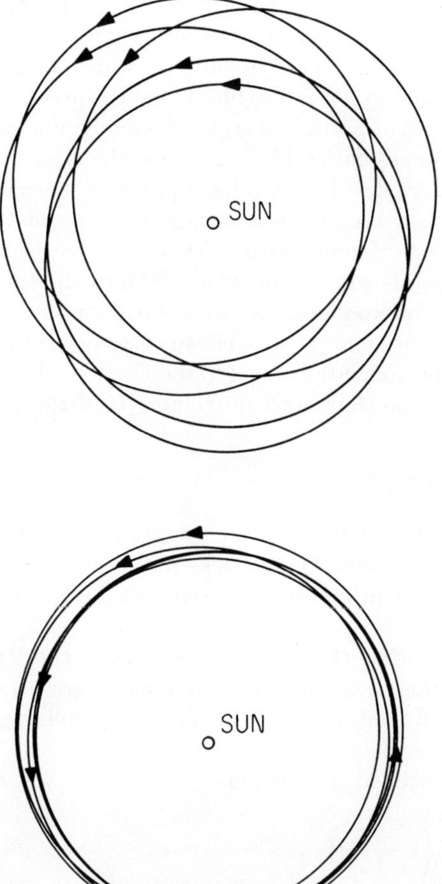

Fig. 2. The condensation process will result in a large number of small grains in eccentric Kepler orbits (top). Inelastic collisions between the grains will not spread the orbits because of the negative diffusion coefficient. Baxter and Thompson (1971, 1973). Instead the collisions will lead to equalization of the orbital elements (bottom) so that a jet stream is formed. From Alfvén and Arrhenius (1972).

assemblages with these characteristics are properly called jet streams. Such jet streams are today probably represented by groups of asteroids moving in closely similar orbits (Arnold, 1969; Danielsson, 1969, 1971). It is also possible that the particles that make up comets and meteor streams have these characteristics (Mendis, 1973).

6. Accretion of Planetary Embryos

Investigations of the lunar surface have demonstrated a number of processes leading to adhesion of colliding particles and resulting in a net growth of aggregate size (Asunmaa et al., 1970; Arrhenius and Asunmaa, 1973). This occurs when the relative velocity between the particles is low enough, or if the target is an already accreted fluffy aggregate, large enough to dissipate the projectile energy within it. Before this stage of low relative velocities in the jet stream is reached, particle collisions result in fragmentation or vaporization. Their effect is mainly a decrease of the particle size while the resultant fragments or condensates remain parts of the stream and eventually collide again. The importance of high-energy impact processes is reflected by the large fraction of melted and quenched silicate droplets (chondrules), which form a major part of the most common meteorites. However, it is also likely that the presence of gas in jet streams leads to viscous dissipation of particle energies, thereby reducing the relative velocities at collision. The need for assuming this comes from the observation in carbonaceous chondrites of abundant crystals likely to be of primordial origin and having a fragile texture, which have been brought together into the ultimate aggregate now observed, without destruction of temperature or impact sensitive features (Fig. 1). This requires that the crystals were aggregated without suffering high-energy collisions and such an effect can be produced only by gas friction.

The approximate dimensions of the Earth's original jet stream can be visualized in the form of a torus with the large radius r_0 approximately equal to the Earth's orbital radius with the small diameter $2x$ such that the characteristic volume U of the jet stream is

$$U = 2\pi^2 r_0 x^2 = \tfrac{1}{2} r_0 T_K{}^2 v_i{}^2 \tag{1}$$

where T_K is the Kepler orbital period of the Earth and v_i is the "internal velocity" in the stream representing the relative velocity between the particles in the jet stream. (The results quoted in this section are derived in detail in Alfvén and Arrhenius, 1970b, Section 9).

When the condition has been reached such that the relative velocities in the jet stream are low enough to permit net accretion, a number of individual aggregates (embryos) in the stream begin to accrete, and continue to grow further by collision with individual grains and with each other.

The rate of mass increase of an embryo (assumed spherical) is

$$\frac{dM_e}{dt} = v_i \rho \pi R^2 \left(1 + \frac{v_e{}^2}{v_i{}^2}\right) \tag{2}$$

where ρ is the space density of condensable substances in the jet stream, πR^2 is the geometrical cross section of the embryo for capture of the condensable substances, and v_e is the escape velocity of the embryo, given by

$$v_e = \left(\frac{2\kappa M_e}{R}\right)^{1/2} = (\tfrac{8}{3}\pi\kappa\theta)^{1/2} R \tag{3}$$

θ being the density (assumed here to be uniform) of the embryo, and κ the gravitational constant. The factor in parentheses in equation 2 represents the increase in the effective capture cross section of the embryo due to gravitational attraction. The gravitational accretion becomes important when the embryo has reached a size of the order of 100 km, and the rate of accretion increases rapidly afterward.

The rapid increase in the growth rate with the size of the embryo results in a runaway accretion process (Safronov, 1954). The rate of accretion becomes catastrophically rapid at a time τ_c after the beginning of accretion when the largest embryo in the jet stream sweeps up all the other material in the jet stream to form the protoplanet. If there were an unlimited supply of particles to the jet stream, the radius of this protoplanet would theoretically become infinite in a finite time τ_a, given by

$$\tau_a = \left(\frac{3\pi}{2\kappa}\right)^{1/2} \frac{\theta^{1/2}}{\rho} = 8.4 \times 10^3 \,\frac{\theta^{1/2}}{\rho} \tag{4}$$

If M is the final mass of the planet, the distributed density ρ of condensables may be approximated by $\rho = M/U$, so that equation 4 may also be written as

$$\tau_a = 8.4 \times 10^3 \theta^{1/2} \frac{U}{M} \tag{5}$$

The time τ_c at which the catastrophic growth takes place may be approximated by

$$\tau_c = (2\tau_i \tau_a)^{1/2} \tag{6}$$

where the injection time τ_i is the time during which condensing grains are continuously fed to the jet stream, replenishing those removed by accretion. This represents the time span during which the grains were condensing from the plasma, and hence the total time during which gas was injected into the circumsolar region. In the part of this region where meteorites formed, measurements of formation intervals (Podosek, 1970) indicate that the injection time cannot possibly have been less than 0.15 – 0.5 · 10^8 yr. As, on the other hand, it could not possibly be of the order 10^9 yr, an intermediate value of 3×10^8 yr has been used for τ_i. Other estimates have led to the order of 10^8 yr (Safronov, 1954, 1958, 1960, 1969; Urey, 1962). As shown in Section 8, the exact value is not very important in the case of the Earth.

The order-of-magnitude consideration of the time parameter is, however, of crucial importance. As pointed out by Levin (1972), much of the confusion in the discussion of the origin of the Earth arises from ignoring the strictures that the accretion mechanism imposes on the time factor, and from the resulting *ad hoc* assumptions of accretion times many orders of magnitude shorter than the time indicated by any quantitative accumulation theory.

Applying the above relationships to the bodies in our solar system and adopting the above value for τ_i, we find essentially three types of cases. Mercury, Venus, Earth, and Jupiter all have values for τ_c of the order 10^7 yr (3.5×10^7 yr for Earth), which probably is shorter than the total time of injection of material, τ_i. At the other extreme are Uranus and Neptune, for which the values of τ_c calculated in this manner would be larger than the age of the solar system. An intermediate group is formed by the Moon, Mars, and Saturn, for which τ_c most likely is of the same order of magnitude as τ_i.

We conclude that for Uranus and Neptune, significant growth of embryos cannot have occurred while the parent jet streams were maintained at constant volume U by continuous injection of material during τ_i. Only after τ_i could a contraction of the jet stream occur, first slowly and then rapidly increasing the space density of matter and thereby accelerating the process leading up to a catastrophic accumulation. The accumulation process would consequently continue for a time substantially longer than 10^8 yr for these two planets.

In the case of the Moon, Mars, and Saturn the catastrophic termination of accretion roughly coincided with the end of injection of matter by condensation; the present uncertainty in the value of τ_i makes it impossible to state which time was the longer.

In the third case, which includes the Earth and hence is of particular interest to us, the catastrophic accumulation of the protoplanet and the exhaustion of the parent jet stream occurred very early in the process of formation of the solar system, according to equation 6, 3.5×10^7 yr after the onset of condensation in the terrestrial region of space. The mass present at that time sufficed to give rise to a protoplanet with about half the present radius (Fig. 3). During the remaining part of the time period of injection of material, assumed to last approximately 3×10^8 yr, growth was maintained at a low and steady rate, determined by the rate of injection of newly condensed material

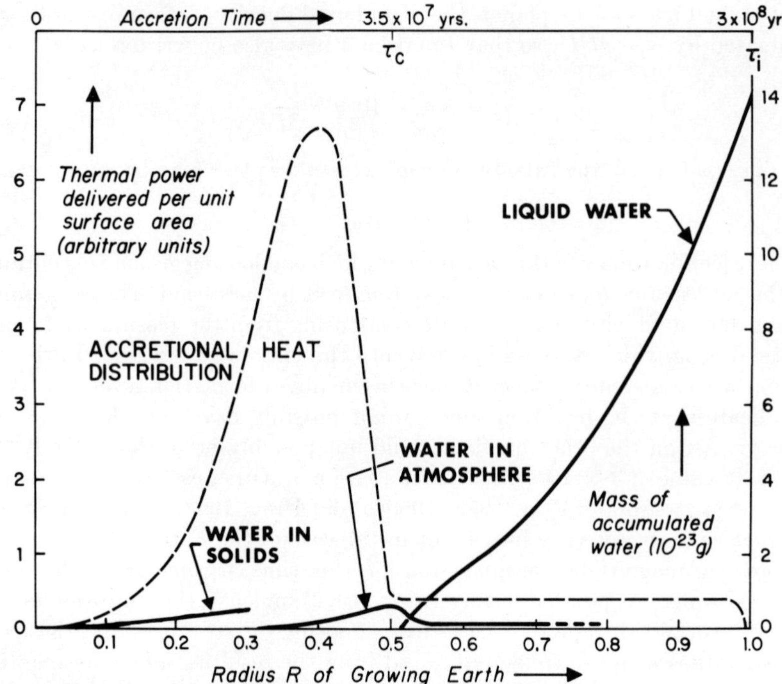

Fig. 3. The dashed curve and the left-hand ordinate scale show the thermal power (in arbitrary units) delivered per unit surface area of the growing Earth by impacting planetesimals. The lower abscissa shows the radius of the growing Earth in fractions of the present size. The upper (nonlinear) abscissa scale shows the time elapsed from inception of accretion. The three solid curves show the accumulation of water on Earth according to equation 17. The left curve represents the amount retained in the cooly accreted inner core; the middle curve shows the accumulated water in the atmosphere, and the right-hand curve shows the accumulated liquid water. The final mass of accumulated water has been adjusted to equal the present ocean mass.

into the jet stream and hence by the rate of inflow of gas into this part of the circumsolar region. At the end of the injection time τ_i, the jet stream was rapidly exhausted and the accretion of the planet terminated, as shown in Fig. 3.

7. Heat Release and Volatilization of Water at Accretion

We have shown above the mass and time relationships of accretion of planets in general with special consideration of the Earth. The heating of the accreted material, carrying in it the volatile sources of the ocean and the atmosphere, is of crucial importance for fractionation of the volatiles and their ultimate disposition. The major amount of heat in the accretion process derives from the conversion of kinetic energy of the infalling bodies into thermal energy at impact.

When a grain hits an embryo, the velocity at impact is

$$v_p = (v_e^2 + v_i^2)^{1/2} \tag{7}$$

where v_e is the escape velocity for the embryo given by equation 3, and v_i is the original velocity of the grain relative to the embryo. In the later stage of accretion, v_i becomes small compared to v_e. Hence, the amount of kinetic energy released at each impact is at least $\frac{1}{2}mv_e^2$, where m is the mass of the impacting grain. A fraction γ of this energy will be converted to thermal energy of fusion within the grain, melting a mass-fraction α of the grain, given by

$$\alpha = \frac{\gamma v_e^2}{2L} \tag{8}$$

L being the latent heat of fusion for the grain material. If we take iron-magnesium silicates to be representatives of the solid material in the grains, the latent heat of fusion (Fe_2SiO_4:295 J/g, $MgSiO_3$:616 J/g, Mg_2SiO_4:455 J/g) may be taken to be of the order of 500 J/g for our estimate. As an example, when the embryo has grown to a size of half the present size of the Earth, we find on putting $R = 0.5R_{\oplus}$, $\theta = 5.5$ g/cm^3, and $L = 500$ J/g.

$$\alpha = 25\gamma$$

Thus, even if γ is as low as 1%, one-fourth of the grain will be melted. It is likely that some of the target material will also be heated at the same time. The above is, however, a very conservative estimate, since γ is likely to be larger. Hence we can conclude that a considerable fraction of the grain will be heated to sufficiently high temperatures for the major part of its volatile components to be released in the form of gas.

The extent to which water vapor and other volatile compounds will be retained as an atmosphere around the protoplanet is determined by the balance between thermal escape of the molecules and the increasing gravitational retention by the protoplanet as its mass grows. Thus there will be a gradual accumulation of water vapor with time, and under suitable conditions this may condense to form liquid water.

These conditions are largely determined by the temperature at the surface of the growing protoplanet, which in its turn depends on the heat release at the impact of individual bodies on it as discussed above, and on the rate at which such impacts occur. Before we proceed in Section 9 to outline the process of the accumulation of water, we shall briefly review the characteristics of the accretional heat distribution.

8. Temperature Distribution in the Growing Protoplanet

The kinetic energy of an impacting planetesimal is almost directly converted to heat energy when it is brought to rest on the surface of the embryo. The thermal power w delivered per unit area of the surface of a growing embryo by the impacting planetesimals is given by

$$4\pi R^2 w = \frac{v_p^2}{2}\frac{dM_e}{dt} \tag{9}$$

Substituting equation 2 into this equation, we obtain

$$w = \frac{\rho}{8}\frac{(v_i^2 + v_e^2)^2}{v_i} \tag{10}$$

If a fraction $\gamma' w$ of this heat is dissipated in melting and vaporization of projectile and target material, then the rest $(1 - \gamma')w$, will be used up in heating the surface of the embryo. Equations 3 and 10 now give us the profile of $(1 - \gamma')w$ as a function of radius R of the growing embryo, assuming γ' to be constant. It is reasonable to assume that this heat is balanced by radiation from the surface of the embryo. Hence the profile of $(1 - \gamma')\, w$ will also represent the profile of the temperature of the surface layer of the growing embryo as a function of its radius. This profile has been plotted in Fig. 3, where we note that the temperature first reaches a maximum and then falls to a very low value at the end of the time τ_c. The fraction of the mass accumulated by the time τ_c is reached is

$$\phi = \frac{\tau_c}{\tau_i} = \left(\frac{2\tau_a}{\tau_i}\right)^{1/2} \tag{11}$$

The radius of the protoplanet at this time, R_c, equals $\beta R_\oplus$, where $R_\oplus$ is the final radius, with

$$\beta = \phi^{1/3} = (2\tau_a/\tau_i)^{1/6} \tag{12}$$

Using the values 2×10^6 yr found for τ_a for the Earth, and taking $\tau_i = 3 \times 10^8$ yr, we find

$$\beta = (\tfrac{4}{300})^{1/6} \approx 0.5 \tag{13}$$

The result is not very sensitive to the choice of value for τ_i; values of 10^8 and 10^9 yr change the value for β to 0.58 and 0.40, respectively.

We conclude, therefore, that the inner core of the Earth accreted cold (Fig. 3), the accretion temperature rose to maximum at the formation of the outer core and then fell abruptly and remained low (averaged over the entire surface of the Earth) during the accretion of the mantle. It is tempting to see in this primeval heat distribution of the Earth an explanation of the fact that in its present state, our planet is known to have a solid inner core and mantle and a liquid outer core. This requires that since the formation, the heat distribution has not changed very much due to the thermal conduction. However, radioactive decay would add another component to the heat profile in a manner depending on the largely unknown distribution of uranium, thorium, and potassium. Hence, it is possible that also the central part of the Moon, although accumulated cold, is now partially melted, as suggested by seismic evidence (Latham et al., 1973).

9. A Simple Model for Accumulation of Water

The rate of increase of mass with radius of an embryo of uniform density is

$$\frac{dM_e}{dR} = 4\pi R^2\theta \tag{14}$$

Let us suppose that each mass unit of impacting matter releases ϵ mass units of water. Then the rate of increase of water content in the environment of the embryo is

$$\frac{dM_{H_2O}}{dR} = \epsilon\frac{dM_e}{dR} = \epsilon 4\pi R^2\theta \tag{15}$$

The water vapor in the upper atmosphere will approach an equilibrium temperature T and a corresponding Maxwellian velocity distribution. The molecules that have thermal velocity v in excess of the escape velocity v_e for the embryo can escape immediately from the neighborhood of the embryo. As shown by Jeans, if the root mean square velocity of a gas is only of the order of 20% of the escape velocity, the gas can escape entirely in the course of a billion years or so. Let us make a conservative estimate of the retention of water molecules and assume that all molecules having velocities higher than 0.2 v_e will escape from the gravitational field of an embryo.

Hence, we have to multiply the right-hand side of equation 15 by the fraction representing the number of molecules that are retained:

$$\frac{dM_{H_2O}}{dR} = \epsilon 4\pi R^2 \theta \frac{4}{\sqrt{\pi}} \int_0^{X(R)} e^{-x^2} x^2 \, dx \tag{16}$$

with

$$x = v\left(\frac{m_{H_2O}}{2kT}\right)^{1/2}$$

$$X(R) = 0.2 v_e \left(\frac{m_{H_2O}}{2kT}\right)^{1/2} = 0.2\left(\frac{8}{3}\pi\kappa\theta\right)^{1/2} R\left(\frac{m_{H_2O}}{2kT}\right)^{1/2}$$

where m_{H_2O} and k are the mass of a water molecule and the Boltzmann constant, respectively. Therefore, the total mass of water that has accumulated when the embryo had a radius R is

$$M_{H_2O}(R) = \epsilon 16\pi^{1/2}\theta \int_0^R R^2 \left[\int_0^{X(R)} e^{-x^2} x^2 \, dx\right] dR \tag{17}$$

Is the accumulation of water described by equation 17 up to the time when the planet has attained its final size sufficient to account for the ocean mass? In order to answer this question, we need to specify the value of the parameter ϵ. Instead, we shall turn the question around and ask what value of ϵ will give a total accumulation equal to the present ocean mass; we can then examine the implications of this value of ϵ.

The relevant temperature T of the water vapor that will determine its rate of gravitational escape is a characteristic temperature at the top of the atmosphere that forms by the release of the occluded gases. This temperature is not related to the accretionally heated surface temperature of the embryo, but is determined by the radiation fields of the Sun and of the plasma in the primordial magnetosphere surrounding the Earth (De and Arrhenius, 1973). Assuming that the thermal conditions at the top of the atmosphere were comparable to those in the Earth's exosphere today, we choose a characteristic temperature of 1000°K. Our analysis does not change appreciably if T is lower than 1000°K. If T were as high as 3000°K, this would lower the total accumulation of water by about a factor of 2.

For the density θ, we adopt for convenience the average density 5.5 g/cm^3 of Earth. It is possible that the Earth formed from relatively homogeneous material of lower density. The high-density core would in this case be produced by a phase transformation setting in when the Earth had reached about 0.8 of its present radius (Lodochnikov, 1939; Ramsey, 1948, 1949, 1967; see also discussion in Levin, 1972 and Alfvén and Arrhenius, 1973b). The original density of this material is then likely to be of the order of 3 to 4 g/cm^3—but as far as the present analysis is concerned, the assumption of average density is not critical.

Figure 3 shows the accumulation of water with increasing radius of the protoplanet calculated on the basis of equation 17. The total accumulation when the radius reaches the present value has been matched to equal the present ocean mass. The value of ϵ needed for this is $\epsilon \approx 3.2 \times 10^{-4}$.

Meteorite materials of the type discussed in Section 4 have values of ϵ in the range 10^{-2} to 10^{-3}, hence primordial grains in principle would satisfy the required value for ϵ. Figure 3 also shows the primeval heat structure of the Earth resulting from accretion, as discussed in Section 8. The ordinate (left) for this curve is given in arbitrary units and is proportional to the temperature. We note that after the low temperature accretion of the inner core, the temperature of the surface layer of the embryonic Earth continues to rise and culminates at $R \approx 0.4R_{\oplus}$. Hence water vapor cannot condense during this period and must remain in the atmosphere. However, the gravitational retention of water vapor at this stage is very small. As the accretion proceeds, now at a low rate determined by the injection of source gas into the terrestrial region, the surface temperature of the protoplanet falls to a low average value that is probably close to the present surface temperature of the Earth. This would allow the water vapor to condense and begin the formation of a proto-ocean.

10. Accretional Heat Front and State of Water

As shown in Section 8 and Fig. 3 for the case of the Earth, heat delivery to the surface layer of the protoplanet first reached a maximum and then declined to a low mean value when the size of the present outer core was reached. After this culmination, the accretion of the outer regions of the Earth proceeded at a low rate, controlled by the continued injection rate of matter (assumed here to be constant) into the terrestrial region of space and terminating at the time τ_i when this injection ceased. During the era preceding τ_i, the average rate of heating of the surface protoplanet hence must have been low. At the same time, however, the local heating at each individual impact site continued to be high and actually increased as a function of R as the escape velocity of the Earth increased due to its increasing mass. The transformation of kinetic energy of the infalling bodies to thermal energy has been discussed in Section 7. Since the major fraction of mass, and hence potential thermal energy, is concentrated in the largest embryos impacting on the growing Earth (Gurevich and Lebedinskij, 1950), it is these large projectiles that control the thermal evolution.

Assuming that the size distribution of accreting planetesimals was such as to place the major fraction of mass in bodies sufficiently large to penetrate the atmosphere and the ocean, the major fraction of heat was delivered in large impacts repeated relatively rarely at any given location (once every 10 to a few hundred years in any impact area) during the era of mantle and crust formation. Each major impact is likely to have created a deep subsurface region of molten rock that, in contrast to secondary ejecta and a thin surface crust, would cool slowly. In such melt reservoirs differentiation of magma could take place with the heavy components sinking to the bottom and the light materials accumulating at the top. Although the average surface temperature of the Earth during this era would have remained low, each individual impact region would, in the course of time, be remelted and differentiated many times over. Radial progression of this accretional heat front, discontinuous in space and time, resulted in the selective removal toward the surface of light differentiates forming the Earth's crust, and of volatiles forming the atmosphere and the ocean.

The water vapor released at individual impacts would, after time τ_c, condense and contribute to the growing proto-ocean due to the low average surface temperature during this era.

11. Details of Model

The development discussed in Sections 8 and 9 has purposely been made simplistic in order to illustrate in principle the energetics of growth of the planet and the course of retention of oceanic and atmospheric components with time. There are several complicating factors, some of which can be discussed qualitatively with some assurance at the present time; for others, observational basis is still lacking. Some of the resulting modifications and uncertainties are discussed in the following sections.

A. Atmospheric Loss Mechanism

In the calculation in Section 9, it was assumed that water vapor is lost from the exosphere by molecular evaporation. If one assumes solar energy flux of at least the present magnitude, water vapor in the upper atmosphere will be dissociated and form a number of species, including atomic and molecular hydrogen, hydroxyl and oxygen ions; of these, the hydrogen species have a high escape rate and are preferentially lost to space. The escape rate is probably controlled by the transfer rate of water vapor from the troposphere across the stratospheric cold trap (Harteck and Jensen, 1948; Urey, 1952, 1959).

It is thus generally believed that a part of the terrestrial oxygen is the residue of water from which the hydrogen component has escaped. An estimate of the relative importance of this selective loss can be obtained from the budget shown in Table I.

TABLE I

Oxygen Reservoirs	Mass of Stored Oxygen (10^{23}g)
Hydrosphere (including sediment porewater)	16.7
Limestone	4
Excess in oxidized iron compounds	0.2
Atmosphere	0.05
Sulfates	0.04

The table shows that if we make the extreme assumption that the oxygen now present in carbonates derives entirely from dissociated water by reaction of such oxygen with primordial carbon compounds, then limestone would be a major store of such oxygen. However, the carbonates may partly or entirely have formed by other reactions instead; carbon dioxide may have been a primordial gas component of planetesimals (Gibson and Moore, 1973a), it may have been produced by reaction of planetesimal carbon with oxygen in iron silicate in the accretional heat front (Ringwood, 1959), or carbonates could have formed by reaction of methane and water with silicates (Urey, 1952). Hence the largest conceivable loss of water by escape of hydrogen would amount to about 25% of the present mass of water; the actual amount is probably much smaller.

The amount of atmospheric oxygen used up by oxidation of transition element compounds, primarily those of iron, has been estimated on the basis of the extreme assumption of an original oxygen-iron average oxidation state corresponding to FeO; furthermore all iron in present-day sediments occurs as Fe_2O_3 and forms on the average 3.5% of shale and deep-sea sediments. The total thus obtained is only a small fraction of the oxygen in the present ocean. However, this calculation ignores the unknown amount of water-derived oxygen bound to divalent or trivalent iron in the mantle and in crustal igneous rocks (see Holland, 1964). Particularly the amount in the mantle constitutes a substantial uncertainty.

The rate of removal of gas from bodies in space is also affected by interaction with corpuscular radiation from the Sun. It is sometimes assumed that a "solar gale" arose after the planets had formed, removing all planetary atmospheres in the inner part of the solar system.

The need for such an *ad hoc* mechanism was rooted in the belief that the primordial components were missing from the Earth's atmosphere. As discussed in Section 4, it is now realized that on the contrary, our present atmosphere can only be understood as a product of the primordial accumulation, modified by loss of hydrogen and helium, by photochemical and biological processes, and by reaction with the solid Earth, from which radiogenic gases have also been added. The records from the Moon and from meteorites also have failed to give evidence of any major enhancement of solar corpuscular radiation after the formative era. For a discussion of the corpuscular radiation effects during this era, see Alfvén and Arrhenius, 1973, Section 11.8.

B. Effect of Atmosphere and Ocean on Accretional Heating

The developing hydrosphere and atmosphere could, in principle, introduce effects on the distribution of heat received in the accretional process. This is partly because some of the projectile energy will be dissipated by frictional heating of the atmosphere and the ocean and partly because these will decrease the efficiency of cooling by reradiation into space from collision-heated spots on the surface. The latter effect would become important if a large fraction of accumulated water were evaporated into a hot atmosphere. This is, however, not likely to have taken place since such a runaway greenhouse effect (Rasool and de Bergh, 1970) would probably be irreversible, whereas the geological record shows existence of sediments and organic life on Earth already at the -3 Gy level (Engel et al., 1968). The lack of development of a hot atmosphere can be understood, since the calculated size distribution of accumulating planetesimals place the major amount of mass in large projectiles (Section 10). This would concentrate the accretional heat to limited regions, and with sufficient intervening time available for efficient reradiation of surficial heat into space.

At a large projectile mass-surface ratio, the energy dissipation in the atmosphere and the ocean would also become small compared to the energy release after penetration to the solid surface (Lin, 1966). Terrestrial experience gives no guidance concerning the nature of impact processes of the magnitude involved here. Until these effects could be studied directly in the preserved impact record of the Moon, it would be difficult to predict the relative distribution of projectile matter between ejecta dissipating energy over wide regions, and the retained projectile fraction implanted in the target and melting itself as well as the target material. In the projectile mass range covered by controlled experiments, the mass of ejecta exceeds that of the projectile in hypersonic impacts (Gault et al., 1968; Neukum et al., 1970). At projectile masses far beyond this range, however, the fraction of projectile material retained in the target would be expected to increase, particularly at impact speeds several times the sound velocity in the projectile material. This is indicated by the effects of the largest impacts on the lunar surface. Hence local implantation of kinetic energy converted to heat is likely to have been an important process at the accretion of the Earth.

12. Volatiles in the Lithosphere

Crustal igneous rocks on Earth have a low but persistent content of water and occasionally very high contents of carbon dioxide (von Eckermann, 1948, 1958; Tuttle and Gittens, 1966). Because of the unknown extent of these components with depth in the Earth, the total store of volatiles in the solid Earth is highly uncertain.

The question how and when these volatiles became buried is important to the problem of the formation of the ocean. One suggestion has been that an excess over the present amount was introduced into the interior of the Earth during its early history. This situation would be or would become metastable, causing a net transport of water from the lithosphere to add to the volume of the ocean during a substantial fraction of geological time and possibly still today. No observational basis seems to exist for this assumption, which was originally made to secure a storage place for the present ocean and atmosphere while the original atmosphere was supposed to be destroyed. As discussed above, such a catastrophe is counterindicated by the noble gas distribution in the atmosphere, hence the need for temporary ocean storage has disappeared.

To explain the present content of reactive volatiles (primarily water and carbon dioxide) in igneous rocks, Fanale (1971), on the basis of a proposal that the Earth became completely melted (Hanks and Anderson, 1969), suggested that the volatiles were partitioned in equilibrium between the melted Earth and a hot atmosphere in contact with it. This would seem excluded on the basis of quantitative considerations of the accumulation process (Safronov, 1954, 1958, 1959, 1960, 1969; Alfvén and Arrhenius, 1970a, b; Section 6 in this chapter). These indicate early exhaustion of the Earth's jet stream, and slow subsequent growth during the major part of the approximately 10^8-yr accretion period. If this is correct, the average temperature of the Earth's surface must have been low during accumulation of the mantle and the crust. The thorough outgassing of the noble gases recognized by Fanale is, as demonstrated by the late bombardment effects on the Moon, the natural consequence of the local heating at each individual impact and does not in itself require simultaneous heating of the whole Earth. It is furthermore doubtful that a thoroughly melted Earth would have had time to cool to yield a still-preserved crust 0.7 Gy after formation, particularly with a hot atmosphere containing a major part of the present ocean and of the carbon dioxide reservoir. Finally, the spotty occurrence of deep-seated igneous rocks rich in carbon dioxide suggests that it was introduced locally by a mechanism such as described below, rather than by equilibration of a molten Earth with a hot, massive atmosphere.

There is indeed a straightforward and observationally supported way in which the igneous rocks of the crust and upper mantle would seem to be continuously impregnated with reactive volatiles from the atmosphere and the ocean. The evidence for convection-driven lateral movement of large plates of the Earth's crust suggests strongly that water and carbonate-containing sediments and hydrated submarine eruptives are sinking and assimilating into the upper mantle in subduction zones, compensating for the rise of magma and generation of new crust in the sea floor spreading zones. This vertical mixing is sufficiently fast (approximately 5 cm/yr) to have drowned all ocean sediments appreciably older than a few per cent of the estimated age of the Earth. Hence all reactive volatiles now found in igneous rocks can be understood as contamination mainly from the ocean, introduced into the solid Earth much later than the time of formation of the primordial crust. A potential measure of the efficiency of this cycling is the remaining effusion from the Earth's interior of stable end products from such radioactive species that decayed practically completely a short time after the formation of the Earth (Xe^{129} from I^{129}, half-life approximately 15 My; see Boulos and Manuel, 1971). Another suggested indicator would be He^3, possibly inherited as a cosmic ray spallation product from primordial material (Clarke et al., 1969). It would, however, seem difficult to understand how helium could survive accretional degassing while neon, argon and krypton were transferred to the primordial atmosphere with such efficiency that no traces have been found of their primordial component in terrestrial igneous rocks.

It should be clear from this discussion that an efficient mechanism for circulation of volatiles between the ocean-atmospheric system and the upper mantle has been operating through the geological eras recorded on the ocean floor and presumably during the entire history of the Earth after its formation. This does not exclude the possibility that a fraction of the primordial volatiles were left behind in the growing lithosphere as a result of incomplete outgassing at accumulation of the Earth.

At atmospheric pressure the equilibrium solubilities in silicate melts of most gases are modest. However, considerable excess amounts of gas can be incorporated, at the moment of shock, in melted, gas-rich materials and can be retained in disequilibrium in such melts when they solidify due to the inefficiency of diffusion-limited removal processes. On the other hand, convection in such melts, and stripping by boiling of components such as hydrocarbons and monoxides of carbon, silicon, and potassium, contribute toward relieving such disequilibria. These retention and removal phenomena are exemplified in the lunar rocks. Conditions in the lunar crust also indicate that in the culminating stage of accretional heating (which on Earth probably occurred at the outer core and on the Moon not far below the present surface), the removal of any water vapor possibly associated with the molten and vaporized projectile material was highly efficient, resulting in oxygen partial pressure less than 10^{-14} b. The sporadic occurrences of volatiles in lunar materials are considered to derive from post-formative impact of volatile-rich projectiles on the cold lunar surface and in some instances perhaps to be due to vapor transport through crustal fractures from the coldly accreted inner core (which could be considerably warmer today due to radioactive heating).

During the accretion of the Earth's mantle and crust, the large impacts could well have implanted hydroxyl-containing material sufficiently deep so that the solubility in the melt remained comparatively high, and removal was not complete before solidification in spite of repeated remelting by new impacts and gravitational upward removal of light components resulting in formation of the crust. Because of the complexity of these processes and our lack of knowledge of large-scale impact effects, it is difficult now to estimate the ultimate efficiency of the materials separation by the accretional heat front.

A continued systematic search for primordial gas components in the effluents from the Earth's crust and mantle could narrow the limits of uncertainty. Improved knowledge of the temperature distribution in the mantle would also contribute to the vertical transport efficiency problem, since at least at moderate pressures the large cations of the elements contributing to radioactive heating are concentrated in the light component migrating toward the surface in the accretional heat front.

13. The Ocean and the Earth-Moon System

It is likely that the evolution of the ocean has been markedly affected by the fact that an abnormally massive body causing significant tidal effects exists in the vicinity of the Earth. A similar case is that of Neptune with the captured satellite Triton, which has a tidally modified orbit (McCord, 1966).

After the recent exploration of the Moon, two types of theories for its origin remain to be discussed. One postulates the formation of the Moon in an independent solar orbit (Gerstenkorn, 1969) or coupled by resonance to the Earth (Alfvén and Arrhenius, 1969, 1972) and in either case subsequently captured by tidal interaction. The other (Ringwood, 1970) proposes that the Moon formed around the Earth by hydromagnetic transfer of angular momentum to a primordial plasma emplaced around the planet in

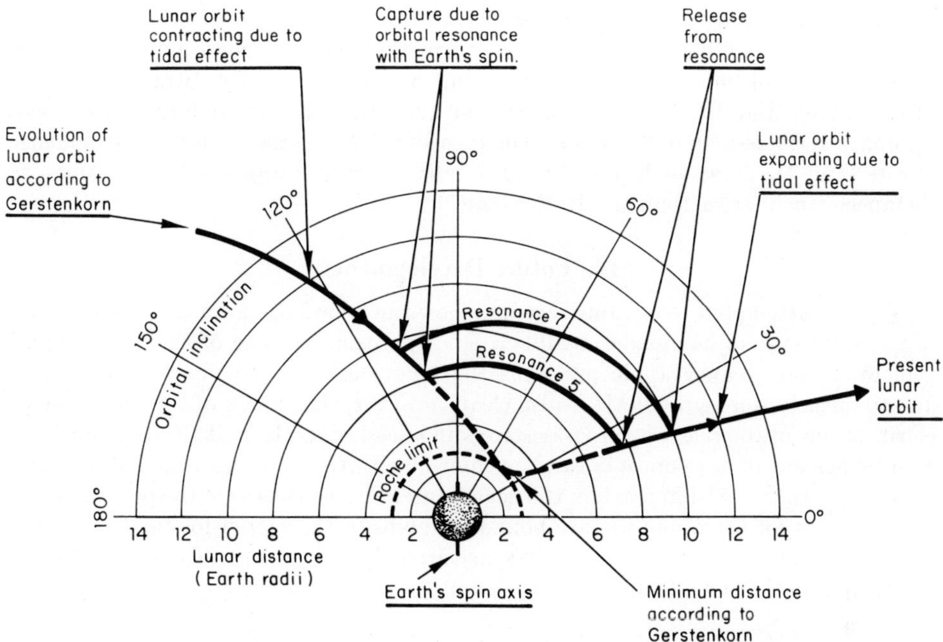

Fig. 4. Noncatastrophic capture: spin-orbit resonance prevents the Moon from reaching the Roche limit. The retrograde lunar capture orbit contracts due to tidal dissipation, until resonance between the lunar orbit period and the spin period of the Earth locks the Moon in a slowly expanding orbit. Since the Moon never comes very close, no breakup or autoejection occurs and the tides do not reach catastrophic heights. When the orbital inclination has decreased below a critical angle (suggested in the diagram at about 25°), the resonance locking is broken and the Moon recedes to its present orbit at 60 $R_{\oplus}$. From Alfven and Arrhenius (1969).

the same way as the (structurally very different) regular satellite systems seem to have formed.

The former hypothesis would appear more likely in view of the fact that the Moon is much more massive (mass ratio 1:80 relative to Earth) than the regular satellites of Jupiter, Uranus, and Saturn where the ratios of satellite mass to central body are less than $1:10^4$.

A comparison of Earth with the regular planet-satellite systems of Jupiter, Saturn, and Uranus (Alfvén and Arrhenius, 1972, Fig. 1) suggests that the Earth indeed may have had a regular satellite system, composed of about half a dozen bodies, each with a mass of only a fraction of a percent of the lunar mass. These proper satellites could have been swept up by the Moon during the postcapture evolution of its orbit; the major maria may be the impact sites, and the active time interval -4.0 to -3.0 Gy would mark this series of events.

Regardless of the ultimate origin of the Moon, tidal forces in the early evolution of the Earth-Moon system should be of considerable importance, and the question arises of the relative role of the ocean in the tidal dissipation. Since dissipation in the solid Earth is considered insignificant (Munk, 1968), the ocean would provide the most important medium for tidal energy exchange.

It was believed earlier that capture of the Moon must have catastrophic tidal effects on Earth, leading to complete evaporation of the ocean to form a hot atmosphere. However, the long duration of the high magnetic field immersion indicated by the magnetization of lunar rocks in the time interval -4 to -3 Gy (Strangway et al., 1972; Alfvén and Lindberg, 1973) suggest that the capture and the subsequent approach and recession of the Moon to its present orbit were associated with resonance effects (Fig. 4). These could possibly also limit the closest approach of the Moon to distances much larger than the Roche limit.

14. Future Developments

We have attempted to demonstrate here how the knowledge gained by exploration of the solar system has made possible a new approach to some of the fundamental geological and oceanographic problems that previously lacked observational basis and frequently were ignored. It is also clear, however, that much of the quantitative clarifications of the relevant processes are still ahead of us. It is likely that considerable refinement of our concepts can be achieved with the new experimental material already existing or within reach in the near future. The awareness of the problems and of the means for their solution are bound to intensify the search for further experimental evidence both on Earth and in space around us. It was at this new frontier of oceanography that Lars Gunnar Sillén's inquisitive and exacting work came to an end.

Acknowledgments

This research was funded by NASA's Apollo Lunar Exploration Office under grant NGL 05-009-154, Lunar and Planetary Program Division under grant NGL 05-009-002, and Planetology Program under grant NGR 05-009-110. The interest and generous support from those NASA offices is gratefully acknowledged. The authors also wish to thank Mrs. Marjorie Sinkankas, Mrs. Dawn Rawls, and Dr. Saara Asunmaa for valuable help.

References

Alfvén, H., 1942–1945. On the cosmogony of the solar system. *Stockholms Observatorium Ann.*, **14** (2); **14** (5); **14** (9).

Alfvén, H., 1954. *On the Origin of the Solar System.* Oxford University Press, London.

Alfvén, H., 1970. Jet streams in space. *Astrophys. Space Sci.*, **6**, 161–174.

Alfvén, H. and G. Arrhenius, 1969. Two alternatives for the history of the Moon. *Science*, **165**, 11–17.

Alfvén, H. and G. Arrhenius, 1970a. Structure and evolutionary history of the solar system, I. *Astrophys. Space Sci.*, **8**, 338–421.

Alfvén, H. and G. Arrhenius, 1970b. Origin and evolution of the solar system, II. *Astrophys. Space Sci.*, **9**, 3–33.

Alfvén, H. and G. Arrhenius, 1972. Origin and evolution of the Earth-Moon system. *The Moon*, **5**, 210–230.

Alfvén, H. and G. Arrhenius, 1973. Structure and evolutionary history of the solar system, III. *Astrophys. Space Sci.*, **12**, in press.

Alfvén, H. and G. Arrhenius, 1973. Structure and evolutionary history of the solar system, IV. *Astrophys. Space Sci.* In preparation.

Alfvén, H. and L. Lindberg, 1973. Magnetic field production in the Earth-Moon system. In preparation.

Anders, E., 1971. Conditions in the early solar system, as inferred from meteorites. In *From Plasma to Planet.* Proc. Nobel Symp. 21. A. Elvius, ed. Wiley, New York, pp. 133–156.

Apollo 16 Preliminary Examination Team, 1973. *Science*, **179**, 23.

Arnold, J. R., 1969. Asteroid families and "jet streams." *Astron. J.*, **74**, 1235–1242.

Arrhenius, G., 1972. Chemical effects in plasma condensation. In *From Plasma to Planet*. Proc. Nobel Symp. 21. A. Elvius, ed., Wiley, New York, pp. 117–132.

Arrhenius, G. and H. Alfvén, 1971. Fractionation and condensation in space. *Earth Planet. Sci. Letters*, **10**, 253–267.

Arrhenius, G. and S. K. Asunmaa, 1973. Aggregation of grains in space. *The Moon*, **8**, in press.

Aston, F. W., 1924. The rarity of the inert gases on the Earth. *Nature*, **114**, 786.

Asunmaa, S. K., S. S. Liang, and G. Arrhenius, 1970. Primordial accretion; inferences from the lunar surface. *Proc. Apollo 11 Lunar Science Conf.*, Vol. 1, Pergamon Press, pp. 1975–1985.

Baxter, D. and W. B. Thompson, 1971. Jetstream formation through inelastic collisions. In *Physical Studies of Minor Planets*. NASA SP-267. T. Gehrels, ed. pp. 319–326.

Baxter, D. and W. B. Thompson, 1973. Elastic and inelastic scattering in orbital clustering. *Astrophys. J.*, In press.

Black, D. C., 1972a. On the origins of trapped helium, neon and argon isotopic variations in meteorites-I. Gas-rich meteorites, lunar soil and breccia. *Geochim. Cosmochim. Acta*, **36**, 347–375.

Black, D. C., 1972b. On the origins of trapped helium, neon and argon isotopic variations in meteorites-II. Carbonaceous chondrites. *Geochim. Cosmochim. Acta*, **36**, 377–394.

Black, L. P., N. H. Gale, S. Moorbath, R. J. Pankhurst, and V. R. McGregor, 1971. Isotopic dating of very early Precambrian amphibolite facies gneisses from the Godthaab Distict, West Greenland. *Earth Planet. Sci. Letts.*, **12**, 245–259.

Boulos, M. S. and O. K. Manuel, 1971. Xenon record of extinct radioactivities in the earth. *Science*, **174**, 1334–1336.

Cameron, A. G. W., 1964. Interpretation of xenon measurements. In *The Origin and Evolution of Atmospheres and Oceans*. P. J. Brancazio and A. G. W. Cameron, eds. Wiley, New York, 235–248.

Clarke, W. B., M. A. Beg, and H. Craig, 1969. Excess He^3 in the sea: evidence for terrestrial primordial helium. *Earth Planet. Sci. Letts.*, **6**, 213–220.

Danielsson, L., 1969. Statistical arguments for asteroidal jet streams. *Astrophys. Space Sci.*, **5**, 53.

Danielsson, L., 1971. Profile of a jetstream. In *Physical Studies of Minor Planets*. NASA SP-267, T. Gehrels, ed., pp. 353–362.

De, B. and G. Arrhenius, 1973. Inhomogeneous plasmas and primordial condensation: inferences from present-day observations. In preparation.

v. Eckermann, H., 1948. The alkaline district of Alnö Island. *Sveriges Geol. Undersöhn Årsbok, Ser. Ca.*, **36**, 176 pp.

v. Eckermann, H., 1958. The alkaline and carbonatitic dikes of the Alnö formation on the mainland north-west of Alnö Island. *Kungl. Svenska Vetenskaps Akademiens Handl.*, 4th series, **7**, No. 2.

Engel, A. E. J., B. Nagy, L. A. Nagy, C. G. Engel, G. O. W. Kremp, and C. M. Drew, 1968. Alga-like forms in Onverwacht Series, South Africa: oldest recognized lifelike forms on Earth. *Science*, **161**, 1005–1008.

Fanale, F. P., 1971. A case for catastrophic early degassing of the Earth. *Chem. Geol.*, **8**, 79–105.

Fuchs, L. H., 1969. Occurrence of cordierite and aluminous orthoenstatite in the Allende meteorite. *Amer. Mineralogist*, **54**, 1645–1653.

Gault, D. E., W. L. Quaide, and V. R. Oberbeck, 1968. Impact cratering mechanics and structures. In *Shock Metamorphism of Natural Materials*. B. M. French and N. M. Short, eds. Mono Book Corp., Baltimore, pp. 87–99.

Gerstenkorn, H., 1969. The earliest past of the Earth-Moon system. *Icarus*, **11**, 189–207.

Gibson, E. K., Jr., 1973. *Thermochim. Acta*. In press.

Gibson, E. K. and S. M. Johnson, 1971. *Geochim. Cosmochim. Acta*, **2** (Suppl. 2), 1351.

Gibson, E. K. and S. M. Johnson, 1972. *Thermochim. Acta*, **4**, 49.

Gibson, E. K. and G. W. Moore, 1973a. Volatile-rich lunar soil: evidence of possible cometary impact. *Science*, **179**, 69–71.

Gibson, E. K. and G. W. Moore, 1973b. *Geochim. Cosmochim. Acta*. In press.

Grossman, L., 1972. Condensation in the primitive solar nebula. *Geochim. Cosmochim. Acta*, **36**, 597–619.

Gurevich, L. E. and A. I. Lebedinskij, 1950. On the formation of planets. 1. Gravitational condensation. *Izv. Akad. Nauk S.S.S.R., Ser. Fiz*, **14**, 765–775.

Hanks, T. C. and D. L. Anderson, 1969. The early thermal history of the Earth. *Phys. Earth Planet. Inter.*, **2** (1), 19–29.

Harteck, P. and J. H. D. Jensen, 1948. *Z. Naturforschung*, **3a**, 591.

Hartmann, W. K., 1972. *Moons and Planets: An Introduction to Planetary Science*. Bogden and Quigley, Tarrytown-on-Hudson, N.Y. and Belmont, Calif., pp. 404.

Hattori, T., T. Nakano, and C. Hayashi, 1969. Thermal and dynamical evolution of gas clouds of various masses. *Prog. Theoret. Phys.*, **42**, 781–798.

Holland, H. O., 1964. On the chemical evolution of the terrestrial and cytherean atmospheres. In *The Origin and Evolution of Atmospheres and Oceans*. P. J. Brancazio and A. G. W. Cameron, eds., Wiley, New York, pp. 86–102.

Kumar, S. S., 1972. On the formation of Jupiter. *Astrophys. Space Sci.*, **16**, 52–54.

Larimer, J. W., 1967. Chemical fractionation in meteorites-I. Condensation of the elements. *Geochim. Cosmochim. Acta*, **31**, 1215–1238.

Larimer, J. W. and E. Anders, 1967. Chemical fractionation in meteorites-II. Abundance patterns and their interpretation. *Geochim. Cosmochim. Acta*, **31**, 1239–1270.

Larimer, J. W. and E. Anders, 1970. Chemical fractionation in meteorites-III. Major element fractionations in chondrites. *Geochim. Cosmochim. Acta*, **34**, 367–387.

Latham, G., J. Dorman, F. Duennebier, M. Ewing, D. Lammlein, and Y. Nakamura, 1973. Moonquakes, meteoroids, and the state of the lunar interior. In *Lunar Science IV*. J. W. Chamberlain and C. Watkins, eds. The Lunar Science Institute, Houston.

Lehnert, B., 1970. On the conditions for cosmic grain formation. *Cosmical Electrodyn.* **1**, 219–232.

Levin, B. J., 1972. Origin of the Earth. In *The Upper Mantle*. A. R. Ritsema, ed. Tectonophysics, **13**, 7–29.

Lin, S. C., 1966. Cometary impact and the origin of tektites. *J. Geophys. Res.*, **71**, 2427–2437.

Lodochnikov, V. N., 1939. Some general problems connected with magma producing basaltic rocks. *Zap. Mineral. O-va.*, **64**, 207–223.

Lord, H. C., 1965. Molecular equilibrium and condensation in a solar nebula and cool stellar atmospheres. *Icarus*, **4**, 279–288.

Martin and Donnay, 1972. Hydroxyl in the mantle. *Amer. Mineralogist*, **57**, 554–570.

McCord, T. B., 1966. Dynamical evolution of the Neptunian system. *Astron. J.*, **71**, 585–590.

Mendis, D. A., 1973. The comet-meteor stream complex. *Astrophys. Space Sci.* In press.

Meyer, C., Jr., 1969. Sputter condensation of silicates. Ph.D. thesis Scripps Institution of Oceanography, University of California, San Diego.

Meyer, C., Jr., 1971. An experimental approach to circumstellar condensation. *Geochim. Cosmochim. Acta*, **35**, 551–566.

Munk, W. H., 1968. Once again—tidal friction. *Q. J. R. Astron. Soc.*, **9**, 352–375.

Neukum, G., A. Mehl, H. Fechtig, and J. Zahringer, 1970. Impact phenomena of micrometeorites on lunar surface material. *Earth Planet. Sci. Letters*, **8**, 31–35.

Podosek, F. A., 1970. Dating of meteorites by the high-temperature release of iodine-correlated Xe^{129}. *Geochim. Cosmochim. Acta*, **34**, 341–365.

Ramsey, W. H., 1948. On the constitution of the terrestrial planets. *Monthly Not. R. Astron. Soc.*, **108**, 406–413.

Ramsey, W. H., 1949. On the nature of the Earth's core. *Monthly Not. R. Astron. Soc., Geophys. Suppl.*, **5**, 409–426.

Ramsey, W. H., 1967. On the constitutions of Uranus and Neptune. *Planet. Space Sci.*, **15**, 1609–1623.

Rasool, S. I. and C. de Bergh, 1970. The runaway greenhouse and the accumulation of CO_2 in the Venus atmosphere. *Nature*, **226**, 1037–1039.

Ringwood, A. E., 1959. On the chemical evolution and densities of the planets. *Geochim. Cosmochim. Acta*, **15**, 257–283.

Ringwood, A. E., 1970. Petrogenesis of Apollo 11 basalts and implications for lunar origin. *J. Geophys. Res.*, **75**, 6453–6479.

Rubey, W. W., 1951. Geologic history of sea water. An attempt to state the problem. *Bull. Geol. Soc. Amer.*, **62, 1111–1147.**

Rubey, W. W., 1955. Development of the hydrosphere and atmosphere with special reference to probable composition of the early atmosphere. *Geol. Soc. Amer., Special Paper 62*, 631–650.

Safronov, V. S., 1954. On the growth of planets in the protoplanetary cloud. *Astron Zh.*, **31**, 499–510.

Safronov, V. S., 1958. On the growth of terrestrial planets. *Vopr. Kosmog., Akad. Nauk S.S.S.R.*, **6**, 63–77.

Safronov, V. S., 1959. On the initial temperature of the earth. *Izv. Akad. Nauk S.S.S.R., Ser. Geofiz.*, **1**, 139–143.

Safronov, V. S., 1960. Accumulation of planets of the earth's group. *Vopr. Kosmog., Akad. Nauk S.S.S.R.*, **7**, 59–65.

Safronov, V. S., 1969. *Evolution of the Preplanetary Cloud and the Formation of the Earth and Planets.* Nauka, Moscow, 241 pp. In Russian.

Schmidt, O. Yu, 1944. Meteoritic theory of the origin of the Earth and planets. *Dokl. Akad. Nauk SSSR*, **45** (6), 245–249.

Signer, P. and H. E. Suess, 1963. Rare gases in the sun, in the atmosphere, and in meteorites. In *Earth Science and Meteoritics.* J. Geiss and E. D. Goldberg, eds. North-Holland Publ. Co., Amsterdam, pp. 241–272.

Sillén, L. G., 1965. Oxidation states of Earth's ocean and atmosphere, I. A model calculation on earlier states. The myth of the "probiotic" soup. *Arkiv. Kemi.* **24**, 431–456.

Sillén, L. G., 1966. Oxidation states of Earth's ocean and atmosphere, II. The behavior of Fe, S and Mn in earlier states. Regulating mechanisms for O_2 and N_2. *Arkiv. Kemi.*, **25**, 159–176.

Strangway, D. W., W. A. Gose, G. W. Pearce, and J. G. Carnes, 1972. Magnetism and the history of the Moon. Proc. 18th Conf. on Magnetism and Magnetic Materials. *J. Appl. Phys.* In press.

ter Haar, D., 1967. On the origin of the solar system. *Ann. Rev. Astron. Astrophys.*, **5**, 267–278.

Trulsen, J., 1971. Theory of jet streams. In *From Plasma to Planet.* Proc. Nobel Symp. 21. A. Elvius, ed. Wiley, New York, pp. 179–194.

Tuttle, O. F. and J. Gittens, ed., 1966. *Carbonatites*, Wiley, Interscience, New York, 591 pp.

Urey, H. C., 1952. *The Planets: Their Origin and Development.* Yale University Press, New Haven, 245 pp.

Urey, H. C., 1959. The atmosphere of the planets. In *Handbuch der Physik*, Springer, Berlin. Vol. 52, 363–418.

Urey, H. C., 1962. The origin of the Moon and its relationship to the origin of the solar system. In *The Moon.* Proc. 14th I.A.U. Symp. Z. Kopal and Z. K. Mikhailov, eds. Academic Press, London, pp. 133–148.

Wasson, J. T., 1969. Primordial rare gases in the atmosphere of the Earth. *Nature*, **223**, 163–165.

Wiik, H. B., The chemical composition of some stony meteorites. *Geochim. Cosmochim. Acta*, **9**, 279–289.

AUTHOR INDEX

C

G

H

L

SUBJECT INDEX